Unified Calculus
and Analytic Geometry

By Earl D. Rainville

ELEMENTARY DIFFERENTIAL EQUATIONS, *Second Edition*

A SHORT COURSE IN DIFFERENTIAL EQUATIONS, *Second Edition*

SPECIAL FUNCTIONS

UNIFIED CALCULUS AND ANALYTIC GEOMETRY

ANALYTIC GEOMETRY, *Fifth Edition* (*with* Clyde E. Love)

DIFFERENTIAL AND INTEGRAL CALCULUS, *Fifth Edition* (*with* Clyde E. Love)

INTERMEDIATE DIFFERENTIAL EQUATIONS (*published by* John Wiley & Sons, Inc.)

Unified
Calculus and Analytic
Geometry

BY EARL D. RAINVILLE

Professor of Mathematics,
The University of Michigan

New York   THE MACMILLAN COMPANY

Library of Congress catalog card number: 61-5159

The Macmillan Company, New York
Brett-Macmillan Ltd., Galt, Ontario

Printed in the United States of America

Some material included in this book is from Love and Rainville: *Differential and Integral Calculus*, Fifth Edition, copyright 1954 by The Macmillan Company; Love and Rainville: *Analytic Geometry*, Fifth Edition, copyright 1955 by The Macmillan Company; Rainville: *Elementary Differential Equations*, Second Edition, © 1958 by The Macmillan Company; and Rainville: *A Short Course in Differential Equations*, Second Edition, © 1958 by The Macmillan Company.

Preface

This book is intended as a text for courses which furnish the backbone of the student's collegiate mathematics. Before going into the course, the student should know the basic principles and formulas of elementary trigonometry and advanced high school, or beginning college, algebra. At the end of the course, he should be prepared for advanced calculus, or advanced mathematics for engineers, for more thorough courses in differential equations, and even for the milder versions of first courses in the Laplace transform, Fourier series, complex variables, matrices, theory of equations, theory of numbers, linear vector spaces, etc.

Throughout the book I have attempted to effect a balance between the desire for rigor and the cold fact of the probable state of mathematical maturity of the student. If we proceed to teach without rigor, what we teach is not mathematics. If, at this stage, we teach entirely rigorously, we gain much stature for the course and lose—the student.

I have tried to state definitions and theorems with care, to prove some things rigorously, to present others with discussions aimed only at making the facts seem plausible. By means of what I hope are illuminating discussions in the text, I attempt to increase both the student's maturity and his knowledge of the subject. There are in this book not only a large number of illustrative examples but also well over five thousand exercises for the student. The exercises have been constructed carefully. They are supposed not only to develop gradually a considerable manipulative skill but also in numerous instances to add appreciably to the student's basic knowledge. The instructor will notice many exercises clearly intended to prepare the student for specific problems which he may encounter in more advanced courses.

I have included a few topics which are not often discussed at this stage in the student's training. For example, the error function is studied in § 349 to show the student how easily some so-called nonelementary functions may be handled.

When calculus and analytic geometry are combined, there is a strong tendency to neglect the geometry so much that at times the student is at a loss as to what he can use his calculus upon. I feel that there is, for instance, little point to teaching a student how to obtain the area bounded by two plane curves before he can sketch the curves without time-consuming point plotting. The instructor will find in this book a thorough treatment of the analytic geometry needed. Solid analytic geometry, in particular, receives much more attention than is usually accorded it in combined courses.

A shorter course may be taught from this book by omitting all or any of the following: §§ 121–123, 156–161, 171–172, Chapters 21–22; §§ 253–254, Chapter 31; §§ 271–272, 278, 290, Chapter 36; §§ 327, 338–339, 348–349, Chapter 42; and all or part of the five chapters on differential equations. I strongly advise against omitting Newton's method, Chapter 21, but it, like the other sections listed above, may be omitted without interrupting the continuity of the course. Sections explicitly concerned with applications may also be omitted safely, if such omission seems desirable.

By explicit agreement with the interested parties, I have been allowed to incorporate in this book portions of three other Macmillan books, my *Elementary Differential Equations* (2nd edition, 1958), the Love and Rainville *Differential and Integral Calculus* (5th edition, 1954), and the Love and Rainville *Analytic Geometry* (5th edition, 1955). I have particularly taken from those books large numbers of exercises.

I am indebted to Professor Phillip E. Bedient of Franklin and Marshall College and to Professor Ralph L. Shively of Western Reserve University for a critical reading of certain portions of the manuscript for this book.

EARL D. RAINVILLE

Contents

Chapter 14.   The Central Conics   200

Chapter 15.   Parametric Equations.   Motion   218

Chapter 16.   Hyperbolic Functions   244

*Unified Calculus
and Analytic Geometry*

1

One-dimensional Geometry

1. Inequality Symbols

We shall frequently employ the following symbols with which the student may already be familiar:

$$> \quad \text{to mean "is greater than";}$$
$$< \quad \text{to mean "is less than";}$$
$$\neq \quad \text{to mean "is not equal to."}$$

The symbol $\leq$ means "is less than or equal to." The statement $x \leq 4$ means that either x is 4 or x is less than 4. We use $\geq$ in a similar way.

Example (a).

$$7 > 3, \qquad 2 < 6, \qquad -3 \neq 5,$$
$$-4 > -5, \qquad -3 < -1, \qquad -4 \neq 4.$$

Example (b). The one-valued square root, as defined in algebra, has the properties:

$$\sqrt{x^2} = \quad x, \qquad \text{for } x \geq 0,$$
$$= -x, \qquad \text{for } x < 0.$$

Example (c). If $y \geq 0$, $\sqrt{4 + y} \geq 2$.

2. The Absolute-Value Symbol

The symbol $|x|$, which may be read "absolute value of x," is defined by

(1)
$$|x| = \quad x, \qquad \text{for } x \geq 0,$$
$$= -x, \qquad \text{for } x < 0.$$

Example (a). $|3| = |-3| = 3$.
Example (b). If $a > 0$, $|x| \leq a$ is equivalent to $-a \leq x \leq a$.
Example (c). From Example (b) of § 1 and the definition (1) above, it follows that

(2)
$$\sqrt{x^2} = |x|.$$

1

A fundamental property of the absolute-value symbol is that *the absolute value of the sum of two numbers is never larger than the sum of their absolute values*:

$$|a + b| \leq |a| + |b|.$$

In § 5 we shall obtain a geometric interpretation for the absolute value of the difference of two real numbers.

3. *Linear Coordinate*

Let us confine our attention to a specific straight line. On that line choose a fixed point O as a point of reference. Select a fixed direction as the positive direction on the line; the opposite direction then becomes the negative direction. In Figure 1 the positive direction is to the right, the negative direction to the left.

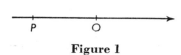

Figure 1

The position of any point P on the line is determined when the direction of P from O and the distance between P and O are specified. We associate with each point P a real number x called the *coordinate* of P; the sign of x indicates the direction of P from O and $|x|$ is the distance between P and O. We have thus set up a one-to-one correspondence between the real numbers, as coordinates, and the points on a line.

The coordinate of a point will be written in parentheses, $P: (x)$. The point O is called the origin of coordinates, or simply the *origin*; its coordinate is (0).

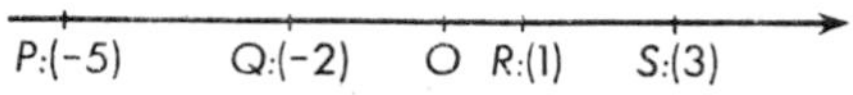

In Figure 2 the point R has the coordinate (1), indicating that R is one unit of length to the right of O. Figure 2 also shows the points $P: (-5)$, $Q: (-2)$, and $S: (3)$. To avoid stuffy writing, it is conventional to refer to "the point (-2)," meaning Q, rather than to "the point whose coordinate is (-2)."

$$P{:}(-5) \qquad Q{:}(-2) \qquad O \quad R{:}(1) \qquad S{:}(3)$$

Figure 2

4. *Directed Distance Between Two Points*

Consider any two points A_1 and A_2 on our line. Let A_1 have the coordinate (x_1), A_2 the coordinate (x_2). The *directed distance* from A_1 to A_2 is defined by

$$(1) \qquad\qquad A_1 A_2 = x_2 - x_1.$$

Notice that if A_2 lies to the right of A_1, then $x_2 > x_1$ so that $A_1 A_2$ is positive. If A_2 lies to the left of A_1, $x_2 < x_1$ and $A_1 A_2$ is negative. If A_2 coincides with A_1, $A_1 A_2 = 0$. It follows from (1) that

$$(2) \qquad\qquad A_2 A_1 = - A_1 A_2.$$

Example. In Figure 2, $PS = 3 - (-5) = 8$, $SQ = -2 - 3 = -5$.

Theorem 1 below follows rapidly from the definition (1) and should be proved by the student.

THEOREM 1. *For any three points A_1, A_2, A_3 on a line*

$$(3) \qquad A_1A_2 + A_2A_3 = A_1A_3.$$

It is important that equation (3) is independent of the relative positions of the three given points.

5. Undirected Distance Between Two Points

The *undirected distance* between any two points (x_1) and (x_2) on the line is defined by

$$(1) \qquad D_{12} = |x_2 - x_1|.$$

Then D_{12} is, in the ordinary sense, the length of the line segment joining (x_1) and (x_2); D_{12} is never negative.

Since the origin has the coordinate (0), it follows that $|x| = |x - 0|$ is the length of the line segment joining the point (x) with the origin.

In equation (2) of § 2 we found that $\sqrt{x^2} = |x|$. Thus the definition (1) above may be put in the form

$$(2) \qquad D_{12} = \sqrt{(x_2 - x_1)^2}.$$

Equation (2) is in a desirable form for the purpose of generalization to two or more dimensions. See §§ 10 and 217.

6. Mid-point of a Line Segment

Let $A_1: (x_1)$ and $A_2: (x_2)$ be any two points on our line. We wish to find the coordinate of the mid-point M_{12} of the line segment joining A_1 with A_2. See Figure 3.

Let M_{12} have the coordinate x_m. We know that $A_1M_{12} = M_{12}A_2$ whether A_1 is to the right or the left of A_2. Hence

$$(1) \qquad x_m - x_1 = x_2 - x_m,$$

from which we obtain

$$(2) \qquad x_m = \tfrac{1}{2}(x_1 + x_2).$$

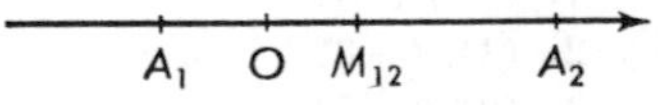

Figure 3

7. Division of a Line Segment

Consider the line segment joining $A_1: (x_1)$ and $A_2: (x_2)$. Let the point $P: (x)$ divide the line segment from A_1 to A_2 (Figure 4) in such a way that

Figure 4

$$(1) \qquad \frac{A_1P}{A_1A_2} = k.$$

Since $A_1P = x - x_1$ and $A_1A_2 = x_2 - x_1$, it follows from (1) that

$$(2) \qquad\qquad x = x_1 + k(x_2 - x_1).$$

If k is negative, A_1P and A_1A_2 are of opposite signs and A_1 must lie between P and A_2. If $k > 1$, A_2 lies between A_1 and P. If $0 < k < 1$, P lies between A_1 and A_2.

Example (a). Find the trisection points of the line segment joining (-4) with (11).

Let the trisection points be T_1: (t_1) and T_2: (t_2). Since $A_1T_1 = \frac{1}{3}A_1A_2$ and $A_1T_2 = \frac{2}{3}A_1A_2$, we use $k = \frac{1}{3}, \frac{2}{3}$, successively to obtain

$$t_1 = -4 + \tfrac{1}{3}(11 + 4) = 1,$$
$$t_2 = -4 + \tfrac{2}{3}(11 + 4) = 6.$$

Example (b). The line segment from A_1: (-7) to A_2: (-2) is to be extended each way twice its own length. Find the terminal points.

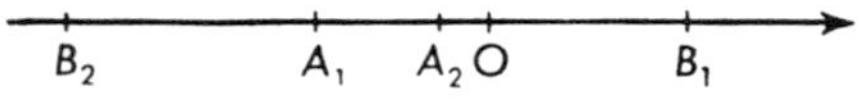

Figure 5

Let the desired points be B_1: (b_1) to the right of A_2, and B_2: (b_2) to the left of A_1, as in Figure 5. Then $A_1B_1 = 3A_1A_2$ and $A_1B_2 = -2A_1A_2$. Therefore

$$b_1 = -7 + 3(-2 + 7) = 8,$$
$$b_2 = -7 - 2(-2 + 7) = -17.$$

Any problem of the type of Examples (a) and (b) can be solved with the aid of common sense and a little arithmetic, with no need for a formula such as (2) of this section. The purpose in using (2) is to prepare the student for analogous problems in two or three dimensions.

EXERCISES

In Exs. 1–10, find (a) the directed distance from the first point to the second, (b) the mid-point.

1. (-3), (5).   *Ans.* (a) 8; (b) (1).
2. (4), (-8).   *Ans.* (a) -12; (b) (-2).
3. (0), (-5).
4. (0), (-9).
5. (3), (10).
6. (2), (13).
7. (-7), (-1).
8. (-1), (-7).
9. (6), (-4).
10. $(x_1 - x_2)$, $(x_1 + x_2)$.

11. The line segment joining (5) to (14) is to be trisected. Find the points of trisection.

12. Trisect the segment from (-4) to (3).

13. The segment from (-6) to (-2) is extended its own length each way. Find the terminal points.

14. The segment from (a) to (b) was trisected and the results found to be (0) and (-7). Find a and b.

15. The segment from (-3) to (4) is to be divided into five equal parts. Find the two innermost points of division.   *Ans.* (-0.2), (1.2).

16. For any four distinct points (x_1), (x_2), (x_3), (x_4) define as the *cross-ratio* of those points the number

$$\{x_1, x_2, x_3, x_4\} = \frac{x_1 - x_3}{x_1 - x_4} \cdot \frac{x_2 - x_4}{x_2 - x_3}.$$

Let $\{x_1, x_2, x_3, x_4\} = \lambda$ and show that the 24 possible cross-ratios formed by using all permutations of the four points yield only the six values

(A) $$\lambda, \frac{1}{\lambda}, 1 - \lambda, \frac{1}{1 - \lambda}, \frac{\lambda - 1}{\lambda}, \frac{\lambda}{\lambda - 1}.$$

These are called the elements of the cross-ratio group. See Exs. 17–21.

17. Let the six elements in (A) of Ex. 16 be denoted by a $a_1, a_2, \ldots, a_6$, respectively. Thus $a_1 = \lambda, a_2 = \frac{1}{\lambda}, a_3 = 1 - \lambda$, etc. Define the symbol $a_k \bigcirc a_m$ to mean the result of substituting a_k for λ in a_m. For example, $a_2 = \frac{1}{\lambda}$ and $a_3 = 1 - \lambda$; so,

$$a_2 \bigcirc a_3 = 1 - \left(\frac{1}{\lambda}\right) = 1 - \frac{1}{\lambda} = \frac{\lambda - 1}{\lambda} = a_5.$$

Form a multiplication table for the a's; i.e., verify the answer below in which all the pertinent "products" $a_k \bigcirc a_m$ are indicated in the following manner:

In the table the rows are numbered at the left, the columns at the top. The intersection of the row numbered k and the column numbered m contains the subscript in the result of performing the operation $a_k \bigcirc a_m$. For instance, row number 2 and column number 5 have a 3 at their intersection, which means that $a_2 \bigcirc a_5 = a_3$. Row number 5 and column number 2 intersect at a 6, meaning that $a_5 \bigcirc a_2 = a_6$.

Ans.

↱	1	2	3	4	5	6
1	1	2	3	4	5	6
2	2	1	5	6	3	4
3	3	4	1	2	6	5
4	4	3	6	5	1	2
5	5	6	2	1	4	3
6	6	5	4	3	2	1

18. The elements a_k and a_m are said to *commute*, or to *be commutative*, under the operation used if $a_k \bigcirc a_m = a_m \bigcirc a_k$. If $a_k \bigcirc a_m \neq a_m \bigcirc a_k$ the two elements are *noncommutative* under the operation. From the table in Ex. 17 determine all noncommutative pairs of a's.

19. Examine the table in Ex. 17 for other properties of $a_k \circ a_m$. When does $a_k \circ a_m = a_m$? When does $a_k \circ a_m = a_k$? What subscripts appear in any one row? In any one column?

20. Repeat Ex. 17 but using only the three elements a_1, a_4, a_5. What happens if you try to form a multiplication table containing only a_1, a_4, and a_6?

21. Find multiplication tables containing only two different a's.

22. Let $b_1 = 1$, $b_2 = i = \sqrt{-1}$, $b_3 = -1$, $b_4 = -i$ and let the operation symbol $\circ$ denote ordinary multiplication. Form and examine, in the sense of Exs. 17–21, a multiplication table for the four b's.

Two-dimensional Geometry

8. Rectangular Coordinates

In a plane choose two straight lines perpendicular to each other. Call those lines the *axes* and their point of intersection the *origin*. Give each axis a linear coordinate system as in Chapter 1, using O as the origin for both axes. In Figure 6 we have chosen a horizontal line as the x-axis with an x-coordinate system, and a vertical line as the y-axis with a y-coordinate system. The positive direction on each axis is the direction which bears the letter indicating the coordinate system for that axis.

Given any point P in the plane of the x- and y-axes, project P onto each axis as shown in Figure 6. We associate with P an ordered pair of real numbers (x, y) called the *rectangular coordinates* of P and defined as follows: The x-coordinate of P is the x-coordinate of A, the point of projection of P onto the x-axis;

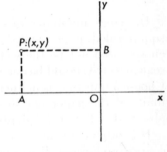

Figure 6

the y-coordinate of P is the y-coordinate of B, the point of projection of P onto the y-axis. For the point P shown in Figure 6, the x-coordinate is negative, the y-coordinate positive. With any ordered pair of real numbers (x, y) associate the point whose coordinates are respectively x and y as described above. We have thus stipulated a one-to-one correspondence between the points in a plane and the set of all ordered pairs of real numbers.

As in the one-dimensional analog we shall often write "the point $(-2, \frac{1}{2})$" as a short form of "the point whose rectangular coordinates are $(-2, \frac{1}{2})$."

When, as in Figure 6, the axes have been chosen horizontal and vertical, with positive directions to the right and upward, it is common practice to call the horizontal coordinate the *abscissa* of P and the vertical coordinate the *ordinate* of P. Coordinates are always enclosed by parentheses, with the abscissa written first.

The axes divide the plane into four quadrants numbered as shown in Figure 7. The signs of the coordinates associated with points in the various quadrants are as indicated in the following scheme:

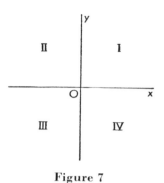

Figure 7

First quadrant: (+, +),
Second quadrant: (−, +),
Third quadrant: (−, −),
Fourth quadrant: (+, −).

Except where the contrary is indicated, it will be assumed that segments oblique to the axes are *undirected*, segments parallel to an axis are *directed*. Segments parallel to Ox will be considered positive to the right, negative to the left; segments parallel to Oy, positive upward, negative downward.

9. *Units*

Drawings involving rectangular coordinates are most easily made on square-ruled paper called *coordinate paper*. The unit of measurement chosen need not be the width of one space on the coordinate paper. The scale selected should be one which exhibits the drawing to its best advantage. Choose a unit that is neither so large that some of the points fall beyond the limits of the paper nor so small that the properties of the figure become obscured. The scale adopted should be clearly indicated.

It is often convenient to adopt different scales on the two axes, which of course produces a distortion of the figure. Except where the contrary is stated, we shall assume always that the unit for ordinates is the same as that for abscissas.

To plot a point whose coordinates are irrational, we employ decimal approximations. For instance, to plot the point $(\sqrt{2}, \sqrt{3})$, we may take $\sqrt{2} = 1.41$, $\sqrt{3} = 1.73$. Of course $(\sqrt{2}, \sqrt{3})$ and $(1.41, 1.73)$ are not at all the same point; we are merely doing the best we can for plotting purposes. Such approximations are permissible only in plotting, which is an inaccurate process at best, or in applications where an approximate result is satisfactory.

10. *Distance Between Two Points*

Let d be the undirected distance between the points P_1: (x_1, y_1) and P_2: (x_2, y_2), as shown in Figure 8. By the theorem of Pythagoras

(1)
$$d = \sqrt{\overline{P_1Q}^2 + \overline{QP_2}^2}.$$

But

$$P_1Q = M_1M_2 = x_2 - x_1,$$
$$QP_2 = M_2P_2 - M_2Q = y_2 - y_1.$$

Therefore the distance between the points (x_1, y_1) and (x_2, y_2) is given by

(2) $d = \sqrt{(x_2 - x_1)^2 + (y_2 - y_1)^2}.$

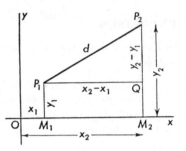

Figure 8

By drawing the figure in various positions, the student may convince himself that the formula holds, no matter where the points P_1, P_2 may be situated.   Compare (2) above with equation (2) of § 5.

Example (a).   Find the distance between the points $(3, 2)$ and $(-5, 4)$.
By formula (2), we find

$$d = \sqrt{(-8)^2 + 2^2} = \sqrt{68} = 2\sqrt{17}.$$

Example (b).   Show that the points $P_1: (5, 0)$, $P_2: (2, 1)$, $P_3: (4, 7)$ are the vertices of a right triangle.

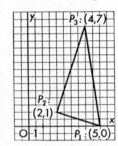

By (2),

$$P_1P_2 = \sqrt{9 + 1} = \sqrt{10},$$
$$P_2P_3 = \sqrt{4 + 36} = \sqrt{40},$$
$$P_1P_3 = \sqrt{1 + 49} = \sqrt{50},$$

so that

$$\overline{P_1P_2}^2 + \overline{P_2P_3}^2 = \overline{P_1P_3}^2.$$

Figure 9

Example (c).   A moving point P remains always equidistant from $P_1: (-1, 0)$ and $P_2: (0, -2)$.   Express this fact by an algebraic equation.

Let the coordinates of the moving point P be denoted by (x, y).   Then, since by hypothesis

$$PP_1 = PP_2,$$

it follows that

$$\sqrt{(x + 1)^2 + y^2} = \sqrt{x^2 + (y + 2)^2}.$$

Square and simplify:

$$x^2 + 2x + 1 + y^2 = x^2 + y^2 + 4y + 4,$$

or

$$2x - 4y - 3 = 0.$$

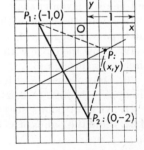

Figure 10

The locus of P is, of course, the perpendicular bisector of the segment P_1P_2.

EXERCISES

In Exs. 1–4, draw the figure on coordinate paper, choosing a suitable scale in each instance.

1. Triangle with vertices $(0, 3)$, $(-1, -2)$, $(4, 1)$.
2. Triangle with vertices $(3, 4)$, $(-2, 2)$, $(5, -2)$.
3. Quadrilateral with vertices $(-1, 2)$, $(-1, -1)$, $(3, -4)$, $(5, 4)$.
4. Quadrilateral with vertices $(2, 3)$, $(-2, -3)$, $(3, -5)$, $(4, 1)$.

In Exs. 5–8, find the distance between the given points.

5. $(2, 1)$, $(5, 5)$.   6. $(-2, 4)$, $(3, 6)$.
7. $(\frac{1}{2}, 1)$, $(-\frac{3}{2}, -3)$.   8. $(\frac{2}{3}, -\frac{1}{3})$, $(\frac{5}{6}, -\frac{1}{2})$.

9. What can be said of the coordinates of all points on the x-axis? On the y-axis? On the line through O bisecting the first and third quadrants? The second and fourth quadrants? On the line parallel to the y-axis two units to the right of it? Two units to the left?

10. Where does a point lie if its abscissa is zero? If its ordinate is zero? If abscissa and ordinate are equal? Are numerically equal but of opposite sign?

11. Show that the points $(-1, -2)$, $(5, 4)$, $(-3, 0)$ are the vertices of a right triangle, and find its area.   *Ans.* 12.

12. Show that the points $(4, 0)$, $(2, 1)$, $(-1, -5)$ are the vertices of a right triangle and find its area.   *Ans.* $\frac{15}{2}$.

13. Show that the points $(-2, 4)$, $(3, -1)$, $(-1, -3)$ are the vertices of an isosceles triangle, and find its area.   *Ans.* 15.

14. Show that the points $(1, -3)$, $(3, 2)$, $(-2, 4)$ are the vertices of an isosceles triangle, and find its area.   *Ans.* $\frac{29}{2}$.

15. Show that the points $(1, 4)$, $(7, 0)$, $(5, -3)$, $(-1, 1)$ are the vertices of a rectangle, and find its area.   *Ans.* 26.

16. Show that the points $(-1, -3)$, $(-2, 0)$, $(1, 6)$, $(2, 3)$ are the vertices of a parallelogram. Is the parallelogram a rectangle?

17. Explain why it is impossible to show graphically that a given point lies on a given circle, although it may be feasible to show graphically that a given point does not lie on a given circle.

18. Draw the circle with center at $(1, 2)$ and passing through $(8, 3)$. Does this circle pass through $(-4, -3)$? Through $(5, 8)$? Through $(0, 9)$? See Ex. 17.

19. Draw the circle with center at $(-3, 1)$ and passing through $(5, 4)$. Does this circle pass through $(3, 7)$? Through $(-6, 9)$? See Ex. 17.

20. Draw the circle with center at $(-5, -2)$ and tangent to the y-axis. Does this circle pass through $(-2, 2)$? Through $(-4, 3)$? See Ex. 17.

21. At what points does the circle of Ex. 20 cut the x-axis?

22. Find the radius of a circle with center at $(2, 3)$, if a chord of length 8 is bisected at $(-1, 4)$.   *Ans.* $\sqrt{26}$.

23. Find the radius of a circle with center at $(-2, 1)$, if a chord of length 10 is bisected at $(-3, 0)$.   *Ans.* $3\sqrt{3}$.

24. The center of a circle is at $(4, 2)$ and its radius is 5. Find the length of the chord which is bisected at $(2, -1)$.   *Ans.* $4\sqrt{3}$.

25. The center of a circle is at $(-3, -2)$ and its radius is 7.   Find the length of the chord which is bisected at $(3, 1)$.   *Ans.* 4.

26. At what points does the circle of Ex. 25 cut the y-axis?

In Exs. 27–30, do the given points lie in a straight line?

27. $(1, -1)$, $(-1, -5)$, $(2, 1)$.
28. $(-3, -2)$, $(23, 15)$, $(-24, -16)$.
29. $(-2, 2)$, $(5, -8)$, $(-7, 9)$.
30. $(9, -14)$, $(5, -8)$, $(-9, 13)$.

In Exs. 31–33, express the given statement by an algebraic equation.   What is the locus of the point (x, y) in each exercise?   Draw the figure.

31. The point (x, y) is equidistant from $(0, 0)$ and $(4, -2)$.   *Ans.* $2x - y = 5$.
32. The point (x, y) is equidistant from $(4, -1)$ and $(-2, 3)$.   *Ans.* $3x - 2y = 1$.
33. The point (x, y) is at a distance 5 from $(0, -3)$.   *Ans.* $x^2 + y^2 + 6y - 16 = 0$.

11. *Mid-point of a Line Segment*

Let $P_m: (x_m, y_m)$ be the mid-point of the line segment joining $P_1: (x_1, y_1)$ to $P_2: (x_2, y_2)$.   The projection A_m (Figure 11) of P_m onto the x-axis is the mid-point of the projection of the segment P_1P_2 onto that axis.   In § 6 we found the coordinate (x_m) of the mid-point of the segment joining (x_1) to (x_2). The same formula applies with x's replaced by y's.   Hence

(1) $$x_m = \tfrac{1}{2}(x_1 + x_2), \qquad y_m = \tfrac{1}{2}(y_1 + y_2).$$

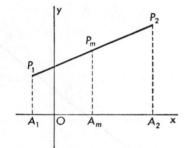
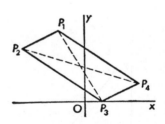

Figure 11   **Figure 12**

Example (a).   Show that the quadrilateral with vertices $P_1: (-\tfrac{3}{2}, 4)$, $P_2: (-\tfrac{7}{2}, 3)$, $P_3: (1, 0)$, $P_4: (3, 1)$ is a parallelogram.

Let us use the theorem that a quadrilateral whose diagonals bisect each other is a parallelogram.   For the mid-point of P_1P_3, we have (Figure 12)

$$x = \tfrac{1}{2}(-\tfrac{3}{2} + 1) = -\tfrac{1}{4}, \qquad y = \tfrac{1}{2}(4 + 0) = 2;$$

for the mid-point of P_2P_4,

$$x = \tfrac{1}{2}(-\tfrac{7}{2} + 3) = -\tfrac{1}{4}, \qquad y = \tfrac{1}{2}(3 + 1) = 2.$$

Since the two mid-points coincide, our problem is solved.

Example (*b*). The directed line segment from (1, 3) to (4, 8) is extended its own length. Find the terminal point.

Let the terminal point be (x, y). Then (4, 8) is the mid-point of the segment from (1, 3) to (x, y). Therefore

$$\frac{x+1}{2} = 4, \qquad \frac{y+3}{2} = 8,$$

from which it follows that the terminal point is (7, 13).

12. *Division of a Line Segment*

Consider the line through the points P_1: (x_1, y_1) and P_2: (x_2, y_2). Let P: (x, y) be a point on that line such that

$$(1) \qquad\qquad \frac{P_1P}{P_1P_2} = k.$$

By projecting the line segments joining P_1, P_2, and P onto each axis in turn, and using the known result (2) of § 7, we obtain

$$(2) \qquad x = x_1 + k(x_2 - x_1), \qquad y = y_1 + k(y_2 - y_1).$$

Example (*a*). The segment joining P_1: (1, 3), P_2. (5, −2) is trisected. Find the point of trisection nearer to P_1.

In Figure 13, $P_1P = \frac{1}{3}P_1P_2$; so $k = \frac{1}{3}$, and

$$x = 1 + \tfrac{1}{3}(5 - 1) = \tfrac{7}{3}, \qquad y = 3 + \tfrac{1}{3}(-2 - 3) = \tfrac{4}{3}.$$

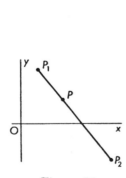

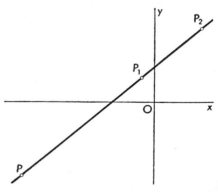

Figure 13   Figure 14

Example (*b*). The segment joining P_1: $(-\frac{1}{2}, 1)$ to P_2: (2, 3) is extended beyond P_1 so that its length is tripled. Find the terminal point P: (x, y). See Figure 14.

Here P_1P is twice the length of P_1P_2, but they are in opposite directions. Therefore $k = -2$ and we obtain

$$x = -\tfrac{1}{2} - 2(2 + \tfrac{1}{2}) = -\tfrac{11}{2}, \qquad y = 1 - 2(3 - 1) = -3.$$

EXERCISES

In Exs. 1–4, find the point midway between the given points.

1. $(5, 6)$, $(3, -2)$.   **2.** $(4, 8)$, $(-4, -3)$.
3. $(3, 0)$, $(-\frac{1}{2}, 4)$.   **4.** $(\frac{3}{2}, -6)$, $(-\frac{1}{3}, \frac{1}{2})$.
   5. Show in two ways that the quadrilateral with vertices $(0, -1)$, $(1, 2)$, $(-4, 7)$, $(-5, 4)$ is a parallelogram.
   6. Show in two ways that the quadrilateral with vertices $(11, 1)$, $(0, 0)$, $(-1, -3)$, $(10, -2)$ is a parallelogram.
   7. Show in a new way that the points $(-1, -2)$, $(5, 4)$, $(-3, 0)$ are the vertices of a right triangle. (Ex. 11, page 10.)
   8. Show in a new way that the points $(4, 0)$, $(2, 1)$, $(-1, -5)$ are the vertices of a right triangle. (Ex. 12, page 10.)
   9. The segment joining $(5, 11)$ and $(-3, -1)$ is to be divided into four equal parts. Find the points of division.
   10. Trisect the segment joining $(-2, 3)$ and $(7, 1)$.   *Ans.* $(1, \frac{7}{3})$, $(4, \frac{5}{3})$.
   11. The center of a circle is at $(2, -5)$; one point on the circle is $(-4, 2)$. Find the other end of the diameter through $(-4, 2)$.
   12. Three consecutive vertices of a parallelogram are $(1, -3)$, $(-3, -1)$, $(3, 5)$. Find the fourth vertex.   *Ans.* $(7, 3)$.
   13. Three vertices of a parallelogram are $(1, -3)$, $(-3, -1)$, $(3, 5)$. Find the fourth vertex.   *Ans.* $(-5, -9)$, $(-1, 7)$, or $(7, 3)$.
   14. The segment joining $(-4, 7)$, $(5, -2)$ is divided into two segments, one of which is five times as long as the other. Find the point of division.
                             Ans. $(-\frac{5}{2}, \frac{11}{2})$; $(\frac{7}{2}, -\frac{1}{2})$.
   15. The segment joining $(2, -4)$, $(9, 3)$ is divided into two segments, one of which is three-fourths as long as the other. Find the point of division.
                                Ans. $(5, -1)$; $(6, 0)$.
   16. The segment from $(-1, 4)$ to $(2, -2)$ is extended three times its own length. Find the terminal point.   *Ans.* $(11, -20)$.
   17. The segment joining $(-2, -3)$, $(6, 1)$ is extended each way a distance equal to one-fourth its own length. Find the terminal points.   *Ans.* $(8, 2)$; $(-4, -4)$.

13. *Inclination; Slope*

   The *angle of inclination*, also called simply the *inclination*, of a straight line is the smallest positive angle from the positive x-axis to the line—the

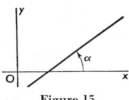
Figure 15

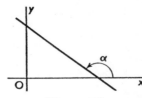
Figure 16

angles α in Figures 15–16. By special definition, the inclination of a line parallel to Ox is zero.

The *slope* of a line is the *tangent of the angle of inclination*. Slope is usually denoted by m:

(1) $m = \tan \alpha.$

If the axes are in the conventional position, a line sloping *upward to the right* has *positive slope*, since the tangent of a positive acute angle is positive; a line sloping *downward to the right* has *negative slope*. The slope of a line parallel to the x-axis is zero.

It should be noted that the idea of slope is meaningless in the case of a line parallel to the y-axis (including the y-axis itself), since $\tan \alpha$ "approaches infinity" (i.e., exceeds all bounds) as α approaches $90°$. Therefore, *in all discussions involving slopes, lines parallel to the y-axis are excluded.*

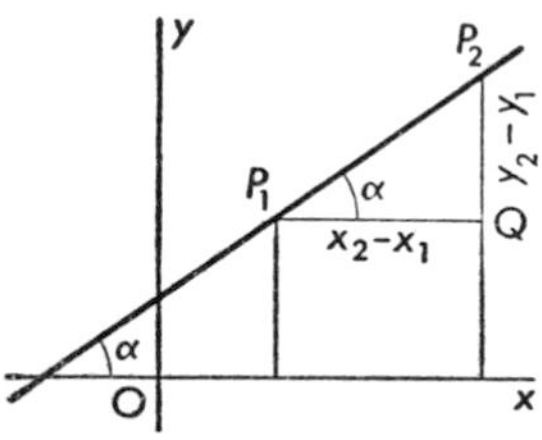

From Figure 17 we obtain

$$m = \tan \alpha = \frac{QP_2}{P_1Q}.$$

The slope of the line joining the points P_1: (x_1, y_1) and P_2: (x_2, y_2) is

Figure 17

(2) $m = \dfrac{y_2 - y_1}{x_2 - x_1},$ $x_2 \neq x_1.$

When the scales in the two directions are not the same, the defining formula (1) is *replaced by* (2).

14. *Parallel and Perpendicular Lines*

If two lines are parallel, they have the same slope; and conversely.
Given two perpendicular lines L_1, L_2, with slopes

$$m_1 = \tan \alpha_1, \qquad m_2 = \tan \alpha_2,$$

let L_1 denote the one with positive slope, so that

$$\alpha_2 = 90° + \alpha_1.$$

By trigonometry,

$\tan \alpha_2 = \tan (90° + \alpha_1)$

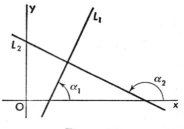

$$= -\cot \alpha_1 = -\frac{1}{\tan \alpha_1},$$

whence

Figure 18

(1) $m_2 = -\dfrac{1}{m_1}.$

On the other hand, if (1) is true, then

(2) $\tan \alpha_2 = -\cot \alpha_1.$

Since α_1 and α_2 are each positive and less than 180°, it follows from (2) that they differ by 90°.   Hence, if (1) holds, the lines L_1 and L_2 are perpendicular.

Of course any line parallel to the x-axis is perpendicular to any line parallel to the y-axis.

THEOREM 2.   *For lines not parallel to the axes, two lines are perpendicular if and only if their slopes are negative reciprocals.*

Example (a).   Verify that the points P_1: $(-1, 3)$, P_2: $(0, 5)$, P_3: $(3, 1)$ are the vertices of a right triangle (Figure 19).

From the figure we see that if there is a right angle it must be at P_1.   The slopes of P_1P_2, P_1P_3 are respectively

$$m_1 = \frac{5-3}{0+1} = 2, \qquad m_2 = \frac{1-3}{3+1} = -\frac{1}{2},$$

from which it follows that P_1P_2 and P_1P_3 are perpendicular.

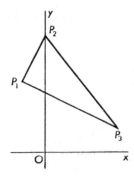

Figure 19

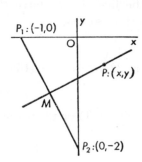

Figure 20

Example (b).   A moving point P: (x, y) remains always equidistant from P_1: $(-1, 0)$ and P_2: $(0, -2)$.   Express this fact by an algebraic equation. [Example (c), § 10.]

We know that P must lie on the perpendicular bisector of the line segment joining P_1 and P_2.   Let M (Figure 20) be the mid-point of P_1P_2.   Then M is the point $(-\frac{1}{2}, -1)$.

The slope of MP is

$$m_1 = \frac{y+1}{x+\frac{1}{2}}.$$

The slope of P_1P_2 is

$$m_2 = \frac{-2-0}{0+1} = -2.$$

By Theorem 2,

$$\frac{y+1}{x+\frac{1}{2}} = \frac{1}{2} \quad \text{or} \quad 2x - 4y - 3 = 0.$$

15. *Angle Between Two Lines*

By the angle *from* a line L_1 *to* a line L_2 we shall understand the positive angle through which L_1 must be rotated to come to coincidence with L_2 (the angles φ in Figures 21–22).

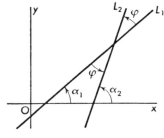
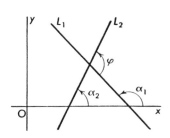

Figure 21   **Figure 22**

Let the lines L_1, L_2 have the inclinations α_1, α_2. Then in Figure 21, $\alpha_2 = \alpha_1 + \varphi$, so that

(1) $$\varphi = \alpha_2 - \alpha_1.$$

In Figure 22, $\alpha_1 = \alpha_2 + (180° - \varphi)$, from which

(2) $$\varphi = 180° + (\alpha_2 - \alpha_1).$$

From either (1) or (2) it follows that

$$\tan \varphi = \tan (\alpha_2 - \alpha_1) = \frac{\tan \alpha_2 - \tan \alpha_1}{1 + \tan \alpha_1 \tan \alpha_2}.$$

But the slopes of the lines are

$$\tan \alpha_1 = m_1, \qquad \tan \alpha_2 = m_2,$$

so that:

The angle from a line of slope m_1 to a line of slope m_2 is given by the formula

(3) $$\mathbf{\tan \varphi = \frac{m_2 - m_1}{1 + m_1 m_2}.}$$

This result will be more easily remembered if we realize that it is not, properly speaking, a new formula at all, but merely a restatement of the formula for the tangent of the difference of two angles.

Formula (3) fails if one line, say L_2, is parallel to Oy, but in that case $\varphi = 90° - \alpha_1$, so that $\tan \varphi = \cot \alpha_1 = \dfrac{1}{m_1}.$

Example. Find the interior angles of the triangle with vertices $(1, 1)$, $(4, 3)$, $(5, 2)$. (We shall be content to find the tangents, without troubling to look up the angles themselves in a table of "natural tangents.")

Let the lines forming the triangle be denoted by L_1, L_2, L_3 as shown in Figure 23. We readily find the slopes of these lines to be

$$m_1 = -1, \qquad m_2 = \tfrac{1}{4}, \qquad m_3 = \tfrac{2}{3}.$$

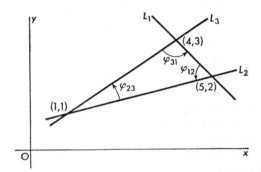

Figure 23

Let φ_{12} (read φ one two) denote the angle from L_1 to L_2, φ_{23} from L_2 to L_3, φ_{31} from L_3 to L_1. By (3),

$$\tan \varphi_{12} = \frac{\tfrac{1}{4} + 1}{1 - \tfrac{1}{4}} = \frac{5}{3}.$$

Similarly,

$$\tan \varphi_{23} = \tfrac{5}{14}, \qquad \tan \varphi_{31} = -5.$$

Check:

$$\tan (\varphi_{12} + \varphi_{23}) = \frac{\tfrac{5}{3} + \tfrac{5}{14}}{1 - \tfrac{5}{3} \cdot \tfrac{5}{14}} = 5 = -\tan \varphi_{31},$$

$$\varphi_{12} + \varphi_{23} = 180° - \varphi_{31}, \qquad \varphi_{12} + \varphi_{23} + \varphi_{31} = 180°.$$

EXERCISES

In Exs. 1–6, find the slope of the line joining the given points.

1. $(6, 2)$, $(3, -4)$.
2. $(2, -1)$, $(-3, 4)$.
3. $(4, 0)$, $(1, -2)$.
4. $(-2, -1)$, $(5, 3)$.
5. $(\tfrac{1}{2}, -\tfrac{1}{2})$, $(0, \tfrac{1}{3})$.
6. $(\tfrac{3}{2}, \tfrac{1}{3})$, $(\tfrac{5}{6}, \tfrac{1}{2})$.

Verify the statements in Exs. 7–14 by methods based on §§ 13–15.*

7. The points $(6, -1)$, $(3, 0)$, $(5, 6)$ are the vertices of a right triangle.
8. The points $(-1, \tfrac{1}{2})$, $(0, -\tfrac{5}{2})$, $(5, \tfrac{5}{2})$ are the vertices of a right triangle.
9. The triangle with vertices $(-3, 3)$, $(-1, -1)$, $(3, -3)$ is isosceles.
10. The triangle with vertices $(4, -2)$, $(8, 2)$, $(7, -1)$ is isosceles.
11. The points $(4, 0)$, $(12, 3)$, $(7, 4)$, $(-1, 1)$ are vertices of a parallelogram.

---

* The student will frequently be asked to solve a previous exercise in a new way. This is so that, by weighing the merits of the various methods, he may learn how to pick the best one in a given problem.

12. The points $(-7, -11)$, $(11, 5)$, $(6, 11)$, $(-12, -5)$ are vertices of a parallelogram. Draw the figure. Prove that the parallelogram is not a rectangle.

13. The circle having the points $(-4, 3)$, $(6, 3)$ as ends of a diameter also passes through $(-2, 7)$.

14. The perpendicular bisector of the line joining $(9, 5)$ and $(-7, 3)$ passes through $(3, -12)$.

In Exs. 15–18, determine whether the given points lie on a straight line.

15. $(-10, -4)$, $(0, -1)$, $(30, 8)$.
16. $(-22, -12)$, $(-1, 2)$, $(25, 19)$.
17. $(9, 10)$, $(4, 3)$, $(-3, -7)$.
18. $(-4, 9)$, $(-2, 6)$, $(8, -9)$.
19. Show that the quadrilateral with vertices $(0, 1)$, $(4, 2)$, $(3, 6)$, $(-5, 4)$ has two right angles. Find the area. *Ans.* $A = \frac{51}{2}$.
20. Show that the quadrilateral with vertices $(10, 10)$, $(-14, -2)$, $(-10, -10)$, $(4, -24)$ can be divided into two right triangles. Find the area. *Ans.* $A = 400$.

In Exs. 21–24, express the given statement by an algebraic equation.

21. The point (x, y) is equidistant from $(0, 0)$ and $(4, -2)$. (Ex. 31, page 11.)
22. The point (x, y) is equidistant from $(4, -1)$ and $(-2, 3)$. (Ex. 32, page 11.)
23. The point (x, y) lies on a circle which has the segment from $(2, -4)$ to $(5, 6)$ as a diameter. *Ans.* $x^2 + y^2 - 7x - 2y - 14 = 0$.
24. The point (x, y) lies on a circle which has the segment from $(0, -1)$ to $(\frac{1}{3}, \frac{4}{3})$ as a diameter. *Ans.* $3x^2 + 3y^2 - x - y - 4 = 0$.

In Exs. 25–30, if the line L_1 passes through the first pair of points, L_2 through the second pair, find the angle from L_1 to L_2.

25. $(2, 0)$, $(3, 5)$; $(5, 2)$, $(4, 6)$.   *Ans.* $\tan \varphi = \frac{3}{19}$.
26. $(4, 3)$, $(6, -2)$; $(9, 5)$, $(6, -2)$.   *Ans.* $135°$.
27. $(1, 9)$, $(2, 6)$; $(3, 3)$, $(-1, 5)$.   *Ans.* $45°$.
28. $(-5, -3)$, $(2, 6)$; $(6, 4)$, $(8, 2)$.   *Ans.* $\tan \varphi = 8$.
29. $(4, 0)$, $(0, 7)$; $(4, -5)$, $(1, 10)$.   *Ans.* $\tan \varphi = -\frac{1}{3}$.
30. $(-2, 0)$, $(8, 6)$; $(0, 6)$, $(7, 3)$.   *Ans.* $\tan \varphi = -\frac{18}{13}$.

In Exs. 31–34, find the interior angles; check the answers.

31. The triangle of Ex. 7.   **32.** The triangle of Ex. 8.
33. The triangle of Ex. 9.   **34.** The triangle of Ex. 10.

16. *Curves*

Consider any equation involving x and y or either of them. The set of all points whose coordinates satisfy the equation is called the *curve* representing that equation. The curve is also called the *graph* of the equation or the *locus* (Latin for "place") of the equation. For brevity we often refer to "the curve (1)" as a short form of "the curve representing equation (1)."

Example. Sketch the curve

(1)
$$y^2 = x.$$

To find points on the graph of (1) we may choose values of x and compute y from (1) or choose y and compute x from (1). Naturally we do the latter for this equation. The number and distribution of y values to be used is a matter of judgment; an adequate computation of points on (1) appears in the table.

y	y^2 or x
0.0	0.00
0.5	0.25
1.0	1.00
1.5	2.25
2.0	4.00
3.0	9.00
4.0	16.00

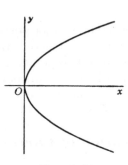

Figure 24

Using the information in the table, we plot the points $(0, 0)$, $(0.25, 0.5)$, $(1, 1)$, etc. Since in (1) a change from y to $(-y)$ does not alter the equation, the table yields also the points $(0.25, -0.5)$, $(1, -1)$, $(2.25, -1.5)$, and so on. Finally we draw a smooth curve (Figure 24) through the points plotted. This curve is a parabola. Parabolas will be studied in more detail in § 63.

One of the many advantages of calculus (the subject which we begin to study in the next chapter) is that it greatly reduces the number of points which need to be plotted to obtain a good sketch of a curve whose equation is given. A knowledge of calculus also permits us to obtain for many curves much additional information which would not be accessible from point plotting no matter what number of points were plotted. Therefore we shall delay most of the sketching of curves until the pertinent tools of calculus have been introduced.

The set of points whose coordinates satisfy a given equation may be empty. There are, for example, no real values of x and y which satisfy the equation

(2)
$$x^2 + y^2 = -4.$$

There is only one point, the origin, on the curve

(3)
$$x^2 + y^2 = 0.$$

The student should not lean heavily on any intuitive feeling about the appearance of curves.   A simple equation may yield a curve which looks bizarre to the beginner.   A curve does not need to do any "curving."   For instance, the equation

(4) $$y = 2x + 1$$

represents a straight line, and we shall see in Ex. 40, page 46, that the points on the curve

(5) $$|x| + |y| = 1,$$

form a square.

On the other hand, a major portion of those curves which enter our work do bend gracefully.   Just as the straight line is often described as the shortest distance between two points, a curve has been loosely described as the loveliest distance between two points.   The student who bears that loose description in mind may be led to spare his instructor the pain involved in examining ugly drawings.

17. *Classification of Curves*

An algebraic plane curve is one whose equation in rectangular coordinates is a polynomial in x and y, equated to zero: for example,

$$x^2 - xy + x + 3y - 5 = 0,$$
$$x^3 + 2x^2y - y^3 + 5y = 0.$$

Any nonalgebraic curve is called *transcendental*; for example,

$$y = \sin x, \qquad y = \log_{10} x, \qquad y = 2^x.$$

An algebraic curve whose equation is of the nth degree is called a *curve of the nth degree*.   For example, the curve

$$3x^2y + 2x^2 - y = 6$$

is of third degree; the curve

$$y^2 = \frac{x + 3}{x^2 + 2x}$$

is of fourth degree.

Since an irrational equation may not be fully equivalent to the one obtained by rationalizing, its locus may be only a part of the curve corresponding to the rational form.   For instance, the equation

$$y = \sqrt{x}$$

represents only the upper half of the curve of Figure 24, page 19,

$$y^2 = x.$$

18. *Symmetry*

Two points P_1, P_2 are said to be *symmetric* with respect to a line if that line is the perpendicular bisector of the segment P_1P_2; the line is then called a *line of symmetry*. Each of the points P_1, P_2 is the *image*, or *reflection*, of the other in the line L. A curve or other plane figure is *symmetric with respect to a line* if, corresponding to every point P_1 of the figure, the image-point P_2 in that line also belongs to the figure. This means that the figure is *unchanged by reflection* in the line of symmetry. In Figure 25 the curve is symmetric with respect to the line L.

Figure 25   Figure 26

Two points P_1, P_2 are said to be *symmetric with respect to a point C* if C is the mid-point of P_1P_2. A plane figure is symmetric with respect to a point C if, corresponding to every point P_1 of the figure, there is a point P_2, also belonging to the figure, such that C is the mid-point of P_1P_2. The point C is called the *center of symmetry*, or simply the *center* (Figure 26).

THEOREM 3. *A curve is symmetric with respect to the x-axis if its equation is unchanged* when y is replaced by $-y$; and conversely. A curve is sym-metric with respect to the y-axis if its equation is unchanged when x is replaced by $-x$; and conversely.*

THEOREM 4. *A curve is symmetric with respect to the origin if its equation is unchanged when x is replaced by $-x$ and y by $-y$ simultaneously; and conversely.*

Proof of Theorem 3. By hypothesis, if any pair of coordinates (x, y) satisfy the equation, the coordinates $(x, -y)$ of the image-point with respect to the x-axis also satisfy the equation. Proof of the converse and of Theorem 4 is left to the student.

19. *Points of Intersection of Two Curves*

In rectangular coordinates, the points of intersection of two curves are points whose coordinates *satisfy both equations*, and there are no other points having this property. Hence *the points of intersection of two curves are found by solving the equations of the curves as simultaneous equations.* Intersections of a curve with the coordinate axes are called *intercepts*.

* Precisely, if the new form of the equation is *equivalent* to the original form—that is, if each form is satisfied by all the values of the variables that satisfy the other.

It may happen that all the values of x and y, found by solving two simultaneous equations, are imaginary; or the equations may be "incompatible," not satisfied by any pairs of values either real or imaginary (Ex. 40 below). Of course in either case the result means that the curves have no intersection.

A check should always be made by substituting the values of x and y in both equations and noting whether the equations hold.

Example. Find the points of intersection of the curve (a straight line)

(1) $$2x + y = 10$$

and the curve (a circle)

(2) $$x^2 + y^2 = 25.$$

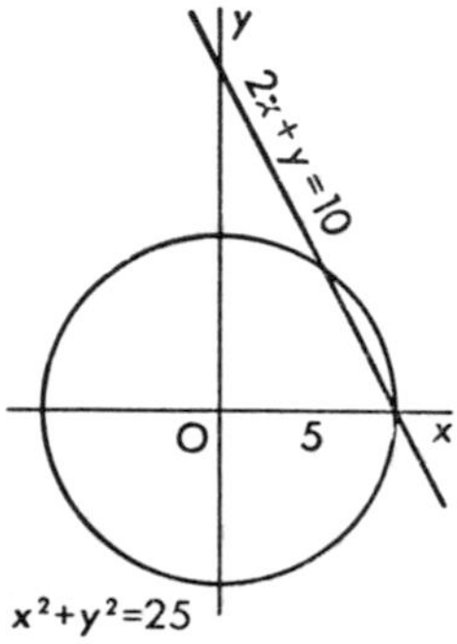

Substituting the value of y from (1) in (2), we get

$$x^2 + (10 - 2x)^2 = 25,$$

or

$$5x^2 - 40x + 75 = 0,$$
$$x^2 - 8x + 15 = 0,$$

so that

$$x = 3 \text{ or } 5.$$

By (1),

$$y = 4 \text{ or } 0,$$

Figure 27

and the points are (3, 4), (5, 0).

We know that when two equations in x and y are solved as simultaneous, the number of solutions (i.e., the number of pairs of values of x and y satisfying both equations) is not greater than the product of the degrees of the equations.

THEOREM 5. *The number of points of intersection of two curves is not greater than the product of the degrees of their equations.*

EXERCISES

In Exs. 1–6, determine whether the points lie on the curve.

1. Curve $x + 3y = 7$; points (1, 2), (2, −3), (10, −1), (0, 2).
2. Curve $3x - 2y + 1 = 0$; points (1, 1), (1, 2), (3, 5), ($\frac{1}{2}$, $\frac{5}{4}$).
3. Curve $y^2 = 4ax$; points ($2a$, a), ($-a$, $-2a$), ($4a$, $-4a$), ($\frac{1}{4}a$, a).
4. Curve $x^2 + y^2 = 5$; points (−2, −1), ($\sqrt{2}$, $\sqrt{3}$), (1.41, 1.73).
5. Curve $y = x^3 + 2x^2 - x - 3$; points (1, −1), (−2, −1), (−4, −30).
6. Curve $x^2 - xy + 4y = 3$; points (3, −6), (−2, −1), (2, −$\frac{1}{2}$).
7. For what values of c does the curve $cy = x^3$ pass through (a) (1, 2); (b) (2, 4); (c) (0, 3); (d) (3, 0); (e) (0, 0)?
8. Given that the point (x_1, y_1) lies on the curve $x^2 - 4y^2 = 25$, express this fact analytically.
9. What is the condition that the curve $y = ax^2 + bx + c$ shall pass through (0, 0)? Through (1, 2)? Through (−2, 3)?

In Exs. 10–13, determine the constants so that the curve shall pass through the given points.   Check the answers.

10. Curve $Ax + By = 5$; points $(3, 1)$, $(-1, -2)$.   *Ans. $3x - 4y = 5$.*
11. Curve $y = mx + b$; points $(1, 2)$, $(5, -6)$.
12. Curve $x^2 + y^2 + ax + by = 0$; points $(4, 2)$, $(6, 8)$.
                    Ans. $x^2 + y^2 + 2x - 14y = 0$.
13. Curve $y = ax^2 + bx + c$; points $(1, 6)$, $(-2, -6)$, $(0, 4)$.
                    Ans. $y = 4 + 3x - x^2$.
  14. On the curve $y^2 = x^3$, find the points (a) whose abscissa is 1; (b) whose abscissa is -3; (c) whose ordinate is -8.   *Ans. (b) None.*
  15. On the curve $y^2 = 4ax$, find the points (a) whose abscissa is a; (b) whose ordinate is $-a$; (c) whose ordinate is zero.
  16. On the curve $y^2 = 4y - x + 2$, find the points (a) whose abscissa is -3; (b) whose abscissa is 7; (c) whose ordinate is 6.

In Exs. 17–26, find the intercepts on the axes, test for symmetry, plot an adequate number of points, and draw the curve on a suitable scale.

17. $y^2 = x + 4$.   **18.** $x^2 = y - 2$.
19. $y = x^2 - x$.   **20.** $y = 6 - x - x^2$.
21. $xy = 4$.   **22.** $y = x^3 - 9x$.
23. $4y^2 - 2y + x = 0$.   **24.** $x = (y^2 - 4)^2$.
25. $y = x^3 + 3x^2 + 2x$.   **26.** $y = x^3 - 3x^2 - 4x$.

Without formal proofs, state how many lines of symmetry are possessed by each of the figures in Exs. 27–32.

  27. (a) A circle; (b) a circular arc.
  28. (a) A straight line; (b) a straight line segment.   *Ans. (b) Two.*
  29. A triangle.   Discuss special cases fully.
  30. A quadrilateral.   Discuss all special cases.
  31. Two intersecting lines taken together.
  32. Two parallel lines taken together.
  33. Show that two circles taken together always have one line of symmetry. When are there two such lines?   When more than two?
  34. When do three circles have one or more lines of symmetry?
  35. Prove analytically that if a curve is symmetric with respect to Ox and Oy, it is symmetric with respect to the origin.   Show by an example that the converse is not true.
  36. Prove that: *If a curve is symmetric with respect to one axis and the origin, it is symmetric with respect to the other axis also.*
  37. By finding the mid-point and slope of the line segment joining the points (h, k) and (k, h), prove that: *In any equation, the effect of interchanging x and y is to reflect the curve in the line $y = x$.*

In Exs. 38–49, find the points of intersection of the given curves; check your answers.

  38. $x + y = 7$, $3x - y = 5$.
  39. $2x - 3y = 13$, $5x + y = 7$.
  40. $x + 2y + 1 = 0$, $4y = 5 - 2x$.   Draw the lines.

41. $2x - 3y = 0$, $6y - 4x = 3$.   Draw the lines.

42. $x^2 + y^2 = 50$, $3y = x + 20$.

43. $x^2 + y^2 = 25$, $3x + y = 5$.

44. $x^2 + y^2 = 5$, $2x - y = 5$.   *Ans.* $(2, -1)$ twice.

45. $x^2 + y^2 = 10$, $x + 3y = 10$.   *Ans.* $(1, 3)$ twice.

46. $y = x^2$, $y^2 = 3y - 2x$.   *Ans.* $(0, 0)$, $(-2, 4)$, $(1, 1)$ twice.

47. $x^2 + y^2 = 5$, $y^2 = 2x + 5$.

48. $y = x^3 - 3x^2 + x$, $2x + y = 1$.   Make an accurate detail of the curves in the interval $0 \leq x \leq 2$.   *Ans.* $(1, -1)$ three times.

49. $y = x^4 - 4x^3 + 6x^2 - 3$, $y = 4x - 4$.   Make a large scale detail of the curves in the interval $0 \leq x \leq 2$.   *Ans.* $(1, 0)$ four times.

In Exs. 50–53, determine the degree of the equation.

50. $x^{\frac{1}{2}} + y^{\frac{1}{2}} = a^{\frac{1}{2}}$.   *Ans.* 2.   **51.** $x^{\frac{1}{3}} + y^{\frac{1}{3}} = a^{\frac{1}{3}}$.   *Ans.* 3.

52. $x^{\frac{2}{3}} + y^{\frac{2}{3}} = a^{\frac{2}{3}}$.   *Ans.* 6.   **53.** $x^{\frac{3}{2}} + y^{\frac{3}{2}} = a^{\frac{3}{2}}$.   *Ans.* 6.

20. *Straight Lines*

In § 13 we obtained a formula for the slope of the straight line joining any two points (x_1, y_1), (x_2, y_2) with unequal abscissas:

$$(1) \qquad\qquad m = \frac{y_2 - y_1}{x_2 - x_1}, \qquad x_2 \neq x_1.$$

Consider a straight line through two given points (x_1, y_1), (x_2, y_2), with $x_2 \neq x_1$, and compute its slope by (1).   Let (x, y) be a variable point on the line.   Then also by (1)

$$\frac{y - y_1}{x - x_1} = m,$$

so that the straight line is represented by the equation

$$(2) \qquad\qquad y - y_1 = m(x - x_1).$$

Equation (2) is called the point-slope form of the equation of a straight line. By using (2) we may write at once the equation of a line through a given point with a given slope.

Any line whose slope exists has an equation of the form (2) and therefore intersects the y-axis ($x = 0$) at some point $(0, b)$.   Then b is called the *y-intercept* of the line.   By employing (2) with (x_1, y_1) replaced by $(0, b)$, we obtain the equation

$$(3) \qquad\qquad y = mx + b.$$

which is called the *slope-intercept form* of the equation of a straight line.

If two points on a line have equal abscissas, $x_2 = x_1$, all points on the line have the same abscissa and the line is represented by the equation

$$(4) \qquad\qquad x = x_1,$$

in which x_1 is the common abscissa and (x, y) is a variable point on the line. Equation (4) represents a vertical line, one parallel to the y-axis.

We have shown that every line in the xy-plane has an equation of the form (3) or of the form (4). Equations (3) and (4) are both included in the general equation of the first degree:

$$(5) \qquad\qquad Ax + By + C = 0,$$

with constant A, B, C.

THEOREM 6. *Every straight line may be represented by an equation of the first degree.*

Next we prove that equation (5) always represents a straight line.

THEOREM 7. *The locus of every equation of the first degree is a straight line.*

Proof. We need to show that if A and B are not both zero, (5) represents a straight line. Either $B = 0$ or $B \neq 0$. If $B = 0$, $A \neq 0$, and (5) may be written

$$x = -\frac{C}{A},$$

which is of the form (4) above with $x_1 = -\dfrac{C}{A}$. Therefore, if $B = 0$, (5) represents a vertical line.

If $B \neq 0$, we may solve (5) for y and thus obtain

$$y = mx + b$$

in which $m = -\dfrac{A}{B}$ and $b = -\dfrac{C}{B}$. This is the equation of a line with slope m and y-intercept b.

The slope-intercept form

$$(6) \qquad\qquad y = mx + b$$

and the point-slope form

$$(7) \qquad\qquad y - y_1 = m(x - x_1)$$

are both extremely useful.

RULE. *To reduce the equation of any line (not parallel to the y-axis) to the slope-intercept form, solve the equation for y. When this has been done, the coefficient of x is the slope and the constant term is the y-intercept.*

Example (a). To reduce the equation

$$3x + 4y - 6 = 0$$

to the slope-intercept form, write

$$4y = -3x + 6,$$
$$y = -\tfrac{3}{4}x + \tfrac{3}{2},$$

from which we find that the slope is $-\tfrac{3}{4}$ and the y-intercept $\tfrac{3}{2}$.

Example (*b*).   Find the equation of the line through $(-3, 5)$ and $(2, 4)$.
By (1) of this section the slope of the line is

$$m = \frac{4 - 5}{2 + 3} = -\frac{1}{5}.$$

Equation (7) now yields

$$y - 5 = -\tfrac{1}{5}(x + 3),$$

or

(8) $x + 5y = 22.$

Check.   For $(2, 4)$, $x + 5y = 2 + 20 = 22$;
For $(-3, 5)$, $x + 5y = -3 + 25 = 22.$

The student should prove the following theorem with the aid of the slope-intercept form.

THEOREM 8.   *The lines*

$$A_1x + B_1y + C_1 = 0,$$
$$A_2x + B_2y + C_2 = 0,$$

are parallel if and only if

$$\begin{vmatrix} A_1 & B_1 \\ A_2 & B_2 \end{vmatrix} = 0.$$

By reduction to the slope-intercept form, it is easily seen that the lines

$$Ax + By + C = 0,$$
$$Ax + By + K = 0,$$

are parallel and that the lines

$$Ax + By + C = 0,$$
$$Bx - Ay + K = 0,$$

are perpendicular.   Hence, if a line is to be parallel to a given line, the coefficients of x and y in the required equation may be taken *the same as those in the given equation*; if a line is to be perpendicular to a given line, the coefficients of x and y in the required equation may be found by *interchanging the coefficients of x and y and changing the sign of one of them.*   In each case, of course, the constant term must be determined by an additional condition.

Example (*c*).   Write the equation of a line through the point $(3, -1)$ perpendicular to the line $3x + 2y = 6$.

The left member of the required equation will be $2x - 3y$; if the new equation is to be satisfied by the coordinates $(3, -1)$, the right member must be what the left member becomes when we put 3 for x and (-1) for y. Hence the required equation is

$$2x - 3y = 9.$$

Example (d). Find the equation of the line through $(3, -6)$ perpendicular to the line joining $(4, 1)$ and $(2, 5)$.

By (1), the slope of the line joining $(4, 1)$ and $(2, 5)$ is -2, whence the slope of the required line is $\frac{1}{2}$, and by (2) its equation is

$$y + 6 = \tfrac{1}{2}(x - 3),$$

or

$$x - 2y = 15.$$

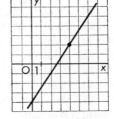

Figure 28

When the slope and one point of a line are given, the line can be drawn, if desired, *without writing the equation*. For example, to draw the line of slope $\frac{3}{2}$ through the point $(4, 2)$: starting at $(4, 2)$, we measure off 2 units to the right and then 3 upward (or 4 to the right and 6 upward, or 2 to the left and 3 downward, etc.); through the point thus reached and $(4, 2)$ we draw the line. See Figure 28.

EXERCISES

In Exs. 1–6, draw the line.

1. $y = 0$.
2. $x = 0$.
3. $x = 5$.
4. $2y = 3$.
5. $4y + 1 = 0$.
6. $3x - 4 = 0$.

In Exs. 7–10, draw the line; then write its equation.

7. Of slope $\frac{1}{4}$ through $(3, 1)$.
8. Of slope $\frac{3}{2}$ through $(-2, 4)$.
9. Of slope $-\frac{7}{3}$ through $(0, -5)$.
10. Of slope $-\frac{1}{2}$ through $(-4, 0)$.

In Exs. 11–19, write the equation of the line.

11. Through $(4, 1)$ and (a) parallel, (b) perpendicular to the line through $(7, 3)$, $(5, -1)$.   *Ans.* (a) $2x - y = 7$, (b) $x + 2y = 6$.
12. Through $(2, -3)$ and (a) parallel, (b) perpendicular to the line through $(0, -4)$, $(3, -2)$.   *Ans.* (a) $2x - 3y = 13$, (b) $3x + 2y = 0$.
13. Through $(4, 0)$ and (a) parallel, (b) perpendicular to the line through $(-1, -5)$, $(2, -4)$.
14. Through $(1, -5)$ and (a) parallel, (b) perpendicular to the line through $(-3, -2)$, $(-5, 3)$.
15. Through $(6, 1)$, $(4, 4)$.
16. Through $(-4, -1)$, $(5, -2)$.
17. Through $(-2, 3)$, $(3, -2)$.
18. Through $(3, 5)$, $(3, -7)$.
19. Through $(-1, 5)$ and (a) parallel, (b) perpendicular to the line through $(1, 3)$, $(1, -4)$.

In Exs. 20–25, reduce the equation to the slope-intercept form.

20. $2x - 7y + 5 = 0$.
21. $x + 3y - 4 = 0$.
22. $3x + 6y - 2 = 0$.
23. $4x - 2y + 3 = 0$.
24. $x + y = 7$.
25. $5x + 3y = 0$.

In Exs. 26–33, write, at sight, the equation of the line through the given point (a) parallel, (b) perpendicular to the given line.

26. Point $(3, 5)$, line $4x - y = 5$.   *Ans.* (a) $4x - y = 7$; (b) $x + 4y = 23$.
27. Point $(2, 4)$, line $2x + 3y = 6$.   *Ans.* (a) $2x + 3y = 16$; (b) $3x - 2y = -2$.
28. Point $(1, 2)$, line $2x + y = 7$.
29. Point $(-2, 4)$, line $3x + 5y = 8$.
30. Point $(-1, -4)$, line $4x - 2y = 3$.
31. Point $(0, -2)$, line $x + 3y = 7$.
32. Point $(0, -1)$, line $2y + 3 = 0$.
33. Point $(2, 4)$, line $4x + 3 = 0$.
34. Show that the lines $3x - y = 7$, $2x + 6y = 5$, $9x = 3y - 4$, and $x + 3y = 8$ form a rectangle.
35. Show that the following lines: $x = 2y + 4$, $3x + 2y = 5$, $3x - 6y = 7$, and $3x + 2y = -1$ form a parallelogram.
36. Find the locus of the centers of circles touching the line $3x + 7y = 4$ at $(-1, 1)$.
37. Find the locus of the centers of circles touching the line $5x + y = 6$ at $(2, -4)$.
38. Show that a circle can be drawn which touches the lines $x - y + 1 = 0$ and $7x + y = 13$ at $(4, 5)$ and $(2, -1)$, respectively.
39. Can a circle be drawn touching the lines $x + y = 6$ and $7x + 20y = 73$ at $(7, -1)$ and $(-1, 4)$, respectively?

21. *Area of a Triangle*

Consider a triangle with vertices P_1: (x_1, y_1), P_2: (x_2, y_2), P_3: (x_3, y_3). In Figure 29, if from the area of the trapezoid $M_3M_2P_2P_3$ we subtract the areas of the trapezoids $M_3M_1P_1P_3$ and $M_1M_2P_2P_1$, there remains the area of the triangle. Now, from the figure,

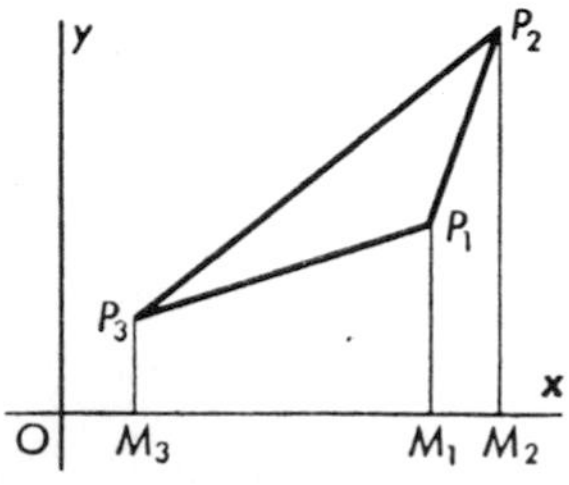

Figure 29

$$M_3M_2P_2P_3 = \tfrac{1}{2}(x_2 - x_3)(y_2 + y_3),$$
$$M_3M_1P_1P_3 = \tfrac{1}{2}(x_1 - x_3)(y_1 + y_3),$$
$$M_1M_2P_2P_1 = \tfrac{1}{2}(x_2 - x_1)(y_2 + y_1).$$

Thus

$$A = \tfrac{1}{2}[(x_2 - x_3)(y_2 + y_3) - (x_1 - x_3)(y_1 + y_3) - (x_2 - x_1)(y_2 + y_1)],$$

or, after some rearrangement,

(1) $$A = \tfrac{1}{2}[x_1(y_2 - y_3) + x_2(y_3 - y_1) + x_3(y_1 - y_2)].$$

Since the right member of (1) is the expansion, by minors of the first column, of the determinant below, we have proved that:

The area of the triangle with vertices (x_1, y_1), (x_2, y_2), (x_3, y_3) *is*

(2) $$A = \tfrac{1}{2} \begin{vmatrix} x_1 & y_1 & 1 \\ x_2 & y_2 & 1 \\ x_3 & y_3 & 1 \end{vmatrix}.$$

One qualifying remark is necessary. It can be shown that the formula gives a positive or negative answer according as motion around the triangle in the order P_1, P_2, P_3 is counterclockwise or clockwise. To avoid confusion, it is best to arrange the vertices in the counterclockwise order, so that the formula will always yield a positive result.

EXERCISES

In Exs. 1–8, find the area of the triangle with vertices as given.

1. $(2, -5)$, $(6, 2)$, $(4, 1)$.   *Ans.* 5.
2. $(2, 3)$, $(1, 1)$, $(-2, -2)$.   *Ans.* $\frac{3}{2}$.
3. $(-3, -2)$, $(7, 4)$, $(-8, -1)$.
4. $(1, -2)$, $(-1, 6)$, $(-4, -1)$,
5. $(3, 7)$, $(5, -2)$, $(6, 1)$.
6. $(9, 2)$, $(4, 6)$, $(-4, 0)$.
7. $(2, 0)$, $(11, 6)$, $(-4, -4)$. Interpret the result.
8. $(1, 1)$, $(-5, 9)$, $(4, -3)$. Interpret the result.
9. Three vertices of a parallelogram are $(3, 2)$, $(-1, 7)$, $(4, -3)$. Find the area and draw the appropriate parallelograms.
10. Three vertices of a parallelogram are $(0, -1)$, $(2, 5)$, $(-5, -3)$. Find the area and draw the appropriate parallelograms.

In Exs. 11–14, find the area of the quadrilateral having the given points as consecutive vertices. Check by dividing into triangles in two ways.

11. $(5, 2)$, $(4, 3)$, $(2, 4)$, $(-8, -1)$.
12. $(3, -5)$, $(9, 5)$, $(0, 5)$, $(-2, 1)$.
13. $(3, -2)$, $(-1, -3)$, $(7, -2)$, $(5, 3)$.
14. $(8, -2)$, $(5, 6)$, $(4, 1)$, $(-7, 4)$.

In Exs. 15–18, find the distance of the point from the line.

15. Point $(12, 7)$, line through $(5, 3)$, $(2, -3)$.   *Ans.* $2\sqrt{5}$.
16. Point $(5, -3)$, line through $(1, -1)$, $(-3, -4)$.   *Ans.* 4.
17. Point $(27, 20)$, line through $(0, 0)$, $(40, 30)$. Plot the points.   *Ans.* $\frac{1}{5}$.
18. Point $(2, 5)$, line through $(-5, -5)$, $(7, 12)$. Plot the points.
19. Prove that if the coordinates of the vertices of a parallelogram are whole numbers, the parallelogram contains a whole number of units of area. Is this theorem true for any polygon?
20. Prove that if the coordinates of the vertices of a polygon are rational numbers, the area of the polygon is also a rational number.
21. Prove that if the coordinates of the vertices of a triangle are even numbers, the area of the triangle is an even number. Is this theorem true for any polygon?

22. *Two-Point Form; Intercept Form*

We have already (§ 20) written the equation of a line through two points by utilizing the point-slope form, equation (2), page 24. That method fails if the given points have the same abscissa.

The equation of the line through any two points (x_1, y_1), (x_2, y_2) may be written in the form

(1)
$$\begin{vmatrix} x & y & 1 \\ x_1 & y_1 & 1 \\ x_2 & y_2 & 1 \end{vmatrix} = 0.$$

For, by § 21, this equation merely expresses the fact that the moving point (x, y) forms with the fixed points (x_1, y_1), (x_2, y_2) a triangle of area zero. See also Ex. 24 below.

It is to be noted that formula (1) holds in all cases—even when the line is parallel to the y-axis.

If a line has intercepts on both axes, the equation of the line can be written in terms of those intercepts.

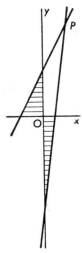

The equation of the straight line with x-intercept a and y-intercept b is

(2)
$$\frac{x}{a} + \frac{y}{b} = 1.$$

This equation, called the *intercept form*, fails in case the line passes through the origin or is parallel to either axis.

Equation (2) may be obtained by writing the equation of the line joining $(a, 0)$ with $(0, b)$, or by any one of numerous other methods.

Example. A line forms with the axes a triangle of area 1 and passes through the point P: $(1, 4)$. Find the dimensions of the triangle.

Use of the intercept form is suggested by the fact that we can then express the first condition at once. It is apparent that the intercepts of the line must be of opposite sign: therefore

Figure 30

(3)
$$-\tfrac{1}{2}ab = 1.$$

Substituting the coordinates $(1, 4)$ in (2), we get

(4)
$$\frac{1}{a} + \frac{4}{b} = 1.$$

Equations (3) and (4) give

$$a = -1, b = 2 \quad \text{or} \quad a = \tfrac{1}{2}, b = -4.$$

EXERCISES

In Exs. 1–4, draw the line with the given numbers as x- and y-intercepts, respectively. Write the equation of the line.

1. $2, -3$.

2. $-5, 4$.

3. $\frac{1}{3}, \frac{2}{5}$.

4. $-\frac{2}{3}, -\frac{1}{4}$.

In Exs. 5–10, reduce the equation to the intercept form.   Draw the line.

5. $3x + 5y = 30$.

6. $5x - 2y = -10$.

7. $3x - 4y = -24$.

8. $x + 2y = 9$.

9. $2x + 3y = 1$.

10. $7x - y = -1$.

In Exs. 11–17, find the equation of the line.   Check the answer.

11. Through $(3, 4)$, with equal intercepts.

12. Through $(-5, 2)$, with equal intercepts.

13. Through $(-7, 4)$, with intercepts numerically equal but of opposite sign.
$Ans.$ $x - y = -11$.

14. Through $(-8, 6)$, with x-intercept twice the y-intercept.

15. Through $(\frac{12}{5}, 1)$, forming with the axes a triangle of area 5.
$Ans.$ $5x - 2y = 10; 5x + 8y = 20; 5x + 18y = 30; 5x - 72y = -60$.

16. Through $(-2, 4)$, forming with the axes a triangle of area 9.   Why are there only two solutions?

17. Through $(1, 3)$, forming with the axes a triangle of area 6.   (Three solutions.)

18. A line passes through $(2, 2)$, and the segment of the line intercepted between the axes is of length $\sqrt{5}$.   Find the equation of the line.
$Ans.$ $2x - y = 2; x - 2y = -2$.

19. A rectangle is inscribed, base to base, in a right triangle of base b and height h.   What relation must hold between the base and altitude of the rectangle?

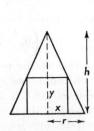

Figure 31

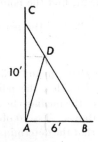

Figure 32

20. A circular cylinder is inscribed in a circular cone of radius r and height h. What relation must hold between the radius and height of the cylinder?   (Figure 31.)
$Ans.$ $\dfrac{x}{r} + \dfrac{y}{h} = 1$.

21. A beam BC leans against a wall AC and is stayed by a strut AD.   If D is 2 ft. out from the wall, find the length of the strut.   (Figure 32.) $Ans.$ 6 ft. 11.5 in.

22. In Ex. 21, if a strut 6 ft. long is used, at what height above the ground will it reach the beam?   *Ans.* 5 ft. 3.5 in.

23. Show that *three points* (x_1, y_1), (x_2, y_2), (x_3, y_3) *lie in a straight line if and only if*

$$\begin{vmatrix} x_1 & y_1 & 1 \\ x_2 & y_2 & 1 \\ x_3 & y_3 & 1 \end{vmatrix} = 0.$$

24. Without expanding the determinant, verify formula (1) of this section, by showing (a) that the equation is of first degree; (b) that it is satisfied by the coordinates of the given points.

25. Show that if no two of the three lines

$$A_1 x + B_1 y + C_1 = 0,$$
$$A_2 x + B_2 y + C_2 = 0,$$
$$A_3 x + B_3 y + C_3 = 0,$$

are parallel, the three lines are concurrent if and only if

$$\begin{vmatrix} A_1 & B_1 & C_1 \\ A_2 & B_2 & C_2 \\ A_3 & B_3 & C_3 \end{vmatrix} = 0.$$

In Exs. 26–32, choose coordinate axes so that the vertices of the triangle become $(a, 0)$, $(-a, 0)$, (b, c).

26. Show that the medians of a triangle are concurrent (Ex. 25).

27. Show that the altitudes of a triangle are concurrent (Ex. 25).

28. Show that the perpendicular bisectors of the sides of a triangle are concurrent (Ex. 25).

29. In Ex. 26, find the point of intersection of the medians.   *Ans.* $(\frac{1}{3}b, \frac{1}{3}c)$.

30. In Ex. 27, find the point of intersection of the altitudes.   *Ans.* $\left(b, \dfrac{a^2 - b^2}{c}\right)$.

31. In Ex. 28, find the point of intersection of the perpendicular bisectors.

Ans. $\left(0, \dfrac{b^2 + c^2 - a^2}{2c}\right)$.

32. Prove that, in any triangle, the point of intersection of the perpendicular bisectors of the sides, the point of intersection of the altitudes, and the point of intersection of the medians lie in a straight line. Use the results of Exs. 29–31 above and Ex. 23 above. Try to obtain the result without expanding the determinant.

33. Show that the determinant in Ex. 25 is always zero if the three lines are parallel and never zero if two are parallel but not coincident, with the third intersecting them.

23. *Circles*

A *circle* is the locus of a point that moves at a constant distance from a fixed point. The fixed point is the *center*, and the constant distance is the *radius*. The radius as thus defined is, of course, merely a number of linear units; the term is also used, as in elementary geometry, to mean a line-segment joining the center and a point of the curve. A *diameter* of a circle may mean either a straight line through the center, or the segment of such a line lying inside the curve.

Given a circle of radius a with center at C: (h, k), assume a point P: (x, y) on the curve. Then

Figure 33

$$CP = \sqrt{(x - h)^2 + (y - k)^2} = a;$$

if the center is at the origin,

$$\sqrt{x^2 + y^2} = a.$$

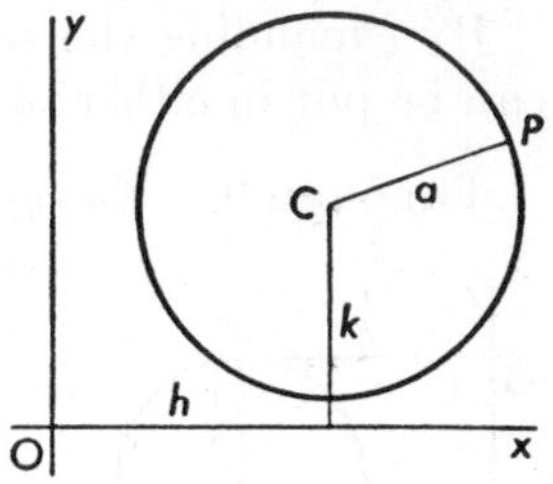

Hence:

The equation of a circle of radius a is:

if the center is the origin,

$$(1) \qquad x^2 + y^2 = a^2;$$

if the center is the point (h, k),

$$(2) \qquad (x - h)^2 + (y - k)^2 = a^2.$$

It follows from (2) that the equation of a circle is always of the second degree.

The most general equation of the second degree in x and y may contain, at most, terms in x^2, xy, y^2, x, y, and a constant: i.e., it may be written in the form

$$Ax^2 + Bxy + Cy^2 + Dx + Ey + F = 0.$$

Consider now the special case in which $A = C$ and $B = 0$:

$$(3) \qquad Ax^2 + Ay^2 + Dx + Ey + F = 0, \qquad A \neq 0.$$

We may always divide this equation through by A, transpose the constant term to the right member, and complete the squares in x and y (see the example below). The equation then has the form

$$(2) \qquad (x - h)^2 + (y - k)^2 = a^2,$$

and consequently represents a circle whenever the right member is positive.

When an equation of form (3) is reduced to form (2), it may happen that the right member becomes 0:

$$(x - h)^2 + (y - k)^2 = 0.$$

Since this equation holds only when $x = h$ and $y = k$, the locus is the single point (h, k)—a so-called point-circle.

Finally, it may happen that the right member of (2) is negative: In this case there is clearly no locus.

In some problems it is convenient to take, as the general form, the equation

$$(4) \qquad x^2 + y^2 + Dx + Ey + F = 0.$$

That this is allowable follows from the fact that, in (3), the coefficient of the square terms can always be reduced to unity by dividing through by A.

By expanding the squares in (2) we see that the equation of any circle can be put in either of the forms (3) or (4).

THEOREM 9.   *An equation of the second degree in which x^2 and y^2 have equal coefficients and the xy-term is missing represents a circle (exceptionally, a single point, or no locus).*

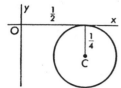

Figure 34

Example.   Find the center and radius of the circle

$$4x^2 + 4y^2 - 4x + 2y + 1 = 0.$$

Transpose the constant term to the right member and divide by 4:

$$x^2 + y^2 - x + \tfrac{1}{2}y = -\tfrac{1}{4}.$$

Then complete the squares in x and y:

$$x^2 - x + \tfrac{1}{4} + y^2 + \tfrac{1}{2}y + \tfrac{1}{16} = -\tfrac{1}{4} + \tfrac{1}{4} + \tfrac{1}{16},$$

or

$$(x - \tfrac{1}{2})^2 + (y + \tfrac{1}{4})^2 = \tfrac{1}{16}.$$

The center is the point C: $(\tfrac{1}{2}, -\tfrac{1}{4})$, and the radius is $\tfrac{1}{4}$.

EXERCISES

In Exs. 1–13, write the equation of the circle.

1. With center at $(2, -3)$, radius 5.
2. With center at $(-4, 1)$, radius 6.
3. With radius a and touching both axes.
4. With center at $(2a, a)$ and touching the y-axis.
5. With center at (a, b) and passing through the origin.
6. With center at $(-1, -3)$ and passing through $(-2, 0)$.
7. With center at $(-4, 2)$ and passing through $(0, 5)$.
8. With the points $(2, 5)$, $(6, -1)$ as ends of a diameter.
9. With the points $(0, 2a)$, $(2b, 0)$ as ends of a diameter.
10. With center at $(0, 0)$ and touching the line $3x + 4y = 10$.   Find two points on the line.   Then obtain the distance from $(0, 0)$ to the given line with the aid of equation (2), § 21.
11. With center at $(0, 0)$ and touching the line $5x - 12y = 52$.   See Ex. 10.
12. With center at $(-1, -2)$ and touching the line $x - 2y = -7$.   See Ex. 10.
13. With center at $(4, 3)$ and touching the line $3x + y = -15$.   See Ex. 10.
14. Using equation (2) of this section, find the condition that a circle shall (a) touch the x-axis; (b) pass through $(0, 0)$; (c) have its center on Oy; (d) touch both axes; (e) have its center on the line $3x + 4y = 12$.

In Exs. 15–24, draw the circle.

15. $x^2 + y^2 - 4x - 6y = 12.$ **16.** $x^2 + y^2 - 8x + 2y = 8.$
17. $x^2 + y^2 = 6x - 8y.$ **18.** $x^2 + y^2 = 2ay.$

19. $3x^2 + 3y^2 = y + 2$.   20. $2x^2 + 2y^2 = 6 - x$.
21. $4x^2 + 4y^2 + 4x = 12y - 1$.   22. $3x^2 + 3y^2 + 8x + 6y + 7 = 0$.
23. $2x^2 + 2y^2 = 2x + 2y - 1$.   24. $4x^2 + 4y^2 = 4y - 8x - 5$.

In Exs. 25–28, show that the circles are tangent to each other, and draw the figure.

25. $x^2 + y^2 - 6x + 1 = 0$, $x^2 + y^2 - 2y + 8x - 1 = 0$.
26. $x^2 + y^2 - 2x - 3 = 0$, $x^2 + y^2 + 4x - 8y + 11 = 0$.
27. $x^2 + y^2 = 2(y - x + 1)$, $x^2 + y^2 - 4x + 6y = 36$.
28. $x^2 + y^2 = 10x + 11$, $x^2 + y^2 - 2x - 6y + 9 = 0$.
29. Prove that equation (3) of this section represents a point-circle if and only if $D^2 + E^2 - 4AF = 0$.
30. Prove that equation (3) of this section has no locus if and only if

$$D^2 + E^2 - 4AF < 0.$$

31. A point moves so that the sum of the squares of its distances from the points $(a, 0)$, $(-a, 0)$ is constant (equal to k^2). Find the equation of its locus, and draw the curve for the cases $k^2 = 6a^2$, $k^2 = 4a^2$, $k^2 = 3a^2$, $k^2 = 2a^2$.
32. A point moves so that the square of its distance from a fixed point is proportional to its distance from a fixed line. Find the equation of its locus, and draw the curve for various cases. Use the fixed point $(0, 0)$ and fixed line $x = -a$.
33. A cone is inscribed in a sphere of radius a. Express the radius of the cone in terms of its altitude, and draw the graph.   *Ans.* $r = \sqrt{2ah - h^2}$.
34. Prove that an angle inscribed in a semicircle is a right angle.
35. On the line $x + 2y = 3$, find points at a distance 5 from $(1, 6)$.
   Ans. $(1, 1)$, $(-3, 3)$.
36. On the circle $x^2 + y^2 + 2x - 8y + 7 = 0$, find points at a distance 5 from $(2, -2)$.   *Ans.* $(2, 3)$, $(-2, 1)$.
37. Find the points of intersection of the circles

$$x^2 + y^2 - 18x - 4y + 35 = 0, \quad x^2 + y^2 + 2x + 6y - 15 = 0.$$

Draw the figure.   *Ans.* $(2, 1)$, $(4, -3)$.
38. Find the points of intersection of the circles

$$x^2 + y^2 - 6x - 8y - 24 = 0, \quad x^2 + y^2 = 6x + 8y.$$

Interpret the result.
39. Find the points of intersection of the circles

$$x^2 + y^2 - 4x - 2y + 1 = 0, \quad x^2 + y^2 + 4x + 3 = 0.$$

Interpret the result.

24. Polar Coordinates

Instead of locating a point by its distance from two perpendicular lines, we frequently, in ordinary usage, locate it by its distance and "bearing" from some fixed point: one town is 5 miles southeast of another; one boundary marker is 90 ft. N. 10° E. of another; etc. This method also has its counterpart in analytic geometry.

Let us choose a fixed line Ox in the coordinate plane and a point O on this line. The position of any point P (Figure 35) in the plane is determined if we know the length of the line OP together with the angle that this line

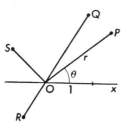

makes with Ox, both the distance and the angle being measured in a definite sense. The segment OP and the angle xOP are the *polar coordinates* of P: they are called the *radius vector* and the *polar angle*, respectively, and are denoted by r, θ. The fixed line Ox is the *initial line*, or *polar axis*, and the point O is the *pole*, or *origin*.

The polar coordinates of a point are written as P: (r, θ), or simply (r, θ). The polar angle is *positive* when measured *counterclockwise, negative clockwise*; the radius vector is *positive* if laid off *on the terminal side of θ,*

Figure 35

negative in the opposite direction, i.e., *on the terminal side produced through O*. Figure 35 shows Q: $(2, 60°)$, R: $(-1, 60°)$, S: $(-1, -45°)$.

To plot a point whose polar coordinates are given, we begin by drawing the line on which the radius vector lies—i.e., the line making an angle θ with Ox—and then lay off on that line, in the proper sense, the distance r.

Point plotting using polar coordinates is most easily done on "polar coordinate paper," which is paper ruled in concentric circles and straight lines.

Although to every pair of polar coordinates corresponds a single point, the same point may be represented by various pairs of coordinates. For instance, in Figure 35, the coordinates $(2, 60°)$, $(-2, 240°)$, $(-2, -120°)$ all represent the point Q.

Example. Trace the curve $r = 2a \cos \theta$.

θ	0	$\frac{1}{6}\pi$	$\frac{1}{4}\pi$	$\frac{1}{3}\pi$	$\frac{1}{2}\pi$
r	$2a$	$\sqrt{3}\,a$	$\sqrt{2}\,a$	a	0

By plotting these points, we get the upper half of the curve. Since for values of θ in the *second* quadrant $\cos \theta$, and hence r, is negative, the curve falls in the *fourth* quadrant; the values of $\cos \theta$ are numerically the same as in the first quadrant, but in reverse order, so that the lower half of the curve is symmetric to the upper half. In the third quadrant $\cos \theta$ takes the same values as in the first, but negative: the upper half is repeated. Similarly, for θ in the fourth quadrant, the lower half is repeated. Since

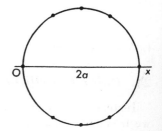

$$\cos (\theta \pm 2n\pi) = \cos \theta, \qquad n = 1, 2, \cdots,$$

values of $\theta > 2\pi$ or $\theta < 0$ will merely repeat the same curve.

Figure 36

Symmetry tests for equations in polar coordinates will be taken up in § 163.

25. *Distance Between Two Points*

We already know a formula for the distance between two points in terms of the rectangular coordinates of those points. Let us now obtain the corresponding formula in terms of the polar coordinates of the two points. In Figure 37, the required distance D, between the points (r_1, θ_1) and (r_2, θ_2), can be found by using the law of cosines from trigonometry:

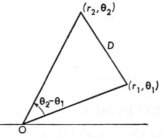

Figure 37

(1) $D^2 = r_1{}^2 + r_2{}^2 - 2r_1r_2 \cos(\theta_2 - \theta_1).$

From (1) we obtain easily the polar equation of any circle. Let (r, θ) be a variable point on the circle, (r_1, θ_1) the center, and a the radius. Then, by (1),

(2) $$r^2 + r_1{}^2 - 2r_1r \cos(\theta - \theta_1) = a^2.$$

Equation (1) is equivalent to the earlier formula

(3) $$D^2 = (x_1 - x_2)^2 + (y_1 - y_2)^2.$$

Example. Show that the points $(3, 90°)$, $(\sqrt{3}, 0°)$, $(3, 150°)$ are the vertices of a right triangle. (Figure 38.)

Designate the points by P_1, P_2, P_3, in the order given. By the distance formula, we obtain

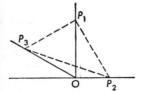

Figure 38

$$\overline{P_1P_2}{}^2 = 9 + 3 - 6\sqrt{3} \cos 90° = 12 - 0 = 12,$$
$$\overline{P_1P_3}{}^2 = 9 + 9 - 18 \cos 60° = 18 - 9 = 9,$$
$$\overline{P_2P_3}{}^2 = 3 + 9 - 6\sqrt{3} \cos 150° = 12 - 6\sqrt{3}\left(-\frac{\sqrt{3}}{2}\right) = 21.$$

Thus the triangle is a right triangle with its right angle at P_1.

26. *Choice of Coordinate System*

A coordinate system is a tool; it is not inherently present in a specific geometric problem. With both polar and rectangular coordinates available, we use whichever appears simpler for the particular problem under consideration. At times it will prove beneficial to change from one coordinate system to the other. The requisite formulas will be obtained on page 38.

Experience and common sense are both helpful in the efficient selection of the coordinate system to be used. As an example, compare the formulas for the rectangular coordinates of the mid-point of a line segment with the corresponding formulas in polar coordinates as exhibited in Exs. 33–34 below.

With the axes placed as in Figure 39, let a point P have the rectangular coordinates x, y and the polar coordinates r, θ. Then, from the figure,

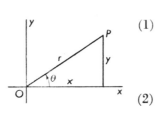

(1)

$$\begin{cases} x = r \cos \theta, \\ y = r \sin \theta, \\ x^2 + y^2 = r^2, \end{cases}$$

(2)

$$\begin{cases} r = \sqrt{x^2 + y^2}, \\ \cos \theta = \dfrac{x}{\sqrt{x^2 + y^2}}, \\ \sin \theta = \dfrac{y}{\sqrt{x^2 + y^2}}. \end{cases}$$

Figure 39

EXERCISES

In Exs. 1–4, plot the points whose polar coordinates are given.

1. $(3, 45°)$, $(2, -30°)$, $(-2, 135°)$.
2. $(1, 90°)$, $(-3, 180°)$, $(\frac{1}{2}, 120°)$.
3. $(4, 270°)$, $(-2, 60°)$, $(3, 0°)$.
4. $(2, 225°)$, $(1, -60°)$, $(0, 20°)$.

In Exs. 5–12, find the distance between the given points.

5. $(4, 0°)$, $(2\sqrt{3}, 30°)$.   *Ans.* 2.
6. $(3, 30°)$, $(8, 90°)$.   *Ans.* 7.
7. $(3, 15°)$, $(5, 135°)$.   *Ans.* 7.
8. $(7, -20°)$, $(8, 100°)$.   *Ans.* 13.
9. $(7, 30°)$, $(3\sqrt{2}, 75°)$.   *Ans.* 5.
10. $(7, 15°)$, $(5\sqrt{2}, 150°)$.   *Ans.* 13.
11. $(5, 0°)$, $(3\sqrt{2}, 45°)$.   *Ans.* $\sqrt{13}$.
12. $(-5, 0°)$, $(3\sqrt{2}, 45°)$.   *Ans.* $\sqrt{73}$.
13. Does the circle with center at $(3, 10°)$ and radius 7 pass through the point $(5, 130°)$?   *Ans.* Yes.
14. Does the circle with center at $(8, 20°)$ and radius 7 pass through the point $(5, 80°)$?   *Ans.* Yes.

In Exs. 15–18, show that the given points lie on a straight line.

15. $(6, 90°)$, $(3, 30°)$, $(2\sqrt{3}, 0°)$.
16. $(1, 30°)$, $(2, 90°)$, $(-2, 150°)$.
17. $(-6, 15°)$, $(3, 135°)$, $(2\sqrt{3}, 105°)$.
18. $(6, 0°)$, $(12, 60°)$, $(4\sqrt{3}, -30°)$.

In Exs. 19–21, show that the given points are the vertices of a right triangle, and find its area.

19. $(2, 45°)$, $(\sqrt{2}, 90°)$, $(-2, 135°)$.   *Ans.* 2.
20. $(2, 60°)$, $(2\sqrt{3}, 90°)$, $(1, 120°)$.   *Ans.* $\sqrt{3}$.
21. $(4, 45°)$, $(\sqrt{2}, 90°)$, $(-12, 135°)$.   *Ans.* 20.

In Exs. 22–28, express the statement by an equation.

22. The point (r, θ) lies on a circle of radius 5 with center at $(5, 0°)$.
$$Ans. \ r = 10 \cos \theta.$$

23. The point (r, θ) lies on a circle of radius 3 with center at $(-3, 0°)$.
$$Ans. \ r = -6 \cos \theta.$$

24. The point (r, θ) is at a distance 4 from $(3, 30°)$.
$$Ans. \ r^2 - 6r \cos (\theta - 30°) - 7 = 0.$$

25. A right triangle has its right angle at (r, θ) and its other vertices fixed at $(4, 30°)$ and $(3, 120°)$. $Ans. \ r = 4 \cos (\theta - 30°) + 3 \cos (\theta - 120°)$.

26. A right triangle has its right angle at (r, θ) and its other vertices fixed at $(5, 30°)$ and $(2, 90°)$. $Ans. \ r^2 - 2r \sin \theta - 5r \cos (\theta - 30°) + 5 = 0$.

27. The point (r, θ) is equidistant from $(2, 90°)$ and $(-2, 150°)$. $Ans. \ \theta = 30°$.

28. The point (r, θ) is equidistant from $(2, 30°)$ and $(3, 60°)$.
$$Ans. \ 2r[3 \cos (\theta - 60°) - 2 \cos (\theta - 30°)] = 5.$$

In Exs. 29–32, plot the curve with due regard to the symmetry properties of the sine and cosine.

29. $r = 2a \sin \theta$.

30. $r = a \cos^2 \theta$.

31. $r = a \sin^2 \theta$.

32. $r = a(1 + \sin \theta)$.

In Figure 40, the point $M:(r_m, \ \theta_m)$ is the mid-point of the line segment joining $P_1:(r_1, \ \theta_1)$ to $P_2:(r_2, \ \theta_2)$. The point A is the mid-point of OP_1. By elementary geometry we know that

$$\angle OAM = 180° - (\theta_2 - \theta_1),$$

$AM = \frac{1}{2}OP_2$, etc.

33. Use the law of sines to show that the polar coordinate θ_m for the point M in Figure 40 is given by

$$\tan \theta_m = \frac{r_1 \sin \theta_1 + r_2 \sin \theta_2}{r_1 \cos \theta_1 + r_2 \cos \theta_2}.$$

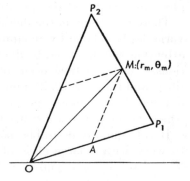

Figure 40

34. Use the law of cosines to show that the polar coordinate r_m for the point M in Figure 40 is given by

$$r_m{}^2 = \tfrac{1}{4}r_1{}^2 + \tfrac{1}{4}r_2{}^2 + \tfrac{1}{2}r_1r_2 \cos (\theta_2 - \theta_1).$$

35. Write the polar equation of a circle of radius a through the pole, if a diameter through O makes an angle α with Ox. $Ans. \ r = 2a \cos (\theta - \alpha)$.

36. Find the polar equation of the tangent line to the circle $r = a$ at the point (a, β). $Ans. \ r \cos (\theta - \beta) = a$.

37. Find the polar equation of the tangent line at the point (r_2, θ_2) on the circle with center at (r_1, θ_1).
$$Ans. \ rr_2 \cos (\theta - \theta_2) - rr_1 \cos (\theta - \theta_1) + r_1r_2 \cos (\theta_1 - \theta_2) = r_2{}^2.$$

Functions. Limits

27. Functions

When two quantities x and y are related so that for some range of values of x the value of y is determined by that of x, we say that y is a *function* of x. For a square with side of length c, the area is given by

$$(1) \qquad\qquad A = c^2, \qquad c > 0.$$

Thus A is a function of c, the range of values of c being determined by the physical meaning of the quantities involved.

There is nothing in the definition of the term *function* to require that the variables be related by an equation or by any set of formulas. Most of our attention will, however, be devoted to a study of functions defined by equations. Such functions occur often in mathematics and in physical applications, and they furnish illuminating examples of the power of the tools to be developed throughout the present course of study. The quantities with which we shall deal are restricted to real values.

It is frequently desirable, particularly in the development of the theory, to work with a large class of functions rather than with a specific one. Therefore we use a symbol such as $f(x)$, which is read "f of x," to denote a function of x. We write

$$(2) \qquad\qquad y = f(x)$$

to convey the fact that y is a function of x, without designating the particular manner in which y is related to x. Letters other than f are used in the same way: we may write

$$(3) \qquad\qquad z = w(v), \qquad u = s(v),$$

to indicate that z and u are both functions of v, without (since w and s are different letters) the two functions necessarily being the same.

Although the function symbol is of most value when the function is not stipulated, a little work with specific functions is an aid in becoming familiar with the notation.

Example (a). Let $f(x) = x^2 - 2$. Find $f(4), f(-3), f(0), f(c+1), f(-x)$.

40

Since $f(x) = x^2 - 2$,

$$f(4) = (4)^2 - 2 = 14.$$

In the same way

$$f(-3) = (-3)^2 - 2 = 7,$$
$$f(0) = 0^2 - 2 = -2,$$
$$f(c + 1) = (c + 1)^2 - 2 = c^2 + 2c - 1,$$

and

$$f(-x) = (-x)^2 - 2 = x^2 - 2 = f(x).$$

Example (b).   Let $h(y) = \sin 2y - 2 \cos y$.   Find $h(0), h(\frac{1}{2}\pi), h(\pi), h(\frac{1}{4}\pi)$.
From

$$h(y) = \sin 2y - 2 \cos y$$

it follows that

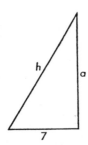

$$h(0) = \sin 0 - 2 \cos 0 = 0 - 2 = -2,$$
$$h(\tfrac{1}{2}\pi) = \sin \pi - 2 \cos \tfrac{1}{2}\pi = 0 - 0 = 0,$$
$$h(\pi) = \sin 2\pi - 2 \cos \pi = 0 + 2 = 2,$$
$$h(\tfrac{1}{4}\pi) = \sin \tfrac{1}{2}\pi - 2 \cos \tfrac{1}{4}\pi = 1 - \sqrt{2}.$$

Example (c).   A right triangle has a fixed base of length 7. Express the length of the altitude of the triangle as a function of the length of the hypotenuse.

The theorem of Pythagoras yields

$$h^2 = 49 + a^2$$

Figure 41   or

(4) $$a = \sqrt{h^2 - 49}, \qquad h > 7.$$

In (4) a is expressed as a function (explicit) of h.

28. *Graph of a Function*

The curve

(1) $$y = f(x)$$

is called the *graph of the function* $f(x)$.   Many properties of the function are made more vivid by this graphic representation.

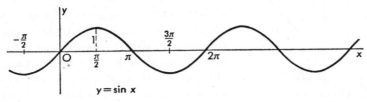

Figure 42

The graphs of the trigonometric functions sin x, cos x, tan x, as shown in Figures 42, 43, 44, exhibit for those functions many properties already familiar to the student. These three graphs are discussed in more detail in § 90.

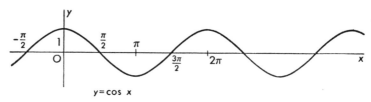

$y = \cos x$

Figure 43

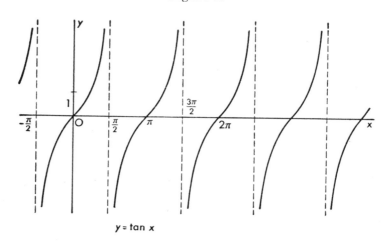

$y = \tan x$

Figure 44

The function $|x|$ was defined (without use of the functional notation) in § 2. The curve

(2)
$$y = |x|$$

is shown in Figure 45. As we already know, this is the same function as

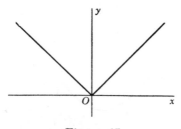

Figure 45

(3)
$$y = \sqrt{x^2}.$$

When the relation $y = f(x)$ is such that there is only one value of y for each admissible x, then $f(x)$ is said to be a *one-valued* function of x. The equivalent term *single-valued* function is also used. Graphically this means that if the function is defined for $x = a$, the vertical line $x = a$ intersects the curve in one and only one point.

Frequently, however, the law connecting x and y determines two or more values of y, in general distinct, for each value of x. Say that there are n values of y corresponding to each value of x. It is then possible to group the values of y so as to form n distinct one-valued functions, called the *branches* of the original function. The graph consists of n branches (not necessarily disconnected), each of which is met by the line $x = a$ in exactly one point.

Example. The equation

(4) $$y^2 = x, \qquad x \geqq 0,$$

defines a two-valued function whose branches are

$$y = \sqrt{x}, \qquad y = -\sqrt{x}.$$

The graphs of these functions are respectively the upper and lower halves of the curve (a parabola) shown in Figure 24, page 19.

When a many-valued function arises, we must as a rule form from it a *one-valued function* by naming the particular branch from which the value of y is to be taken. The reason is easily seen: until this has been done, there is no way to tell which of the several possible values is meant. If three grades of gasoline are for sale at 32¢, 30¢, 27¢, then the cost C is a three-valued function of the quantity of gasoline Q. The customer must make the function definite (i.e., one-valued) by saying which kind he wants. See Figure 46, which shows the three branches

$$C = 0.32\,Q, \qquad C = 0.30\,Q, \qquad C = 0.27\,Q.$$

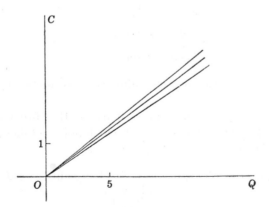

Figure 46

In this book we shall restrict ourselves to the study of one-valued functions except when the contrary is specifically stated. The word "function" is to denote a one-valued function without constant reiteration of its single-valued character.

29. *The Signum Function*

It is sometimes convenient to make use of what is called the *signum* (Latin for "sign") *function*. In practice, signum is usually abbreviated to sgn. We define this function by

$$(1) \qquad \begin{aligned} \operatorname{sgn} x &= -1, & \text{for } x < 0, \\ &= 0 \;\;, & \text{for } x = 0, \\ &= +1, & \text{for } x > 0. \end{aligned}$$

The graph of $y = \operatorname{sgn} x$ is shown in Figure 47. Except at zero, the value of the signum function is determined by the algebraic sign of its argument. When the argument x is positive, sgn x has the value plus one; when x is negative, sgn x has the value minus one.

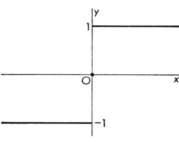

Figure 47

The signum function may be used to write in a single formula what would otherwise be given by two or more formulas. Suppose we wish to use the function $g(x)$ for values of $x < c$ and the function $h(x)$ for values of $x > c$. We write

$$(2) \quad \begin{aligned} F(x) &= \tfrac{1}{2}[1 - \operatorname{sgn}(x - c)]g(x) \\ &\quad + \tfrac{1}{2}[1 + \operatorname{sgn}(x - c)]h(x). \end{aligned}$$

Since $\operatorname{sgn}(x - c) = -1$ for $x < c$ and $\operatorname{sgn}(x - c) = +1$ for $x > c$, we may conclude that

$$(3) \qquad \begin{aligned} F(x) &= g(x), & \text{for } x < c, \\ &= \tfrac{1}{2}[g(c) + h(c)], & \text{for } x = c, \\ &= h(x), & \text{for } x > c. \end{aligned}$$

At $x = c$, $F(x)$ takes on the average value, the arithmetic mean of the values of $g(x)$ and $h(x)$.

Given a function $f(x)$, let us replace it by another function which agrees with $f(x)$ everywhere except at $x = c$, at which point it takes on some value k chosen by us. We write

$$(4) \qquad w(x) = f(x) \operatorname{sgn}|x - c| + (1 - \operatorname{sgn}|x - c|)k$$

and find that

$$\begin{aligned} w(x) &= f(x), & \text{for } x \neq c \\ &= k, & \text{for } x = c. \end{aligned}$$

Example. Sketch the curve

$$(5) \qquad y = \tfrac{1}{2}(1 + \operatorname{sgn} x) \sin x.$$

For $x < 0$, sgn $x = -1$, so $y = 0$. For $x = 0$, $y = 0$. For $x > 0$, $\frac{1}{2}(1 + \text{sgn } x) = +1$, so $y = \sin x$. Therefore the curve is as exhibited in Figure 48.

It follows from the definition of absolute value that

(6) $x = |x| \text{ sgn } x$

and that

(7) $|x| = x \text{ sgn } x.$

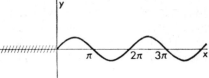

Figure 48

EXERCISES

In Exs. 1–10, certain functions are explicitly defined. Perform the indicated operations in each exercise.

1. If $f(x) = x^3 - 2x + 1$, find $f(0)$, $f(1)$, $f(2)$, $f(-2)$, $f(\frac{1}{2})$.   *Ans.* $f(-2) = -3$.
2. If $f(x) = x^4 - 2x^3 + 3x^2 + 4x - 1$, find $f(0)$, $f(2)$, $f(-2)$, $f(3)$, $f(\frac{1}{2})$.
$$\textit{Ans. } f(3) = 65, f(\tfrac{1}{2}) = \tfrac{25}{16}.$$
3. If $\varphi(y) = y(y - 2)^2$, find $\varphi(c)$, $\varphi(0)$, $\varphi(-2)$, $\varphi(x + 2)$.
$$\textit{Ans. } \varphi(x + 2) = x^2(x + 2).$$
4. If
$$F(a) = \frac{a^2 - a}{a^2 + 1},$$

find $F(0)$, $F(1)$, $F(2)$, $F(\tan x)$.   *Ans.* $F(\tan x) = \sin x(\sin x - \cos x)$.
5. If
$$f(x) = \frac{x^2 - 4x + 5}{12x - 3x^2},$$

show that $f(4 - x) = f(x)$.
6. If $H(\varphi) = \cos \varphi + \sin \varphi$, find $H(0)$, $H(\pi)$, $H(\pi + \varphi)$, $H(2\pi + \varphi)$.
$$\textit{Ans. } H(\pi + \varphi) = -H(\varphi).$$
7. If $f(x) = \sin 2x$, find $f(\frac{1}{2}\pi)$, $f(\pi - x)$, $f(-x)$, $f(0)$, $f(x - \frac{1}{2}\pi)$.
$$\textit{Ans. } f(\pi - x) = f(-x) = f(x - \tfrac{1}{2}\pi) = -f(x).$$
8. If $w(x) = \tan x$, find $w(\frac{1}{6}\pi)$, $w(\frac{2}{3}\pi)$, $w(x + \frac{1}{2}\pi)$, $w(x + \pi)$, $w(2x)$.
9. If $f(\beta) = \sin^2 \beta - \cos \beta$, find $f(\frac{1}{2}\pi)$, $f(\pi)$, $f(0)$, $f(\pi - \beta)$, $f(-\beta)$.
$$\textit{Ans. } f(\pi - \beta) = \sin^2 \beta + \cos \beta.$$
10. If $f(x) = \cos x$, find $f(x + \frac{1}{2}\pi)$, $f(\pi - x)$, $f(x + \frac{3}{2}\pi)$, $f(-x)$.

In Exs. 11–25, express the function by a formula and draw the graph, indicating that portion of the graph which has a meaning in the problem.

11. The value of a farm at \$60 per acre, with buildings worth \$4,000, as a function of the number of acres.
12. The volume of a sphere as a function of the radius.
13. The radius of a sphere as a function of the volume.
14. The volume of a cube as a function of the length of an edge.
15. The surface area of a cube as a function of the length of an edge.

16. The length e of an edge of a cube as a function of the surface area A of the cube. $\qquad$ *Ans.* $e = \sqrt{\dfrac{A}{6}}.$

17. The surface area of a cube as a function of the volume of the cube.

18. The present value V of a square tract of land as a function of the length of one side k (in yards), if it will be worth \$3.00 per sq. yd. after being inclosed by a fence costing \$2.00 per yd., with a 12-ft. gate costing \$25.

Ans. $V = 3k^2 - 8k - 17; k \geq 4.$

19. Temperature in °F. as a function of temperature in °C., (a) in general; (b) for a body of water in liquid form. *Ans.* (a) $F = \frac{9}{5}C + 32, C \geq -273.$

20. The altitude of a right triangle as a function of the base, if the hypotenuse is given.

21. The hypotenuse of a right triangle as a function of the base, if the altitude is given.

22. The base of a right triangle of given altitude, in terms of the hypotenuse.

23. The height of a cylindrical cup as a function of the radius, if 4π sq. in. of sheet metal are used.

24. In Ex. 23, the radius as a function of the height. *Ans.* $r = -h + \sqrt{h^2 + 4}.$

25. The current I from a battery as a function of the external resistance R, the electromotive force E and internal resistance r being constant. (Current equals electromotive force divided by the sum of the two resistances.)

26. In Ex. 25, express R as a function of I, and draw the curve.

27. A man drives from Detroit to Chicago, say 300 mi., at an average speed of 60 mi. per hr., stops 1 hr. in Chicago, and returns at a speed of 50 mi. per hr. Neglecting variations of speed en route, write formulas expressing x (distance from Detroit) as a function of t, and draw the graph.

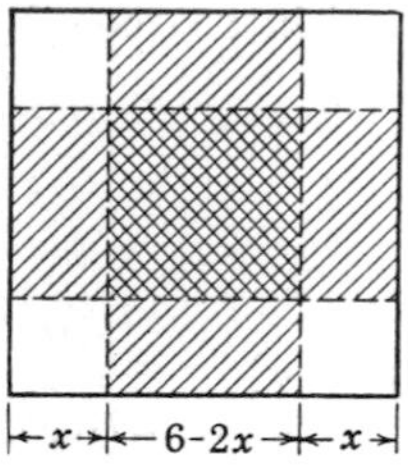

28. In Ex. 27, graph t as a function of x.

29. In Ex. 27, graph the speed v as a function of t.

30. In Ex. 27, graph the speed v as a function of x.

31. An open-top box is made by cutting equal squares of side x out of the corners of a piece of cardboard 6 in. square and turning up the sides (Figure 49). Plot the volume V as a function of x. *Ans.* $V = 4x(3 - x)^2; 0 \leq x \leq 3.$

$\leftarrow x \rightarrow\!\leftarrow\! 6-2x \rightarrow\!\leftarrow\! x \rightarrow$

Figure 49

32. In Ex. 31, find x if $V = 12.5$ cu. in. *Ans.* $x_1 = 0.5; x_2 = 1.60$ in.

33. Draw the graph of letter postage in the United States. What is the independent variable?

In Exs. 34–39, draw the curve.

34. $y = \frac{1}{2}(1 - \operatorname{sgn} x)x^2.$ **35.** $y = x - |x|.$

36. $y = x^2 + \operatorname{sgn}(x - 1).$ **37.** $y = x^2 \operatorname{sgn}(x - 1).$

38. $y = \sqrt{x^2 - 2ax + a^2}.$ **39.** $y = \sqrt{x^4 - 2x^2 + 1}.$

40. Draw the curve (a square) whose equation is $|x| + |y| = 1.$

41. The sides of three squares are 1, c, x. If the area of the third square equals the difference in area of the other two, graph x as a function of c.

42. A certain telegram costs 70¢ for the first 15 words or less, plus 5¢ for each additional word. Graph the cost as a function of the number of words.

43. A driver, starting with 10 gal. of gasoline, buys 5 gal. at the end of each 100 mi. If the car travels 20 mi. per gal., graph the quantity of gasoline in the tank, as a function of distance.

44. Solve Ex. 43 if the car travels 15 mi. per gal. Determine analytically and graphically how far the car can go. *Ans.* 375 mi.

30. *Definition of a Limit*

Let $f(x)$ be a function of x and let a be constant. If there is a number L such that, *in order to make the value of $f(x)$ as close to L as may be desired, it is sufficient to choose x close enough to a, but different from a,* then we say that the limit of $f(x)$, as x approaches a, is L. We write

$$\text{Lim}_{x \to a} f(x) = L,$$

which is read "the limit of $f(x)$, as x approaches a, is L." The same idea is to be conveyed by writing:

$$\text{as } x \to a, \quad f(x) \to L,$$

read "as x approaches a, $f(x)$ approaches L." If efficient use is to be made of the definition of a limit, the phrases "as close to L as may be desired" and "close enough to a" must be expressed in mathematical symbols. Therefore we restate the definition as follows: We say that

$$(1) \qquad\qquad \text{Lim}_{x \to a} f(x) = L,$$

if for every positive number ϵ (arbitrarily small), there exists a number δ such that, in order to make

$$(2) \qquad\qquad |f(x) - L| < \epsilon,$$

it is sufficient that x satisfy

$$(3) \qquad\qquad |x - a| < \delta, \qquad x \neq a.$$

The above concept of a limit is the mathematical refinement of an intuitive notion which is still of importance in rough everyday use, that the limit L is a number which $f(x)$ approaches as closely as may be desired, as x creeps up on a. The idea of a moving point, x moving toward a, $f(x)$ moving toward L, is a relic of the Newtonian* calculus.

A graphical interpretation of the definition of a limit is helpful. Consider a sketch of the graph of $y = f(x)$ near $x = a$. In Figure 50 is shown a representative graph in which $\text{Lim}_{x \to a} f(x)$ exists; in Figure 51 is shown a graph in which $\text{Lim}_{x \to a} f(x)$ does not exist.

---

* Sir Isaac Newton (1642–1727) and Gottfried Wilhelm Leibniz (1646–1716), independently of each other, developed the calculus. Before them, the nearest approach to calculus was a set of isolated, partially developed ideas, scattered throughout the mathematical literature.

In Figure 50, if it is desired to force $f(x)$ to differ from L by less than a pre-scribed quantity ϵ, $|f(x) - L| < \epsilon$, then all that is needed is to choose x any-where within a certain amount δ of the value $x = a$, $0 < |x - a| < \delta$. That is, it is possible near $x = a$ on the curve in Figure 50 to restrict the y variation to as little as may be desired by sufficiently narrowing the vertical band around $x = a$.   For the curve of Figure 50, $\lim\limits_{x \to a} f(x) = L$.

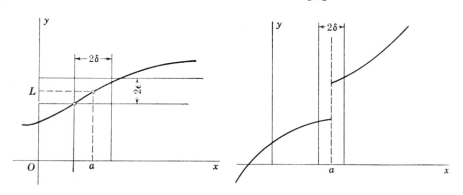

Figure 50   Figure 51

Now consider the situation near $x = a$ for the curve shown in Figure 51. There, no matter how narrow a band be chosen about $x = a$, the y variation can never be made arbitrarily small.   For the curve of Figure 51, $\lim\limits_{x \to a} f(x)$ does not exist.

The existence or nonexistence of $f(a)$, the value of $f(x)$ at $x = a$, has noth-ing whatever to do with the existence or nonexistence of the limit of $f(x)$ as x approaches a.

A major difference between calculus and the subjects which usually pre-cede it in the mathematical curriculum is that calculus uses limiting processes.

Example (a).   Show that

$$\lim_{x \to 3} (2x + 1) = 7.$$

Analysis of the problem.   Given an ϵ, we wish to satisfy the inequality

$$|(2x + 1) - 7| < \epsilon$$

by choosing x "sufficiently close" to 3.   The inequality yields

$$|2x - 6| < \epsilon,$$

or

$$|x - 3| < \frac{\epsilon}{2}.$$

Proof of the desired limit property.   We are now in a position to choose the δ in (3) for this problem.

Let $\delta = \frac{\epsilon}{2}.$ Then for all x such that

$$|x - 3| < \frac{\epsilon}{2}, \qquad x \neq 3,$$

it follows that
$$|2x - 6| < \epsilon,$$

from which
$$|(2x + 1) - 7| < \epsilon,$$

so that, by the definition of this section,

$$\operatorname*{Lim}_{x \to 3} (2x + 1) = 7.$$

Example (b).   Show that

$$\operatorname*{Lim}_{x \to 2} (x^2 + 1) = 5.$$

Analysis.   Since we wish to obtain

$$|x^2 + 1 - 5| < \epsilon,$$

we write it in the form

$$|x^2 - 4| < \epsilon,$$

or

$$|x - 2| \cdot |x + 2| < \epsilon.$$

Recall that one property of the absolute value symbol is that

$$|A + B| \leq |A| + |B|.$$

Since $x + 2 = x - 2 + 4$, it follows that

$$|x + 2| \leq |x - 2| + 4.$$

Thus, if we choose
$$|x - 2| < \delta,$$

then
$$|x + 2| < \delta + 4.$$

Therefore it is desirable to find a δ such that

$$\delta(\delta + 4) = \epsilon.$$

Since δ is required to be positive, we find that

$$\delta = -2 + \sqrt{4 + \epsilon}.$$

Proof of the desired limit property.   Choose

$$\delta = \sqrt{4 + \epsilon} - 2.$$

Then, for
$$|x - 2| < \sqrt{4 + \epsilon} - 2,$$
it can be seen, because $|x + 2| \leqq |x - 2| + 4$, that
$$|x + 2| < \sqrt{4 + \epsilon} + 2.$$

By multiplication of corresponding members of the above two inequalities, we find that
$$|x - 2| \cdot |x + 2| < (\sqrt{4 + \epsilon})^2 - (2)^2,$$
or
$$|x^2 - 4| < 4 + \epsilon - 4,$$
so that
$$|x^2 + 1 - 5| < \epsilon,$$
as desired.   Therefore
$$\text{Lim}_{x \to 2} (x^2 + 1) = 5.$$

The procedure used in Examples (*a*) and (*b*) above quickly grows tedious. Hence we proceed to obtain theorems to remove the necessity of going through all those details in the evaluation of limits.

31. *Theorems on Limits*

We shall need the following theorems on limits.   Proofs are omitted, except that a proof of Theorem 10 can be found in the next section.

THEOREM 10.   *The limit of the sum of two (or more) functions is equal to the sum of their limits:*

$$\text{Lim}_{x \to a} \left[u(x) + v(x) \right] = \text{Lim}_{x \to a} u(x) + \text{Lim}_{x \to a} v(x).$$

THEOREM 11.   *The limit of the product of two (or more) functions is equal to the product of their limits:*

$$\text{Lim}_{x \to a} \left[u(x)v(x) \right] = \left[\text{Lim}_{x \to a} u(x) \right]\left[\text{Lim}_{x \to a} v(x) \right].$$

THEOREM 12.   *The limit of the quotient of two functions is equal to the quotient of their limits, provided the limit of the denominator is not zero:*

$$\text{Lim}_{x \to a} \frac{u(x)}{v(x)} = \frac{\text{Lim}_{x \to a} u(x)}{\text{Lim}_{x \to a} v(x)}, \qquad \text{if } \text{Lim}_{x \to a} v(x) \neq 0.$$

In these theorems it is assumed that the limits of the two functions exist. However, even though neither function separately approaches a limit, the sum, product, or quotient may do so.

Theorem 12 tells us nothing about what happens to the ratio $\dfrac{u}{v}$ if $v \to 0$.

If u approaches a nonzero limit and $v \to 0$, the ratio $\dfrac{u}{v}$ can be made to assume values numerically larger than any preassigned quantity. Let us prove that statement.

Let $u \to k \neq 0$ as $x \to a$. Then, by the definition of a limit, we may choose x close enough to a to make u lie between $\frac{1}{2}k$ and $\frac{3}{2}k$. For such values of x, $|u| > \frac{1}{2}|k|$. At the same time, since $v \to 0$, we may choose x close enough to a to make $|v| < \epsilon$, with ϵ as small as desired. Now let x be chosen closer to a than either of the above two choices. Then $|u| > \frac{1}{2}|k|$ and $|v| < \epsilon$ are both true and it follows that $\left|\dfrac{u}{v}\right| > \dfrac{|k|}{2\epsilon}$, which can be made as large as we wish by choosing ϵ sufficiently small.

If $u \to 0$ and $v \to 0$ as $x \to a$, the limit of the ratio $\dfrac{u}{v}$ may exist, as it does in Example (b) below. We shall find that the entire differential calculus is based upon limits of ratios whose numerators and denominators each approach zero.

Example (a). Evaluate $\operatorname{Lim}_{x \to 3} (x^3 + 2x)$.

By Theorem 11,

$$\operatorname{Lim}_{x \to 3} (x^3) = \operatorname{Lim}_{x \to 3} (x \cdot x \cdot x) = 3 \cdot 3 \cdot 3 = 27.$$

By Theorem 10,

$$\operatorname{Lim}_{x \to 3} (x^3 + 2x) = \operatorname{Lim}_{x \to 3} (x^3) + \operatorname{Lim}_{x \to 3} (2x) = 27 + 6 = 33.$$

Example (b). Evaluate $\operatorname{Lim}_{x \to 2} \dfrac{x^3 - 2x^2 - 3x + 6}{x - 2}$.

By Theorems 10 and 11,

$$\operatorname{Lim}_{x \to 2} (x^3 - 2x^2 - 3x + 6) = 8 - 8 - 6 + 6 = 0,$$

$$\operatorname{Lim}_{x \to 2} (x - 2) = 0.$$

But, for all values of x except $x = 2$,

$$\frac{x^3 - 2x^2 - 3x + 6}{x - 2} \equiv \frac{(x - 2)(x^2 - 3)}{x - 2} \equiv x^2 - 3,$$

so that

$$\operatorname{Lim}_{x \to 2} \frac{x^3 - 2x^2 - 3x + 6}{x - 2} = \operatorname{Lim}_{x \to 2} (x^2 - 3) = 1.$$

32. *Proof of a Theorem on Limits*

Let us prove one of the results stated in § 31.   Theorem 10 may be restated as follows:

THEOREM 10.   *If*

(1) $$\operatorname*{Lim}_{x \to a} f_1(x) = L_1$$

and

(2) $$\operatorname*{Lim}_{x \to a} f_2(x) = L_2,$$

then

(3) $$\operatorname*{Lim}_{x \to a} \left[f_1(x) + f_2(x) \right] = L_1 + L_2.$$

Proof.   Because of (1) and the definition of a limit, we know that for any $\epsilon_1 > 0$, there exists a δ_1 such that, if x satisfies

$$|x - a| < \delta_1, \qquad x \neq a,$$

then

$$|f_1(x) - L_1| < \epsilon_1.$$

Similarly, because of (2), for any $\epsilon_2 > 0$, there exists a δ_2 such that, if x satisfies

$$|x - a| < \delta_2, \qquad x \neq a,$$

then

$$|f_2(x) - L_2| < \epsilon_2.$$

Now suppose we are given an ϵ for which we wish to make

(4) $$|\{f_1(x) + f_2(x)\} - (L_1 + L_2)| < \epsilon.$$

We can choose $\epsilon_1 = \frac{1}{2}\epsilon$, $\epsilon_2 = \frac{1}{2}\epsilon$, and let δ be smaller than either of δ_1 and δ_2, the δ's which correspond respectively to ϵ_1 and ϵ_2.   Then for all x which satisfy

$$|x - a| < \delta, \qquad x \neq a,$$

it is also true that $|x - a| < \delta_1$ and $|x - a| < \delta_2$, and therefore that

(5) $$|f_1(x) - L_1| < \frac{\epsilon}{2}$$

and

(6) $$|f_2(x) - L_2| < \frac{\epsilon}{2}.$$

Since

$$|f_1(x) + f_2(x) - (L_1 + L_2)| \leq |f_1(x) - L_1| + |f_2(x) - L_2|,$$

it follows from (5) and (6), that

$$|f_1(x) + f_2(x) - (L_1 + L_2)| < \frac{\epsilon}{2} + \frac{\epsilon}{2}$$

or

$$|f_1(x) + f_2(x) - (L_1 + L_2)| < \epsilon,$$

as desired.

By similar, sometimes more complicated, devices, the other theorems on limits which are quoted in § 31 can be proved.

33. *Right-hand and Left-hand Limits*

Once in a while it is convenient to employ a restricted version of limit as described below. We write

$$(1) \qquad \qquad \mathrm{Lim}_{x \to a^+} f(x) = L,$$

and mean by $x \to a^+$ that each x involved is greater than a. A limit such as that in (1) is called a right-hand limit; the independent variable x approaches a from the right. A left-hand limit,

$$(2) \qquad \qquad \mathrm{Lim}_{x \to a^-} f(x) = M,$$

with x remaining less than a, is also used.

If the ordinary limit exists, then the right-hand and left-hand limits each exist and all three have the same value. If the right- and left-hand limits exist and have the same value, then the limit itself exists and has that value.

34. *Limit of* $\dfrac{sin\ α}{α}$ *as* α *Approaches Zero*

The answer to Example (a), § 31, could be obtained by merely replacing x, in the function $x^3 + 2x$, by its limiting value 3. In Example (b), direct substitution produced the meaningless symbol $\frac{0}{0}$, so that a preliminary simplification was necessary, but this simplification was easily discovered. To show that the problem is not always quite so simple, and at the same time to establish a result of great intrinsic importance, we obtain the following result.

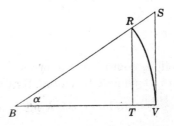

Figure 52

THEOREM 13.   *If* α *is measured in radians,*

$$(1) \qquad \qquad \mathbf{Lim}_{α \to 0} \frac{sin\ α}{α} = 1.$$

Consider Figure 52 in which RV is a circular arc with radius r and with center at B. The angles RTB and SVB are right angles. Since the triangle

RTB is contained in the sector RVB, and the sector is in turn contained in the larger triangle SVB, it follows that:

$$\text{Area of } \triangle RTB < \text{Area of sector } RVB < \text{Area of } \triangle SVB.$$

Since

$$\text{Area of } \triangle RTB = \tfrac{1}{2}\overline{BT} \cdot \overline{RT} = \tfrac{1}{2}r \cos \alpha \cdot r \sin \alpha,$$

$$\text{Area of sector } RVB = \frac{\alpha}{2\pi} \, (\pi r^2) = \tfrac{1}{2}\alpha r^2,$$

and

$$\text{Area of } \triangle SVB = \tfrac{1}{2}\overline{BV} \cdot \overline{SV} = \tfrac{1}{2}r \cdot r \tan \alpha,$$

we may conclude that, for $0 < \alpha < \dfrac{\pi}{2}$,

(2) $$\tfrac{1}{2}r^2 \cos \alpha \sin \alpha < \tfrac{1}{2}\alpha r^2 < \tfrac{1}{2}r^2 \tan \alpha.$$

Let us divide each member of the inequalities (2) by the positive quantity $\tfrac{1}{2}r^2 \sin \alpha$, and thus obtain

$$\cos \alpha < \frac{\alpha}{\sin \alpha} < \frac{1}{\cos \alpha},$$

which can be rewritten, by inverting each member, in the form

$$\frac{1}{\cos \alpha} > \frac{\sin \alpha}{\alpha} > \cos \alpha.$$

As α approaches zero, both $\cos \alpha$ and $\dfrac{1}{\cos \alpha}$ approach unity. Then $\dfrac{\sin \alpha}{\alpha}$, which is hemmed in between them, must also approach unity. That is,

$$\lim_{a \to 0^+} \frac{\sin \alpha}{\alpha} = 1.$$

That the left-hand limit also has the value unity follows from the fact that

$$\frac{\sin \alpha}{\alpha} = \frac{\sin (-\alpha)}{(-\alpha)}.$$

This completes the proof of (1).

It should be noted that direct substitution of $\alpha = 0$ in the expression $\dfrac{\sin \alpha}{\alpha}$ produces the void result $\tfrac{0}{0}$. Thus the difficulty arising here is the same, in kind, as the one we met in Example (*b*), § 31.

A variety of other important limits may be evaluated by judicious use of (1).

Example. Evaluate $\lim\limits_{\theta \to 0} \dfrac{\sin 3\theta}{\theta}$.

Since

$$\frac{\sin 3\theta}{\theta} \equiv 3 \cdot \frac{\sin 3\theta}{3\theta},$$

we need merely to take $\alpha = 3\theta$ in (1):

(3)
$$\operatorname*{Lim}_{\theta \to 0} \frac{\sin 3\theta}{\theta} = 3 \operatorname*{Lim}_{\theta \to 0} \frac{\sin 3\theta}{3\theta} = 3.$$

Lest anyone should think that (1) justifies us in assigning a value to the nonsense symbol $\dfrac{\sin 0}{0}$, we note that the "value" suggested by (1) would be in conflict with (3); see also Exs. 43, 46, 47, below.

EXERCISES

Evaluate the limits in Exs. 1–30.

1. $\operatorname*{Lim}_{x \to 4} (x^2 - 3x + 1)$.   *Ans.* 5.

2. $\operatorname*{Lim}_{x \to -2} (x^2 + 4x + 5)$.   *Ans.* 1.

3. $\operatorname*{Lim}_{z \to 1} (z^3 + 2z^2 - 4z + 1)$.

4. $\operatorname*{Lim}_{y \to 3} (2y^3 - y + 10)$. 61

5. $\operatorname*{Lim}_{t \to 1} \dfrac{t^2 + t + 1}{2t^3 - t + 3}$.   *Ans.* $\frac{3}{4}$.

6. $\operatorname*{Lim}_{x \to 0} \dfrac{2x^2 - x + 3}{5x^2 + 4x + 6}$.   *Ans.* $\frac{1}{2}$.

7. $\operatorname*{Lim}_{y \to 2} \dfrac{y^3 + 2y^2 - 4}{y^2 - y}$. $\frac{12}{2} = 6$

8. $\operatorname*{Lim}_{x \to -1} \dfrac{2x^3 + 5x^2 - 3}{x^2 - x + 3}$. $\frac{0}{3} = 0$

9. $\operatorname*{Lim}_{\varphi \to \frac{1}{4}\pi} \dfrac{\sin^2 \varphi}{\tan \varphi}$.   *Ans.* $\frac{1}{2}$.

10. $\operatorname*{Lim}_{\theta \to \frac{\pi}{6}} \dfrac{\cos 2\theta}{\sin \theta \tan \theta}$.   *Ans.* $\sqrt{3}$.

11. $\operatorname*{Lim}_{x \to 3} \dfrac{x^2 - 9}{x^2 - x - 6}$.   *Ans.* $\frac{6}{5}$.

12. $\operatorname*{Lim}_{x \to 1} \dfrac{x^2 - 1}{2x^2 + x - 3}$.   *Ans.* $\frac{2}{5}$.

13. $\operatorname*{Lim}_{x \to -1} \dfrac{3x^2 + x - 2}{2x^2 + x - 1}$.

14. $\operatorname*{Lim}_{x \to 2} \dfrac{3x^2 - 5x - 2}{x^2 - x - 2}$.

15. $\operatorname*{Lim}_{x \to 2} \dfrac{x^3 - 2x - 4}{2x^3 - 3x^2 - 4}$.   *Ans.* $\frac{5}{6}$.

16. $\operatorname*{Lim}_{y \to 3} \dfrac{y^3 - 10y + 3}{y^3 - 7y - 6}$.   *Ans.* $\frac{17}{20}$.

17. $\operatorname*{Lim}_{x \to 1} \dfrac{2x^3 - 3x + 1}{2x^3 - 3x^2 + 1}$.   *Ans.* No limit.

18. $\operatorname*{Lim}_{x \to 2} \dfrac{2x^3 - x^2 - 5x - 2}{3x^3 - 11x^2 + 8x + 4}$.   *Ans.* No limit.

19. $\operatorname*{Lim}_{\beta \to -2} \dfrac{2\beta^3 + 7\beta^2 + 4\beta - 4}{\beta^3 + 2\beta^2 - 4\beta - 8}$.   *Ans.* $\frac{5}{4}$.

20. $\operatorname*{Lim}_{\alpha \to \frac{1}{2}} \dfrac{8\alpha^3 - 4\alpha^2 - 2\alpha + 1}{4\alpha^2 - 4\alpha + 1}$.   *Ans.* 2.

21. $\operatorname*{Lim}_{x \to 2} \dfrac{x^4 - 5x + 6}{2x^3 - 9x^2 + 12x - 4}$.

22. $\operatorname*{Lim}_{x \to 3} \dfrac{x^3 + x^2 - 4x - 12}{2x^3 - 11x^2 + 12x + 9}$.

23. $\lim\limits_{x \to 0} \dfrac{\sin x}{\tan x}$.   *Ans.* 1.   **24.** $\lim\limits_{\theta \to 0} \dfrac{\tan \theta}{\tan 2\theta}$.   *Ans.* $\frac{1}{2}$.

25. $\lim\limits_{\theta \to 0} \dfrac{\sin 2\theta}{\tan \theta}$.   *Ans.* 2.   **26.** $\lim\limits_{\theta \to \frac{\pi}{2}} \dfrac{\cos 2\theta}{\tan \theta}$.   *Ans.* 0.

27. $\lim\limits_{x \to \pi} \dfrac{1 + \cos x}{\sin^2 x}$.   **28.** $\lim\limits_{x \to 0} \dfrac{\sin^2 x}{1 - \cos x}$.

29. $\lim\limits_{\alpha \to 0} \dfrac{\sin \alpha - \tan \alpha}{\sin^3 \alpha}$.   *Ans.* $-\frac{1}{2}$.   **30.** $\lim\limits_{\alpha \to 0} \dfrac{\sin 2\alpha \tan \alpha}{1 - \cos \alpha}$.   *Ans.* 4.

31. Show that, if $P(x)$ is a polynomial in x,

$$\lim_{x \to a} P(x) = P(a).$$

32. Show that, if $P_1(x)$ and $P_2(x)$ are polynomials,

$$\lim_{x \to a} \frac{P_1(x)}{P_2(x)} = \frac{P_1(a)}{P_2(a)}, \qquad P_2(a) \neq 0.$$

33. Under what circumstances may the limit in Ex. 32 exist when $P_2(a) = 0$? Give examples.

34. Show, by means of an example, that the limit in Ex. 32 does not always exist when $P_1(a) = P_2(a) = 0$.

35. Prove that

$$\lim_{x \to a} \sqrt{u} = \sqrt{\lim_{x \to a} u}, \qquad u > 0.$$

(Put $u = v^2$ and apply Theorem 11, § 31.)

36. Prove that, if p and q are integers,

$$\lim_{x \to a} (u^{\frac{p}{q}}) = (\lim_{x \to a} u)^{\frac{p}{q}}, \qquad u > 0.$$

Evaluate the limits in Exs. 37–42.

37. $\lim\limits_{x \to 2^+} \dfrac{\sqrt{x - 2}}{\sqrt{x^2 - 4}}$.   *Ans.* $\frac{1}{2}$.   **38.** $\lim\limits_{x \to 3^+} \dfrac{x - 3}{\sqrt{x^2 - 9}}$.   *Ans.* 0.

39. $\lim\limits_{x \to 1} \dfrac{(1 - x^2)^{\frac{1}{3}}}{(1 - x^3)^{\frac{1}{3}}}$.   *Ans.* $(\frac{2}{3})^{\frac{1}{3}}$.   **40.** $\lim\limits_{x \to 1^-} \dfrac{\sqrt{1 - x^3}}{\sqrt{1 - x^2}}$.   *Ans.* $\frac{1}{2}\sqrt{6}$.

41. $\lim\limits_{x \to 2^+} \dfrac{(x^4 - 4x^3 + 5x^2 - 4x + 4)^{\frac{1}{2}}}{(x^2 - 3x + 2)^{\frac{1}{2}}}$.   *Ans.* $5^{\frac{1}{2}}$.

42. $\lim\limits_{x \to 1^+} \dfrac{(x^2 + 4x - 5)^{\frac{1}{2}}}{(x^2 - 4x + 3)^{\frac{1}{2}}}$.   *Ans.* 0.

Use the result $\lim\limits_{\alpha \to 0} \dfrac{\sin \alpha}{\alpha} = 1$ to evaluate the limits in Exs. 43–50.

43. $\lim\limits_{\alpha \to 0} \dfrac{\sin k\alpha}{\alpha}$.   *Ans.* k.   **44.** $\lim\limits_{\theta \to 0} \dfrac{\sin^2 \theta}{\theta}$.   *Ans.* 0.

45. $\underset{\alpha \to 0}{\text{Lim}} \dfrac{\tan \alpha}{\alpha}.$ *Ans.* 1.   **46.** $\underset{\alpha \to 0}{\text{Lim}} \dfrac{\sin \alpha^2}{\alpha}.$ *Ans.* 0.

47. $\underset{\theta \to 0}{\text{Lim}} \dfrac{\sin \theta}{\theta^2}.$ *Ans.* No limit.   **48.** $\underset{x \to 0}{\text{Lim}} \; x \csc x.$ *Ans.* 1.

49. $\underset{x \to 0}{\text{Lim}} \dfrac{\tan ax}{\sin bx}.$ *Ans.* $\dfrac{a}{b}.$ **50.** $\underset{x \to \frac{1}{2}\pi}{\text{Lim}} \dfrac{\cos x}{x - \frac{1}{2}\pi}.$ *Ans.* −1.

51. Let $\alpha°$ denote the measure in degrees of an angle whose radian measure is α. Use the fact that $\sin \alpha° = \sin \alpha$, and that $\alpha° = \dfrac{180°}{\pi} \alpha$, together with Theorem 13, to show that

$$\underset{\alpha° \to 0}{\text{Lim}} \frac{\sin \alpha°}{\alpha°} = \frac{\pi}{180°}.$$

$$\Bigg|\ 4$$

Continuity

35. Definitions

A function $f(x)$ is said to be *continuous* at $x = a$ if all three of the following conditions are satisfied:

(1) $$f(a) \text{ exists};$$

(2) $$\lim_{x \to a} f(x) \text{ exists};$$

(3) $$\lim_{x \to a} f(x) = f(a).$$

Example (a). At $x = 2$, $f(x) = x^2 + 1$ is continuous because

$$\lim_{x \to 2} (x^2 + 1) = 5, \qquad f(2) = (2)^2 + 1 = 5.$$

Indeed, by Ex. 31, page 56, every polynomial in x is continuous for every finite x.

If any one or more of conditions (1), (2), and (3) is not satisfied, the function $f(x)$ is said to be *discontinuous* at $x = a$ or to have a *discontinuity* at $x = a$.

Example (b). At $x = 3$ the function

$$H(x) = \frac{x^2 - 9}{x - 3}$$

is discontinuous because $H(3)$ does not exist. It so happens, since

$$\frac{x^2 - 9}{x - 3} = \frac{(x - 3)(x + 3)}{x - 3} = x + 3, \qquad x \neq 3,$$

that $\lim\limits_{x \to 3} H(x) = 6$, but that is not enough to save the day.

Example (c). At $x = 0$, the signum function, page 44, is discontinuous. Although sgn 0 exists, sgn $0 = 0$, the limit involved does not exist. Indeed,

$$\lim_{x \to 0^+} \text{sgn } x = +1, \qquad \lim_{x \to 0^-} \text{sgn } x = -1.$$

Therefore condition (2) breaks down for sgn x at $x = 0$.

58

When $f(a)$ exists and

(4)
$$\text{Lim}_{x \to a^+} f(x) = f(a),$$

the function $f(x)$ is said to have *right-hand continuity* at $x = a$. If $f(a)$ exists and

(5)
$$\text{Lim}_{x \to a^-} f(x) = f(a),$$

$f(x)$ is said to have *left-hand continuity* at $x = a$.

Example (d). Examine $f(x) = \sqrt{x}$ at $x = 0$.

Here $f(0) = 0$. But $f(x)$ is not defined (we deal in real values only) for $x < 0$, so $\text{Lim}_{x \to 0} f(x)$ does not exist. However,

$$\text{Lim}_{x \to 0^+} \sqrt{x} = 0.$$

Hence, since $f(0)$ is also zero, $f(x) = \sqrt{x}$ has right-hand continuity at $x = 0$.

Continuity implies both right-hand and left-hand continuity. Since we are concerned with only single-valued functions, the existence of both right-hand and left-hand continuity at a point implies ordinary continuity at that point.

The following theorem is easily proved with the aid of Theorems 10, 11, 12, page 50.

Theorem 14. *If $u(x)$ and $v(x)$ are both continuous at $x = a$, it follows that $u(x) \cdot v(x)$, and $u(x) + v(x)$ are continuous at $x = a$, and that if $v(a) \neq 0$,*

$$\frac{u(x)}{v(x)}$$

is continuous at $x = a$.

36. *Missing Point Discontinuities*

Consider a function $f(x)$ which is not defined when $x = a$, but such that $\text{Lim}_{x \to a} f(x)$ exists,

(1)
$$\text{Lim}_{x \to a} f(x) = L.$$

The function is discontinuous at $x = a$ because condition (1), § 35, is not satisfied. Graphically the curve appears, to the eye, to be continuous, but the single point $x = a$ is missing.

It is always possible to repair such missing-point discontinuities by replacing the original function $f(x)$ with another function $\varphi(x)$, defined as follows:

(2)
$$\begin{cases} \varphi(x) = f(x); & x \neq a, \\[2mm] \varphi(x) = L; & x = a. \end{cases}$$

The function $\varphi(x)$ is the same as $f(x)$ wherever $f(x)$ was defined, but $\varphi(x)$ is continuous at $x = a$.

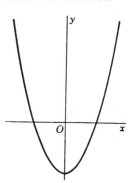

Example. In Example (*b*), § 31, we found that the function

$$(3) \qquad f(x) = \frac{x^3 - 2x^2 - 3x + 6}{x - 2}$$

is undefined when $x = 2$, but that

$$\operatorname*{Lim}_{x \to 2} \frac{x^3 - 2x^2 - 3x + 6}{x - 2} = 1.$$

Since

$$\frac{x^3 - 2x^2 - 3x + 6}{x - 2} = x^2 - 3, \qquad x \neq 2,$$

Figure 53

the graph of $y = f(x)$ is the parabola (See § 63) $y = x^2 - 3$, except for an invisible break at $x = 2$.

37. *Finite Discontinuities*

It may happen that, at $x = a$, the function has both a left-hand and a right-hand limit, but the two are not equal:

$$\operatorname*{Lim}_{x \to a^-} f(x) = L_1, \qquad \operatorname*{Lim}_{x \to a^+} f(x) = L_2, \qquad L_1 \neq L_2.$$

At such a point the function has a *finite discontinuity*: the curve takes a vertical *jump* of width $L_2 - L_1$.

Example. The first-class postage P (in cents) is defined in terms of the weight W (in ounces) as follows:

$$P = 0, \qquad W = 0;$$
$$P = 4, \qquad 0 < W \leq 1;$$
$$P = 8, \qquad 1 < W \leq 2; \text{ etc.}$$

The function has finite discontinuities at $W = 0, 1, 2, \text{ etc.}*$

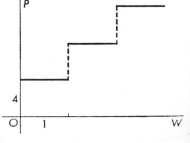

Figure 54

38. *Infinite Discontinuities*

A frequently occurring type of discontinuity is that in which the function *increases numerically without limit* as x approaches a: we say that the function

---

* Many familiar functions have a great number of relatively small finite discontinuities—e.g., the cost of a quantity of gasoline at 30 cents per gallon, jumping by 1 cent at intervals of $\frac{1}{30}$ gallon; price of a stock on the New York Exchange, changing by eighths at irregular time-intervals; etc. For most purposes such a function may be replaced by a function varying continuously.

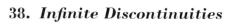

has an *infinite discontinuity* at $x = a$. Graphically this means that the curve
approaches the line $x = a$, usually with-
out ever reaching it, at the same time
receding indefinitely from the x-axis.
It may happen that $f(x)$ becomes large
and positive, or large and negative, on
both sides of the line $x = a$ (Figure 55);
if so, we write

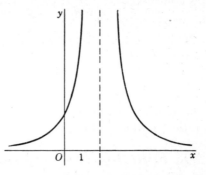

$$\operatorname{Lim}_{x \to a} f(x) = \infty \quad \text{or} \quad \operatorname{Lim}_{x \to a} f(x) = -\infty,$$

as the case may be.

Figure 55

It should be clearly understood, however, that any "equation" such as those
above is not an equation at all, in the true sense, for the reason that *the
symbol ∞ does not represent a number*. The symbols written tell us, not that
$f(x)$ approaches some vague, indefinite, very large limiting value, but that
it increases numerically beyond any limit whatever.

Example (a). As x approaches 1, the function (Figure 55)

$$y = \frac{1}{(x - 1)^2}$$

increases without limit: that is,

$$\operatorname{Lim}_{x \to 1} \frac{1}{(x - 1)^2} = \infty.$$

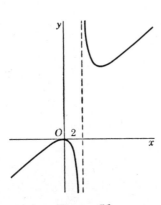

Figure 56

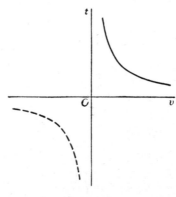

Figure 57

Example (b). As x approaches 2, the function (Figure 56)

$$y = \frac{x^2}{x - 2}$$

becomes indefinitely large, positive if $x > 2$, negative if $x < 2$:

$$\mathrm{Lim}_{x \to 2^+} \frac{x^2}{x - 2} = \infty, \qquad \mathrm{Lim}_{x \to 2^-} \frac{x^2}{x - 2} = -\infty.$$

Example (c). The time required to travel 100 mi. at a constant speed v is (Figure 57)

$$t = \frac{100}{v}; \qquad \mathrm{Lim}_{v \to 0^+} \frac{100}{v} = \infty.$$

This merely states the fact that by moving slowly enough, we could, theoretically at least, take any conceivable amount of time to cover the distance.*

39. *Function with Argument Approaching Infinity*

We frequently have to investigate the behavior of a function as the independent variable increases, or decreases, without bound.

If there is a constant c such that $|f(x) - c|$ can be made as small as desired by choosing x sufficiently large, we write

$$\mathrm{Lim}_{x \to \infty} f(x) = c.$$

Graphically this means that the curve $y = f(x)$ approaches the line $y = c$, as $x \to \infty$.

In a similar manner, if there is a constant k, such that $|f(x) - k|$ can be made arbitrarily small by choosing x negative and of sufficiently great magnitude, we say that

$$\mathrm{Lim}_{x \to -\infty} f(x) = k.$$

As x increases without bound, it may happen that $f(x)$ does likewise. If both are positive, we write

$$\mathrm{Lim}_{x \to \infty} f(x) = \infty,$$

with appropriate changes in notation when either or both are negative.

Finally, it may be that $f(x)$ approaches no limit, finite or infinite, as $x \to \infty$, or as $x \to -\infty$. Consider the behavior of the curve $y = \tan x$, as $x \to \infty$ or as $x \to -\infty$.

Example (a). To evaluate

$$\mathrm{Lim}_{x \to \infty} \frac{x^2 - 1}{x^2 + 1},$$

divide numerator and denominator by x^2:

$$\mathrm{Lim}_{x \to \infty} \frac{x^2 - 1}{x^2 + 1} = \mathrm{Lim}_{x \to \infty} \frac{1 - \dfrac{1}{x^2}}{1 + \dfrac{1}{x^2}} = 1.$$

---

* A glacier would require many centuries to travel 100 mi.

The graph of the function is shown in Figure 58.

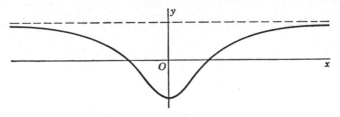

Figure 58

Example (b).

$$\text{Lim}_{x \to \infty} \frac{x^2}{x - 2} = \text{Lim}_{x \to \infty} \frac{x}{1 - \dfrac{2}{x}} = \infty,$$

$$\text{Lim}_{x \to -\infty} \frac{x^2}{x - 2} = -\infty.$$

Thus in this case no limit is approached as x increases in either direction. (Figure 56.)

Example (c).   In Example (c), § 38,

$$t = \frac{100}{v}; \qquad \text{Lim}_{v \to \infty} \frac{100}{v} = 0.$$

This merely says that if the speed could be made great enough, we could cover the distance in any desired time, no matter how short.*   (Figure 57.)

40. *Rational Algebraic Functions*

In regard to rational algebraic functions, the question of continuity is completely covered by the following theorems.

Theorem 15.   *A polynomial is continuous for all values of x.*

Theorem 16.   *A rational algebraic fraction is continuous except for those values of x for which the denominator vanishes.*

These theorems are immediate consequences of Exs. 31–32, page 56. Under Theorem 16, at a point where the denominator vanishes, only two kinds of discontinuity are possible: a missing-point discontinuity or an infinite discontinuity.

In the above, it is understood that x is free to assume any real value.   In applications where, owing to the nature of the problem, the variable is restricted in range, an entirely different situation may arise.   This matter will be discussed in § 70.

---

* Light travels 100 mi. in a very small fraction of a second.

EXERCISES

Find the points of discontinuity of the functions in Exs. 1–25.

1. $\dfrac{x^2 + 5}{x^2 - 9}$.   *Ans.* $x = \pm 3$.   **2.** $\dfrac{2x + 1}{x^2 - 4x + 4}$.   *Ans.* $x = 2$.

3. $\dfrac{x - 1}{x^2 + 4}$.   **4.** $\dfrac{x + 2}{3x^2 - 2x + 1}$.

5. $\dfrac{x^2 - 2x}{x^3 - 2x^2 + 2x}$.   *Ans.* $x = 0$.   **6.** $\dfrac{4(x + 1)^2}{2x^3 - 5x^2 - 4x + 3}$.

7. $\dfrac{x^4 - x + 2}{x^3 - 12x + 16}$.   **8.** $\dfrac{3}{2x^3 + 5x^2 - 7}$.

9. $\sin \theta$.   *Ans.* None.   **10.** $\cot \theta$.   *Ans.* $n\pi$, n any integer.

11. $\csc \theta$.   **12.** $\sec \theta$.   **13.** $(1 - x)^{\frac{1}{3}}$.

14. $\sqrt{x^2 - a^2}$.   **15.** $(1 - x)^{-\frac{1}{3}}$.   **16.** $(1 - x)^{-\frac{1}{2}}$.

17. $\sqrt{1 + \sqrt{x}}$.   **18.** $\dfrac{\sqrt{a + x}}{x^2 - a^2}$.

19. $\sqrt{x^2 - 2ax + a^2}$.   *Ans.* None.   **20.** $\dfrac{\sqrt{2ax - x^2}}{a^2 - x^2}$.

21. The cost of sending a telegram, as a function of the number of words.
                    Ans. Everywhere discontinuous.

22. The weight of a U. S. coin, as a function of the value.

23. $y = x - |x|$.   *Ans.* None.

24. $y = \operatorname{sgn} x$.   *Ans.* $x = 0$.

25. $y = \frac{1}{2}(1 + \operatorname{sgn} x) \sin x$.   *Ans.* None.

26. Given two continuous functions, what can be said of the continuity of their sum? Their product? Their quotient?

27. Show that as x approaches zero, the function $\sin \dfrac{\pi}{x}$ oscillates between -1 and 1, without approaching any limit.

28. Discuss the behavior of $\tan \dfrac{\pi}{x}$ near the origin.

29. Show that the function $y = x \sin \dfrac{1}{x}$ is discontinuous at the origin. What type of discontinuity is present?

30. Show that the function $y = x \tan \dfrac{1}{x}$ is discontinuous at the origin.

Evaluate the limits in Exs. 31–52.

31. $\operatorname*{Lim}_{x \to \infty} \dfrac{2}{x^2 - 3}$.   **32.** $\operatorname*{Lim}_{x \to \infty} \dfrac{2x^2}{x^2 - 3}$.

33. $\operatorname*{Lim}_{x \to -\infty} \dfrac{x^3}{4x^3 + 1}$.   *Ans.* $\frac{1}{4}$.   **34.** $\operatorname*{Lim}_{x \to -\infty} \dfrac{4x^2}{3x^2 - x}$.   *Ans.* $\frac{4}{3}$.

35. $\lim\limits_{x \to \infty} \dfrac{7x^3}{x^2 + 4}.$ *Ans.* No limit (∞).

36. $\lim\limits_{x \to -\infty} \dfrac{(x + 1)^4}{(2x - 1)^3}.$ *Ans.* No limit ($-\infty$).

37. $\lim\limits_{x \to \infty} \dfrac{(x - 2)(4x^3 + 1)}{(2x^2 + 1)^2}.$ **38.** $\lim\limits_{x \to \infty} \dfrac{(x - 1)^3}{(x^2 + 1)^2}.$

39. $\lim\limits_{x \to \infty} 2^{\frac{1}{x}}.$ *Ans.* 1. **40.** $\lim\limits_{x \to -\infty} 2^{\frac{1}{x}}.$ *Ans.* 1.

41. $\lim\limits_{x \to 0^+} 2^{\frac{1}{x}}.$ *Ans.* No limit (∞). **42.** $\lim\limits_{x \to 0^-} 2^{\frac{1}{x}}.$ *Ans.* 0.

43. $\lim\limits_{x \to \infty} \dfrac{1}{1 + 2^{\frac{1}{x}}}.$ *Ans.* $\frac{1}{2}$. **44.** $\lim\limits_{x \to -\infty} \dfrac{1}{1 + 2^{\frac{1}{x}}}.$ *Ans.* $\frac{1}{2}$.

45. $\lim\limits_{x \to 0^+} \dfrac{1}{1 + 2^{\frac{1}{x}}}.$ *Ans.* 0. **46.** $\lim\limits_{x \to 0^-} \dfrac{1}{1 + 2^{\frac{1}{x}}}.$ *Ans.* 1.

47. $\lim\limits_{x \to \infty} \dfrac{2}{2 + 3^{\frac{1}{x}}}.$ **48.** $\lim\limits_{x \to -\infty} \dfrac{3}{5 + 2^{\frac{1}{x}}}.$

49. $\lim\limits_{x \to \infty} \sin x.$ *Ans.* No limit. **50.** $\lim\limits_{x \to \infty} \tan x.$ *Ans.* No limit.

51. $\lim\limits_{x \to \infty} \dfrac{\sin x}{x}.$ *Ans.* 0. **52.** $\lim\limits_{x \to \infty} \dfrac{\tan x}{x}.$ *Ans.* No limit.

53. Sketch the curve $y = 2^{\frac{1}{x}}$. See Exs. 39–42.

54. Sketch the curve $y = \dfrac{1}{1 + 2^{\frac{1}{x}}}.$ See Exs. 43–46.

55. Sketch the curve $y = \dfrac{3}{5 + 2^{\frac{1}{x}}}.$

41. *The Intermediate Value Theorem*

The function $f(x)$ is said to be continuous over the closed interval $a \leqq x \leqq b$ if $f(x)$ is continuous at every interior point $a < x < b$ and $f(x)$ has right-hand continuity at $x = a$ and left-hand continuity at $x = b$.

LEMMA 1. *If $f(x)$ is continuous over the closed interval $a \leqq x \leqq b$, if $f(a) < 0$ and $f(b) > 0$, there exists a number c in the open interval $a < c < b$ for which $f(c) = 0$.*

In Lemma 1 the signs of $f(a)$ and $f(b)$ may be reversed, as may be seen by applying the lemma to the negative of $f(x)$.

Proof of Lemma 1 belongs, in the author's opinion, in a more advanced course. Here we shall attempt in two ways to make the truth of the result plausible.   Examine a representative graph such as that in Figure 59.   As x varies from a to b, the value of $f(x)$, starting with a negative value and proceeding without jumping (continuity) to a positive value, must somewhere take on the value zero for an x between a and b.

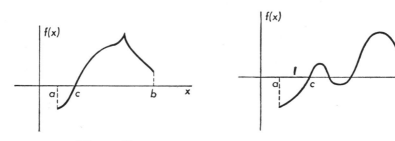

Figure 59   **Figure 60**

Consider next the following argument.   Since $f(x)$ is continuous and is negative at $x = a$, there must exist an interval I of nonzero length, and with a for its left end point, such that $f(x)$ is negative over that entire interval.   But $f(b)$ is positive, so the interval I cannot occupy all the original interval $a \le x \le b$.   Hence there is a point c (Figure 60) such that for some $\epsilon > 0$

(1) $f(x) < 0,$ for x in the range $c - \epsilon < x < c$

and

(2) $f(x) > 0,$ for x in the range $c < x < c + \epsilon.$

That is, $f(x)$ is negative for all x near enough to c and to the left of c.   Also $f(x)$ is positive for all x near enough to c and to the right of c.

Now $f(c)$ exists (continuity).   But $f(c)$ cannot be positive because of (1), and $f(c)$ cannot be negative because of (2).   Hence $f(c) = 0$ and c lies between a and b, $a < c < b$.

From Lemma 1 the intermediate value theorem follows at once.

THEOREM 17.   *If the single-valued function $f(x)$ is continuous over the closed interval $a \le x \le b$, then in that interval $f(x)$ takes on every value between $f(a)$ and $f(b)$.*

If $f(a) = f(b)$, there is nothing to prove.
If $f(a) < f(b)$, let λ be any number between them,

$$f(a) < \lambda < f(b).$$

We need to show that there is a number c in $a < c < b$ such that $f(c) = \lambda$. Put $\varphi(x) = f(x) - \lambda$.   Then $\varphi(x)$ is continuous over $a \le x \le b$.   Also $\varphi(a) < 0$ and $\varphi(b) > 0$.   Then Lemma 1 may be applied to $\varphi(x)$, thus yielding a number c such that $a < c < b$ and $\varphi(c) = 0$.   But $\varphi(c) = 0$ means $f(c) = \lambda$, as desired.

If $f(a) > f(b)$, let μ be any number between them,

$$f(b) < \mu < f(a).$$

Use $\psi(x) = \mu - f(x)$ and apply Lemma 1 to $\psi(x)$ to obtain a number c such that $a < c < b$ and $\psi(c) = 0$. Thus $f(c) = \mu$, as desired.

Another important result, the proof of which is beyond us in this course, will now be stated. A proof of this theorem will be found in more advanced books.

THEOREM 18. *If* $f(x)$ *is continuous over the closed interval* $a \leqq x \leqq b$, $f(x)$ *takes on a greatest value and a least value in the closed interval.*

The theorem states that there is at least one point x_1 in $a \leqq x_1 \leqq b$, such that

$$f(x_1) \geqq f(x)$$

for all x in $a \leqq x \leqq b$. There may be many such points, each with the same maximum value for $f(x)$. The situation with regard to least (minimum) values is similar.

In Theorem 18 the interval must be a closed one for the conclusion to follow from the hypothesis. For example, the $f(x) = \dfrac{1}{x}$ has no greatest value in the interval $0 < x \leqq 1$, although $f(x)$ is continuous over that interval. The discontinuity at $x = 0$ causes the trouble. Of course a function may be discontinuous and still take on a greatest and a least value. Theorem 18 states that a function continuous over a closed interval must take on a greatest and a least value in that interval. If a function is discontinuous, it is on its own; the theorem simply yields no conclusion for that function.

The student should draw graphs illustrating the theorem and graphs showing some pertinent types of behavior for functions which fail to satisfy the hypothesis of the theorem.

The lemma and theorems stated in this section may well be considered obvious* by the student. We shall not argue that point. What we do state is that the theorems are true. That the obvious is not always true is commonplace in mathematics. Demonstration of such a statement is a bit elusive because what is obvious to one person may not be obvious to another.

A widely used example will now be exhibited. Many people consider the truth of the following statement to be obvious: "If arcs of two continuous curves approach each other in position, they do so in length."† Let us be precise.

---

* The word "obvious" is a dangerous one. It is often said, not always facetiously, that when a mathematician says something is obvious he means one of two things: either the statement isn't true or he can't prove it.

† The sad fact is that a continuous curve need not have a length in the sense in which length of an arc is defined in calculus. Unfortunately, continuous curves for which arc length does not exist are not elementary, so no such examples are given here.

In an xy-plane the line segment along the x-axis from the origin to the point $(2, 0)$ has the length 2. Consider a sequence of curves

$$(3) \qquad\qquad\qquad\qquad y = f_n(x),$$

one for each positive integer n, with the following properties:

(*a*) For each n, the curve (3) passes through the points $(0, 0)$ and $(2, 0)$;

(*b*) For each n, the curve (3) is continuous over the closed interval $0 \leq x \leq 2$;

(*c*) As $n \to \infty$, $f_n(x) \to 0$ for each x in $0 \leq x \leq 2$.

Our contention is that it is obvious but not true that the length of the curve (3) from $(0, 0)$ to $(2, 0)$ approaches 2 as $n \to \infty$.

Let the curves (3) be defined as follows. For $n = 1$, the curve is to be a semicircle (radius unity) with the segment from $(0, 0)$ to $(2, 0)$ as diameter. The length of the arc is π.

For $n = 2$, the curve (3) is to consist of two semicircles, one with the segment from $(0, 0)$ to $(1, 0)$ as diameter, the other having the segment from $(1, 0)$ to $(2, 0)$ as diameter. Each semicircle has radius $\frac{1}{2}$ and length $\frac{1}{2}\pi$. The total length of arc from $(0, 0)$ to $(2, 0)$ is π.

For general n, the curve (3) is to consist of n semicircles, each of radius $\dfrac{1}{n}$, side by side from $(0, 0)$ to $(2, 0)$. The total length of arc is $n\left(\dfrac{\pi}{n}\right) = \pi$. Figure 61 shows the curve for $n = 4$.

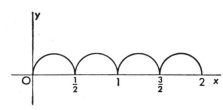

Figure 61

The curves (3), as described above, satisfy conditions (*a*) and (*b*) for each n. Since, for any n the maximum value of $f_n(x)$ is $\dfrac{1}{n}$, it follows that (*c*) is also satisfied. But the length of arc is always π, so the length of arc does not approach 2 as $n \to \infty$.

The Derivative.   Slope.
Rate of Change

42. The Derivative

Given a continuous function

(1) $$y = f(x),$$

let us choose some fixed value of x, the corresponding value of y being given by (1). Now consider another value of x, differing from the first one by an amount (positive or negative) which we will call the *increment* of x, and will denote by the symbol Δx. For this value of x, y will have a new value, differing from the original by an amount Δy. In other words, *when x changes to the value $x + \Delta x$, y changes to the value $y + \Delta y$*, and we have

$$y + \Delta y = f(x + \Delta x),$$
(2) $$\Delta y = f(x + \Delta x) - f(x).$$

Now let us form the ratio $\dfrac{\Delta y}{\Delta x}$, and investigate the behavior of this ratio when Δx approaches zero. Since $f(x)$ is continuous, the Δy of equation (2) also approaches zero. We have found that when both numerator and denominator of a fraction approach zero, the fraction itself may, or may not, approach a limit. In Figure 62, let the curve AB represent the graph of the given function. The ratio $\dfrac{\Delta y}{\Delta x}$ is the slope of the line joining the points $P: (x, y)$ and $P': (x + \Delta x, \ y + \Delta y)$. As Δx approaches zero, P' approaches P along the curve, and in all ordinary cases the line PP' approaches a certain straight line (PT in the figure) as a

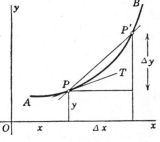

Figure 62

limiting position. That is, for a sufficiently well-behaved curve, the ratio

69

$\dfrac{\Delta y}{\Delta x}$ *approaches a limit*, the slope of the line PT. This limit is called the *derivative* of y with respect to x.

FUNDAMENTAL DEFINITION. *The* **derivative** *of y with respect to x is the limit of the ratio* $\dfrac{\Delta y}{\Delta x}$ *when Δx approaches zero.*

The derivative is designated by the symbol $\dfrac{dy}{dx}$:

$$\frac{dy}{dx} = \operatorname*{Lim}_{\Delta x \to 0} \frac{\Delta y}{\Delta x} = \operatorname*{Lim}_{\Delta x \to 0} \frac{f(x + \Delta x) - f(x)}{\Delta x}.$$

Other symbols for the derivative are y', $f'(x)$, $D_x y$, $\dfrac{d}{dx} f(x)$. But since the symbol y' does not explicitly indicate the independent variable, this notation should be used only when no confusion or ambiguity can arise.

Functions can be found which, though continuous, do not possess a derivative for any value of x. Such functions, being extremely artificial, are very unlikely to occur in elementary applications. Their importance is theoretical rather than practical.

The operation of finding the derivative is called **differentiation**. *Only differentiable functions* (those having a derivative) *are studied in this book.* When the derivative fails to exist for particular values of x, those values are either excluded or specially investigated.

We have now listed three fundamental requirements of the calculus. Each function to be studied must, for some range of values of the independent variable, be *continuous, one-valued,* and *differentiable.*

43. *Determination of the Derivative*

Our first problem is to prove, for the elementary functions, the existence of the derivative—i.e., to prove that when Δx approaches zero, $\dfrac{\Delta y}{\Delta x}$ approaches a definite limit—and at the same time to derive formulas for the derivative in terms of x, for the various functions. This problem will occupy us extensively for some time.

To obtain the derivative of any function, the general process is as follows:

1. *Replace x by $x + \Delta x$, and y by $y + \Delta y$:*

(1) $$y = f(x),$$
(2) $$y + \Delta y = f(x + \Delta x).$$

2. *By subtraction, eliminate y between* (1) *and* (2), *thus obtaining a formula for Δy in terms of x and Δx:*

(3) $$\Delta y = f(x + \Delta x) - f(x).$$

3. *By some suitable transformation, throw the right member of* (3) *into a form which contains* Δx *explicitly as a factor.*

4. *Divide through by* Δx:

$$\frac{\Delta y}{\Delta x} = \frac{f(x + \Delta x) - f(x)}{\Delta x}.$$

5. *Determine the limit as* Δx *approaches zero.*

The transformation required in step 3 varies with different classes of functions and must be discovered by trial. For the transcendental functions, evaluation of the limit in the final step is not always a simple problem. We shall see how to overcome these difficulties as they arise.

Example (a). Differentiate the function $y = x^3 - 2x$.

1. $y + \Delta y = (x + \Delta x)^3 - 2(x + \Delta x)$.

2. $\quad \Delta y = (x + \Delta x)^3 - 2(x + \Delta x) - x^3 + 2x$

3. $\quad\quad = x^3 + 3x^2\,\Delta x + 3x\,\overline{\Delta x}^2 + \overline{\Delta x}^3 - 2x - 2\Delta x - x^3 + 2x$

$\quad\quad = 3x^2\,\Delta x + 3x\,\overline{\Delta x}^2 + \overline{\Delta x}^3 - 2\Delta x$.

4. $\quad \dfrac{\Delta y}{\Delta x} = 3x^2 + 3x\,\Delta x + \overline{\Delta x}^2 - 2$.

5. $\quad y' = 3x^2 - 2$. $\hspace{2cm}$ (Theorems 10, 11, page 50.)

Example (b). Find the derivative of the function $x = \dfrac{1}{t}$.

1. $x + \Delta x = \dfrac{1}{t + \Delta t}$.

2. $\quad \Delta x = \dfrac{1}{t + \Delta t} - \dfrac{1}{t}$

3. $\quad\quad = \dfrac{t - (t + \Delta t)}{(t + \Delta t)t} = \dfrac{-\Delta t}{(t + \Delta t)t}$.

4. $\quad \dfrac{\Delta x}{\Delta t} = \dfrac{-1}{(t + \Delta t)t}$.

5. $\quad \dfrac{dx}{dt} = -\dfrac{1}{t^2}$.

$\hspace{6cm}$ (Theorem 12, page 50.)

Example (c). Differentiate the function

$$y = \sqrt{x}, \quad x > 0.$$

1. $y + \Delta y = \sqrt{x + \Delta x}$.

2. $\quad \Delta y = \sqrt{x + \Delta x} - \sqrt{x}$

3. $\quad\quad = (\sqrt{x + \Delta x} - \sqrt{x}) \cdot \dfrac{\sqrt{x + \Delta x} + \sqrt{x}}{\sqrt{x + \Delta x} + \sqrt{x}}$

$\quad\quad = \dfrac{(x + \Delta x) - x}{\sqrt{x + \Delta x} + \sqrt{x}} = \dfrac{\Delta x}{\sqrt{x + \Delta x} + \sqrt{x}}$.

4. $\dfrac{\Delta y}{\Delta x} = \dfrac{1}{\sqrt{x + \Delta x} + \sqrt{x}}.$

5. $\dfrac{dy}{dx} = \dfrac{1}{2\sqrt{x}}.$ (Ex. 35, page 56.)

EXERCISES

Differentiate the functions in Exs. 1–28.

1. $y = 3x^2 - x + 1.$ *Ans.* $y' = 6x - 1.$

2. $y = 4 + 2x - x^2.$ *Ans.* $y' = 2 - 2x.$

3. $y = \frac{1}{2}x^2 - 4x.$

4. $x = y^2 + 4y - 1.$ *Ans.* $\dfrac{dx}{dy} = 2y + 4.$

5. $y = x^3 - 2x + 3.$ *Ans.* $y' = 3x^2 - 2.$

6. $x = 2t^3 - t^2 + 5.$ *Ans.* $\dfrac{dx}{dt} = 6t^2 - 2t.$

7. $z = \frac{1}{2}x^4 - 7x + 4.$

8. $y = t^4 - 3t^3.$ *Ans.* $\dfrac{dy}{dt} = 4t^3 - 9t^2.$

9. $y = \frac{1}{2}(x^2 + 1)^2.$ *Ans.* $y' = 2x(x^2 + 1).$

10. $y = \frac{1}{2}(3x^2 - 1)^2.$ *Ans.* $y' = 6x(3x^2 - 1).$

11. $y = \dfrac{1}{x + c}.$ *Ans.* $\dfrac{dy}{dx} = \dfrac{-1}{(x + c)^2}.$

12. $y = \dfrac{1}{3 - x}.$ *Ans.* $\dfrac{dy}{dx} = \dfrac{1}{(3 - x)^2}.$

13. $x = \dfrac{3t}{t + 2}.$

14. $x = \dfrac{y}{4 - y}.$

15. $y = 1 + 3x - \dfrac{1}{x}.$ *Ans.* $y' = 3 + \dfrac{1}{x^2}.$

16. $y = \dfrac{2x - 1}{3x + 4}.$ *Ans.* $\dfrac{dy}{dx} = \dfrac{11}{(3x + 4)^2}.$

17. $y = \dfrac{1}{x^2}.$ *Ans.* $\dfrac{dy}{dx} = \dfrac{-2}{x^3}.$

18. $v = \dfrac{2}{t^3}.$ *Ans.* $\dfrac{dv}{dt} = \dfrac{-6}{t^4}.$

19. $y = \sqrt{x + 4}.$ *Ans.* $\dfrac{dy}{dx} = \dfrac{1}{2\sqrt{x + 4}}.$

20. $y = \sqrt{3 - 4x}.$ *Ans.* $\dfrac{dy}{dx} = \dfrac{-2}{\sqrt{3 - 4x}}.$

21. $y = \sqrt{a^2 - x^2}.$ *Ans.* $\dfrac{dy}{dx} = \dfrac{-x}{\sqrt{a^2 - x^2}}.$

22. $u = \sqrt{a^2 + y^2}.$ $Ans. \dfrac{du}{dy} = \dfrac{y}{\sqrt{a^2 + y^2}}.$

23. $y = 2x + \sqrt{x}.$ $Ans.\ y' = 2 + \dfrac{1}{2\sqrt{x}}.$

24. $x = t^2 - \sqrt{t}.$ $Ans.\ x' = 2t - \dfrac{1}{2\sqrt{t}}.$

25. $y = \dfrac{1}{\sqrt{x}}.$ $Ans.\ \dfrac{dy}{dx} = \dfrac{-1}{2x^{\frac{3}{2}}}.$

26. $u = t^{\frac{3}{2}}.$ $Ans.\ \dfrac{du}{dt} = \dfrac{3}{2}t^{\frac{1}{2}}.$

27. $y = \dfrac{1}{\sqrt{x+3}}.$ $Ans.\ \dfrac{dy}{dx} = \dfrac{-1}{2(x+3)^{\frac{3}{2}}}.$

28. $y = x\sqrt{x+1}.$ $Ans.\ \dfrac{dy}{dx} = \dfrac{3x+2}{2\sqrt{x+1}}.$

29. For the function $y = \sqrt{3 - 4x}$, show that the derivative does not exist at the point $x = \frac{3}{4}$.   (Ex. 20.)

44. *Tangents to Plane Curves*

A straight line that intersects a curve in two or more distinct points is called a *secant*.

Let P be a fixed point of a plane curve, and P' a neighboring point. If P' be made to approach P along the curve, the secant PP' approaches, in general, a definite limiting position, PT in Figure 63. If the secant line has such a limiting position, then the straight line which is that limit, PT in Figure 63, is called the *tangent to the curve at P*, or is said to *touch the curve at P*. The point P is the *point of contact*.

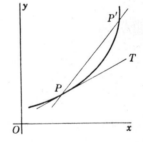

Figure 63

The slope of the tangent to the curve at any point is called simply the *slope of the curve* at that point. When P' approaches P, the slope of the secant *approaches as its limit the slope of the curve*.

45. *Derivative Interpreted as Slope*

In Figure 62, page 69, the slope of the secant PP' is $\dfrac{\Delta y}{\Delta x}$.   As Δx approaches zero, P' approaches P along the curve, so that the slope of the secant approaches as its limit the slope of the curve at P.   But this limit has been defined as the derivative of y with respect to x.   *The derivative of a function is identical with the slope of the graph of the function.*

More explicitly, this means that if, in the formula for y', we substitute any given value of x, the *number* thus obtained is the slope of the curve at the point whose abscissa is the given x.

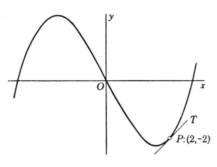

Figure 64

Example. Find the slope of the curve $y = \frac{1}{4}x^3 - 2x$ at the point P: $(2, -2)$.

By the method of § 43, the derivative is

$$y' = \tfrac{3}{4}x^2 - 2.$$

When $x = 2$, this takes the value

$$y' = 1,$$

which is the slope at the given point (slope of the tangent PT, Figure 64).

Let us verify that the term *slope of a curve* does not conflict with the previously used term *slope of a line*. The equation of a line of slope m can be written

(1) $$y = mx + b.$$

From (1) we obtain

$$y + \Delta y = m(x + \Delta x) + b,$$
$$\Delta y = m\,\Delta x,$$

(2) $$\frac{\Delta y}{\Delta x} = m.$$

Hence, for the straight line (1),

$$\frac{dy}{dx} = m;$$

the two uses of the word "slope" are in agreement.

46. *Rate of Change*

The idea of *rate of change* of a function occurs constantly in everyday experience. Such familiar expressions as miles per hour, miles per gallon, pressure per square inch, value per acre, price per ton, all represent rates.

Given a function

$$y = f(x)$$

let us assign to x an arbitrary increment Δx, thus causing in y a (positive or negative) change Δy. The ratio $\dfrac{\Delta y}{\Delta x}$ is called the *average* rate of change over the interval Δx. If we let Δx approach zero, this ratio in general approaches a limiting value, which is defined as the *rate of change of y corresponding to the given value of* x, *or the* instantaneous rate:

$$\frac{dy}{dx} = \lim_{\Delta x \to 0} \frac{\Delta y}{\Delta x} = \textit{rate of change of } y \textit{ with respect to } x.$$

In order to understand and appreciate these ideas, nothing more than ordinary experience is needed. As an illustration, suppose that two posts, at a measured distance apart, are set up beside a highway, and that a car is driven past them. Let Δx be the distance between the posts, and Δt the time required to pass. Then, if the car travels at a uniform speed, that speed is merely $\frac{\Delta x}{\Delta t}$. But if the speed is variable, this ratio is the *average* speed. If we wish to know the speed at a particular instant, say when passing the first post, common sense would suggest that the posts be placed close together. For then Δt will be small, and there will not be time for the speed to change a great deal, so that the average will be nearly equal to the instantaneous speed. While in practice, of course, this process could not be pushed beyond a certain point, it is clear that our ordinary idea of instantaneous speed is expressed exactly by $\frac{dx}{dt}$, the *limit* of $\frac{\Delta x}{\Delta t}$ as Δt approaches zero.

Comparing the definitions of derivative and rate of change, we have another fundamental relation: *The derivative of a function is identical with its rate of change.*

Thus in our future work it must always be borne in mind that the three quantities—derivative, slope of graph, rate of change—are all equal to each other.

When the slope of a curve is positive (as on the arc AB), the ordinate y is increasing (as x increases); when the slope is negative (as on BC), the ordinate is decreasing. This merely says that a function increases or decreases according as its rate of change is positive or negative.

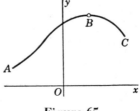

Figure 65

Example (a). Find the rate at which the reciprocal of a number changes as the number increases.

Let n equal the number, r its reciprocal:

$$r = \frac{1}{n}.$$

By the method of § 43 (or directly from Example (b) of that section) we find

$$\frac{dr}{dn} = -\frac{1}{n^2}.$$

At the instant, say, when n passes through the value 2, the reciprocal is diminishing one-fourth as fast as the number is increasing.

Example (*b*).   The surface area of a sphere, initially zero, increases uniformly at the rate of 4 sq. in. per sec.   Find the rate at which the radius is increasing at the end of 2 sec.

Let: $t =$ time (sec.),
   $r =$ radius of sphere (in.),
   $S =$ surface area (sq. in.).

Since S is increasing at a constant rate, S is proportional to the elapsed time; indeed,

$$S = 4t.$$

But also, $S = 4\pi r^2$, so that $4t = 4\pi r^2$, from which it follows that

$$r = \frac{\sqrt{t}}{\sqrt{\pi}}.$$

By the method of § 43, we find

$$\frac{dr}{dt} = \frac{1}{2\sqrt{\pi} \cdot \sqrt{t}}.$$

When $t = 2$,

$$\frac{dr}{dt} = \frac{1}{2\sqrt{2\pi}} = 0.20 \text{ in. per sec.}$$

EXERCISES

In Exs. 1–10, find the slope of the curve at the given point.

1. $y = x^2 - 4x$, $(3, -3)$.   *Ans.* 2.
2. $y = 1 - 2x^2$, $(1, -1)$.   *Ans.* -4.
3. $y = 2x^3 + x$, $(1, 3)$.   *Ans.* 7.
4. $y = x^3 - x^2$, $(1, 0)$.   *Ans.* 1.

5. $y = \dfrac{1}{x^2}$, $(1, 1)$.   *Ans.* -2.   **6.** $y = \dfrac{1}{x+1}$, $(1, \frac{1}{2})$.   *Ans.* $-\frac{1}{4}$.

7. $y^2 = 4x$, $(1, -2)$.   *Ans.* -1.
8. $y^2 = x - 4$, $(5, 1)$.   *Ans.* $\frac{1}{2}$.
9. $y^2 = 2x + 1$, $(4, 3)$.   *Ans.* $\frac{1}{3}$.
10. $y^2 = 6x - 2$, $(1, -2)$.   *Ans.* $-\frac{3}{2}$.

11. The dimensions of a box are b, $b + 1$, $b + 3$.   Find how fast the total surface area A increases as b increases.

$$Ans. \quad \frac{dA}{db} = 12b + 16.$$

12. For the box of Ex. 11, find how fast the volume increases as b increases.

13. Find how fast (a) the circumference, (b) the area, of a circle increases when the radius increases.

14. Find how fast (a) the volume, (b) the surface area, (c) the diagonal, of a cube increases when the length of the edge increases.

15. Find how fast (a) the volume, (b) the surface area, of a sphere increases as the radius increases.

16. The radius of a sphere, initially zero, increases at the rate of 3 ft. per sec. Find how fast the volume is increasing after $\frac{1}{2}$ sec. *Ans.* 27π cu. ft. per sec.

17. The base of a box is a square of side l; the volume V is constant. How fast does l change as the depth h changes?

$$Ans. \ \frac{dl}{dh} = -\frac{V^{\frac{1}{2}}}{2h^{\frac{3}{2}}}.$$

18. A right circular cylinder has a fixed height of 4 units. Find the rate of change of its volume V with respect to the radius r of its base.

$$Ans. \ \frac{dV}{dr} = 8\pi r.$$

19. In Ex. 18, find the rate of change of the total surface area A with respect to r.

$$Ans. \ \frac{dA}{dr} = 4\pi(r + 2).$$

Algebraic Functions

47. Introduction

In this and later chapters (11–13) we develop certain *standard formulas* by means of which any elementary function may be differentiated. The use of these formulas obviates the necessity of evaluating a special limit in every problem, thus effecting a great saving of time.

At present we confine our attention to algebraic functions. However, the formulas of §§ 49, 51 are direct consequences of the definition of the derivative and are valid for all functions that are *continuous, one-valued,* and *differentiable.*

48. Derivative of a Constant

We note first that *the derivative of a constant is zero*:

$$(1) \qquad \frac{dc}{dx} = 0.$$

This result appears geometrically from the fact that the curve $y = c$ is a straight line parallel to Ox, so that the slope is everywhere zero. Likewise, since a constant never changes in value, its rate of change is always zero. Formally, if $y = c$, then $y + \Delta y = c$, and hence

$$\Delta y = 0, \qquad \frac{\Delta y}{\Delta x} = 0,$$

$$\frac{dy}{dx} = \operatorname*{Lim}_{\Delta x \to 0} \frac{\Delta y}{\Delta x} = 0.$$

49. Derivative of a Sum; a Product; a Quotient

If u and v are functions of x, the following formulas are true by the definition of the derivative (see proofs below):

$$(2) \qquad \frac{d}{dx}(u + v) = \frac{du}{dx} + \frac{dv}{dx},$$

$$(3) \qquad \frac{d}{dx}(uv) = u\frac{dv}{dx} + v\frac{du}{dx},$$

78

(4)
$$\frac{d}{dx}\left(\frac{u}{v}\right) = \frac{v\dfrac{du}{dx} - u\dfrac{dv}{dx}}{v^2}.$$

These formulas may be stated in words as follows:

(2) *The derivative of the sum of two functions is equal to the sum of their derivatives.*

(3) *The derivative of the product of two functions is equal to the first function times the derivative of the second plus the second times the derivative of the first.*

(4) *The derivative of the quotient of two functions is equal to the denominator times the derivative of the numerator minus the numerator times the derivative of the denominator, all divided by the square of the denominator.*

Proof of (2).   Let x assume an increment Δx, and denote by Δu and Δv the corresponding increments of u and v.   Then

$$y = u + v,$$
$$y + \Delta y = u + \Delta u + v + \Delta v,$$
$$\Delta y = \Delta u + \Delta v,$$
$$\frac{\Delta y}{\Delta x} = \frac{\Delta u}{\Delta x} + \frac{\Delta v}{\Delta x},$$
$$\frac{dy}{dx} = \lim_{\Delta x \to 0}\frac{\Delta y}{\Delta x} = \frac{du}{dx} + \frac{dv}{dx}.$$

Proof of (3).

$$y = uv,$$
$$y + \Delta y = (u + \Delta u)(v + \Delta v),$$
$$\Delta y = u\,\Delta v + v\,\Delta u + \Delta u\,\Delta v,$$
$$\frac{\Delta y}{\Delta x} = u\frac{\Delta v}{\Delta x} + v\frac{\Delta u}{\Delta x} + \Delta u\frac{\Delta v}{\Delta x},$$
$$\frac{dy}{dx} = \lim_{\Delta x \to 0}\frac{\Delta y}{\Delta x} = u\frac{dv}{dx} + v\frac{du}{dx}.$$

Proof of (4).

$$y = \frac{u}{v},$$
$$y + \Delta y = \frac{u + \Delta u}{v + \Delta v},$$
$$\Delta y = \frac{u + \Delta u}{v + \Delta v} - \frac{u}{v} = \frac{uv + v\,\Delta u - uv - u\,\Delta v}{(v + \Delta v)v},$$
$$\frac{\Delta y}{\Delta x} = \frac{v\dfrac{\Delta u}{\Delta x} - u\dfrac{\Delta v}{\Delta x}}{(v + \Delta v)v},$$
$$\frac{dy}{dx} = \lim_{\Delta x \to 0}\frac{\Delta y}{\Delta x} = \frac{v\dfrac{du}{dx} - u\dfrac{dv}{dx}}{v^2}.$$

Formulas (2) and (3) can be extended to the case where n functions are involved.   For three functions, (3) becomes

$$\frac{d}{dx} uvw = vw \frac{du}{dx} + wu \frac{dv}{dx} + uv \frac{dw}{dx}.$$

In the special case when $u = c$, a constant, (3) and (4) become

(3')
$$\frac{d}{dx} cv = c \frac{dv}{dx},$$

(4')
$$\frac{d}{dx} \frac{c}{v} = - \frac{c \frac{dv}{dx}}{v^2}.$$

All the formulas appearing in heavy type should be carefully memorized, preferably in words.

On pages 198–199 there is a collection of fundamental differentiation formulas, each of which is derived either in this chapter or in one of Chapters 11, 12, or 13.   These basic formulas carry boldface (heavy type) equation numbers and retain those numbers throughout the various chapters involved.

50. *Derivative of* x^n

If
$$y = x^n,$$
then

(1)
$$\frac{dy}{dx} = nx^{n-1}.$$

When n is a positive integer, this formula may be established as follows:

$$y + \Delta y = (x + \Delta x)^n$$
$$= x^n + nx^{n-1} \Delta x + \frac{n(n-1)}{2!} x^{n-2} \overline{\Delta x}^2 + \cdots + \overline{\Delta x}^n,$$
$$\Delta y = nx^{n-1} \Delta x + \frac{n(n-1)}{2!} x^{n-2} \overline{\Delta x}^2 + \cdots + \overline{\Delta x}^n,$$
$$\frac{\Delta y}{\Delta x} = nx^{n-1} + \frac{n(n-1)}{2!} x^{n-2} \Delta x + \cdots + \overline{\Delta x}^{n-1},$$
$$\frac{dy}{dx} = \lim_{\Delta x \to 0} \frac{\Delta y}{\Delta x} = nx^{n-1}.$$

In particular, if $n = 1$, i.e., if $y = x$,

$$\frac{dx}{dx} = 1.$$

Although the above proof is valid only for positive integral values of n, formula (1) is true for all values of the exponent.   The general proof will be given later; meanwhile the truth of the statement will be assumed.

Example (a). The derivative of

$$y = 2x^3 - 5x^2 + 3x + 2$$

is

$$y' = 6x^2 - 10x + 3.$$

Example (b). The derivative of

$$y = \frac{x^2 + 1}{4x + 3}$$

is

$$y' = \frac{(4x + 3)2x - (x^2 + 1)4}{(4x + 3)^2}$$

$$= \frac{4x^2 + 6x - 4}{(4x + 3)^2}.$$

Example (c). To differentiate

$$y = \frac{1}{\sqrt{x}},$$

we write

$$y = x^{-\frac{1}{2}}$$

from which we obtain

$$\frac{dy}{dx} = -\frac{1}{2} x^{-\frac{3}{2}} = \frac{-1}{2x^{\frac{3}{2}}}.$$

EXERCISES

Differentiate the functions in Exs. 1–28.

1. $y = x^3 - 6x + 2.$

2. $y = x^4 + 2x^3 - x + 1.$

3. $y = 3x^2 - x^4 - 3x^5.$

4. $y = 4 - 2x + x^3 - 2x^6.$

5. $y = 2x^{-1} - 3x^{-2}.$

     Ans. $y' = -2x^{-2} + 6x^{-3}.$

6. $y = 4x^{-2} + x^{-3}.$

     Ans. $y' = -8x^{-3} - 3x^{-4}.$

7. $y = \dfrac{2}{t^2} - \dfrac{1}{t^4}$ See Ex. 5.

     Ans. $\dfrac{dy}{dt} = -\dfrac{4}{t^3} + \dfrac{4}{t^5}.$

8. $x = \dfrac{1}{t} - \dfrac{3}{t^2}$ See Ex. 5.

     Ans. $\dfrac{dx}{dt} = -\dfrac{1}{t^2} + \dfrac{6}{t^3}.$

9. $z = \dfrac{1}{5} + \dfrac{2x}{7} - \dfrac{x^2}{4}.$

     Ans. $\dfrac{dz}{dx} = \dfrac{2}{7} - \dfrac{x}{2}.$

10. $x = \dfrac{3}{4} - \dfrac{y^2}{3} + \dfrac{2y^3}{5}.$

     Ans. $\dfrac{dx}{dy} = -\dfrac{2y}{3} + \dfrac{6y^2}{5}.$

11. $y = x^{\frac{1}{2}} - x^{-\frac{3}{2}}.$

12. $y = x^{-\frac{1}{2}} - x^{\frac{1}{2}}.$

13. $x = \sqrt{t} - 4\sqrt{t^3}.$

14. $x = t\sqrt{t} - \dfrac{2}{\sqrt{t}}.$

15. $y = 2x^{\frac{1}{2}} + x^2.$

16. $y = 4 - x^{-\frac{3}{4}}.$

17. $y = (1 - x^2)(2 + 3x)$.

18. $y = (t^3 + 2)(t^2 - t + 1)$.   *Ans.* $\dfrac{dy}{dt} = 5t^4 - 4t^3 + 3t^2 + 4t - 2$.

19. $y = \dfrac{1}{2 - 3x}$.   Use (4'), page 80.   *Ans.* $y' = \dfrac{3}{(2 - 3x)^2}$.

20. $y = \dfrac{4}{1 + 2x}$.   Use (4'), page 80.   *Ans.* $y' = \dfrac{-8}{(1 + 2x)^2}$.

21. $z = \dfrac{3}{t^2 - 1}$.   *Ans.* $\dfrac{dz}{dt} = \dfrac{-6t}{(t^2 - 1)^2}$.

22. $x = \dfrac{5}{1 - 3t^2}$.   *Ans.* $\dfrac{dx}{dt} = \dfrac{30t}{(1 - 3t^2)^2}$.

23. $y = \dfrac{x^2}{1 - x}$.   *Ans.* $\dfrac{dy}{dx} = \dfrac{2x - x^2}{(1 - x)^2}$.

24. $y = \dfrac{2x}{x^2 + 1}$.   *Ans.* $\dfrac{dy}{dx} = \dfrac{2(1 - x^2)}{(x^2 + 1)^2}$.

25. $f(x) = \dfrac{x^2 - 1}{x^2 + 1}$.   *Ans.* $f'(x) = \dfrac{4x}{(x^2 + 1)^2}$.

26. $F(t) = \dfrac{1 + 2t}{4 - t^2}$.   *Ans.* $F'(t) = \dfrac{2(4 + t + t^2)}{(4 - t^2)^2}$.

27. $\varphi(t) = \dfrac{t^2 + 2t}{1 - 2t}$.   *Ans.* $\varphi'(t) = \dfrac{2(1 + t - t^2)}{(1 - 2t)^2}$.

28. $f(v) = \dfrac{v^2 + v - 1}{v^2 - v}$.   *Ans.* $f'(v) = \dfrac{-2v^2 + 2v - 1}{(v^2 - v)^2}$.

In Exs. 29–34, find the slope at the point indicated.

29. $y = x^3 - 4x^2 + 3x + 5$, at $x = 2$.   *Ans.* -1.
30. $y = 1 + 9x - 2x^3$, at $x = -1$.   *Ans.* 3.

31. $y = \dfrac{x}{x^2 + 4}$, at $x = 1$.   *Ans.* $\frac{3}{25}$.

32. $y = \dfrac{x - 2}{1 - x^2}$, at $x = 3$.   *Ans.* $-\frac{1}{32}$.

33. $y = x^3 - x^2 + 2$, where the curve crosses Ox.   *Ans.* 5.
34. $y = x^4 - 3x^3 - x^2 + 13x - 10$, where the curve crosses Ox.   *Ans.* -51; 6.

In Exs. 35–38, find the point where the tangent is parallel to Ox. Sketch the curve. These curves, called *parabolas*, will be studied in more detail in § 63.

35. $y = x^2 + 4x + 2$.   **36.** $y = 3x^2 - 2x + 1$.
37. $3x^2 - 9x + 7y + 5 = 0$.   **38.** $2x^2 + x + 5y + 2 = 0$.

In Exs. 39–46, find the points where the tangent is parallel to Ox.

39. $y = x^3 + 3x^2 + 1$.   *Ans.* (0, 1), $(-2, 5)$.
40. $y = 3x^4 + 4x^3 - 12x^2 + 2$.   *Ans.* (0, 2), $(1, -3)$, $(-2, -30)$.

41. $y = x^4 - 2x^3 - 3x^2 + 4x + 3$.   *Ans.* $(-1, -1)$, $(\frac{1}{2}, \frac{65}{16})$, $(2, -1)$.

42. $5y = x^4 - 14x^2 - 24x + 7$.   *Ans.* $(-2, 3)$, $(-1, \frac{18}{5})$, $(3, -22)$.

43. $y = x^4 + 2x^3 + 8x^2 - 10x + 3$.   *Ans.* $(\frac{1}{2}, \frac{5}{16})$.

44. $y = x^4 + 2x^2 - 40x + 36$.   *Ans.* $(2, -20)$.

45. $y = \dfrac{x + 1}{x^2 + 2x + 5}$.   *Ans.* $(1, \frac{1}{4})$, $(-3, -\frac{1}{4})$.

46. $y = \dfrac{x + 2}{x(x + 3)}$.   *Ans.* None.

47. Find the rate at which the radius r of a sphere increases as the volume V increases.

$$\text{\textit{Ans.} } \frac{dr}{dV} = (4\pi)^{-\frac{1}{3}}(3V)^{-\frac{2}{3}}.$$

48. A body of gas is contained in a vessel of volume v; the pressure is given by the formula $p = \dfrac{k}{v}$. Find the rate at which pressure increases with decreasing volume, at the instant when $v = 3$.

49. Suppose the container of Ex. 48 is a cube with its edge c units in length. Find the rate at which the pressure p varies with varying edge length, when $c = 2$ units.

$$\text{\textit{Ans.} } \frac{dp}{dc} = -\frac{3k}{16}.$$

50. Use $(4')$ of § 49 to prove that (1) of § 50 holds for negative integral values of n.

51. The force between two magnetic poles at a distance r apart is $F = \dfrac{k}{r^2}$. Find the rate at which F changes with respect to r, when $r = 4$.

51. *The Chain Rule*

Given y as a function of x, it is frequently convenient to think of y as a function of an auxiliary variable u, where u in turn is a function of x. For example, the formula of § 50 would fail entirely to find the derivative of such a function as

$$y = \sqrt{x^2 + 1};$$

it will appear presently that the difficulty may be overcome by merely putting $y = \sqrt{u}$, where $u = x^2 + 1$.

Let

$$y = f(u), \text{ where } u = \varphi(x).$$

Assign to x an increment Δx, and denote by Δu and Δy the corresponding changes in u and y. Then

$$\frac{\Delta y}{\Delta x} = \frac{\Delta y}{\Delta u} \cdot \frac{\Delta u}{\Delta x},$$

and when Δx approaches zero, we find (assuming that the limits of all three ratios exist)

$$\mathrm{Lim}_{\Delta x \to 0} \frac{\Delta y}{\Delta x} = \mathrm{Lim}_{\Delta x \to 0} \frac{\Delta y}{\Delta u} \cdot \mathrm{Lim}_{\Delta x \to 0} \frac{\Delta u}{\Delta x},$$

or

(5)
$$\frac{dy}{dx} = \frac{dy}{du} \cdot \frac{du}{dx}.$$

Equation (5) is called the *chain rule*. It is an extremely useful tool and will be employed over and over again throughout much of the remainder of this book.

Two other formulas follow very quickly. Writing (5) in the form

$$\frac{dy}{du} = \frac{\dfrac{dy}{dx}}{\dfrac{du}{dx}},$$

let us interchange u and x:

(5′)
$$\frac{dy}{dx} = \frac{\dfrac{dy}{du}}{\dfrac{dx}{du}}, \qquad \frac{dx}{du} \neq 0.$$

In (5′), put $u = y$:

(5″)
$$\frac{dy}{dx} = \frac{1}{\dfrac{dx}{dy}}, \qquad \frac{dx}{dy} \neq 0.$$

Formula (5″) says that the rate of change of y with respect to x and the rate of change of x with respect to y are reciprocals. This fact appears constantly in ordinary experience. Say that a car is traveling at a speed (time-rate of change of distance) of 30 mi. per hr. Then time is elapsing at a rate (distance-rate of change of time) of 2 min. ($\frac{1}{30}$ hr.) per mi.:

$$\frac{dx}{dt} = 30,$$

$$\frac{dt}{dx} = \frac{1}{30}.$$

52. *The General Power Formula*

Formula (1) of § 50 enables us to differentiate any power of x. By means of the chain rule, we are able to differentiate *any power of any function of x*. To do this, let

$$y = u^n, \text{ where } u = \varphi(x).$$

Then by (1), § 50,

$$\frac{dy}{du} = nu^{n-1},$$

and we have by the chain rule (5)

(6) $$\frac{d}{dx} u^n = nu^{n-1} \frac{du}{dx}.$$

An important special case of this formula is the case $n = \frac{1}{2}$:

(6′) $$\frac{d}{dx} \sqrt{u} = \frac{\dfrac{du}{dx}}{2 \sqrt{u}}.$$

Example (a).   Find the derivative of

$$y = (3x^2 + 1)^4.$$

This function is of the form u^n, with $u = 3x^2 + 1$, $n = 4$.   Hence (6) gives

$$\begin{aligned} y' &= 4(3x^2 + 1)^3 \cdot 6x \\ &= 24x(3x^2 + 1)^3. \end{aligned}$$

Example (b).   Differentiate the function

$$x = \sqrt{l^2 + 1}.$$

By (6′), we have

$$\frac{dx}{dl} = \frac{2l}{2 \sqrt{l^2 + 1}} = \frac{l}{\sqrt{l^2 + 1}}.$$

Example (c).   Differentiate

$$y = (4x + 1)^2(x^2 - 2)^3.$$

By (3) and (6), we have

$$\begin{aligned} y' &= (4x + 1)^2 3(x^2 - 2)^2 2x + (x^2 - 2)^3 2(4x + 1)4 \\ &= (4x + 1)(x^2 - 2)^2[6(4x + 1)x + 8(x^2 - 2)] \\ &= (4x + 1)(x^2 - 2)^2(32x^2 + 6x - 16). \end{aligned}$$

53. *Higher Derivatives*

The derivative of y with respect to x is itself a function of x and may in turn be differentiated.   The derivative of the first derivative is called the *second derivative*, and is written $\dfrac{d^2y}{dx^2}$; further differentiations give $\dfrac{d^3y}{dx^3}, \dfrac{d^4y}{dx^4}$, etc.   Other symbols for the higher derivatives are y'', y''', $y^{(4)}$, $\cdots$, and $f''(x), f'''(x), f^{(4)}(x), \cdots$.

Since y'' is the derivative of y', we see by § 46 that *the second derivative of a function is the rate of change of slope of the graph.*

Example. In Example (*b*), § 52,

$$\frac{dx}{dt} = \frac{t}{\sqrt{t^2 + 1}},$$

so that, by (4),

$$\frac{d^2x}{dt^2} = \frac{\sqrt{t^2 + 1} \cdot 1 - \dfrac{t \cdot 2t}{2\sqrt{t^2 + 1}}}{t^2 + 1}$$

$$= \frac{1}{(t^2 + 1)^{\frac{3}{2}}}.$$

It is sometimes necessary to express $\dfrac{d^2y}{dx^2}$ in terms of the derivatives of x with respect to y.   To do this, let us in (5′), § 51, replace u by y and y by y':

(1)
$$\frac{dy'}{dx} = \frac{\dfrac{dy'}{dy}}{\dfrac{dx}{dy}}.$$

But by (5″),

$$\frac{dy'}{dy} = \frac{d}{dy}\left(\frac{1}{\dfrac{dx}{dy}}\right) = -\frac{\dfrac{d^2x}{dy^2}}{\left(\dfrac{dx}{dy}\right)^2}.$$

Substituting in (1), we find

(2)
$$\frac{d^2y}{dx^2} = -\frac{\dfrac{d^2x}{dy^2}}{\left(\dfrac{dx}{dy}\right)^3}, \qquad \frac{dx}{dy} \neq 0.$$

Suppose $f(x)$ contains $(x - a)$ as a factor precisely n times.   Then

(3)
$$f(x) = (x - a)^n g_0(x), \qquad g_0(a) \neq 0.$$

From (3), with the aid of the formula for the derivative of a product, we obtain

$$f'(x) = (x - a)^n g_0'(x) + n(x - a)^{n-1} g_0(x)$$
$$= (x - a)^{n-1}[(x - a)g_0'(x) + ng_0(x)].$$

Hence

(4)
$$f'(x) = (x - a)^{n-1} g_1(x), \qquad g_1(a) \neq 0.$$

That is, the derivative of $f(x)$ contains $(x - a)$ as a factor one time less than did $f(x)$.   Iteration of this fact yields the following result.

THEOREM 19.   *If $f(x)$ contains $(x - a)$ as a factor precisely n times, the kth derivative of $f(x)$ contains $(x - a)$ as a factor precisely $(n - k)$ times.   That is, if*

$$(5) \qquad f(x) = (x - a)^n g_0(x), \qquad g_0(a) \neq 0,$$

then

$$(6) \qquad f^{(k)}(x) = (x - a)^{n-k} g_k(x), \qquad g_k(a) \neq 0.$$

The above theorem will be of much help to us in our study of the applications of the derivative in the next chapter.

EXERCISES

In Exs. 1–40, find the first derivative.

1. $y = (1 + 2x)^3$.   Ans. $y' = 6(1 + 2x)^2$.

2. $y = (2 - x)^4$.   Ans. $y' = -4(2 - x)^3$.

3. $y = (4 - 3t)^5$.   Ans. $\dfrac{dy}{dt} = -15(4 - 3t)^4$.

4. $x = \frac{1}{2}(5t - 1)^8$.   Ans. $\dfrac{dx}{dt} = 20(5t - 1)^7$.

5. $y = (a - x)^{-2}$.   Ans. $\dfrac{dy}{dx} = 2(a - x)^{-3}$.

6. $x = 4\sqrt{3 + y}$.   Ans. $\dfrac{dx}{dy} = \dfrac{2}{\sqrt{3 + y}}$.

7. $y = 6(1 - 3x)^{\frac{3}{2}}$.   Ans. $y' = -27(1 - 3x)^{\frac{1}{2}}$.

8. $y = \dfrac{2}{(1 + 3x)^2}$.   Ans. $y' = \dfrac{-12}{(1 + 3x)^3}$.

9. $a^2 y = (x^2 + a^2)^{\frac{3}{2}}$.   Ans. $a^2 \dfrac{dy}{dx} = 3x(x^2 + a^2)^{\frac{1}{2}}$.

10. $x = \sqrt{2ay - y^2}$.   Ans. $\dfrac{dx}{dy} = \dfrac{a - y}{\sqrt{2ay - y^2}}$.

11. $x = (16 - t^4)^{-\frac{3}{2}}$.   Ans. $\dfrac{dx}{dt} = 6t^3(16 - t^4)^{-\frac{5}{2}}$.

12. $u = (v^4 + 3v^2 - 1)^{\frac{5}{2}}$.   Ans. $\dfrac{du}{dv} = 5v(2v^2 + 3)(v^4 + 3v^2 - 1)^{\frac{3}{2}}$.

13. $y = x^3(x + 1)^2$.   Ans. $y' = x^2(x + 1)(5x + 3)$.

14. $f(x) = x(x^2 - a^2)^{\frac{1}{2}}$.   Ans. $f'(x) = (2x^2 - a^2)(x^2 - a^2)^{-\frac{1}{2}}$.

15. $f(t) = t^3(t^2 + b^2)^{-\frac{1}{2}}$.   Ans. $f'(t) = t^2(2t^2 + 3b^2)(t^2 + b^2)^{-\frac{3}{2}}$.

16. $y = \dfrac{(1 + x)^2}{x}$.   Ans. $y' = \dfrac{x^2 - 1}{x^2}$.

17. $y = \dfrac{(2x + 1)^3}{x^2}$.   Ans. $y' = 8 - 6x^{-2} - 2x^{-3}$.

18. $y = \dfrac{(x - 2)^3}{x^2}$.   Use three methods and check your answers against one another. *Hint*: consider y as a product, as a quotient, or with the binomial expanded.

19. $x = \dfrac{t}{\sqrt{a^2 - t^2}}$.   *Ans.* $\dfrac{dx}{dt} = \dfrac{a^2}{(a^2 - t^2)^{\frac{3}{2}}}$.

20. $y = (a^{\frac{2}{3}} - x^{\frac{2}{3}})^{\frac{3}{2}}$.   *Ans.* $y' = -x^{-\frac{1}{3}}(a^{\frac{2}{3}} - x^{\frac{2}{3}})^{\frac{1}{2}}$.

21. $y = \dfrac{1}{(3 - 4x)^5}$.   *Ans.* $\dfrac{dy}{dx} = \dfrac{20}{(3 - 4x)^6}$.

22. $\varphi = \dfrac{7}{\sqrt{9 + t^4}}$.   *Ans.* $\dfrac{d\varphi}{dt} = \dfrac{-14t^3}{(9 + t^4)^{\frac{3}{2}}}$.

23. $y = x\sqrt{(a^2 - x^2)^3}$.   *Ans.* $y' = (a^2 - 4x^2)\sqrt{a^2 - x^2}$.

24. $y = \dfrac{\sqrt{a^2 + x^2}}{x}$.   *Ans.* $y' = -a^2 x^{-2}(a^2 + x^2)^{-\frac{1}{2}}$.

25. $y = (1 + x)^2(2 - x)^3$.   *Ans.* $y' = (1 + x)(2 - x)^2(1 - 5x)$.

26. $y = (x^2 + 1)^3(x^2 - 2)^2$.   *Ans.* $y' = 2x(x^2 + 1)^2(x^2 - 2)(5x^2 - 4)$.

27. $f(x) = (2 + 3x)^4(5 - 2x)^3$.   *Ans.* $f'(x) = 6(2 + 3x)^3(5 - 2x)^2(8 - 7x)$.

28. $\varphi(t) = (4 + 3t)^2(2 - 5t)^3$.   *Ans.* $\varphi'(t) = -3(4 + 3t)(2 - 5t)^2(16 + 25t)$.

29. $y = (2x + 1)^3(x^2 - 1)^{\frac{3}{2}}$.   *Ans.* $y' = 3(2x + 1)^2(x^2 - 1)^{\frac{1}{2}}(4x^2 + x - 2)$.

30. $y = (x^2 - 1)^{\frac{1}{2}}(3x - 2)^2$.   *Ans.* $y' = (x^2 - 1)^{-\frac{1}{2}}(3x - 2)(9x^2 - 2x - 6)$.

31. $F(y) = \dfrac{(y^2 + 1)^2}{y^2 - 1}$.   *Ans.* $F'(y) = 2y(y^2 + 1)(y^2 - 3)(y^2 - 1)^{-2}$.

32. $\psi(x) = \dfrac{2x}{\sqrt{x + 1}}$.   *Ans.* $\psi'(x) = (x + 2)(x + 1)^{-\frac{3}{2}}$.

33. $y = \dfrac{1}{x^3(x + 2)^2}$.   *Ans.* $y' = -(5x + 6)x^{-4}(x + 2)^{-3}$.

34. $y = \dfrac{1}{(x + 2)^2(2x - 1)^3}$.   *Ans.* $y' = -10(x + 1)(x + 2)^{-3}(2x - 1)^{-4}$.

35. $x = \left(\dfrac{t}{1 + t}\right)^{\frac{1}{2}}$.   *Ans.* $\dfrac{dx}{dt} = \dfrac{1}{2} t^{-\frac{1}{2}}(1 + t)^{-\frac{3}{2}}$.

36. $y = \left(\dfrac{z^3}{a + z}\right)^{\frac{1}{2}}$.   *Ans.* $\dfrac{dy}{dz} = \dfrac{1}{2}(3a + 2z)z^{\frac{1}{2}}(a + z)^{-\frac{3}{2}}$.

37. $y = x^3(x + 1)^2(2x - 3)^2$.   *Ans.* $y' = x^2(x + 1)(2x - 3)(14x + 9)(x - 1)$.

38. $z = [1 + (x^2 - 1)^3]^{\frac{3}{2}}$.   *Ans.* $z' = 9x(x^2 - 1)^2\sqrt{1 + (x^2 - 1)^3}$.

39. $f(x) = \sqrt{1 + \sqrt{1 - x}}$.   *Ans.* $f'(x) = \dfrac{-1}{4\sqrt{1 - x}\sqrt{1 + \sqrt{1 - x}}}$.

40. $y = \dfrac{1}{(1 + \sqrt{1 - x})^2}$.   *Ans.* $y' = \dfrac{1}{\sqrt{1 - x}\,(1 + \sqrt{1 - x})^3}$.

In Exs. 41–44, find the slope of the curve at the given point.

41. $y = (3x + 1)^2$, $(-1, 4)$.   *Ans.* -12.

42. $y = \sqrt{25 - x^2}$, $(3, 4)$.   *Ans.* -0.75.

43. $y = \dfrac{x}{(x^2 + 1)^2}$, $\left(1, \dfrac{1}{4}\right)$.   *Ans.* -0.25.

44. $6y = (2x + 1)^2(x - 3)^3$, $(1, -12)$.   *Ans.* 2.

In Exs. 45–49, find the second derivative.

45. $y = x(x + 1)^3$.   *Ans.* $y'' = 6(x + 1)(2x + 1)$.

46. $y = x^2(2x - 1)^2$.   *Ans.* $y'' = 2(24x^2 - 12x + 1)$.

47. $y = \dfrac{-1}{\sqrt{a^2 + x^2}}$.   *Ans.* $y'' = (a^2 - 2x^2)(a^2 + x^2)^{-\frac{5}{2}}$.

48. $x = \dfrac{(1 + t)^2}{t^2}$.   *Ans.* $\dfrac{d^2x}{dt^2} = \dfrac{6}{t^4} + \dfrac{4}{t^3}$.

49. $u = (1 - 3v)^2(2 + v)^3$.   *Ans.* $\dfrac{d^2u}{dv^2} = 6(2 + v)(1 + 36v + 30v^2)$.

50. Find $\dfrac{d^2y}{dx^2}$ from the equation $y = \sqrt{1 - 2xt + t^2}$.

$$Ans. \quad \frac{d^2y}{dx^2} = -t^2(1 - 2xt + t^2)^{-\frac{3}{2}}.$$

51. Find $\dfrac{d^2y}{dt^2}$ from the equation of Ex. 50.   *Ans.* $\dfrac{d^2y}{dt^2} = (1 - x^2)(1 - 2xt + t^2)^{-\frac{3}{2}}$.

52. For the curve $y = (2x + 1)^3$, find the rate of change of slope at $(1, 27)$.

Ans. 72.

53. For the curve $y = \dfrac{(1 + x)^2}{x}$, find the rate of change of slope at $(1, 4)$.   *Ans.* 2.

54. If $y = x(x + 1)^3$, find y'''.   *Ans.* $y''' = 24x + 18$.

55. If $\varphi(x) = \sqrt{ax + b}$, find $\varphi^{(4)}(x)$.   *Ans.* $\varphi^{(4)}(x) = -\frac{15}{16}a^4(ax + b)^{-\frac{7}{2}}$.

56. If $y = uv$, where u and v are any functions of x, derive the formula

$$y'' = uv'' + 2u'v' + u''v.$$

Obtain the formula for y'''.

54. Implicit Functions

In general, an equation involving x and y determines a value (or values) of y corresponding to each value of x and therefore determines y as a function of x. Hitherto we have been concerned with functions defined *explicitly* by an equation of the form

$$y = f(x).$$

It may happen, however, that x and y are connected by an equation not solved for y; for example, $x^3 + y^3 = 3axy$.

In such a case y is called an *implicit function* of x, and the relation is expressed by writing

$$F(x, y) = 0.$$

The definition becomes explicit if we solve for y; e.g., if

$$x^2 + y^2 = a^2, \text{ then } y = \pm \sqrt{a^2 - x^2}.$$

Frequently, however, it is not desirable to change to the explicit form, even when such a change is feasible.

55. *Derivatives in Implicit Form*

To find the derivative of a function defined implicitly, we apply the following procedure.

Rule. *Differentiate each term of the equation*

$$F(x, y) = 0$$

with respect to x, bearing in mind that y is a function of x.

In this connection it must be remembered that, by (6), the derivative of y^n with respect to x is $ny^{n-1}\dfrac{dy}{dx}$.

Example (a). Find y', if

$$x^3 + y^3 - 3axy = 0.$$

Differentiating each term in turn, we have

$$3x^2 + 3y^2y' - 3a(xy' + y) = 0,$$

from which it follows that

$$(y^2 - ax)y' + x^2 - ay = 0,$$

$$y' = -\frac{x^2 - ay}{y^2 - ax}.$$

Example (b). Find y'', if $x^2 - y^2 = a^2$.

Differentiating, we get

$$2x - 2yy' = 0,$$

or

(1) $$y' = \frac{x}{y}.$$

A second differentiation gives

$$y'' = \frac{y - xy'}{y^2},$$

or, after substitution of the value of y' from (1),

$$y'' = \frac{y - \dfrac{x^2}{y}}{y^2} = \frac{y^2 - x^2}{y^3};$$

since $x^2 - y^2 = a^2$, this reduces to

$$y'' = -\frac{a^2}{y^3}.$$

EXERCISES

In Exs. 1–12, find the derivative of y with respect to x.

1. $x^2 + y^2 = a^2$.   *Ans.* $y' = -\dfrac{x}{y}$.

2. $x^3 - y^3 = a^3$.   *Ans.* $y' = \dfrac{x^2}{y^2}$.

3. $y^2(x + y) = b^3$.   *Ans.* $y' = -\dfrac{y}{2x + 3y}$.

4. $4x^2 + y^2 = 4cy$.   *Ans.* $y' = \dfrac{4x}{2c - y}$.

5. $x^2 + xy + y^2 = 1$.   *Ans.* $y' = -\dfrac{2x + y}{x + 2y}$.

6. $x^2 - 3xy + y^2 = 6x - 2y$.   *Ans.* $y' = \dfrac{2x - 3y - 6}{3x - 2y - 2}$.

7. $(x - y)^2 = 2ay$.   *Ans.* $\dfrac{dy}{dx} = \dfrac{x - y}{x - y + a}$.

8. $(x + y)^2 = 2ax$.   *Ans.* $\dfrac{dy}{dx} = \dfrac{a - x - y}{x + y}$.

9. $x^{\frac{1}{2}} + y^{\frac{1}{2}} = a^{\frac{1}{2}}$.   *Ans.* $y' = -x^{-\frac{1}{2}}y^{\frac{1}{2}}$.
10. $x^{\frac{2}{3}} + y^{\frac{2}{3}} = a^{\frac{2}{3}}$.   *Ans.* $y' = -x^{-\frac{1}{3}}y^{\frac{1}{3}}$.

11. $(x^2 + y^2)^2 = ay^3$.   *Ans.* $\dfrac{dy}{dx} = \dfrac{4x(x^2 + y^2)}{y(3ay - 4x^2 - 4y^2)}$.

12. $(x^2 + y^2)^3 = a^4x^2$.   *Ans.* $\dfrac{dy}{dx} = \dfrac{x[a^4 - 3(x^2 + y^2)^2]}{3y(x^2 + y^2)^2}$.

13. If $x = t^3 - 3t^2$, find $\dfrac{dt}{dx}$.   *Ans.* $\dfrac{dt}{dx} = \dfrac{1}{3t(t - 2)}$.

14. If $y = (x^3 + 1)^2$, find $\dfrac{dx}{dy}$.   *Ans.* $\dfrac{dx}{dy} = \dfrac{1}{6x^2(x^3 + 1)}$.

15. If $z^2 - 2zy + 3y^2 = 4$, find $\dfrac{dz}{dy}$.   *Ans.* $\dfrac{dz}{dy} = \dfrac{z - 3y}{z - y}$.

16. If $4c^2\theta t = (\theta^2 - t^2)^2$ and $\dfrac{d\theta}{dt}$.   *Ans.* $\dfrac{d\theta}{dt} = \dfrac{t\theta^2 - t^3 + c^2\theta}{\theta^3 - t^2\theta - c^2t}$.

17. If $y^2 = 4ax$, find y''.   *Ans.* $y'' = \dfrac{-4a^2}{y^3}$.

18. If $x^2 = 4ay$, find y''. $y'' = \dfrac{1}{2a}$

19. If $x^2 + y^2 = a^2$, find y''.   *Ans.* $y'' = \dfrac{-a^2}{y^3}$.

20. If $x^3 - y^3 = a^3$, find y''.   *Ans.* $y'' = -2a^3xy^{-5}$.

21. If $x^3 = a^2t$, find $\dfrac{d^2x}{dt^2}$.   *Ans.* $\dfrac{d^2x}{dt^2} = -\dfrac{2a^4}{9x^5}$.

22. If $x^3 = az^2$, find $\dfrac{d^2x}{dz^2}$.

Ans. $\dfrac{d^2x}{dz^2} = -\dfrac{2a}{9x^2}$.

23. If $x^{\frac{1}{2}} + y^{\frac{1}{2}} = a^{\frac{1}{2}}$, find $\dfrac{d^2y}{dx^2}$.

Ans. $\dfrac{d^2y}{dx^2} = \tfrac{1}{2}a^{\frac{1}{2}}x^{-\frac{3}{2}}$.

24. If $x^{\frac{2}{3}} + y^{\frac{2}{3}} = a^{\frac{2}{3}}$, find $\dfrac{d^2y}{dx^2}$.

Ans. $\dfrac{d^2y}{dx^2} = \tfrac{1}{3}a^{\frac{2}{3}}x^{-\frac{4}{3}}y^{-\frac{1}{3}}$.

In Exs. 25–34, find the slope of the curve at the given point.

25. $x^2 + y^2 + 4x - 2y - 5 = 0$ at $(1, 0)$.　　　　Ans. 3.
26. $x^2 + 2y^2 - 6x + 4y - 13 = 0$ at $(-1, 1)$.　　　Ans. 1.
27. $(x + y)^2 + 3x - 15 = 0$ at $(2, 1)$.　　　　Ans. -1.5.
28. $(x - y)^2 = 4y$ at $(0, 4)$.　　　　　Ans. 2.
29. $x(y^2 - x^2) = 3$ at $(1, 2)$.　　　　Ans. -0.25.
30. $y(x - y^2) = 3$ at $(4, 1)$.　　　　Ans. -1.
31. $y(x - y^2) = 2$ at $(3, 1)$.　　Ans. Slope does not exist.

32. $y^2 = \dfrac{b^3}{2x + b}$ at $(0, b)$.　　　　Ans. -1.

33. $y^2 = \dfrac{2a^3x}{x^2 + a^2}$ at (a, a).　　　　Ans. 0.

34. $y^3 = \dfrac{2ax^3}{x + a}$ at (a, a).　　　　Ans. $\tfrac{5}{6}$.

Polynomial Curves

56. Tangents and Normals to Plane Curves

The equation of a line of slope m through the point (x_1, y_1) is

(1) $$y - y_1 = m(x - x_1).$$

Hence, to find the tangent at any point of a plane curve, we have only to find the slope of the curve (i.e., the value of y') at that point, and substitute for m in the above formula.

The normal* to a curve at the point (x_1, y_1) is defined to be the line through that point and perpendicular to the tangent line there.

The equation of the normal is found from that of the tangent by recalling that if two lines are perpendicular, the slope of one is the negative reciprocal of the slope of the other.

Example (a). Find the tangent and normal to the curve

(2) $$4x^2 + 9y^2 = 25$$

at the point P: $(2, -1)$.

The curve (2) is an ellipse. Ellipses will be treated in more detail in § 109, page 201.

Differentiation of both members of (2) yields

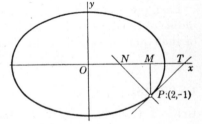

(3) $$8x + 18yy' = 0.$$

Figure 66

At the point of contact $(2, -1)$, x has the value 2, y the value (-1), and we shall denote the slope there by m. Thus at $(2, -1)$, equation (3) yields

$$16 - 18m = 0; \qquad m = \tfrac{8}{9}.$$

By (1) the equation of the tangent line is

$$y + 1 = \tfrac{8}{9}(x - 2),$$

---

* The word "normal" is used in advanced mathematics as meaning "perpendicular." It is in this sense rather than in the sense of "natural" or "usual" that the word is used here.

or

(4)
$$8x - 9y = 25.$$

The normal line is perpendicular to the line (4) and passes through $(2, -1)$. Hence that normal is

$$9x + 8y = 10.$$

Example (b). Find the tangents of slope 2 to the circle

(5)
$$x^2 + y^2 = 5.$$

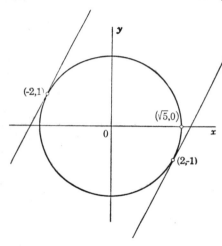

Figure 67

From equation (5) it follows that

(6)
$$x + yy' = 0.$$

The slope of the tangent line is to be 2. Therefore, the coordinates of the point of contact must satisfy the equation

(7)
$$x + 2y = 0,$$

found by using $y' = 2$ in equation (6).

The coordinates of the point of contact must also satisfy the equation of the original curve (5). By solving the simultaneous equations (5) and (7), we determine the points of contact $(-2, 1)$ and $(2, -1)$.

Each point of contact, together with the given slope 2, yields the equation of one of the desired tangent lines. With the aid of the point-slope form (1) of the equation of a line, the desired tangents may now be found to be

$$2x - y = -5, \qquad 2x - y = 5.$$

EXERCISES

In Exs. 1–17, find the equations of the tangent and the normal at the point indicated.

1. $y = 3x^2 - x + 1$ at $(1, 3)$.
   Ans. Tangent: $5x - y = 2$; Normal: $x + 5y = 16$.

2. $y = 2x^3 - x^2 + 1$ at $(1, 2)$.
   Ans. Tangent: $4x - y = 2$.

3. $y = 3 + 2x - x^3$ at $x = 1$.
   Ans. Normal: $x - y = -3$.

4. $x^2 - 4x + 2y - 5 = 0$ at $x = 3$.

5. $y = (2x + 1)^3$ at $x = -1$.
   Ans. Normal: $x + 6y = -7$.

6. $y = (1 - x^2)^2$ at $x = 0$.

7. $y = x^2 + x$ at its points of intersection with the line $y = 6$.
   Ans. Tangents: $5x - y = 4$, $5x + y = -9$.

8. $y = x^3 + 3x^2 - x - 3$ at its points of intersection with the x-axis.
   Ans. Tangents: $8x - y = -24$, $4x + y = -4$, $8x - y = 8$.

9. $a^2y = x^3$ at (a, a).
   Ans. Normal: $x + 3y = 4a$,

10. $xy^2 = a^3$ at its points of intersection with the line $x = \frac{1}{4}a$.

Ans. Tangents: $4x - y = 3a$, $4x + y = 3a$.

11. $xy - 3x + y = 0$ at $x = 2$.   *Ans.* Tangent: $x - 3y = -4$.

12. $x^2 - xy + 3y - 9 = 0$ at $x = -1$.

13. $(x + y)^2 + 3x - 1 = 0$ at $(0, 1)$.   *Ans.* Tangent: $5x + 2y = 2$.

14. $(x - 2y)^2 + 4y - 4 = 0$ at $(-2, 0)$.

15. The *cissoid* $y^2 = \dfrac{x^3}{2a - x}$ at (a, a).   *Ans.* Tangent: $2x - y = a$.

16. The *trisectrix* $y^2 = \dfrac{x^2(3a - x)}{a + x}$ at (a, a).

17. The *folium* $x^3 + y^3 = 3axy$ at $(\frac{3}{2}a, \frac{3}{2}a)$.   *Ans.* Normal: $x - y = 0$.

In Exs. 18–26, find tangent lines as directed.

18. To the curve $y = x^3 - 2x + 4$ parallel to the line $y = x$.

Ans. $y = x + 2$, $y = x + 6$.

19. To the curve $y = x^4 - 14x^2 + 19x + 4$ parallel to the line $5x + y = 4$.

Ans. $5x + y = 15$, $5x + y = 12$, $5x + y = -113$.

20. To the curve $y = x^4 + 2x^3 - 2x^2 - 3x + 3$ perpendicular to the line $x - 3y = 2$.   *Ans.* $3x + y = 3$, $3x + y = -5$, $48x + 16y = 45$.

21. To the curve $y = x^4 - 4x^3 + 2x^2 - 4x + 15$ perpendicular to the line $x + 8y = 7$.   *Ans.* $8x - y = 30$.

22. To the curve $y = x^4 - 4x^3 - 2x^2 + 16x - 10$ parallel to the line $y = 4x - 1$.

Ans. $4x - y = 3$, $4x - y = 19$ (twice).

23. To the curve $y = \frac{1}{4}x^4 + x^3 + x^2 - 2x - 3$ parallel to the line $2x + y = 1$.

Ans. $8x + 4y = -11$, $2x + y = -3$ (twice).

24. To the curve $y = x^4 - 4x^3 + 6x^2 - 4x + 3$ with slope zero.

Ans. $y = 2$ (three times).

25. To the curve $y = x^4 + 4x^3 - 8x^2 + 3x + 70$ with slope 3.

Ans. $3x - y = -70$, $3x - y = -67$, $3x - y = 58$.

26. To the curve $y = x^2(x^2 + 2x - 2)$ parallel to the x-axis.

Ans. $y = 0$, $y = -8$, $y = -\frac{3}{16}$.

27. Determine a, b, c so that the curve $y = ax^2 + bx + c$ shall be tangent to the line $3x - y = 5$ at $(2, 1)$ and shall also pass through $(3, -1)$.

Ans. $y = -5x^2 + 23x - 25$.

28. Make the curve $y = ax^2 + bx + c$ be tangent to the line $2x - y = 3$ at $(3, 3)$ and also pass through $(-1, 3)$.   *Ans.* $y = \frac{1}{2}x^2 - x + \frac{3}{2}$.

29. Make the curve $y = ax^3 + bx^2 + cx + d$ be tangent to the line $y = 4(x + 1)$ at $(1, 8)$ and also be tangent to the line $y = 4(2x + 3)$ at $(-1, 4)$.

Ans. $y = 2x^3 - x^2 + 7$.

30. Make the curve $y = ax^3 + bx^2 + cx + d$ be tangent to the line $3x - y = 3$ at the point $(1, 0)$ and also pass through $(-1, -6)$ and $(0, -2)$.

Ans. $y = x^3 - x^2 + 2x - 2$.

31. Find the equation of a circle tangent to the line $3x + y = -5$ at $(-1, -2)$ and also passing through $(1, 2)$.   *Ans.* $x^2 + y^2 - 4x + 2y - 5 = 0$.

32. Find the equation of a circle tangent to the line $3x + y = 1$ at $(-1, 4)$, and also passing through $(-1, 2)$.   *Ans.* $x^2 + y^2 + 8x - 6y + 15 = 0$.

57. *Increasing and Decreasing Functions*

Consider a function

(1) $$y = f(x)$$

which has a continuous derivative on some range of x-values. We know (§ 46) that the derivative y' is the rate of change of y with respect to x. If

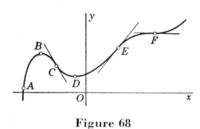

Figure 68

$y' > 0$ in some x-interval, the rate of change of y is positive, so that y increases as x increases in that interval. If $y' < 0$ in some interval, y decreases as x increases in that interval. The same conclusions are exhibited vividly by the graph of the function because y' is also the slope of the curve (1). In Figure 68, as x increases, *the curve rises if the slope is positive*, as on the arc AB; *it falls if the slope is negative*, as along BD:

> *If $y' > 0$, y increases;*
> *If $y' < 0$, y decreases.*

The above results are useful not only as employed in this chapter but also in demonstrating the validity of certain inequalities which are valuable in many phases of advanced mathematics. In §§ 89 and 105 some of those inequalities will be obtained.

58. *Maxima and Minima*

At a point such as B (Figure 68), where the function is algebraically greater than at any neighboring point, the function is said to have a *maximum value*, and the point is called a *maximum point*. Similarly, at D the function has a *minimum value*. *At such points the tangent is parallel to Ox*; i.e.,

$$y' = 0.$$

But the vanishing of the derivative does not mean that the function is necessarily a maximum or a minimum; the tangent is parallel to Ox at F, yet the function is neither a maximum nor a minimum there. From the figure, we deduce the following test:

At a point where $y' = 0$, if y' changes from positive to negative (as x increases), y is a maximum; if y' changes from negative to positive, y is a minimum; if y' does not change sign, y is neither a maximum nor a minimum.

The points at which $y' = 0$ are called *critical points*, and the corresponding values of x are the *critical values* of x: in Figure 68, B, D, F are critical points.

Maxima and minima collectively are called *extremes*: in the figure, B and D are extremes.

It should be clearly understood that an extreme is not necessarily the greatest (or least) value that the function attains anywhere in its range—the ordinate of F, for example, is greater than that of B. An extreme is merely greater (or less) than any *neighboring* value. The greatest value that the function can assume anywhere in its range (if such a value exists) is the *absolute maximum*; a maximum (such as at B) that is merely greater than any other in the neighborhood is a *relative maximum*.

In the majority of applications, we are concerned with the absolute maximum or minimum. When the function is a polynomial, there can never be an absolute extreme if x is unrestricted; but even in the case of polynomials such extremes frequently occur in practical problems, owing to the fact that x is limited in its range. This matter will be discussed more fully in § 70.

Example. Locate and classify the critical points of

$$y = \tfrac{1}{3}x^3 - \tfrac{1}{2}x^2 - 2x + 2.$$

We find

$$y' = x^2 - x - 2 = (x + 1)(x - 2).$$

Setting

$$y' = 0,$$

we get the critical values $x = -1$ or 2, and the critical points $(-1, \tfrac{19}{6})$, $(2, -\tfrac{4}{3})$. Now as x (increasing) passes through -1, y' changes from positive to negative: thus y assumes the maximum value $\tfrac{19}{6}$. As x passes through 2, y' changes from negative to positive: y assumes the minimum value $-\tfrac{4}{3}$. The curve is shown in Figure 69, page 100.

59. *Concavity*

The second derivative is the rate of change of the first derivative. It follows that when y'' is positive, y' is increasing; as x increases, the tangent turns in a counterclockwise sense and the curve is *concave upward*. When y'' is negative, y' decreases; the curve is *concave downward*.

At a maximum point the curve is concave downward, and hence y'', if it is not zero, must be negative. At a minimum, y'', if not zero, must be positive. If the second derivative is easily obtained and if it does not happen to be zero at the critical point in question, it is usually more convenient to determine whether we have a maximum or a minimum by finding the sign of y''; but the test of § 58 has the advantage of being perfectly general.

In summary, the test is as follows:

At a point where $y' = 0$, if $y'' < 0$, y is a maximum; if $y'' > 0$, y is a minimum; if $y'' = 0$, the test fails.

Example (a).　　Examine the function

$$y = \tfrac{1}{3}x^3 - \tfrac{1}{2}x^2 - 2x + 2$$

for maxima and minima.　(See the example, § 58.)

We have

$$y' = x^2 - x - 2 = (x + 1)(x - 2),$$
$$y'' = 2x - 1.$$

At $x = -1$, $y'' = -3$: y is a maximum.　At $x = 2$, $y'' = 3$: y is a minimum.

Example (b).　　Examine the function

$$y = x(x - 1)^3$$

for maxima and minima.

We find

$$y' = 3x(x - 1)^2 + (x - 1)^3 = (x - 1)^2(4x - 1),$$
$$y'' = 4(x - 1)^2 + 2(x - 1)(4x - 1) = 6(x - 1)(2x - 1).$$

The critical points ($y' = 0$) are ($\tfrac{1}{4}$, $-\tfrac{27}{256}$), (1, 0).　When $x = \tfrac{1}{4}$, $y'' = \tfrac{9}{4}$: y is a minimum.　When $x = 1$, $y'' = 0$: the test fails.　Turning to the test of § 58, we find that as x passes through 1, y' does not change sign: the point is neither a maximum nor a minimum.　The curve is shown in Figure 70, page 101.

The results of this and the preceding section give useful information regarding the behavior of a function as determined by the behavior of its derivatives.　However, we shall find in the next chapter that in specific applications of the theory, the nature of the various critical values can often be determined very easily by inspection.　In such a case, of course, it is unnecessary to apply either of the above tests, except perhaps as a check.

In the exercises below, it is advised that no attempt be made to trace the curve; this is better postponed until our analysis is complete (§§ 60–61).

EXERCISES

In Exs. 1–15, locate the critical points, and determine the maxima and minima by the tests of §§ 58–59.

1. $y = 7 - 8x + x^2$.
2. $y = 3x^2 + 12x - 1$.
3. $y = (3x - 1)^2$.
4. $y = -4(x + 3)^2$.
5. $y = 2x^3 + 3x^2 - 12x + 7$.　　*Ans.* (1, 0) minimum; (−2, 27) maximum.
6. $y = 5 + 9x - \tfrac{1}{3}x^3$.　　*Ans.* (3, 23) maximum; (−3, −13) minimum.
7. $y = x^3 + 3x^2 + 30x - 4$.　　*Ans.* No critical point.
8. $y = -20 + 18x - \tfrac{3}{2}x^2 - x^3$.　*Ans.* (2, 2) maximum; (−3, −60.5) minimum.
9. $y = x^3 + 3x^2 + 3x - 4$.　　*Ans.* No extreme.
10. $y = \tfrac{1}{4}x^4 - x^3 + 4x + 3$.　　*Ans.* (−1, $\tfrac{1}{4}$) minimum.
11. $y = x^2(x - 2)^2$.　　*Ans.* (0, 0) and (2, 0) minima; (1, 1) maximum.
12. $a^3y = x^4$.　　*Ans.* (0, 0) minimum.
13. $9a^3y = x(4a - x)^3$.　　*Ans.* (a, 3a) maximum.

14. $a^3y = x^2(2a^2 - x^2)$.   *Ans.* $(0, 0)$ minimum; (a, a) and $(-a, a)$ maxima.

15. $a^3y = x^3(4a - 3x)$.   *Ans.* (a, a) maximum.

16. Determine a, b, c, d so that the curve $y = ax^3 + bx^2 + cx + d$ shall have critical points at $(-1, -1)$ and $(-3, 3)$.   *Ans.* $y = x^3 + 6x^2 + 9x + 3$.

17. Make the curve $y = ax^3 + bx^2 + cx + d$ have critical points at $(0, 2)$ and $(-2, 6)$.   *Ans.* $y = x^3 + 3x^2 + 2$.

18. Make the curve $y = ax^3 + bx^2 + cx + d$ pass through the points $(0, 6)$ and $(3, 0)$ and have a critical point at $(2, 2)$.   *Ans.* $y = -x^3 + 5x^2 - 8x + 6$.

19. Make the curve $y = ax^3 + bx^2 + cx + d$ have a critical point at $(0, -2)$ and also be tangent to the line $3x + y + 3 = 0$ at $(-1, 0)$.   *Ans.* $y = x^3 + 3x^2 - 2$.

20. Make the curve $y = ax^4 + bx^3 + cx^2 + dx + e$ pass through $(2, -36)$, with critical points at $(0, -4)$, $(1, 0)$.   *Ans.* $y = -4(x^2 - 1)^2$.

21. Make the curve $y = ax^4 + bx^3 + cx^2 + dx + e$ pass through $(-1, 8)$, be tangent to the line $y = 11x - 5$ at $(1, 6)$, and have a critical point at $(0, 3)$.

22. What is the condition that the cubic $y = ax^3 + bx^2 + cx + d$ shall have two extremes?   *Ans.* $b^2 - 3ac > 0$.

60. *Points of Inflection*

A *point of inflection* is a point at which the curve changes from concave upward to concave downward, or vice versa (the points C, E, F in Figure 68, page 96).

At a point of inflection the tangent reverses the sense in which it turns, which means that y' changes from an increasing to a decreasing function, or vice versa. Hence at such a point y'' changes sign, and if it is continuous, must vanish.   Conversely, *a point at which y'' vanishes is a point of inflection, provided y'' changes sign at that point.*

Since y''—i.e., the rate of change of the slope—is zero at a point of inflection, the tangent is sometimes said to be *stationary for an instant* at such a point, and in the neighborhood of the point it turns very slowly.   Hence the inflectional tangent agrees more closely with the curve near its point of contact than does an ordinary tangent; it is therefore especially useful in tracing the curve to *draw the tangent at each point of inflection.*

A point at which y'' vanishes without changing sign is not a point of inflection; the result merely means that near that point the tangent turns even more slowly than near a point of inflection.

As noted in §§ 58–59, a point where $y' = 0$ is a maximum or a minimum, provided $y'' \neq 0$.   If y' and y'' both equal zero, the point is in general a point of inflection with a horizontal tangent (the point F in Figure 68); but if y'' vanishes without changing sign, the point is a maximum or minimum.

By combining Theorem 19, page 87, with the above discussion we obtain the following useful result.

THEOREM 20.   *If $x = a$ is a root of odd order—simple, triple, etc.—of the equation $y' = 0$, then $x = a$ yields a maximum or minimum; if $x = a$ is a root of even order, $x = a$ yields a point of inflection with horizontal tangent.*

61. *Sketching of Polynomial Curves*

The theory in §§ 57–60 may now be summarized in the form of a definite sequence of steps, as follows:

1. *Find the points of intersection with the axes.*
2. *Determine the behavior of y for large values of x.*
3. *Locate the points where y′ = 0, and determine the maxima and minima.*
4. *Locate the points where y″ = 0 (points of inflection, in most cases), and draw the tangent at each of those points.*
5. *If necessary, plot a few additional points.*

Any step that leads to serious algebraic difficulties may be omitted, provided sufficient information is obtainable without it.

Example (a).   Trace the curve

$$y = \tfrac{1}{3}x^3 - \tfrac{1}{2}x^2 - 2x + 2.$$

1. When $x = 0$, $y = 2$.   The x-intercepts are irrational and will not be determined.

2. When x is numerically large, the sign of y is the same as the sign of the highest-degree term in x.   Hence, when x is large and negative, y is large and negative; when x is large and positive, y is large and positive.

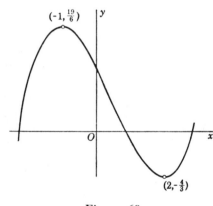

Figure 69

3. $y' = x^2 - x - 2$
$= (x + 1)(x - 2)$:

the critical points are $(-1, \tfrac{19}{6})$, $(2, -\tfrac{4}{3})$.   Without reference to previous examples (§§ 58–59), the situation at once becomes clear when the result of step 2 is considered: since y is large and negative when x is large and negative, the curve must come up through the third quadrant, rise to a maximum at $(-1, \tfrac{19}{6})$, fall to a minimum at $(2, -\tfrac{4}{3})$, and then rise indefinitely (since when x is large and positive y is large and positive).

4. $y'' = 2x - 1$.

Equating this to zero, we get $x = \tfrac{1}{2}$; the point $(\tfrac{1}{2}, \tfrac{11}{12})$ is a point of inflection, the slope at that point being $-\tfrac{9}{4}$.

Example (b).   Trace the curve $y = x(x - 1)^3$.

1. When $x = 0$, $y = 0$; when $y = 0$, $x = 0$ or 1.
2. When x is large and either positive or negative, y is large and positive.

3. $y' = (x - 1)^3 + 3x(x - 1)^2 = (x - 1)^2(4x - 1)$.

Thus the critical points are $(\frac{1}{4}, -\frac{27}{256})$, $(1, 0)$. The result of step 2 shows that the former point is a minimum, the latter a point of inflection with horizontal tangent. This last is verified by the fact that $x = 1$ is a *double root* of $y' = 0$ (Theorem 20).

4. $y'' = 2(x - 1)(4x - 1) + 4(x - 1)^2$
$ = 6(x - 1)(2x - 1).$

The points of inflection are $(\frac{1}{2}, -\frac{1}{16})$, with slope $\frac{1}{4}$, and $(1, 0)$, with slope zero.

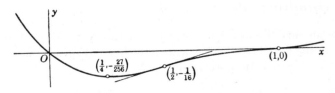

Figure 70

EXERCISES

In Exs. 1–34, trace the curve, choosing a suitable scale in each problem.

1. $y = 3x - x^3$.
2. $y = 3x^2 - x^3$.
3. $y = x^3 - 6x^2 + 20$.
4. $y = x^3 + 3x^2 + 3x - 7$.
5. $y = 10 - x - x^3$.
6. $y = (x - 6)^2(9 - x)$.
7. $3y = x^3 - 9x^2 + 12$.
8. $y = x^3 + 6x^2 + 15x + 18$.
9. $y = x^4 - 2x^2 - 8$.
10. $y = x^2(3x^2 + 8x + 6)$.
11. $y = x^4 + 8x^3 + 24x^2 + 32x$.
12. $y = 8x(2x^3 - 4x^2 + 3x - 1)$.
13. $y = x^4 - 2x^3 - 8x - 11$.
14. $y = x^4 - 8x^3 + 18x^2 - 24$.
15. $a^3y = (a^2 - x^2)(x^2 - 5a^2)$.
16. $a^3y = (x^2 - a^2)(x^2 - 23a^2)$.
17. $y = \frac{1}{2}x^4 - x^3 + x - 2$.
18. $y = x^4 - 4x^3 + 16x - 16$.
19. $y = x^4 - 8x^3 + 18x^2 - 16x + 5$.
20. $y = x^5 - 5x$.
21. $a^4y = x^4(5a - 4x)$.
22. $y = x^5 - 20x^2$.
23. $y = 3x^5 - 20x^3$.
24. $y = (2x + 1)^5 - 32$.
25. $8y = 3x^5 - 50x^3 + 135x$.
26. $y = 3x^5 - 10x^3 + 15x$.
27. $y = \frac{1}{4}x^4 - \frac{3}{2}x^2 - 2x + 2$.
28. $120y = 3x^5 + 40x^3 + 240x$.
29. $y = x^5 - 10x^3 - 20x^2 - 15x - 4$.
30. $y = 6x^5 - 15x^4 + 20x^3 - 30x^2 + 30x$.
31. $y = 64x^3(x - 1)^3$.
32. $a^4y = x(x^2 - 15a^2)^2$.
33. $y = x^2(x - 1)^4$.
34. $a^5y = x^5(6a - 5x)$; $(0.8)^5 = 0.33$.

35. Plot the curves $y = x$, $y = x^2$, $y = x^3$, $y = x^4$, $y = x^5$, all on the same axes, in the interval $-1 \leq x \leq 1$.

36. Make the curve $y = ax^3 + bx^2 + cx + d$ have at $(-1, 2)$ a point of inflection with a horizontal tangent, and also pass through $(0, 4)$.

         Ans. $y = 2(x^3 + 3x^2 + 3x + 2)$.

37. Make the curve $y = ax^3 + bx^2 + cx + d$ pass through $(1, 5)$ and have a point of inflection at $(2, 1)$, with inflectional tangent $3x + y = 7$.

Ans. $y = 15 - 15x + 6x^2 - x^3$.

38. Make the curve $y = ax^4 + bx^3 + cx^2 + dx + e$ have a critical point at $(0, 0)$ and an inflection point at $(-1, 2)$ with inflectional tangent $2x + y = 0$.

Ans. $y = 2x^2(x^2 + 3x + 3)$.

39. Make the curve $y = ax^4 + bx^3 + cx^2 + dx + e$ pass through the points $(0, 0)$, $(2, 24)$, and also have an inflection point with horizontal tangent at $(1, 9)$.

Ans. $y = 3x(x^3 - 6x + 8)$.

62. *The Quadratic Polynomial*

We have already discussed in some detail the general linear polynomial $y = mx + b$, the graph of which is a straight line. Consider next the quadratic polynomial

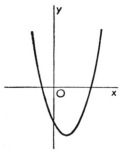

Figure 71

(1) $y = Ax^2 + Bx + C, \qquad A \neq 0.$

At once

$$y' = 2Ax + B.$$
$$y'' = 2A.$$

Since y'' is constant, the curve (1) is concave upward for all x if $A > 0$, concave downward for all x if $A < 0$. The one extreme occurs at $x = -\dfrac{B}{2A}$. For that x, equation (1) yields a minimum y if $A > 0$, a maximum y if $A < 0$. There are no inflection points.

We shall see later in this chapter that the curve (1) is a parabola. Parabolas will be defined geometrically in the next section. The geometric viewpoint will permit us later (Chapter 14) to see that the parabola is but one of a larger class of curves, the conic sections, which possess many geometric properties in common.

By interchanging the roles of x and y in (1) we see that

(2) $x = Ay^2 + By + C, \qquad A \neq 0,$

is also a parabola and that it is concave to the right if $A > 0$, concave to the left if $A < 0$.

63. *The Parabola*

We define a parabola as the locus of points equidistant from a fixed point F and a fixed line DD'. Call the point F the *focus* and the line DD' the *directrix*. Call the line through F, perpendicular to DD', the *axis of the parabola*.

To express the locus analytically, we need a coordinate system. Choose as x-axis the axis of the curve and as y-axis the perpendicular bisector of the segment joining F to DD', as shown in Figure 72. Let the coordinates of F be $(a, 0)$. Then the directrix is the line $x = -a$.

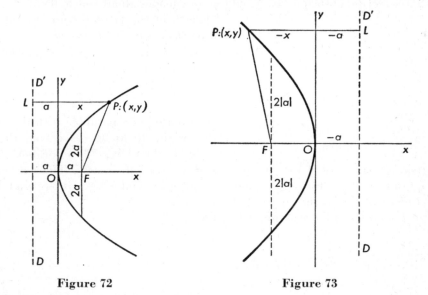

Figure 72   Figure 73

Let P: (x, y) be a variable point on the desired locus. The distance from P to the point $(a, 0)$ is equal to the distance from P to the line $x = -a$. If $a > 0$, as in Figure 72,

(1)
$$\sqrt{(x - a)^2 + y^2} = a + x.$$

If $a < 0$, as in Figure 73,

(2)
$$\sqrt{(x - a)^2 + y^2} = -a - x.$$

From either (1) or (2) it follows that

(3)
$$y^2 = 4ax.$$

By § 62 the curve (3) is concave to the right if $a > 0$, concave to the left if $a < 0$. Hence a parabola is concave in the direction away from its directrix. Since y may be changed to $(-y)$ without affecting equation (3), *the parabola is symmetric with respect to its axis.*

The mid-point of the perpendicular segment from the focus to the directrix is called the *vertex* of the parabola. For the parabola (3) the vertex is at the origin. The chord through the focus perpendicular to the axis of the parabola is called the *latus rectum, or right chord.* In equation (3) the value $x = a$ yields $y = \pm 2a$. Hence the length of the latus rectum is $4|a|$. We conclude that *for a parabola, the length of the latus rectum is four times the distance from focus to vertex.*

It is important that the student distinguish between the tools used and the conclusions drawn from them. The coordinate system and equation (3) of this section are tools. The definitions of focus, directrix, axis, vertex, and latus rectum of the parabola and the conclusions about concavity, symmetry, and length of the latus rectum are all *independent of the coordinate system.*

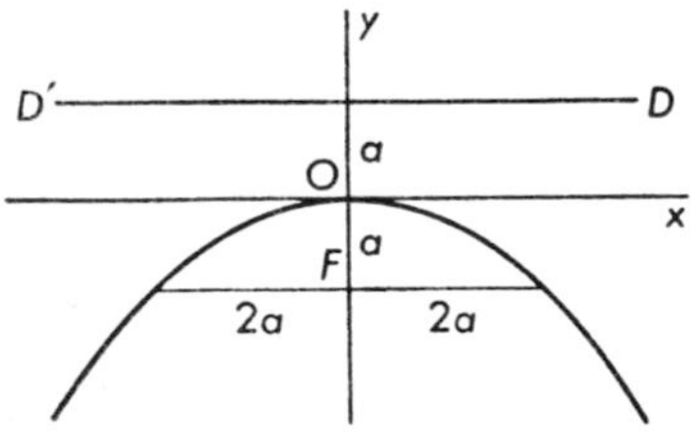

Figure 74

Interchanging x and y in equation (3) leads to the conclusion that

$$(4) \qquad x^2 = 4ay$$

is the equation of a parabola with the vertex at the origin, focus at $(0, a)$ and the line $y = -a$ as directrix. The parabola (4) is concave upward if $a > 0$, concave downward if $a < 0$. The axis of the parabola (4) is the y-axis, and the curve is symmetric with respect to it. Figure 74 shows the curve (4) for negative a.

Example. Find the tangent to the parabola

$$(5) \qquad y^2 = 4ax$$

at a point (x_1, y_1) on the curve.

From (5) we obtain

$$2yy' = 4a.$$

Therefore at (x_1, y_1) the slope of the parabola (5) is

$$(6) \qquad m = \frac{2a}{y_1}.$$

The equation of a line through (x_1, y_1) with slope given by (6) is

$$y - y_1 = \frac{2a}{y_1}(x - x_1),$$

or

$$(7) \qquad y_1y - y_1{}^2 = 2ax - 2ax_1.$$

We have not yet imposed the condition

$$(8) \qquad y_1{}^2 = 4ax_1$$

to force the point (x_1, y_1) to be on the curve (5). Using equation (8) to simplify (7), we obtain the result: The equation of the tangent to the parabola

$$y^2 = 4ax$$

at the point (x_1, y_1) on the curve is

$$(9) \qquad y_1y = 2ax + 2ax_1.$$

In this section we have chosen axes in a convenient position to facilitate our study of the parabola. In § 65 we shall translate the axes parallel to their original positions so as to arrive at equations which yield every parabola whose own axis is parallel to one of the coordinate axes.

64. *Translation of Axes*

We have had many illustrations of the fact that a problem may be greatly simplified by taking the axes in a convenient position. It may happen, however, that the position of the axes is pre-determined by the statement of the problem; it is then desirable that we have methods for shifting the axes to a more suitable position. Such methods will be developed as need arises.

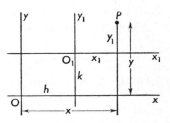

Figure 75

Consider now the *translation* of axes, in which the axes are moved parallel to their original positions. Let Ox, Oy be the original axes, O_1x_1, O_1y_1 the new, and suppose the new origin O_1 to be the point (h, k) referred to the old axes. If we denote by (x, y) the coordinates of any point P in the original system, by (x_1, y_1) the coordinates of the same point* in the new system, then the two sets of coordinates are connected by the formulas

(1)
$$\begin{cases} x = x_1 + h, \\ y = y_1 + k. \end{cases}$$

65. *The Parabola: Standard Forms*

To find the equation of a parabola with vertex at (h, k) and axis horizontal, let us introduce (temporarily) new axes O_1x_1, O_1y_1, where O_1 is the vertex and O_1x_1 the axis of the parabola (Figure 76). In the x_1y_1-coordinate system the equation of the parabola is

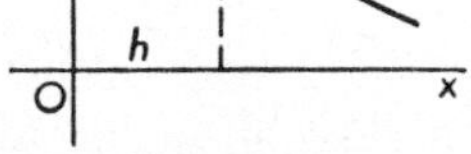

(1) $y_1{}^2 = 4ax_1.$

By the equations for the translation of axes in the preceding section,

(2) $x_1 = x - h, \qquad y_1 = y - k.$

Equations (1) and (2) yield

(3) $(y - k)^2 = 4a(x - h).$

Figure 76

In the same way we may obtain the equation of a parabola with vertex at (h, k) and axis vertical. In summary:

* Note that x_1 and y_1 are variables, so that we are departing from our usual convention whereby the coordinates (x_1, y_1) denote a fixed point.

The equation of a parabola with vertex at (h, k) and axis parallel to Ox is

(3) $$(y - k)^2 = 4a(x - h);$$

the parabola is concave to the right if $a > 0$, concave to the left if $a < 0$.

The equation of a parabola with vertex at (h, k) and axis parallel to Oy is

(4) $$(x - h)^2 = 4a(y - k);$$

the parabola is concave upward if $a > 0$, concave downward if $a < 0$.

Note that in expanded form equations (3) and (4) are precisely the equations of the quadratic polynomial curves discussed in § 62.

Example. Discuss the curve

(5) $$2x^2 + 2x + 3y = 0.$$

Complete the square in x:

(6)
$$x^2 + x + \tfrac{1}{4} = -\tfrac{3}{2}y + \tfrac{1}{4},$$
$$(x + \tfrac{1}{2})^2 = -\tfrac{3}{2}(y - \tfrac{1}{6}).$$

We now see that the curve (5) is a parabola with vertex at $(-\tfrac{1}{2}, \tfrac{1}{6})$, axis

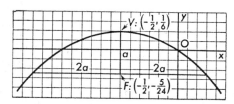

Figure 77

parallel to Oy, and with $4a = -\tfrac{3}{2}$, $a = -\tfrac{3}{8}$. The curve is concave downward with its focus at $(-\tfrac{1}{2}, -\tfrac{5}{24})$. Since $2|a| = \tfrac{3}{4}$, the ends of the latus rectum are $\tfrac{3}{4}$ of a unit to the right and left of the focus.

Unless for some reason we are interested in more distant regions, it is usually sufficient to draw only the part of the curve shown in Figure 77—i.e., extending a moderate distance beyond the ends of the latus rectum.

EXERCISES

In Exs. 1–20, reduce the equation to a standard form; plot the vertex, focus, and ends of the latus rectum; trace the curve.

1. $y^2 = 7x$.
2. $y^2 = -20x$.
3. $x^2 + 8y = 0$.
4. $x^2 = 10y$.
5. $y^2 - 12x + 24 = 0$.
6. $y^2 + 8x + 16 = 0$.
7. $x^2 + 2y + 2 = 0$.
8. $x^2 - 4y + 12 = 0$.
9. $x^2 = 4(x + y)$.
10. $y^2 = 12(y - x)$.
11. $y^2 + 2x + 6y + 17 = 0$.
12. $x^2 - 2x + 2y + 7 = 0$.
13. $y^2 - x + y = 0$.
14. $y^2 + x + y = 0$.
15. $2x^2 - 2x + y - 1 = 0$.
16. $2x^2 + 2x + y - 1 = 0$.
17. $2y^2 - x - 8y + 8 = 0$.
18. $2y^2 + x + 12y + 18 = 0$.
19. $4x^2 + 6x - y + 2 = 0$.
20. $4x^2 - 6x + y + 1 = 0$.

In Exs. 21–29, find the equation of the parabola.

21. With vertex $(-2, 3)$ and focus $(-4, 3)$.

22. With vertex $(5, 1)$ and focus $(5, -2)$.

23. With vertex $(2, -3)$ and directrix $y = -7$.

24. With vertex $(2, 4)$ and directrix $x = -3$.

25. With latus rectum joining $(-4, 1)$, $(2, 1)$.

$$\textit{Ans. } x^2 + 2x - 6y - 2 = 0;\; x^2 + 2x + 6y - 14 = 0.$$

26. With latus rectum joining $(2, 5)$, $(2, -3)$.

27. With directrix $y = 3$, axis $x = 0$, and latus rectum 4.   (Two answers.)

28. With directrix $x + 1 = 0$, axis $y = 2$, and latus rectum 2.   (Two answers.)

29. With vertex on Oy, axis parallel to Ox, and passing through $(2, 2)$, $(8, -1)$.

$$\textit{Ans. } (y - 1)^2 = \tfrac{1}{2}x;\; (y - 5)^2 = \tfrac{9}{2}x.$$

30. Prove that the tangents at the ends of the latus rectum of a parabola intersect on the directrix.

31. Prove that any tangent to a parabola intersects the directrix and the latus rectum (produced) at points equally distant from the focus.

32. Show that if the axes of two parabolas are parallel, the parabolas cannot intersect in more than two points.

33. Show that if a line is parallel to the axis of a parabola, it intersects the curve in one and only one point; and conversely.

34. Show that a parabola is the locus of a point moving so that the square of its distance from one of two fixed perpendicular lines is proportional to its distance from the other.

35. If P is a point on a parabola, show that the distance of P from the axis is a mean proportional between the latus rectum and the distance of P from the tangent at the vertex.

36. If a parabola with horizontal axis passes through the points (x_1, y_1), (x_2, y_2), (x_3, y_3), prove that its equation is

$$\begin{vmatrix} y^2 & x & y & 1 \\ y_1^2 & x_1 & y_1 & 1 \\ y_2^2 & x_2 & y_2 & 1 \\ y_3^2 & x_3 & y_3 & 1 \end{vmatrix} = 0.$$

37. In the equation of Ex. 36, show that the coefficient of x vanishes if any two of y_1, y_2, y_3 are equal. How do we know in advance that this must be so? What becomes of the curve under these conditions?

38. In Ex. 36, investigate the case $x_1 = x_2 = x_3$.

39. In Ex. 36, under what condition does the equation degenerate to a linear equation? Interpret the condition geometrically.

40. Derive an equation analogous to that of Ex. 36 for the parabola with vertical axis.

41. In the equation of Ex. 36, show that the coefficient of x vanishes only if two of the numbers y_1, y_2, y_3 are equal.

42. Find the equation of a parabola with axis parallel to Ox and passing through $(5, 4)$, $(11, -2)$, $(21, -4)$. $\textit{Ans. } y^2 - 2x - 4y + 10 = 0.$

43. Find the equation of a parabola with axis parallel to Oy and passing through $(1, 9)$, $(-2, 9)$, $(-1, 1)$. $\textit{Ans. } 4x^2 + 4x - y + 1 = 0.$

44. Find the locus of the center of a circle which passes through $(-2, 3)$ and touches the line $x = 6$.   *Ans.* $y^2 + 16x - 6y - 23 = 0$.

45. Find the locus of the center of a circle which passes through $(2, 5)$ and touches the line $y = -7$.   *Ans.* $x^2 - 4x - 24y - 20 = 0$.

46. Find the equation of a circle through $(0, 5)$, $(3, 4)$, touching the line $y + 5 = 0$.
                    Ans. $x^2 + y^2 = 25$; $(x - 60)^2 + (y - 180)^2 = (185)^2$.

47. Find the locus of the center of a circle which touches the circle $x^2 + y^2 = 4$ and the line $x = 3$.   *Ans.* $y^2 = 25 - 10x$; $y^2 = 1 - 2x$.

48. A circle touches the line $y = 2$ and the circle $x^2 + y^2 = 16$.   Find the locus of its center.   *Ans.* $x^2 + 12y = 36$; $x^2 - 4y = 4$.

49. Find the equation of a parabola with vertex on the line $y = x$, axis parallel to Ox, and passing through $(6, -2)$, $(3, 4)$.
                    Ans. $y^2 - 4x - 4y + 12 = 0$; $5y^2 - 36x - 28y + 140 = 0$.

50. Find the equation of a parabola with vertex on the line $y = x + 2$, axis parallel to Oy, latus rectum 6, and passing through $(-3, -1)$.
          Ans. $(x + 3)^2 = \pm 6(y + 1)$; $(x + 9)^2 = 6(y + 7)$; $(x - 3)^2 = -6(y - 5)$.

In Exs. 51–58, find the points of intersection of the given curves and draw the figure.

51. $x^2 = 4y$, $x^2 = y + 3$.   *Ans.* $(2, 1)$, $(-2, 1)$.
52. $x^2 = 3y$, $x^2 = y - 2$.
53. $y^2 = 4x$, $x^2 - 3x + y = 0$.   *Ans.* $(0, 0)$, $(1, 2)$ twice, $(4, -4)$.
54. $y^2 + y = x$, $x^2 + 12y = 8x$.   *Ans.* $(0, 0)$, $(2, 1)$ twice, $(12, -4)$.
55. $(y - 1)^2 = x + 7$, $x^2 + (y + 5)^2 = 85$.
                    Ans. $(2, 4)$, $(9, -3)$, $(-6, 2)$, $(-7, 1)$.
56. $y^2 + x - 2y + 2 = 0$, $x^2 + 9x + 6y + 2 = 0$.
                    Ans. $(-1, 1)$, $(-2, 2)$, $(-5, 3)$, $(-10, -2)$.
57. $x^2 + y^2 = 2x + 5y - 7$, $x^2 = 2x + y - 3$.   *Ans.* $(1, 2)$ four times.
58. $x^2 = 4y$, $y^2 = 6y - 4x + 3$.   *Ans.* $(2, 1)$ three times, $(-6, 9)$.

59. Prove that the cubic $y = ax^3 + bx^2 + cx + d$ is symmetric with respect to its point of inflection.   (Find the point of inflection; translate to that point as new origin.)

Applications of the Derivative

66. *Applications of Maxima and Minima*

It was shown in § 58 that, at a point where its first derivative vanishes, a function assumes an extreme value, provided the derivative changes sign at that point. This result finds application in a great variety of problems, some of which will now be considered.

When the derivative is equated to zero, it may happen, of course, that several critical values are obtained. In practice, the value that gives the desired maximum or minimum can often be selected at once by inspection.

Example (a). A box is to be made of a piece of cardboard 16 × 10 in. by cutting equal squares out of the corners and turning up the sides. Find the volume of the largest box that can be made in this way. (Figure 78.)

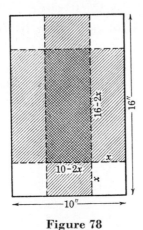

Figure 78

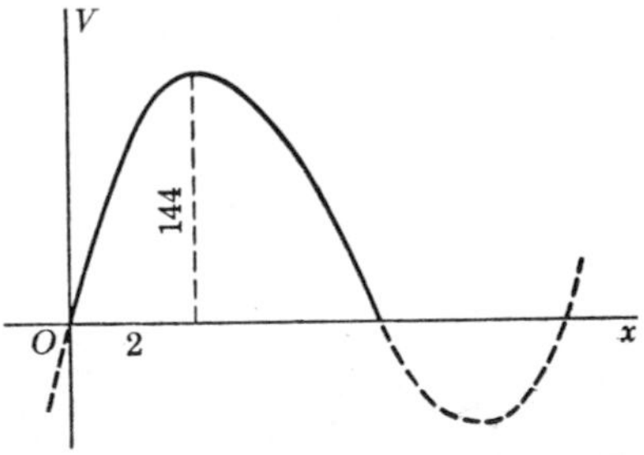

Figure 79

Let x be the length of the side of each of the squares cut out. Then the volume of the box is

$$V = x(10 - 2x)(16 - 2x), \qquad 0 \leq x \leq 5,$$
$$= 160x - 52x^2 + 4x^3,$$

109

whence
$$V' = 160 - 104x + 12x^2$$
$$= 4(x - 2)(3x - 20).$$

Setting
$$V' = 0,$$

we get the critical values $x = 2, \frac{20}{3}$. By the nature of the problem, x is restricted to values between 0 and 5, so that the value $\frac{20}{3}$ must be rejected. Since the volume is zero when $x = 0$ and again when $x = 5$, it must reach a maximum at some intermediate point; it therefore follows without the application of further tests that the critical value $x = 2$ gives the required maximum volume (Figure 79):

$$V_{\text{max.}} = 2(10 - 4)(16 - 4) = 144 \text{ cu. in.}$$

The minimum volume, of course, is $V = 0$, occurring at the end points $x = 0, x = 5$. The reason why our analysis fails to show these minima is that V is discontinuous at $x = 0, 5$, and all our present theory rests on the assumption that $f(x)$ and $f'(x)$ are continuous. Extremes occurring in connection with discontinuities will be discussed in § 70.

Example (b). Find the area of the largest rectangle that can be inscribed in a given circle.

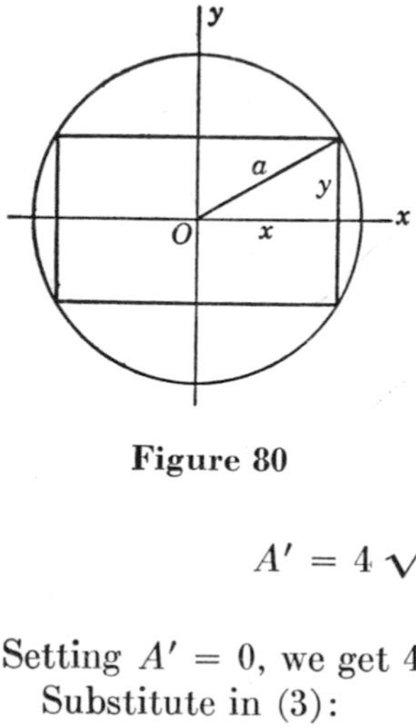

Figure 80

The area of the rectangle is

(1) $$A = 4xy,$$

where x and y are connected by the relation

(2) $$x^2 + y^2 = a^2.$$

Substituting $y = \sqrt{a^2 - x^2}$ in (1), we find

(3) $$A = 4x\sqrt{a^2 - x^2},$$

so that

$$A' = 4\sqrt{a^2 - x^2} - \frac{4x^2}{\sqrt{a^2 - x^2}} = \frac{4a^2 - 8x^2}{\sqrt{a^2 - x^2}}.$$

Setting $A' = 0$, we get $4a^2 - 8x^2 = 0,$ $x = \frac{1}{2}\sqrt{2}\, a.$
Substitute in (3):

$$A_{\text{max.}} = 2a^2.$$

Example (c). Find the altitude of the largest circular cylinder that can be inscribed in a circular cone of radius r and height h.
The volume of the cylinder is

$$V = \pi x^2 y.$$

Figure 81 shows a section by a plane through the axis.   By similar triangles,

$$\frac{x}{r} = \frac{h-y}{h}, \qquad x = \frac{r}{h}(h-y),$$

so that

$$V = \frac{\pi r^2}{h^2}(h-y)^2 y,$$

$$\frac{dV}{dy} = \frac{\pi r^2}{h^2}[(h-y)^2 - 2(h-y)y]$$

$$= \frac{\pi r^2}{h^2}(h-y)(h-3y).$$

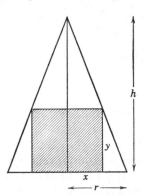

Figure 81

To make V a maximum, set $V' = 0$.   Then $y = h$ or $y = \frac{1}{3}h$.   But $y = h$ leads to $V = 0$, surely not the largest V.   That $y = \frac{1}{3}h$ yields the maximum V is intuitively reasonable and can be checked by noting that

$$\frac{d^2 V}{dy^2} = \frac{\pi r^2}{h^2}(-4h + 6y)$$

is negative for $y = \frac{1}{3}h$.

67. *Use of an Auxiliary Variable*

If the function under consideration is most readily expressed in terms of two variables, a relation between these two variables must be found from the conditions of the problem.   By means of this relation one of the variables can be eliminated, after which the maximum or minimum can be found as in § 66.   However, it is often more convenient not to perform the elimination but to proceed as in the following examples.

Example (a).   Find the shape of the largest rectangle that can be inscribed in a given circle.   (See Figure 80, page 110.)

The area of the rectangle is

(1) $A = 4xy,$

where x and y are connected by the relation

(2) $x^2 + y^2 = a^2.$

Differentiating (1) with respect to x and equating the derivative to zero, we have

$$A' = 4(xy' + y) = 0,$$

or

$$y' = -\frac{y}{x}.$$

Differentiating (2), we get, since a is constant,

$$2x + 2yy' = 0, \qquad y' = -\frac{x}{y}.$$

Equating values of y', we find

$$-\frac{y}{x} = -\frac{x}{y},$$

whence

(3) $$y = x;$$

the maximum rectangle is a square.

If it is desired to find the actual maximum value of A, we solve the simultaneous equations (2), (3), which yield

$$x = y = \tfrac{1}{2}\sqrt{2}\,a,$$

and

$$A_{\text{max.}} = 2a^2.$$

Example (*b*). A cylindrical tin boiler, open at the top, has a copper bottom. If sheet copper is five times as expensive as tin, per unit area, find the most economical proportions.

Let r denote the radius, h the height; let k be the unit cost of tin. Then the cost C, which is to be a minimum, is

(4) $$C = 2\pi krh + 5\pi kr^2 = \pi k(2rh + 5r^2).$$

The volume

(5) $$V = \pi r^2 h$$

is to be held constant.

From (4) we get

(6) $$\frac{dC}{dr} = \pi k\left(2r\frac{dh}{dr} + 2h + 10r\right)$$

and from (5) it follows that

(7) $$\pi\left(r^2\frac{dh}{dr} + 2rh\right) = 0,$$

since V is constant.

Seeking a minimum cost, we may set $\dfrac{dC}{dr} = 0$, eliminate $\dfrac{dh}{dr}$ with the aid of (7) and thus arrive at $h = 5r$. This is certainly an easy way to solve the problem, but it has one disadvantage in that it tempts us to rely on intuition to see that $h = 5r$ actually leads to the minimum C. An alternative procedure follows:

From (7) we obtain $r\dfrac{dh}{dr} = -2h$ so that (6) may now be written in the form

(8)
$$\frac{dC}{dr} = 2\pi k(5r - h).$$

Now set $C' = 0$ and obtain $h = 5r$.   But also note that (8) yields

(9)
$$\frac{d^2C}{dr^2} = 2\pi k\left(5 - \frac{dh}{dr}\right) = 2\pi k\left(5 + \frac{2h}{r}\right).$$

Thus C'' is positive for $h = 5r$.   We may then conclude that C is a minimum at $h = 5r$.

It is just as reasonable to attack this problem by holding the cost fixed and seeking a maximum volume.   Either method leads eventually to the two equations $C' = 0$ and $V' = 0$.

We must, however, hold either C or V constant.   With no restrictions on V or C, surely the minimum cost is attained by not building the boiler; that is, $r = h = 0$ yields a minimum C for V unrestricted.   This type of "solution" is not popular in industry.

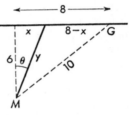

Example (c).   A man in a rowboat 6 mi. from shore desires to reach a point on the shore at a distance of 10 mi. from his present position.   If he can walk 4 mi. per hr. and row 2 mi. per hr., in what direction should he row in order to reach his destination in the shortest possible time?

Figure 82

Let x and y be distances defined by Figure 82, with the man starting at M. Since he rows the distance y at 2 mi. per hr. and walks the distance $(8 - x)$ at 4 mi. per hr., the time required for him to reach his goal G is

$$T = \frac{y}{2} + \frac{8 - x}{4},$$

with
$$y^2 = x^2 + 36.$$

To find the minimum time, we have

$$T' = \tfrac{1}{2}y' - \tfrac{1}{4} = 0, \qquad y' = \tfrac{1}{2};$$
$$2yy' = 2x, \qquad y' = \frac{x}{y}.$$

Equating the values of y' and noting that

$$\frac{x}{y} = \sin\theta,$$

we find $\theta = 30°$.

EXERCISES

1. The sum of two numbers is k. Find the minimum value of the sum of their squares.
Ans. $\frac{1}{2}k^2$.

2. What number exceeds its square by the maximum amount?
Ans. $\frac{1}{2}$.

3. What positive number added to its reciprocal gives the minimum sum?

4. The sum of two positive numbers is 4. Find the smallest value possible for the sum of the cube of one number and the square of the other.
Ans. $\frac{256}{27}$.

5. Find two numbers whose sum is a, if the product of one by the square of the other is to be a maximum.
Ans. $\frac{1}{3}a$, $\frac{2}{3}a$.

6. Find two numbers whose sum is a, if the product of one by the cube of the other is to be a maximum.
Ans. $\frac{1}{4}a$, $\frac{3}{4}a$.

7. Find two numbers whose sum is a, if the product of the square of one by the cube of the other is to be a maximum.
Ans. $\frac{2}{5}a$, $\frac{3}{5}a$.

8. A rectangular field is to be enclosed and divided into five lots by parallels to one of the sides. What should be the shape of the field of fixed area to make the amount of fencing a minimum?
Ans. Width $= \frac{1}{3} \times$ length.

9. What should be the shape of a rectangular field of given area, if it is to be enclosed by the least amount of fencing?
Ans. A square.

10. A rectangular field of given area is to be fenced off along the bank of a river. If no fence is needed along the river, what is the shape of the rectangle requiring the least amount of fencing?
Ans. Width $= \frac{1}{2} \times$ length.

11. A rectangular lot is to be fenced off along a highway. If the fence on the highway costs m dollars per yard, on the other sides n dollars per yard, find the area of the largest lot that can be fenced off for k dollars.
Ans. $\dfrac{k^2}{8n(m+n)}$.

12. A rectangular lot is bounded at the back by a river. No fence is needed along the river and there is to be a 20-ft. opening in front. If the fence along the front costs \$3 per ft., along the sides \$1 per ft., find the dimensions of the largest lot which can be thus fenced in for \$600.
Ans. 110 ft. by 165 ft.

13. Find the rectangle of maximum perimeter inscribed in a given circle.
Ans. A square.

14. If the hypotenuse of a right triangle is given, show that the area is a maximum when the triangle is isosceles.

15. Find the most economical proportions for a covered box of fixed volume whose base is a rectangle with one side three times as long as the other.
Ans. Altitude $= \frac{3}{2} \times$ shorter side of base.

16. Solve Ex. 15 if the box has an open top.
Ans. Altitude $= \frac{3}{4} \times$ shorter side of base.

17. Find the most economical proportions for a quart can.
Ans. Diameter $=$ height.

18. Find the most economical proportions for a cylindrical cup.
Ans. Radius $=$ height.

19. Find the most economical proportions for a box with an open top and a square base.
Ans. Side of base $= 2 \times$ altitude.

20. A box is to be made of a piece of cardboard 12 in. square by cutting equal squares out of the corners and turning up the sides. Find the volume of the largest box that can be made in this way.
Ans. 128 cu. in.

21. Find the volume of the largest box that can be made by cutting equal squares out of the corners of a piece of cardboard of dimensions 6 in. by 16 in., and then turning up the sides. *Ans.* $\frac{1600}{27}$ cu. in.

22. Find the depth of the largest box that can be made by cutting equal squares of side x out of the corners of a piece of cardboard of dimensions $6a$, $6b$, $(b \leqq a)$, and then turning up the sides. To select that value of x which yields a maximum volume, apply the test of § 59; or, as an exercise in algebra, show that

$$(a + b + \sqrt{a^2 - ab + b^2}) \geqq 3b.$$

Check Exs. 20, 21. *Ans.* Depth $= a + b - \sqrt{a^2 - ab + b^2}$.

23. The perimeter of an isosceles triangle is P inches. Find the maximum area.

Ans. $P^2 \dfrac{\sqrt{3}}{36}$ sq. in.

24. The sum of the length and girth of a container of square cross-section is a inches. Find the maximum volume. *Ans.* $\frac{1}{108}a^3$ cu. in.

25. Find the proportions of the largest circular cylinder that can be inscribed in a given sphere. *Ans.* Diameter $= \sqrt{2} \times$ height.

26. In Ex. 25, find the shape of the cylinder if its convex surface area is to be a maximum. *Ans.* Diameter $=$ height.

27. The strength of a rectangular beam is proportional to the breadth and the square of the depth. Find the shape of the strongest beam that can be cut from a log of given size. *Ans.* Depth $= \sqrt{2} \times$ breadth.

28. The stiffness of a rectangular beam is proportional to the breadth and the cube of the depth. Find the shape of the stiffest beam that can be cut from a log of given size. *Ans.* Depth $= \sqrt{3} \times$ breadth.

29. Compare for strength and stiffness, against both edgewise and sidewise thrust, two beams of equal length, one 2 in. by 8 in., the other 4 in. by 6 in. (See Exs. 27–28.) Which shape is more often used for floor joists? Why?

30. A cylindrical glass jar has a plastic top. If the plastic is half as expensive as glass, per unit area, find the most economical proportions for the jar. *Ans.* Height $= \frac{3}{2} \times$ radius of the base.

31. Find the dimensions of the largest rectangular building that can be placed on a right-triangular lot, facing one of the perpendicular sides. (Figure 83.) *Ans.* $x = \frac{1}{2}a$.

32. A Norman window consists of a rectangle surmounted by a semicircle. What shape gives the most light for a given perimeter? *Ans.* Breadth $=$ height.

33. Solve Ex. 32 if the semicircle is of stained glass admitting only half the normal amount of light.

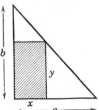

Figure 83

34. Find the shortest distance from the point $(c, 0)$ to the curve $x^2 - y^2 = a^2$. *Ans.* $\sqrt{a^2 + \frac{1}{2}c^2}$.

35. Find the point on the curve $a^2y = x^3$ that is nearest the point $(4a, 0)$.

Ans. (a, a).

36. Find the shortest distance from the point $(0, 8a)$ to the curve $ax^2 = y^3$.

Ans. $2a \sqrt{11}$.

37. Find the shortest distance from the point (4, 2) to the curve (an ellipse) $x^2 + 3y^2 = 12$.   *Ans.* $\sqrt{2}$.

38. A cylindrical tin boiler, open at the top, has a copper bottom. If sheet copper is m times as expensive as tin, per unit area, find the most economical proportions.   *Ans.* Height = m × radius.

39. Solve Ex. 38 if the boiler is to have a tin cover. Deduce the answer directly from that of Ex. 38.

40. The base of a covered box is a square. The bottom and back are made of pine, the remainder of oak. If oak is m times as expensive as pine, find the most economical proportions.

$$Ans.\ \text{Side of base} = \frac{3m+1}{2m+2} \times \text{height}.$$

41. A silo consists of a cylinder surmounted by a hemisphere. If the floor, walls, and roof are equally expensive per unit area, find the most economical proportions.   *Ans.* Diameter = total height.

42. For the silo of Ex. 41, find the most economical proportions if the floor is twice as expensive as the walls, per unit area, and the roof is three times as expensive as the walls, per unit area.   *Ans.* Diameter = $\frac{2}{7}$ × total height.

43. Two posts, one 10 ft. high and the other 15 ft. high, stand 30 ft. apart. They are to be stayed by wires attached to a single stake at ground level, the wires running to the tops of the posts. Where should the stake be placed, to use the least amount of wire?   *Ans.* 12 ft. from the shorter post.

44. A lot has the form of a right triangle, with perpendicular sides 90 and 120 ft. long. Find the length and width of the largest rectangular building that can be erected, facing the hypotenuse of the triangle.   *Ans.* 36 ft. by 75 ft.

45. Solve Ex. 44 if the lengths of the perpendicular sides are a, b.

$$Ans.\ \frac{ab}{2\sqrt{a^2+b^2}},\ \frac{\sqrt{a^2+b^2}}{2}.$$

46. An oil can consists of a cylinder surmounted by a cone. If the diameter of the cone is five-sixths of its height, find the most economical proportions.
                      Ans. Height of cone = 2 × height of cylinder.

47. A ship lies 8 mi. from shore, and opposite a point 15 mi. farther along the shore, another ship lies 12 mi. offshore. A boat from the first ship is to land a passenger and then proceed to the other ship. What is the least distance the boat can travel?   *Ans.* 25 mi.

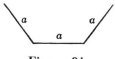

48. A trapezoidal gutter is to be made from a strip of tin by bending up the edges. If the cross-section has the form shown in Figure 84, what width across the top gives maximum carrying capacity?   *Ans.* 2a.

Figure 84

49. Solve Ex. 48 if the strip is 11 in. wide and the base 7 in. wide.

50. In Ex. 48, if the strip is L inches wide, and the width across the top is T inches, what base width gives the maximum capacity?   *Ans.* $\frac{1}{3}L$ inches.

51. From a strip of tin 14 in. wide a trapezoidal gutter is to be made by bending up the sides at an angle of 45°. Find the width of the base, for greatest carrying capacity.   *Ans.* 3.17 in.

52. A page is to contain 24 sq. in. of print. The margins at top and bottom are $1\frac{1}{2}$ in., at the sides 1 in. Find the most economical dimensions for the page.

Ans. Printed portion 4 in. by 6 in.

53. A light is to be placed above the center of a circular area of radius a. What height gives the best illumination on a circular walk surrounding the area? (When light from a point-source strikes a surface obliquely, the intensity of illumination is $I = \dfrac{k \sin \theta}{d^2}$, where θ is the angle of incidence and d the distance from the source.)

Ans. $h = \frac{1}{2} \sqrt{2}\, a$.

54. It is shown in the theory of attraction that a wire bent in the form of a circle of radius a exerts upon a particle in the axis of the circle (i.e., in the line through the center of the circle perpendicular to its plane) an attraction proportional to $\dfrac{h}{(a^2 + h^2)^{\frac{3}{2}}}$, where h is the height of the particle above the plane of the circle. Find h, for maximum attraction. (Compare with Ex. 53.) *Ans.* $h = \frac{1}{2} \sqrt{2}\, a$.

55. In Ex. 54, if the wire has instead the form of a square of side $2l$, the attraction is proportional to $\dfrac{h}{(h^2 + l^2) \sqrt{h^2 + 2l^2}}$. Find h, for maximum attraction. *Ans.* $h = 0.786l$.

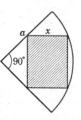

56. Cut the largest possible rectangle from a circular quadrant, as shown in Figure 85. *Ans.* $x = 0.54a$.

57. Inscribe a circular cylinder of maximum convex surface area in a given circular cone.

Ans. Diameter of cylinder = radius of cone.

Figure 85

58. Find the circular cone of maximum volume inscribed in a sphere of radius a. *Ans.* Altitude $= \frac{4}{3}a$.

59. A sphere is cut to the shape of a circular cone. How much of the material can be saved? (Ex. 58.) *Ans.* 30%.

60. Find the circular cone of minimum volume circumscribed about a sphere of radius a. *Ans.* Altitude $= 4a$.

61. Find the largest right pyramid with a square base that can be inscribed in a sphere of radius a. *Ans.* Altitude $= \frac{4}{3}a$.

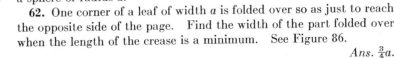

62. One corner of a leaf of width a is folded over so as just to reach the opposite side of the page. Find the width of the part folded over when the length of the crease is a minimum. See Figure 86. *Ans.* $\frac{3}{4}a$.

63. Solve Ex. 62 if the area folded over is to be a minimum. *Ans.* $\frac{2}{3}a$.

Figure 86

64. An Indian tepee is made by stretching skins or birch bark over a group of poles tied together at the top. If poles of given length are to be used, what shape gives maximum volume? *Ans.* Radius $= \sqrt{2} \times$ height.

65. Solve Ex. 64 if poles of any length can be found, but only a limited amount of covering material is available. *Ans.* Height $= \sqrt{2} \times$ radius.

66. A man on an island a miles south of a straight beach wishes to reach a point on shore b miles east of his present position. If he can row r miles per hour and walk w miles per hour, in what direction should he row, to reach his destination as soon as possible?   See Figure 87.

Ans. If $r < w$, and if $b > \dfrac{ra}{\sqrt{w^2 - r^2}}$, $\sin \theta = \dfrac{r}{w}$;

otherwise, directly toward his destination.

67. A man on an island 12 mi. south of a straight beach wishes to reach a point on shore 20 mi. east.   If a motorboat, making 20 mi. per hr., can be hired at a rate of $2.00 per hr. for the time it is actually used, and the cost of land transportation is $0.06 per mi., how much must he pay for the trip?   *Ans.* $2.16.

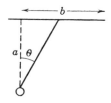

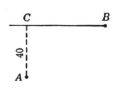

Figure 87   **Figure 88**

68. A man in a motorboat at A (Figure 88) receives a message at noon, calling him to B.   A bus making 40 mi. per hr. leaves C, bound for B, at 1:00 P.M.   If $AC = 40$ mi., what must be the speed of the boat to enable the man to catch the bus?   *Ans.* At least 28.3 mi. per hr.

69. In Ex. 68, if the speed of the boat is 30 mi. per hr., what is the greatest distance offshore from which the bus can be caught?   *Ans.* $\frac{120}{7} \sqrt{7} = 45.3$ mi.

68. *Distance from a Point to a Line*

We shall now use the method of § 67 to obtain a formula for the distance from a given point (x_1, y_1) to a given line

$$(1) \qquad\qquad Ax + By + C = 0.$$

Let D be the distance from (x_1, y_1) to a variable point (x, y) on the line (1). Then

$$(2) \qquad\qquad D^2 = (x - x_1)^2 + (y - y_1)^2.$$

We therefore seek to make the D of (2) a minimum, with the variables x and y restricted by (1).

From (2) we obtain

$$(3) \qquad\qquad DD' = x - x_1 + (y - y_1)y'$$

and from (1) we get

$$(4) \qquad\qquad A + By' = 0.$$

Setting $D' = 0$ and eliminating y' by using (4) leads us to

(5) $$x - x_1 - \frac{A}{B}(y - y_1) = 0.$$

In (5) we assume $B \neq 0$. For $B = 0$, the conclusion in Theorem 21 below is easily verified.

Equations (5) and (1) may be put in the form

(6) $$B(x - x_1) - A(y - y_1) = 0,$$
(7) $$A(x - x_1) + B(y - y_1) = -Ax_1 - By_1 - C.$$

We need to solve (6) and (7) for $(x - x_1)$ and $(y - y_1)$ and put the results into (2) to find the minimum D. Equations (6) and (7) give us

(8) $$(B^2 + A^2)(x - x_1) = -A(Ax_1 + By_1 + C),$$
(9) $$(B^2 + A^2)(y - y_1) = -B(Ax_1 + By_1 + C).$$

Using (8) and (9) in equation (2) we find that

$$D^2_{\min} = \frac{(A^2 + B^2)(Ax_1 + By_1 + C)^2}{(A^2 + B^2)^2},$$

which yields the desired minimum value of D.

THEOREM 21. *The undirected distance from the point (x_1, y_1) to the line $Ax + By + C = 0$ is*

$$D = \left| \frac{Ax_1 + By_1 + C}{\sqrt{A^2 + B^2}} \right|.$$

For a discussion of directed distance between a point and a line see pages 71–73 of Love and Rainville's *Analytic Geometry*, 5th ed., New York: The Macmillan Company, 1955.

Example (a). The distance from the point $(4, 7)$ to the line $3x - 2y = 5$ is, by Theorem 21,

$$D = \left| \frac{(3 \cdot 4) - (2 \cdot 7) - 5}{\sqrt{9 + 4}} \right| = \frac{7}{\sqrt{13}}.$$

Example (b). Find the locus of points at a distance $\sqrt{5}$ from the line

(10) $$x - 2y = 2.$$

Let (x, y) now be a point on the desired locus. By Theorem 21 the distance from (x, y) to the line (10) is

$$D = \left| \frac{x - 2y - 2}{\sqrt{5}} \right|$$

in which (x, y) now plays the role of the (x_1, y_1) of Theorem 21. We are given that $D = \sqrt{5}$.   Hence either

$$\frac{x - 2y - 2}{\sqrt{5}} = \sqrt{5}$$

or

$$\frac{x - 2y - 2}{\sqrt{5}} = -\sqrt{5}.$$

The desired locus therefore consists of the two lines

(11) $x - 2y = 7, \qquad x - 2y = -3.$

Each of the lines (11) is parallel to the line (10) and at a distance $\sqrt{5}$ from it.   As a check, choose any two points at random on either of the lines (11) and compute the distances from those points to the line (10).

Example (c).   Find the equations of the lines bisecting the angles between the lines

(12) $x + y = 2, \qquad x - 7y = -2.$

A variable point (x, y) on the desired locus must be equidistant from the two lines (12).   Hence either

(13) $$\frac{x + y - 2}{\sqrt{2}} = \frac{x - 7y + 2}{\sqrt{50}}$$

or

(14) $$\frac{x + y - 2}{\sqrt{2}} = -\frac{x - 7y + 2}{\sqrt{50}}.$$

Equations (13) and (14) reduce to

(15) $x + 3y = 3, \qquad 3x - y = 4,$

which are therefore the equations of the required angle bisectors.

EXERCISES

In Exs. 1–8, find the distance from the point to the line.

1. $x = 3y - 12$, $(5, -1)$.   *Ans.* $2\sqrt{10}$.
2. $x + y = -7$, $(4, -1)$.   *Ans.* $5\sqrt{2}$.
3. $3x + 4y = 11$, $(2, 5)$.   4. $4x - 3y = 11$, $(1, 1)$.
5. $3x - y = 25$, $(2, 1)$.   6. $2x + y = 16$, $(-3, 2)$.
7. $y = -4x$, $(8, 2)$.   8. $y = x$, $(3, 7)$.

9. Plot the points $(0, -10)$, $(8, 1)$, $(15, 10)$.   How far is the second point from the line joining the other two?

10. Solve Ex. 9 for the points $(-10, -20)$, $(17, 0)$, $(30, 10)$.

11. A circle of radius 3 touches the line $12x - 5y = 7$.   Find the locus of its center.

12. A circle of radius 4 touches the line $3x + 4y = 8$.   Find the locus of its center.

13. A moving point remains equidistant from the point $(a, 0)$ and the line $y = x$. Find the equation of its locus.   *Ans.* $x^2 + 2xy + y^2 - 4ax + 2a^2 = 0$.

14. The distance of a point from the origin is twice its distance from the line $x - y = a$.   Find the equation of its locus.

$$Ans.\ x^2 - 4xy + y^2 - 4ax + 4ay + 2a^2 = 0.$$

In Exs. 15–20, find the bisectors of the angles between the lines.

15. $x + 7y = 8,\ x - y = 10.$ *Ans.* $2x - 6y = 21,\ 3x + y = 29.$
16. $2x - y = 1,\ 11x + 2y = 5.$ *Ans.* $x + 7y = 0,\ 21x - 3y = 10.$
17. $x = 2,\ y = 7.$ **18.** $4x = 3y,\ y = 1.$
19. $3x + 4y = 7,\ 3x - 4y = 11.$ **20.** $3x + 4y = 7,\ 4x - 3y = 11.$

In Exs. 21–22, use the method of Example (c) to find the bisectors of the angles between the lines, and interpret your results.

21. $y = 2x - 7,\ 2x - y = 3.$ **22.** $y = 11 - 3x,\ 3x + y = 7.$
23. A circle touches the lines $4x + y = 7,\ x + 4y = 13.$ Find the locus of its center.   *Ans.* $x + y = 4,\ x - y = -2.$
24. Find the equations of the lines through $(7, -4)$ passing at a distance 1 from the point $(2, 1)$.   *Ans.* $3x + 4y = 5;\ 4x + 3y = 16.$
25. Find the equations of the lines through $(3, 0)$ passing at a distance $\sqrt{5}$ from $(4, -3)$.   *Ans.* $x + 2y = 3;\ 2x - y = 6.$
26. A point moves so that the ratio of its distances from two intersecting lines is constant.   Prove that the locus of the moving point is two straight lines.

69. *Time Rates*

The fact that the derivative of a function is identical with its rate of change leads to a great variety of applications; those in which time is the independent variable are especially important.

Example (a).   A balloon, leaving the ground 60 ft. from an observer, rises vertically at the rate of 10 ft. per sec.   How fast is the balloon receding from the observer, after 8 sec.?

In time t, the balloon rises a distance $10t$, so that

$$s = \sqrt{3600 + 100t^2},$$

$$\frac{ds}{dt} = \frac{100t}{\sqrt{3600 + 100t^2}}.$$

When $t = 8$,

$$\frac{ds}{dt} = \frac{800}{\sqrt{3600 + 6400}} = 8\ \text{ft. per sec.}$$

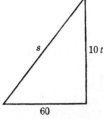

Figure 89

Note that the given value $t = 8$ is employed only *after the differentiation has been performed.*

Example (b).   As a man walks across a bridge at the rate of 5 ft. per sec., a boat passes directly beneath him at 10 ft. per sec.   If the bridge is 30 ft. above the water, how fast are the man and the boat separating 3 sec. later?

In t seconds, the man covers a distance $5t$, the boat a distance $10t$. By elementary geometry, the distance between them is

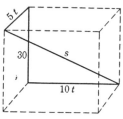

$$s = \sqrt{(5t)^2 + (10t)^2 + (30)^2}$$
$$= \sqrt{125t^2 + 900};$$

$$\frac{ds}{dt} = \frac{125t}{\sqrt{125t^2 + 900}}.$$

After 3 sec.,

$$\frac{ds}{dt} = \frac{375}{\sqrt{2025}} = \frac{25}{3} \text{ ft. per sec.}$$

Figure 90

Frequently, the problem of rates is most conveniently solved by expressing the variable whose rate of change is to be found in terms of another variable whose rate is *known*, and then differentiating *with respect to time* the equation connecting them. It will be recalled that a similar device was employed in § 67.

Example (c). A man on a wharf 20 ft. above the water pulls in a rope, to which a boat is attached, at the rate of 4 ft. per sec. At what rate is the boat approaching the wharf when there is 25 ft. of rope out?

Let x denote the distance of the boat from the wharf, r the length of rope. Then, *given* $\dfrac{dr}{dt}$, we have to *find* $\dfrac{dx}{dt}$. To do this, as suggested above, we express x in terms of r (implicitly or explicitly) and differentiate with respect to t:

$$x = \sqrt{r^2 - 400}, \qquad \frac{dx}{dt} = \frac{r \dfrac{dr}{dt}}{\sqrt{r^2 - 400}}.$$

Substitute $r = 25$, $\dfrac{dr}{dt} = -4$:

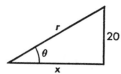

$$\frac{dx}{dt} = \frac{-100}{\sqrt{225}} = -\frac{20}{3} \text{ ft. per sec.}$$

Figure 91

Example (d). Water is flowing into a conical reservoir, 20 ft. deep and 10 ft. across the top, at the rate of 15 cu. ft. per min. Find how fast the surface is rising when the water is 8 ft. deep. The volume of water is

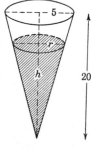

$$V = \tfrac{1}{3}\pi r^2 h.$$

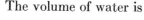

By similar triangles,

$$\frac{r}{h} = \frac{5}{20}, \qquad r = \frac{1}{4}h.$$

Hence

$$V = \frac{\pi h^3}{48}, \qquad \frac{dV}{dt} = \frac{\pi h^2}{16}\frac{dh}{dt}.$$

Figure 92

But we have given that

$$\frac{dV}{dt} = 15,$$

so that

$$\frac{\pi h^2}{16}\frac{dh}{dt} = 15, \qquad \frac{dh}{dt} = \frac{240}{\pi h^2}.$$

When $h = 8$,

$$\frac{dh}{dt} = \frac{15}{4\pi} = 1.19 \text{ ft. per min.}$$

EXERCISES

1. Water is flowing into a vertical cylindrical tank at the rate of 12 cu. ft. per min. If the radius of the tank is 3 ft., how fast is the surface rising?
                                   Ans. 0.42 ft. per min.

2. Water flows into a vertical cylindrical tank at 6 cu. ft. per min.; the surface rises 6 in. per min. Find the radius of the tank.   *Ans.* 1.95 ft.

3. A rectangular trough is 10 ft. long and 3 ft. wide. Find how fast the surface rises if water flows in at the rate of 6 cu. ft. per min.   *Ans.* 0.2 ft. per min.

4. A triangular trough 10 ft. long is 4 ft. across the top, and 4 ft. deep. If water flows in at the rate of 6 cu. ft. per min., find how fast the surface is rising when the water is 6 in. deep.   *Ans.* 1.2 ft. per min.

5. A man 6 ft. tall walks away from a lamp post 10 ft. high at the rate of 4 mi. per hr. How fast does the end of his shadow move?   *Ans.* 10 mi. per hr.

6. In Ex. 5, how fast does the shadow lengthen?

7. A boy on a bike rides north 5 mi., then turns east (Figure 93). If he rides 10 mi. per hr., at what rate was his distance to the starting point S changing 2 hr. after he left that point?
                     Ans. $3\sqrt{10}$ mi. per hr.

Figure 93

8. A train, starting at noon, travels north at 40 mi. per hr. Another train, starting from the same point at 2 P.M., travels east at 50 mi. per hr. Find, to the nearest mile per hour, how fast the two trains are separating at 3 P.M.
                     Ans. 56 mi. per hr.

Figure 93

9. In Ex. 8, how fast are the trains separating after a long time?

10. A 15-ft. ladder leans against a vertical wall. If the top slides downward at the rate of 2 ft. per sec., find how fast the lower end is moving when it is 12 ft. from the wall.   *Ans.* 1.5 ft. per sec.

11. In Ex. 10, find the rate of change of the slope of the ladder.

12. A trapezoidal trough is 12 ft. long, 6 ft. wide at the top, 3 ft. wide at the bottom, and 3 ft. deep. If water flows in at 6 cu. ft. per min., find how fast the water surface is rising when the water is 1 ft. deep.   *Ans.* $\frac{1}{8}$ ft. per min.

13. For the trough of Ex. 12, find how fast the water surface is rising when the water is 2 ft. deep.   *Ans.* 0.1 ft. per min.

14. A light at eye level stands 20 ft. from a house and 15 ft. from the path leading from the house to the street. A man walks along the path at 6 ft. per sec. How fast does his shadow move along the wall when he is 10 ft. from the house?
                                   Ans. 18 ft. per sec.

15. In Ex. 14, when the man is 10 ft. from the house, find the time-rate of change of that portion of his shadow which lies on the ground.   *Ans.* 18.3 ft. per sec.

16. A light is placed on the ground 40 ft. from a building. A man 6 ft. tall walks from the light toward the building at the rate of 5 ft. per sec. Find the rate at which the length of his shadow on the wall is changing when he is 20 ft. from the building.   *Ans.* −3 ft. per sec.

17. Solve Ex. 16, if the light is 8 ft. above the ground.   *Ans.* 1 ft. per sec.

18. One city, *A*, is 30 mi. north and 55 mi. east of another city, *B*. At noon, a car starts west from *A* at 40 mi. per hr.; at 12:10 P.M., another car starts east from *B* at 60 mi. per hr. Find, in two ways, when the cars will be nearest together.   *Ans.* 12:39 P.M.

19. For the conditions of Ex. 18, draw the appropriate figures for times before 12:39 P.M., and after that time. Show that, in terms of time after noon, the formulas for distance between the two cars (one formula associated with each figure) are equivalent.

20. For Ex. 18, compute the time-rate of change of the distance between the cars at (a) 12:15 P.M.; (b) 12:30 P.M.; (c) 1:15 P.M.   *Ans.* (a) −80 mi. per hr.; (c) 89.4 mi. per hr.

21. One city, *C*, is 30 mi. north and 35 mi. east of another city, *D*. At noon, a car starts north from *C* at 40 mi. per hr.; at 12:10 P.M., another car starts east from *D* at 60 mi. per hr. Find when the cars will be nearest together.   *Ans.* 12:17 P.M.

22. For the conditions of Ex. 21, draw the appropriate figures for times before 12:45 P.M., and after that time. Show that, in terms of time after noon, the formulas for distance between the two cars (one formula associated with each figure) are equivalent.

23. For Ex. 21, compute the time-rate of change of the distance between the cars at (a) 12:15 P.M.; (b) 12:45 P.M.   *Ans.* (a) −4 mi. per hr.

24. One city, *E*, is 20 mi. north and 20 mi. east of another city, *F*. At noon, a car starts south from *E* at 40 mi. per hr.; at 12:10 P.M., another car starts east from *F* at 60 mi. per hr. Find the rate at which the cars approach each other between 12:10 P.M. and 12:30 P.M. What happens at 12:30 P.M.?   *Ans.* 72.1 mi. per hr.

25. A kite is 120 ft. high, with 130 ft. of cord out. If the kite moves horizontally 6.5 mi. per hr. directly away from the boy flying it, how fast is the cord being paid out?   *Ans.* 2.5 mi. per hr.

26. In Ex. 25, find the rate at which the slope of the cord is decreasing.

27. A car drives from *A* toward *C* at 30 mi. per hr. Another car, starting from *B* at the same time, drives toward *A* at 20 mi. per hr. If *AB* = 20 mi., find when the cars will be nearest together. See Figure 94.   *Ans.* $\frac{7}{19}$ hr.

Figure 94

28. Solve Ex. 27 if the second car starts 30 min. later.   *Ans.* $\frac{1}{19}$ hr. after the second car starts.

29. Two railroad tracks intersect at right angles. At noon there is a train on each track approaching the crossing at 40 mi. per hr., one being 100 mi., the other 200 mi. distant. Find (*a*) when they will be the nearest together, and (b) what will be their minimum distance apart.   *Ans.* (a) 3:45 P.M.; (b) 70.7 mi.

30. An elevated train on a track 30 ft. above the ground crosses a street at the rate of 20 ft. per sec. at the instant that a car approaching at the rate of 30 ft. per sec. is 40 ft. up the street.   Find how fast the train and the car are separating 1 sec. later. *Ans.* $\frac{5}{7}\sqrt{14} = 2.67$ ft. per sec.

31. In Ex. 30, find when the train and the car are nearest together.   *Ans.* $\frac{12}{13}$ sec.

32. From a car traveling east at 40 mi. per hr., an airplane traveling horizontally north at 100 mi. per hr. is visible 1 mi. east, 2 mi. south, and 2 mi. up.   Find when the two will be nearest together. *Ans.* $1\frac{7}{29}$ min.

33. In Ex. 32, find how fast the two will be separating after a long time.

Ans. $20\sqrt{29} = 107.7$ mi. per hr.

34. An arc light hangs at a height of 30 ft. above the center of a street 60 ft. wide.   A man 6 ft. tall walks along the sidewalk at the rate of 4 ft. per sec.   How fast is his shadow lengthening when he is 40 ft. up the street?   *Ans.* 0.8 ft. per sec.

35. In Ex. 34, how fast is the tip of the shadow moving?   *Ans.* 5 ft. per sec.

36. A ship sails east 20 mi. and then turns N. 30° W.   If the ship's speed is 10 mi. per hr., find how fast it will be leaving the starting point 5 hr. after the start.

37. In Ex. 36, find when the ship will be nearest the starting point after making its turn. *Ans.* 3 hr.

38. In Ex. 36, when would the ship have been nearest the starting point if it had turned N. 45° W.? *Ans.* 3 hr. 25 min.

70. *Discontinuous Derivatives*

Our treatment of maxima, minima, and inflection points has centered on functions which have continuous first and second derivatives.   Since continuity of $f(x)$ requires only that

$$\operatorname*{Lim}_{\Delta x \to 0} [f(x + \Delta x) - f(x)] = 0$$

and differentiability of $f(x)$ requires that

$$\operatorname*{Lim}_{\Delta x \to 0} \frac{f(x + \Delta x) - f(x)}{\Delta x}$$

exists, we know that continuity does not imply the existence of the derivative.   In particular, a continuous function $f(x)$ may have a derivative which is discontinuous.   If $f(x)$ and $f'(x)$ are continuous, $f''(x)$, the derivative of $f'(x)$, may be discontinuous.

When discontinuities are present in a derivative, the location of extremes or inflection points of the corresponding graph should be examined with even more than customary caution.   At a point of discontinuity of y or y', the graph of

$$y = f(x)$$

may have an extreme even though y' does not vanish or even exist, as in Example (*b*) below.   In order to produce an inflection point, the essential thing is that y'' change sign, not that it vanish.   If y'' is discontinuous, it

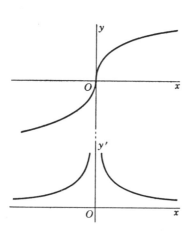

Figure 95

may change sign by jumping over the value zero, as in Example (*a*) below.

Example (*a*). The function

$$(1) \qquad y = x^{\frac{1}{3}}$$

is everywhere continuous, but the curve comes in to the origin tangent to the y-axis; thus the slope,

$$y' = \frac{1}{3x^{\frac{2}{3}}},$$

has an infinite discontinuity at that point. The graphs of y and y' are shown in Figure 95. The curve (1) has a point of inflection at the origin. Since

$$y'' = \frac{-2}{9x^{\frac{5}{3}}},$$

it is clear that y'' changes sign, not by vanishing but by virtue of an infinite discontinuity:

$$\operatorname*{Lim}_{x \to 0^-} y'' = +\infty, \qquad \operatorname*{Lim}_{x \to 0^+} y'' = -\infty.$$

An inflection effected by a finite jump occurs in Ex. 17 below. It is even possible for an extreme and an inflection to occur at the same point (Ex. 12 below).

Example (*b*). The function

$$(2) \qquad y = |x|$$

is everywhere continuous, but the slope y' jumps from -1 to 1 at $x = 0$. Both y and y' are shown in Figure 96. The function $|x|$ assumes its minimum value zero at $x = 0$, although the derivative does not vanish (or exist) there.

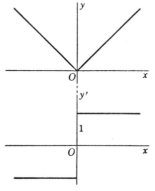

Figure 96

If a function $f(x)$ and its first derivative $f'(x)$ are both continuous, the function is said to be *smooth*. A smooth function may, of course, have a discontinuous second derivative. An important instance of this occurs in highway or railroad construction. Say that a level highway AO begins at O to climb a grade OBC. The pavement must be unbroken (y continuous) and smooth (y' continuous), but in general y''—rate of change of grade—will be discon-

Figure 97

tinuous at O and B. A similar situation arises in connection with horizontal turns: the turn would usually be "eased"—y' continuous—but the rate of change of direction may jump abruptly.

In practical applications, as we have seen many times, the independent variable is usually confined, by the nature of the problem, to a limited range. Then a function which would be continuous if x were unrestricted has only one-sided continuity at the ends of the interval and in many cases assumes extreme values at those points, although as a rule the derivative does not vanish there.

Example (c). The cost of a quantity of gasoline at \$0.30 per gallon is, in dollars,

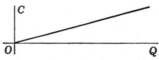

$$C = 0.30Q.$$

Figure 98

The minimum cost is zero, occurring at $Q = 0$, although

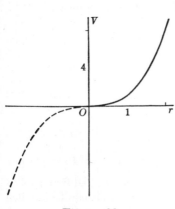

$$\frac{dC}{dQ} = 0.30.$$

Example (d). The volume of a sphere is (Figure 99)

$$V = \frac{4}{3}\pi r^3, \qquad \frac{dV}{dr} = 4\pi r^2.$$

The minimum volume is zero, occurring at $r = 0$. Here it is true that $\frac{dV}{dr} = 0$ when $r = 0$, but the theory of § 60 (here inapplicable, of course) would show this to be not a minimum but a point of inflection.

Similar remarks apply to most of our problems in maxima and minima in §§ 66–67

Figure 99

and in the exercises following. In any practical case the situation would almost always be just as clear as in the above examples.

EXERCISES

In Exs. 1–8, examine the curve for maxima and minima. Rationalize the equation and plot the curve; indicate the portion representing the original equation.

1. $y = x^{\frac{2}{3}}$.

2. $y = (4 - x^2)^{\frac{1}{3}}$.

3. $y = -\sqrt{1 + x}$.

4. $y = (1 + x)^{\frac{3}{2}}$.

5. $y = \sqrt{x^2 - a^2}$.

6. $y = \sqrt{2ax - x^2}$.

7. $y = \sqrt{1 - \sqrt{x}}$.

8. $y = \sqrt{1 + \sqrt{x}}$.

In Exs. 9–14, draw the graphs of y, y', and y''.

9. $y = x - |x|$.

10. $y = x^2 \operatorname{sgn} x$.

11. $y = x - \operatorname{sgn} x$.

12. $y = \sqrt{x^4 - 2x^2 + 1}$.

13. $y = \sqrt{1 + |x|}$.   **14.** $y = \sqrt{|x| - 1}$.

15. A cone with radius of base R and height H is given. A cylinder of height h is inscribed in the cone. Show that the volume of the cylinder is given by

$$V = \pi R^2 H^{-2} h (H - h)^2.$$

Draw the curve representing V as a function of h, and indicate that portion of the curve which has physical meaning in the problem.

16. A box is to be made from a rectangular piece of cardboard, of dimensions 4 in. by 6 in., by cutting equal squares out of the corners and turning up the sides. Graph the volume of the box as a function of the length of side of the squares cut out, and indicate the portion of the graph which has physical meaning.

17. In Figure 97, let the coordinates of B and C with O as origin be (5, 25), (10, 50), the x-unit being 100 ft., the y-unit 1 ft. If OB, BC are parabolic arcs with equations of the form $y = ax^2 + bx + c$, the slope being zero at O and C, determine y as a function of x; investigate y'' for continuity; find the maximum grade.
  Ans. $y = x^2$, $0 \leq x \leq 5$; $y = -x^2 + 20x - 50$, $5 \leq x \leq 10$; maximum grade 10%.

18. Graph the difference in area between a square of side 1 and a square of side l.

19. Graph the difference in volume between a sphere of radius r and a cylinder of radius r, height 1. Discuss extremes.

20. Graph the difference in volume V between two boxes of dimensions l, 2, 2 and l, l, 2. Discuss extremes.

21. In Ex. 20, what value of l makes $V = 1$?   *Ans.* 0.293, 1.707, 2.225.

22. Sketch the curve

$$y = \sqrt{x + \sqrt{x - \tfrac{1}{4}}} + \sqrt{x - \sqrt{x - \tfrac{1}{4}}}.$$

Hint: Examine the curve for $x < \tfrac{1}{4}$, $\tfrac{1}{4} \leq x \leq \tfrac{1}{2}$, $\tfrac{1}{2} < x$; rationalize the equation.

In Exs. 23–26, a cylinder is to be cut from a sphere of diameter 1 ft. and then packed in a rectangular box. Find the volume of the largest cylinder that can be handled in this way, if the dimensions of the box are as given.

23. Box 10 in. by 10 in. by 8 in.   *Ans.* $V = 96\sqrt{3}\,\pi = 166.3\pi$ cu. in.

24. Box 10 in. by 8 in. by 8 in.   *Ans.* $V = 64\sqrt{5}\,\pi = 143.1\pi$ cu. in.

25. Box 12 in. by 12 in. by 6 in.   *Ans.* $V = 162\pi$ cu. in.

26. Box 10 in. by 6 in. by 4 in.   *Ans.* $V = 40\pi$ cu. in.

27. Express $\cos 3\theta$ as a function of $\cos \theta$ by the addition formula. Putting $x = \cos \theta$, $y = \cos 3\theta$, graph $\cos 3\theta$ as a function of $\cos \theta$; find the extremes.
          Ans. $\cos 3\theta = 4 \cos^3 \theta - 3 \cos \theta$; $(\pm \tfrac{1}{2}, \mp 1)$, $(\pm 1, \pm 1)$.

28. Solve Ex. 27 for the functions $\sin 3\theta$, $\sin \theta$.
          Ans. $\sin 3\theta = 3 \sin \theta - 4 \sin^3 \theta$; $(\pm \tfrac{1}{2}, \pm 1)$, $(\pm 1, \mp 1)$.

9

The Differential

71. Differentials

Consider an interval in which a curve relating x and y has a slope y'. Let $P: (x, y)$ be a point on the curve, as shown in Figures 100 and 101. A change Δx in the value of x changes y by some amount Δy. In the figures, P' is the point $(x + \Delta x, y + \Delta y)$; Δy is the distance QP'. Unless the equation of the curve is particularly simple, it may be difficult to compute Δy. We seek for Δy an approximation which must satisfy two requirements: First, it must be possible for us to prove that the difference between the approximation and Δy can be made arbitrarily small by taking Δx sufficiently small; second, the approximation must be easy to compute.

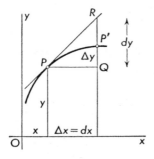

Figure 100

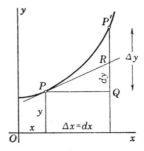

Figure 101

In Figures 100 and 101 the tangent line at P intersects the ordinate through P' at the point R. Examination of the figures shows that it is plausible that the length QR is an approximation to $QP' = \Delta y$ for small Δx. Let us see whether QR satisfies our two requirements.

At P the slope of the curve is $\dfrac{QR}{PQ}$. Now $PQ = \Delta x$, so that we obtain

(1) $$QR = y' \, \Delta x.$$

We already know how easy it is to compute the slope y'. Hence our second requirement is satisfied by QR.

129

The difference between QR and QP' is given by

$$P'R = QR - QP' = y' \, \Delta x - \Delta y.$$

Our first requirement demands that we show that $P'R \to 0$ as $\Delta x \to 0$. We shall do even better by showing that $\dfrac{P'R}{\Delta x} \to 0$ as $\Delta x \to 0$. Indeed,

(2)
$$\operatorname*{Lim}_{\Delta x \to 0} \frac{P'R}{\Delta x} = \operatorname*{Lim}_{\Delta x \to 0} \left(y' - \frac{\Delta y}{\Delta x} \right) = y' - y' = 0$$

because

$$\operatorname*{Lim}_{\Delta x \to 0} \frac{\Delta y}{\Delta x} = y',$$

since we are working in an interval where the slope exists. In a sense, (2) shows that $P'R \to 0$ more rapidly than $\Delta x \to 0$.

The quantity QR is called the *differential* of y and is denoted by dy. By equation (1)

(3)
$$dy = y' \, \Delta x.$$

Theoretically we are still at liberty to define dx—i.e., the differential of the independent variable—in any way we please. But if in (3) we put

$$y = x, \qquad y' = 1,$$

the result is

(4)
$$dx = \Delta x.$$

Thus in order to avoid conflict when (3) is applied to the function $y = x$, we adopt (4) as our definition. That is, *the differential of the independent variable is equal to the increment of that variable.*

We may therefore write

(5)
$$dy = y' \, dx = y' \, \Delta x,$$

and state the definition as follows:

*The **differential** of any function is equal to its derivative multiplied by the differential of the independent variable.*

Starting with page 70, we have been using $\dfrac{dy}{dx}$ (as well as y') to denote the derivative of y with respect to x. Our two newly defined quantities, dy and dx, are such that their ratio is the derivative $\dfrac{dy}{dx}$. If that were not true, we would be forced to abandon one or the other of the notations. From now on, the derivative may be looked upon as the single quantity $\dfrac{dy}{dx}$ or as the ratio dy divided by dx, whichever suits our purpose. No attempt is made to carry this idea to higher derivatives; from our standpoint there is no meaning to d^2y by itself.

It follows from the above definitions that *all the fundamental formulas for derivatives become differential formulas if we merely multiply through by dx.* For instance, the product formula is

$$d(uv) = u\,dv + v\,du;$$

in words, the differential of the product of two functions is equal to the first function times the differential of the second plus the second times the differential of the first.

Example (a).
$$y = x^3 - 2x,$$
$$dy = 3x^2\,dx - 2dx.$$

Example (b).
$$y = \frac{z^2 - 1}{z^2 + 1},$$
$$dy = \frac{(z^2 + 1)2z\,dz - (z^2 - 1)2z\,dz}{(z^2 + 1)^2}$$
$$= \frac{4z\,dz}{(z^2 + 1)^2}.$$

Example (c).
$$y^3 + 2xy = 3.$$
$$3y^2\,dy + 2x\,dy + 2y\,dx = 0,$$
$$dy = \frac{-2y\,dx}{3y^2 + 2x}.$$

Here we have an excellent example in support of the statement made in the first paragraph of this chapter to the effect that it may be difficult to compute Δy. From

$$y^3 + 2xy = 3$$

and

$$(y + \Delta y)^3 + 2(x + \Delta x)(y + \Delta y) = 3,$$

it follows rapidly that

$$(\Delta y)^3 + 3y(\Delta y)^2 + (3y^2 + 2x + 2\Delta x)(\Delta y) + 2y\,\Delta x = 0.$$

The determination of Δy from the above cubic equation is surely not simple compared to the determination of dy as accomplished at the beginning of this example.

We see now that the technique of differentiation is the same, except for a slight change in form, whether derivatives or differentials are used. It follows that differentials would hardly be worth bothering with if they were to be used merely as an additional tool in differentiation. The importance of differentials lies elsewhere, as will become apparent in several places later in the book.

72. *Differential of Arc Length*

To obtain the length of an arc of a curve, the average person may well bend a wire to fit that arc, then straighten the wire and measure its length.

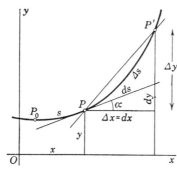

We wish to replace that intuitive concept with a mathematical definition of arc length. Actually, we now define only the differential of arc length and leave until later (§ 279) the computation of lengths of curves.

We shall use Figure 102 to guide us to a reasonable definition. Let s denote the length of the arc of the curve measured from some initial point P_0 to the point $P: (x, y)$, and suppose for definiteness that s increases as x increases. For the change Δs in arc length from P to P' we obtain

Figure 102

$$\frac{\Delta s}{\Delta x} = \frac{\Delta s}{\overline{PP'}} \cdot \frac{\overline{PP'}}{\Delta x} = \frac{\Delta s}{\overline{PP'}} \cdot \frac{\sqrt{\overline{\Delta x^2} + \overline{\Delta y^2}}}{\Delta x}$$

$$= \frac{\Delta s}{\overline{PP'}} \cdot \sqrt{1 + \left(\frac{\Delta y}{\Delta x}\right)^2},$$

in which $\overline{PP'}$ is the length of the chord from $P: (x, y)$ to $P': (x + \Delta x, y + \Delta y)$. If the curve is well-behaved near P, it is reasonable to expect that

$$\operatorname*{Lim}_{\Delta x \to 0} \frac{\Delta s}{\overline{PP'}} = 1,$$

which yields

(1) $$\frac{ds}{dx} = \operatorname*{Lim}_{\Delta x \to 0} \frac{\Delta s}{\Delta x} = \sqrt{1 + \left(\frac{dy}{dx}\right)^2}.$$

If s decreases as x increases, then

$$\frac{\Delta s}{\Delta x} = -\frac{\Delta s}{\overline{PP'}} \cdot \sqrt{1 + \left(\frac{\Delta y}{\Delta x}\right)^2},$$

and

(2) $$\frac{ds}{dx} = -\sqrt{1 + \left(\frac{dy}{dx}\right)^2}.$$

Equations (1) and (2) furnish us with a desirable starting point. We define the *differential of arc length ds* by

(3) $$ds = \pm \sqrt{(dx)^2 + (dy)^2}.$$

Thus $|ds|$ is the hypotenuse of the right triangle with sides $|dx|$ and $|dy|$.

If the tangent to the curve at P makes an angle α with Ox, then

(4) $$\cos \alpha = \frac{dx}{ds}, \qquad \sin \alpha = \frac{dy}{ds}.$$

The formula for differential of arc length in polar coordinates will be derived in § 279. From equation (3) and the relations $x = r\cos\theta$, $y = r\sin\theta$, it will be found that

(5) $$ds = \pm \sqrt{(dr)^2 + r^2(d\theta)^2}.$$

We are in no position now to make use of the above definitions and results. They do, however, play a significant role in several later developments. See §§ 279–280.

EXERCISES

In Exs. 1–24 find the differential of the given function.

1. $y = 2x^4 - 7x^3 + x - 3$.

Ans. $dy = 8x^3\, dx - 21x^2\, dx + dx = (8x^3 - 21x^2 + 1)\, dx$.

2. $z = (1 - 2t + t^3)^{-\frac{2}{3}}$. Ans. $dz = \frac{3}{2}(2 - 3t^2)(1 - 2t + t^3)^{-\frac{5}{3}}\, dt$.

3. $x = (3t + 2)^4$. **4.** $y = (1 - x^3)^2$.

5. $z = \sqrt{4 - 3x}$. **6.** $\beta = \dfrac{3}{\sqrt{1 - 2\alpha}}$.

7. $u = \sqrt{2y - y^2}$. Ans. $du = (1 - y)(2y - y^2)^{-\frac{1}{2}}\, dy$.

8. $x = \frac{1}{3}t^3 - \sqrt{t} + \dfrac{1}{t^2}$. Ans. $dx = \left(t^2 - \dfrac{1}{2\sqrt{t}} - \dfrac{2}{t^3}\right)\, dt$.

9. $y = x(3 + 2x)^4$. **10.** $w = x^2(1 - x^2)^{\frac{1}{2}}$.

11. $u = \dfrac{v^3}{v + 2}$. **12.** $x = \dfrac{t^2}{\sqrt{1 - t}}$.

13. $y = \sqrt{x^2 - a^2}$, a held constant. Ans. $dy = \dfrac{x\, dx}{\sqrt{x^2 - a^2}}$.

14. $y = \sqrt{x^2 - a^2}$, x held constant. Ans. $dy = \dfrac{-a\, da}{\sqrt{x^2 - a^2}}$.

15. $x = t^2(t^2 + 4)^{\frac{3}{2}}$. **16.** $x = y^3(9 - y^2)^{\frac{1}{2}}$.

17. $r = \dfrac{s}{\sqrt{1 - s^2}}$. **18.** $r = \dfrac{\sqrt{1 - s^2}}{s}$.

19. $y = (1 + \sqrt{x})^4$. **20.** $y = \sqrt{1 + \sqrt{x}}$.

21. $x = \dfrac{t}{(2 - 3t)^4}$. Ans. $dx = \dfrac{(9t + 2)\, dt}{(2 - 3t)^5}$.

22. $y = \dfrac{(1 - x)^2}{(1 - 2x)^2}$. Ans. $dy = \dfrac{2(1 - x)\, dx}{(1 - 2x)^3}$.

23. $r = \sqrt{\dfrac{1 - s}{1 + s}}.$ *Ans.* $dr = \dfrac{-ds}{(1 - s)^{\frac{1}{2}}(1 + s)^{\frac{3}{2}}}.$

24. $y = \dfrac{(x^3 - x)^2}{x + 1}.$ *Ans.* $dy = x(x - 1)(5x^2 + x - 2)\, dx.$

In Exs. 25–32, find dy.

 25. $y^2 = 4ax.$

 26. $\dfrac{x^2}{a^2} - \dfrac{y^2}{b^2} = 1.$ *Ans.* $dy = \dfrac{b^2 x\, dx}{a^2 y}.$

 27. $x^2 + xy + y^2 = 4.$
 28. $3x^2 - 6xy + 3y^2 - 7x + 2y - 1 = 0.$

 29. $x^{\frac{2}{3}} + y^{\frac{2}{3}} = a^{\frac{2}{3}}.$ **30.** $y^2 = \dfrac{x^2}{x^2 - a^2}.$

 31. $y^2 = \dfrac{x^3}{2a - x}.$ **32.** $y^3 = \dfrac{x^2}{a - x}.$

73. *Approximate Formulas*

Very often we wish to compute, or to estimate within safe limits, the change in the value of a function caused by a small change in the value of the independent variable. When Δx is small, dy and Δy are, in general, nearly equal, and in many cases *the value of dy furnishes a sufficiently good approximation to the value of* Δy.

In any approximate computation, the amount by which the computed value of the function differs from the true value is called the *error* of the computation. Of course in using any approximate formula, we should make sure that the error committed is within the allowable limit of error for the problem. This question will be considered more fully in § 343.

Example (a). Find an approximate formula for the area of a narrow circular ring.

The area of a circle of radius r is

$$A = \pi r^2.$$

When the radius increases by an amount Δr, the area increases by an amount ΔA which is approximated by

$$dA = 2\pi r\, dr = 2\pi r\, \Delta r.$$

(Since r is the independent variable, $dr = \Delta r$.) Hence the area of a narrow circular ring is approximately the *product of the circumference by the width*.

Example (b). Find an approximate value for $\sqrt{8.73}$.

Put $y = \sqrt{x}$, from which

(1) $dy = \dfrac{dx}{2\sqrt{x}}.$

For x we choose a number which is close to 8.73 and for which we know the square root.   Choose

$$x = 9 \quad \text{and} \quad \Delta x = dx = -0.27$$

so that $x + dx = 8.73$.   From (1) it follows that

$$dy = \frac{-0.27}{2\sqrt{9}} = \frac{-0.27}{6} = -0.045.$$

Then

$$\sqrt{8.73} = y + dy = 3 - 0.045 = 2.955$$

approximately.   To five decimal places the correct value is 2.95466.

EXERCISES

1. Find approximately the volume of a thin spherical shell.
Ans. Surface area × thickness.

2. Find an approximate formula for the volume of a thin cylindrical shell of given height.   *Ans. Circumference × height × thickness.*

3. Find approximately the volume of wood required to make a cubical box of edge length 5 ft., using boards $\frac{1}{2}$ in. thick.   *Ans. 6.25 cu. ft.*

4. The base of a right triangle is fixed at 3 ft., the hypotenuse is 5 ft. long and subject to change.   Find the approximate change in altitude when the hypotenuse is changed by a small amount Δh.   *Ans. 1.25 Δh.*

5. The diameter of a circle is measured and found to be 4 ft. with a maximum error of 0.1 in.   Find the approximate maximum error in the computed area.
Ans. 7.54 sq. in.

6. The diameter of a sphere is measured and found to be 4 ft. with a maximum error of 0.1 in.   Find the approximate maximum error in the computed volume.
Ans. 362 cu. in.

7. Find the approximate maximum error in computing the surface area of the sphere of Ex. 6.   *Ans. 30.2 sq. in.*

8. Find approximately the change in the reciprocal of a number x produced by a small change in the number.   Investigate also the case when the number itself is small.

9. Divide 1 by 9.83.   Use Ex. 8.   *Ans. 0.1017.*

10. Divide 1 by 25.3.   *Ans. 0.0395.*

11. The diameter of a circle is to be measured and its area computed.   If the diameter can be measured with a maximum error of 0.001 in., and the area must be accurate to within 0.1 sq. in., find the largest diameter for which the process can be used.   *Ans. Nearly 64 in.*

12. The diameter of a sphere is to be measured, and its volume computed.   If the diameter can be measured with a maximum error of 0.001 in., and the volume must be accurate to within 0.1 cu. in., find the largest diameter for which the process can be used.   *Ans. Nearly 8 in.*

13. A closed cylindrical tank of circular cross-section has a radius of 2 ft. and a height of 6 ft.   Find the approximate volume of asbestos required to line the tank completely with a lining 1 in. thick.   *Ans. 8.4 cu. ft.*

14. A bin is 10 ft. by 9 ft. by 8 ft. Find approximately the change in the volume when the bin is completely lined with paper $\frac{1}{16}$ in. thick. *Ans.* -2.52 cu. ft.

15. The volume of a body of gas is measured; the pressure is then computed from the formula

$$p = \frac{k}{v}.$$

If the allowable error in p is $0.001k$, and the maximum error in measuring v is 0.4 cu. ft., what is the volume of the smallest container to which the process can be applied? *Ans.* 20 cu. ft.

16. Suppose that the container in Ex. 15 is a cube of edge length s. Find the approximate error in the computed value of p due to a small error in measuring s.

17. In Ex. 16, if $s = 10 \pm 0.3$, how accurately can p be determined?

Ans. $dp \leqq 9(10)^{-5}k$.

18. The attraction between two magnetic poles is inversely proportional to the square of the distance between them: $F = \dfrac{k}{r^2}$. If the distance is slightly increased, how is the attraction affected?

19. The attraction between two magnetic poles is measured, and the distance between them computed (cf. Ex. 18). If $k = 1$ and $F = 6.3 \pm 0.1$, find r.

Ans. 0.398 ∓ 0.003 in.

20. A 16-lb. shot is made of iron weighing 444 lb. per cu. ft. If the weight must be accurate within 1 oz., find the radius. *Ans.* 2.459 ± 0.003 in.

21. A hollow sphere of outer radius 1 ft. is made of metal weighing about 400 lb. per cu. ft. The volume of metal is found by weighing to be 2 cu. ft., with an uncertainty of 0.1 cu. ft. due to the uncertain density. Find the inner radius.

Ans. 9.67 ∓ 0.15 in.

In Exs. 22–29, use differentials to approximate to the desired number.

22. The square root of 623.	*Ans.* 24.96.
23. The square root of 286.	*Ans.* 16.91.
24. The square root of 36.3.	*Ans.* 6.025.
25. The square root of 101.2.	*Ans.* 10.06.
26. The cube root of 9.	*Ans.* 2.083.
27. The cube root of 339.	*Ans.* 6.973.
28. The cube root of 3.4.	*Ans.* 1.504.
29. The fourth root of 17.	*Ans.* 2.031.

30. Find the change in the lateral surface area of a right circular cone, with radius of base fixed as r, when the altitude h changes by a small amount Δh.

31. Solve Ex. 30 if the radius changes (altitude fixed). *Ans.* $\dfrac{\pi(h^2 + 2r^2)\,\Delta r}{\sqrt{r^2 + h^2}}$.

32. Find the lateral surface area of a circular cone of radius 5 ft., height 12 ft., if the radius is uncertain by $\frac{1}{4}$ in. (Ex. 31.) *Ans.* $(65 \pm 0.3)\pi$ sq. ft.

33. For what values of x may $\sqrt[3]{x + 1}$ be replaced by $\sqrt[3]{x}$, if the allowable inaccuracy is 0.01? *Ans.* $x > 192$.

10

Integration

74. *Integration*

We have been occupied up to this point with the problem: Given a function, to find its derivative (or differential). Many of the most important applications of the calculus lead to the inverse problem: *Given the derivative of a function, to find the function.* The required function is called an *integral* of the given derivative, and the process of finding it is called *integration.* The given function is the *integrand.*

If $f(x)$ is a given function and $F(x)$ is a function whose derivative is $f(x)$, the relation between them is expressed by writing

$$F(x) = \int f(x) \, dx,$$

where the symbol $\int$, called the *integral sign*, indicates that we are to perform the operation of integration upon $f(x) \, dx$; i.e., we are to find a function whose derivative is $f(x)$ or whose differential is $f(x) \, dx$. For reasons that will appear later, we always write after the integral sign the differential $f(x) \, dx$ rather than the derivative $f(x)$.

Example (a). Evaluate $\int x^2 \, dx$.

Since differentiation reduces the exponent by 1, integration must *increase* the exponent by 1 (in order that, upon differentiating our answer, we may return to the original exponent). Thus our first guess at the answer may be x^3. But

$$d(x^3) = 3x^2 \, dx;$$

an unwanted factor 3 presents itself. To correct this, we amend our first guess by dividing by 3. Now, $d(\frac{1}{3}x^3) = x^2 \, dx$, but the addition of any constant whatever to $(\frac{1}{3}x^3)$ does not alter the differential. Hence

(1) $$\int x^2 \, dx = \tfrac{1}{3}x^3 + C,$$

where C is an arbitrary constant. Equation (1) is equivalent to the statement that $d(\frac{1}{3}x^3 + C) = x^2\,dx$.

It is natural to inquire whether there may be other correct, and essentially different, functions for the right member of (1); i.e., whether any function can have the differential $(x^2\,dx)$ and differ from $\frac{1}{3}x^3$ by other than a constant. The answer, contained in the following theorem, is "No!".

THEOREM 22. *Two functions having the same derivative differ only by a constant.*

Let $\varphi(x)$ and $\psi(x)$ be the two functions, and place

$$y = \varphi(x) - \psi(x).$$

By hypothesis,

$$y' = \varphi'(x) - \psi'(x) = 0.$$

The rate of change of y with respect to x is everywhere zero; hence y is constant.

In the following examples, the student should try to obtain the answer for himself, by intelligent guesswork, and should finally verify by differentiation.

Example (b). $\displaystyle \int \sqrt{1 + 5x}\,dx = \frac{2}{15}(1 + 5x)^{\frac{3}{2}} + C.$

Example (c). $\displaystyle \int (a^2 - y^2)^6\,y\,dy = -\frac{1}{14}(a^2 - y^2)^7 + C.$

Example (d). $\displaystyle \int \frac{dt}{\sqrt{1 - t}} = \int (1 - t)^{-\frac{1}{2}}\,dt = -2(1 - t)^{\frac{1}{2}} + C.$

It is now clear that a function whose derivative is given is not completely determined, since it contains an arbitrary additive constant, the *constant of integration.* For this reason, the function $\displaystyle \int f(x)\,dx$ is called the *indefinite integral of $f(x)$.*

75. General Properties of Indefinite Integrals

The following properties of indefinite integrals are easily verified by differentiation:

$$\int du = u + C.$$

$$\int (du + dv + \cdots + dz) = \int du + \int dv + \cdots + \int dz.$$

$$\int c\,du = c \int du.$$

The first formula is merely the definition of an integral.

The second formula shows that if the integrand consists of a sum of terms, each term may be integrated separately.

The third formula says that if the integrand contains a constant factor, that factor may be written before the integral sign.   As a corollary, we may *introduce a constant factor into the integrand*, provided we place its reciprocal before the integral sign.   But it is *never* allowable to introduce variable factors by this rule, for the reason that an answer obtained in this way cannot possibly be correct.   Given

$$(1) \qquad F(x) = \int f(x) \, dx,$$

write

$$(2) \qquad F(x) = \frac{1}{u} \int uf(x) \, dx,$$

or

$$uF(x) = \int uf(x) \, dx.$$

Differentiate:

$$(3) \qquad uF'(x) \, dx + F(x) \, du = uf(x) \, dx.$$

But, from (1), $F'(x) = f(x)$, so that (3) becomes

$$F(x) \, du = 0.$$

Since $F(x) \neq 0$, we must have $du = 0$, $u = $ a constant if (2) is to be true.

76. *The Power Formula*

In the formula
$$d(u^n) = nu^{n-1} \, du,$$

let us replace n by $n + 1$:

$$d(u^{n+1}) = (n + 1)u^n \, du.$$

Divide by $n + 1$ (since this is impossible when $n = -1$, that value must be excluded), and reverse the equation:

$$u^n \, du = \frac{d(u^{n+1})}{n + 1}.$$

Integrating, we obtain the *general power-formula of integration*:

$$(1) \qquad \int u^n \, du = \frac{u^{n+1}}{n + 1} + C, \qquad n \neq -1.$$

This formula, *correctly applied*, serves to evaluate each of the examples of § 74, and in fact every integral occurring in this chapter.   (In Chapter 23, analogous formulas will be developed for the other types of elementary integrals.) Thus the hit-or-miss method of § 74 may now be replaced by straightforward use of the formula. But aside from mere algebraic mistakes, it often happens, especially at first, that the student interprets the formula incorrectly: thus it is just as important as ever that each answer be checked by differentiation.

Example (a).

$$\int \left(3x^3 + 1 + \frac{1}{2x^2} \right) dx = 3 \int x^3 \, dx + \int dx + \frac{1}{2} \int x^{-2} \, dx$$

$$= \frac{3x^4}{4} + x - \frac{1}{2} x^{-1} + C$$

$$= \frac{3x^4}{4} + x - \frac{1}{2x} + C.$$

After a little practice, the answer can be written at once, both intermediate steps being omitted.

Example (b). Evaluate $\int (a^2 - y^2)^5 y \, dy.$

This resembles (1) with $u = a^2 - y^2$, $n = 5$. Since

$$d(a^2 - y^2) = -2y \, dy,$$

we introduce the factor (-2) under the integral sign, with its reciprocal in front:

$$\int (a^2 - y^2)^5 y \, dy = -\frac{1}{2} \int (a^2 - y^2)^5 (-2y) \, dy = -\frac{(a^2 - y^2)^6}{12} + C.$$

This integral could also be evaluated by expanding $(a^2 - y^2)^5$ and integrating the resulting row of powers, but this would be an exceedingly slow and tiresome method.

Example (c). Evaluate $\int (a^2 - x^2)^2 \, dx.$

This resembles Example (b), but only superficially. In any attempt to use formula (1) directly, it is found that when we choose $u = a^2 - x^2$, $n = 2$, then the differential

$$du = d(a^2 - x^2) = -2x \, dx$$

is not present in our integrand. The (-2) can be inserted, but nothing can be done about that missing factor x.

We are therefore forced to have recourse to expansion of $(a^2 - x^2)^2$, followed by a term-by-term integration:

$$\int (a^2 - x^2)^2 \, dx = \int (a^4 - 2a^2x^2 + x^4) \, dx$$

$$= a^4x - \tfrac{2}{3}a^2x^3 + \tfrac{1}{5}x^5 + C.$$

Example (d). Evaluate $\int (2x + 3) \, dx$.

First method. $\int (2x + 3) \, dx = x^2 + 3x + C$.

Second method.

$$\int (2x + 3) \, dx = \frac{1}{2} \int (2x + 3) 2 dx = \frac{(2x + 3)^2}{4} + C_1.$$

This simple example is introduced to exhibit a very common phenomenon. We shall meet many cases where two answers, both correct, differ widely in appearance; yet it will always be possible to show that they differ at most by a constant, however improbable this may seem at first sight. Here we have only to expand the second form:

$$\frac{(2x + 3)^2}{4} + C_1 = x^2 + 3x + \frac{9}{4} + C_1 = x^2 + 3x + C.$$

This shows that the arbitrary constants C, C_1 merely differ by $\frac{9}{4}$.

In the exercises, when the result of an integration is given, it is not implied that the one given is the only correct form or even necessarily better than any other.

EXERCISES

Evaluate the following integrals; check by differentiation.

1. $\int (x^3 - 2x) \, dx$.

2. $\int (4x - x^2) \, dx$.

3. $\int (6x^3 - 3x + 1) \, dx$.

4. $\int (10x^4 + 6x^2 - 1) \, dx$.

5. $\int \frac{dv}{v^2}$. *Ans.* $-\frac{1}{v} + C$.

6. $\int \frac{6 \, dz}{z^4}$. *Ans.* $-\frac{2}{z^3} + C$.

7. $\int (4 - y^{-2}) \, dy$.

8. $\int \left(\frac{1}{y^3} - y \right) dy$.

$\qquad\qquad\qquad\qquad\qquad$ *Ans.* $\frac{2}{3} t^{\frac{3}{2}} - 2 t^{\frac{1}{2}} + C$.

9. $\int \left(\sqrt{t} - \frac{1}{\sqrt{t}} \right) dt$.

10. $\int \left(u^{\frac{3}{2}} + \frac{1}{u^{\frac{3}{2}}} \right) du$. *Ans.* $\frac{2}{5} u^{\frac{5}{2}} - 2u^{-\frac{1}{2}} + C$.

11. $\int (y - 2)^3 \, dy$.

12. $\int (a + x)^4 \, dx$.

13. $\int \frac{dx}{(x + 1)^3}$.

14. $\int \frac{du}{(u - 4)^2}$.

15. $\int (4x + 1)^2 \, dx$. *Ans.* $\frac{1}{12}(4x + 1)^3 + C$.

16. $\displaystyle\int \frac{dx}{(2x-7)^4}.$ Ans. $-\frac{1}{6}(2x-7)^{-3}+C.$

17. $\displaystyle\int \frac{dx}{\sqrt{3x-4a}}.$ **18.** $\displaystyle\int \frac{dv}{(4v+3a)^{\frac{1}{3}}}.$

19. $\displaystyle\int (x^4 + a^4)^2\, dx.$ **20.** $\displaystyle\int (x^4 - 2a^2x^2)\, dx.$

21. $\displaystyle\int \left(x - \frac{1}{x}\right)^2 dx.$ **22.** $\displaystyle\int x(4-x)^2\, dx.$

23. $\displaystyle\int \frac{dy}{\sqrt{1-3y}}.$ **24.** $\displaystyle\int \frac{dz}{(4-z)^3}.$

25. $\displaystyle\int x(1+x^2)^4\, dx.$ **26.** $\displaystyle\int \frac{y\, dy}{(1+y^2)^2}.$

27. $\displaystyle\int (1+x^2)^3\, dx.$ **28.** $\displaystyle\int y^2(a^2 - y^2)\, dy.$

29. $\displaystyle\int \frac{u\, du}{\sqrt{a^2 + u^2}}.$ **30.** $\displaystyle\int u^2(a^2 - u^2)^2\, du.$

31. $\displaystyle\int x(x^3 + 2)^2\, dx.$ **32.** $\displaystyle\int x^2(x^3 + 2)^4\, dx.$

33. $\displaystyle\int \frac{x^3 + a^3}{x^2}\, dx.$ **34.** $\displaystyle\int \frac{a^2 - y^2}{y^2}\, dy.$

35. $\displaystyle\int (x^7 + 3x)^5\, dx.$ **36.** $\displaystyle\int x^5(x-2)^5(x-1)\, dx.$

In Exs. 37–40, integrate by two different methods and show that your answers are equivalent.

37. $\displaystyle\int x(2 - x^2)\, dx.$ **38.** $\displaystyle\int y^2(1 - y^3)^2\, dy.$

39. $\displaystyle\int u^{\frac{1}{2}}(u^{\frac{3}{2}} - 5)^2\, du.$ **40.** $\displaystyle\int \frac{(\sqrt{x} - 1)^2\, dx}{\sqrt{x}}.$

77. The Definite Integral

Let $f(x)$ be a given continuous function, $F(x)$ an integral of $f(x)$, and $x = a$ and $x = b$ two given values of x. The *change in the value of the integral* $F(x)$ as x changes from a to b, i.e., the quantity $F(b) - F(a)$, is called the *definite integral of $f(x)$ between the "limits" a and b*, or simply the *definite integral from a to b*, and is denoted by the symbol $\displaystyle\int_a^b f(x)\, dx$. It is called the *definite integral* because its value is independent of the constant of integration.

The numbers a and b are called the *lower limit* and the *upper limit*, respectively. Thus the definite integral is merely *the value of the indefinite integral at the upper limit, minus its value at the lower limit.* The symbol $\left[F(x) \right]_a^b$ means $F(b) - F(a)$:

(1) $$\int_a^b f(x) \, dx = \left[F(x) \right]_a^b = F(b) - F(a).$$

Since the constant of integration disappears, there is no object in writing it at all.

The assumption of continuity is introduced temporarily for simplicity. See § 211.

Example (a). $\displaystyle\int_0^1 (x + 1)^2 \, dx = \left[\frac{(x + 1)^3}{3} \right]_0^1 = \frac{8}{3} - \frac{1}{3} = \frac{7}{3}.$

Example (b). $\displaystyle\int_{-a}^a (a^2 - t^2) \, dt = \left[a^2 t - \tfrac{1}{3} t^3 \right]_{-a}^a$
$$= a^3 - \tfrac{1}{3}a^3 - (-a^3 + \tfrac{1}{3}a^3) = \tfrac{4}{3}a^3.$$

Example (c). $\displaystyle\int_0^a z(a^2 - z^2)^3 \, dz = -\left[\frac{(a^2 - z^2)^4}{8} \right]_0^a = \frac{a^8}{8}.$

The variable whose differential occurs—respectively x, t, z, in the examples—is called the *variable of integration.*

78. *General Properties of Definite Integrals*

The following properties are possessed by all definite integrals:

(1) $$\int_a^b f(x) \, dx = -\int_b^a f(x) \, dx;$$

(2) $$\int_a^b f(x) \, dx = \int_a^c f(x) \, dx + \int_c^b f(x) \, dx;$$

(3) $$\int_a^b f(x) \, dx = \int_a^b f(z) \, dz.$$

In words, these formulas say respectively:

(1) Interchanging the limits changes the sign of the integral.

(2) The interval of integration can be broken up into any number of subintervals, and the integration can be performed over each interval separately. (While the theorem is usually employed in this way, it is true whether or not c lies between a and b.)

(3) It makes no difference what letter is used for the variable of integration; i.e., *the definite integral of a given integrand is independent of the variable of integration.*

The first two are established very easily by writing out, by the defining formula (1), § 77, the values of the various integrals. The truth of (3) appears from a glance at that same formula, where the result involves the limits a and b but not the variable of integration x. In Example (a), § 77,

$$\int_0^1 (x+1)^2\, dx = \int_0^1 (y+1)^2\, dy = \int_0^1 (t+1)^2\, dt = \tfrac{7}{3}.$$

79. *Even and Odd Functions*

A function that *remains unchanged* when x is replaced by $-x$, i.e., such that

(1) $$f(-x) = f(x),$$

is called an *even function*. This means geometrically that the curve

$$y = f(x)$$

is symmetric with respect to the y-axis. Familiar examples of even functions are x^{2n} (n an integer), $\cos \theta$, $t \sin t$, etc.

A function such that

(2) $$f(-x) = -f(x)$$

is called an *odd function*. Geometrically, the curve $y = f(x)$ is symmetric with respect to the origin. Examples are x^{2n+1}, $x^{\frac{1}{3}}$, $\sin \theta$, $\tan \theta$.

THEOREM 23. *Any function defined throughout an interval $-a \leqq x \leqq a$ can be expressed as the sum of an even function and an odd function in that interval.*

Proof. We prove that this can be done by doing it. For x in the interval $-a \leqq x \leqq a$, write

(3) $$f(x) = \tfrac{1}{2}[f(x) + f(-x)] + \tfrac{1}{2}[f(x) - f(-x)],$$

an identity. The introduction of $f(-x)$ is permissible because our interval is symmetric with respect to $x = 0$; both $f(x)$ and $f(-x)$ exist for any x in that interval.

It is important that the separation (3) of a function into its even and odd parts is unique.

THEOREM 24. *If $E_1(x)$ and $E_2(x)$ are even functions of x and $O_1(x)$ and $O_2(x)$ are odd functions of x, then from*

(4) $$E_1(x) + O_1(x) = E_2(x) + O_2(x)$$

in some interval, it follows that in the same interval

(5) $$E_1(x) = E_2(x), \qquad O_1(x) = O_2(x).$$

Proof. In (4) change x to $(-x)$ to get

(6) $$E_1(x) - O_1(x) = E_2(x) - O_2(x).$$

Add and subtract the members of (4) and (6) to arrive at (5).

THEOREM 25.   *If $f(x)$ is an even function of x and $f(x)$ has a derivative $f'(x)$, then $f'(x)$ is an odd function of x.*

THEOREM 26.   *If $f(x)$ is an odd function of x and $f(x)$ has a derivative $f'(x)$, then $f'(x)$ is an even function of x.*

Proof of Theorems 25 and 26.   We know that

$$(7) \qquad f'(x) = \lim_{\Delta x \to 0} \frac{f(x + \Delta x) - f(x)}{\Delta x}$$

and, directly from the definition of a limit, that

$$(8) \qquad \lim_{h \to 0} g(h) = \lim_{h \to 0} g(-h).$$

From (7) and (8) it follows that

$$f'(-x) = \lim_{\Delta x \to 0} \frac{f(-x + \Delta x) - f(-x)}{\Delta x}$$
$$= \lim_{\Delta x \to 0} \frac{f(-x - \Delta x) - f(-x)}{-\Delta x}.$$

If $f(x)$ is an even function of x, $f(-x - \Delta x) = f(x + \Delta x)$, and therefore

$$f'(-x) = \lim_{\Delta x \to 0} \frac{f(x + \Delta x) - f(x)}{-\Delta x} = -f'(x),$$

so that $f'(x)$ is an odd function of x.   If $f(x)$ is an odd function of x,

$$f(-x - \Delta x) = -f(x + \Delta x),$$

and therefore

$$f'(-x) = \lim_{\Delta x \to 0} \frac{-f(x + \Delta x) + f(x)}{-\Delta x} = f'(x),$$

so that $f'(x)$ is an even function of x.

The student should prove the following lemma by first separating $H(x)$ into its even and odd parts and then employing Theorems 24, 25, and 26.

LEMMA 2.   *If $H'(x)$ is an even function of x, $H(x)$ is the sum of a constant $H(0)$ and an odd function of x; if $H'(x)$ is an odd function of x, $H(x)$ is an even function of x.*

THEOREM 27.   *If $f(x)$ is an even function of x,*

$$\int_{-a}^{a} f(x)\, dx = 2 \int_{0}^{a} f(x)\, dx.$$

THEOREM 28.   *If $f(x)$ is an odd function of x,*

$$\int_{-a}^{a} f(x)\, dx = 0.$$

In Theorems **27** and **28** it is assumed that the integrals involved exist.

Proof of Theorems 27 and 28. Let the indefinite integral of $f(x)\,dx$ be denoted by

(9)
$$\int f(x)\,dx = H(x) + C.$$

We know that $H'(x) = f(x)$ and that

(10)
$$\int_{-a}^{a} f(x)\,dx = H(a) - H(-a).$$

If $f(x)$ is an even function in the interval $-a \leq x \leq a$, $H'(x)$ is an even function, and by Lemma 2, $H(x)$ is an odd function of x plus the constant $H(0)$. Put

(11)
$$H(x) = O(x) + H(0).$$

Then, by (10),

$$\int_{-a}^{a} f(x)\,dx = O(a) + H(0) - O(-a) - H(0) = 2O(a)$$

or

$$\int_{-a}^{a} f(x)\,dx = 2[H(a) - H(0)] = 2\int_{0}^{a} f(x)\,dx,$$

by (11).

If $f(x)$ is an odd function of x, $H'(x)$ is odd, so $H(x)$ is an even function of x. Then $H(-a) = H(a)$ and Theorem 28 follows from equation (10).

Since many integrals of these precise types occur, the theorems are frequently applicable. Theorem 27 saves time and reduces the danger of mistake; Theorem 28 is even more useful, since whenever it applies, there is no need to find the indefinite integral at all.

When the integrand consists of several terms, some odd, some even (the limits being, of course, $-a$ to a), the odd terms may be dropped at once.

Example (a).

$$\int_{-a}^{a} (a^2 - l^2)\,dl = 2\int_{0}^{a} (a^2 - l^2)\,dl$$
$$= 2\left[a^2 l - \tfrac{1}{3}l^3 \right]_{0}^{a} = \tfrac{4}{3}a^3.$$

[Cf. Example (b), § 77.]

Example (b). $\displaystyle \int_{-1}^{1} \frac{x\,dx}{\sqrt{2 - x^8}} = 0.$

This is a so-called elliptic integral: the indefinite integral is not only beyond our present reach—it can never be evaluated in terms of elementary functions. But Theorem 28 gives the value of the definite integral at a glance.

Example (c).

$$\int_{-2}^{2} (x^5 - 3x^3 + 2x^2 - x)\, dx = 4 \int_{0}^{2} x^2\, dx$$

$$= \left[\frac{4x^3}{3} \right]_{0}^{2} = \frac{32}{3}.$$

EXERCISES

Evaluate the definite integrals in Exs. 1–20.

1. $\int_{1}^{2} x^3\, dx.$ *Ans.* $\frac{15}{4}$.   **2.** $\int_{0}^{2} (y - 1)^2\, dy.$ *Ans.* $\frac{2}{3}$.

3. $\int_{-1}^{2} (3 - 2v + 6v^2)\, dv.$ *Ans.* 24.

4. $\int_{-1}^{2} (1 - 3x^2)\, dx.$ *Ans.* -6.

5. $\int_{0}^{3} z(1 + 2z)\, dz.$ *Ans.* $\frac{45}{2}$.   **6.** $\int_{0}^{2} \sqrt{4\beta + 1}\, d\beta.$ *Ans.* $\frac{13}{3}$.

7. $\int_{-2}^{-3} (5 + 2w)^5\, dw.$ *Ans.* 0.   **8.** $\int_{-2}^{0} x^2(3 - x)\, dx.$ *Ans.* 12.

9. $\int_{1}^{2} (x - 4)(3x - 2)\, dx.$ **10.** $\int_{1}^{2} (3x - 4)(x + 2)\, dx.$

11. $\int_{1}^{2} \frac{dy}{(3 - y)^3}.$ *Ans.* $\frac{3}{8}$.   **12.** $\int_{1}^{2} \frac{du}{(2 + u)^2}.$ *Ans.* $\frac{1}{12}$.

13. $\int_{0}^{2} (1 - \alpha^2)^2\, d\alpha.$ *Ans.* $\frac{46}{15}$.   **14.** $\int_{\frac{1}{2}}^{1} \left(1 - \frac{1}{x^2}\right)^2 dx.$ *Ans.* $\frac{5}{6}$.

15. $\int_{0}^{1} \frac{dy}{(1 + 4y)^3}.$ *Ans.* $\frac{3}{25}$.   **16.** $\int_{1}^{3} \frac{v^4 + 1}{v^2}\, dv.$ *Ans.* $\frac{28}{3}$.

17. $\int_{1}^{4} \frac{1 + y}{\sqrt{y}}\, dy.$ *Ans.* $\frac{20}{3}$.

18. $\int_{0}^{a} \frac{x^3\, dx}{\sqrt{a^4 + x^4}}.$ *Ans.* $\frac{1}{2}a^2(\sqrt{2} - 1)$.

19. $\int_{\frac{1}{4}}^{1} \frac{\sqrt{1 - \sqrt{y}}}{\sqrt{y}}\, dy.$ *Ans.* $\frac{1}{3}\sqrt{2}$.

20. $\int_{0}^{1} (1 - x^{\frac{3}{2}})^4 \sqrt{x}\, dx.$ *Ans.* $\frac{2}{15}$.

In Exs. 21–29, use the properties of integrals with odd, or even, functions as integrands, to simplify the evaluation of the integral.

21. $\int_{-2}^{2} (x^3 - 7x^5)\, dx.$ *Ans.* 0.   **22.** $\int_{-a}^{a} x^3 \sqrt{a^2 - x^2}\, dx.$ *Ans.* 0.

23. $\int_{-1}^{1} (6y^2 - 5y^4)\, dy.$ *Ans.* 2.   **24.** $\int_{-2}^{2} (1 - \tfrac{1}{4}t^2)^2\, dt.$ *Ans.* $\tfrac{32}{15}.$

25. $\int_{-4}^{4} (2v^3 + \tfrac{3}{8}v^2 - 17v - 3)\, dv.$ *Ans.* −8.

26. $\int_{-a}^{a} x^2(7x^3 + 15ax^2 - 13a^2x + 6a^3)\, dx.$ *Ans.* $10a^6.$

27. $\int_{-2}^{2} x(9 - x^6)^{\frac{1}{2}}\, dx.$ *Ans.* 0.

28. $\int_{-1}^{1} (u^7 + 1)(3u^2 + 1)\, du.$ *Ans.* 4.

29. $\int_{-2}^{2} (x^5 - x^3 + 3x^2 - 4)\, dx.$ *Ans.* 0.

30. Show that the product or quotient of two odd functions is even.

31. Show that the product or quotient of an odd function by an even function is odd.

32. Prove Lemma 2, page 145.

80. *The Sigma Notation*

We shall have frequent occasion to speak of *sums* of a considerable number of terms, usually an unspecified number n:

$$u_1 + u_2 + u_3 + \cdots + u_n.$$

To save the bother of writing out such expressions always in full, a single symbol is commonly used in mathematics. The symbol $\sum\limits_{i=1}^{n}$ means that we are to substitute $i = 1, 2, 3, \ldots, n$ successively in the expression following, and add the results; for example:

$$\sum_{i=1}^{n} u_i = u_1 + u_2 + u_3 + \cdots + u_n,$$

$$\sum_{k=0}^{n} a_k x^{n-k} = a_0 x^n + a_1 x^{n-1} + \cdots + a_{n-1} x + a_n.$$

81. *Plane Area*

Calculus grew out of the attempts, eventually successful in the seventeenth century, of mathematicians* to solve two major problems. The first prob-

---

* Particularly Sir Isaac Newton, 1642–1727, and Gottfried Wilhelm Leibnitz (or Leibniz), 1646–1716; these two men, independently of each other, produced the great bulk of basic ideas and techniques which form the elementary calculus.

lem was to obtain the tangent line to a curve at a given point on it; that
was solved by introducing and applying the notion of a derivative. The
second problem was to obtain the area bounded by a curve $y = f(x)$, the
x-axis, and two ordinates $x = a$ and $x = b$.

This second problem is solved by a judicious extension of the elementary
concept of the area of a rectangle as the product of its base and its altitude.

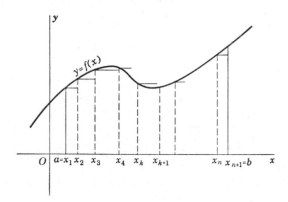

Figure 103

In Figure 103, let the interval $a \leqq x \leqq b$ be divided into n parts in any
manner, the divisions being at x_1, x_2, x_3, $\cdots$, x_{n+1}, with $x_1 = a$, $x_{n+1} = b$.
Erect rectangles, using the ordinates at x_1, x_2, x_3, $\cdots$, x_n, as shown in
the figure. In order to have a simple notation for the width of the bases
of these rectangles, let $\Delta x_1 = x_2 - x_1$, $\Delta x_2 = x_3 - x_2$, $\cdots$; i.e., let
$\Delta x_k = x_{k+1} - x_k$, for $k = 1, 2, 3, \cdots , n$.

It is reasonable that, if the maximum width of the rectangles shown be
taken sufficiently small, and the number of these rectangles correspondingly
large, then the sum of the areas of the rectangles will approximate, as closely
as desired, a quantity which agrees with our intuitive concept of the required
area. Even the oft-quoted average man on the street would, if presented
with the curve $y = f(x)$ drawn carefully on graph paper, obtain an approximation to the area we wish by counting the squares enclosed by its boundaries. We wish to replace his rough idea by a specific formula. Therefore
we proceed to lay down as our definition of the area A bounded by the curve
$y = f(x)$, the x-axis, and the ordinates $x = a$ and $x = b$, the following:

(1)
$$A = \lim_{\text{max. } \Delta x_k \to 0} \sum_{k=1}^{n} f(x_k)\, \Delta x_k,$$

in which, since the widths Δx_k of the rectangles approach zero, the number
of them, n, must approach infinity.

At once we are confronted with the question of whether the limit in (1) exists and, if it does exist, with the problem of determining how to compute that limit. A sufficient condition for the existence of the limit in (1), together with a remarkably simple method for obtaining its value, is contained in the following theorem.

THE FUNDAMENTAL THEOREM OF THE INTEGRAL CALCULUS

THEOREM 29. *If $f(x)$ is continuous in the interval $a \leq x \leq b$, if*

$$a = x_1 < x_2 < x_3 \cdots < x_n < x_{n+1} = b,$$

and if $\Delta x_k = x_{k+1} - x_k$, for $k = 1, 2, 3, \cdots, n$, then

$$(2) \qquad \underset{\text{max. } \Delta x_k \to 0}{\text{Lim}} \sum_{k=1}^{n} f(x_k) \, \Delta x_k = \int_a^b f(x) \, dx.$$

From equations (1) and (2) above, it follows that the area A is given by

$$(3) \qquad A = \int_a^b f(x) \, dx,$$

which is the basic formula we needed for the computation of the area shown in Figure 103.

The proof of Theorem 29 will be omitted; a rigorous analytic approach to our subject properly belongs in advanced calculus, or in a course in functions of a real variable. Here we content ourselves with the discussion in the next section, a treatment intended to make Theorem 29 plausible, not to prove it.

In § 83 we shall use formulas (2) and (3) to compute some elementary areas, thus obtaining a mild verification of those formulas.

82. *Plane Area: An Intuitive Approach*

Consider the area bounded by the continuous curve $y = f(x)$, the x-axis, the fixed ordinate $x = a$, and a variable ordinate $x = x$, as shown in Figure 104. For the moment, let the function $f(x)$ be increasing with increasing x. Then, when x is increased by an amount Δx, the area A will increase by an amount ΔA, the area $KLRP$. Now,

$$\text{Area } KLQP < \text{Area } KLRP < \text{Area } KLRS,$$

and

$$\text{Area } KLQP = \overline{KP} \cdot \overline{KL} = f(x) \, \Delta x,$$

$$\text{Area } KLRP = \Delta A,$$

$$\text{Area } KLRS = f(x + \Delta x) \, \Delta x.$$

Therefore we have

$$f(x)\,\Delta x < \Delta A < f(x + \Delta x)\,\Delta x,$$

(1) $$f(x) < \frac{\Delta A}{\Delta x} < f(x + \Delta x).$$

In the inequalities (1), let $\Delta x \to 0$. Then $f(x)$ stays fixed and $f(x + \Delta x) \to$ $f(x)$ because $f(x)$ is continuous. Since $\dfrac{\Delta A}{\Delta x}$ is pinned in between two quanti-ties, $f(x)$ and the quantity $f(x + \Delta x)$ which approaches $f(x)$ (because of continuity), then $\dfrac{\Delta A}{\Delta x}$ must also ap-

proach $f(x)$. Since $\dfrac{\Delta A}{\Delta x} \to \dfrac{dA}{dx}$, as $\Delta x \to 0$, we can conclude that

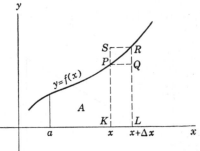

(2) $$\frac{dA}{dx} = f(x).$$

Because the derivative of A is $f(x)$, it follows that

$$A = \int f(x)\,dx = F(x) + C.$$

Figure 104

Since the position of the fixed ordinate $x = a$ is given, the constant of inte-gration may be determined by the fact that $A = 0$ when $x = a$:

$$0 = F(a) + C,$$

$$C = -F(a),$$

(3) $$A = F(x) - F(a).$$

For the area bounded by $y = f(x)$, the x-axis, and the ordinates $x = a$ and $x = b$, equation (3) becomes

(4) $$A = F(b) - F(a).$$

In view of the definition of the definite integral, equation (4) yields

(5) $$A = \int_a^b f(x)\,dx,$$

in agreement with the formula for area as dictated by Theorem 29.

The above discussion is readily modified to apply to a function which steadily decreases with increasing x, or which remains constant. If the interval between the ordinates $x = a$ and $x = b$ can be broken up into sub-intervals, on each of which the function increases, decreases, or remains constant, the argument leading to (5) goes through just as easily.

For brevity and simplicity in this first course, we shall make free use of intuitive reasoning. All the many formulas that we shall obtain will fall into one or the other of two classes: definitions or theorems. For many theorems we shall omit formal proofs, being content merely to show the meaning and reasonableness of the result; but every formula or theorem that we accept on this basis can be shown to rest on the firm foundation of analysis.

83. *Simple Verifications*

Let us verify that the definition of area presented in § 81 yields the desired result ($\frac{1}{2}$ base $\times$ altitude) for a right triangle. Figure 105 shows a right triangle bounded by the x-axis, the vertical line $x = b$, and the line

$$y = \frac{hx}{b}.$$

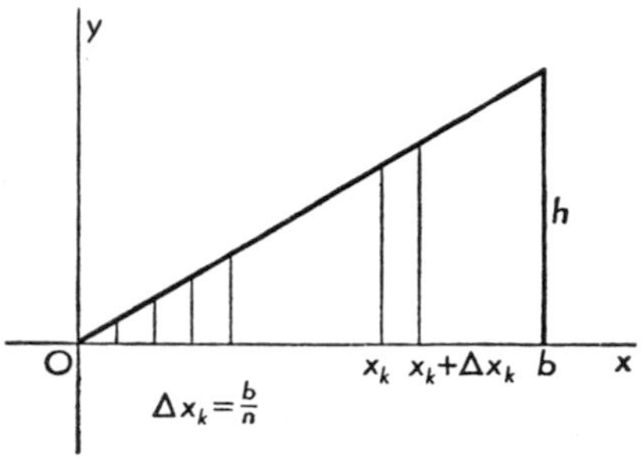

In the definition of area

$$(1) \qquad A = \operatorname*{Lim}_{\text{max. } \Delta x_k \to 0} \sum_{k=1}^{n} f(x_k)\, \Delta x_k$$

we choose to use n intervals of equal length. Put

Figure 105

$$f(x) = \frac{hx}{b}, \qquad x_k = \frac{(k-1)b}{n}, \qquad \Delta x_k = \Delta x = \frac{b}{n}.$$

Then (1) becomes

$$A = \operatorname*{Lim}_{\Delta x \to 0} \sum_{k=1}^{n} \frac{h}{b} \cdot \frac{(k-1)b}{n} \cdot \frac{b}{n},$$

or

$$(2) \qquad A = \operatorname*{Lim}_{n \to \infty} \frac{bh}{n^2} \sum_{k=1}^{n} (k-1).$$

In algebra* we found that the sum of any arithmetic series is one-half the product of the number of terms by the sum of the first term and the last term:

$$(3) \qquad \sum_{k=1}^{n} [a + (k-1)d] = \tfrac{1}{2}n[2a + (n-1)d].$$

* See any college algebra; for example, J. R. Britton and L. C. Snively, *Algebra for College Students*, 2nd ed., New York: Rinehart and Co., 1954, page 292.

For $a = 0$, $d = 1$, equation (3) yields

$$(4) \qquad \sum_{k=1}^{n} (k - 1) = \tfrac{1}{2}n(n - 1).$$

Then equation (2) becomes

$$A = \underset{n \to \infty}{\text{Lim}} \frac{bh}{n^2} \cdot \frac{n(n - 1)}{2} = \frac{1}{2} bh \underset{n \to \infty}{\text{Lim}} \frac{n - 1}{n} = \frac{1}{2} bh,$$

as desired.

Because of Theorem 29, page 150, we may obtain the desired area more simply by employing a definite integral.   Since, in this example,

$$f(x) = \frac{hx}{b},$$

it follows that

$$A = \int_0^b f(x)\, dx = \frac{h}{b} \int_0^b x\, dx$$

$$= \frac{h}{b} \left[\frac{1}{2} x^2 \right]_0^b = \frac{1}{2} bh.$$

Next let us verify Theorem 29 for the area exhibited in Figure 106.   Again we use only the one choice of intervals of equal length.   The desired area is that bounded by the x-axis, the vertical line $x = 1$, and the pertinent arc of the parabola

$$(5) \qquad\qquad y = x^2.$$

Here $f(x) = x^2$ and the definite integral method for obtaining areas gives us

$$(6) \qquad A_1 = \int_0^1 x^2\, dx = \tfrac{1}{3} \left[x^3 \right]_0^1 = \tfrac{1}{3}.$$

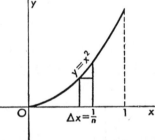

Figure 106

It is our purpose to determine whether the result in (6) agrees, as Theorem 29 states it does, with the result given by

$$(7) \qquad\qquad A_2 = \underset{\Delta x_k \to 0}{\text{Lim}} \sum_{k=1}^{n} f(x_k)\, \Delta x_k.$$

For this example,

$$f(x) = x^2, \quad x_k = \frac{k - 1}{n}, \quad \Delta x_k = \Delta x = \frac{1}{n}.$$

Hence (7) yields

$$A_2 = \underset{n \to \infty}{\text{Lim}} \sum_{k=1}^{n} \left(\frac{k-1}{n}\right)^2 \frac{1}{n}$$

$$= \underset{n \to \infty}{\text{Lim}} \frac{1}{n^3} \sum_{k=1}^{n} (k-1)^2.$$

It is easy to show by induction that

(8) $$\sum_{k=1}^{n} (k-1)^2 = \frac{n(n-1)(2n-1)}{6},$$

or the result may be obtained by replacing n by $(n-1)$ in Ex. 11 on page 287 of Britton and Snively's *Algebra for College Students*, cited near the beginning of this section.

With the aid of equation (8) we may write

$$A_2 = \underset{n \to \infty}{\text{Lim}} \frac{n(n-1)(2n-1)}{6n^3} = \underset{n \to \infty}{\text{Lim}} \frac{2n^2 - 3n + 1}{6n^2} = \frac{1}{3}.$$

Therefore the A_1 of (6) and the A_2 of (7) are equal, as predicted by Theorem 29, page 150.

EXERCISES

In each exercise compute by the two methods employed in this section the area bounded by the given curves and straight lines. Use equation (1) of § 81 and recompute the area by formula (3) of § 81. In your work equations (4) and (8) of the present section and the sum

(9) $$\sum_{k=1}^{n} (k-1)^3 = \tfrac{1}{4}n^2(n-1)^2$$

may be used. A set of formulas equivalent to (4), (8), and (9) is

(10) $$\sum_{k=1}^{n} 1 = n, \qquad \sum_{k=1}^{n} k = \tfrac{1}{2}n(n+1),$$

$$\sum_{k=1}^{n} k^2 = \tfrac{1}{6}n(n+1)(2n+1), \qquad \sum_{k=1}^{n} k^3 = \tfrac{1}{4}n^2(n+1)^2.$$

1. $y = x^3,\ y = 0,\ x = 1.$ *Ans.* $\tfrac{1}{4}$.

2. $y = 4x(1-x),\ y = 0.$ *Ans.* $\tfrac{2}{3}$.

3. $y = x^2,\ y = 0,\ x = 1,\ x = 2.$ *Ans.* $\tfrac{7}{3}$.

4. $y = 2x - 3,\ y = 0,\ x = 2,\ x = 5.$ *Ans.* 12.

5. $y = x^2,\ y = 0,\ x = 1,\ x = 3.$ *Ans.* $\tfrac{26}{3}$.

84. *Computation of Plane Areas*

The formula for area in § 81, properly extended, enables us to compute areas bounded, in any manner whatever, by curves whose equations are given in rectangular coordinates. We merely take an element, parallel to either axis according to convenience, express its area in terms of the coordinates, and integrate over the whole region. The process is best explained by means of examples.

In plane-area problems, a rough check on the answer may be obtained by circumscribing about the area a rectangle with its sides parallel to the axes and comparing the area of the rectangle with the result obtained by integration. In problems where the numerical work is simple, so that the answer is likely to be either correct or widely incorrect, this check is especially valuable.

In every problem the student should *make a sketch of the area to be found, draw an element in a general position, and obtain the area of the element directly from the figure.*

Example (a). Find the area in the first quadrant bounded by the parabola $y^2 = 4ax$, the x-axis, and the line $x = a$. (Figure 107.)

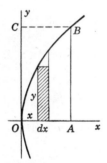

Figure 107

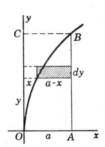

Figure 108

With the element parallel to Oy, we have

$$A = \int_0^a y\, dx = 2a^{\frac{1}{2}} \int_0^a x^{\frac{1}{2}}\, dx = \tfrac{4}{3}a^{\frac{1}{2}} \left[x^{\frac{3}{2}} \right]_0^a = \tfrac{4}{3}a^2.$$

Since the area $OABC$ is $2a^2$, the result is roughly checked.

Example (b). Find the above area by another method.

Take the element parallel to Ox (Figure 108). The base of the rectangle is evidently $a - x$, the altitude dy, whence

$$A = \int_0^{2a} (a - x)\, dy = \int_0^{2a} \left(a - \frac{y^2}{4a} \right) dy$$

$$= \left[ay - \frac{y^3}{12a} \right]_0^{2a} = \frac{4}{3} a^2.$$

85. *Integral with Negative Integrand*

In the definite integral $\int_a^b f(x)\,dx$, let the limits be so chosen that the lower limit is algebraically less than the upper limit. With this convention x increases, so that dx is positive.

Suppose first that the integrand $f(x)$ keeps the same sign, either positive or negative, throughout the interval. Then, when the integral is evaluated, the result will have the same sign as $f(x)$. For, in Theorem 29, each of the

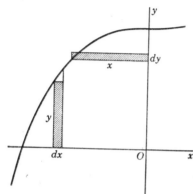

Figure 109

terms occurring in the summation will have the same sign as $f(x)$, and the limit of the sum must have that same sign.

Now, if we are using the integral to compute an area in the ordinary sense of elementary geometry, the formula must always be so written that the element is positive, since area is essentially positive.

Example. Find the area in the second quadrant bounded by the curve

$$y = x^3 + 1.$$

With vertical rectangles,

$$A = \int_{-1}^0 y\,dx = \int_{-1}^0 (x^3 + 1)\,dx = \left[\frac{1}{4}x^4 + x\right]_{-1}^0 = \frac{3}{4}.$$

With horizontal rectangles, since x is negative, the area of the element is $(-x)\,dy$, and

$$A = \int_0^1 (-x)\,dy = -\int_0^1 (y - 1)^{\frac{1}{3}}\,dy$$

$$= -\frac{3}{4}\left[(y - 1)^{\frac{4}{3}}\right]_0^1 = \frac{3}{4}.$$

If the curve crosses the axis within the interval of integration, and we wish to find the area in the above sense, we may integrate over the positive and negative regions separately, changing the sign in the latter. (Of course considerations of symmetry may enable us to shorten the process.)

86. *Area Between Two Curves*

In finding the area between two curves, uncertainty as to signs sometimes arises when some of the coordinates are negative. It need not, if we merely remember that in analytic geometry all coordinates are *directed* line segments.   In Figure 110, the height of the element is

$$QP = QM + MP = MP - MQ = y_h - y_l.$$

In Figure 111, the height is

$$QP = QM - PM = MP - MQ = y_h - y_l.$$

Always, a vertical element will be positive, if we use the y *of the higher point minus the y of the lower point.*

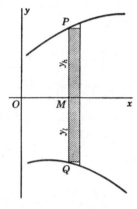

Figure 110

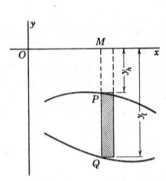

Figure 111

A horizontal element will be positive if we use the x *of the right-hand point minus the x of the left-hand point,* as is done in Example (*c*) below.

Example (a).   Find the area between the curves (Figure 112)

$$x^2 = 2ay, \qquad x^2 = 4ay - a^2.$$

We easily find that these parabolas intersect at $(\pm a, \frac{1}{2}a)$.   The area of a vertical element is $(y_h - y_l)\,dx$, where y_h and y_l are the ordinates of the

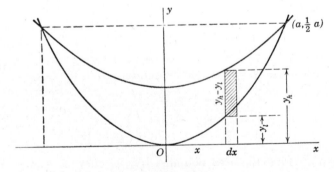

Figure 112

higher and lower curves respectively. Instead of integrating from $-a$ to a, we may, owing to the symmetry with respect to Oy, integrate from 0 to a and multiply by 2:

$$A = \int_{-a}^{a} (y_h - y_l)\, dx = 2 \int_{0}^{a} \left(\frac{x^2}{4a} + \frac{a}{4} - \frac{x^2}{2a} \right) dx$$

$$= 2 \int_{0}^{a} \left(\frac{a}{4} - \frac{x^2}{4a} \right) dx = \frac{1}{2} \left[ax - \frac{x^3}{3a} \right]_{0}^{a} = \frac{1}{3} a^2.$$

The area of the circumscribing rectangle is a^2, which yields a rough check on our result.

Example (b). Find the area bounded by the curve $x^2 + 4y - 8 = 0$ and the line $x = 2y$.

Obtain the intersections of the given curves by solving their equations simultaneously. In this example, the intersections are found to be at $(2, 1)$ and $(-4, -2)$. Next put the equation of the parabola into standard form, $x^2 = -4(y - 2)$. Then sketch the curves, Figure 113, and draw in an

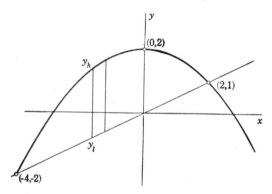

Figure 113

appropriate element, as shown. Using that element, we arrive at the desired area as follows:

$$A = \int_{-4}^{2} (y_h - y_l)\, dx$$

$$= \int_{-4}^{2} (2 - \tfrac{1}{4}x^2 - \tfrac{1}{2}x)\, dx$$

$$= \left[2x - \frac{x^3}{12} - \frac{x^2}{4} \right]_{-4}^{2}$$

$$= 4 - \tfrac{2}{3} - 1 - (-8 + \tfrac{16}{3} - 4) = 9.$$

Example (c). Find the area bounded by the curve $x = y^2 - 1$ and the line $y = x - 1$.

As in Example (a), we find the intersections, and sketch the figure, Figure 114. This time a horizontal element is suggested by the figure. The length of the element is the x-coordinate on the right (that of the straight line) minus the x-coordinate on the left (that of the parabola). Therefore we conclude that

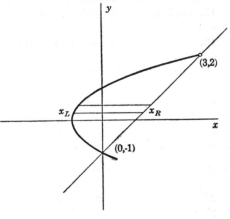

$$A = \int_{-1}^{2} (x_R - x_L)\, dy$$

$$= \int_{-1}^{2} (y + 1 - y^2 + 1)\, dy$$

$$= \left[2y + \frac{y^2}{2} - \frac{y^3}{3} \right]_{-1}^{2} = \frac{9}{2}.$$

Figure 114

EXERCISES

1. Find the area bounded by the curve $y = 4 - x^2$ and the x-axis. Solve in two ways. *Ans.* $\frac{32}{3}$.

2. Find the area bounded by the curve $a^2y = x^3$, the x-axis, and the line $x = 2a$. Solve in two ways. *Ans.* $4a^2$.

3. Find the area bounded by the curve $y^2 - 3x + 3 = 0$ and the line $x = 4$. *Ans.* 12.

4. Find the area bounded by the curve $ay = x^2$ and the lines $y = a$ and $y = 4a$. *Ans.* $\frac{28}{3}a^2$.

5. Find the area bounded by the curve $y = 8 - x^3$ and the axes. Solve in two ways.

6. A trapezoid has its vertices at $(0, 0)$, (a, h), $(a + b_1, h)$, $(b_2, 0)$, with all letters denoting positive quantities. Set up a single integral for the area of the trapezoid, evaluate the integral, and compare your answer with the known elementary formula $A = \frac{1}{2}h(b_1 + b_2)$.

7. Find the area bounded by a parabola and any right chord. (Use the parabola $y^2 = 4ax$, chord $x = x_1$.) *Ans.* Two-thirds of the circumscribing rectangle.

8. Solve Ex. 7 by another method.

9. Find the area in the third quadrant bounded by the curve $x = y^2 + 2y$. *Ans.* $\frac{4}{3}$.

10. Find the area bounded by the curve $x = y^2 + 2y$ and the line $x = 3$.

11. Find the area bounded by the curve $y^2 + 2x - 2y - 3 = 0$ and the y-axis. *Ans.* $\frac{16}{3}$.

12. Find the area bounded by the curve $y = 3x(x - 2)^2$ and the x-axis. *Ans.* 4.

13. Find the area bounded by the curve $y = x(x - 1)^2$, the y-axis, and the line $y = 2$. *Ans.* $\frac{10}{3}$.

14. Find the area in the second quadrant bounded by the curve $2x^2 + 4x + y = 0$. *Ans.* $\frac{8}{3}$.

15. Find the area bounded by the curve $y = 4x - x^2$ and the line $y = 3$. *Ans.* $\frac{4}{3}$.

16. Find the area bounded by the curve $y = 4x - x^2$ and the lines $x = 0$ and $y = 4$.   Solve in two ways.   *Ans.* $\frac{8}{3}$.

17. Find the area bounded by the curve $y = 4x - x^2$ and the lines $x = -2$ and $y = 4$.   *Ans.* $\frac{64}{3}$.

18. Find the area bounded by the curve $y = 12x - x^3$ and the line $y = 16$.
                                                                Ans. 108.

19. Find each of the two areas bounded by the curves $y = x^3 - 4x$ and $y = x^2 + 2x$.   *Ans.* $\frac{16}{3}$, $\frac{63}{4}$.

20. Find the area bounded by the curve $a^3y = (x^2 - a^2)^2$ and the x-axis.
                                                            Ans. $\frac{16}{15}a^2$.

21. Find the area, in the first quadrant, bounded by the curve $x^2y = a^3$, the lines $x = 2a$, $y = 4a$, and the axes.   *Ans.* $\frac{7}{2}a^2$.

In Exs. 22–37, find the area between the two curves.

22. $2x^2 + 4x + y = 0$, $y = 2x$.   *Ans.* 9.

23. $y^2 = -4x$, $y = 2(x + 2)$.   *Ans.* 9.

24. $y^2 = 2x + 3$, $y = x$.   *Ans.* $\frac{16}{3}$.

25. $y = x^4$, $y = 5x + 6$.   *Ans.* 18.9.

26. A parabola and a chord through the vertex.   (Use $y^2 = 4ax$, $y = mx$.)
                                                            Ans. $\dfrac{8a^2}{3m^3}$.

27. $x^2 = ay$, $a^2y = x^3$.

28. $y = x$, $a^2y = x^3$.

29. $y^2 = 1 - x$, $y = 1 + x$.   *Ans.* $\frac{9}{2}$.

30. $y^2 = -x$, $x^2 = 6 - 5y$.   *Ans.* 5.4.

31. $y^2 = -x$, $x^2 + 3y + 4x + 6 = 0$.   *Ans.* $\frac{5}{3}$.

32. $y = x^2 - 2x$, $x + 2y + 1 = 0$.   Check by Ex. 26.

33. $y = x^2(x - 3)$, $y = x^2$.   *Ans.* $\frac{64}{3}$.

34. $y = x^2(x - 3)$, $y = 4(x - 3)$; the total area.   *Ans.* 32.75.

35. $x^2 = y + 1$, $x = (y + 1)^2$.   Solve in two ways.   *Ans.* $\frac{1}{3}$.

36. $y = x^2(x - 3)$, $y^2 + 8y - 16x + 48 = 0$.   *Ans.* $\frac{17}{12}$.

37. $y = x^3 + 3x^2 - 4$, $y = 2x^3$.   *Ans.* $\frac{27}{4}$.

38. Find the area bounded by $y^2 = 4a(y - x)$, $y^2 = 2a(x + 2y - 3a)$, and the x-axis.   *Ans.* $2a^2$.

39. Evaluate $\displaystyle\int_0^a \sqrt{a^2 - x^2}\, dx$ by considering the geometric meaning of the integral.   *Ans.* $\frac{1}{4}\pi a^2$.

Trigonometric Functions

87. Elementary Properties

The trigonometric functions are one-valued and continuous for all values of the argument x, except that the tangent and secant become infinite when $x = \pm(n + \frac{1}{2})\pi$, the cotangent and cosecant become infinite when $x = \pm n\pi$, where n is zero or a positive integer. The sine and cosine and their reciprocals, the cosecant and secant, are periodic with the period 2π; the tangent and cotangent are periodic with the period π.

A student of calculus may save himself a great deal of time and trouble by memorizing thoroughly the fundamental facts and formulas of trigonometry. It is strongly recommended that such a review be made before proceeding further.

88. Derivative of sin x

From
$$y = \sin x,$$
it follows readily that
$$y + \Delta y = \sin(x + \Delta x)$$
$$= \sin x \cos \Delta x + \cos x \sin \Delta x.$$
Then
$$\Delta y = \sin x \cos \Delta x + \cos x \sin \Delta x - \sin x$$
$$= \cos x \sin \Delta x - \sin x(1 - \cos \Delta x).$$

Eventually we shall let $\Delta x \to 0$. By Theorem 13,

$$\lim_{\alpha \to 0} \frac{\sin \alpha}{\alpha} = 1;$$

therefore, we favor sine functions involving Δx. From trigonometry we know that $\sin^2 A = \frac{1}{2}(1 - \cos 2A)$. Hence

$$1 - \cos \Delta x = 2 \sin^2(\tfrac{1}{2}\Delta x)$$

so that we may write

$$\Delta y = \cos x \sin \Delta x - 2 \sin x \sin^2(\tfrac{1}{2}\Delta x).$$

161

This leads us to

$$\frac{\Delta y}{\Delta x} = \cos x \, \frac{\sin \Delta x}{\Delta x} - 2 \sin x \, \frac{\sin^2 \left(\frac{1}{2}\Delta x\right)}{\Delta x},$$

or

(1) $$\frac{\Delta y}{\Delta x} = \cos x \, \frac{\sin \Delta x}{\Delta x} - \sin x \, \frac{\sin \left(\frac{1}{2}\Delta x\right)}{\frac{1}{2}\Delta x} \cdot \sin \left(\tfrac{1}{2}\Delta x\right).$$

Now

$$\operatorname*{Lim}_{\Delta x \to 0} \frac{\sin \Delta x}{\Delta x} = 1, \; \operatorname*{Lim}_{\Delta x \to 0} \frac{\sin \left(\frac{1}{2}\Delta x\right)}{\frac{1}{2}\Delta x} = 1, \; \operatorname*{Lim}_{\Delta x \to 0} \sin \left(\tfrac{1}{2}\Delta x\right) = 0.$$

Thus, when we let $\Delta x \to 0$ in each member of (1), we obtain

$$y' = \cos x \cdot 1 - \sin x \cdot 1 \cdot 0,$$

or

$$\frac{dy}{dx} = \frac{d}{dx} \sin x = \cos x.$$

If u is any function of x, it follows by the chain rule, § 51, that

$$\frac{d}{dx} \sin u = \frac{d}{du} \sin u \cdot \frac{du}{dx}.$$

We have thus derived another of the fundamental differentiation formulas to be listed on pages 198–199:

(7) $$\frac{d}{dx} \sin u = \cos u \, \frac{du}{dx}.$$

Radian measure of angles is almost always used in calculus in preference to degree measure of angles. In Ex. 51, page 57, it was found that

$$\operatorname*{Lim}_{\alpha^\circ \to 0} \frac{\sin \alpha^\circ}{\alpha^\circ} = \frac{\pi}{180^\circ}.$$

With the aid of the above limit, it can be seen that, if x° is measured in degrees, then equation (1) yields

$$\frac{d}{dx^\circ} \sin x^\circ = \frac{\pi}{180^\circ} \cos x^\circ.$$

The highly undesirable factor $\left(\dfrac{\pi}{180^\circ}\right)$ would also appear in the derivatives of the other trigonometric functions, if degree measure were to be used. Therefore, in calculus we use radian measure whenever feasible, although in numerical studies (surveying, etc.) it is common practice to retain degree measure of angles.

89. *Derivatives of cos x, tan x, Etc.*

The derivatives of the other trigonometric functions may also be obtained directly from the definition of the derivative, but they are more easily found from (7) above.

To differentiate cos x, we write

$$\frac{d}{dx} \cos x = \frac{d}{dx} \sin\left(\frac{\pi}{2} - x\right) = -\cos\left(\frac{\pi}{2} - x\right)$$
$$= -\sin x.$$

If u is any function of x, we find by the chain rule of § 51 another of the formulas to be listed on pages 198–199:

$$(8) \qquad\qquad \frac{d}{dx} \cos u = -\sin u \frac{du}{dx}.$$

The remaining trigonometric functions may be differentiated by expressing them in terms of the sine and cosine. If u is any function of x, the results are:

$$(9) \qquad\qquad \frac{d}{dx} \tan u = \sec^2 u \frac{du}{dx},$$

$$(10) \qquad\qquad \frac{d}{dx} \cot u = -\csc^2 u \frac{du}{dx},$$

$$(11) \qquad\qquad \frac{d}{dx} \sec u = \sec u \tan u \frac{du}{dx},$$

$$(12) \qquad\qquad \frac{d}{dx} \csc u = -\csc u \cot u \frac{du}{dx}.$$

Example (a). If $y = \sin 4x^2$, then

$$\frac{dy}{dx} = 8x \cos 4x^2.$$

Example (b). If $r = (2 + 3 \cot 4\theta)^5$, then

$$\frac{dr}{d\theta} = 5(2 + 3 \cot 4\theta)^4 \cdot 3 \cdot (-4 \csc^2 4\theta)$$
$$= -60 \csc^2 4\theta(2 + 3 \cot 4\theta)^4.$$

Example (c). Show that $\sin \varphi > \dfrac{2\varphi}{\pi}$ for $0 < \varphi < \dfrac{1}{2} \pi$.

Put

$$(1) \qquad\qquad y = \sin \varphi - \frac{2\varphi}{\pi}.$$

The desired inequality will be obtained by showing that y is positive for the given range of φ values.

From (1) it follows that

(2)
$$y' = \cos \varphi - \frac{2}{\pi},$$

(3)
$$y'' = -\sin \varphi.$$

Since $\sin \varphi$ is positive in the range $0 < \varphi < \frac{1}{2}\pi$, equation (3) tells us that the y-curve is concave downward throughout that range. Therefore, since y is zero at $\varphi = 0$ and at $\varphi = \frac{1}{2}\pi$, the direction of concavity of the curve (1) shows that y must be positive between $\varphi = 0$ and $\varphi = \frac{1}{2}\pi$.

As a check, note that at $\varphi = 0$, $y' = 1 - \frac{2}{\pi}$ is positive, so that y is increasing for small positive φ. The known continuity of y and its derivatives is being used several times in the argument presented. The student should sketch the pertinent portion of the curve (1).

EXERCISES

In Exs. 1–42, find the first derivative of the given function.

1. $y = \sin 4x.$ 　　　　　　　　　　　　　　　　*Ans.* $\dfrac{dy}{dx} = 4 \cos 4x.$

2. $x = \cos 3t.$ 　　　　　　　　　　　　　　　　*Ans.* $\dfrac{dx}{dt} = -3 \sin 3t.$

3. $x = \sec 2u.$ 　　　　　　　　　　　　　　*Ans.* $\dfrac{dx}{du} = 2 \sec 2u \tan 2u.$

4. $y = -2 \csc 2t.$ 　　　　　　　　　　　　*Ans.* $\dfrac{dy}{dt} = 4 \csc 2t \cot 2t.$

5. $t = \tan 3y.$ 　　　　　　　　　　　　　　　*Ans.* $\dfrac{dt}{dy} = 3 \sec^2 3y.$

6. $\theta = 4 \cot \frac{1}{2}\varphi.$ 　　　　　　　　　　　*Ans.* $\dfrac{d\theta}{d\varphi} = -2 \csc^2 \frac{1}{2}\varphi.$

7. $y = \csc (3x - 1).$ 　　　　　**8.** $y = \tan \left(\dfrac{\pi}{4} - \dfrac{x}{2} \right).$

9. $r = \cos \frac{1}{2}\theta^2.$ 　　　　　　　**10.** $r = \sin \left(\dfrac{\pi}{3} - \dfrac{\theta}{2} \right).$

11. $x = \cot (1 - t^2).$ 　　　　　**12.** $x = \sec \dfrac{2\pi - \theta}{3}.$

13. $u = z \sin 4z.$ 　　　　　　　**14.** $u = \sin^2 3z.$
15. $y = x^2 \cos^3 x.$ 　　　　　**16.** $y = (1 - x)^3 \sin^2 x.$
17. $x = \sec 2t - \tan 2t.$ 　　　**18.** $x = \csc^2 (1 + 4t).$
19. $\alpha = \sin^2 \beta \cos \beta.$ 　　　　**20.** $\alpha = \sec^2 \beta \tan^2 \beta.$
21. $f(x) = \tan x - x.$ 　　　　**22.** $F(x) = x + \cot x.$

23. $y = \cos^4 t - \sin^4 t.$ 　　　　　　　　　　*Ans.* $\dfrac{dy}{dt} = -2 \sin 2t.$

24. $y = \sec^2 \theta - \tan^2 \theta.$ 　　　　　　　　　　*Ans.* $\dfrac{dy}{d\theta} = 0.$

25. $r = \cos \theta \cot \theta.$ *Ans.* $\dfrac{dr}{d\theta} = -\cos \theta (1 + \csc^2 \theta).$

26. $w = \sin^4 y \cos^4 y.$ *Ans.* $\dfrac{dw}{dy} = \dfrac{1}{2} \sin^3 2y \cos 2y.$

27. $x = 2 \cos^2 \dfrac{t}{2}.$ *Ans.* $\dfrac{dx}{dt} = -\sin t.$

28. $z = 4 \sin^2 3u.$ *Ans.* $\dfrac{dz}{du} = 12 \sin 6u.$

29. $y = \sin (\cos x).$ *Ans.* $y' = -\sin x \cos (\cos x).$

30. $y = \tan (x \sin x).$ *Ans.* $y' = (x \cos x + \sin x) \sec^2 (x \sin x).$

31. $v = (1 + \sin^4 y)^{\frac{1}{2}}.$ **32.** $v = (1 - 4 \cos 5y)^{-\frac{1}{2}}.$

33. $r = (2 \tan^3 2\theta - 1)^{\frac{1}{3}}.$ **34.** $r = \dfrac{\cos 2\theta}{1 - \sin 2\theta}.$

35. $y = \dfrac{\tan 2x}{1 - \cot 2x}.$ **36.** $y = \dfrac{1}{(\sec^2 3x - 4)^{\frac{1}{2}}}.$

37. $x = \dfrac{1 - \tan^2 v}{\tan^4 v}.$ **38.** $x = \dfrac{1}{(\cos \varphi - \sin \varphi)^2}.$

39. $y = \left(\dfrac{1 - \cos \theta}{1 + \cos \theta}\right)^3.$ **40.** $y = \dfrac{(1 + \sec x)^2}{(1 - \sec x)^3}.$

41. $u = x \csc^3 (x^2).$ **42.** $v = (1 - x^2) \tan (1 - x^2).$

43. From the equation $y = \sin (ax)$, find the first four derivatives of y with respect to x.

44. Find $y^{(4)}$ and $y^{(8)}$ from the equation $y = \cos 2x$.

45. Show that if A, B, k are constants, from $y = A \cos kx + B \sin kx$, we obtain $\dfrac{d^2y}{dx^2} = -k^2 y.$

46. From each of the three trigonometric formulas for $\cos 2x$, deduce by differentiation the trigonometric formula for $\sin 2x$.

47. From the trigonometric formula for $\sin (x + \alpha)$, deduce by differentiation the trigonometric formula for $\cos (x + \alpha)$.

48. From the trigonometric formula for $\tan 2x$, deduce by differentiation the trigonometric formula for $\cos 2x$.

49. Show that $\tan x$ increases as x increases, for all values of x for which $\tan x$ is defined.

50. Derive (9) from the fact that $\tan x = \dfrac{\sin x}{\cos x}.$

51. Derive (10).   **52.** Derive (11).   **53.** Derive (12).

54. Assuming that you know $\dfrac{d}{dx} \sin u = \cos u \dfrac{du}{dx}$, find $\dfrac{d}{dx} \cos x$ from the relation $\cos x = 1 - 2 \sin^2 (\frac{1}{2}x).$

55. Show that $\sin x + \cos x > 1$ for $0 < x < \frac{1}{2}\pi.$

56. Show that $12\pi \sin x > (24 + \pi^2)x - 4x^3$ for $0 < x < \frac{1}{2}\pi.$

57. Use the method, but not the result, of Example (c) to show that $\cos x > 1 - \dfrac{2x}{\pi}$ for $0 < x < \frac{1}{2}\pi.$

90. *Graphs of Trigonometric Functions*

To draw the graph of the function

$$y = \sin x,$$

we may proceed as in § 61. On account of the periodicity of the sine function, it will be sufficient to determine the appearance of the curve in the interval from $x = 0$ to $x = 2\pi$; the remainder of the curve must consist of repetitions of this portion.

1. When $x = 0$, $y = 0$; when $y = 0$, $x = 0$, π, 2π.
2. Evidently, large values of x need not be considered.
3. $y' = \cos x$: hence the critical points are $(\frac{1}{2}\pi, 1)$, a maximum, and $(\frac{3}{2}\pi, -1)$, a minimum.
4. $y'' = -\sin x$: the points of inflection are $(0, 0)$, with slope 1, $(\pi, 0)$, with slope -1, and $(2\pi, 0)$, with slope 1.

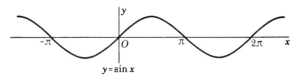

$y = \sin x$

Figure 115

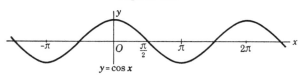

$y = \cos x$

Figure 116

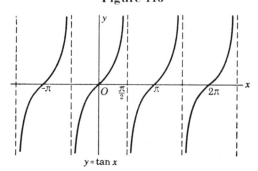

$y = \tan x$

Figure 117

The curve consists of an infinite succession of waves along the x-axis, as shown in Figure 115.

The graphs of the cosine and tangent are shown in Figures 116 and 117; they are obtained in a similar way, except that in the case of the tangent the points of discontinuity $x = \pm(n + \frac{1}{2})\pi$ must be specially investigated in addition to the usual discussion.

EXERCISES

Trace the curve in each exercise.

1. $y = \sec x$.
2. $y = \csc x$.
3. $y = \cot x$.
4. $y = \frac{1}{2}\cos 2x$.
5. $y = -2 \sin \frac{1}{2}x$.
6. $y = 3 \tan 2x$.
7. $y = 4 \cos \frac{1}{3}x$.
8. $y = -\frac{1}{2}\sin 4x$.
9. $x = \cos^2 t$.
10. $x = \sin^2 t$.
11. $z = \sin^2 3x$.
12. $z = \cos^2 \frac{1}{2}x$.
13. $y = \sin^3 x$.
14. $y = \cos^3 x$.
15. $y = \sin^2 x + \sin x$.
16. $y = \cos^2 x - \cos x$.
17. $u = 2 \sin v - 1$.
18. $u = 1 - 3 \cos 2v$.
19. $y = \sin 2x - 2 \cos x + 2$.
20. $y = \cos x - \frac{1}{2}\sin 2x - 1$.
21. $y = 2 \cos^3 x - 3 \sin x$.
22. $y = x - \sin x$.
23. $y = \cos 2x - x$.
24. $y = 2x + \cos x$.
25. $y = \dfrac{\cos x}{x}$.
26. $y = \dfrac{\sin x}{x}$.
27. $y = \dfrac{\tan x}{x}$.
28. $y = x - \tan x$.

91. *Maxima and Minima*

Many problems requiring the determination of maxima and minima may be solved very neatly by expressing the function in terms of trigonometric functions of an angle.

Example (a).   Find the shape of the largest rectangle that can be inscribed in a given circle.   [Example (a), § 67.]

The area of the rectangle is

$$A = 4xy.$$

But $x = a \cos \theta, \qquad y = a \sin \theta,$

$$A = 4a^2 \cos \theta \sin \theta = 2a^2 \sin 2\theta:$$

$$\frac{dA}{d\theta} = 4a^2 \cos 2\theta = 0, \qquad \theta = \frac{\pi}{4},$$

$$y = x.$$

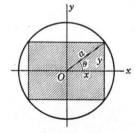

Figure 118

Example (b).   A man in a rowboat 6 mi. from shore desires to reach a point on the shore at a distance of 10 mi. from his present position.   If he can walk 4 mi. per hr. and row 2 mi. per hr., in what direction should he row in order to reach his destination in the shortest possible time?   [Example (c), § 67.]

The time required is

$$T = \frac{y}{2} + \frac{8 - x}{4}.$$

Since

$$y = 6 \sec \theta, \qquad x = 6 \tan \theta,$$

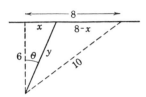

$$T = \frac{6 \sec \theta}{2} + \frac{8 - 6 \tan \theta}{4}$$

$$= 3 \sec \theta + 2 - \tfrac{3}{2} \tan \theta,$$

$$\frac{dT}{d\theta} = 3 \sec \theta \tan \theta - \tfrac{3}{2} \sec^2 \theta$$

$$= 3 \sec^2 \theta \,(\sin \theta - \tfrac{1}{2}) = 0,$$

$$\theta = 30°.$$

Figure 119

EXERCISES

Solve the following exercises by making use of trigonometric functions.

1. Find the shape of the rectangle of maximum perimeter inscribed in a circle.
Ans. A square.

2. A cylinder is inscribed in a given sphere. Find the shape of the cylinder if its convex surface area is a maximum. *Ans.* Diameter = height.

3. Find the weight of the heaviest circular cylinder that can be cut from a 16-lb. shot. *Ans.* 9.2 lb.

4. The stiffness of a rectangular beam is proportional to the breadth and the cube of the depth. Find the shape of the stiffest beam that can be cut from a log of given size. *Ans.* Depth = $\sqrt{3}$ × breadth.

5. The strength of a rectangular beam is proportional to the breadth and the square of the depth. Find the shape of the strongest beam that can be cut from a log of given size. *Ans.* Depth = $\sqrt{2}$ × breadth.

6. A trapezoidal gutter is to be made from a strip of metal 22 in. wide by bending up the edges. If the base is 14 in. wide, what width across the top gives the greatest carrying capacity? *Ans.* 16 in.

7. Solve Ex. 6, if the strip is 13 in. wide and the base width 7 in. *Ans.* 9 in.

8. Solve Ex. 6, if the strip is 9 in. wide and the base width 3 in. *Ans.* 6 in.

9. Solve Ex. 6, if the strip width is w and the base width b.
Ans. $\tfrac{1}{2}[b + \sqrt{b^2 + 2(w - b)^2}]$.

10. Find the conical tent of largest volume that can be constructed having a given slant height. *Ans.* $r = \sqrt{\tfrac{2}{3}}\, s$.

11. A gutter having a triangular cross-section is to be made by bending a strip of tin in the middle. Find the angle between the sides when the carrying capacity is a maximum. *Ans.* 90°.

12. Find the altitude of the circular cone of maximum convex surface area inscribed in a sphere of radius a. *Ans.* Altitude = $\tfrac{4}{3}a$.

13. A sphere is cut in the shape of a circular cone. How much of the material can be saved? *Ans.* About 30%.

14. A wall 8 ft. high is 12 ft. from a house. Find the length of the shortest ladder that will reach the house when one end rests on the ground outside the wall.

Ans. 28.1 ft.

15. Solve Ex. 14, if the height of the wall is b and its distance from the house is c.

Ans. $(b^{\frac{2}{3}} + c^{\frac{2}{3}})^{\frac{3}{2}}$.

16. Solve Ex. 53, page 117.

17. A man in a motorboat at A receives a message at noon, calling him to B. A bus making 40 mi. per hr. leaves C, bound for B, at 1:00 P.M. If $AC = 30$ mi., what must be the speed of the boat, to enable the man to catch the bus?   *Ans.* 24 mi. per hr.

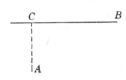

Figure 120

18. Solve Ex. 17, if $AC = 20$ mi., and the bus makes 50 mi. per hr., leaving C at 12:18 P.M., bound for B.

Ans. 40 mi. per hr.

19. A pole 27 ft. long is carried horizontally along a corridor 8 ft. wide and into a second corridor at right angles to the first. How wide must the second corridor be?   *Ans.* $5\sqrt{5} = 11.18$ ft.

20. Solve Ex. 19, if the pole is of length L and the first corridor is of width C.

Ans. $(L^{\frac{2}{3}} - C^{\frac{2}{3}})^{\frac{3}{2}}$.

21. A sphere of radius a is dropped into a conical vessel full of water. Find the altitude of the smallest cone that will permit the sphere to be entirely submerged.

Ans. Altitude $= 4a$.

22. A sphere is cut in the form of a right pyramid with a square base. How much of the material can be saved?   *Ans.* 19%.

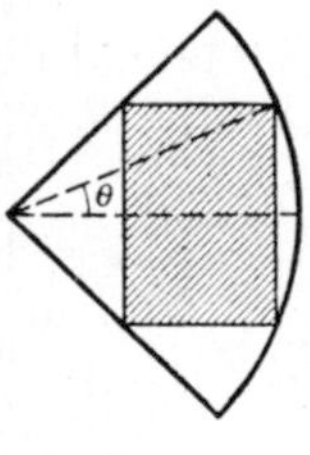

23. Find the area of the largest rectangle that can be cut from a circular quadrant as in Figure 121.

Ans. $\theta = 22\frac{1}{2}°$; $A = (\sqrt{2} - 1)a^2 = 0.414a^2$.

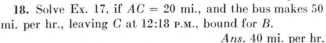

24. In Ex. 23, draw the graph of A as a function of θ, indicating the portion of the curve that has a meaning.

25. A corridor 4 ft. wide opens into a room 100 ft. long and 32 ft. wide, at the middle of one side. Find the length of the longest thin rod that can be carried horizontally into the room.

Ans. $20\sqrt{5} = 44.72$ ft.

Figure 121

26. Solve Ex. 25 if the room is 56 ft. long.   *Ans.* 43.86 ft.

Inverse Trigonometric Functions

92. *Inverse Functions*

Consider an equation solved explicitly for x in terms of y:

$$(1) \qquad\qquad x = \varphi(y).$$

Except where φ is independent of y, equation (1) will also define y as a function of x:

$$(2) \qquad\qquad y = f(x).$$

When two functions $\varphi(y)$ and $f(x)$ are connected in this way, each is said to be the inverse of the other. Note that here "inverse" does not mean "reciprocal."

If $\varphi(y)$ is an algebraic function, $f(x)$ can sometimes be explicitly expressed in algebraic symbols. In fact, nothing is new in such cases except the name "inverse function," for the situation has been familiar to us since the days of elementary algebra. For example,

(a) $\qquad\qquad$ If $x = 2y + 4$, then $y = \frac{1}{2}x - 2$;

(b) $\qquad\qquad$ If $x = y^2$, $\qquad$ then $y = \pm \sqrt{x}$.

93. *Inverse Trigonometric Functions*

Let y be defined as a function of x by the equation

$$\sin y = x;$$

i.e., x is the sine of y, or what is exactly the same thing, y *is an angle whose sine is x.* When this equation is solved for y, a new kind of function, neither algebraic nor trigonometric, is obtained; we must therefore devise a new symbol to denote this function.

An *angle whose sine is x* is represented by the symbol arcsin x, or sin⁻¹ x:

$$y = \textbf{arcsin } x \quad \textit{if} \quad \sin y = x.$$

That is, the function arcsin x is the *inverse* of the sine, by the definition of § 92.

Similarly, we lay down the definitions

$$y = \textbf{arccos } x \quad \textit{if} \quad \cos y = x;$$
$$y = \textbf{arctan } x \quad \textit{if} \quad \tan y = x;$$

etc.   The new functions here defined are called *inverse trigonometric functions.*
The graph of the inverse function

(1) $y = \arcsin x$

is obtained by interchanging the roles of x and y in the graph (Figure 115, page 166) of $y = \sin x$.   Thus, the graph of (1) can be found by reflecting the graph of

(2) $y = \sin x$

in the line $y = x$.   The curve (1) consists of an infinite succession of waves along the y-axis, as shown in Figure 122.

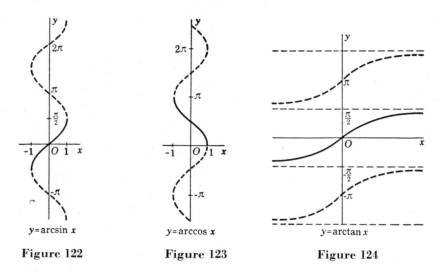

$y=$arcsin x	$y=$arccos x	$y=$arctan x
Figure 122	**Figure 123**	**Figure 124**

The curves $y = $ arccos x, $y = $ arctan x appear in Figures 123, 124.   They are obtained, of course, by reflection of Figures 116, 117.

94. *Restriction to a Single Branch*

When either the given or the inverse function is one-valued, it by no means follows that the other is one-valued.   Both were so in (*a*), § 92, but in (*b*), the given function was one-valued, the inverse two-valued; and in fact, examples are easily found to illustrate any sort of combination.

When an angle is given, its sine, cosine, etc., are uniquely determined; i.e., the trigonometric functions are one-valued. On the other hand, if the sine is given, the angle is not uniquely determined; for instance, there are infinitely many angles whose sine is $\frac{1}{2}$, viz. $\frac{\pi}{6}, \frac{5\pi}{6}$, or an angle differing from one of these by any multiple of 2π. The inverse trigonometric functions are *infinitely many-valued*; corresponding to a given value of the variable there are infinitely many values of the function. Geometrically, this means that a line $x = k$, if it meets the curve at all, meets it in an infinite number of points; the truth of this statement is evident from a glance at Figures 122–124.

We shall hereafter, unless the contrary is noted, *confine our attention to a single branch* of each of these functions; the branch chosen is the one drawn full in each figure. In order to distinguish between the single-valued function and its infinitely many-valued counterpart, we use a *capital letter to denote the single-valued function.* Thus in our future work the three principal inverse trigonometric functions are subject to the following restrictions:

(1) $$-\frac{\pi}{2} \leqq \textbf{Arcsin } x \leqq \frac{\pi}{2};$$

(2) $$0 \leqq \textbf{Arccos } x \leqq \pi;$$

(3) $$-\frac{\pi}{2} < \textbf{Arctan } x < \frac{\pi}{2}.$$

With (1) in effect, we have now, uniquely,

$$\text{Arcsin } \frac{1}{2} = \frac{\pi}{6}.$$

Any other angle whose sine is $\frac{1}{2}$ is readily expressed in terms of Arcsin $\frac{1}{2}$:

$$\frac{5\pi}{6} = \pi - \text{Arcsin } \frac{1}{2}; \qquad \frac{13\pi}{6} = 2\pi + \text{Arcsin } \frac{1}{2}; \text{ etc.}$$

Also,

$$\text{Arcsin } (-1) = -\frac{\pi}{2}, \qquad \text{not } \frac{3\pi}{2};$$

$$\text{Arccos } \frac{1}{2} \sqrt{2} = \frac{\pi}{4}, \qquad \text{Arccos } \left(-\frac{1}{2} \sqrt{2}\right) = \frac{3\pi}{4};$$

$$\text{Arctan } (-1) = -\frac{\pi}{4}, \qquad \text{not } \frac{3\pi}{4}.$$

The student must note these conventions carefully, since failure to observe them leads to frequent errors.*

* It must be clearly understood that in calculus, just as surely as in trigonometry, there are infinitely many angles corresponding to a given value of the sine. We have merely agreed that the symbol Arcsin x shall denote *that one* of these angles (there will always be one and only one) that lies in the interval between $-\frac{\pi}{2}$ and $\frac{\pi}{2}$.

In dealing with the other three functions, we shall restrict ourselves to *positive values of x.* The conventions are as follows:

$$0 \leq \text{Arccot } x \leq \frac{\pi}{2}, \qquad x \geq 0;$$

$$0 \leq \text{Arcsec } x \leq \frac{\pi}{2}, \qquad x \geq 1;$$

$$0 \leq \text{Arccsc } x \leq \frac{\pi}{2}, \qquad x \geq 1.$$

These last three functions are distinctly troublesome when x is negative. For instance, it will appear presently that

(4) $$\text{Arccot } x = \frac{\pi}{2} - \text{Arctan } x, \qquad x > 0;$$

also that

(5) $$\text{Arccot } x = \text{Arctan } \frac{1}{x}, \qquad x > 0.$$

These are useful formulas to have; yet no convention can be laid down under which both formulas are true when x is negative. (For instance, try $x = -1$.) Thus our agreement to consider these functions only for positive x makes greatly for simplicity.*

This book will make very little use of the three minor functions, chiefly because of the difficulty just mentioned.

95. *Elementary Properties*

Discovery of the elementary properties of the inverse trigonometric functions will be left largely to the student. However, since this new language may be troublesome at first, numerous examples are provided.

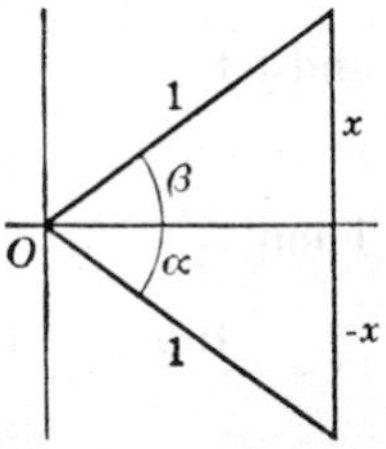

Example (a). Prove that

$$\text{Arcsin } (-x) = - \text{Arcsin } x.$$

Put

$$\alpha = \text{Arcsin } (-x), \qquad \beta = \text{Arcsin } x,$$

so that

$$\sin \alpha = -x, \qquad \sin \beta = x.$$

Figure 125

By (1), § 94, both α and β are acute angles, one negative, the other positive,

---

* The restriction is not serious. Of course it is possible to avoid the three minor functions completely; on the rather infrequent occasions when it seems simpler to use them, x is usually positive. If they are to be used when x is negative, great care must be exercised. Much confusion exists; many standard handbooks contain formulas that are invalid for negative x, with no warning given.

so that they may be represented as in Figure 125.   The truth of the formula appears from a glance at the figure.

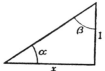

Figure 126

Example (b).   Prove that

$$\text{Arccot } x = \tfrac{1}{2}\pi - \text{Arctan } x.$$

Put

$$\alpha = \text{Arccot } x, \qquad \beta = \text{Arctan } x.$$

By § 94, both are positive acute and may be represented as in Figure 126.   Then α and β are complementary angles: $\alpha + \beta = \tfrac{1}{2}\pi$.

Example (c).   Prove that

$$\sin (2 \text{ Arcsin } x) = 2x \sqrt{1 - x^2}.$$

Put

$$\alpha = \text{Arcsin } x,$$

whence

$$\sin \alpha = x.$$

By trigonometry,

$$\cos \alpha = \pm \sqrt{1 - \sin^2 \alpha} = \pm \sqrt{1 - x^2}.$$

But since (§ 94) α lies in either the first or the fourth quadrant, the cosine is positive and we have definitely

(1)
$$\cos \alpha = \sqrt{1 - x^2},$$
$$\sin (2 \text{ Arcsin } x) = \sin 2\alpha = 2 \sin \alpha \cos \alpha = 2x \sqrt{1 - x^2}.$$

Example (d).   Simplify the expression (Arctan 2 + Arctan 3).
Put

$$\alpha = \text{Arctan } 2, \qquad \beta = \text{Arctan } 3,$$

from which

$$\tan \alpha = 2, \qquad \tan \beta = 3,$$

and let

$$\gamma = \text{Arctan } 2 + \text{Arctan } 3 = \alpha + \beta.$$

Then

$$\tan \gamma = \tan (\alpha + \beta) = \frac{\tan \alpha + \tan \beta}{1 - \tan \alpha \tan \beta}$$
$$= \frac{2 + 3}{1 - 2 \cdot 3} = -1.$$

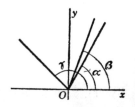

Figure 127

Since the sum of two positive acute angles must lie in either the first or the second quadrant,

$$\text{Arctan } 2 + \text{Arctan } 3 = \tfrac{3}{4}\pi.$$

This example, typical of many similar situations, shows that when $\tan \gamma = -1$, we must not hastily conclude that $\gamma = -\tfrac{1}{4}\pi$.

Example (e).   Simplify the equation

(2)   Arcsin x + Arcsin y = $\frac{1}{3}\pi$.

Put

(3) α = Arcsin x, β = Arcsin y,

so that (2) becomes

(4) $\alpha + \beta = \frac{1}{3}\pi$.

From (3),

$$\sin \alpha = x, \qquad \cos \alpha = \sqrt{1 - x^2};$$
$$\sin \beta = y, \qquad \cos \beta = \sqrt{1 - y^2}.$$

It can be shown by trial (see Ex. 48 below) that in simplifying the sum of two Arcsines or two Arccosines, the best procedure is to take the cosine of the sum.   (To simplify the sum of an Arcsine and an Arccosine, it is best to take the sine of the sum.)   Hence, taking the cosine of both members of (4), we get

$$\sqrt{1 - x^2} \cdot \sqrt{1 - y^2} - xy = \frac{1}{2},$$

or, after isolating the radical, squaring, and simplifying,

(5) $4x^2 + 4xy + 4y^2 = 3.$

Thus, from equation (2), equation (5) follows.   Therefore every point on the curve (2) must lie on the curve (5), but by no means do the coordinates of all points on the locus (5) need to satisfy equation (2).   Equation (2) consists of only a part of the curve (5).   For instance, the point $(-\frac{1}{2}, -\frac{1}{2})$ is on the curve; its coordinates satisfy equation (5).   Because of the principal value convention,

$$\text{Arcsin}\left(-\frac{1}{2}\right) = -\frac{\pi}{6},$$

so that, for $x = y = -\frac{1}{2}$, the left member of equation (2) becomes

$$-\frac{\pi}{6} - \frac{\pi}{6} = -\frac{\pi}{3} \neq \frac{\pi}{3}.$$

The coordinates of the point $(-\frac{1}{2}, -\frac{1}{2})$ satisfy equation (5), but not equation (2).   Similar remarks apply to Exs. 42–47 below.

EXERCISES

1. Find Arcsin $(\frac{1}{2}\sqrt{3})$, Arcsin $(-\frac{1}{2}\sqrt{3})$, Arcsin $(-\frac{1}{2}\sqrt{2})$, Arcsin (1).
2. Find Arctan $(\frac{1}{3}\sqrt{3})$, Arctan $(-\frac{1}{3}\sqrt{3})$, Arctan $(-\sqrt{3})$.
3. Find Arccos (-1), Arccos (0), Arccos $(-\frac{1}{2}\sqrt{3})$, Arccos $(\frac{1}{2})$.
4. Find Arcsec $(\sqrt{2})$, Arccot $(\sqrt{3})$, Arcsec 2.

Establish the formulas in Exs. 5–22.

5. $\text{Arctan}\,(-x) = -\,\text{Arctan}\,x.$ **6.** $\text{Arccos}\,(-x) = \pi - \text{Arccos}\,x.$

7. $\text{Arccos}\,x = \tfrac{1}{2}\pi - \text{Arcsin}\,x.$ **8.** $\text{Arctan}\,\dfrac{1}{x} = \text{Arccot}\,x.$

9. $\text{Arcsin}\,\dfrac{1}{x} = \text{Arccsc}\,x.$ **10.** $\text{Arccos}\,\dfrac{1}{x} = \text{Arcsec}\,x.$

11. $\text{Arcsin}\,\dfrac{x}{\sqrt{1 + x^2}} = \text{Arctan}\,x.$ **12.** $\text{Arctan}\,\dfrac{x}{\sqrt{1 - x^2}} = \text{Arcsin}\,x.$

13. $\sin\,(\text{Arccos}\,x) = \sqrt{1 - x^2}.$ **14.** $\cos\,(\text{Arctan}\,x) = \dfrac{1}{\sqrt{1 + x^2}}.$

15. $\tan\,(2\,\text{Arctan}\,x) = \dfrac{2x}{1 - x^2}.$ **16.** $\sin\,(2\,\text{Arccos}\,x) = 2x\,\sqrt{1 - x^2}.$

17. $\cos\,(2\,\text{Arccos}\,x) = 2x^2 - 1.$ **18.** $\cos\,(2\,\text{Arctan}\,x) = \dfrac{1 - x^2}{1 + x^2}.$

19. $\sin\,(2\,\text{Arctan}\,x) = \dfrac{2x}{1 + x^2}.$ **20.** $\cos\,(2\,\text{Arcsin}\,x) = 1 - 2x^2.$

21. $\tan\,(2\,\text{Arcsin}\,x) = \dfrac{2x\,\sqrt{1 - x^2}}{1 - 2x^2}.$ **22.** $\tan\,(2\,\text{Arccos}\,x) = \dfrac{2x\,\sqrt{1 - x^2}}{2x^2 - 1}.$

In Exs. 23–28, evaluate the given expression.

23. $\tan\,(\text{Arctan}\,\tfrac{2}{3} - \text{Arctan}\,\tfrac{1}{5}).$ *Ans.* $\tfrac{7}{17}.$
24. $\cos\,(\text{Arcsin}\,\tfrac{5}{13} + \text{Arccos}\,\tfrac{4}{5}).$ *Ans.* $\tfrac{33}{65}.$
25. $\cos\,(\text{Arctan}\,\tfrac{12}{5} - \text{Arcsin}\,\tfrac{3}{5}).$ *Ans.* $\tfrac{56}{65}.$
26. $\tan\,(\text{Arcsin}\,\tfrac{4}{5} - \text{Arctan}\,2).$ *Ans.* $\dfrac{-2}{11}.$

27. $\sin\,(\text{Arctan}\,\tfrac{6}{7} - \text{Arctan}\,\tfrac{1}{4}).$ *Ans.* $\dfrac{\sqrt{5}}{5}.$

28. $\sin\,(\text{Arctan}\,\tfrac{2}{3} + \text{Arctan}\,\tfrac{4}{7}).$ *Ans.* $\dfrac{2\,\sqrt{5}}{5}.$

In Exs. 29–41, simplify the given expression, in the sense of Example (d) above.

29. $\text{Arctan}\,\tfrac{3}{8} + \text{Arctan}\,\tfrac{8}{3}.$ *Ans.* $\tfrac{1}{2}\pi.$
30. $\text{Arcsin}\,\tfrac{5}{13} + \text{Arcsin}\,\tfrac{12}{13}.$ *Ans.* $\tfrac{1}{2}\pi.$
31. $\text{Arccos}\,\tfrac{4}{5} + \text{Arctan}\,\tfrac{4}{3}.$ *Ans.* $\tfrac{1}{2}\pi.$
32. $\text{Arctan}\,\tfrac{1}{3} + \text{Arctan}\,\tfrac{1}{2}.$ *Ans.* $\tfrac{1}{4}\pi.$
33. $\text{Arctan}\,\tfrac{5}{12} + \text{Arcsin}\,\tfrac{12}{13}.$ *Ans.* $\tfrac{1}{2}\pi.$
34. $\text{Arctan}\,\tfrac{1}{13} + \text{Arctan}\,\tfrac{1}{4}.$ *Ans.* $\text{Arctan}\,\tfrac{1}{3}.$
35. $\text{Arctan}\,\tfrac{1}{2} - \text{Arctan}\,\tfrac{1}{3}.$ *Ans.* $\text{Arctan}\,\tfrac{1}{7}.$
36. $2\,\text{Arctan}\,2 + \text{Arctan}\,\tfrac{4}{3}.$ *Ans.* $\pi.$
37. $2\,\text{Arctan}\,\tfrac{1}{2} - \text{Arctan}\,\tfrac{4}{3}.$ *Ans.* $0.$
38. $2\,\text{Arctan}\,\tfrac{1}{2} - \text{Arctan}\,\tfrac{1}{7}.$ *Ans.* $\tfrac{1}{4}\pi.$
39. $\text{Arctan}\,\tfrac{4}{3} - 2\,\text{Arctan}\,3.$ *Ans.* $-\tfrac{1}{2}\pi.$

40. Arctan 2 + Arctan 4 + Arctan 13. $\qquad$ *Ans.* $\frac{5}{4}\pi$.
41. Arctan $\frac{1}{3}$ + Arctan $\frac{4}{3}$ − Arctan $\frac{1}{2}$. $\qquad$ *Ans.* $\frac{1}{4}\pi$.

In Exs. 42–47, change the equation to algebraic form, with the realization that the new form may contain points not satisfying the original equation. Point out what steps in your procedure may introduce extraneous portions of the curve.

42. Arcsin x + Arcsin y = $\frac{1}{2}\pi$. $\qquad$ *Ans.* $x^2 + y^2 = 1$.
43. Arctan x + Arctan y = $\frac{1}{4}\pi$. $\qquad$ *Ans.* $xy + x + y = 1$.
44. Arccos x + Arcsin y = $\frac{1}{6}\pi$. $\qquad$ *Ans.* $4x^2 - 4xy + 4y^2 = 3$.
45. 2 Arcsin x + Arcsin y = π. $\qquad$ *Ans.* $y^2 = 4x^2(1 - x^2)$.
46. Arctan x − 2 Arctan y = π. $\qquad$ *Ans.* $xy^2 = x - 2y$.
47. Arctan x + Arctan y = $\frac{1}{2}\pi$. $\qquad$ *Ans.* $xy = 1$.
48. In Example (*e*) § 95, simplify by taking the sine of both members.

96. *Derivatives of the Inverse Trigonometric Functions*

To differentiate the function

$$y = \text{Arcsin } x,$$

let us pass to the form

(1) $\qquad$ $\sin y = x.$

Equation (1) yields

$$\cos y \, \frac{dy}{dx} = 1,$$

$$\frac{dy}{dx} = \frac{1}{\cos y}.$$

Since $\sin y = x$, and $-\frac{1}{2}\pi \leq y \leq \frac{1}{2}\pi$, it follows that

$$\cos y = \sqrt{1 - \sin^2 y} = \sqrt{1 - x^2},$$

so that

$$\frac{d}{dx} \text{Arcsin } x = \frac{1}{\sqrt{1 - x^2}}.$$

Differentiation of the other functions may be left to the reader. If u is any function of x, the general formulas for the three principal functions are:

(13) $\qquad$ $\dfrac{d}{dx} \text{Arcsin } u = \dfrac{\dfrac{du}{dx}}{\sqrt{1 - u^2}};$

(14) $\qquad$ $\dfrac{d}{dx} \text{Arccos } u = - \dfrac{\dfrac{du}{dx}}{\sqrt{1 - u^2}};$

(15) $\qquad$ $\dfrac{d}{dx} \text{Arctan } u = \dfrac{\dfrac{du}{dx}}{1 + u^2}.$

Example (a).   If $\theta = \text{Arctan } \frac{1}{3}t$,

$$\frac{d\theta}{dt} = \frac{\frac{1}{3}}{1 + \frac{1}{9}t^2} = \frac{3}{9 + t^2}.$$

Example (b).   If $y = \text{Arcsin } (2 \cos \theta)$,

$$\frac{dy}{d\theta} = \frac{-2 \sin \theta}{\sqrt{1 - 4 \cos^2 \theta}}.$$

Example (c).   A man on a wharf 20 ft. above the water pulls in a rope, to which a boat is tied, at the rate of 4 ft. per sec.   Find the rate of change of the angle θ (Figure 128) when there is 25 ft. of rope out.

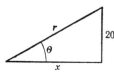

Figure 128

By the figure,

$$\theta = \text{Arcsin } \frac{20}{r},$$

$$\frac{d\theta}{dt} = \frac{-\frac{20}{r^2}\frac{dr}{dt}}{\sqrt{1 - \frac{400}{r^2}}} = \frac{-20\frac{dr}{dt}}{r\sqrt{r^2 - 400}}.$$

We have given

$$\frac{dr}{dt} = -4,$$

so that when $r = 25$,

$$\frac{d\theta}{dt} = \frac{16}{75} \text{ rad. per sec.}$$

EXERCISES

In Exs. 1–28, find the first derivative of the function given.

1. $y = \text{Arcsin } 5x$.   *Ans.* $y' = \dfrac{5}{\sqrt{1 - 25x^2}}$.

2. $u = \text{Arctan } \frac{1}{2}t$.   *Ans.* $u' = \dfrac{2}{4 + t^2}$.

3. $\theta = \text{Arctan } a\varphi$.   *Ans.* $\dfrac{d\theta}{d\varphi} = \dfrac{a}{1 + a^2\varphi^2}$.

4. $f(y) = \text{Arcsin } y^2$.   *Ans.* $f'(y) = \dfrac{2y}{\sqrt{1 - y^4}}$.

5. $x = \text{Arcsin } (1 - 2v)$.   *Ans.* $\dfrac{dx}{dv} = \dfrac{-1}{\sqrt{v - v^2}}$.

6. $y = \text{Arctan } (1 + 2x)$.   *Ans.* $y' = \dfrac{1}{1 + 2x + 2x^2}$.

7. $x = \text{Arcsin } \sqrt{t}$.   **8.** $\theta = \text{Arccos } 2t$.

9. $y = \text{Arctan } t^3$.   **10.** $y = (\text{Arctan } t)^3$.

11. $x = \text{Arccos } \sqrt{1 - y}$.

12. $z = x \text{ Arctan } 3x$.

13. $u = x^2 \text{ Arcsin } x$.

14. $w = \dfrac{\text{Arcsin } \alpha}{\alpha}$.

15. $y = \dfrac{\text{Arctan } 2x}{x}$.

16. $y = \dfrac{\text{Arcsin } x^2}{x^2}$.

17. $y = (1 + x^2) \text{ Arctan } x - x$.

Ans. $y' = 2x \text{ Arctan } x$.

18. $y = \text{Arctan}^2 (x^3)$.

Ans. $y' = \dfrac{6x^2 \text{ Arctan } (x^3)}{1 + x^6}$.

19. $y = \sqrt{\text{Arcsin } x}$.

Ans. $\dfrac{dy}{dx} = \dfrac{1}{2 \sqrt{1 - x^2} \cdot \sqrt{\text{Arcsin } x}}$.

20. $y = \text{Arcsin } \sqrt{1 + \dfrac{1}{x}}$. (Note that x must be negative, so that in simplifying

the answer we must use $\sqrt{x^2} = -x$.)

Ans. $\dfrac{dy}{dx} = \dfrac{1}{2x \sqrt{-x - 1}}$.

21. $y = (x - 1) \sqrt{2x - x^2} + \text{Arcsin } (x - 1)$.

Ans. $y' = 2 \sqrt{2x - x^2}$.

22. $y = 2 \text{ Arcsin } \sqrt{\dfrac{x}{2}}$.

Ans. $y' = \dfrac{1}{\sqrt{2x - x^2}}$.

23. $y = x \text{ Arcsin } x + \sqrt{1 - x^2}$.

Ans. $y' = \text{Arcsin } x$.

24. $y = \dfrac{x}{\sqrt{a^2 - x^2}} - \text{Arcsin } \dfrac{x}{a}$.

Ans. $\dfrac{dy}{dx} = \dfrac{x^2}{(a^2 - x^2)^{\frac{3}{2}}}$.

25. $y = a^2 \text{ Arcsin } \dfrac{x}{a} - x \sqrt{a^2 - x^2}$.

Ans. $\dfrac{dy}{dx} = \dfrac{2x^2}{\sqrt{a^2 - x^2}}$.

26. $y = \text{Arcsin } \dfrac{x}{a} + \dfrac{\sqrt{a^2 - x^2}}{x}$.

Ans. $y' = -\dfrac{\sqrt{a^2 - x^2}}{x^2}$.

27. $y = \text{Arcsin } \dfrac{a}{x}$. *Ans.* $\dfrac{dy}{dx} = \dfrac{-a}{x \sqrt{x^2 - a^2}}$, $x > a$; $\dfrac{dy}{dx} = \dfrac{a}{x \sqrt{x^2 - a^2}}$, $x < -a$.

28. $y = \text{Arctan } \dfrac{a}{x}$.

Ans. $y' = \dfrac{-a}{a^2 + x^2}$.

29. Derive (15) from (13). (Ex. 11, page 176).

30. Derive the formula $\dfrac{d}{dx} \text{Arccot } u = \dfrac{-\dfrac{du}{dx}}{1 + u^2}$, $u > 0$.

31. Derive the formula $\dfrac{d}{dx} \text{Arcsec } u = \dfrac{\dfrac{du}{dx}}{u \sqrt{u^2 - 1}}$, $u > 1$.

32. Derive the formula $\dfrac{d}{dx} \text{Arccsc } u = \dfrac{-\dfrac{du}{dx}}{u \sqrt{u^2 - 1}}$, $u > 1$.

33. If $\tan \theta = \dfrac{y}{x}$, where x and y are functions of t, show that

$$\frac{d\theta}{dt} = \frac{x\,\dfrac{dy}{dt} - y\,\dfrac{dx}{dt}}{x^2 + y^2}.$$

34. A ladder 13 ft. long leans against a vertical wall. If the top slides down at 3 ft. per sec., how fast is the angle of elevation of the ladder decreasing, when the lower end is 9 ft. from the wall?   *Ans.* $\frac{1}{3}$ rad. per sec.

35. A ship, moving 8 mi. per hr., sails north for 30 min., then turns east. If a searchlight at the point of departure follows the ship, how fast is the light rotating 2 hr. after the start?   *Ans.* 0.2 rad. per hr.

36. A balloon, leaving the ground 80 ft. from an observer, rises 10 ft. per sec. How fast is the angle of elevation of the line of sight increasing, after 6 sec.?

Ans. $\frac{2}{25}$ rad. per sec.

37. The base of a right triangle grows 2 ft. per sec., the altitude grows 4 ft. per sec. If the base and altitude are originally 10 ft. and 6 ft., respectively, find the time-rate of change of the base angle, when that angle is 45°.   *Ans.* $\frac{1}{14}$ rad. per sec.

38. Prove that an angle is a maximum or minimum when its tangent is a maximum or minimum, and conversely. (Let $\theta = \text{Arctan } m$, where m is a function of x; compare the conditions for extreme θ and extreme m.)

39. Prove that an acute angle is a maximum or minimum when its sine is a maximum or minimum, and conversely.

40. Prove that an acute angle is a maximum or minimum when its cosine is a minimum or maximum, and conversely.

41. A rowboat is pushed off from a beach at 8 ft. per sec. A man on shore holds a rope, tied to the boat, at a height of 4 ft. Find how fast the angle of elevation of the rope is decreasing, after 1 sec.   *Ans.* $\frac{2}{5}$ rad. per sec.

42. A kite is 60 ft. high, with 100 ft. of cord out. If the kite is moving horizontally 4 mi. per hr. directly away from the boy flying it, find the rate of change of the angle of elevation of the cord.   *Ans.* $-\frac{22}{625}$ rad. per sec.

43. A ship, moving at 8 mi. per hr., sails E. for 2 hr., then turns N. 30° W. A searchlight, placed at the starting point, follows the ship. Find how fast the light is rotating, (a) 3 hr. after the start; (b) just after the turn.

Ans. (a) $\frac{1}{3}\sqrt{3}$ rad. per hr.; (b) $\frac{1}{4}\sqrt{3}$ rad. per hr.

44. In Ex. 43, find when the light rotates most rapidly.   *Ans.* After 3 hr.

45. Prove that the results in Exs. 43–44 are independent of the speed of the ship.

46. A ship, moving at 10 mi. per hr., sails E. for 2 hr., then turns N. 30° E. A searchlight, placed at the starting point, follows the ship. Find how fast the light is rotating (a) 4 hr. after the start; (b) just after the turn.

Ans. (a) $\frac{1}{12}\sqrt{3}$ rad. per hr.; (b) $\frac{1}{4}\sqrt{3}$ rad. per hr.

47. Using the methods of § 70, show that in Ex. 46 the maximum rate of rotation of the light occurs at the time the ship turns.

48. The lower edge of a picture is a feet, the upper edge b feet, above the eye of an observer. At what horizontal distance should he stand, if the vertical angle subtended by the picture is to be greatest?   *Ans.* $\sqrt{ab}$ feet.

Exponential and Logarithmic Functions

97. The Exponential Function

The number $a^n (a > 0)$ is defined in algebra for all rational values of n. In calculus it becomes necessary to attach a meaning to the function

$$y = a^x, \qquad a > 0$$

as x varies continuously.

Let x_0 be any irrational number. Then a^{x_0} is defined as the limit of a^x, where x is rational, as x approaches x_0. That the limit exists is proved in more advanced texts. The function

$$y = a^x, \qquad a > 0,$$

called the *exponential function*, thus becomes defined for all values of x. It is one-valued and continuous and obeys the laws of exponents:

(1) $$a^x \cdot a^t = a^{x+t},$$
(2) $$(a^x)^t = a^{xt}.$$

The exponential function is positive for all values of x.

98. The Logarithm

The inverse of the exponential function is the *logarithm*, defined by the statement that

$$y = \log_a x \quad if \quad x = a^y, \qquad a > 1.$$

This function is one-valued and continuous for all *positive* values of x. The number a is called the *base* of the system of logarithms. The assumption $a > 1$ is introduced for simplicity; this condition is satisfied in all cases of practical importance.

The following facts concerning the function $y = \log_a x$ follow at once from the definition:

(a) *Negative numbers have no (real) logarithms.*
(b) *Numbers between 0 and 1 have negative logarithms.*
(c) *Numbers greater than 1 have positive logarithms.*
(d) *As $x \to 0^+$, $y \to -\infty$.*
(e) *The logarithm of 1 is 0.*
(f) *As $x \to \infty$, $y \to \infty$.*

It is easily discovered that some of these properties would not hold if a were less than 1.

99. *Fundamental Properties of Logarithms*

Further important properties of the logarithmic function are as follows:

(1) $$\log_a xy = \log_a x + \log_a y;$$

(2) $$\log_a \frac{x}{y} = \log_a x - \log_a y;$$

(3)* $$\log_a x^n = n \log_a x;$$
(4) $$\log_a a^x = x;$$
(5) $$a^{\log_a x} = x.$$

Since (1), (2), and (3) have been met in the study of trigonometry, their proofs will be omitted. Formulas (4) and (5) are restatements of the definition of logarithm. To prove (5) formally, set

$$a^{\log_a x} = t,$$

and take logarithms to the base a on each side:

$$\log_a x = \log_a t,$$

whence $t = x$.

100. *Change of Base*

Given a table of logarithms to any base b, the logarithm of any number x to the base a can be found by the *formula for change of base*:

(1) $$\log_a x = \frac{\log_b x}{\log_b a}.$$

To prove this formula, let

$$m = \log_a x \quad \text{and} \quad n = \log_b x;$$

then

$$x = a^m = b^n.$$

---

* If n is a positive or negative even integer, the function $\log_a x^n$ has a meaning even when x is negative, and this case frequently arises. With proper modification, (3) still applies:

$$\log x^n = n \log (-x) \quad \text{if} \quad x < 0, \qquad n = \pm 2, \pm 4, \pm 6, \cdots.$$

Taking logarithms to the base b, we get

$$m \log_b a = n,$$

which gives the formula at once.

Taking $x = b$ in (1), we obtain the formula

(2) $$\log_a b = \frac{1}{\log_b a}.$$

101. *The Number e*

It will be found, in § 104 below, that the problem of differentiating $y = \log_a x$ leads to a need for evaluation of

(1) $$\operatorname*{Lim}_{z \to \infty} \left(1 + \frac{1}{z}\right)^z.$$

First, let z take on only positive integral values. Consider the sequence of numbers v_n (i.e., $v_1, v_2, v_3, \cdots, v_n, v_{n+1}, \cdots$),

(2) $$v_n = \left(1 + \frac{1}{n}\right)^n; \qquad n \text{ integral}, n > 0.$$

We wish to show that v_n approaches* a limit, as $n \to \infty$.
Application of the binomial theorem to (2) yields

$$v_n = \left(1 + \frac{1}{n}\right)^n = 1 + \sum_{k=1}^{n} \frac{n(n-1)(n-2)\cdots(n-k+1)}{k!} \left(\frac{1}{n}\right)^k$$

$$= 1 + \frac{n}{1}\left(\frac{1}{n}\right) + \sum_{k=2}^{n} \frac{1 \cdot \left(1 - \frac{1}{n}\right)\left(1 - \frac{2}{n}\right) \cdots \left(1 - \frac{k-1}{n}\right)}{k!}.$$

Hence, for $n > 2$,

(3) $$v_n = 2 + \sum_{k=2}^{n} \frac{1 \cdot \left(1 - \frac{1}{n}\right)\left(1 - \frac{2}{n}\right) \cdots \left(1 - \frac{k-1}{n}\right)}{k!}.$$

* The student may find it helpful to examine v_n numerically as n increases. From (2) it follows that

$$\log_{10} v_n = n \log_{10} \left(1 + \frac{1}{n}\right).$$

In the table below, the v_n for $n > 3$ were computed with the aid of a seven-place log table.

n	1	2	3	10	100	1000
v_n	2	2.25	2.37	2.594	2.705	2.717

From (3) we obtain the next number v_{n+1} in the sequence in the form

(4) $$v_{n+1} = 2 + \sum_{k=2}^{n+1} \frac{1 \cdot \left(1 - \frac{1}{n+1}\right)\left(1 - \frac{2}{n+1}\right) \cdots \left(1 - \frac{k-1}{n+1}\right)}{k!}.$$

Since

$$1 - \frac{j}{n+1} > 1 - \frac{j}{n}$$

for each of $j = 1, 2, \cdots, (k-1)$, we may conclude that each term in the summation in (4) is larger than the corresponding term in the summation in (3), and (4) has an extra term, that in which $k = n + 1$.   Hence

(5) $$v_{n+1} > v_n;$$

the v_n increase steadily as n increases.
   Furthermore, equation (3) yields

(6) $$v_n < 2 + \sum_{k=2}^{n} \frac{1}{k!}.$$

But $k! = 1 \cdot 2 \cdot 3 \cdots k > 2^{k-1}$, so

$$v_n < 2 + \sum_{k=2}^{n} \frac{1}{2^{k-1}} = 2 + \left(1 - \frac{1}{2^{n-1}}\right).$$

Hence

(7) $$v_n < 3 - \frac{1}{2^{n-1}}.$$

Therefore

(8) $$v_n < 3.$$

We now know that the elements v_n of the sequence (2) steadily increase and are always less than 3.   Then the v_n approaches a limit; call that limit e.

LEMMA 3.   *For integral n*

(9) $$\lim_{n \to \infty} \left(1 + \frac{1}{n}\right)^n = e.$$

We have shown that $e \leq 3$.   Actually

$$e = 2.718 \quad 281 \quad 828 \quad 5 \cdots.$$

With the aid of Lemma 3 we may now obtain the desired result.

THEOREM 30. $\mathrm{Lim}_{z \to \infty} \left(1 + \dfrac{1}{z}\right)^z = e.$

Proof. At any stage, z lies between two consecutive integers,

(10) $$n \leq z < n + 1.$$

From (10) it follows that

$$\frac{1}{n+1} < \frac{1}{z} \leq \frac{1}{n}$$

and

(11) $$1 + \frac{1}{n+1} < 1 + \frac{1}{z} \leq 1 + \frac{1}{n}.$$

From (10) and (11) we get

(12) $$\left(1 + \frac{1}{n+1}\right)^n < \left(1 + \frac{1}{z}\right)^z \leq \left(1 + \frac{1}{n}\right)^{n+1}.$$

Now, because of the result in Lemma 3,

$$\mathrm{Lim}_{n \to \infty} \left(1 + \frac{1}{n+1}\right)^n = \frac{\mathrm{Lim}_{n \to \infty} \left(1 + \dfrac{1}{n+1}\right)^{n+1}}{\mathrm{Lim}_{n \to \infty} \left(1 + \dfrac{1}{n+1}\right)} = \frac{e}{1} = e,$$

and

$$\mathrm{Lim}_{n \to \infty} \left(1 + \frac{1}{n}\right)^{n+1} = \left[\mathrm{Lim}_{n \to \infty} \left(1 + \frac{1}{n}\right)^n\right]\left[\mathrm{Lim}_{n \to \infty} \left(1 + \frac{1}{n}\right)\right] = e \cdot 1 = e.$$

Hence, by (12), $\left(1 + \dfrac{1}{z}\right)^z$ lies between two numbers, each of which is approaching e as z (and therefore also n) approaches ∞. Thus $\left(1 + \dfrac{1}{z}\right)^z$ must also $\to e$ as $z \to \infty$.

The function

(13) $$y = e^x$$

is of great importance in calculus and its applications. A table of values of e^x and its reciprocal e^{-x} will be found on pp. 701–706; with the help of the table the curve (13) is easily plotted by points. See Figure 129, page 186.

102. *Natural Logarithms*

Only two systems of logarithms are of actual importance in practice. Logarithms to the base 10, called *common logarithms*, possess the great advantage that the "mantissa," or fractional part of the logarithm, is independent of the position of the decimal point in the given number; common logarithms are therefore used very generally in computing.   However, in the applications of calculus it is more convenient to use the base e.

Logarithms to the base e are called *natural logarithms*, and e is the *natural base*.   The reason for these names will appear in § 104.   Since the natural logarithm enters our work often, it is worthwhile to use a special symbol for it.   We write ln x for $\log_e x$; that is,

(1) $\ln x = \log_e x.$

A table of common logarithms gives

$$\log_{10} e = \log_{10} 2.718\,28 = 0.434\,29.$$

This important number, called the *modulus* of the common system, will hereafter be noted by M:

$$\log_{10} e = M = 0.434\,29;$$

$$\ln 10 = \frac{1}{M} = 2.302\,59.$$

.We thus derive from (1), § 100, the following formulas:

(2) $\log_{10} x = M \ln x, \qquad \ln x = \frac{1}{M} \log_{10} x.$

A brief table of natural logarithms will be found on pages 699–700.   For numbers beyond the range of the table, or with no table of natural logarithms at hand, any natural logarithm may evidently be found from a table of common logarithms with the help of (2).

The curve

$$y = \ln x$$

is shown in Figure 130.   It can be obtained from the curve $y = e^x$ of Figure 129 by interchanging the roles of x and y; i.e., by reflection in the line $y = x$.

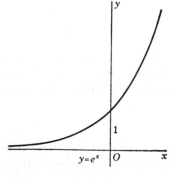

Figure 129

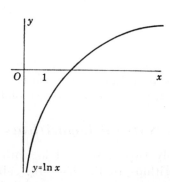

Figure 130

The following examples and exercises illustrate the use of the material so far developed in this chapter.

Example (a). Find x, if

$$\ln x = \ln 2 - 2 \ln 3 + \tfrac{1}{2} \ln 5.$$

By (3), § 99,

$$2 \ln 3 = \ln 9,$$
$$\tfrac{1}{2} \ln 5 = \ln \sqrt{5},$$
$$\ln x = \ln 2 - \ln 9 + \ln \sqrt{5}.$$

Hence,* by (1) and (2), § 99,

$$\ln x = \ln \frac{2 \sqrt{5}}{9},$$

$$x = \frac{2 \sqrt{5}}{9}.$$

Example (b). Find the inverse of the function

$$(3) \qquad\qquad y = \sin 5e^{x^3}.$$

The problem means, of course, that we are to solve the equation for x. Pass to the inverse trigonometric form:†

$$\arcsin y = 5e^{x^3}.$$

Take the natural logarithm:

$$\ln \arcsin y = \ln 5 + \ln e^{x^3} = \ln 5 + x^3,$$
$$x = (\ln \arcsin y - \ln 5)^{\frac{1}{3}}.$$

EXERCISES

In Exs. 1–13, find x without using a table.

1. (a) $\log_{10} x = 3$; (b) $\log_{10} x = \tfrac{2}{3}$; (c) $\log_{10} x = -3$; (d) $\log_{10} x = -\tfrac{1}{2}$.
2. (a) $\ln x = 4$; (b) $\ln x = \tfrac{3}{2}$; (c) $\ln x = -3$; (d) $\ln x = -\tfrac{2}{3}$.
3. (a) $\log_a x = 0$; (b) $\log_a x = 1$; (c) $\log_a x = -2$; (d) $\log_a x = \tfrac{3}{2}$.
4. $\ln x = \ln 3 + \ln 4 + \ln 6$.   *Ans.* 72.
5. $\ln x = \ln 7 + \ln 6 - \ln 3$.   *Ans.* 14.
6. $\log_{10} x = \log_{10} 7 + \log_{10} 6 - \log_{10} 3$.
7. $\ln x = 2 \ln 3 - \ln 6 + \ln 5$.   *Ans.* 7.5.
8. $\ln x = 3 \ln \tfrac{1}{2} - 2 \ln 2 + \ln 5 + \ln 6$.   *Ans.* $\tfrac{15}{16}$.
9. $\ln x = 4 + \ln 7$.   *Ans.* $7e^4$.
10. $\log_{10} x = 4 + \log_{10} 7$.

---

* After a little practice, we shall be able to write the result almost instantly, performing all intermediate steps mentally.

† Since, in (3), the quantity $5e^{x^3}$ may represent any angle whose sine is y—not necessarily the acute angle—what is needed here is the many-valued function arcsin y, not the single-valued function Arcsin y.

11. $\ln x = \frac{1}{2} \ln 6 + \frac{3}{2} \ln 3 - 3$. *Ans.* $9e^{-3} \sqrt{2}$.

12. $\ln x = \frac{3}{2} \ln 2 - \frac{1}{2} \ln 3 + \ln 6 - 1$. *Ans.* $\dfrac{4\sqrt{6}}{e}$.

13. $\log_{10} x = \frac{3}{2} + \frac{1}{2} \log_{10} 5 - \frac{3}{2} \log_{10} 2$. *Ans.* 25.

14. Show that negative numbers have no (real) logarithms.

15. Show that numbers between 0 and 1 have negative logarithms.

16. Show that numbers greater than 1 have positive logarithms.

17. Simplify: (a) $e^{\ln 5}$; (b) $e^{-\ln y}$; (c) $e^{4 \ln x}$; (d) $e^{-2 \ln 4}$; (e) $e^{2x + \ln x}$; (f) $e^{-2+2 \ln 3}$; (g) $e^{2 \ln 4 - 3 \ln x}$. *Ans.* (c) x^4; (f) $9e^{-2}$; (g) $16x^{-3}$.

18. Simplify: (a) $\ln e^{3x}$; (b) $\ln (3e^{-x})$; (c) $\ln (4x^3)^{\frac{1}{2}}$; (d) $\ln (4e^2 \cos y)$.

In Exs. 19–30, find the inverse of the given function; i.e., solve the equation for x.

19. $y = e^{5x}$. *Ans.* $x = \frac{1}{5} \ln y$.

20. $y = 3e^{-2x}$. *Ans.* $x = -\frac{1}{2} \ln \dfrac{y}{3}$.

21. $y = 10^{x+3}$. *Ans.* $x = -3 + \log_{10} y$.

22. $y = 10^{2x-1}$.

23. $y = \sin 4x$. *Ans.* $x = \frac{1}{4} \arcsin y$.

24. $y = 2 \tan (3x)$. *Ans.* $x = \frac{1}{3} \arctan (\frac{1}{2}y)$.

25. $y = \arcsin e^{-x}$. *Ans.* $x = -\ln \sin y$.

26. $y = 3 \arctan (x + 2)$. *Ans.* $x = -2 + \tan (\frac{1}{3}y)$.

27. $y = \ln (3x + 1)$. *Ans.* $x = \frac{1}{3}(e^y - 1)$.

28. $y = \frac{1}{2} \ln (4x)$. *Ans.* $x = \frac{1}{4}e^{2y}$.

29. $y = \ln \tan x$.

30. $y = 3 + \frac{1}{2} \ln \sin (4x)$.

31. Show that the function $y = \operatorname{Arcsin} e^{x^2}$ is imaginary except at one point.

32. Show that the curve $y = \operatorname{Arcsin} e^{\sin^2 x}$ consists of a set of isolated points.

In Exs. 33–38, break up the given expression into sums and differences of simpler logarithms.

33. $\ln \dfrac{x(2x + 1)}{x + 4}$.

34. $\ln \dfrac{x^2 - 9}{x^2(x^2 - 1)}$.

35. $\ln \dfrac{4x^2}{x^2 - 5x + 4}$.

36. $\ln \sqrt{\dfrac{x^3}{x + 4}}$.

37. $\ln \dfrac{4x^5 e^{-x}}{(x + 1)^3}$. *Ans.* $2 \ln 2 + 5 \ln x - x - 3 \ln (x + 1)$.

38. $\ln \dfrac{e^{3x} - e^{-3x}}{x^4(e^{3x} + e^{-3x})}$. *Ans.* $\ln (e^{3x} - e^{-3x}) - 4 \ln x - \ln (e^{3x} + e^{-3x})$.

In Exs. 39–46, solve for x by first taking logarithms of each member of the equation.

39. $3^x = 4$. *Ans.* $x = \dfrac{2 \ln 2}{\ln 3}$. **40.** $5^x = 2$. *Ans.* $x = \dfrac{\ln 2}{\ln 5}$.

41. $7 \cdot 3^{2x} = 6$. **42.** $8 \cdot 3^{-x} = 7$.

43. $2^{3x} = 3^{2x-1}$. $\qquad\qquad\qquad Ans.\ x = \dfrac{\ln 3}{\ln 9 - \ln 8}$.

44. $5^{2x} = 2^{3x+1}$.

45. $10^x = 5^{3x-2}$.

46. $a^{x^2} = (a^x)^x$, $a > 0$. $\qquad\qquad\qquad Ans.\ x = 1;\ x = 2$.

47. Show that, for $0 < a < x$,

$$\ln (x - \sqrt{x^2 - a^2}) = 2 \ln a - \ln (x + \sqrt{x^2 - a^2}).$$

48. Show that, for $a > 0$, $x > 0$,

$$\ln (\sqrt{x + a} + \sqrt{x}) = \ln a - \ln (\sqrt{x + a} - \sqrt{x}).$$

49. Show that, for $\dfrac{-\pi}{2} < \theta < \dfrac{\pi}{2}$,

$$\ln (\sec \theta - \tan \theta) = - \ln (\sec \theta + \tan \theta).$$

50. Let $\alpha = \left(1 + \dfrac{1}{n+1}\right)^{\frac{1}{n}}$, $\alpha > 1$. Show that

(A) $$n\alpha^n > \sum_{k=0}^{n-1} \alpha^k.$$

Add n times the right member of (A) to each member of (A) to obtain

$$n \sum_{k=0}^{n} \alpha^k > (n + 1) \sum_{k=0}^{n-1} \alpha^k,$$

or

(B) $$n(\alpha^{n+1} - 1) > (n + 1)(\alpha^n - 1).$$

Use the fact that $\alpha^n = 1 + \dfrac{1}{n+1}$ to conclude that

$$\alpha^{n+1} > 1 + \dfrac{1}{n}$$

and from it that $v_{n+1} > v_n$, in which v_n is defined by equation (2), § 101.

103. *Exponential and Logarithmic Equations*

Equations involving exponential functions only, or logarithms only, may in simple cases be solved by applying the theory of §§ 98–99.

Example (a). Solve for x the equation

$$e^x - e^{-x} = 2.$$

Multiplying by e^x, we get

$$e^{2x} - 1 = 2e^x,$$
$$e^{2x} - 2e^x - 1 = 0.$$

This is a quadratic equation in e^x as the unknown quantity, whose solution is found by elementary algebra to be

$$e^x = 1 + \sqrt{2}.$$

(The root $e^x = 1 - \sqrt{2}$ must be rejected, since e^x is never negative.) Hence

$$x = \ln (1 + \sqrt{2}).$$

Check:

$$e^{\ln (1+\sqrt{2})} - e^{-\ln (1+\sqrt{2})} = 1 + \sqrt{2} - \frac{1}{1 + \sqrt{2}}$$

$$= 1 + \sqrt{2} - \frac{1 - \sqrt{2}}{(1 + \sqrt{2})(1 - \sqrt{2})}$$

$$= 1 + \sqrt{2} + 1 - \sqrt{2}$$

$$= 2.$$

Example (b).   Solve the equation

$$\ln (2x + 7) - \ln (x - 1) = \ln 5.$$

Combining the logarithms in the left member, we get

$$\ln \frac{2x + 7}{x - 1} = \ln 5,$$

whence

$$\frac{2x + 7}{x - 1} = 5,$$

and

$$x = 4.$$

Check: $\ln 15 - \ln 3 = \ln 5.$

EXERCISES

Solve the equations in Exs. 1–18.

1. $e^x + 6e^{-x} = 5.$	*Ans.* $x = 0.693, 1.099.$
2. $e^x + 15e^{-x} = 8.$	*Ans.* $x = 1.099, 1.609.$
3. $e^x + 1 = 6e^{-x}.$	*Ans.* $x = 0.693.$
4. $2e^x + 1 = e^{-x}.$	*Ans.* $x = -0.693.$
5. $e^{2x} + 20e^{-x} = 21.$	*Ans.* $x = 0, 1.386.$
6. $1 - 3e^x = 4e^{-x}(e^{-x} + 1).$	*Ans.* No real solutions.
7. $3^x + 8 \cdot 3^{-x} = 6.$	*Ans.* $x = 0.631, 1.262.$
8. $4^x + 2 \cdot 4^{-x} = 3.$	*Ans.* $x = 0, 0.5.$
9. $\ln (x - 1) + \ln (x - 2) = \ln 6.$	*Ans.* $x = 4.$
10. $\ln (x + 1) + \ln (x - 3) = \ln 5.$	*Ans.* $x = 4.$
11. $\ln (1 - x) + \ln (x + 7) = \ln 15.$	*Ans.* $x = -2, -4.$
12. $\ln (5 - 3x) + \ln (1 + x) = \ln 4.$	*Ans.* $x = 1, -\frac{1}{3}.$

13. $\log_{10} (2x - 5) + \log_{10} (x - 1) = \log_{10} 2.$ *Ans. x = 3.*
14. $\ln (x^2 - 3x + 7) + \ln (x + 3) = \ln 17.$ *Ans. x = -2.*
15. $\ln (x + 4) - \ln (2x - 1) + \ln (x - 3) = \ln 2.$ *Ans. x = 5.*
16. $\log_{10} (x + 5) - \log_{10} (x - 1) + \log_{10} 5 + \log_{10} (x + 2) = 2.$

Ans. x = 3, 10.

17. $\ln (x - 3) + \ln (x + 1) - \ln (x^2 - x + 2) + \ln (2 - x) = 2 \ln 2.$

Ans. No solutions.

18. $\ln (x^2 + 2x + 4) - \ln (x^2 + x + 2) + \ln (1 - x) = \ln 3.$

Ans. x = -1, -2.

In Exs. 19–23, write the equation in a form free from logarithms. State the range of values of x and y for which the original equation is valid.

19. $\ln x + \ln y - \ln (x - y) = \ln 3.$ *Ans. $xy - 3x + 3y = 0$, for $x > y > 0$.*
20. $\frac{1}{2} \ln (x - a) - \frac{1}{2} \ln (x + a) - \ln y + \ln a = 0.$

Ans. $y^2(x + a) = a^2(x - a)$, for $x > a > 0$, $y > 0$.

21. $\ln (x^2 + 4) - 2 \ln y + 3 = 0.$ *Ans. $y^2 = e^3(x^2 + 4)$, for $y > 0$.*
22. $x + \ln y - \ln x = 0.$ *Ans. $y = xe^{-x}$, for $x > 0$, $y > 0$.*
23. $2 \ln (1 - x) - \ln (1 + x) + 3 \ln y = 2 \ln 3.$

Ans. $y^3(1 - x)^2 = 9(1 + x)$, for $|x| < 1$, $y > 0$.

In Exs. 24–31, find the inverse of the given function.

24. $y = \frac{1}{2}(e^{3x} - e^{-3x}).$ *Ans. $x = \frac{1}{3} \ln (y + \sqrt{y^2 + 1}).$*
25. $4y = e^x - 8e^{-x}.$ *Ans. $x = \ln (y + \sqrt{y^2 + 2}) + \ln 2.$*
26. $y = \ln (x + 1) - \ln (x - 1).$ *Ans. $x = \dfrac{e^y + 1}{e^y - 1}.$*
27. $y = \ln (x + 1) + \ln (x - 1).$ *Ans. $x = \sqrt{1 + e^y}.$*
28. $y = 2 \ln x - \ln (x + 1).$ *Ans. $x = \frac{1}{2}e^y(1 + \sqrt{1 + 4e^{-y}}).$*
29. $y = \ln (e^{2x} - 1).$ *Ans. $x = \frac{1}{2} \ln (1 + e^y).$*
30. $y = \frac{1}{2} \ln (3e^{\frac{1}{2}x} - 2).$ *Ans. $x = 2 \ln (e^{2y} + 2) - 2 \ln 3.$*
31. $y = \ln (1 - \sqrt{4 - x^2}).$ *Ans. $x = \pm \sqrt{(1 + e^y)(3 - e^y)}$, for $y \le 0$.*

104. *Derivative of the Logarithm*

To obtain the derivative of the logarithm, we proceed by the method of § 43:

$$y = \log_a x,$$
$$y + \Delta y = \log_a (x + \Delta x),$$
$$\Delta y = \log_a (x + \Delta x) - \log_a x = \log_a \frac{x + \Delta x}{x}$$
$$= \log_a \left(1 + \frac{\Delta x}{x}\right).$$

Hence

$$\frac{\Delta y}{\Delta x} = \frac{1}{\Delta x} \log_a \left(1 + \frac{\Delta x}{x}\right).$$

Let us multiply and divide by x and then employ (3), § 99:

$$\frac{\Delta y}{\Delta x} = \frac{1}{x} \cdot \frac{x}{\Delta x} \log_a \left(1 + \frac{\Delta x}{x}\right)$$

$$= \frac{1}{x} \log_a \left(1 + \frac{\Delta x}{x}\right)^{\frac{x}{\Delta x}}.$$

Hence

(1) $$\frac{dy}{dx} = \lim_{\Delta x \to 0} \frac{\Delta y}{\Delta x} = \frac{1}{x} \lim_{\Delta x \to 0} \log_a \left(1 + \frac{\Delta x}{x}\right)^{\frac{x}{\Delta x}}$$

(2) $$= \frac{1}{x} \log_a \left[\lim_{\Delta x \to 0} \left(1 + \frac{\Delta x}{x}\right)^{\frac{x}{\Delta x}} \right],$$

making use of the continuity of the logarithmic function.

Now, putting

$$\frac{x}{\Delta x} = z,$$

we see that the limit occurring in (2) is, if $\Delta x > 0$,

$$\lim_{z \to \infty} \left(1 + \frac{1}{z}\right)^z = e,$$

by Theorem 30.   (The argument must be slightly modified for negative Δx.)
Hence

(3) $$\frac{d}{dx} \log_a x = \frac{1}{x} \log_a e.$$

In order to remove the awkward factor $\log_a e$, choose the base a so that $\log_a e = 1$; i.e., take $a = e$. Then $\log_a x$ becomes ln x, $\log_a e$ becomes unity, and equation (3) simplifies to the form

$$\frac{d}{dx} \ln x = \frac{1}{x}.$$

This is the reason for the use of logarithms to the base e in calculus.*
By the chain rule of § 51, if u is any function of x,

$$\frac{d}{dx} \log_a u = \frac{\frac{du}{dx}}{u} \cdot \log_a e,$$

* Since the undesirable factor $\log_a e$ has appeared in consequence of an intrinsic property of the logarithmic function, with no way of removing it except by adoption of e as base, the terms "natural base" and "natural logarithm" are seen to be justified.   While it is clearly a nuisance to have to use two systems of logarithms—one for computing, the other in applications of calculus—it would be a much greater nuisance to use (3) every time a logarithm is differentiated.   Compare with similar remarks in § 88 concerning the use of radian measure of angles—which, in the same line of thought, might be called "natural measure."

and as special cases,

$$(16) \qquad \frac{d}{dx} \ln u = \frac{\dfrac{du}{dx}}{u},$$

$$(17) \qquad \frac{d}{dx} \log_{10} u = \frac{M \dfrac{du}{dx}}{u}.$$

In differentiating the logarithm of a complicated expression, a great deal of labor may often be saved if we make judicious use of (1), (2), and (3) of § 99.

Example (a). Differentiate $y = \ln \sqrt{1 + 3x}$.

Let us write y in the form

$$y = \tfrac{1}{2} \ln (1 + 3x).$$

Then

$$y' = \frac{1}{2} \cdot \frac{3}{1 + 3x}.$$

Example (b). Differentiate $x = \ln \dfrac{z^3(z^2 - 1)^2}{(z^2 + 1)^2}.$

Write

$$x = 3 \ln z + 2 \ln (z^2 - 1) - 2 \ln (z^2 + 1);$$

$$\frac{dx}{dz} = \frac{3}{z} + \frac{4z}{z^2 - 1} - \frac{4z}{z^2 + 1}$$

$$= \frac{3(z^4 - 1) + 4z^2(z^2 + 1) - 4z^2(z^2 - 1)}{z(z^4 - 1)}$$

$$= \frac{3z^4 + 8z^2 - 3}{z(z^4 - 1)}.$$

EXERCISES

In Exs. 1–32, find the derivative of the given function. When necessary, use M to denote $\log_{10} e$.

1. $y = \ln (3 - 2x)$.
2. $y = \ln (4x + 1)$.
3. $y = \ln (cx)$.
4. $y = \ln (x^2 + 3x - 7)$.
5. $y = \ln (a^2 - x^2)^{\frac{3}{2}}$.
6. $u = \ln (2t - t^2)$.
7. $x = \ln \sec \theta$.
8. $x = \ln \sin (3v)$.

9. $y = \log_{10} \cos \dfrac{x}{a}.$
$\qquad$ *Ans.* $\dfrac{dy}{dx} = -\dfrac{M}{a} \tan \dfrac{x}{a}.$

10. $\alpha = \log_{10} (1 + 3 \tan \beta)$.
$\qquad$ *Ans.* $\dfrac{d\alpha}{d\beta} = \dfrac{3M \sec^2 \beta}{1 + 3 \tan \beta}.$

11. $x = \ln \dfrac{3t + 1}{3t - 1}.$
$\qquad$ *Ans.* $\dfrac{dx}{dt} = \dfrac{-6}{9t^2 - 1}.$

12. $w = \ln (b^2 - x^2)^{\frac{3}{2}}$.

$Ans. \dfrac{dw}{dx} = \dfrac{-3x}{b^2 - x^2}$.

13. $y = \ln \sqrt{a^2 + x^2}$.

$Ans. \dfrac{dy}{dx} = \dfrac{x}{a^2 + x^2}$.

14. $u = \ln \dfrac{1 - v^2}{1 + v^2}$.

$Ans. \dfrac{du}{dv} = \dfrac{-4v}{1 - v^4}$.

15. $y = 4 \ln \sqrt{\dfrac{1 + x^3}{1 - x^3}}$.

$Ans. \dfrac{dy}{dx} = \dfrac{12x^2}{1 - x^6}$.

16. $r = \log_{10} \sec^2 3\theta$.

$Ans. \dfrac{dr}{d\theta} = 6M \tan 3\theta$.

17. $y = z^3 \ln z$.

18. $w = \dfrac{1}{\ln x}$.

19. $x = \ln^2 t$.

20. $y = \dfrac{\ln x}{x^2}$.

21. $u = x \ln (1 + x)$.

22. $v = x^2 \ln (1 - x)$.

23. $y = \ln \ln x$.

24. $x = \ln \ln (1 + \sin t)$.

25. $r = \cos \ln \theta$.

26. $y = \csc \ln x$.

27. $y = x^3(3 \ln x - 1)$.

$Ans. y' = 9x^2 \ln x$.

28. $w = t^2(\cos \ln t - \sin \ln t)$.

$Ans. w' = t(\cos \ln t - 3 \sin \ln t)$.

29. $u = t^3(\sin \ln t - \cos \ln t)$.

$Ans. u' = 2t^2(2 \sin \ln t - \cos \ln t)$.

30. $y = x \ln (a^2 + x^2) + 2a \operatorname{Arctan} \dfrac{x}{a} - 2x$.

$Ans. y' = \ln (a^2 + x^2)$.

31. $y = \ln \sqrt{\dfrac{1 + \sin x}{1 - \sin x}}$.

$Ans. \dfrac{dy}{dx} = \sec x$.

32. $y = \ln \tan \left(\dfrac{\pi}{4} + \dfrac{x}{2} \right)$.

$Ans. \dfrac{dy}{dx} = \sec x$.

In Exs. 33–36, find y'.

33. $x \ln y - y \ln x = c$.

$Ans. y' = \dfrac{y(y - x \ln y)}{x(x - y \ln x)}$.

34. $x \ln (x^2 + y^2) - y = c$.

$Ans. y' = \dfrac{2x^2 + (x^2 + y^2) \ln (x^2 + y^2)}{(x - y)^2}$.

35. $4 \ln (\sec y + \tan y) - 2x - \sin 2x = c$.

$Ans. y' = \cos y \cos^2 x$.

36. $\ln (x^2 + y^2) + 4 \operatorname{Arctan} \dfrac{y}{x} = c$.

$Ans. y' = \dfrac{2y - x}{y + 2x}$.

37. For the function $y = x^2 \ln x$, find the first four derivatives.

38. For the function $y = (x^3 - 1) \ln x$, find $\dfrac{d^4y}{dx^4}$.

$Ans. \dfrac{d^4y}{dx^4} = \dfrac{6(x^3 + 1)}{x^4}$.

39. For the curve $y = \ln x$, find the equation of a tangent line parallel to the line $2x - y = 4$.

$Ans. 2x - y = 1 + \ln 2$.

40. For the curve $y = x \ln x$, find the equation of a tangent line perpendicular to the line $x + 2y = 7$.

$Ans. 2x - y = e$.

41. Find the tangent to the curve $y = \ln x$ at any point (x_1, y_1). By finding the y-intercept of the tangent, derive a ruler-and-compass construction for the tangent at any point of the curve. *Ans.* $x_1y - x = x_1y_1 - x_1.$

Of the statements in Exs. 42–45, which ones are true, and why?

42. If $t^2 = k$, and $x^2 = k$, then $t = x$.   *Ans.* False.

43. If $\sin t = k$, and $\sin x = k$, then $t = x$.   *Ans.* False.

44. If $\log_a x = k$, and $\log_a t = k$, then $t = x$.

45. If $k = a^x$, and $k = a^t (a \neq 1)$, then $t = x$. Take the logarithm in each equation.

46. By setting $y = x^n$, taking the logarithm, and differentiating, prove the formula $\dfrac{d}{dx} x^n = nx^{n-1}$ for all values of n.

Sketch carefully each of the curves in Exs. 47–54, locating all maximum, minimum, and inflection points.

47. $y = \ln (x - 1)$.   **48.** $y = \ln (x + 1)$.

49. $y = x - \ln x$.   **50.** $y = x^2 - 2 \ln x$.

51. $y = \ln \ln x$.   **52.** $y = \ln \cos x$.

53. $y = \frac{1}{2} \ln (x^2 - 1)$.   **54.** $y = 9 \ln (x + 1) - \ln (x - 1)$.

105. *Derivative of the Exponential Function*

If
$$y = a^x,$$
then
$$\ln y = x \ln a.$$

Differentiating by the rule for implicit functions, we find

$$\frac{1}{y} \frac{dy}{dx} = \ln a,$$

$$\frac{dy}{dx} = y \ln a = a^x \ln a;$$

i.e.,

$$\frac{d}{dx} a^x = a^x \ln a.$$

If u is a function of x, this formula becomes

(18) $$\frac{d}{dx} a^u = a^u \ln a \cdot \frac{du}{dx}.$$

For the case $a = e$, we have the important special case*

---

* The number e has a way of appearing in many physical problems (for simple illustrations, see §§ 138, 140), frequently for reasons that are rather obscure. In this it resembles that other remarkable number, π, which turns up in a multitude of situations having no apparent connection with circles.

(19) $$\frac{d}{dx}\, e^u = e^u \frac{du}{dx}.$$

Example (a).   If $y = e^{2x^3}$,

$$y' = e^{2x^3} \cdot 6x^2 = 6x^2 e^{2x^3}.$$

Example (b).   If $y = \sin^2 e^{3x}$,

$$y' = 2 \sin e^{3x} \cos e^{3x} \cdot e^{3x} \cdot 3 = 3e^{3x} \sin 2e^{3x}.$$

Example (c).   Show that $e^{-x} > (1 - x)$ for $x > 0$.
Put

(1) $$y = e^{-x} - 1 + x.$$

We need to show that y is positive for $x > 0$.   From (1) it follows that

(2) $$y' = 1 - e^{-x},$$
(3) $$y'' = e^{-x}.$$

At $x = 0$, $y = 0$ and $y' = 0$.   Because of (3) the y-curve is concave upward for all x.   Therefore $y > 0$ for $x > 0$, which yields the desired inequality.

106. *Variable with Variable Exponent*

Let

$$y = u^v, \qquad u > 0$$

where both u and v are functions of x.

While it is easy to develop the general formula (Ex. 47 below) for the derivative of this function, it is usually simpler not to use the formula but *to take the logarithm of both members* before differentiating.

Example.   Differentiate $y = x^x$.

We have

$$\ln y = x \ln x,$$
$$\frac{y'}{y} = 1 + \ln x,$$
$$y' = y(1 + \ln x) = x^x(1 + \ln x).$$

EXERCISES

In Exs. 1–26, find the first derivative of the given function.

1. $y = e^{-4x}$.
2. $x = e^{-t^2}$.
3. $v = e^{\tan \theta}$.
4. $v = e^{-\sin 2\theta}$.
5. $y = xe^{3x}$.
6. $y = 4x^2 e^{-x}$.
7. $u = \ln (e^{2x} - 1)$.
8. $v = \ln (4 + e^{-2t})$.
9. $r = e^\theta \sin 3\theta$.
10. $z = e^{-2\theta} \sin 2\theta$.

11. $x = e^{2t}(\cos t - 2 \sin t)$.

12. $x = e^{t}(2 \cos 2t - \sin 2t)$.

13. $y = a \sin e^{-\frac{x}{a}}$.

14. $y = b \operatorname{Arcsin} e^{-\frac{x}{b}}$.

15. $y = 5^{2x}$.

16. $x = 10^{-3t}$.

17. $x = 10^{\tan \theta}$.

18. $w = 3^{-u^2}$.

19. $y = (4 - 3e^{2x})^{\frac{3}{2}}$.

20. $z = \tan^2 (1 - e^{-u})$.

21. $w = e^{-3v}(1 - e^{3v})^{\frac{1}{2}}$.

22. $x = t^2 e^{-\frac{1}{t}}$.

23. $z = \dfrac{e^{3y}}{y^2}$.

24. $y = x + x^3 e^{-3 \ln x}$.   *Ans.* $y' = 1$

25. $y = (1 + e^{-x})^3(1 - e^{-x})^{\frac{1}{2}}$.   **26.** $x = \dfrac{e^{2t} - e^{-2t}}{e^{2t} + e^{-2t}}$.

27. Find y' from the equation $x^2 e^y - y^2 e^x = 1$.

28. Find y' from the equation $e^{xy} - xe^y = 3$.   *Ans.* $y' = \dfrac{e^y - ye^{xy}}{x(e^{xy} - e^y)}$.

29. Find y'' from the equation $y = xe^{-x^2}$.   *Ans.* $y'' = 2xe^{-x^2}(2x^2 - 3)$.

30. Find $\dfrac{d^2x}{dt^2}$ from the equation $x = t^3 e^{-t}$.   *Ans.* $\dfrac{d^2x}{dt^2} = te^{-t}(t^2 - 6t + 6)$.

31. Find $y^{(n)} = \dfrac{d^n y}{dx^n}$ from the equation $y = e^{ax}$.

32. Find $y^{(n)}$ from the equation $y = xe^x$.

33. From $u = e^{-t} \sin t$, show that $\dfrac{d^2u}{dt^2} + 2 \dfrac{du}{dt} + 2u = 0$.

34. From $y = e^{3x} \sin 2x$, show that $y'' - 6y' + 13y = 0$.

35. From $x = e^{-\frac{1}{2}t} \cos t$, show that $4 \dfrac{d^2x}{dt^2} + 4 \dfrac{dx}{dt} + 5x = 0$.

In Exs. 36–44, sketch the curve carefully.

36. $y = e^{-3x}$.

37. $y = 1 + e^x$.

38. $y = 4(e^{-x} - 1)$.

39. $y = e^x - x$.

40. $y = e^{-x^2}$.

41. $y = e^{-\frac{1}{x}}$.

42. $y = e^{-x} \sin x$.

43. $y = \operatorname{Arcsin} e^{-x}$.

44. $y = e^{\sin x}$.

45. For the curve $y = e^{-2x}$, find the tangent line parallel to the line $x + y = 4$.
                     Ans. $x + y = \frac{1}{2}(1 + \ln 2)$.

46. For the curve $y = e^{3x}$, find the tangent line perpendicular to the line $x + 6y = 7$.   *Ans.* $y - 6x = 2 - 2 \ln 2$.

47. If u and v are functions of x, find the derivative of u^v.

$$\textit{Ans. } \frac{d}{dx} u^v = vu^{v-1} \frac{du}{dx} + u^v \ln u \frac{dv}{dx}.$$

48. Differentiate $y = x^{e^x}$.   *Ans.* $y' = x^{e^x - 1} e^x (1 + x \ln x)$.

49. Differentiate $y = x^{x^2}$.   *Ans.* $y' = x^{1+x^2}(1 + 2 \ln x)$.

50. Differentiate $y = e^{x^x}$.   *Ans.* $y' = x^x e^{x^x}(1 + \ln x)$.

51. Differentiate $y = (\ln x)^x$.   *Ans.* $y' = (\ln x)^{x-1} (1 + \ln x \ln \ln x)$.

52. Differentiate $y = x^{\ln x}$.   *Ans.* $y' = 2(\ln x)x^{\ln x - 1}$.

53. Show that $e^{-x} > 1 - x + \frac{1}{2}x^2 - \frac{1}{6}x^3$ for $x > 0$.

Fundamental Differentiation Formulas

(1) $\dfrac{dc}{dx} = 0;$

(2) $\dfrac{d}{dx}(u + v) = \dfrac{du}{dx} + \dfrac{dv}{dx};$

(3) $\dfrac{d}{dx}uv = u\dfrac{dv}{dx} + v\dfrac{du}{dx};$ (3') $\dfrac{d}{dx}cv = c\dfrac{dv}{dx};$

(4) $\dfrac{d}{dx}\dfrac{u}{v} = \dfrac{v\dfrac{du}{dx} - u\dfrac{dv}{dx}}{v^2};$ (4') $\dfrac{d}{dx}\dfrac{c}{v} = -\dfrac{c\dfrac{dv}{dx}}{v^2};$

(5) $\dfrac{dy}{dx} = \dfrac{dy}{du} \cdot \dfrac{du}{dx};$ (5') $\dfrac{dy}{dx} = \dfrac{\dfrac{dy}{du}}{\dfrac{dx}{du}};$ (5'') $\dfrac{dy}{dx} = \dfrac{1}{\dfrac{dx}{dy}};$

(6) $\dfrac{d}{dx}u^n = nu^{n-1}\dfrac{du}{dx};$ (6') $\dfrac{d}{dx}\sqrt{u} = \dfrac{\dfrac{du}{dx}}{2\sqrt{u}};$

(7) $\dfrac{d}{dx}\sin u = \cos u\dfrac{du}{dx};$

(8) $\dfrac{d}{dx}\cos u = -\sin u\dfrac{du}{dx};$

(9) $\dfrac{d}{dx}\tan u = \sec^2 u\dfrac{du}{dx};$

(10) $\dfrac{d}{dx}\cot u = -\csc^2 u\dfrac{du}{dx};$

(11) $\dfrac{d}{dx}\sec u = \sec u \tan u\dfrac{du}{dx};$

(12) $\dfrac{d}{dx}\csc u = -\csc u \cot u\dfrac{du}{dx};$

(13) $\dfrac{d}{dx}\text{Arcsin } u = \dfrac{\dfrac{du}{dx}}{\sqrt{1 - u^2}},$ $-\dfrac{\pi}{2} \leqq \text{Arcsin } u \leqq \dfrac{\pi}{2};$

(14) $\dfrac{d}{dx}\text{Arccos } u = -\dfrac{\dfrac{du}{dx}}{\sqrt{1 - u^2}},$ $0 \leqq \text{Arccos } u \leqq \pi;$

(15) $\dfrac{d}{dx}\text{Arctan } u = \dfrac{\dfrac{du}{dx}}{1 + u^2},$ $-\dfrac{\pi}{2} < \text{Arctan } u < \dfrac{\pi}{2};$

(16) $\dfrac{d}{dx}\ln u = \dfrac{\dfrac{du}{dx}}{u};$

(17) $\dfrac{d}{dx} \log_{10} u = \dfrac{M \dfrac{du}{dx}}{u}$;

(18) $\dfrac{d}{dx} a^u = a^u \ln a \dfrac{du}{dx}$;

(19) $\dfrac{d}{dx} e^u = e^u \dfrac{du}{dx}$.

MISCELLANEOUS EXERCISES

Differentiate the following functions.

1. $u = x \operatorname{Arcsin} \dfrac{x}{3}$.

2. $u = x \sqrt{1 - 4x^2}$.

3. $y = (t^3 + 2)e^{-2t}$.

4. $y = z^2 \ln \sin z$.

5. $w = \operatorname{Arctan}(1 + v^2)$.

6. $w = \dfrac{v^3}{\sqrt{1 - 6v^2}}$.

7. $y = \ln \dfrac{x^4}{(1 - x^2)^3}$.

8. $y = \cos x \cot x$.

9. $y = (a^{\frac{2}{3}} - x^{\frac{2}{3}})^{\frac{3}{2}}$.

10. $y = e^{-x} \ln x$.

11. $x = \dfrac{t^4}{(1 - t^2)^3}$.

12. $r = \ln^2 \cos \theta$.

13. $r = \ln \cos^2 \theta$.

14. $y = z^3(1 - z^2)^{\frac{1}{2}}$.

15. $l = e^{-x}(1 - e^{2x})^{-\frac{1}{2}}$.

16. $r = \dfrac{\cos^3 2\theta}{(1 + \sin 2\theta)^3}$.

17. $\alpha = \cos 2\beta \sin 3\beta$.

18. $\psi = 4^{3x}$.

19. $y = \operatorname{Arctan} \ln x$.

20. $y = \operatorname{Arcsin} e^{-5x}$.

21. $x = \sin^2 (\frac{1}{4}\pi - 2t)$.

22. $z = \ln(1 - e^{-3v})$.

23. $y = \ln \ln (1 + e^x)$.

24. $y = 4x^2 e^{-\frac{1}{2}x}$.

25. $x = t \ln \sqrt{1 + t}$.

26. $v = e^{e^{-x}}$.

27. $\theta = \operatorname{Arcsin}(1 - r)$.

28. $r = \sqrt{\dfrac{1 - \cos \theta}{1 + \cos \theta}}$.

29. $y = \sec^4 3x$.

30. $y = \csc^2 x \cot^3 x$.

31. $v = (e^{4z} - 1)^{-\frac{1}{2}}$.

32. $v = \tan^2 (1 + 3x)$.

33. $u = (1 - x^2)^{\frac{1}{2}}(1 + x^2)^{-\frac{1}{2}}$.

34. $u = v^2 e^{-v^2}$.

35. $A = \dfrac{t^3}{\sqrt{2at - t^2}}$.

36. $\beta = \sqrt[3]{1 - 4 \ln \alpha}$.

37. $z = \log_{10}(9u^2 - 1)$.

38. $t = \log_{10} \dfrac{4e^z - 1}{4e^z + 1}$.

39. $V = \sin 2\theta \cos^2 \theta$.

40. $W = \sin^3 2\theta \cos^4 2\theta$.

The Central Conics

107. Conic Sections

In § 63, page 102, we defined a parabola as the locus of points equidistant from a fixed point and a fixed line. The locus of points P for which the distance from P to a fixed point F is in a constant ratio to the distance from P to a fixed line DD' is called a *conic section*, or simply a *conic*.

The fixed point is called the *focus* of the conic, the fixed line the *directrix*, and the constant ratio the *eccentricity*. In Figure

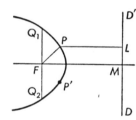

131, if F is the focus, DD' the directrix, and P a point on the conic, then

$$\frac{FP}{LP} = e,$$

or

$$(1) \qquad FP = e \times LP,$$

Figure 131

where e denotes the eccentricity.

If $e = 1$, the distances FP and LP are equal, and the conic is a parabola. The conic sections are classified according to their eccentricity as follows:

> If $e < 1$, the conic is an *ellipse*;
> If $e = 1$, the conic is a *parabola*;
> If $e > 1$, the conic is a *hyperbola*.

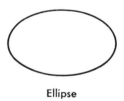

Ellipse   Parabola   Hyperbola

Figure 132

Equation (1) would still be true if the point P were in the position P', symmetric to P with respect to the line FM. Hence the line through the focus perpendicular to the directrix is a line of symmetry for the curve. It follows that the line through the focus parallel to the directrix intersects the curve in two points: the chord Q_1Q_2 joining these points is called the *latus rectum*, or *right chord*.

108. *The Circle; Degenerate Conics*

In addition to the three typical conics mentioned above, it will be convenient to include under that term various other loci.

First, when $e = 0$ the definition fails. But when e *approaches zero*, the ellipse approaches a circle (Ex. 25, page 206). We therefore consider the circle a special case of the ellipse.

Second, we consider the "point-ellipse" of § 111, two intersecting lines (§ 116), and two parallel or coincident lines to be conics of exceptional type. These loci are called *degenerate conics*. Two parallel or coincident lines may be obtained as limiting forms of the parabola.

Every plane section of a circular cone is a curve of the class that we have called *conic sections* (provided the forms just discussed are included); this, of course, is the reason for the name. The student may amuse himself by discovering intuitively how the cutting plane must be passed in order to obtain the various sections.*

We shall soon find that every conic section may be represented by an equation of the second degree. In Chapter 20 we show that every equation of the second degree represents a conic section, if degenerate conics are included.

109. *Ellipse Referred to Its Axes*

By § 107, the ellipse is *the conic section for which* $e < 1$. Let F be the focus and DD' the directrix. The line FM through the focus perpendicular to the directrix intersects the curve in two points, say V_1 and V_2 (two points, because the segment FM can be divided both internally and externally in the ratio e). These points are the *vertices*; and C, the mid-point of V_1V_2, is the *center* (Figure 133).

Let us set

$$CV_1 = a$$
$$CF = c$$
$$CM = d.$$

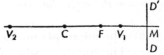

Figure 133

Then, applying (1), § 107, to the points V_1 and V_2, we have

$$a - c = e(d - a), \qquad a + c = e(d + a).$$

* Two parallel lines cannot be cut from a cone. They can, however, be cut from a cylinder, which is the form approached by a cone with a fixed right section as the vertex recedes indefinitely.

By subtraction and addition we find

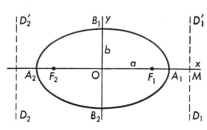

Figure 134

$$2c = 2CF = 2ae, \qquad c = ae,$$
$$2ed = 2e \cdot CM = 2a, \qquad d = \frac{a}{e}.$$

Let us now (Figure 134) choose our origin at the center C, so that the focus F becomes $(ae, 0)$ and the equation of the directrix DD' is

(1) $$x = \frac{a}{e}.$$

Then, if $P: (x, y)$ is a point on the curve, we have

$$\sqrt{(x - ae)^2 + y^2} = e\left(\frac{a}{e} - x\right) = a - ex,$$
$$x^2 - 2aex + a^2e^2 + y^2 = a^2 - 2aex + e^2x^2,$$
$$x^2(1 - e^2) + y^2 = a^2(1 - e^2),$$

(2) $$\frac{x^2}{a^2} + \frac{y^2}{a^2(1 - e^2)} = 1.$$

For simplicity, let us put

(3) $$b^2 = a^2(1 - e^2),$$

where b is real because $e < 1$, $a^2(1 - e^2) > 0$. This reduces (2) to the *standard form*

(4) $$\frac{x^2}{a^2} + \frac{y^2}{b^2} = 1, \qquad a > b.$$

From (4) we see that:

(a) The curve is symmetric with respect to Ox and Oy. From the latter statement it follows that there is *a second focus, the point* $(-ae, 0)$, and *a second directrix, the line* $x = -\dfrac{a}{e}$.

(b) The intercepts on the axes are $(\pm a, 0)$, $(0, \pm b)$.

(c) The equation, when solved for y, has the form

(5) $$y = \pm \frac{b}{a}\sqrt{a^2 - x^2};$$

thus y is imaginary when x is numerically greater than a. Similarly, x is imaginary when y is numerically greater than b.

It is convenient occasionally to speak of the two lines of symmetry as the *axes* of the curve, but usually we consider the axes to be the *segments* of these lines included within the curve; the segment A_2A_1 is the *major axis,* the segment B_2B_1, the *minor axis*. It follows from (3) that, for the ellipse, a is *always greater than b*—hence the terms *major* and *minor*.

From equation (4), the ends of the axes may be plotted immediately. By (3),

$$ae = \sqrt{a^2 - b^2};$$

i.e., *the distance from center to foci is* $\sqrt{a^2 - b^2}$. By (5), when

$$x = ae, \qquad y = \pm \frac{b}{a}\sqrt{a^2 - a^2e^2} = \pm \frac{b^2}{a},$$

so that *the length of the latus rectum is* $\dfrac{2b^2}{a}$. The ends of the latera recta are

then easily plotted; this gives a total of eight points (see Figure 135) on the curve, from which a fairly accurate sketch can be made.

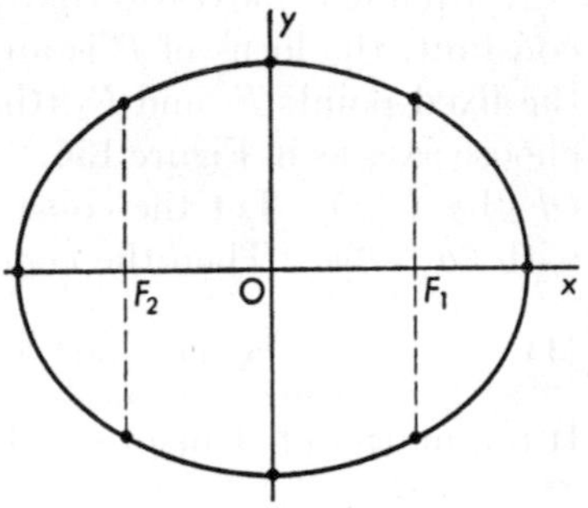

If we had taken the focus on the y-axis and the directrix parallel to the x-axis, the above discussion would have been the same except that x and y would have been interchanged. Hence the equation

Figure 135

$$(6) \qquad \frac{y^2}{a^2} + \frac{x^2}{b^2} = 1, \qquad a > b,$$

represents *the ellipse with center at the origin and major axis on* Oy.

Example. Trace the ellipse

$$4x^2 + 6y^2 = 3.$$

Divide by 3, to reduce the right member to unity:

$$\frac{4x^2}{3} + 2y^2 = 1.$$

Divide numerator and denominator in the first term by 4, in the second by 2, to reduce the numerator-coefficients to unity:

$$(7) \qquad \frac{x^2}{\frac{3}{4}} + \frac{y^2}{\frac{1}{2}} = 1.$$

Since the denominator of x^2 is the larger, we have equation (4) rather than (6): an ellipse with its major axis on Ox. From (7) we read off

$$a = \tfrac{1}{2}\sqrt{3} = 0.87, \qquad b = \tfrac{1}{2}\sqrt{2} = 0.71;$$

the foci are at distance $\sqrt{a^2 - b^2} = \tfrac{1}{2}$ to right and left of the center; the ends of the latera recta are at distance

$$\frac{b^2}{a} = \frac{\frac{1}{2}}{\frac{1}{2}\sqrt{3}} = \frac{1}{3}\sqrt{3} = 0\,57$$

above and below the foci. The eccentricity is

$$e = \frac{\sqrt{a^2 - b^2}}{a} = \frac{\frac{1}{2}}{\frac{1}{2}\sqrt{3}} = \frac{1}{3}\sqrt{3};$$

the directrices are the lines $x = \pm \dfrac{a}{e} = \pm \dfrac{\frac{1}{2}\sqrt{3}}{\frac{1}{3}\sqrt{3}} = \pm \dfrac{3}{2}.$

110. *Some Properties of the Ellipse*

If a point P moves so that the sum of its distances to two fixed points is constant, the locus of P is an ellipse. Let us prove that statement. Call the fixed points F_1 and F_2 (they turn out to be the foci of the ellipse), and choose axes as in Figure 136. Let the directed distance OF_1 be denoted by c, OF_2 by $(-c)$. Let the constant sum of the distances F_1P and F_2P be $2a$, with $2a > 2c$. Then the coordinates (x, y) of P must satisfy the equation

(1) $$\sqrt{(x - c)^2 + y^2} + \sqrt{(x + c)^2 + y^2} = 2a.$$

It is a matter of elementary algebra to rationalize equation (1) and arrive at

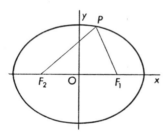

(2) $$\frac{x^2}{a^2} + \frac{y^2}{a^2 - c^2} = 1.$$

Since $a > c$, reference to § 109 shows that the locus of P is an ellipse with foci at F_1 and F_2.

Indeed, every ellipse has the above property; i.e., *an ellipse is the locus of a point which moves so that the sum of its distances from two fixed points is constant.* The fixed points are the foci; the constant sum is the *length of the major axis.*

Figure 136

Next, consider any ellipse. Choose axes so that the foci are F_1: $(ae, 0)$, F_2: $(-ae, 0)$; the directrices $x = \pm \dfrac{a}{e}$; and P: (x, y) any point of an ellipse.

By (1), § 107,

$$F_1P = e\left(\frac{a}{e} - x\right) = a - ex,$$

$$F_2P = e\left(\frac{a}{e} + x\right) = a + ex,$$

so that

(3) $$F_1P + F_2P = 2a.$$

It is a simple matter to find the equation of the tangent line at a point (x_1, y_1) on the ellipse:

(4)
$$\frac{x^2}{a^2} + \frac{y^2}{b^2} = 1.$$

The equation of the tangent line is

(5)
$$\frac{x_1 x}{a^2} + \frac{y_1 y}{b^2} = 1$$

and should be derived by the student by the method used in the corresponding example for the parabola, page 104.

Example. Prove that the tangents at the ends of a latus rectum of an ellipse intersect on a directrix.

For the focus $(ae, 0)$ of the ellipse (4), the corresponding end points of the latus rectum are $\left(ae, \frac{b^2}{a} \right)$ and $\left(ae, -\frac{b^2}{a} \right)$. Using equation (5), we find that the tangent line at the point $\left(ae, \frac{b^2}{a} \right)$ is

$$\frac{aex}{a^2} + \frac{b^2 y}{ab^2} = 1,$$

or

(6)
$$ex + y = a.$$

The tangent line at the point $\left(ae, -\frac{b^2}{a} \right)$ is

$$\frac{aex}{a^2} - \frac{b^2 y}{ab^2} = 1,$$

or

(7)
$$ex - y = a.$$

The lines (6) and (7) intersect at $\left(\frac{a}{e}, 0 \right)$ which is a point on a directrix of the ellipse.

EXERCISES

In Exs. 1–10, find the center and foci, plot the vertices and the ends of the latera recta, and draw the curve. Find the eccentricity and the equations of the directrices.

1. $\dfrac{x^2}{25} + \dfrac{y^2}{16} = 1.$ 2. $\dfrac{x^2}{25} + \dfrac{y^2}{9} = 1.$

3. $\dfrac{x^2}{144} + \dfrac{y^2}{169} = 1.$ 4. $\dfrac{x^2}{36} + \dfrac{y^2}{100} = 1.$

5. $2x^2 + y^2 = 8$.
7. $3x^2 + 5y^2 = 15$.
9. $144x^2 + 225y^2 = 400$.

6. $3x^2 + 4y^2 = 12$.
8. $2x^2 + 3y^2 = 6$.
10. $4x^2 + y^2 = 1$.

In Exs. 11–24, find the equation of the ellipse, assuming form (4), § 109.

11. Eccentricity $\frac{1}{3}$, distance between foci 2.   *Ans.* $8x^2 + 9y^2 = 72$.
12. Eccentricity $\frac{1}{2}$, distance between directrices 24.   *Ans.* $3x^2 + 4y^2 = 108$.
13. Major axis 8, distance between foci 6.   *Ans.* $7x^2 + 16y^2 = 112$.
14. Minor axis 10, distance between foci 24.   *Ans.* $\dfrac{x^2}{169} + \dfrac{y^2}{25} = 1$.
15. Distance between foci 2, between directrices 8.   *Ans.* $3x^2 + 4y^2 = 12$.
16. Distance between foci 4, between directrices 36.   *Ans.* $8x^2 + 9y^2 = 288$.
17. Latus rectum 4, distance between foci $4\sqrt{2}$.   *Ans.* $x^2 + 2y^2 = 16$.
18. Distance between foci $8\sqrt{6}$, rectangle on the axes of area 80.
    Ans. $x^2 + 25y^2 = 100$.
19. Eccentricity $\frac{2}{3}$, latus rectum $\frac{2}{3}$.   *Ans.* $25x^2 + 45y^2 = 9$.
20. Passing through (4, 3), (6, 2).   *Ans.* $x^2 + 4y^2 = 52$.
21. Passing through (1, 2), (3, 1).   *Ans.* $3x^2 + 8y^2 = 35$.
22. Passing through (2, 3), latus rectum three times the distance from center to focus.   *Ans.* $3x^2 + 4y^2 = 48$.
23. Latus rectum $\frac{60}{19}$, distance between directrices $2\sqrt{19}$.
    Ans. $15x^2 + 19y^2 = 60$; $10x^2 + 19y^2 = 90$.
24. Distance between foci $\frac{4}{3}\sqrt{33}$, passing through (2, 1).   *Ans.* $x^2 + 12y^2 = 16$.

25. Show that as e approaches zero, with a kept fixed, the ellipse approaches a circle. Let $e \to 0$ in (2), § 109. As this happens, how do the foci and directrices move?

26. The orbits of the planets in our solar system are ellipses with the sun at one focus. The eccentricities are tabulated below. For each planet, as a measure of the nearly circular character of its orbit, determine to the nearest hundredth the ratio of the length of the minor axis to the length of the major axis.

Mercury: $e = 0.206$.   *Ans.* 0.98.
Venus: $e = 0.007$.   *Ans.* 1.00.
Earth: $e = 0.017$.   *Ans.* 1.00.
Mars: $e = 0.093$.   *Ans.* 1.00.
Jupiter: $e = 0.048$.   *Ans.* 1.00.
Saturn: $e = 0.056$.   *Ans.* 1.00.
Uranus: $e = 0.047$.   *Ans.* 1.00.
Neptune: $e = 0.008$.   *Ans.* 1.00.
Pluto: $e = 0.249$.   *Ans.* 0.97.

27. In the asteroid belt between the orbits of Mars and Jupiter some asteroids are known to have orbits with eccentricities as high as $\frac{2}{3}$. For such an elliptic orbit, find the ratio of minor to major axis.   *Ans.* 0.75.

28. Show that the ordinates of the ellipse $\dfrac{x^2}{a^2} + \dfrac{y^2}{b^2} = 1$ are $\dfrac{b}{a}$ times those of the circle $x^2 + y^2 = a^2$.

29. The orbit of the earth is an ellipse with the sun at a focus; the semimajor axis is 93 million miles, the eccentricity $\frac{1}{60}$, nearly. Find the greatest and least distances of the earth from the sun.

30. In Figure 133, page 201, show that $CF:CV_1 = CV_1:CM$.

31. A line segment of fixed length moves with its ends following two perpendicular lines. The line is divided by a point P into two segments of lengths a, b. Find the locus of P. *Ans.* An ellipse.

32. A point moves so that the sum of its distances from $(4, 0)$, $(-4, 0)$ is 9. Find the equation of its locus. (§ 110.)

33. A circle touches the circle $(x + 1)^2 + y^2 = 9$ and passes through $(1, 0)$. Find the locus of its center. *Ans.* $20x^2 + 36y^2 = 45$.

34. A moving circle is tangent to each of the fixed circles $(x - c)^2 + y^2 = c^2$, $(x + c)^2 + y^2 = 16c^2$. Find the locus of its center.

Ans. $84x^2 + 100y^2 = 525c^2$; $20x^2 + 36y^2 = 45c^2$.

35. Derive the equation of the tangent line (5), § 110.

36. Tangents are drawn to the ellipse $\dfrac{x^2}{a^2} + \dfrac{y^2}{b^2} = 1$ and to the circle $x^2 + y^2 = a^2$

at points having the same abscissa. Show that these tangents cross Ox together.

37. Show that the tangents at the ends of the latera recta of an ellipse have slopes $\pm e$.

38. Prove that the perpendicular from a focus to any tangent to an ellipse, and the line joining the center to the point of contact, intersect on the directrix.

39. Prove that the product of the distances from the foci to any tangent to an ellipse is constant (equal to b^2 for an ellipse in standard form).

111. *Other Standard Forms*

By translation of axes (§ 64) we may establish the following standard forms:

The equation of an ellipse with center at (h, k) and major axis parallel to Ox is

(1) $$\frac{(x-h)^2}{a^2} + \frac{(y-k)^2}{b^2} = 1, \qquad a > b.$$

The equation of an ellipse with center at (h, k) and major axis parallel to Oy is

(2) $$\frac{(y-k)^2}{a^2} + \frac{(x-h)^2}{b^2} = 1, \qquad a > b.$$

The equation

(3) $$Ax^2 + Cy^2 + Dx + Ey + F = 0,$$

where A and C have *the same sign*, can in general be reduced by completing the squares in x and y, to one of the standard forms. (See the example below Theorem 31.) There are two exceptional cases. When the left member is written as the sum of two squares, the right member may be zero, or it may be negative. In the former case the locus is the single point (h, k)—the so-called point-ellipse; in the latter case, there is no locus.

THEOREM 31. *An equation of the second degree in which the xy-term is missing and the coefficients of x² and y² have the same sign represents an ellipse with axes parallel to the coordinate axes (exceptionally, a single point, or no locus).*

Example. Draw the curve

$$9x^2 + 4y^2 - 36x + 8y + 31 = 0.$$

Transpose the constant and complete the squares:

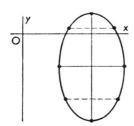

Figure 137

$$9(x^2 - 4x + 4) + 4(y^2 + 2y + 1) = -31 + 36 + 4,$$

$$9(x - 2)^2 + 4(y + 1)^2 = 9,$$

$$\frac{(x - 2)^2}{1} + \frac{(y + 1)^2}{\frac{9}{4}} = 1.$$

The center is at $(2, -1)$, major axis parallel to Oy, semiaxes $a = \frac{3}{2}$, $b = 1$, distance from center to foci $\sqrt{a^2 - b^2} = \sqrt{\frac{5}{4}} = \frac{1}{2}\sqrt{5}$, latus rectum $= \frac{4}{3}$.

EXERCISES

In Exs. 1–18, find the center and foci, plot the ends of the axes and of the latera recta, and draw the curve.

1. $\dfrac{(x - 2)^2}{25} + \dfrac{(y - 1)^2}{9} = 1.$

2. $\dfrac{(x - 4)^2}{4} + \dfrac{(y + 2)^2}{9} = 1.$

3. $\dfrac{(x + 1)^2}{1} + \dfrac{(y + 3)^2}{9} = 1.$

4. $\dfrac{(x + 5)^2}{1} + \dfrac{(y - 4)^2}{\frac{1}{4}} = 1.$

5. $\dfrac{(x + 2a)^2}{a^2} + \dfrac{y^2}{2a^2} = 1.$

6. $\dfrac{(x + a)^2}{4a^2} + \dfrac{(y - 2a)^2}{a^2} = 1.$

7. $x^2 + 2y^2 - 6x + 5 = 0.$
8. $x^2 + 9y^2 + 18y = 0.$
9. $x^2 + 9y^2 + 3x - 18y + 9 = 0.$
10. $x^2 + 2y^2 + 4x - 12y + 16 = 0.$
11. $2x^2 + y^2 - 4x - 2y = 1.$
12. $3x^2 + 2y^2 - 36x - 16y + 134 = 0.$
13. $3x^2 + y^2 = 6cx.$
14. $x^2 + 4y^2 = 4cy.$
15. $16x^2 + 12y^2 - 12y - 9 = 0.$
16. $7x^2 + 2y^2 + 14x - 8y + 1 = 0.$
17. $3x^2 + 4y^2 - 18x + 8y + 19 = 0.$
18. $9x^2 + 10y^2 - 90x - 40y + 175 = 0.$

In Exs. 19–24, find the points of intersection and draw the curves.

19. $x^2 = 3y,\ 3x^2 + y^2 - 24y + 36 = 0.$ *Ans.* $(\pm3, 3),\ (\pm6, 12).$
20. $y^2 = 4x,\ 4x^2 + 9y^2 = 8x + 72y - 112.$ *Ans.* $(4, 4),\ (1, 2).$

21. $x^2 = y + 10$, $y^2 + 5(x - 1)^2 = 81$.

         Ans. $(-3, -1)$, $(-2, -6)$, $(1, -9)$, $(4, 6)$.

22. $4x^2 + y^2 = 100$, $4(x + 3)^2 + 7y^2 = 448$.   *Ans.* $(-3, \pm 8)$, $(4, \pm 6)$.

23. $x^2 + y^2 + 4ax = 0$, $2x^2 + y^2 = 4ax$.   *Ans.* $(0, 0)$ twice. ·

24. $x^2 + y^2 - 4ax = 0$, $2x^2 + y^2 = 4ax$.   *Ans.* $(0, 0)$ four times.

25. A circle is tangent to the circles $x^2 + y^2 = 4$, $x^2 + y^2 = 12y + 64$. Find the locus of its center and draw the figure.

     Ans. $4x^2 + 3y^2 - 18y - 81 = 0$; $16x^2 + 7y^2 - 42y - 49 = 0$.

112. *Hyperbola Referred to Its Axes*

By definition, the hyperbola is *the conic section for which $e > 1$.*

The derivation of equation (2), § 109, does not depend upon the fact that $e < 1$; we therefore conclude at once that, with the axes chosen as in § 109, the equation of the hyperbola is

(1)
$$\frac{x^2}{a^2} + \frac{y^2}{a^2(1 - e^2)} = 1.$$

But, since now $e > 1$, it follows that $\dfrac{a}{e} < a < ae$; hence the directrices pass between the vertices, and the foci lie in the axis produced each way. From the fact that $e > 1$, it also follows that the quantity $a^2(1 - e^2)$ is negative; therefore to make b real, we set

(2) $b^2 = a^2(e^2 - 1)$,

and write (1) in the form

(3) $\dfrac{x^2}{a^2} - \dfrac{y^2}{b^2} = 1$.

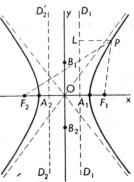

Figure 138

This equation shows that:

(*a*) The curve is symmetric with respect to both axes. Hence there are two foci, the points $(\pm ae, 0)$, and two directrices, the lines $x = \pm \dfrac{a}{e}$.

(*b*) The intercepts on Ox are $(\pm a, 0)$; on Oy, imaginary.

(*c*) The equation when solved for y has the form

(4) $y = \pm \dfrac{b}{a} \sqrt{x^2 - a^2}$;

thus y is imaginary if, and only if, $x^2 < a^2$: i.e., if $-a < x < a$. The curve consists of two disconnected branches, one to the right of the line $x = a$, the other to the left of the line $x = -a$.

(*d*) *The length of the latus rectum is* $\dfrac{2b^2}{a}$.

As in the case of the ellipse, the lines of symmetry are sometimes spoken of as the *axes* of the curve, but unless the contrary is indicated, the axes will be considered to be the *segments* A_2A_1 of length $2a$ and B_2B_1 of length $2b$; the former is the *transverse axis*, the latter the *conjugate axis*. The conjugate axis does not intersect the curve but plays an important part in its theory. The ends A_2, A_1 of the transverse axis are the *vertices*; the point of intersection of the axes is the *center*.

It follows from (2) that *the distance from center to foci is*

(5) $\;$ /
$$ae = \sqrt{a^2 + b^2}.$$

It should also be noted that in the case of the hyperbola, b may be *greater than*, *equal to*, or *less than* a, according to the value of e.

With the foci on the y-axis and directrices parallel to the x-axis, the analysis is the same except that x and y are interchanged; hence the equation

(6)
$$\frac{y^2}{a^2} - \frac{x^2}{b^2} = 1$$

represents a *hyperbola with transverse axis along Oy.*

It is customary to call the ellipse and hyperbola the *central conics*, since each has a center of symmetry.

113. *Asymptotes*

Given the standard equation of the hyperbola

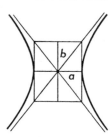

Figure 139

(1)
$$\frac{x^2}{a^2} - \frac{y^2}{b^2} = 1,$$

let us clear of fractions:

(2) $\qquad b^2x^2 - a^2y^2 = a^2b^2.$

When this curve and the straight line

(3) $\qquad bx - ay = 0$

are drawn on the same axes, the hyperbola approaches the straight line more and more closely, as the distance from the center increases, but without ever reaching the line. To prove this, let P: (x_1, y_1) be a point on the hyperbola in the first or third quadrant. The distance of P from the line (3) is

(4)
$$d = \frac{bx_1 - ay_1}{\sqrt{a^2 + b^2}}.$$

Since P is on the curve, its coordinates satisfy (2):

$$b^2x_1{}^2 - a^2y_1{}^2 = a^2b^2,$$

whence

$$bx_1 - ay_1 = \frac{a^2b^2}{bx_1 + ay_1}.$$

Substituting this value of $bx_1 - ay_1$ in (4), we find

$$d = \frac{a^2b^2}{\sqrt{a^2 + b^2}} \cdot \frac{1}{bx_1 + ay_1}.$$

Evidently d can never equal zero, but as P recedes, so that x_1 and y_1 both increase indefinitely, d becomes smaller and smaller, approaching the limit zero.

A similar result is easily established for the line

(5) $$bx + ay = 0$$

when P lies in the second or fourth quadrant.

The lines (3) and (5), which together may be written as

(6) $$y = \pm \frac{b}{a} x,$$

are called *asymptotes* of the hyperbola (1). A general definition of asymptote will be given in § 151. In practice it is soon discovered that the asymptotes are of great aid in sketching a hyperbola.

From (6) we derive the following theorem, which gives a convenient method for drawing the asymptotes of any hyperbola whose axes are given.

THEOREM 32. *The asymptotes of a hyperbola are the diagonal lines of the rectangle whose center is the center of the curve and whose sides are parallel to and equal to the axes of the curve.*

To draw a hyperbola whose equation is in a standard form, we plot the vertices and the ends of the latera recta, and draw the asymptotes.

Example. Trace the curve

$$4y^2 = x^2 - 1.$$

First reduce to standard form:

$$\frac{x^2}{1} - \frac{y^2}{\frac{1}{4}} = 1.$$

Since x^2 is in the *positive term*, this is form (3), § 112; the transverse axis is along the x-axis. We read off $a = 1$, $b = \frac{1}{2}$; the foci are at distance $\sqrt{a^2 + b^2} = \frac{1}{2}\sqrt{5} = 1.12$ to right and left of the center; the ends of the latera recta are at distance $\frac{b^2}{a} = \frac{1}{4}$ above and below the foci; the asymptotes are the diagonals of the rectangle of sides $2a$, $2b$. The eccentricity is

$$e = \frac{\sqrt{a^2 + b^2}}{a} = \frac{1}{5}\sqrt{5};$$ the directrices are the lines

$$x = \pm \frac{a}{e} = \pm \frac{2}{5}\sqrt{5}.$$

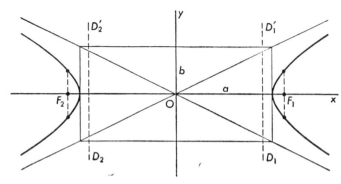

Figure 140

114. *Equilateral, or Rectangular, Hyperbola*

The hyperbola for which a and b are equal is called, on account of the equality of the semiaxes, the *equilateral* hyperbola. Since the rectangle of Figure 139, page 210, is in this case a square, the asymptotes of the equilateral hyperbola are at right angles: for this reason it is also called the *rectangular* hyperbola. Since $ae = \sqrt{a^2 + b^2}$, the eccentricity of the equilateral hyperbola is $e = \sqrt{2}$.

When the hyperbola is equilateral, equation (3) of § 112 assumes the form

$$x^2 - y^2 = a^2.$$

115. *Some Properties of the Hyperbola*

The hyperbola has properties which parallel those of the ellipse, as described in § 110. The student should prove the following statements.

If a point P moves so that the difference of its distances to two fixed points is constant, the locus of P is a hyperbola.

A hyperbola is the locus of a point which moves so that the difference of its distances from two fixed points is constant. The fixed points are the *foci* and the constant difference is *the length of the transverse axis.*

That is, in Figure 138, page 209,

(1) $$F_2P - F_1P = 2a,$$

or, for a point P' on the left-hand branch,

$$F_1P' - F_2P' = 2a.$$

The tangent line at the point (x_1, y_1) on the hyperbola

(2)
$$\frac{x^2}{a^2} - \frac{y^2}{b^2} = 1$$

has the equation

(3)
$$\frac{x_1 x}{a^2} - \frac{y_1 y}{b^2} = 1.$$

EXERCISES

In Exs. 1–10, locate the center, vertices, foci, and ends of the latera recta, draw the asymptotes, and trace the curve. Determine the eccentricity and write the equations of the directrices and asymptotes.

1. $\dfrac{x^2}{16} - \dfrac{y^2}{9} = 1.$

2. $\dfrac{x^2}{25} - \dfrac{y^2}{144} = 1.$

3. $\dfrac{y^2}{9} - \dfrac{x^2}{1} = 1.$

4. $\dfrac{y^2}{4} - \dfrac{x^2}{2} = 1.$

5. $2y^2 - 9x^2 = 18.$

6. $3x^2 - 4y^2 = 12.$

7. $5x^2 = 4y^2 + 20.$

8. $x^2 = 3y^2 - 27.$

9. $y^2 = x^2 - a^2.$

10. $y^2 = x^2 + a^2.$

In Exs. 11–22, find the equation of the hyperbola, assuming form (3), § 112.   Draw the curve.

11. Distance between foci 18, between directrices 2.   *Ans.* $8x^2 - y^2 = 72.$

12. Eccentricity 2, distance between foci $4\sqrt{2}$.   *Ans.* $3x^2 - y^2 = 6.$

13. Latus rectum 1, slope of asymptotes $\pm\frac{1}{2}$.   *Ans.* $x^2 - 4y^2 = 4.$

14. Latus rectum 6, distance between foci twice the distance between directrices.
        Ans. $x^2 - y^2 = 9.$

15. Eccentricity 3, latus rectum $\frac{8}{3}$.   *Ans.* $72x^2 - 9y^2 = 2.$

16. Latus rectum $\frac{14}{3}$, distance between directrices $\frac{9}{2}$.   *Ans.* $7x^2 - 9y^2 = 63.$

17. Distance between directrices unity, passing through (2, 3).
        Ans. $3x^2 - y^2 = 3;\ 12x^2 - y^2 = 39.$

18. Latus rectum 2, passing through (6, 3).   *Ans.* $x^2 - 3y^2 = 9.$

19. Latus rectum 18, distance between foci 12.   *Ans.* $3x^2 - y^2 = 27.$

20. Eccentricity 2, distance between directrices $\sqrt{2}$.   *Ans.* $3x^2 - y^2 = 6.$

21. Passing through (2, 1), (4, 3).   *Ans.* $2x^2 - 3y^2 = 5.$

22. Foci $(\pm4, 0)$, slope of asymptotes ± 3.   *Ans.* $45x^2 - 5y^2 = 72.$

23. Prove equation (1), § 115.   (Compare with § 110.)

24. A point moves so that the difference of its distances from $(ae, 0)$, $(-ae, 0)$ is $2a$.   Find the equation of its locus.

25. A circle passes through a given point and touches a given circle.   Find the locus of its center, for all possible cases.   (§§ 110, 115.)

26. The sound of a gun and the ring of the ball on the target are heard simultaneously at P.   Show that the locus of P is one branch of a hyperbola.

27. A point moves so that the difference of its distances from $(4, 0)$, $(-4, 0)$ is 6. Find the equation of its locus.

28. A point moves so that the difference of its distances from $(0, 3)$, $(0, -3)$ is 2. Find the equation of its locus.

29. A circle touches the circle $x^2 + y^2 + 2cx = 0$ and passes through $(c, 0)$. Find the locus of its center.   *Ans.* $12x^2 - 4y^2 = 3c^2$.

30. Prove analytically that a line parallel to an asymptote of a hyperbola intersects the curve in one and only one point.

31. Show that the product of the distances of any point of a hyperbola from its asymptotes is constant.

32. Show that: A *hyperbola* is the locus of a point moving so that the product of its distances from two intersecting lines is constant. (Take the lines $y = \pm mx$.)

33. If the angle between the transverse axis and an asymptote of a hyperbola is denoted by α, show that $\sec \alpha = e$.

34. A moving circle is tangent externally to each of the two fixed circles $(x - 2c)^2 + y^2 = c^2$, $(x + 2c)^2 + y^2 = 4c^2$. Find the locus of its center.

Ans. $60x^2 - 4y^2 = 15c^2$.

35. Derive the equation of the tangent line (3) directly above these exercises.

36. Show that the tangents at the ends of the latera recta of a hyperbola have slopes $\pm e$.

37. Prove that the perpendicular from a focus to any tangent to a hyperbola, and the line joining the center to the point of contact, intersect on the directrix.

38. Prove that the product of the distances from the foci to any tangent to a hyperbola is constant (equal to b^2 for a hyperbola in standard form).

116. *Standard Forms*

By translating the coordinate axes, we obtain for the hyperbola formulas analogous to those of § 111 for the ellipse. The resulting formulas are as follows:

The equation of a hyperbola with center at (h, k) and transverse axis parallel to Ox is

$$(1) \qquad \frac{(x - h)^2}{a^2} - \frac{(y - k)^2}{b^2} = 1.$$

The equation of a hyperbola with center at (h, k) and transverse axis parallel to Oy is

$$(2) \qquad \frac{(y - k)^2}{a^2} - \frac{(x - h)^2}{b^2} = 1.$$

The equation

$$(3) \qquad Ax^2 + Cy^2 + Dx + Ey + F = 0,$$

where A and C have *opposite* signs, can be reduced, by completing the squares in x and y, to one of the forms (1) or (2). The only exceptional case is the one in which, when the left member has been expressed as the difference of two squares, the right member reduces to zero:

$$\frac{(x-h)^2}{a^2} - \frac{(y-k)^2}{b^2} = 0.$$

This equation can be factored, and therefore represents two straight lines intersecting at (h, k).

THEOREM 33. *An equation of the second degree in which the xy-term is missing and the coefficients of x^2 and y^2 have unlike signs represents a hyperbola with its axes parallel to the coordinate axes (exceptionally, two intersecting lines).*

Example. Trace the curve

$$x^2 - 2y^2 + 4x + 4y + 4 = 0.$$

Completing squares, we get

$$(x+2)^2 - 2(y-1)^2 = -2,$$

or, dividing by -2,

$$\frac{(y-1)^2}{1} - \frac{(x+2)^2}{2} = 1.$$

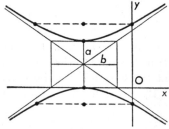

Figure 141

This is a hyperbola with center at $(-2, 1)$ and transverse axis parallel to Oy; the semiaxes are $a = 1$, $b = \sqrt{2}$. The vertices are at the distance 1, the foci at the distance $\sqrt{a^2 + b^2} = \sqrt{3}$, above and below the center. The ends of the latera recta are at distance 2 to right and left of the foci.

EXERCISES

In Exs. 1–14, locate the center, vertices, foci, and ends of the latera recta, draw the asymptotes, and draw the curve.

1. $\dfrac{(x-1)^2}{16} - \dfrac{(y-2)^2}{9} = 1.$

2. $\dfrac{(x-3)^2}{4} - \dfrac{(y+2)^2}{1} = 1.$

3. $\dfrac{(y+1)^2}{1} - \dfrac{(x+4)^2}{3} = 1.$

4. $\dfrac{(y+2)^2}{9} - \dfrac{(x-4)^2}{7} = 1.$

5. $\dfrac{y^2}{4} - \dfrac{(x+3)^2}{5} = 1.$

6. $\dfrac{x^2}{8} - \dfrac{(y-3)^2}{8} = 1.$

7. $3x^2 - y^2 + 12cx + 9c^2 = 0.$

8. $4x^2 - y^2 + 2cy + 3c^2 = 0.$

9. $5x^2 - 4y^2 = 20x + 24y + 36.$

10. $9x^2 - y^2 = 90x - 12y - 225.$

11. $x^2 - 3y^2 - 2x - 2 = 0.$

12. $x^2 - y^2 + 6x + 2y = -10.$

13. $16x^2 - 4y^2 = 12y - 16x + 1.$

14. $4x^2 - 3y^2 = 6(x + y).$

In Exs. 15–23, find the points of intersection and draw the curves.

15. $x^2 - 4y^2 + 2x + 8y + 1 = 0$, $2y = x + 3$.   *Ans.* None.

16. $9x^2 - y^2 + 18x + 2y + 17 = 0$, $3x + y + 2 = 0$.

17. $(x-1)^2 = y + 1$, $5x^2 - y^2 = 4x$.   *Ans.* $(0, 0)$, $(1, -1)$, $(4, 8)$, $(-1, 3)$.

18. $2x^2 - y^2 - 8x - y + 8 = 0$, $4x^2 - 3y^2 - 16x - 3y + 18 = 0$.

19. $x^2 - y^2 - 2ay = 0$, $x^2 + y^2 - 2ay = 0$.   *Ans.* (0, 0) four times.

20. $2x^2 + y^2 - 8x - 4y + 10 = 0$, $x^2 - 3y^2 + 10x + 12y - 23 = 0$.

                                                 Ans. (1, 2) four times.

21. $x^2 - y^2 = 4x + 4y - 1$, $x^2 - y^2 = 4x + 2y - 7$.   *Ans.* (2, −3) twice.

22. $x^2 - y^2 + 3x - y + 8 = 0$, $x^2 - y^2 + 4x - 4y + 16 = 0$.

23. $x^2 - y^2 + 5x + 3y + 2 = 0$, $x^2 - y^2 + 2x = 4$.   *Ans.* (−4, 2).

117. *Polar Equation of a Conic*

The polar equation of any conic assumes a simple form if we choose a focus as the pole and take the initial line perpendicular to the corresponding directrix. In Figure 142, let $P: (r, \theta)$ be a random point on the conic and let Q be at one end of the latus rectum. Drop perpendiculars as indicated from P and Q to the initial line OA and the directrix AB. For convenience, let the length of the latus rectum be $2L$.

By the definition of eccentricity e (page 200), we may write

$$PO = e \cdot PB, \qquad QO = e \cdot QM.$$

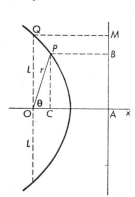

Figure 142

Therefore $PB = \dfrac{r}{e}$ and $QM = \dfrac{L}{e}$. But also,

$$PB = OA - OC$$
$$= QM - OC,$$

from which it follows that

(1) $$\frac{r}{e} = \frac{L}{e} - r \cos \theta.$$

When solved for r, equation (1) takes the form

(2) $$r = \frac{L}{1 + e \cos \theta}.$$

Other forms for the polar equation of a conic appear in the exercises.

EXERCISES

In Exs. 1–11, derive the polar equation of the conic with focus as pole, eccentricity and directrix as stipulated.

1. With $e = 2$ and directrix perpendicular to Ox through $(4, \pi)$.

                                  Ans. $r = \dfrac{8}{1 - 2 \cos \theta}$.

2. With $e = \frac{1}{2}$ and directrix perpendicular to Ox through $(6, \pi)$.

3. With $e = \frac{1}{3}$ and directrix parallel to Ox through $(2, \frac{1}{2}\pi)$.

                                  Ans. $r = \dfrac{2}{3 + \sin \theta}$.

4. With $e = 2$ and directrix parallel to Ox through $(4, \frac{1}{2}\pi)$.

5. With $e = 6$ and directrix parallel to Ox through $(1, \frac{3}{2}\pi)$.

$$Ans. \; r = \frac{6}{1 - 6 \sin \theta}.$$

6. With $e = 3$ and directrix parallel to Ox through $(2, \frac{3}{2}\pi)$.

7. With $e = 1$ and directrix perpendicular to Ox through $(4, 0)$.

8. With $e = \frac{1}{2}$ and directrix perpendicular to Ox through $(3, 0)$.

9. With eccentricity e and directrix perpendicular to Ox through $\left(\frac{L}{e}, \pi\right)$.

$$Ans. \; r = \frac{L}{1 - e \cos \theta}.$$

10. With eccentricity e and directrix parallel to Ox through $\left(\frac{L}{e}, \frac{1}{2}\pi\right)$.

$$Ans. \; r = \frac{L}{1 + e \sin \theta}.$$

11. With eccentricity e and directrix parallel to Ox through $\left(\frac{L}{e}, \frac{3}{2}\pi\right)$.

$$Ans. \; r = \frac{L}{1 - e \sin \theta}.$$

In Exs. 12–17, sketch the conic.

12. $r(3 + 2 \sin \theta) = 6$.

13. $r(1 - \cos \theta) = 4$.

14. $r(1 - \sin \theta) = 2$.

15. $r(5 + \cos \theta) = 20$.

16. $r(2 + 3 \sin \theta) = 6$.

17. $r(1 + 3 \cos \theta) = 15$.

18. Find the polar equation of a central conic, with center at the pole and transverse axis along Ox, by transforming to polar coordinates equation (4) § 109.

19. Derive the polar equation of a parabola with vertex at the pole and focus at $(a, 0)$ directly, and also by transforming the equation $y^2 = 4ax$.

$$Ans. \; r \sin \theta \tan \theta = 4a.$$

20. Chords are drawn from the vertex of a parabola. Show that the locus of their mid-points is a parabola whose latus rectum is half as long as that of the original parabola. Use the answer to Ex. 19.

21. Find the locus of the mid-points of the focal radii of the conic (2) of this section.

$$Ans. \; r = \frac{\frac{1}{2}L}{1 + e \cos \theta}.$$

22. Find the locus of the mid-points of chords drawn through a fixed point on a circle.

Parametric Equations.   Motion

118. *Parametric Equations*

In both pure and applied mathematics, a curve often arises most naturally as the locus of points whose coordinates are determined by two equations

$$(1) \qquad x = f(t), \quad y = g(t),$$

giving x and y in terms of a third variable t.   The variable t is then called a *parameter*; the equations (1) are parametric equations of the curve.   To obtain the rectangular equation of the curve, we need to eliminate the parameter.   As we shall see, such elimination may not be feasible; it may not be wise even when feasible.

A curve can be drawn by plotting points directly from its parametric equations, assigning suitable values to the parameter and computing corresponding values of x and y.   For the location of maxima, minima, and points of inflection, we must develop a technique for obtaining the derivatives of y with respect to x from the parametric equations (1).

Example (a).   Find $\dfrac{dy}{dx}$ and $\dfrac{d^2y}{dx^2}$ from

$$x = t^3 + 2t - 4, \qquad y = t^3 - t + 2.$$

First we obtain the derivatives of x and of y with respect to t:

$$\frac{dx}{dt} = 3t^2 + 2, \qquad \frac{dy}{dt} = 3t^2 - 1.$$

Then, by the chain rule of § 51, the ratio of these gives the desired first derivative,

$$(2) \qquad \frac{dy}{dx} = \frac{3t^2 - 1}{3t^2 + 2}.$$

Equation (2) exhibits $\dfrac{dy}{dx}$ in terms of t.   We wish to differentiate both members of (2) with respect to x, and t is a function of x.   Therefore we need to use the formula for a derivative of a function of a function,

218

(3)
$$\frac{dF}{dx} = \frac{dF}{dt} \cdot \frac{dt}{dx}$$

which is (5) of § 51, except for changes in notation. Employing the idea in (3) when differentiating the right member of equation (2), we get

(4)
$$\frac{d^2y}{dx^2} = \frac{(3t^2 + 2)(6t) - (3t^2 - 1)(6t)}{(3t^2 + 2)^2} \cdot \frac{dt}{dx}.$$

But $\frac{dt}{dx}$ is the reciprocal of $\frac{dx}{dt}$, as shown in (5″) of § 51. Hence (4) yields

$$\frac{d^2y}{dx^2} = \frac{18t}{(3t^2 + 2)^2} \cdot \frac{1}{3t^2 + 2}$$
$$= \frac{18t}{(3t^2 + 2)^3}.$$

Example (b). Find $\frac{dy}{dx}$ and $\frac{d^2y}{dx^2}$ from

(5)
$$x = t^3 + 1, \qquad y = 4t^2 - 4t.$$

As a mild variation of the method used in Example (a), let us employ differentials. From (5) we get

(6)
$$dx = 3t^2 \, dt, \qquad dy = 4(2t - 1) \, dt.$$

Then

(7)
$$y' = \frac{dy}{dx} = \frac{4(2t - 1)}{3t^2}.$$

The differential of y' may be obtained from (7). It is given by

(8)
$$dy' = \frac{8(1 - t) \, dt}{3t^3}.$$

Now

$$y'' = \frac{d^2y}{dx^2} = \frac{dy'}{dx},$$

so we combine (8) and (6) to obtain

(9)
$$\frac{d^2y}{dx^2} = \frac{8(1 - t) \, dt}{3t^3 \cdot 3t^2 \, dt} = \frac{8(1 - t)}{9t^5}.$$

EXERCISES

In Exs. 1–12, find the first and second derivatives of y with respect to x from the parametric equations given.

1. $x = 1 + t^2$, $y = 4t - 3$.   *Ans.* $y'' = -t^{-3}$.
2. $x = t^3 + 7$, $y = 6t^2 - 1$.   *Ans.* $y'' = -\frac{4}{3}t^{-4}$.

3. $x = t^3 - 1$, $y = t^2 + t$. *Ans.* $y'' = \dfrac{-2(t + 1)}{9t^5}$.

4. $x = 3(t - 2)^2$, $y = 9t^2 + 4$. *Ans.* $y'' = -(t - 2)^{-3}$.

5. $x = \dfrac{1}{t^2}$, $y = t^2 - 4t + 1$. *Ans.* $y'' = t^5(2t - 3)$.

6. $x = \dfrac{1}{t^2}$, $y = t^2 - t$. *Ans.* $y'' = \tfrac{1}{4}t^5(8t - 3)$.

7. $x = \dfrac{1}{t^3}$, $y = t^3 + 3t$. *Ans.* $y'' = \tfrac{2}{3}t^7(3t^2 + 2)$.

8. $x = \dfrac{1}{(t + 1)^2}$, $y = t^2 + 3$. *Ans.* $y'' = \tfrac{1}{2}(t + 1)^5(4t + 1)$.

9. $x = \sqrt{1 - t}$, $y = t^3 - 3t$. *Ans.* $y'' = 6(1 + 4t - 5t^2)$.

10. $x = \sqrt{t + 2}$, $y = t^2 - 3$. *Ans.* $y'' = 4(3t + 4)$.

11. $x = (t - 2)^{\frac{3}{2}}$, $y = t^2 - 1$. *Ans.* $y'' = \dfrac{4(t - 4)}{9(t - 2)^2}$.

12. $x = \dfrac{1}{(t - 1)^2}$, $y = \dfrac{1}{t + 2}$. *Ans.* $y'' = \dfrac{-(t - 1)^5(t + 8)}{4(t + 2)^3}$.

From the parametric equations in each of Exs. 13–17, find $y' = \dfrac{dy}{dx}$ from the quotient dy divided by dx.

13. $x = 1 + t^2$, $y = t^3 - 2$. *Ans.* $y' = \tfrac{3}{2}t$.

14. $x = 2 - 3t + t^3$, $y = 3t^2 - 7$. *Ans.* $y' = \dfrac{2t}{t^2 - 1}$.

15. $x = (\beta^2 - 1)^2$, $y = 4\beta^3$. *Ans.* $y' = \dfrac{3\beta}{\beta^2 - 1}$.

16. $x = \dfrac{1}{u^2}$, $y = u^4 - 2u^2 + \dfrac{4}{u}$. *Ans.* $y' = 2u(1 + u^3 - u^5)$.

17. $x = \dfrac{1}{t + 1}$, $y = \dfrac{1}{t - 1}$. *Ans.* $y' = \left(\dfrac{t + 1}{t - 1}\right)^2$.

In each of Exs. 18–24, find $y'' = \dfrac{d^2y}{dx^2}$ by first obtaining y' and then $\dfrac{dy'}{dx}$.

18. Ex. 13. *Ans.* $y'' = \dfrac{3}{4t}$.

19. Ex. 14. *Ans.* $y'' = \dfrac{-2(t^2 + 1)}{3(t^2 - 1)^3}$.

20. Ex. 15. *Ans.* $y'' = \dfrac{-3(\beta^2 + 1)}{4\beta(\beta^2 - 1)^3}$.

21. Ex. 16. *Ans.* $y'' = u^3(6u^5 - 4u^3 - 1)$.

22. Ex. 17. *Ans.* $y'' = 4\left(\dfrac{t + 1}{t - 1}\right)^3$.

23. $x = t^2 - 3$, $y = t^3 + t + 1$.   *Ans.* $y'' = \dfrac{3t^2 - 1}{4t^3}$.

24. $x = 1 - \dfrac{1}{t}$, $y = 6 - \dfrac{7}{t} + \dfrac{2}{t^2}$.   *Ans.* $y'' = 4$.

119. *Point Plotting*

To plot, by points, a curve represented by parametric equations, we merely assign suitable values to the parameter and compute the corresponding values of x and y.

Example. Plot the curve

(1) $x = a \cos^3 \theta$, $y = a \sin^3 \theta$.

θ	0	$\frac{1}{6}\pi$	$\frac{1}{4}\pi$	$\frac{1}{3}\pi$	$\frac{1}{2}\pi$
x	a	$\frac{3}{8}\sqrt{3}\,a$	$\frac{1}{4}\sqrt{2}\,a$	$\frac{1}{8}a$	0
y	0	$\frac{1}{8}a$	$\frac{1}{4}\sqrt{2}\,a$	$\frac{3}{8}\sqrt{3}\,a$	a

Plotting these points, we get the portion of Figure 143 lying in the first quadrant. Taking the cube root of the square of each member, we may write the given equations in the form

(2) $x^{\frac{2}{3}} = a^{\frac{2}{3}} \cos^2 \theta$, $y^{\frac{2}{3}} = a^{\frac{2}{3}} \sin^2 \theta$;

adding, we get the rectangular equation

$$x^{\frac{2}{3}} + y^{\frac{2}{3}} = a^{\frac{2}{3}}.$$

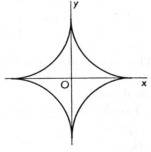

From this it follows that the curve is symmetric with respect to both axes, whence the balance of the curve may be obtained by reflection. This curve is the *hypocycloid of four cusps*.

Figure 143

The student is warned not to confuse parametric representation with polar coordinates. The parameter θ occurring here is quite different from the polar angle θ.

120. *Curve Tracing from Parametric Equations*

Consider the curve of Example (*b*), § 118:

(1) $x = t^3 + 1$, $y = 4t^2 - 4t$.

It is possible to eliminate the parameter t from equations (1) and obtain the rectangular equation

(2) $y^3 + 48y(x - 1) - 64(x - 1)(x - 2) = 0$.

Direct study of (2) is not particularly pleasant if we seek critical points and inflection points. Let us therefore study the curve from its parametric equations (1).

We already know, from Example (*b*), page 219, that

$$\text{(3)} \qquad \frac{dy}{dx} = \frac{4(2t - 1)}{3t^2}$$

and

$$\text{(4)} \qquad \frac{d^2y}{dx^2} = \frac{8(1 - t)}{9t^5}.$$

For a critical point we must have $y' = 0$. Hence, by (3), $t = \frac{1}{2}$. For $t = \frac{1}{2}$, $x = \frac{9}{8}$, $y = -1$, and y'' is positive. Therefore the point $(\frac{9}{8}, -1)$ is a minimum point.

Let us set $y'' = 0$. Then $t = 1$, which leads to $x = 2$, $y = 0$, $y' = \frac{4}{3}$. It follows that $(2, 0)$ is a point of inflection and that the inflectional tangent has the slope $\frac{4}{3}$.

It is useful to note that the slope does not exist at $t = 0$. When $t = 0$, $x = 1$, $y = 0$. There is a vertical tangent line at the point $(1, 0)$.

From the sign of the second derivative in (4) we obtain the direction of concavity of the curve. The results are:

> For $t < 0$, $y'' < 0$, curve concave downward;
> For $0 < t < 1$, $y' > 0$, curve concave upward;
> For $t > 1$, $y'' < 0$, curve concave downward.

The curve is shown in Figure 144. Note that there is an inflection point at $(1, 0)$ where the direction of concavity changed because of discontinuity in the derivatives.

For either of two reasons, parametric equations may represent only a portion of the curve which results from elimination of the parameter. The parameter may in a physical problem be restricted. For example, if the coordinates are functions of time t, usually there is physical meaning to the results only for $t \geq 0$, for times after some initial instant. Also, if we permit only real values of the parameter, the functions involved may automatically exclude some portions of the curve. See Example (*b*) below.

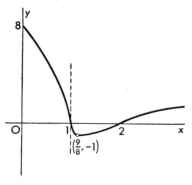

Figure 144

Parametric equations for a curve are not unique. The number of different parametric representations for any specified curve is unlimited.

Example (a).   Draw the curve whose parametric equations are

(5) $x = -2 - 3t, \qquad y = 1 + t.$

Elimination of the parameter at once yields

(6) $x + 3y = 1,$

so that the locus is the straight line shown in Figure 145, assuming that there are no restrictions on the parameter except that it be real.

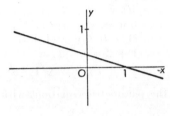

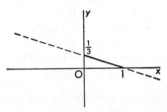

Figure 145   **Figure 146**

Example (b).   Draw the curve

(7) $x = \cos^2 t, \quad y = \tfrac{1}{3} \sin^2 t.$

Since $\cos^2 t + \sin^2 t = 1$, we are again, as in Example (a), led to

(6) $x + 3y = 1.$

This time, however, the properties of the trigonometric functions automatically restrict x and y.   For real t, $\cos^2 t$ lies between zero and unity. Hence the locus of (7) is that portion of the line (6) for which

$$0 \le x \le 1,$$

the portion shown solid in Figure 146.   Note the restriction on y, $0 \le y \le \tfrac{1}{3}$, obtained in a similar manner.

EXERCISES

In Exs. 1–13, obtain all maxima, minima, and inflection points without eliminating the parameter.   Discuss the direction of concavity and sketch the curve carefully.

1. $x = t^3 - 1$, $y = t^2 + t$.   (Ex. 3, page 220.)
2. $x = t^{-2}$, $y = t^2 - 4t + 1$.   (Ex. 5, page 220.)
3. $x = t^{-2}$, $y = t^2 - t$.   (Ex. 6, page 220.)
4. $x = t^{-3}$, $y = t^3 + 3t$.   (Ex. 7, page 220.)
5. $x = (t + 1)^{-2}$, $y = t^2 + 3$.   (Ex. 8, page 220.)
6. $x = (1 - t)^{\frac{1}{2}}$, $y = t^3 - 3t$.   (Ex. 9, page 220.)
7. $x = (t + 2)^{\frac{1}{2}}$, $y = t^2 - 3$.   (Ex. 10, page 220.)
8. $x = 1 + t^2$, $y = 4t - 3$.   (Ex. 1, page 219.)
9. $x = t^3 + 7$, $y = 6t^2 - 1$.   (Ex. 2, page 219.)
10. $x = 1 + t^2$, $y = t^3 - 2$.   (Ex. 13, page 220.)

11. $x = (\beta^2 - 1)^2$, $y = 4\beta^3$.   (Ex. 15, page 220.)
12. $x = (t + 1)^{-1}$, $y = (t - 1)^{-1}$.   (Ex. 17, page 220.)
13. $x = 1 - t^{-1}$, $y = 6 - 7t^{-1} + 2t^{-2}$.   (Ex. 24, page 221.)

In Exs. 14–27, find the rectangular equation and draw the curve. Assuming the parameter restricted to real values, determine whether the parametric equations represent all or part of the curve.

14. $x = 1 - t$, $y = 1 + t$.

15. $x = 2t$, $y = 3 - 4t$.

16. $x = 1 - t^2$, $y = 1 + t^2$.

17. $x = 2t^2$, $y = 3 - 4t^2$.

18. $x = 1 + t$, $y = t^2$.

19. $x = 4t^2$, $y = t - 2$.

20. $x = 2 \sin^2 \varphi$, $y = \cos 2\varphi$.

21. $x = \tan^2 \varphi$, $y = \sec^2 \varphi$.

22. $x = \cos \theta$, $y = \sec \theta$.

23. $x = (1 + t)^{-2}$, $y = (1 + t)^2$.

24. $x = \log_{10} n^2$, $y = \log_{10} 100n$.

25. $x = 1 + 2^{-t}$, $y = 2^t$.

26. $x = \tan \beta$, $y = \sin 2\beta$.

27. $x = \frac{1}{2}(1 + t^2)$, $y = \sqrt{1 - t^4}$.

In Exs. 28–33, plot the curve by points, using the parametric equations with real parameter. Obtain the rectangular equation.

28. $x = t^2 - 1$, $y = t^3 - 5t$.   *Ans.* $y^2 = (x + 1)(x - 4)^2$.

29. $x = 2 - t^2$, $y = t + t^3$.   *Ans.* $y^2 = (2 - x)(3 - x)^2$.

30. $x = \dfrac{1}{1 + t}$, $y = \dfrac{2}{1 + t^2}$.   *Ans.* $y = \dfrac{2x^2}{2x^2 - 2x + 1}$.

31. $x = \dfrac{1}{1 - t}$, $y = \dfrac{1}{1 - t^2}$.   *Ans.* $x^2 - 2xy + y = 0$.

32. $x = \cos \varphi$, $y = \cos \varphi + \sin \varphi$.   *Ans.* $2x^2 - 2xy + y^2 = 1$.

33. $x = \cos \varphi$, $y = \cos \varphi - \sin \varphi$.   *Ans.* $2x^2 - 2xy + y^2 = 1$.

In Exs. 34–39, plot by points that portion of the curve corresponding to $t \geqq 0$. Obtain the rectangular equation.

34. Ex. 18.   **35.** Ex. 19.   **36.** Ex. 23.

37. Ex. 25.   **38.** Ex. 30.   **39.** Ex. 31.

121. *Parametric Equations of a Straight Line*

In terms of a real parameter t, one set of parametric equations for a straight line are the equations

(1) $$x = x_1 + at, \qquad y = y_1 + bt,$$

in which x_1, y_1, a, b are fixed quantities. The point (x_1, y_1) lies on the line (1) because it corresponds to the value $t = 0$. If $a \neq 0$ in (1), then $\dfrac{b}{a}$ is the slope of the line. If $a = 0$ in (1), then the line is $x = x_1$, and the slope does not exist.

For some purposes, parametric equations for a line are convenient. For instance, given

(2) $$x = 2 - 3t, \qquad y = 1 + 4t,$$

we can rapidly obtain several points on the line by using specific values of t. The values $t = 0, -\frac{1}{2}, 2$, for example, yield the points $(2, 1)$, $(\frac{7}{2}, -1)$, $(-4, 9)$ with little work.

On the other hand, parametric equations are not convenient for such tasks as obtaining the intersection of two lines, essentially because there is no reason to expect the parameters in two instances to be the same. Given line (2) and another line

(3) $x = 1 + \beta, \qquad y = 3 - 6\beta$

the intersection can be obtained by eliminating both t and β, but the parametric form has contributed nothing to the solution (because our first step is to eliminate those parameters).

122. *Parametric Equations of a Circle*

The equation of any circle can be put in the form

(1) $(x - h)^2 + (y - k)^2 = r^2,$

or

(2) $\left(\dfrac{x - h}{r}\right)^2 + \left(\dfrac{y - k}{r}\right)^2 = 1.$

We know from trigonometry two functions, sine and cosine, which have the property that the sum of their squares is unity. Therefore we can at once write equations

(3) $\dfrac{x - h}{r} = \cos \varphi, \qquad \dfrac{y - k}{r} = \sin \varphi,$

which will lead to (2), or (1), when the parameter φ is eliminated. Thus, from (3), we obtain a set of parametric equations

(4) $x = h + r \cos \varphi, \qquad y = k + r \sin \varphi,$

with φ as parameter, for the circle (1).

123. *Parametric Equations of Conics*

Following the technique developed in the preceding section, a set of parametric equations for the ellipse

(1) $\dfrac{(x - h)^2}{a^2} + \dfrac{(y - k)^2}{b^2} = 1$

can be obtained mentally. The desired equations are

(2) $x = h + a \cos \beta, \qquad y = k + b \sin \beta,$

with parameter β.

In seeking parametric equations for the hyperbola

(3) $$\frac{(x - h)^2}{a^2} - \frac{(y - k)^2}{b^2} = 1,$$

we turn again to trigonometry. Recall that

$$\sec^2 \alpha - \tan^2 \alpha = 1,$$

which suggests the corresponding parametric representation

(4) $$x = h + a \sec \alpha, \qquad y = k + b \tan \alpha,$$

with parameter α, for the hyperbola (3).

For the parabola

(5) $$(y - k)^2 = 4a(x - h),$$

a simple set of parametric equations is

(6) $$x = h + at^2, \qquad y = k + 2at,$$

with parameter t.

The student should keep in mind that any number of different parametric equations can be written down for any curve whose equation is given. The examples in this chapter are merely widely used specific instances.

EXERCISES

In Exs. 1–4, locate three points on the line whose parametric equations are given. Find the slope and draw the line.

1. $x = 2 - t, y = 1 + 2t.$
2. $x = 4 + 3t, y = 7 + t.$
3. $x = 4t, y = 1 - 2t.$
4. $x = -1 + t, y = 2t.$

5. Find the parametric equations of the straight line in terms of the parameter

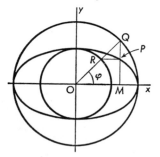

Figure 147

$k = \dfrac{P_1P}{P_1P_2}$, where P: (x, y) is any point on the line, and P_1: (x_1, y_1), P_2: (x_2, y_2) are two given points on the line.

    Ans. $x = x_1 + k(x_2 - x_1), y = y_1 + k(y_2 - y_1).$

6. A circle is drawn on the major axis of the ellipse $\dfrac{x^2}{a^2} + \dfrac{y^2}{b^2} = 1$ as diameter; the ordinate MP of any point P is produced to Q on the circle; the line OQ is drawn, making with Ox an angle φ, called the *eccentric angle corresponding to the point P*. Find the parametric equations of the ellipse in terms of the parameter φ, the eccentric angle.   *Ans.* $x = a \cos \varphi, y = b \sin \varphi.$

In Exs. 7–14, identify the curve; eliminate the parameter and draw the curve.

7. $x = 1 + 2 \cos \varphi, y = -2 + 3 \sin \varphi$.
8. $x = -3 + \cos \varphi, y = 4 - 2 \sin \varphi$.
9. $x = 3 \sin \varphi, y = 1 + \cos \varphi$.
10. $x = -3 + \cos \varphi, y = 4 \sin \varphi$.
11. $x = 2 + 3 \sec t, y = -4 + \tan t$.
12. $x = \tan 3t, y = 2 + \sec 3t$.
13. $x = 4 - \lambda^2, y = -3 - 2\lambda$.
14. $x = -1 + 2\lambda^2, y = 1 + 4\lambda$.

In Exs. 15–24, find at least two different parametric representations for the given curve.

15. $2x - y = 7$.
16. $x + 4y = 9$.
17. $x^2 + (y - 1)^2 = 9$.
18. $(x + 2)^2 + y^2 = 16$.
19. $4x^2 + y^2 = 25$.
20. $(x - 1)^2 + 9y^2 = 16$.
21. $y^2 = -8(x - 1)$.
22. $(x + 2)^2 = 4 + (y - 3)^2$.
23. $y^2 - x^2 = a^2$.
24. $(x + 4)^2 = 12(y + 1)$.

124. *The Problem of the Moving Point*

When a point moves in a plane curve under the action of a given force* or system of forces, an especially convenient way of studying the motion is to express the rectangular coordinates of the point as functions of the time t. The equations giving x and y in terms of t are *parametric equations of the path.*

To simplify the ideas at the outset, we shall first attack the problem of a point moving in a straight line. After a fairly thorough study of such rectilinear motion, we shall move on in § 133 to motion taking place on other plane curves.

125. *Rectilinear Motion*

Consider a point P moving in a straight line. Choose as origin any convenient fixed point in the line of motion, and denote the distance OP by x, positive on one side of O, negative on the other. In accordance with the argument of § 46, the *velocity* at any instant is defined as

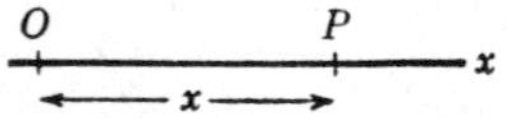

(1) $$v = \frac{dx}{dt}:$$

Figure 148

i.e., *velocity is time-rate of change of distance, measured from a fixed point in the line of motion.*

* The "point" is supposed to be endowed with mass—a "material particle." Further, the argument applies to a body of any size or shape, provided that for present purposes the motion of the entire body is completely characterized by the motion of one of its points. This would be the case, for instance, in computing the range of a projectile or in determining the orbit of a planet.

When the velocity is constant, the motion is said to be *uniform*, and the distance covered in any time is merely proportional to the time.   When the velocity changes from instant to instant, the motion is *accelerated*.

Acceleration, denoted in this book by *a*, is defined by the formula

(2)
$$a = \frac{dv}{dt};$$

i.e., *acceleration is time-rate of change of velocity.*

Since we may write

$$\frac{dv}{dt} = \frac{dv}{dx} \cdot \frac{dx}{dt} = v \frac{dv}{dx},$$

an alternative form of (2) is

(3)
$$a = v \frac{dv}{dx}.$$

When a particle of mass *m* moves with an acceleration *a*, the motion is said to be due to the action of *force*.   Force is defined as the *product of mass by acceleration*:

$$F = ma.$$

If there is no force acting (or if all the forces balance), the particle is *in equilibrium*.   A particle in equilibrium is either at rest or moving uniformly in a straight line.

In view of the relation $F = ma$, equations (2) and (3) yield

(4)
$$F = m \frac{dv}{dt} = m \frac{d^2x}{dt^2},$$

and

(5)
$$F = mv \frac{dv}{dx}.$$

When the acceleration (or force) is given as a function of time, the velocity and position can be found by successive integrations.   For, by (2),

$$dv = a\, dt, \qquad v = \int a\, dt + C_1;$$

by (1),

$$dx = v\, dt, \qquad x = \int v\, dt + C_2.$$

Since two constants of integration are introduced, we must always have given the initial position and velocity, the position at two different times, or some other pair of conditions enabling us to determine the constants.   The given data are called *initial conditions*, or *boundary conditions*.

126. *Falling Body*

When the acceleration is constant, the motion is said to be *uniformly accelerated*. An important instance of uniformly accelerated motion arises when a body moves near the earth's surface in a vertical straight line. The attraction of the earth gives it an acceleration, denoted by g, roughly equal to *32 ft. per sec. per sec.

Take the starting point as origin, and the distance x and velocity v as positive downward. If the body starts, at $x = 0$, with an initial velocity v_0,

$$a = \frac{dv}{dt} = g; \quad \text{when } t = 0, x = 0, v = v_0.$$

From

$$dv = g \, dt,$$

we get

$$v = gt + C_1.$$

The condition $v = v_0$, $t = 0$ gives $C_1 = v_0$, so that

(1) $$v = gt + v_0.$$

Replacing v by $\frac{dx}{dt}$ and integrating again, we get

$$x = \tfrac{1}{2}gt^2 + v_0 t + C_2;$$

since $x = 0$ when $t = 0$, $C_2 = 0$ and

(2) $$x = \tfrac{1}{2}gt^2 + v_0 t.$$

By eliminating t between equations (1) and (2), we arrive at the useful result:

(3) $$v^2 = v_0^2 + 2gx.$$

In all motion problems, we shall disregard negative values of t, assuming the motion to start at $t = 0$.

Example (a). A ball is dropped from a balloon at a height of 640 ft. If the balloon is rising 96 ft. per sec., find the highest point reached by the ball, and the time of flight.

By (2), with $g = 32$,

(4) $$x = 16t^2 - 96t.$$

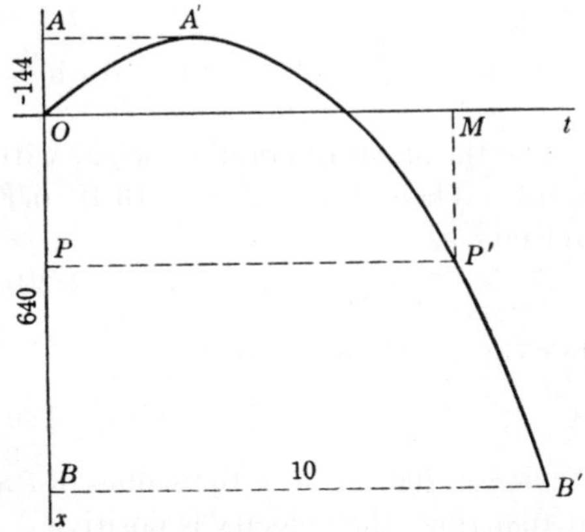

From (4), we obtain

(5) $$v = 32t - 96.$$

Figure 149

* A closer approximation is 32.16 ft. per sec. per sec. Since we are interested in methods, rather than in numerical refinement, the value 32 ft. per sec. per sec. will be used.

At the highest point, $v = 0$; hence

$$t = 3, \qquad x = 144 - 288 = -144 \text{ ft.}$$

The height above the starting point is 144 ft.; the distance above the ground is $640 + 144 = 784$ ft. To find the time of flight (time when the ball strikes the ground), put $x = 640$ in (4):

$$640 = 16t^2 - 96t,$$
$$16(t^2 - 6t - 40) = 0,$$
$$t = -4 \quad \text{or} \quad t = 10.$$

Thus the ball is in the air for 10 sec.

The graph of x as a function of t is the parabolic arc $OA'B'$ (Ox positive downward). The actual path of the ball, of course, is from O to A, then down to the ground at B. To find graphically the position at any time, say, $t = OM$, erect the ordinate MP' and project P' to P. To find the time corresponding to any position P, draw the abscissa PP' and project P' to M. For $x < 0$ (ball above the starting point), t of course is two-valued.

With different initial conditions, a different line of attack may be indicated. In particular, when a (v, x)-pair is given—velocity at a certain position—it is best to start with (3).

Example (b). The velocity 2 ft. below the starting point is 18 ft. per sec. If the start is made from a height of 200 ft., when and with what velocity does the body strike the earth?

With $g = 32$ and the starting point as origin, we have

$$a = v\frac{dv}{dx} = 32; \qquad x = 0 \text{ when } t = 0, \text{ and } v = 18 \text{ when } x = 2.$$

Use the starting point as origin with x (in feet) measured positive downward. Then at $x = 2$, $v = 18$ ft. per sec. Equation (3) yields the initial velocity v_0:

$$(18)^2 = v_0^2 + 2(32)(2), \qquad v_0 = \pm 14.$$

For this problem, (3) becomes

(6)
$$v^2 = 196 + 64x.$$

At $x = 200$, we seek the values of v and t. Since the motion is downward at that time, the velocity is positive. Thus at $x = 200$, the terminal velocity is

$$v_T = \sqrt{196 + 12{,}800} = 114 \text{ ft. per sec.}$$

By (1)

(7)
$$v = 32t \pm 14,$$

with the plus sign holding if the initial impetus was downward, the minus sign holding if the initial impetus was upward. With $v = v_T = 114$, equation (7) yields $t = \frac{2.5}{8}$ sec., or $t = 4$ sec. Thus the body strikes the ground after $\frac{2.5}{8}$, or 4, sec., with a velocity of 114 ft. per sec.

In this problem it could be foreseen that t must turn out as a two-valued function, for the given data do not tell whether the initial velocity of 14 ft. per sec. is upward or downward—either one will produce a velocity of 18 ft. per sec. 2 ft. below the starting point. Yet the time of reaching the earth will be different in the two cases.

It is instructive to solve the problem of Example (b) by starting with equation (3) of § 125 and using integration, thus essentially rederiving the formulas of this section.

127. *Atwood's Machine*

In the apparatus called *Atwood's machine*, two masses m_1, m_2 are joined by a cord hung over a pulley, as in Figure 150. Suppose for definiteness that $m_1 > m_2$. The total mass moved (if the masses of the cord and pulley can be neglected) is

$$m = m_1 + m_2,$$

while the force producing the motion is

$$F = m_1 g - m_2 g.$$

Hence equation (4) of § 125 becomes

$$(m_1 + m_2) \frac{dv}{dt} = (m_1 - m_2)g,$$

or

$$\frac{dv}{dt} = \frac{m_1 - m_2}{m_1 + m_2} g,$$

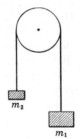

Figure 150

from which the velocity can be determined by integration.

· EXERCISES

In Exs. 1–21, a body moves in a vertical line under gravity alone, air resistance, etc. being neglected.

    1. If the initial velocity is 16 ft. per sec. upward, how far and for how long a time does the body rise?   *Ans.* 4 ft.; 0.5 sec.

    2. If the initial velocity is 40 ft. per sec. upward, how far and for how long a time does the body rise?   *Ans.* 25 ft.; 1.25 sec.

    3. If the velocity after one second is 8 ft. per sec. downward, find (a) the initial velocity and (b) the greatest distance above the starting point.

                                Ans. (a) 24 ft. per sec. upward; (b) 9 ft.

4. If the velocity after 1 sec. is 8 ft. per sec. upward, find (a) the initial velocity and (b) the greatest distance above the starting point.

Ans. (a) 40 ft. per sec. upward; (b) 25 ft.

5. If the body rises 49 ft. before starting to fall, find the initial velocity and the time required to return to the starting point.

Ans. $v_0 = -56$ ft. per sec.; $t = \frac{7}{4}$ sec.

6. During the third second, the body falls 70 ft.   Find the initial velocity.

Ans. -10 ft. per sec.

7. During the third second, the body falls 100 ft.   Find the initial velocity.

Ans. 20 ft. per sec.

8. During the third second, the velocity doubles.   Find the initial velocity.

Ans. -32 ft. per sec.

9. A ball is thrown upward and rises 9 ft. before starting to fall.   Find the total time taken for the ball to return to the starting point.   *Ans.* 1.5 sec.

10. At what times was the ball of Ex. 9 at a distance 8 ft. above its starting point?   *Ans.* $\frac{1}{2}$ sec., 1 sec.

11. From a point 36 ft. above the ground, with what velocity must a stone be thrown to reach the ground in 1 sec.?   *Ans.* 20 ft. per sec.

12. From a point 36 ft. above the ground, with what velocity must a stone be thrown to take 4 sec. to reach the ground?   *Ans.* 55 ft. per sec. upward.

13. From a point 128 ft. above the ground, a stone is thrown in such a way that it is at the same point 4 sec. after it was thrown as it was 3 sec. after it was thrown. How long does it take the stone to reach the ground?   *Ans.* 8 sec.

14. A ball is thrown upward from the ground with a speed of 40 ft. per sec.; at the same instant another ball is dropped (from rest) from a height of 100 ft.   Show that they strike the ground at the same time.

15. One foot below the starting point the velocity is 10 ft. per sec.   If the starting point is at a height of 76 ft., when and with what velocity does the body strike the earth?   *Ans.* $t = 2$ or $2\frac{3}{8}$ sec.

16. Four feet above the starting point the velocity is 12 ft. per sec.   If the starting point is at a height of 176 ft., when and with what velocity does the body reach the earth?   *Ans.* $t = 4$ sec.

17. A stone is thrown vertically upward from the top of a tower.   At the end of 2 sec. it is 400 ft. above the ground and is still rising with a velocity of 10 ft. per sec.   Find the height of the tower and time of flight.   *Ans.* 316 ft.; 7.3 sec.

18. A stone thrown upward from the top of a tower with a velocity of 100 ft. per sec. reaches the ground with a velocity of 140 ft. per sec.   Discuss the motion. Find the height of the tower and the time of flight.   *Ans.* 150 ft.; 7.5 sec.

19. If a stone dropped from a balloon while ascending at the rate of 20 ft. per sec. reaches the ground in 10 sec., find the initial height and the final velocity.

Ans. 1400 ft.; 300 ft. per sec.

20. A body falls under gravity.   Find the distance covered in 6 sec. if at the end of 2 sec. the distance below the starting point is 84 ft.   *Ans.* 636 ft.

21. A stone is thrown upward from the top of a tower.   At the end of 2 sec. it is 84 ft.; at the end of 3 sec., 36 ft. above the ground.   Find the height of the tower.

22. What uniform acceleration will bring an automobile, running at 40 mi. per hr., to rest in 120 ft.?   What time will be required?

Ans. -14.3 ft. per sec.^{2}; 4.1 sec.

23. If a car running at 20 mi. per hr. can be brought to rest in 20 ft., what distance will be required (under the same conditions) at 40 mi. per hr.? *Ans.* 80 ft.

24. The motion of a railroad train is uniformly accelerated. If when the train is 250 ft. past a station, the velocity is 30 ft. per sec., and when 600 ft. past the station it is 40 ft. per sec., find the acceleration, and the velocity when passing the station. *Ans.* $v_0 = 20$ ft. per sec.

25. A cord hangs over a vertical pulley and carries equal weights of 10 lb at each end. If a 1-lb. weight be added at one end, discuss the motion of the system. Find v when the system has moved 6 ft. (§ 127.) *Ans.* 4.3 ft. per sec.

26. The weights in Atwood's machine are 8 and 10 lb. If the smaller weight is originally falling 4 ft. per sec., discuss the motion.

27. The weights in Atwood's machine are 4 and 10 lb.; the cord is 3 ft. long. If the weights are initially equidistant from the pulley, what velocity must be given the system to make the heavier weight strike the pulley? *Ans.* 6.4 ft. per sec.

28. In Atwood's machine, show that the acceleration can be expressed as a function of the ratio $\dfrac{m_1}{m_2}$; hence that the motion depends only on the ratio of the masses, not on their actual values.

29. The weights in Atwood's machine, starting from rest, attain a velocity of 2 ft. per sec. in 1 sec. Find the ratio of the masses. *Ans.* 17:15.

30. The weights in Atwood's machine, starting from rest, attain a velocity of 4 ft. per sec. in the first 2 ft. Find the ratio of the masses. *Ans.* 9:7.

31. Find the ratio of the weights, and the initial velocity, if $v = 4$ when $t = 1$, $v = 6$ when $t = 2$. *Ans.* 17:15; 2 ft. per sec.

32. Find the ratio of the weights and the initial velocity if $v = 2$ when $x = 3$, $v = 3$ when $x = 8$. *Ans.* 65:63; ± 1 ft. per sec.

33. A mass of 12 lb. rests on a smooth horizontal table. A cord attached to this mass runs over a pulley on the edge of the table; from the cord a mass of 4 lb. is suspended. Discuss the motion. If the 12-lb. mass is originally 5 ft. from the edge of the table, find when and with what velocity it reaches the edge.

Ans. 1.1 sec.; 8.9 ft. per sec.

34. In Ex. 33, find the initial velocity if the 12-lb. mass reaches the edge in 1 sec. *Ans.* 1 ft. per sec.

128. *Discussion of the Motion*

In studying a motion, the integrations are really only a preliminary step. When x has been found as a function of t, we proceed to develop the character of the motion. A minimum discussion should answer the following questions:

1. *Where, in what direction, and with what velocity does the motion begin?* ($t = 0$.)

2. *When and where does the body come to rest, and in what direction does it start after each stop?* ($v = 0$.)

3. *What happens after a long time?* ($t \to \infty$.)

Example (a).   Investigate the motion

$$a = 6t - 18; \qquad x = 0, \quad v = 15 \text{ when } t = 0.$$

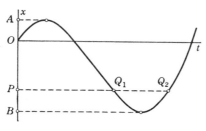

Figure 151

The first integration gives

$$v = 3t^2 - 18t + C_1,$$

or, since $v = 15$ when $t = 0$,

$$v = 3t^2 - 18t + 15$$
$$= 3(t - 1)(t - 5).$$

Integrating again, we get

$$x = t^3 - 9t^2 + 15t + C_2,$$

where $x = 0$, $t = 0$ gives $C_2 = 0$:

$$x = t^3 - 9t^2 + 15t.$$

Since x is a polynomial, its graph may be drawn by the method of § 61. The questions above are answered as follows:

1. $t = 0$: $x = 0$, $v = 15$, $a = -18$.   The motion starts at O, with a velocity of 15 ft. per sec. in the positive direction (as given); the velocity is diminishing.

2. $v = 0$: When $t = 1$ (the stops must, of course, be taken *in chronological order*), $x = 7$, $a = -12$; since $a < 0$, the body turns back in the negative direction.   When $t = 5$, $x = -25$, $a = 12$.   Thus the body moves out to A ($OA = 7$), turns back to B ($OB = -25$), then turns in the positive direction.

3. $t \to \infty$: When t increases indefinitely, both x and v become indefinitely large and positive.   The body goes indefinitely far and indefinitely fast in the positive direction.

From Figure 151 the position at any time, also the time (or times) corresponding to any position, may be read off at once.

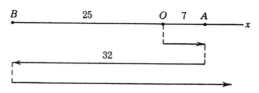

Figure 152

When time is not available for drawing the graph of x, the general character of the motion may be exhibited visually by the device shown in Figure 152.   The three "legs" of which this motion consists are shown by directed lines drawn at successively lower levels: from O to A, from A to B, from B indefinitely to the right.

Example (b).   Study the motion

$$a = 6t - 6; \qquad x = 0 \text{ when } t = 0, \qquad x = 1 \text{ when } t = 1.$$

Integrating twice, we find

$$v = 3t^2 - 6t + C_1,$$
$$x = t^3 - 3t^2 + C_1 t + C_2.$$

Substitution of the (x, t)-pairs gives

$$C_2 = 0;$$
$$1 = 1 - 3 + C_1,$$
$$C_1 = 3.$$

Thus

$$x = t^3 - 3t^2 + 3t,$$

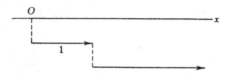

Figure 153

$$v = 3t^2 - 6t + 3 = 3(t - 1)^2.$$

1. $t = 0$: $x = 0$, $v = 3$.
2. $v = 0$: $t = 1$, $x = 1$, $a = 0$.

Since v and a vanish together, the direction of the ensuing motion may be determined by noting that, for $t > 1$, $v > 0$.   The same conclusion follows from the fact that

$$\frac{da}{dt} = 6;$$

thus a will become positive and v will do likewise.

EXERCISES

Discuss fully the rectilinear motions of Exs. 1–16.

1. $a = 2$; when $t = 2$, $x = 3$ and $v = 2$.   *Ans.* $x = t^2 - 2t + 3$.
2. $a = -1$; when $t = 2$, $x = 4$ and $v = 0$.   *Ans.* $x = -\frac{1}{2}t^2 + 2t + 2$.
3. $a = 6(2t - 3)$; when $t = 0$, $x = 2$ and $v = 12$.
                                         Ans. $x = 2t^3 - 9t^2 + 12t + 2$.
4. $a = 6(2t - 1)$; when $t = 0$, $x = 13$ and $v = -12$.
5. $a = 6(t - 2)$; when $t = 1$, $x = 0$ and $v = 3$.   *Ans.* $x = t^3 - 6t^2 + 12t - 7$.
6. $a = 6(t - 1)$; when $t = 0$, $x = 0$, and when $t = 4$, $x = 16$.
                                             Ans. $x = t^2(t - 3)$.
7. $a = 12t^2 - 48t + 44$; when $t = 0$, $x = 10$ and $v = -24$.
8. $a = 12t^2 - 8$; when $t = 0$, $x = 25$, and when $t = 1$, $v = -20$.
9. $a = 12t^2 - 24t - 16$; when $t = 0$, $v = 48$, and when $t = 1$, $x = -3$.
10. $a = 12t^2 - 48t + 20$; when $t = 0$, $x = 40$, and when $t = 1$, $v = 0$.
11. $a = 12(t - 1)(t - 3)$; when $t = 0$, $x = 5$, and when $t = 1$, $x = 0$.
12. $a = 3(t - 2)^2$; when $t = 0$, $x = 5$, and when $t = 1$, $v = 3$.
13. $a = 12t^2 - 48t + 36$; when $t = 0$, $v = 0$, and when $t = 1$, $x = -9$.
14. $a = 12(t - 2)(t - 4)$; when $t = 0$, $x = 15$, and when $t = 1$, $x = -12$.
15. $a = \dfrac{2}{(t + 2)^3}$; when $t = 0$, $x = \dfrac{1}{2}$ and $v = -\dfrac{1}{4}$.   *Ans.* $x = \dfrac{1}{t + 2}$.

16. $a = \dfrac{2}{(t+2)^3}$; when $t = 0$, $x = -\dfrac{1}{2}$ and $v = \dfrac{3}{4}$.   *Ans.* $x = \dfrac{t^2 + t - 1}{t + 2}$.

17. A body moves under an acceleration which increases uniformly at the rate of 6 ft. per sec^3. If at the end of 1 sec. the body is 1 ft., at the end of 2 sec. 2 ft., from the starting point, discuss the motion.   *Ans.* $x = t^3 - 3t^2 + 3t$.

129. *Vectors*

A straight line segment of definite *length*, *direction*, and *sense* is called a *vector*.

Any quantity that is fully characterized when we know its magnitude, direction, and sense may be represented geometrically by a vector (or, as we say for brevity, *is* a vector). The importance of vectors in physics is due to the fact that velocity, acceleration, force, etc., are vector quantities.

Two vectors are said to be *equal* if they have the same magnitude, direction, and sense, even though they do not lie in the same straight line. This agrees with our ordinary ideas. For instance, if two bodies are falling under gravity, they are both subject to the same acceleration, whether or not they happen to be in the same vertical line.

130. *Geometric Addition*

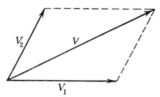

Figure 154

The sum of two vectors V_1, V_2 is called their *resultant*. It is defined as *the diagonal of the parallelogram having V_1, V_2 as adjacent sides.* This is the *parallelogram law.* Composition by this law is called *geometric addition*, or *vector addition.* The sum of two vectors is defined in this way for the reason that in any application the vector V is actually equivalent to the vectors V_1, V_2 combined.

Example. A ship is moving N. at 10 mi. per hr.; a man walks S.E. across the deck at 5 mi. per hr. In what direction and how fast is the man moving, relative to the earth's surface? (Figure 155.)

By the cosine law,

$$v = \sqrt{100 + 25 - 2 \times 50 \cos 45°} = \sqrt{54.3}$$
$$= 7.4 \text{ mi. per hr.}$$

By the sine law,

$$\frac{\sin \alpha}{5} = \frac{\sin 45°}{7.4}, \qquad \sin \alpha = 0.48, \qquad \alpha = 29°.$$

Thus the man is actually moving 29° E. of N., at 7.4 mi. per hr.

In Figure 154, the vectors V_1, V_2 are *components* of V. Fre-

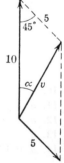

Figure 155

quently, having given a vector V, we wish to resolve it into components. This can be done in an infinite number of ways: If we draw any triangle with V as one side, the other sides, directed as in Figure 154, are components of V.

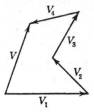

By repeated application of the parallelogram law, the resultant of any number of vectors is easily found. Lay off the vectors end to end to form an open polygon: the closing line, directed from the initial to the terminal point, is the resultant. In Figure 156, V is the resultant of V_1, V_2, V_3, V_4.

Figure 156

131. *Algebraic Addition*

For various reasons it may happen in a particular problem that geometric addition of vectors is not feasible; we then have recourse to *algebraic addition*.

From the definition of vector sum, it follows at once that two vectors may be added algebraically if and only if they have *the same direction*. (For instance, in the above example, if the man were to walk due north or south, his net velocity would be 15 or 5 mi. per hr., respectively.) Thus, to add a number of vectors having different directions:

1. *Resolve all the vectors into components parallel to Ox and Oy.*
2. *Add (algebraically) all the x-components to form V_x, all the y-components to form V_y.*

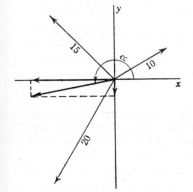

3. *Compound V_x and V_y by the parallelogram law: i.e., draw the vector V of magnitude*

$$V = \sqrt{V_x^2 + V_y^2},$$

inclined to Ox at an angle α such that

$$\tan \alpha = \frac{V_y}{V_x}.$$

Of course the quadrant in which α lies must be determined as in trigonometry, by examining the signs of V_x and V_y.

Figure 157

Example. Three forces act on a particle: 10 lb. inclined at 30° to Ox, 15 lb. at 135°, 20 lb. at 240°. Find the resultant.

We have (Figure 157)

$$F_x = 10 \cos 30° + 15 \cos 135° + 20 \cos 240°$$
$$= 10 \cdot \tfrac{1}{2}\sqrt{3} - 15 \cdot \tfrac{1}{2}\sqrt{2} - 20 \cdot \tfrac{1}{2} = -11.9;$$
$$F_y = 10 \sin 30° + 15 \sin 135° + 20 \sin 240°$$
$$= 10 \cdot \tfrac{1}{2} + 15 \cdot \tfrac{1}{2}\sqrt{2} - 20 \cdot \tfrac{1}{2}\sqrt{3} = -1.7.$$

Thus

$$F = \sqrt{(11.9)^2 + (1.7)^2} = 12.0 \text{ lb.};$$

$$\tan \alpha = \frac{-1.7}{-11.9} = 0.143, \qquad \alpha = 188°.$$

132. *Inclined Plane*

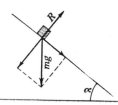

Consider a body of mass m on a smooth plane inclined at an angle α to the horizontal. At any instant the body is subject to two forces: the attraction of gravity, of magnitude mg, and the reaction R of the plane. Resolve the vertical force mg into components $mg \cos \alpha$ and $mg \sin \alpha$, respectively normal and parallel to the plane. The normal component is exactly balanced by the reaction R. Assume that the body is released from rest, or with an initial velocity either directly down or directly up the slope. Then rectilinear motion occurs, owing to the "effective component" $mg \sin \alpha$:

Figure 158

$$ma = mg \sin \alpha, \qquad a = g \sin \alpha.$$

Let x be distance measured down the inclined plane from the starting point. At $t = 0$, let $x = 0$ and $v = v_0$. Then, from $a = g \sin \alpha$, we obtain

$$v = gt \sin \alpha + v_0,$$
$$x = \tfrac{1}{2}gt^2 \sin \alpha + v_0t.$$

The elimination of t from these two equations yields the useful result

$$v^2 = 2xg \sin \alpha + v_0^2.$$

EXERCISES

1. A man can row a boat 5 mi. per hr. He pulls at right angles to the course of a river 2 mi. wide having a current of 3 mi. per hr. Where and when will he reach the opposite shore? *Ans.* 1.2 mi. downstream; 24 min.

2. In Ex. 1, if the man wishes to land directly opposite his starting point, in what direction must he row, and how long will it take him to cross? *Ans.* 30 min.

3. Suppose the man in Ex. 1 wishes to reach a point on the opposite shore 3 mi. downstream from his starting point. At what angle downstream, the α of Figure 159, should he row, and how long will it take him? *Ans.* $\alpha = 36° \, 52'$; 30 min.

4. A steamship is moving at the rate of 12 mi. per hr. A man walks across the deck at right angles to the ship's course at the rate of 5 mi. per hr. If the deck is 40 ft. wide, how far is he finally from his starting point? In what direction?

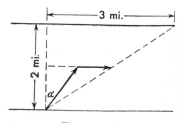

Figure 159

5. Across the deck of a vessel going S. at 10 ft. per sec., a man walks S. 30° E. at 6 ft. per sec. If the deck is 15 ft. wide, how long does it take him to cross, and how far does he travel?   *Ans.* 5 sec.; 77.4 ft.

6. A river flows S. at 5 mi. per hr. A ferryboat, headed E., is making forward progress at 10 mi. per hr. A man sprints across the deck 30° W. of N. at 20 mi. per hr. How fast and in what direction is he actually moving?

7. A river flows S. at 5 mi. per hr. A boat, headed E., is making forward progress at 20 mi. per hr. On the deck is a man capable of sprinting 100 yd. in 10 sec. Can he hold himself motionless, relative to the earth's surface?

Ans. No.

8. Find the resultant of a plane system of forces, $F_1 = 10$ lb., $F_2 = 7$ lb.. $F_3 = 3$ lb., $F_4 = 15$ lb., acting as in Figure 160, in which $\tan \alpha = \frac{4}{3}$.

Ans. $F = 10.8$ lb.; angle with $Ox = 146°\ 19'$.

9. Six forces, of 1, 2, 3, 4, 5, 6 lb., respectively, act at the same point, making angles of 60° with each other. Find their resultant.

Ans. 6 lb., along the line of the 5-lb. force.

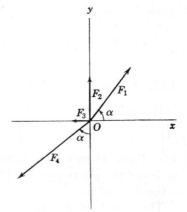

Figure 160

In Exs. 10–12, a body moves on a plane inclined 30° to the horizontal. All distances and velocities are measured along the inclined plane.

10. If the body rises 18 ft. before starting to fall, what was its initial velocity?

Ans. −24 ft. per sec.

11. A body is given an initial velocity of 20 ft. per sec. upward. How far, and for how long, does it travel before starting to fall? *Ans.* 12.5 ft.; $\frac{5}{4}$ sec.

12. A body is given an initial velocity of 16 ft. per sec. upward. How long does it take the body to reach a point 4.5 ft. below its starting point? *Ans.* $\frac{9}{4}$ sec.

13. A body moves on an inclined plane. After 1 sec., the body is 3 ft. below its starting point and has a velocity of 7 ft. per sec., distance and velocity being measured along the plane. Find the angle of inclination of the plane.

Ans. About 14° 30′.

14. If the initial velocity is 16 ft. per sec. upward along an inclined plane and the body moves 12 ft. before starting to return, find the angle of inclination of the plane.   *Ans.* About 19° 30′.

15. It is known that the gravitational attraction of the moon at its surface is approximately $0.165g$, in terms of the gravitational attraction of the earth at its surface. Find the angle of inclination of a plane near the earth's surface which will yield the same equations of motion, along that plane, as the equations of motion of a freely falling body near the surface of the moon. *Ans.* About 9° 30′.

16. A bead is strung on a smooth straight wire inclined at 45° to the horizontal. What initial velocity must the bead be given to raise it to a vertical height of 10 ft.?

Ans. 25.3 ft. per sec.

17. Show that it takes a body twice as long to slide down a plane of 30° inclination as it would take to fall through the "height" of the plane.

18. A hillside slopes gently on one face, steeply on another. Toboggans start at the same time down the two faces. If friction is negligible, find (a) which will reach level ground first, and (b) which will acquire the greater velocity.

19. A car, starting with a velocity of 10 mi. per hr., coasts for 20 sec. down a 2% grade, and then ascends a 3% grade. Neglecting friction, find how far it will go up the grade.   *Ans.* 393 ft.

20. A car, starting from rest, coasts 200 ft. down a 2% grade and then ascends a 10% grade under an acceleration, due to its own power, of 2 ft. per sec. per sec. How far up can it go?   *Ans.* 107 ft.

133. *Velocity and Acceleration in Curvilinear Motion*

If a point moves in a plane curve, its coordinates are functions of time:

(1) $$x = \varphi(t), \qquad y = \psi(t).$$

Equations (1) may be regarded as *parametric equations of the path* (§ 118) in terms of the parameter t. The distance s described along the curve is also a function of time.

The *velocity* at any point P is defined as the *vector, laid off from P on the tangent to the path*, of magnitude

$$v = \operatorname*{Lim}_{\Delta t \to 0} \frac{\Delta s}{\Delta t} = \frac{ds}{dt}.$$

The components of velocity parallel to the axes are

$$v_x = v \cos \alpha, \qquad v_y = v \sin \alpha,$$

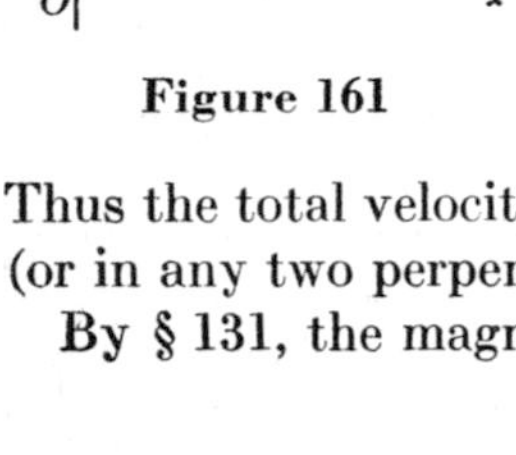

Figure 161

where α is the angle between Ox and the tangent at P. By § 72,

$$v \cos \alpha = \frac{ds}{dt} \cdot \frac{dx}{ds} = \frac{dx}{dt},$$

$$v \sin \alpha = \frac{ds}{dt} \cdot \frac{dy}{ds} = \frac{dy}{dt},$$

so that

$$v_x = \frac{dx}{dt}, \qquad v_y = \frac{dy}{dt}.$$

Thus the total velocity is the vector sum of the velocities parallel to the axes (or in any two perpendicular directions; see Ex. 16 below).

By § 131, the magnitude of the velocity is

$$v = \sqrt{v_x^2 + v_y^2} = \sqrt{\left(\frac{dx}{dt}\right)^2 + \left(\frac{dy}{dt}\right)^2},$$

inclined to the x-axis at an angle α such that

$$\tan \alpha = \frac{v_y}{v_x}.$$

The *acceleration* is the vector a whose components, parallel to the axes, are

(2)
$$a_x = \frac{dv_x}{dt} = \frac{d^2x}{dt^2}, \qquad a_y = \frac{dv_y}{dt} = \frac{d^2y}{dt^2}.$$

The total acceleration is

$$a = \sqrt{a_x{}^2 + a_y{}^2},$$

inclined to the x-axis at an angle β such that

$$\tan \beta = \frac{a_y}{a_x},$$

When each member is multiplied by m, equations (2) yield the components of force:

$$F_x = m\frac{dv_x}{dt}, \qquad F_y = m\frac{dv_y}{dt}.$$

134. *Projectiles*

A simple example of curvilinear motion is furnished by a projectile moving under gravity alone—i.e., in a medium whose resistance can be neglected. This is only a first approximation to actual fact, since in the majority of practical cases the resistance of the medium affects the results materially. (See § 380.)

Let a particle be projected with an initial velocity v_0 inclined at an angle α to the horizontal.   With the starting point as origin and the y-axis *positive upward*, the initial conditions are

$$x = 0, \qquad y = 0, \qquad v_x = v_0 \cos \alpha, \qquad v_y = v_0 \sin \alpha \qquad \text{when } t = 0.$$

The force of gravity acts vertically downward; there is no horizontal force.   Hence the equations of motion are

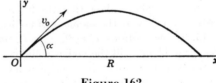

$$\frac{d^2x}{dt^2} = 0, \qquad \frac{d^2y}{dt^2} = -g.$$

Figure 162

These equations may be integrated and the constants determined precisely as in our earlier work; the results are as follows:

(1) $v_x = v_0 \cos \alpha, \qquad v_y = -gt + v_0 \sin \alpha;$
(2) $x = v_0t \cos \alpha, \qquad y = -\tfrac{1}{2}gt^2 + v_0t \sin \alpha.$

EXERCISES

1. Obtain equations (1) and (2), § 134.
2. By eliminating t from (2), § 134, show that the path is a parabola opening downward.

3. Show that a projectile whose initial velocity is horizontal will strike the ground in the same time as a body let fall from rest from the same height.

4. The *time of flight* is the time from the starting point until the projectile strikes the ground. Show that on a horizontal plane the time of flight is

$$T = \frac{2v_0}{g} \sin \alpha.$$

5. The *range* of a projectile is the distance from the starting point to the point where it strikes the ground. Show that the range on a horizontal plane is

$$R = \frac{v_0{}^2}{g} \sin 2\alpha.$$

6. What elevation gives the greatest range on a horizontal plane? (Ex. 5.)

In Exs. 7–12, a point moves in a plane curve, its coordinates being determined by the given formulas. Discuss the motion for $t \geq 0$, and draw the path of the point.

7. $x = 3t, \quad y = 9t(2 - t).$

8. $x = 3(t^2 - 2t + 2), \quad y = 3(t - 2).$

9. $x = \dfrac{1}{t + 2}, \quad y = \dfrac{2(t + 2)}{t + 1}.$

10. $x = t, \quad y = t(4 - t^2).$

11. $x = 2(t - 1), y = \sqrt{t(2 - t)}.$

12. $x = 5 - t, y = \sqrt{t(10 - t)}.$

13. If the motions in Exs. 7 and 8 take place in the same plane, will the bodies collide?   *Ans.* At (6, 0).

14. If the motions $x_1 = t - 2$, $y_1 = t^2$, and $x_2 = t^2 - 8$, $y_2 = \dfrac{4t^2}{t + 1}$, take place in the same plane, show that the bodies will collide, and determine which has the greater velocity at the moment of collision.   *Ans.* At (1, 9); $v_2 > v_1$.

15. If the motions $x_1 = t^2$, $y_1 = t^3$, and $x_2 = 3t - 2$, $y_2 = t^2 + 4$, take place in the same plane, will the bodies collide?   *Ans.* At (4, 8).

16. A point moves in a plane curve, the rectangular coordinates x, y, being functions of the time t. If the axes are rotated to a new system x_1, y_1, by the usual formulas, (page 298),

$$x = x_1 \cos \varphi - y_1 \sin \varphi, \qquad y = x_1 \sin \varphi + y_1 \cos \varphi,$$

prove that

$$\sqrt{\left(\frac{dx}{dt}\right)^2 + \left(\frac{dy}{dt}\right)^2} = \sqrt{\left(\frac{dx_1}{dt}\right)^2 + \left(\frac{dy_1}{dt}\right)^2},$$

and interpret the result physically.

17. A point describes the parabola $y^2 = 4x + 1$, with a constant vertical velocity, $v_y = 4$. Find v_x, a_x, a_y, at (2, 3).   *Ans.* $v_x = 6$; $a_x = 8$.

18. A point describes the parabola $y^2 = 4x + 1$, with a constant horizontal velocity, $v_x = 3$. Find v_y, a_y, a_x, at $(2, 3)$. *Ans.* $v_y = 2$; $a_y = -\frac{4}{3}$.

19. A particle moves on the circle $x^2 + y^2 = 25$, with a constant horizontal velocity $v_x = -2$. Find v_y, a_y, a_x, at $(3, 4)$. *Ans.* $v_y = \frac{3}{2}$; $a_y = -\frac{25}{16}$.

20. A particle starts at the point $(0, -4)$ and moves along the parabola $y = x^2 - 4$, with a variable horizontal velocity given by $v_x = 2t - 1$. At time $t = 2$, find the position of the particle and its various components of velocity and acceleration.
Ans. $(2, 0)$; $v_x = 3$; $v_y = 12$; $a_x = 2$; $a_y = 26$.

21. In Ex. 20, let the particle start at the point $(-2, 0)$, but leave the rest of the problem unchanged. *Ans.* $(0, -4)$; $v_x = 3$; $v_y = 0$; $a_x = 2$; $a_y = 18$.

22. The motion of a certain body is determined by its components of acceleration, $a_x = 2$ and $a_y = -6t$, together with the initial conditions that, when $t = 0$, then $x = 0$, $y = 0$, $v_x = 0$, and $v_y = 1$. Find the equation of the path of the motion.
Ans. $y = (1 - x) \sqrt{x}$.

23. The motion of a certain body is determined by its components of acceleration, $a_x = 1 - t$ and $a_y = 0$, together with the initial conditions that, when $t = 0$, then $x = 1$, $y = 0$, $v_x = 0$, and $v_y = -\frac{1}{2}$. Find the equation of the path of the motion. *Ans.* $3(x - 1) = 2y^2(3 + 2y)$.

24. Starting at the origin, initially at rest, a particle is subjected to a constant horizontal acceleration b, and a constant vertical acceleration c. Find the equation of the path of motion. *Ans.* $by = cx$.

25. In Ex. 24, let the particle have an initial velocity $v_0 \neq 0$, but leave the remainder of the problem unchanged. Show that the path of motion is, in general, a parabola. When will the path be a straight line?

26. Prove that when a point traverses a curve with constant velocity $v = k$, the acceleration is always directed along the normal to the path. (Differentiate both members of the equation $v_x^2 + v_y^2 = k^2$.)

27. A pitcher throws a ball with a speed of 120 ft. per sec., the ball leaving his hand horizontally at a height of 5 ft. If the distance from pitcher to batter is 60 ft., at what height will the ball pass the batter?

28. A stone is thrown horizontally from the top of a tower 400 ft. high, with a velocity of 20 ft. per sec. (a) When, (b) where, and (c) with what velocity does it strike the ground? *Ans.* (a) 5 sec.; (c) 161.2 ft. per sec., at 7° 8' to the vertical.

29. A man on a cliff 160 ft. high throws a stone, with velocity 100 ft. per sec., directly toward a point 120 ft. out from the foot of the cliff. By what distance does the stone miss the mark? *Ans.* 28.1 ft.

Hyperbolic Functions

135. *The Hyperbolic Sine and Cosine*

Two particular combinations of exponential functions appear with such frequency in both pure and applied mathematics that it has been worth while to use special symbols for those combinations. The hyperbolic sine of x, written sinh x, is defined by

(1)
$$\sinh x = \frac{e^x - e^{-x}}{2};$$

the hyperbolic cosine of x, written* cosh x, is defined by

(2)
$$\cosh x = \frac{e^x + e^{-x}}{2}.$$

The use of symbols and names so similar to those of trigonometry may seem unwise. Some justification will appear in § 137 where the basic formulas for these new functions are shown to bear a striking resemblance to those of ordinary trigonometry. It will be shown also that the hyperbolic sine and cosine are related to the equilateral hyperbola in much the same way that the ordinary (circular) sine and cosine are related to the circle.

136. *Other Hyperbolic Functions*

Four more hyperbolic functions are defined in a manner to be expected:

$$\tanh x = \frac{\sinh x}{\cosh x},$$

$$\operatorname{csch} x = \frac{1}{\sinh x},$$

$$\operatorname{sech} x = \frac{1}{\cosh x},$$

$$\coth x = \frac{1}{\tanh x}.$$

---

* Another common notation is Ch x to replace our cosh x, and with it Sh x to replace our sinh x.

244

137. *Basic Formulas of Hyperbolic Trigonometry*

From the definition of sinh x and cosh x, it follows that

$$\sinh^2 x = \tfrac{1}{4}(e^{2x} - 2 + e^{-2x})$$

and

$$\cosh^2 x = \tfrac{1}{4}(e^{2x} + 2 + e^{-2x}),$$

so that

(1) $$\cosh^2 x - \sinh^2 x = 1,$$

an identity similar to the identity $\cos^2 x + \sin^2 x = 1$ in circular trigonometry. Many other such relations will be found in the exercises below.

Directly from the definition we find that

$$y = \sinh u$$

is equivalent to

$$y = \tfrac{1}{2}(e^u - e^{-u}).$$

Hence, if u is a function of x,

$$\frac{dy}{dx} = \frac{1}{2}(e^u + e^{-u})\frac{du}{dx};$$

that is,

(2) $$\frac{d}{dx}\sinh u = \cosh u \,\frac{du}{dx}.$$

The same method yields the result

(3) $$\frac{d}{dx}\cosh u = \sinh u \,\frac{du}{dx}.$$

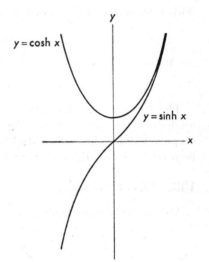

Figure 163

The derivations of the corresponding formulas for the derivatives of the other hyperbolic functions are left as exercises.

The curves $y = \cosh x$ and $y = \sinh x$ are exhibited in Figure 163. Note the important properties:

(a) $\cosh x \geqq 1$ for all real x;

(b) the only real value of x for which $\sinh x = 0$ is $x = 0$;

(c) $\cosh(-x) = \cosh x$; i.e., $\cosh x$ is an even function of x;

(d) $\sinh(-x) = -\sinh x$; $\sinh x$ is an odd function of x.

The hyperbolic functions have no real period. Corresponding to the period 2π possessed by the circular functions, there is a period $2\pi i$ for the six hyperbolic functions.

With regard to the word hyperbolic in the names of the functions being treated here, consider the equations

(4) $x = a \cosh t,$ $y = a \sinh t.$

In the equations (4) let t be a parameter and a a fixed constant. Then those equations are parametric equations of an equilateral hyperbola because from

$$\cosh^2 t - \sinh^2 t = 1$$

it follows that

$$\frac{x^2}{a^2} - \frac{y^2}{a^2} = 1$$

or

$$x^2 - y^2 = a^2.$$

This is analogous to the result that the two equations

$$x = a \cos t, \, y = a \sin t$$

are parametric equations of the circle

$$x^2 + y^2 = a^2.$$

The formulas used to define the hyperbolic sine and cosine also have analogs in the study of the trigonometric functions. The definition given on page 659 for the exponential function with pure imaginary exponent may be used to derive the pertinent formulas.

138. *The Catenary*

Although the proof must be deferred to § 364, we now mention one elementary application of hyperbolic functions.

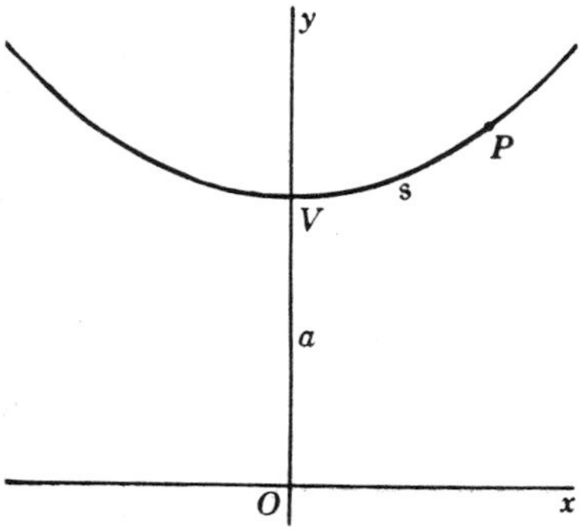

When a flexible, homogeneous cord or wire hangs from two of its points under its own weight (suspended cable, telephone wire, clothesline), it falls in a curve called the *catenary*. With the origin at distance a below the lowest point, the equation is

(1) $y = a \cosh \dfrac{x}{a}.$

y=a cosh $\frac{x}{a}$

Figure 164

We know by observation that the curve has the general form shown in Figure 164. Using the table, pp. 701–706, the student may easily plot the curve.

We shall see in § 364 that the constant in equation (1) is the ratio of the tension exerted at the vertex V divided by the weight per unit length of the cable.

In Figure 164 let s be the length of arc VP from the vertex to any point of the curve. We shall show in Ex. 15, page 476, that

(2) $$s = a \sinh \frac{x}{a}.$$

Suppose a catenary has been formed, as in Figure 165, by suspending a given length of wire or cable between two points A, B at the same height* in a vertical plane. We seek a relation between the length of the cable L, the depth of the dip d, and the constant a. It is assumed that the axes have been chosen so that the equation of the catenary is (1) above. At the point A, $y = a + d$ and $s = \frac{1}{2}L$. Then, by (1) and (2), we have

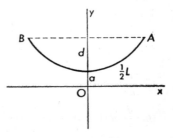

Figure 165

(3) $a + d = a \cosh \dfrac{x}{a}$, $\dfrac{1}{2} L = a \sinh \dfrac{x}{a}$.

Since, for any z, $\cosh^2 z - \sinh^2 z = 1$, equations (3) yield

$$(a + d)^2 - \tfrac{1}{4}L^2 = a^2,$$

or

(4) $$L^2 = 4d(2a + d).$$

EXERCISES

In Exs. 1–16 prove the stated property of the hyperbolic functions. Use the definitions, the results in the text, or the properties obtained in any previous exercise.

1. $\sinh (-x) = - \sinh x$; $\cosh (-x) = \cosh x$; $\tanh (-x) = - \tanh x$.
2. $\operatorname{sech}^2 x = 1 - \tanh^2 x$.
3. $\operatorname{csch}^2 x = \coth^2 x - 1$.
4. $e^x = \cosh x + \sinh x$; $e^{-x} = \cosh x - \sinh x$.
5. $\sinh^2 y = \frac{1}{2}(\cosh 2y - 1)$.
6. $\cosh^2 y = \frac{1}{2}(\cosh 2y + 1)$.
7. $\cosh 2y = \cosh^2 y + \sinh^2 y$
   $$= 2 \cosh^2 y - 1$$
   $$= 2 \sinh^2 y + 1.$$
8. $\sinh 2y = 2 \sinh y \cosh y$.
9. $\sinh (x + y) = \sinh x \cosh y + \cosh x \sinh y$;
   $\sinh (x - y) = \sinh x \cosh y - \cosh x \sinh y$.
10. $\cosh (x + y) = \cosh x \cosh y + \sinh x \sinh y$;
    $\cosh (x - y) = \cosh x \cosh y - \sinh x \sinh y$.

* Of course the wire will hang in a catenary whether or not the points of suspension are at the same height.

11. $\tanh (x + y) = \dfrac{\tanh x + \tanh y}{1 + \tanh x \tanh y}$;

$\tanh (x - y) = \dfrac{\tanh x - \tanh y}{1 - \tanh x \tanh y}$.

12. $\dfrac{d}{dx} \cosh u = \sinh u \dfrac{du}{dx}$.

13. $\dfrac{d}{dx} \tanh u = \operatorname{sech}^2 u \dfrac{du}{dx}$.

14. $\dfrac{d}{dx} \operatorname{csch} u = - \operatorname{csch} u \coth u \dfrac{du}{dx}$.

15. $\dfrac{d}{dx} \operatorname{sech} u = - \operatorname{sech} u \tanh u \dfrac{du}{dx}$.

16. $\dfrac{d}{dx} \coth u = - \operatorname{csch}^2 u \dfrac{du}{dx}$.

In Exs. 17–28, find the first derivative.

17. $y = \sinh 3x$.   **18.** $y = \cosh (2x + 1)$.
19. $y = \tanh (1 - 2x)$.   **20.** $y = \operatorname{sech} 3x$.
21. $x = \cosh^2 4t$.   **22.** $x = \tanh^2 t$.
23. $y = x^2 \sinh 3x$.   **24.** $y = e^{2x} \cosh x$.
25. $y = \cosh x^2$.   **26.** $y = \tanh (x - 1)^2$.
27. $y = \ln \sinh 2x$.   *Ans.* $y' = 2 \coth 2x$.
28. $y = \ln \tanh^2 x$.   *Ans.* $y' = 4 \operatorname{csch} 2x$.
29. Sketch the curve which has for parametric equations

$$x = 3 \cosh t, \qquad y = 4 \sinh t.$$

30. Trace the curve $y = a \sinh \dfrac{x}{a}$. [Reflect the curve $y = ae^{\frac{x}{a}}$ in the origin to obtain $y = -ae^{-\frac{x}{a}}$; average the ordinates.]

31. Trace the curve $y = a \sinh \dfrac{x}{a}$ by the method of § 61. Also use the table, pp. 701–706.

32. Trace the curve $y = a \tanh \dfrac{x}{a}$.   **33.** Trace the curve $y = a \operatorname{sech} \dfrac{x}{a}$.

34. Prove that Arcsin tanh x = Arctan sinh x.
35. Prove that Arcsin tanh x = Arccos sech x, $x \geqq 0$.

139. *Inverse Hyperbolic Functions*

The *inverse hyperbolic sine*, also called *antihyperbolic sine*, is defined and denoted as follows:

$$y = \sinh^{-1} x \quad if \quad x = \sinh y.$$

Similarly for the other inverse functions.

Since the hyperbolic functions are exponential, the inverse functions must be logarithmic.   The explicit formulas are as follows:

(1) $\qquad \sinh^{-1} x = \ln (x + \sqrt{x^2 + 1});$

(2) $\qquad \cosh^{-1} x = \ln (x + \sqrt{x^2 - 1}), \qquad x \geqq 1;$

(3) $\qquad \tanh^{-1} x = \dfrac{1}{2} \ln \dfrac{1 + x}{1 - x}, \qquad |x| < 1;$

(4) $\qquad \coth^{-1} x = \dfrac{1}{2} \ln \dfrac{x + 1}{x - 1}, \qquad |x| > 1;$

(5) $\qquad \operatorname{sech}^{-1} x = \ln \dfrac{1 + \sqrt{1 - x^2}}{x}, \qquad 0 < x \leqq 1;$

(6) $\qquad \operatorname{csch}^{-1} x = \begin{cases} \ln \dfrac{1 + \sqrt{1 + x^2}}{x}, & x > 0; \\[3mm] -\ln \dfrac{1 + \sqrt{1 + x^2}}{-x}, & x < 0. \end{cases}$

The problem of deriving these formulas is similar to Example (a), § 103.   The equation

$$y = \cosh^{-1} x$$

means that

$$\cosh y = x,$$
$$\frac{e^y + e^{-y}}{2} = x, \qquad e^y + e^{-y} - 2x = 0,$$
$$e^{2y} - 2x e^y + 1 = 0.$$

Solving this quadratic in e^y, we get

$$e^y = x \pm \sqrt{x^2 - 1},$$

which gives two values of y:

$$y = \ln (x + \sqrt{x^2 - 1}),$$
$$y = \ln (x - \sqrt{x^2 - 1}).$$

By Ex. 47, page 189, with $a = 1$,

$$\ln (x - \sqrt{x^2 - 1}) = -\ln (x + \sqrt{x^2 - 1}),$$

so that the two values of y are

$$y = \pm \ln (x + \sqrt{x^2 - 1}), \quad x \geqq 1.$$

(It is easily seen that y is imaginary if $x < 1$.)   Thus it turns out that $\cosh^{-1} x$ is two-valued: to make it one-valued, we agree to retain only the positive value.

The other formulas above may be verified by the student.   The derivatives may be found either by differentiation of (1)–(6) or by the indirect method used in § 105.

140. *The Tractrix*

To illustrate the fact that inverse hyperbolic functions appear in comparatively elementary physical problems, we cite an example.

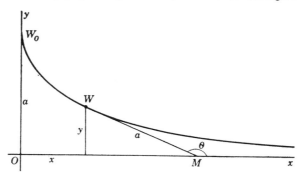

. **Figure 166**

A man, standing at O, holds a rope of length a to which a weight is attached, initially at W_0. The man walks to the right, dragging the weight after him: when the man is at M, the weight is at W. The path of the weight (the tractrix) will at least resemble the curve of Figure 166. In § 365 it will be shown that the equation is

$$x = a \operatorname{sech}^{-1} \frac{y}{a} - \sqrt{a^2 - y^2};$$

from this we can trace the curve accurately (Ex. 21 below).

EXERCISES

1. Trace the curve $y = \sinh^{-1} x$ by reflecting, in the 45°-line, the curve $y = \sinh x$.

2. Trace the curve $y = \cosh^{-1} x$ by reflecting, in the 45°-line, the positive half of the curve $y = \cosh x$.

3. Trace the curve $y = \tanh^{-1} x$.

4. Obtain formula (1), § 139.

5. Obtain formula (3), § 139.

6. Obtain formula (4), § 139.

7. Obtain formula (5), § 139.   (Of the two values that appear, only the positive is retained, by agreement.)

8. Obtain formula (6), § 139.   (Of the two values that appear, one is imaginary when $x < 0$, the other when $x > 0$, so that the function is automatically one-valued.)

In Exs. 9–14, verify the given formula, if u is a function of x.

9. $\dfrac{d}{dx} \sinh^{-1} u = \dfrac{\dfrac{du}{dx}}{\sqrt{1 + u^2}}.$

10. $\dfrac{d}{dx} \tanh^{-1} u = \dfrac{\dfrac{du}{dx}}{1 - u^2}.$

11. $\dfrac{d}{dx} \cosh^{-1} u = \dfrac{\dfrac{du}{dx}}{\sqrt{u^2 - 1}}.$

12. $\dfrac{d}{dx} \coth^{-1} u = \dfrac{\dfrac{du}{dx}}{1 - u^2}.$

13. $\dfrac{d}{dx} \operatorname{sech}^{-1} u = - \dfrac{\dfrac{du}{dx}}{u \sqrt{1 - u^2}}.$

14. $\dfrac{d}{dx} \operatorname{csch}^{-1} u = - \dfrac{\dfrac{du}{dx}}{u \sqrt{1 + u^2}},$ $u > 0;$

$\dfrac{d}{dx} \operatorname{csch}^{-1} u = \dfrac{\dfrac{du}{dx}}{u \sqrt{1 + u^2}},$ $u < 0.$

15. Show that $\tanh^{-1}(-x) = -\tanh^{-1} x.$

16. Show that $\sinh^{-1}(-x) = -\sinh^{-1} x.$

17. Show that $\operatorname{csch}^{-1}(-x) = -\operatorname{csch}^{-1} x.$

18. Show that $\sinh^{-1} \tan \varphi = \ln(\sec \varphi + \tan \varphi),\ \sec \varphi \geqq 1.$

19. Find the slope of the tractrix at any point. (Read off $\tan \theta$ directly from Figure 166.) Hence show that the curve starts at W_0 tangent to the y-axis.

$$Ans. \quad \frac{dy}{dx} = - \frac{y}{\sqrt{a^2 - y^2}}.$$

20. Solve Ex. 19 by finding y' from the equation of the curve. [Formula (5''), page 84.]

21. Trace the tractrix by subtracting abscissas of the circular arc $x = \sqrt{a^2 - y^2}$ from those of the curve $y = a \operatorname{sech} \dfrac{x}{a}.$ (Ex. 33, page 248.)

Curvature

141. *Curvature; Radius of Curvature*

We say in ordinary language that a curve whose direction changes rapidly has great *curvature*, or is sharply curved. Thus a circular arc is said to have greater curvature when the radius is small than when it is large. This somewhat vague idea may be made precise as follows.

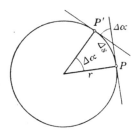

Figure 167

Consider, first, two points P, P' on a circle, and denote the arc PP' by Δs, the angle between the tangents at P, P' by $\Delta\alpha$.

The quotient $\dfrac{\Delta\alpha}{\Delta s}$ is the *change in direction* of the curve, per unit of arc. The central angle subtended by Δs is equal to $\Delta\alpha$; hence, by the formula

$$Arc = radius \times angle,$$

we have

$$\Delta s = r\,\Delta\alpha,$$

so that the change in direction per unit of arc is

$$\frac{\Delta\alpha}{\Delta s} = \frac{1}{r}.$$

That is, in the case of the circle, the quotient $\dfrac{\Delta\alpha}{\Delta s}$ is constant; it is called the *curvature* of the circle.

If now the curve in question is not a circle, the direction of the curve no longer changes uniformly, and the quotient $\dfrac{\Delta\alpha}{\Delta s}$ represents merely the *average curvature* of the arc Δs. But as P' (Figure 168) approaches P along the curve, so that Δs and $\Delta\alpha$ approach zero, the quantity $\dfrac{\Delta\alpha}{\Delta s}$ in general approaches a limit $\dfrac{d\alpha}{ds}$, which is called the *curvature at the point P*.

The curvature (denoted by the Greek letter kappa) at a point is given by

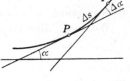

(1) $$\kappa = \operatorname*{Lim}_{\Delta s \to 0} \frac{\Delta \alpha}{\Delta s} = \frac{d\alpha}{ds}.$$

The reciprocal of the curvature is called the *radius of curvature*, and is denoted by ρ:

(2) $$\rho = \frac{1}{\kappa} = \frac{ds}{d\alpha}.$$

Figure 168

However, it is customary to consider κ and ρ as essentially positive (just as, for a circle, the radius of the circle—equal to the radius of curvature—is always positive); and, of course, if s decreases as α increases, the derivative $\dfrac{ds}{d\alpha}$ is a negative quantity. Thus, as our defining formulas, we shall replace (1) and (2) by

(3) $$\kappa = \left| \frac{d\alpha}{ds} \right|,$$

(4) $$\rho = \left| \frac{ds}{d\alpha} \right|.$$

142. *Expression in Rectangular Coordinates*

The definitions above are independent of the particular coordinate system used; the angle α is the angle made by the tangent at P with any fixed line in the plane of the curve. When the equation of the curve is given in rectangular coordinates, it is convenient to take α as the slope-angle of the tangent; i.e., the angle between the tangent and the x-axis. The curvature κ is then easily expressed in terms of the coordinates. For,

$$\tan \alpha = \frac{dy}{dx} = y',$$

$$\alpha = \operatorname{Arctan} y',$$

(1) $$d\alpha = \frac{dy'}{1 + (y')^2} = \frac{y'' \, dx}{1 + (y')^2}.$$

Also, by § 72,

(2) $$ds = \pm \sqrt{1 + (y')^2} \, dx.$$

Substituting (1) and (2) in the defining formulas above, we find

$$\kappa = \frac{|y''|}{[1 + (y')^2]^{\frac{3}{2}}},$$

$$\rho = \frac{[1 + (y')^2]^{\frac{3}{2}}}{|y''|}.$$

Example (a).   Find the radius of curvature of the equilateral hyperbola

(3) $$x^2 - y^2 = a^2$$

at any point (x, y) on the curve.

We have, directly or by Example (b), § 55,

$$y' = \frac{x}{y}, \qquad y'' = -\frac{a^2}{y^3}.$$

Thus

(4) $$\rho = \frac{\left(1 + \frac{x^2}{y^2}\right)^{\frac{3}{2}}}{\dfrac{a^2}{|y^3|}} = \frac{|y^3|\left(1 + \frac{x^2}{y^2}\right)^{\frac{3}{2}}}{a^2} = \frac{(x^2 + y^2)^{\frac{3}{2}}}{a^2}.$$

Example (b).   **In Example (a), find the points of maximum curvature.** [*]

The differentiation is somewhat simpler if, instead of making κ a maximum, we make ρ a minimum.   It will be convenient to express ρ in terms of y by means of (3):

$$\rho = \frac{(a^2 + 2y^2)^{\frac{3}{2}}}{a^2},$$

$$\frac{d\rho}{dy} = \frac{6y(a^2 + 2y^2)^{\frac{1}{2}}}{a^2},$$

so that $$\frac{d\rho}{dy} = 0, \qquad \text{when } y = 0.$$

Thus the curvature is greatest at the vertices.   We actually have maximum κ, rather than minimum or neither, for we know that far out in the first quadrant, and again in the fourth quadrant, the curve is nearly straight.

We might just as easily have happened to express ρ in terms of x.   If so, an interesting situation arises:

$$\rho = \frac{(2x^2 - a^2)^{\frac{3}{2}}}{a^2},$$

$$\frac{d\rho}{dx} = \frac{6x(2x^2 - a^2)^{\frac{1}{2}}}{a^2}$$

$$\frac{d\rho}{dx} = 0 \text{ when } x = 0, \text{ or } x = \pm \tfrac{1}{2}\sqrt{2}\, a.$$

Now all these critical values are barred, since the hyperbola does not reach so far.   We are not yet fully equipped to trace the curve

$$\rho^2 = \frac{(2x^2 - a^2)^3}{a^4},$$

[*] This particular problem can be solved by inspection.   A glance at (4) shows that ρ is least when the quantity $x^2 + y^2$ is least; i.e., at that point of the curve that is nearest the origin.

but it has the form shown in Figure 184, page 287.   However, since we are limited to $|x| \geq a$, $\rho > 0$, only the portions drawn full have a meaning. Hence ρ, as a function of x, has *end-point minima* (§ 70) at $x = \pm a$.

143. *Circle of Curvature*

At any point on a curve $y = f(x)$, where y' and y'' exist and $y'' \neq 0$, there is associated with the curve a circle, which is called the *circle of curvature*. In a sense, the circle of curvature is the circle which comes nearest (of all circles) to fitting the curve in the immediate vicinity of the point under consideration.

At a point (x, y) on $y = f(x)$, let y' and y'' exist with $y'' \neq 0$.   Let a circle, with unspecified radius r and center at (a, b), pass through the point (x, y) and have, at that point, the same y' and y'' as those of the curve $y = f(x)$. The circle has the equation

$$(1) \qquad\qquad (x - a)^2 + (y - b)^2 = r^2.$$

From (1), by differentiating each member twice, we obtain

$$(2) \qquad\qquad x - a + y'(y - b) = 0,$$

$$(3) \qquad\qquad 1 + y''(y - b) + (y')^2 = 0.$$

It is a simple matter to obtain the coordinates a and b, of the center of the circle (1), from equations (2) and (3).   The results are

$$(4) \qquad\qquad a = x - \frac{y'[1 + (y')^2]}{y''},$$

and

$$(5) \qquad\qquad b = y + \frac{1 + (y')^2}{y''}.$$

Next we form the expression $(x - a)^2 + (y - b)^2$ to find the radius of the circle.   From (4) and (5), we get

$$
\begin{aligned}
(x - a)^2 + (y - b)^2 &= \frac{(y')^2[1 + (y')^2]^2}{(y'')^2} + \frac{[1 + (y')^2]^2}{(y'')^2} \\
&= \frac{[1 + (y')^2]^3}{(y'')^2}.
\end{aligned}
$$

Hence

$$r^2 = \frac{[1 + (y')^2]^3}{(y'')^2},$$

so that $r = \rho$, the radius of curvature of $y = f(x)$.

We have shown that the circle of curvature, at a point (x, y) on a curve, is the circle with *center at* (a, b) given by equations (4) and (5), and with *radius equal to the radius of curvature of the curve* at the point under consideration.

Example. Find the circle of curvature of the parabola $y^2 = 2x$ at the point $(\frac{1}{2}, 1)$, at one end of the latus rectum.

From $y = \sqrt{2}\, x^{\frac{1}{2}}$, we obtain

$$y' = \tfrac{1}{2}\sqrt{2}\, x^{-\frac{1}{2}},$$
$$y'' = -\tfrac{1}{4}\sqrt{2}\, x^{-\frac{3}{2}}.$$

Thus at the point $(\frac{1}{2}, 1)$ we have

$$y' = \tfrac{1}{2}\sqrt{2} \cdot \sqrt{2} = 1,$$
$$y'' = -\tfrac{1}{4}\sqrt{2} \cdot (\sqrt{2})^3 = -1.$$

Hence the circle of curvature has for coordinates of its center, from equations (4) and (5),

$$a = \frac{1}{2} - \frac{1(1+1)}{-1} = \frac{5}{2},$$
$$b = 1 + \frac{1+1}{-1} = -1.$$

The radius of the circle of curvature is

$$\rho = \frac{[1+1]^{\frac{3}{2}}}{|-1|} = +2\sqrt{2}.$$

The circle of curvature, then, is

(6) $$(x - \tfrac{5}{2})^2 + (y + 1)^2 = 8.$$

Note the check which is obtained by showing that the circle (6) passes through the given point $(\frac{1}{2}, 1)$.

EXERCISES

In Exs. 1–8, find the radius of curvature at the given point.

1. $y = x - \frac{1}{8}x^2$ at $(1, \frac{7}{8})$.   *Ans.* $\frac{125}{16}$.

2. $y = 2 + 2x - x^2$ at $(\frac{1}{2}, \frac{11}{4})$.   *Ans.* $\sqrt{2}$.

3. $y = x(x + 2)^2$ at $(0, 0)$.   *Ans.* $\dfrac{17\sqrt{17}}{8}$.

4. $y = x^2(x + 2)$ at $(0, 0)$.   *Ans.* $\frac{1}{4}$.

5. $y^2 = x - 2$ at $(3, 1)$.   *Ans.* $\dfrac{5\sqrt{5}}{2}$.

6. $y = \cos x$ at $(\pi, -1)$.   *Ans.* 1.

7. $y = a \sec \dfrac{x}{a}$ at $x = \dfrac{\pi a}{4}$.   *Ans.* $a\sqrt{\frac{3}{2}}$.

8. $y = \ln \tan \dfrac{x}{2}$ at $x = \dfrac{\pi}{4}$.   *Ans.* $2(\frac{3}{2})^{\frac{3}{2}}$.

In Exs. 9–22, find the radius of curvature at any point of the curve. In exercises involving parametric equations, reference may be made to § 118.

9. $y = \tan x$. $\qquad\qquad$ Ans. $\dfrac{(1 + \sec^4 x)^{\frac{3}{2}}}{2 \sec^2 x |\tan x|}$.

10. $y = \cos x$.

11. $y = \ln \sin x$. $\qquad\qquad\qquad\qquad\qquad$ Ans. $|\csc x|$.

12. $y = \ln \sec x$. $\qquad\qquad\qquad\qquad\qquad$ Ans. $|\sec x|$.

13. The parabola $y^2 = 4ax$. $\qquad\qquad\qquad$ Ans. $\dfrac{2(a + x)^{\frac{3}{2}}}{a^{\frac{1}{2}}}$.

14. The hyperbola $2xy = a^2$. $\qquad$ Ans. $\dfrac{(4x^4 + a^4)^{\frac{3}{2}}}{8a^2|x^3|}$.

15. The *four-cusped hypocycloid* $x^{\frac{2}{3}} + y^{\frac{2}{3}} = a^{\frac{2}{3}}$. (Figure 169.) $\qquad\qquad\qquad\qquad$ Ans. $3|axy|^{\frac{1}{3}}$.

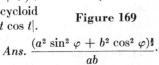

Figure 169

16. $x = 3t + 1$, $y = t^2$, with t as a parameter. $\qquad\qquad\qquad\qquad$ Ans. $\frac{1}{6}(9 + 4t^2)^{\frac{3}{2}}$.

17. $x = 1 - 2t$, $y = t^2 + 3$. $\qquad$ Ans. $2(1 + t^2)^{\frac{3}{2}}$.

18. $x = a \sin^3 t$, $y = a \cos^3 t$, the four-cusped hypocycloid of Ex. 15. $\qquad\qquad\qquad$ Ans. $3|a \sin t \cos t|$.

19. The ellipse $x = a \cos \varphi$, $y = b \sin \varphi$. $\qquad$ Ans. $\dfrac{(a^2 \sin^2 \varphi + b^2 \cos^2 \varphi)^{\frac{3}{2}}}{ab}$.

20. The parabola $x = a \tan^2 \varphi$, $y = 2a \tan \varphi$. $\qquad$ Ans. $2a|\sec^3 \varphi|$.

21. $x = a \tan \varphi$, $y = a \cot \varphi$. $\qquad$ Ans. $\frac{1}{2}a|\tan^3 \varphi|(1 + \cot^4 \varphi)^{\frac{3}{2}}$.

22. $x = a \cos^4 \theta$, $y = a \sin^4 \theta$. $\qquad$ Ans. $2a(\sin^4 \theta + \cos^4 \theta)^{\frac{3}{2}}$.

In Exs. 23–33, find the points of maximum curvature.

23. $3y = x^3$. $\qquad\qquad\qquad\qquad\qquad$ Ans. $x = \pm(\frac{1}{5})^{\frac{1}{4}}$.

24. $4y = x^4$. $\qquad\qquad\qquad\qquad\qquad$ Ans. $x = \pm(\frac{2}{7})^{\frac{1}{6}}$.

25. $21y = x^{14}$. $\qquad\qquad\qquad\qquad\qquad$ Ans. $x = \pm 1$.

26. $x^2y = a^3$. $\qquad\qquad\qquad\qquad\qquad$ Ans. $x = \pm(5)^{\frac{1}{6}}a$.

27. $y = \sin x$.

28. $y = \ln \sin x$. $\qquad\qquad\qquad\qquad\qquad$ Ans. $x = \frac{1}{2}\pi$.

29. $y = a \cosh \dfrac{x}{a}$.

30. A parabola. (Ex. 13.) $\qquad\qquad\qquad\qquad$ Ans. The vertex.

31. $y = e^x$. $\qquad\qquad\qquad\qquad$ Ans. $(-\frac{1}{2} \ln 2, \frac{1}{2} \sqrt{2})$.

32. $y = \ln x$. (Cf. Ex. 31.)

33. $y = \sinh x$. $\qquad\qquad\qquad\qquad$ Ans. $x = \pm \ln (1 + \sqrt{2})$.

34. If x is given as a function of y, derive the formula (see § 51)

$$\rho = \frac{\left[\left(\dfrac{dx}{dy}\right)^2 + 1\right]^{\frac{3}{2}}}{\left|\dfrac{d^2x}{dy^2}\right|}.$$

35. Find the radius of curvature of the tractrix

$$x = a \operatorname{sech}^{-1} \frac{y}{a} - \sqrt{a^2 - y^2}.$$

Ans. (See Ex. 19, page 251.) $\quad -\dfrac{a}{y'}$.

36. Show that when a weight is drawn along the ground as in Figure 166, page 250, the path of the weight continually tends to straighten out. (Ex. 35.)

37. In Example (*b*), § 142, verify in two ways (§§ 59, 60) that ρ is a minimum.

38. Find the point of minimum curvature for the four-cusped hypocycloid. See Figure 169. *Ans.* Midway between the cusps.

In Exs. 39–43, find the equation of the circle of curvature at the given point. Draw the figure.

39. $y = x^2$ at $(0, 0)$. *Ans.* $x^2 + y^2 = y$.
40. $y = x^2$ at $(1, 1)$. *Ans.* $x^2 + y^2 + 8x - 7y = 3$.
41. $y = x^3 - x^2$ at $(0, 0)$. *Ans.* $x^2 + y^2 + y = 0$.
42. $y = x^3 - x^2$ at $(1, 0)$. *Ans.* $x^2 + y^2 = x + y$.

43. The four-cusped hypocycloid $x^{\frac{2}{3}} + y^{\frac{2}{3}} = 2$, at the point of minimum curvature in the first quadrant. See Ex. 38. *Ans.* $x^2 + y^2 = 8x + 8y - 14$.

44. Let x and y be functions of a parameter t. Denote derivatives with respect to t by primes. Show that the formula for curvature κ becomes

$$\kappa = \frac{x'y'' - y'x''}{[(x')^2 + (y')^2]^{\frac{3}{2}}}.$$

Indeterminate Forms

144. Rolle's Theorem

Consider a curve

(1) $$y = f(x)$$

which cuts the x-axis at $x = a$ and $x = b$. That is, $f(a) = 0$ and $f(b) = 0$. If $f(x)$ is continuous over the closed interval $a \leq x \leq b$, we know from Theorem 18, page 67, that $f(x)$ takes on a maximum and a minimum value somewhere in the interval. If $f(x)$ is not identically zero, the maximum and minimum values cannot both be zero. Suppose the maximum is not zero and that the maximum occurs at x_1. Since $f(x_1) \neq 0$, x_1 must lie in the open interval $a < x_1 < b$.

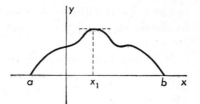

Figure 170

Let us add the condition that the derivative $f'(x)$ exists throughout the open interval $a < x < b$. Then $f'(x_1)$ must exist and (by the definition of a derivative)

(2) $$\underset{\Delta x \to 0}{\text{Lim}} \frac{f(x_1 + \Delta x) - f(x_1)}{\Delta x} = f'(x_1).$$

Now $f(x_1) \geq f(x_1 + \Delta x)$, since a maximum occurs at x_1. Then

(3) $$\frac{f(x_1 + \Delta x) - f(x_1)}{\Delta x} \leq 0, \qquad \text{for } \Delta x > 0,$$

and

(4) $$\frac{f(x_1 + \Delta x) - f(x_1)}{\Delta x} \geq 0, \qquad \text{for } \Delta x < 0.$$

The limit in (2) exists. It cannot be positive because of (3), and it cannot be negative because of (4). Hence the limit is zero, so $f'(x_1) = 0$. The proof is easily adjusted to the situation in which the maximum of $f(x)$ is zero but the minimum is not zero.

We have proved the following theorem, which is used frequently in more advanced mathematics as well as in our study of calculus.

ROLLE'S THEOREM

THEOREM 34. *If $f(x)$ is continuous over the closed interval $a \leqq x \leqq b$, if $f'(x)$ exists over the open interval $a < x < b$, if $f(a) = 0$ and $f(b) = 0$, then there exists an x_1 in the open interval $a < x_1 < b$ such that $f'(x_1) = 0$.*

For a function $f(x)$ which satisfies the conditions imposed in Rolle's theorem, the theorem states that the curve $y = f(x)$ must have a horizontal tangent line at some point between $x = a$ and $x = b$. There may be many such intermediate points. Note also that the function $f(x) \equiv 0$ yields $f'(x) \equiv 0$, so that such a function fits into Rolle's theorem without its being amenable to the proof used here.

145. *The First Law of the Mean*

Examination of Figure 170 suggests that Rolle's theorem may contain (for sufficiently well behaved curves) a property essentially independent of the coordinate system. On an arc of the curve in Figure 170 there is a tangent line parallel to the chord which joins the ends of the arc. We wish to obtain the explicit extension of Rolle's theorem suggested by the above discussion.

In Figure 171, suppose there exists between S and Q the point P at which the tangent line is parallel to the chord SQ. The slope of the chord is

Figure 171

$$\frac{RQ}{SR} = \frac{f(b) - f(a)}{b - a};$$

the slope of the tangent at P is $f'(x_1)$, where x_1 is the abscissa of P. Hence we wish to show that

$$\frac{f(b) - f(a)}{b - a} = f'(x_1).$$

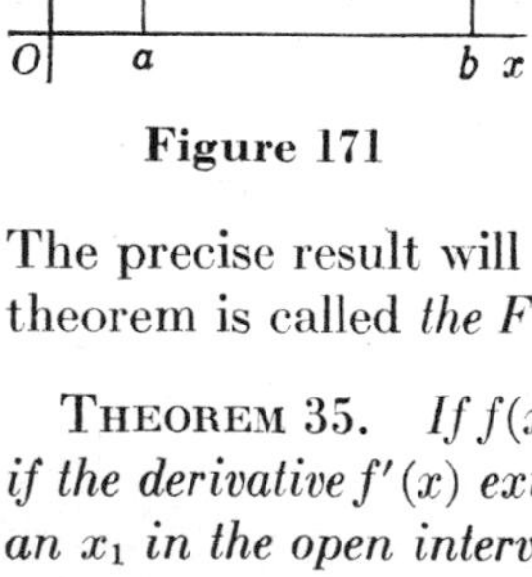

The precise result will now be expressed as a theorem. The formula in the theorem is called *the First Law of the Mean*.

THEOREM 35. *If $f(x)$ is continuous over the closed interval $a \leqq x \leqq b$, and if the derivative $f'(x)$ exists throughout the open interval $a < x < b$, there exists an x_1 in the open interval such that*

$$(1) \qquad f(b) - f(a) = (b - a) f'(x_1), \qquad a < x_1 < b.$$

Theorem 35 differs from Rolle's theorem only in the form of the conclusion and in that the function is not required to vanish at the end points of the interval. It is natural to try to use Rolle's theorem in the proof of Theorem 35. We therefore attempt to set up a function $\varphi(x)$ which retains the continuity and differentiability properties of $f(x)$ and which is such that $\varphi(a) = 0$ and $\varphi(b) = 0$. The continuity and differentiability properties of $f(x)$ will surely be retained if we add to $f(x)$ any polynomial in x. Since we need to satisfy the two conditions

(2) $$\varphi(a) = 0, \qquad \varphi(b) = 0,$$

two constants should suffice, so we add to $f(x)$ a linear polynomial in x.

The determination of $\varphi(x)$ is made simpler by starting with a function which already satisfies one of the conditions (2). Therefore let us set

(3) $$\varphi(x) = f(x) - f(a) + c(x - a)$$

so that $\varphi(x)$ vanishes at $x = a$. We determine the constant c by requiring that $\varphi(b) = 0$. Thus

$$0 = f(b) - f(a) + c(b - a),$$

from which

$$c = -\frac{f(b) - f(a)}{b - a}.$$

Employing the above expression for c in equation (3) yields the desired function

(4) $$\varphi(x) = f(x) - f(a) - \frac{f(b) - f(a)}{b - a}(x - a).$$

Proof of Theorem 35. If $f(x)$ satisfies the conditions of Theorem 35, the function $\varphi(x)$ of (4) satisfies all the requirements of Rolle's theorem, as is easily verified. Therefore there exists an x_1, in the open interval $a < x_1 < b$, such that $\varphi'(x_1) = 0$. Hence, by (4),

(5) $$0 = f'(x_1) - \frac{f(b) - f(a)}{b - a}$$

for some x_1 in $a < x_1 < b$. Since (5) is a rearrangement of (1), the proof of Theorem 35 is now complete.

An interesting application of Theorem 35 is obtained by choosing

(6) $$f(x) = \int_a^x g(y)\, dy.$$

If $g(y)$ is continuous in $a \leq y \leq b$, then $f(x)$ satisfies the conditions of Theorem 35. Now from (6)

$$f'(x) = g(x),$$

so that we may conclude from the theorem that

(7) $\qquad \int_a^b g(y)\, dy - \int_a^a g(y)\, dy = (b-a)g(x_1), \qquad a < x_1 < b.$

The second integral in (7) is zero. Hence

(8) $\qquad \int_a^b g(y)\, dy = (b-a)g(x_1), \qquad a < x_1 < b,$

which is the law of the mean for integrals.

146. *The Indeterminate Forms* $\dfrac{0}{0}$ *and* $\dfrac{\infty}{\infty}$

Theorem 35 of the preceding section furnishes us with a tool which frequently aids in the evaluation of a limit of a quotient,

(1) $$\operatorname*{Lim}_{x \to a} \frac{f(x)}{F(x)},$$

in which both $f(a) = 0$ and $F(a) = 0$.   The quotient $\dfrac{f(x)}{F(x)}$ is said to* *assume*

the "indeterminate form" $\dfrac{0}{0}$ at $x = a$ and is undefined at that point.   Nevertheless the *limit* of the quotient may exist.   This fact is illustrated in the derivation of the fundamental differentiation formulas, where in each case both numerator and denominator of the difference-quotient $\dfrac{\Delta y}{\Delta x}$ approach zero, yet the derivative, which is the limit of that quotient, exists.

If the function $\dfrac{f(x)}{F(x)}$ does approach a limit, it may be possible to evaluate

the limit by means of simple transformations of $\dfrac{f(x)}{F(x)}$, as was done in deriving the differentiation formulas.   In many cases the limit may be obtained by a method that will now be developed.
(L' HOSPITAL'S RULE)

THEOREM 36.   *If* $f(a) = F(a) = 0$ *and if both* $f'(x)$ *and* $F'(x)$ *exist in some interval including the point* $x = a$,

(2) $$\operatorname*{Lim}_{x \to a} \frac{f(x)}{F(x)} = \operatorname*{Lim}_{x \to a} \frac{f'(x)}{F'(x)}$$

in the sense that if the right member of (2) *exists, the left member also exists and their values are equal.*

---

* It should be clearly understood that the symbols $\dfrac{0}{0}$, $\dfrac{\infty}{\infty}$, etc., are never to be taken literally, since, so taken, they have no meaning whatever.   In fact, the term "indeterminate form" is something of a misnomer, since the function is simply not defined at the point in question.   No confusion will arise if we always remember that these symbols are nothing more than convenient shorthand to designate the various situations described.

Proof. Under the assumptions of Theorem 36 we may choose x close enough to a so that the functions $f(y)$ and $F(y)$ are both continuous in the closed interval $a \leq y \leq x$, and their derivatives $f'(y)$ and $F'(y)$ exist in the open interval $a < y < x$.

Now consider the function $\varphi(y)$ defined by

$$(3) \qquad \varphi(y) = f(y)F(x) - f(x)F(y).$$

In the interval $a \leq y \leq x$, $\varphi(y)$ satisfies the conditions of Rolle's theorem, page 260. Note that $f(a) = F(a) = 0$ results in $\varphi(a) = 0$ and the form of $\varphi(y)$ leads to $\varphi(x) = 0$. Then there exists an x_1 in the open interval $a < x_1 < x$ such that $\varphi'(x_1) = 0$. That is,

$$(4) \qquad f'(x_1)F(x) - f(x)F'(x_1) = 0, \qquad a < x_1 < x.$$

Since neither F nor F' can be identically zero (or the problem is trivial), we may choose x close enough to a so that neither $F(x)$ nor $F'(x_1)$ is zero. Hence (4) leads to the result that there exists an x_1 in $a < x_1 < x$ such that

$$(5) \qquad \frac{f(x)}{F(x)} = \frac{f'(x_1)}{F'(x_1)}, \qquad a < x_1 < x.$$

When $x \to a$, $x_1 \to a$, and the conclusion stated in Theorem 36 follows from (5).

Example (a). Evaluate

$$\text{Lim}_{\theta \to \frac{1}{2}\pi} \frac{1 - \sin \theta}{(\pi - 2\theta)^2}.$$

Since $1 - \sin \frac{1}{2}\pi = 0$ and $(\pi - \pi)^2 = 0$, the fraction involved does assume the indeterminate form $\dfrac{0}{0}$ at $\theta = \frac{1}{2}\pi$. Both the functions $(1 - \sin \theta)$ and $(\pi - 2\theta)^2$ are continuous and differentiable for all finite θ. Hence we may apply Theorem 36; i.e., we may differentiate the numerator and denominator separately and replace the old problem by a new one:

$$(6) \qquad \begin{aligned} \text{Lim}_{\theta \to \frac{1}{2}\pi} \frac{1 - \sin \theta}{(\pi - 2\theta)^2} &= \text{Lim}_{\theta \to \frac{1}{2}\pi} \frac{-\cos \theta}{-4(\pi - 2\theta)} \\ &= \frac{1}{4} \text{Lim}_{\theta \to \frac{1}{2}\pi} \frac{\cos \theta}{\pi - 2\theta}. \end{aligned}$$

Again the fraction involved, $\dfrac{\cos \theta}{\pi - 2\theta}$ assumes the form $\dfrac{0}{0}$ at $\theta = \frac{1}{2}\pi$. But the functions $\cos \theta$ and $\pi - 2\theta$ satisfy the conditions of Theorem 36. Hence we apply the process again:

$$(7) \qquad \frac{1}{4} \text{Lim}_{\theta \to \frac{1}{2}\pi} \frac{\cos \theta}{\pi - 2\theta} = \frac{1}{4} \text{Lim}_{\theta \to \frac{1}{2}\pi} \frac{-\sin \theta}{-2} = \frac{1}{4} \cdot \frac{-1}{-2} = \frac{1}{8}.$$

From (6) and (7) we obtain the desired evaluation

$$(8) \qquad \operatorname*{Lim}_{\theta \to \frac{1}{2}\pi} \frac{1 - \sin \theta}{(\pi - 2\theta)^2} = \frac{1}{8}.$$

Theorem 36 applies also when x approaches a from one side only, $x \to a^+$ or $x \to a^-$. By using the substitution $x = \frac{1}{z}$, it is easy to show that Theorem 36 may be extended to the situation in which $x \to \infty$ or $x \to -\infty$.

If $f(x)$ and $F(x)$ both increase indefinitely (in either direction) as x approaches a, the quotient $\frac{f(x)}{F(x)}$ is said to *assume the indeterminate form* $\frac{\infty}{\infty}$ at $x = a$. Here again it may happen that $\operatorname*{Lim}_{x \to a} \frac{f(x)}{F(x)}$ exists, and it can be shown that, subject to certain broad conditions that are satisfied in all ordinary cases, the same method may be applied in this case as in the one just treated.

Thus in all these cases we may differentiate the numerator and the denominator *separately* and take the limit of the new quantity thus formed. It must be borne clearly in mind, however, that the theorem applies only to *quotients* in which the numerator and the denominator *both approach zero or both increase without bound*.

Example (b).   Evaluate $\operatorname*{Lim}_{x \to 0^+} \dfrac{e^{-\frac{1}{x}}}{x}$.

Proceeding directly, we find

$$\operatorname*{Lim}_{x \to 0^+} \frac{e^{-\frac{1}{x}}}{x} = \operatorname*{Lim}_{x \to 0^+} \frac{\frac{1}{x^2} e^{-\frac{1}{x}}}{1} = \operatorname*{Lim}_{x \to 0^+} \frac{e^{-\frac{1}{x}}}{x^2}$$

$$= \operatorname*{Lim}_{x \to 0^+} \frac{\frac{1}{x^2} e^{-\frac{1}{x}}}{2x} = \operatorname*{Lim}_{x \to 0^+} \frac{e^{-\frac{1}{x}}}{2x^3}.$$

Evidently nothing is being accomplished. But, the prominence of $\frac{1}{x}$ in the original expression suggests the substitution $z = \frac{1}{x}$:

$$\operatorname*{Lim}_{x \to 0^+} \frac{e^{-\frac{1}{x}}}{x} = \operatorname*{Lim}_{z \to \infty} z e^{-z} = \operatorname*{Lim}_{z \to \infty} \frac{z}{e^z} = \operatorname*{Lim}_{z \to \infty} \frac{1}{e^z} = 0.$$

Any factor (of the *whole expression*) which approaches a limit different from zero may be replaced by its limit as soon as it makes its appearance (Theorem 11, § 31).

Example (c). $\displaystyle \lim_{\alpha \to 0} \frac{\sin \alpha - \alpha}{\tan^3 \alpha} = \lim_{\alpha \to 0} \frac{\cos \alpha - 1}{3 \tan^2 \alpha \sec^2 \alpha}$

$$= \lim_{\alpha \to 0} \frac{\cos \alpha - 1}{3 \tan^2 \alpha} = \lim_{\alpha \to 0} \frac{-\sin \alpha}{6 \tan \alpha \sec^2 \alpha}$$

$$= \lim_{\alpha \to 0} \frac{-\sin \alpha}{6 \tan \alpha} = \lim_{\alpha \to 0} \frac{-\cos \alpha}{6} = -\frac{1}{6}.$$

Finally, to see that our method, even when applicable, does not always succeed, consider the next example.

Example (d).   Evaluate $\displaystyle \lim_{x \to \infty} \frac{3^x}{2^{x^2}}$.

This is of the type $\dfrac{\infty}{\infty}$:

$$\lim_{x \to \infty} \frac{3^x}{2^{x^2}} = \lim_{x \to \infty} \frac{3^x \ln 3}{2^{x^2} \cdot 2x \ln 2}; \quad \text{etc.}$$

Evidently differentiation will never affect the exponential factors.   But we may write

$$\lim_{x \to \infty} \frac{3^x}{2^{x^2}} = \lim_{x \to \infty} \frac{3^x}{2^{2x}} \cdot \frac{1}{2^{x^2 - 2x}}$$

$$= \lim_{x \to \infty} \left[\left(\frac{3}{4} \right)^x \cdot \frac{1}{2^{x^2 - 2x}} \right] = 0,$$

since each factor approaches zero.   See also Exs. 38 and 49 below.

147. *The Indeterminate Form $0 \cdot \infty$*

Consider the product of two functions $f(x) \cdot F(x)$ such that, as x approaches a, one function approaches zero while the other increases indefinitely.   The product is then said to *take the indeterminate form $0 \cdot \infty$*.

If we write

$$f(x) \cdot F(x) = \frac{f(x)}{\dfrac{1}{F(x)}},$$

it follows that the quotient last written assumes the form $\dfrac{0}{0}$ or $\dfrac{\infty}{\infty}$, and the methods of § 146 may be applied.

Example.   Evaluate $\displaystyle \lim_{x \to 0^+} x^2 \ln x$.

This takes the form $0 \cdot \infty$.   We write

$$\lim_{x \to 0^+} x^2 \ln x = \lim_{x \to 0^+} \frac{\ln x}{\dfrac{1}{x^2}} = \lim_{x \to 0^+} \frac{\dfrac{1}{x}}{\dfrac{-2}{x^3}} = \lim_{x \to 0^+} \left(-\frac{x^2}{2} \right) = 0.$$

EXERCISES

In Exs. 1–18, evaluate the limit by employing Theorem 36.

1. $\lim\limits_{x\to0} \dfrac{x + \tan x}{\sin 3x}.$ *Ans.* $\frac{2}{3}$.

2. $\lim\limits_{x\to\frac{\pi}{2}} \dfrac{1 - \sin x}{\cos 3x}.$ *Ans.* 0.

3. $\lim\limits_{y\to0} \dfrac{\text{Arcsin } y}{y}.$ *Ans.* 1.

4. $\lim\limits_{x\to0} \dfrac{\tan x}{x}.$ *Ans.* 1.

5. $\lim\limits_{x\to0} \dfrac{\ln \sec x}{x^2}.$ *Ans.* $\frac{1}{2}$.

6. $\lim\limits_{y\to1} \dfrac{1 + \cos \pi y}{(y - 1)^2}.$ *Ans.* $\dfrac{\pi^2}{2}$.

7. $\lim\limits_{z\to\infty} \dfrac{\ln z}{z}.$ *Ans.* 0.

8. $\lim\limits_{x\to\infty} (x^2 e^{-x}).$ *Ans.* 0.

9. $\lim\limits_{y\to\infty} \dfrac{e^{2y}}{y^3}.$

10. $\lim\limits_{x\to\infty} \dfrac{\ln^2 x}{x}.$

11. $\lim\limits_{x\to\pi} \dfrac{\ln x - \ln \pi}{\sin 2x}.$

12. $\lim\limits_{x\to1} \dfrac{\ln x}{x^2 - 4x + 3}.$

13. $\lim\limits_{x\to0^+} (\text{Arcsin } x) \ln x.$

14. $\lim\limits_{y\to0^+} y e^{\frac{1}{y}}.$

15. $\lim\limits_{x\to0} \dfrac{x - \sin x}{x(1 - \cos x)}.$ *Ans.* $\frac{1}{3}$.

16. $\lim\limits_{y\to0} \dfrac{y - \tan y}{\sin^3 y}.$ *Ans.* $-\frac{1}{3}$.

17. $\lim\limits_{x\to0} \dfrac{x^2 \sin x}{x - \sin x}.$ *Ans.* 6.

18. $\lim\limits_{x\to0} \dfrac{x e^x - \sin x}{\sin^2 x}.$ *Ans.* 1.

In Exs. 19–28, evaluate each limit by two methods.

19. $\lim\limits_{x\to1} \dfrac{x^2 - 4x + 3}{2x^2 - x - 1}.$

20. $\lim\limits_{x\to-2} \dfrac{2x^2 + 3x - 2}{x^2 + 3x + 2}.$

21. $\lim\limits_{x\to3} \dfrac{x^3 - x^2 - 7x + 3}{x^3 - 8x - 3}.$

22. $\lim\limits_{x\to\infty} \dfrac{3x^4 - x + 1}{2x^4 + x^3 - 6}.$

23. $\lim\limits_{\theta\to0} \dfrac{\sin^2 \theta}{1 - \cos \theta}.$

24. $\lim\limits_{\alpha\to0} \dfrac{1 - \cos^4 \alpha}{\alpha \sin \alpha}.$

25. $\lim\limits_{x\to0} \dfrac{x - \tan x}{\sin x}.$

26. $\lim\limits_{y\to0} \dfrac{\sqrt{y + 4} - 2}{y}.$

27. $\lim\limits_{x\to0} \dfrac{x}{\sqrt{1 + x} - \sqrt{1 - x}}.$

28. $\lim\limits_{x\to0} \dfrac{x^2}{1 - \cos x}.$

In Exs. 29–42, evaluate the limits by any available method.

29. $\lim\limits_{x\to2} \dfrac{x^3 - 7x + 6}{2x^3 - 5x^2 + x + 2}.$ *Ans.* 1.

30. $\lim\limits_{x\to2} \dfrac{x^3 - 7x + 6}{x^3 - 3x^2 + 4}.$ *Ans.* No limit.

31. $\operatorname*{Lim}_{\theta \to 0} \dfrac{\tan \theta - \theta}{\theta^2 \sin \theta}.$ *Ans.* $\frac{1}{3}$.

32. $\operatorname*{Lim}_{\alpha \to 0} \dfrac{\sec \alpha - 1}{\alpha \sin \alpha}.$ *Ans.* $\frac{1}{2}$.

33. $\operatorname*{Lim}_{x \to 0} \dfrac{2 \tan x - \sin 2x}{x^3}.$ *Ans.* 2.

34. $\operatorname*{Lim}_{y \to 0} \dfrac{\tan^2 y - \sin^2 y}{y^3 \sin y}.$ *Ans.* 1

35. $\operatorname*{Lim}_{x \to \infty} \dfrac{\cos x}{x}.$ *Ans.* 0.

36. $\operatorname*{Lim}_{x \to \infty} \dfrac{\tan x}{x}.$ *Ans.* No limit.

37. $\operatorname*{Lim}_{x \to \infty} \dfrac{x - \sin x}{x}.$ *Ans.* 1.

38. $\operatorname*{Lim}_{n \to \infty} \dfrac{e^n}{\pi^n}.$ *Ans.* 0.

39. $\operatorname*{Lim}_{x \to 0} \dfrac{2 \cos x + e^{x^2} - 3}{x^2 - x \sin x}.$ *Ans.* $\frac{7}{2}$.

40. $\operatorname*{Lim}_{x \to 0} \dfrac{e^{-x} + \cos x + \sin x - 2}{x \sin^2 x}.$ *Ans.* $-\frac{1}{3}$.

41. $\operatorname*{Lim}_{x \to \infty} (x \sin e^{-x}).$ *Ans.* 0.

42. $\operatorname*{Lim}_{x \to \infty} \left(\sin \dfrac{1}{x} \csc e^{-x} \right).$ *Ans.* ∞.

Prove the theorems of Exs. 43–48, k being any positive number.

43. $\operatorname*{Lim}_{x \to \infty} \dfrac{x^k}{e^x} = 0.$ **44.** $\operatorname*{Lim}_{x \to \infty} \dfrac{\ln x}{x^k} = 0.$ **45.** $\operatorname*{Lim}_{x \to 0^+} x^k \ln x = 0.$

46. $\operatorname*{Lim}_{x \to \infty} \dfrac{e^x}{x^k} = \infty.$ **47.** $\operatorname*{Lim}_{x \to \infty} \dfrac{x^k}{\ln x} = \infty.$ **48.** $\operatorname*{Lim}_{x \to 0^+} \dfrac{\ln x}{x^k} = -\infty.$

49. Solve Example (d), § 146, by a second method. (Note that $3 = 2^{\log_2 3}$.)

50. If $b > 1$, $k > 1$, prove that $\operatorname*{Lim}_{x \to \infty} \dfrac{a^x}{b^{x^k}} = 0$, regardless of the magnitude of the

ratio $\dfrac{a}{b}$. (Cf. Ex. 49.)

148. *The Indeterminate Form* ∞ − ∞

When two functions $f(x)$, $F(x)$ both become indefinitely large and positive, or large and negative, as x approaches a, the *difference* $f(x) - F(x)$ is said to *assume the indeterminate form* ∞ − ∞. While no general rules can be laid down for evaluating the limit (if any) of this difference, we try to find some transformation that will render the expression amenable to Theorem 36.

Example.   Evaluate $\lim\limits_{x\to\frac{\pi^{+}}{2}} (\sec^3 x - \tan^3 x)$.

This takes the form $-\infty + \infty$.   The transformations required are simple:

$$\lim_{x\to\frac{\pi^{+}}{2}} (\sec^3 x - \tan^3 x) = \lim_{x\to\frac{\pi^{+}}{2}} \left(\frac{1}{\cos^3 x} - \frac{\sin^3 x}{\cos^3 x} \right)$$

$$= \lim_{x\to\frac{\pi^{+}}{2}} \frac{1 - \sin^3 x}{\cos^3 x}$$

$$= \lim_{x\to\frac{\pi^{+}}{2}} \frac{-3 \sin^2 x \cos x}{-3 \cos^2 x \sin x}$$

$$= \lim_{x\to\frac{\pi^{+}}{2}} \tan x = -\infty.$$

That is, the given quantity increases indefinitely in the negative direction, without approaching any limit.

149. *The Indeterminate Forms 0^0, ∞^0, 1^∞*

Consider the function

(1) $$y = [f(x)]^{F(x)}.$$

If

$$\lim_{x\to a} f(x) = 0, \qquad \lim_{x\to a} F(x) = 0,$$

or if

$$\lim_{x\to a} f(x) = \infty, \qquad \lim_{x\to a} F(x) = 0,$$

or if

$$\lim_{x\to a} f(x) = 1, \qquad \lim_{x\to a} F(x) = \infty,$$

the function (1) is said, in the respective cases, to *assume the indeterminate form* 0^0, or ∞^0, or 1^∞.   To investigate any one of these limits, take the logarithm of (1):

$$\ln y = F(x) \ln f(x),$$

and in each case the right-hand member is of the type discussed in § 147.
   If $\ln y$ approaches a limit k, then y itself approaches the limit e^k.

Example.   Evaluate $\lim\limits_{x\to 0^+} (1 - \cos x)^{\frac{1}{\ln x}}$.

Put $y = (1 - \cos x)^{\frac{1}{\ln x}}$.   Then

$$\ln y = \frac{\ln (1 - \cos x)}{\ln x}.$$

Therefore,

$$\operatorname*{Lim}_{x\to 0^+} \ln y = \operatorname*{Lim}_{x\to 0^+} \frac{\ln (1 - \cos x)}{\ln x}$$

$$= \operatorname*{Lim}_{x\to 0^+} \frac{\dfrac{\sin x}{1 - \cos x}}{\dfrac{1}{x}}$$

$$= \operatorname*{Lim}_{x\to 0^+} \frac{x \sin x}{1 - \cos x}$$

$$= \operatorname*{Lim}_{x\to 0^+} \frac{\sin x + x \cos x}{\sin x} = 1 + 1 = 2.$$

From $\ln y \to 2$ it follows that $y \to e^2$.   Hence

$$\operatorname*{Lim}_{x\to 0^+} (1 - \cos x)^{\frac{1}{\ln x}} = e^2.$$

EXERCISES

In Exs. 1–20, evaluate the limits by first converting the problem to a proper form to enable you to use Theorem 36.

1. $\operatorname*{Lim}_{\alpha\to 0} \left(\dfrac{1}{\sin^2 \alpha} - \dfrac{1}{\alpha^2} \right)$.   *Ans.* $\frac{1}{3}$.

2. $\operatorname*{Lim}_{x\to 0} \left(\csc x - \dfrac{1}{e^x - 1} \right)$.   *Ans.* $\frac{1}{2}$.

3. $\operatorname*{Lim}_{\theta\to \frac{\pi}{2}} (\sec \theta - \tan \theta)$.   *Ans.* 0.

4. $\operatorname*{Lim}_{x\to 1} \left(\dfrac{x}{x - 1} - \dfrac{1}{\ln x} \right)$.   *Ans.* $\frac{1}{2}$.

5. $\operatorname*{Lim}_{y\to 0} \left(\dfrac{e^{-y^2}}{y^2} - \dfrac{\sec y}{y^2} \right)$.   *Ans.* $-\frac{3}{2}$.

6. $\operatorname*{Lim}_{x\to 0} \left(\dfrac{1}{\sin^2 x} - \dfrac{\sin x}{x^3} \right)$.   *Ans.* $\frac{1}{2}$.

7. $\operatorname*{Lim}_{x\to 1} x^{\csc \pi x}$.   *Ans.* $e^{\frac{-1}{\pi}}$.   **8.** $\operatorname*{Lim}_{y\to 0} (y + 1)^{\cot 2y}$.   *Ans.* $e^{\frac{1}{2}}$.

9. $\operatorname*{Lim}_{\alpha\to 0} (\cos \alpha - \sin \alpha)^{\frac{1}{\alpha}}$.   *Ans.* e^{-1}.

10. $\operatorname*{Lim}_{x\to 0} (1 + x^2)^{\frac{1}{x}}$.   *Ans.* 1.   **11.** $\operatorname*{Lim}_{\alpha\to 0^+} (\sin \alpha)^{\tan \alpha}$.   *Ans.* 1.

12. $\operatorname*{Lim}_{x\to 0} (1 + \sin^2 x)^{\frac{1}{x^2}}$.   *Ans.* e.   **13.** $\operatorname*{Lim}_{x\to 0} (e^x + 3x)^{\frac{1}{x}}$.   *Ans.* e^4.

14. $\operatorname*{Lim}_{\alpha \to 0^{+}} (\csc \alpha)^{\sin \alpha}$.   *Ans.* 1.   **15.** $\operatorname*{Lim}_{x \to \frac{\pi^{-}}{2}} (\tan x)^{\cos x}$.   *Ans.* 1.

16. $\operatorname*{Lim}_{\alpha \to 0} (\sec \alpha + \tan \alpha)^{\csc \alpha}$.   *Ans.* e.

17. $\operatorname*{Lim}_{x \to 0} (\cos x)^{\frac{1}{x^2}}$.   *Ans.* $e^{-\frac{1}{2}}$.   **18.** $\operatorname*{Lim}_{x \to 0} \left(\dfrac{\sin x}{x} \right)^{\frac{1}{x^2}}$.   *Ans.* $e^{-\frac{1}{6}}$.

19. $\operatorname*{Lim}_{x \to 0^{+}} x^x$.   *Ans.* 1.   **20.** $\operatorname*{Lim}_{x \to 0^{+}} (\tan x)^{\frac{1}{\ln x}}$.   *Ans.* e.

In Exs. 21–34, evaluate the limit by any available method.

21. $\operatorname*{Lim}_{x \to \infty} (e^x - x)$.   *Ans.* $+\infty$.

22. $\operatorname*{Lim}_{x \to 0^{+}} (x + \ln x)$.   *Ans.* $-\infty$.

23. $\operatorname*{Lim}_{x \to \infty} (x - \ln x)$.   *Ans.* $+\infty$.

24. $\operatorname*{Lim}_{\alpha \to \pi^{+}} (\csc^3 \alpha - \cot^3 \alpha)$.   *Ans.* $-\infty$.

25. $\operatorname*{Lim}_{\alpha \to \pi^{-}} (\csc^3 \alpha - \cot^3 \alpha)$.   *Ans.* $+\infty$.

26. $\operatorname*{Lim}_{\alpha \to \pi} (\csc^3 \alpha - \cot^3 \alpha)$.   *Ans.* No limit.

27. $\operatorname*{Lim}_{x \to 0} (\csc^3 x - \cot^3 x)$.   *Ans.* No limit.

28. $\operatorname*{Lim}_{x \to 0} (x \csc^3 x - x \cot^3 x)$.   *Ans.* $\frac{3}{2}$.

29. $\operatorname*{Lim}_{x \to \infty} (1 + x^2 e^x)^{\frac{1}{x}}$.   *Ans.* e.

30. $\operatorname*{Lim}_{x \to \infty} (1 + e^{2x})^{\frac{1}{\ln (1 + e^x)}}$.   *Ans.* e^2.

31. $\operatorname*{Lim}_{x \to 0^{+}} (1 + e^{\frac{4}{x}})^{x}$.   *Ans.* e^4.

32. $\operatorname*{Lim}_{x \to 0^{-}} (1 + e^{\frac{4}{x}})^{x}$.   *Ans.* 1.

33. $\operatorname*{Lim}_{x \to \infty} (1 + x e^{3x^2})^{\frac{1}{x^2}}$.   *Ans.* e^3.

34. $\operatorname*{Lim}_{\beta \to \infty} (1 + \beta \ln \beta)^{\frac{1}{\ln (1 + \beta)}}$.   *Ans.* e.

In Exs. 35–38, evaluate the limit without resorting to differentiation.

35. $\operatorname*{Lim}_{x \to 0^{+}} (1 + \tan x)^{\cot x}$.   Put $\cot x = v$.

36. $\operatorname*{Lim}_{x \to 0} (\sec x)^{2 \cot^2 x}$.   *Ans.* e.

37. $\operatorname*{Lim}_{x \to \frac{\pi}{2}} (\sec^2 x - \tan^2 x)^{\sec x}$.   *Ans.* 1.

38. $\operatorname*{Lim}_{x \to 0^{+}} (\cot x)^{x^3 - e^3 \ln x}$.   *Ans.* 1.

39. Evaluate $\operatorname*{Lim}_{x \to 0} \left(\dfrac{\pi x - 1}{2x^2} + \dfrac{\pi}{x(e^{2\pi x} - 1)} \right)$.   *Ans.* $\dfrac{\pi^2}{6}$.

40. What limiting form is approached, in the first quadrant, by the curve $x^n + y^n = a^n$ as n increases through positive integral values? [Consider inter-sections with lines through O. Putting $y = mx$, find $x = \dfrac{a}{(1 + m^n)^{\frac{1}{n}}}$; investigate $\operatorname*{Lim}_{n \to \infty} x$ for $m < 1$ and $m > 1$.]

> *Ans.* One quadrant of the square $x = \pm a,\, y = \pm a$;
> if n is even, the entire curve approaches the entire square.

41. Find the points of intersection of the curves $x^{100} + y^{100} = 1$, $y = x$. (Cf. Ex. 40.)   *Ans.* $(\pm 0.993,\ \pm 0.993)$.

42. From the fact (Ex. 40) that $\operatorname*{Lim}_{n \to \infty} (1 + m^n)^{\frac{1}{n}} = 1$, $m < 1$, deduce without differentiation the fact that $\operatorname*{Lim}_{n \to \infty} (1 + m^n)^{\frac{1}{n}} = m$, $m > 1$. [Note first that $(1 + m^n)^{\frac{1}{n}} = m(1 + m^{-n})^{\frac{1}{n}}$.]

43. Draw the curve $y = \operatorname*{Lim}_{n \to \infty} (1 + x^n)^{\frac{1}{n}}$, $x > 0$. (Ex. 42.)

Curve Tracing

150. *Introduction*

In this chapter we shall make a systematic attack upon the problem of curve tracing. Factorable equations (so-called degenerate curves) are excluded.

In §§ 150–160 only algebraic curves are under consideration. We shall for simplicity confine our attention chiefly to cases in which either y or y^2 is a rational function of x:

(1) $$y = \frac{P(x)}{Q(x)},$$

or

(2) $$y^2 = \frac{P(x)}{Q(x)},$$

where $P(x)$, $Q(x)$ are polynomials. Since *cubics* (curves of third degree) and *quartics* (curves of fourth degree) are the curves most commonly occurring, most of our work will be with these types.

It will be assumed that $P(x)$ and $Q(x)$ contain no common factor. Hence the only kind of discontinuity that can occur is the infinite discontinuity.

151. *Asymptotes*

As the point of contact of a tangent to a curve recedes indefinitely from the origin, the tangent may or may not approach a limiting position. If it does, the line approached is called an *asymptote*.* Thus an asymptote is sometimes said to be "a tangent whose point of contact lies at infinity"; but of course it is not a tangent in the strict sense.

For example, the hyperbola

$$\frac{x^2}{a^2} - \frac{y^2}{b^2} = 1$$

---

* According to some writers, an asymptote is a line that is approached more and more closely by the *curve*, even though the tangent does not approach a limiting position. For algebraic curves, the two definitions are equivalent. But see Exs. 31–32, page 290.

has the lines

$$y = \pm \frac{b}{a} x$$

as asymptotes. On the other hand, the parabola has no asymptotes, since as the point of tangency recedes, the tangent does not approach any limiting position. Many higher plane curves have one or more asymptotes, and they play an important part in the study of those curves.

For algebraic curves, asymptotes parallel to the axes can be determined by the following rule.

RULE. *If y becomes infinite as x approaches the limit a, the line $x = a$ is an asymptote; if y approaches b as x becomes infinite, the line $y = b$ is an asymptote.*

Example (a). Examine the curve

$$y = \frac{ax^2}{(x - a)(x - 3a)}$$

for horizontal and vertical asymptotes.

Equating the denominator to zero, we find the vertical asymptotes $x = a$, $x = 3a$. As x increases (in either direction), y approaches a (by § 146, or by direct inspection): thus the line $y = a$ is a horizontal asymptote. See Figure 172, page 275.

It can be shown that a curve of the nth degree *may intersect an asymptote in, at most, $(n - 2)$ points.* Although we shall not prove this theorem, it may be made plausible as follows: We know that a curve of nth degree may intersect a straight line in not more than n points. Since a tangent is the limiting position of a secant when two points of intersection come to coincidence, the point of tangency counts as two intersections, so that a tangent may intersect the curve in not more than $n - 2$ other points. While an asymptote is not a tangent in the literal sense, it is the limiting position of a tangent and partakes of the nature of a tangent; hence it is to be expected that the same result will hold.

No curve of types (1)–(2) of § 150 can intersect a vertical asymptote, since if $Q(x) = 0$, y does not exist. These curves may, however, intersect a horizontal asymptote, and such intersections should always be looked for.

Example (b). In the equation of Example (a),

$$y = \frac{ax^2}{(x - a)(x - 3a)},$$

put $y = a$:

$$a(x^2 - 4ax + 3a^2) = ax^2, \qquad x = \tfrac{3}{4}a;$$

thus the curve crosses its horizontal asymptote at $(\tfrac{3}{4}a, a)$. (Figure 172, page 275.)

152. *Restriction to Definite Regions*

It is frequently possible to show that the curve is confined to certain definite portions of the plane, and a result of this kind is of great value in tracing the curve. While no general directions can be given, in case the equation is, or can be, *solved for y* (or some power of *y*), it is highly instructive to note the *changes of sign* of the right member. The process will be explained by examples as need arises.

153. *Summary*

The method of curve tracing outlined in § 61 may now be greatly strengthened, as follows:

1. *Test for symmetry with respect to axes and origin.*
2. *Find the points of intersection with the axes.*
3. *Determine the behavior of y for large values of x. Find the horizontal asymptotes.*
4. *Find the vertical asymptotes.*
5. *Determine as closely as possible those regions of the plane in which the curve lies.*
6. *Find and classify the critical points.*

The above is only a general outline of the process to be followed; other steps will often suggest themselves. In some cases the points of inflection may be found and the inflectional tangents drawn, but this is not worth while if the second derivative is complicated. In fact, any step that leads to serious algebraic difficulty should be omitted if adequate information is obtainable otherwise. The elementary method of point-plotting is not usually worth using extensively, but it is often advisable to plot a few points as a check on the analysis.

154. *Rational Fractions*

Consider the function

(1) $$y = \frac{P(x)}{Q(x)},$$

where

$$P(x) = a_0 x^p + a_1 x^{p-1} + \cdots + a_p,$$
$$Q(x) = b_0 x^q + b_1 x^{q-1} + \cdots + b_q \qquad q \geqq 1.$$

If $q = 0$ (denominator a constant), y is a polynomial; little can be added at this time to the discussion of § 61. If $q = 1$, $p \leqq 2$, the curve is a hyperbola. These cases will therefore be excluded.

Before considering special examples, it will be well to apply our analysis to the rational fraction in general, thus deducing certain results applicable to all curves of this class. The proofs are left to the student.

1. There is no symmetry with respect to Ox.

2. The x-intercepts are the real zeros of P.

3. As x increases in either direction:

(*a*) If P is of higher degree than $Q(p > q)$, y becomes large, though not necessarily of the same sign as x.

(*b*) If P and Q are of the same degree, y approaches $\dfrac{a_0}{b_0}$; the line $y = \dfrac{a_0}{b_0}$ is an asymptote.

(*c*) If P is of lower degree than Q, the x-axis is an asymptote.

4. y increases indefinitely as Q approaches zero. Thus we find the real zeros (if any) of the denominator, $r_1, r_2, \cdots$; the lines $x = r_1, x = r_2, \cdots$ are asymptotes.

5. The fraction *changes sign* when either P or Q does so. Thus we list the zeros of P and Q (already found in steps 2 and 4), *casting out those of even order*, and note for each of the others a change of sign of y and a passage of the curve across the x-axis: by intersection where $P = 0$, by jumping where $Q = 0$.

6. There may be as many as $p + q - 1$ critical points.

Example. Trace the curve (Examples, § 151)

$$y = \frac{ax^2}{(x - a)(x - 3a)}.$$

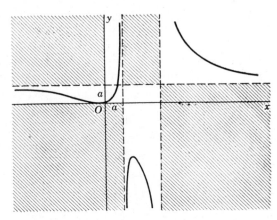

Figure 172

1. No symmetry.

2. $(0, 0)$.

3. The line $y = a$ is an asymptote, intersecting the curve at $(\tfrac{3}{4}a, a)$.

4. The lines $x = a, x = 3a$ are asymptotes.

5. The numerator vanishes at $x = 0$ but does not change sign because of the even exponent; the denominator, and hence the fraction, changes sign

as x goes through a, $3a$. For large positive x, $x^2 > (x - a)(x - 3a)$ and $y > a$; for large negative x, $y < a$. This limits the curve to the unshaded regions.

6. $y' = \dfrac{2a^2x(3a - 2x)}{(x - a)^2(x - 3a)^2}$. Thus the critical points are $(0, 0)$, $(\frac{3}{2}a, -3a)$.

Figure 172 shows the curve, necessarily somewhat distorted because of the small space available.

EXERCISES

In Exs. 1–30, trace the curve.

1. $y = \dfrac{x - 5}{x^2 - 16}$.

2. $y = \dfrac{x - 3}{x^2 - 16}$.

3. $y = \dfrac{x - 1}{x^2 + 1}$.

4. $y = \dfrac{a^3}{x^2 + a^2}$.

5. $y = \dfrac{2x}{1 - x^2}$.

6. $y = \dfrac{2x}{x^2 + 1}$.

7. $y = \dfrac{1 - x^2}{1 + x^2}$.

8. $y = \dfrac{1 + x^2}{1 - x^2}$.

9. $y = \dfrac{x}{(x - 1)(x + 2)}$.

10. $y = \dfrac{1}{x^3 + 2x^2 - 15x}$.

11. $y = \dfrac{x^3}{1 - x^2}$.

12. $y = \dfrac{x^3}{1 - x^4}$.

13. $y = \dfrac{x^3}{1 - x^3}$.

14. $y = \dfrac{x}{x^4 + 1}$.

15. $y = \dfrac{2x - 2}{x^2 - 2x + 5}$.

16. $y = \dfrac{ax^3}{(a - x)^3}$.

17. $y = \dfrac{a^2x}{(x - a)^2}$.

18. $y = \dfrac{(x^2 - 1)^2}{x}$.

19. $y = \dfrac{x^2 + x + 1}{x^2 - 1}$.

20. $y = \dfrac{(2a - x)^3}{ax}$.

21. $y = \dfrac{(x - a)(x - 3a)^2}{ax}$.

22. $y = \dfrac{x^3 + x^2 - 2}{x^3}$.

23. $y = \dfrac{x^2 - 6}{x(x^2 - 4)}$.

24. $y = \dfrac{(x^2 - 2)^2}{x^2(x + 3)^2}$.

25. $y = \dfrac{(x^2 - 4)^2}{x - 4}$.

26. $y = \dfrac{2x^3 - 10}{x^3 - 3x^2 + 2x}$.

27. $y^3 = \dfrac{x}{x^2 - 1}$.

28. $y^3 = \dfrac{x}{x^2 + 1}$.

29. $y = \dfrac{2(x^2 - 4x + 3)}{x^2}$.

30. $y = \dfrac{x + 1}{x^2(x + 9)}$.

31. Draw a curve from which $\tan 2\theta$ may be read if $\tan \theta$ is given.   (Ex. 5.)
32. Draw a curve from which $\sin 2\theta$ may be read if $\tan \theta$ is given.   (Ex. 6.)
33. Draw a curve from which $\cos 2\theta$ may be read if $\tan \theta$ is given.   (Ex. 7.)
34. Draw a curve from which $\sec 2\theta$ may be read if $\tan \theta$ is given.   (Ex. 8.)
35. Draw a curve from which $\sec 2\theta$ may be read if $\cos \theta$ is given.
36. A circular cone is circumscribed about a sphere of radius a. Express the volume of the cone as a function of its radius. Draw the graph, taking $a = 1$.

$$Ans. \ V = \frac{2}{3}\pi a \cdot \frac{r^4}{r^2 - a^2}.$$

37. In Ex. 36, graph the altitude as a function of the radius.

155. *Two-valued Functions*

Consider now the curve

(1) $$y^2 = \frac{P(x)}{Q(x)},$$

where

$$P(x) = a_0x^p + a_1x^{p-1} + \cdots + a_p,$$
$$Q(x) = b_0x^q + b_1x^{q-1} + \cdots + b_q.$$

We exclude the case $q = 0$, $p \leq 2$, since then the curve is a conic.

By way of general analysis, the following remarks may be made:

1. All curves of this class are symmetric with respect to Ox.
2. The x-intercepts are the real zeros of $P(x)$.
3. For large x (in either direction), y may be imaginary. If not:
(a) If $p < q$, the x-axis is an asymptote.
(b) If $p = q$, there are two horizontal asymptotes.
4. A vertical asymptote falling in a region where y is imaginary may be disregarded.
5. y^2 changes from positive to negative, y from real (positive and negative) to imaginary, or vice versa, as x passes through a zero *of odd order* of either $P(x)$ or $Q(x)$.
6. Critical points where y is imaginary are disregarded.

Example. Trace the curve $y^2 = \dfrac{(x + 1)(x + 2)}{x}$.

1. Symmetric with respect to Ox.
2. $(-1, 0)$, $(-2, 0)$.
3. For large positive x, y is real; for large negative x, y is imaginary.
4. $x = 0$.
5. The fraction changes sign as x goes through -2, -1, 0. At the extreme left $y^2 < 0$; thus the curve is absent when $x < -2$, present when $-2 < x < -1$, absent when $-1 < x < 0$, present when $x > 0$.
6. $2yy' = \dfrac{x^2 - 2}{x^2}$, $y' = \dfrac{x^2 - 2}{2x^2y}$.

Thus the critical points are at $x = \sqrt{2}$, $y = \pm(\sqrt{2} + 1)$ and $x = -\sqrt{2}$, $y = \pm(\sqrt{2} - 1)$. The tangent is vertical at $(-2, 0)$, $(-1, 0)$. (See Figure 173.)

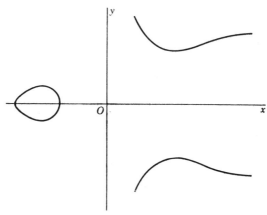

Figure 173

EXERCISES

In Exs. 1–20, trace the curve.

1. $y^2 = x(x^2 - 9)$.

3. $y^2 = x(4 - x^2)$.

2. $y^2 = (x - 1)^2(x - 4)$.

4. $y^2 = x^4 - 10x^2 + 9$.

5. $y^2 = \dfrac{x}{1 + x}$.

6. $y^2 = \dfrac{x}{1 - x}$.

7. $y^2 = \dfrac{1 - x}{3 + x^2}$.

8. $y^2 = \dfrac{x - 2}{x^2 - 3}$.

9. $y^2 = \dfrac{x + 5}{x^2 - 16}$.

10. $y^2 = \dfrac{a^3x}{x^2 - a^2}$.

11. $y^2 = \dfrac{x^3}{1 - x^2}$.

12. $y^2 = \dfrac{x}{(x + 1)(x - 2)}$.

13. $y^2 = \dfrac{x^2 - x}{x^2 - 4}$.

14. $y^2 = \dfrac{(x^2 - 1)(x^2 - 9)}{x(x^2 - 4)}$.

15. $y^2 = \dfrac{(x^2 - 1)(x^2 - 4)}{x^2(x^2 - 9)}$.

16. $y^2 = \dfrac{x^2(x - 3)}{(x - 1)(x + 4)^4}$.

17. $y^2 = \dfrac{x(x - 1)(x - 4)}{(x - 2)^3}$.

18. $y^2 = \dfrac{x(x + 1)}{(x - 1)^2(x - 2)}$.

19. $y^2 = \dfrac{(x - 1)^2(x - 2)}{x(x + 1)}$.

20. $y^2 = \dfrac{x(x^2 - 1)(x^2 - 4)}{(x^2 - 9)(x^2 - 16)^2}$.

21. Graph the eccentricity of the conic $cx^2 + y^2 = c$ in terms of c.

22. In Ex. 21, graph the distance from focus to directrix.

156. *Oblique and Curvilinear Asymptotes*

Asymptotes parallel to the axes are not the only ones which enter the study of simple algebraic curves. On this topic we confine our attention to an illustrative example and a few exercises.

Example. Sketch the curve

(1)
$$y = \frac{x^3}{x - 2}.$$

First, proceed as in the earlier portions of this chapter, thus determining that the curve (1) has the following properties:

(a) $y = 0$ only at $x = 0$;
(b) Minimum point at $(3, 27)$;
(c) Inflection point with horizontal tangent at $(0, 0)$;
(d) Vertical asymptote $x = 2$;
(e) As $x \to \infty$, $y \to \infty$, and as $x \to -\infty$, $y \to \infty$.

The one new tool to be introduced now is based upon carrying out the division of x^3 by $(x - 2)$ on the right in equation (1). That procedure shows that (1) can be rewritten in the form

(2)
$$y = x^2 + 2x + 4 + \frac{8}{x - 2}.$$

As $|x| \to \infty$, equation (2) is well approximated by

(3) $y = x^2 + 2x + 4,$

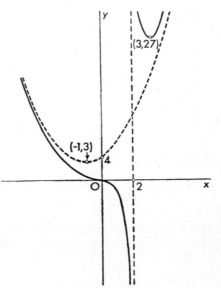

because $\dfrac{8}{x - 2} \to 0$, as $|x| \to \infty$.

Let the y of the cubic (2) be denoted by y_1, the y of the parabola (3) by y_2. Then, from

$$y_1 = x^2 + 2x + 4 + \frac{8}{x - 2}$$

and

$$y_2 = x^2 + 2x + 4,$$

we obtain

(4) $y_1 - y_2 = \dfrac{8}{x - 2}.$

Differentiation of equation (4) yields

$$y_1' - y_2' = -\frac{8}{(x - 2)^2}.$$

Figure 174

It is now easy to see that, as $|x| \to \infty$, $(y_1 - y_2) \to 0$ and also $(y_1' - y_2')$ $\to 0$. Then we call the parabola (3) a *curvilinear asymptote* to the cubic (1). See Figure 174.

EXERCISES

In each exercise find and sketch the curvilinear or rectilinear asymptote, and trace the curve whose equation is given.

1. $y = \dfrac{x^3 + 16}{x}$.

2. $y = \dfrac{2 + x - x^3}{x}$.

3. $y = \dfrac{x^2}{x - 3}$.

4. $y = \dfrac{2x^2}{x + 1}$.

5. $y = \dfrac{x^3}{x + 4}$.

6. $y = \dfrac{x^3}{x^2 + 4}$.

7. $y = \dfrac{x^3 + x^2 - 2}{x^2 + 1}$.

8. $y = \dfrac{x^4}{x^2 - 1}$.

9. $y^2 = \dfrac{4x^2 - 1}{x}$.

10. $y^2 = \dfrac{2x^2}{x + 1}$.

11. $y^2 = \dfrac{x^2 - 16}{x - 5}$.

12. $y^2 = \dfrac{x^2 - 16}{x - 3}$.

13. $y^2 = \dfrac{x^2(x^2 - 8)}{(x + 2)^2}$.

14. $y^2 = \dfrac{x^6}{x^3 - 1}$.

15. Ex. 11, p. 276.   **16.** Ex. 18, p. 276.   **17.** Ex. 25, p. 276.
18. Ex. 36, p. 277.   **19.** Ex. 11, p. 278.   **20.** Ex. 19, p. 278.

21. $y^2 = \dfrac{x^2}{x - 2}$.

22. $y^2 = \dfrac{x^2}{x + 2}$.

23. $y^2 = \dfrac{x^2 - 9}{x - 4}$.

24. $y^2 = \dfrac{x^2 - 9}{x - 2}$.

25. $y = \dfrac{x^3}{x^2 - 4}$.

26. $y^2 = \dfrac{x^3}{x^2 - 4}$.

27. $y = \dfrac{x^3}{4 - x^2}$.

28. $y^2 = \dfrac{x^3}{4 - x^2}$.

157. *Singular Points*

If y is defined implicitly as a function of x by the equation

$$F(x, y) = 0,$$

the derivative in general takes the form of a fraction whose numerator and denominator are functions of x and y:

$$y' = \frac{N(x, y)}{D(x, y)}.$$

(See, for instance, the examples and exercises under § 55.)

If $N(x, y)$ and $D(x, y)$ both vanish at a point (x, y) on the curve, the slope at that point assumes the indeterminate form $\frac{0}{0}$. A point at which the derivative takes this form is called a *singular point*.

To find the singular points of a curve we must therefore find the values of x and y that satisfy the three equations

(1) $F(x, y) = 0,$ $N(x, y) = 0,$ $D(x, y) = 0.$

As we have but two unknowns, x and y, to satisfy three equations, it follows that a curve will have singular points only if these three equations happen to have one or more common solutions.

For the moment, we consider only curves having a singular point at the origin. Singularities occurring elsewhere will be discussed in § 160.

158. *Determination of Tangents by Inspection*

Let the equation of the curve be written in the form

(1) $a_0 + b_0 x + b_1 y + c_0 x^2 + c_1 xy + c_2 y^2 + d_0 x^3 + \cdots + g_n y^n = 0;$

i.e., we arrange the left member in ascending powers of x and y.

By differentiating, we find

$$b_0 + b_1 y' + 2c_0 x + c_1 xy' + c_1 y + 2c_2 yy' + \cdots = 0,$$

$$y' = -\frac{b_0 + 2c_0 x + c_1 y + \cdots}{b_1 + c_1 x + 2c_2 y + \cdots}.$$

The origin is on the curve only if $a_0 = 0$. In that case the equation of the tangent at $(0, 0)$ is found by the usual methods to be

$$b_0 x + b_1 y = 0,$$

provided b_0 and b_1 are not both zero; i.e., the equation of the tangent at the origin may be found by equating to zero the group of terms of the first degree.

If a_0, b_0, and b_1 are all zero, the origin is on the curve and the derivative is indeterminate at that point; hence the origin is a singular point. In this case, since the method of § 56 fails, we proceed as follows:

For convenience let us put

$$c_0 x^2 + c_1 xy + c_2 y^2 \equiv c_2(y - m_1 x)(y - m_2 x).$$

(The argument needs only slight modification when $c_2 = 0$.) Then (1) becomes

$$c_2(y - m_1 x)(y - m_2 x) + d_0 x^3 + \cdots = 0.$$

The abscissas of the points of intersection of the line

$$y = mx$$

with this curve are given by the equation

(2) $\qquad c_2 x^2 (m - m_1)(m - m_2) + x^3 (d_0 + \cdots) + \cdots = 0.$

Two roots of this equation are zero; every line $y = mx$ intersects the curve

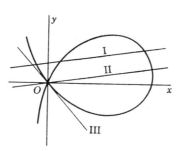

in two coincident points at the origin. But (2) also shows that if we let m approach either m_1 or m_2, the coefficient of x^2 approaches zero; i.e., a third point of intersection of the curve with the line $y = mx$ approaches the origin, and the lines

$$y = m_1 x, \qquad y = m_2 x$$

are both tangent to the curve at the singular point. These lines may, of course, be real and distinct, real and coincident, or imaginary.

Figure 175

To interpret all this geometrically, let us examine Figure 175, which exhibits a typical situation—that in which the curve crosses itself. The random line I intersects the curve in three distinct points. As it moves toward position II, two points approach each other and finally coincide— every line through the singular point intersects the curve twice there. Now as the line rotates to position III, the third point approaches, and ultimately, in the position of tangency, attains coincidence with the other two. Evidently in this figure there are two positions of tangency.

Since

$$c_2 (y - m_1 x)(y - m_2 x) \equiv c_0 x^2 + c_1 xy + c_2 y^2,$$

we see that the equations of the two tangents are obtained by *equating the group of terms of second degree to zero* and factoring the resulting equation.

The argument we have used can be extended to show that if $F(x, y)$ has no terms of degree lower than the kth, any line through the origin meets the curve there in k points, and the k tangents to the curve at the origin are obtained by *equating the group of terms of lowest degree to zero.*

A point at which there are two tangents (whether distinct, coincident, or imaginary) is called a *double point*; one at which there are three tangents is a *triple point*; etc. In most cases that arise in practice, a curve having only one singular point, and that a triple or higher-ordered singularity, is much more easily traced from its polar than from its rectangular coordinate equation. Partly for this reason, and partly because they occur much more often, we shall study chiefly curves whose only singularities are double points.

THEOREM 37. *If the equation $F(x, y) = 0$ contains terms of the second, but none of lower degree, the origin is a double point; the tangents at that point are found by equating to zero, and factoring, the group of terms of second degree.*

As noted above, every line through a double point has at that point two coincident intersections with the curve.   Hence a (nondegenerate) cubic cannot have more than one double point, for if there were two, the straight line through those points would have four intersections with the curve.   By similar argument, it appears that no cubic can have a triple point.

159. *Classification of Double Points*

If the tangents at a double point are real and different, the point is called a *node*; two branches of the curve cross each other, as in Figure 176.

If the tangents are imaginary, the point is an *isolated point*, or *conjugate point*: there is no other portion of the curve in its vicinity.   Such a point is P in Figure 177.

Figure 176   Figure 177

If the tangents are real and coincident, the point is either a *cusp* (Figures 178–179) or a *double cusp* (Figure 180), or in some instances an isolated point.   If the two branches of a cusp lie on opposite sides of the cuspidal

Figure 178   Figure 179   Figure 180

tangent, as in Figure 178, the point is a *cusp of the first kind*; if on the same side, as in Figure 179, a *cusp of the second kind*.

Example (a).   Trace the curve $y^2 = 4x^2(1 - x)$.

1. The curve is symmetric with respect to Ox.
2. The curve intersects the axes at $(0, 0)$, $(1, 0)$.
3. When x is large positive, y is imaginary; x large negative, y large positive and negative.
4. No vertical asymptotes.
5. y is imaginary when $x > 1$.
6. $2yy' = 4(2x - 3x^2)$, $y' = \dfrac{2(2x - 3x^2)}{y}$.   Equating the numerator to

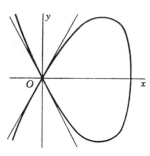

Figure 181

zero, we appear to find the critical values $x = 0$, $x = \frac{2}{3}$. But by the equation of the curve, when $x = 0$, $y = 0$, so that y' takes the form $\frac{0}{0}$, and the origin is a singular point. The only critical points are $(\frac{2}{3}, \pm\frac{4}{9}\sqrt{3})$.

7. Since the equation contains no terms of degree lower than the second, the origin is a singular point (as also discovered above). Equating to zero the terms of lowest degree, i.e., $y^2 - 4x^2 = 0$, we find the two real distinct tangents $y = \pm 2x$; thus the origin is a node. See Figure 181.

Example (b). Trace the curve $y^2 = x^4(1 - x^2)$.

1. The curve is symmetric with respect to both axes.
2. The curve crosses the axes at $(0, 0)$, $(\pm 1, 0)$.
3. When x is large, y is imaginary.
4. There are no vertical asymptotes.
5. y is imaginary outside the interval $-1 < x < 1$.
6. $2yy' = 4x^3 - 6x^5$, $y' = \dfrac{x^3(2 - 3x^2)}{y}$. At $(0, 0)$ the derivative is indeterminate, so that the origin is a singular point; the only critical values are $x = \pm\sqrt{\frac{2}{3}}$.
7. The tangents at the origin are the coincident lines $y^2 = 0$ (the x-axis counted twice). Thus the point is either a cusp or a double cusp; by symmetry, it must be the latter. See Figure 182.

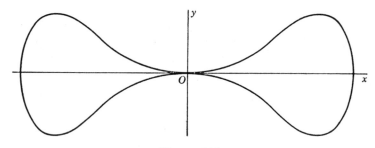

Figure 182

Example (c). Trace the curve $y^3 = x^2(3a - x)$.

1. There is no symmetry.
2. $(0, 0)$, $(3a, 0)$.
3. When x is large positive or negative, y is large negative or positive.
4. No vertical asymptotes.
5. When $x < 3a$, $y > 0$; when $x > 3a$, $y < 0$.

6. $3y^2y' = 3x(2a - x)$, $y' = \dfrac{x(2a - x)}{y^2}$. The slope is indeterminate at $(0, 0)$; the point $(2a, 4^{\frac{1}{3}}a)$ is a maximum.

7. The tangents at $(0, 0)$ are given by $3ax^2 = 0$; the y-axis counted twice. By the result of step 5, the origin is a cusp.

Evidently the slope is infinite—tangent vertical—at $(3a, 0)$; this is also a point of inflection. See Figure 183.

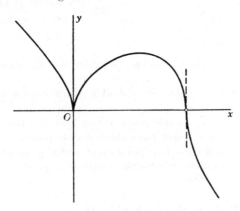

Figure 183

EXERCISES

In Exs. 1–32, trace the curve.

1. $y^2 = 10x^2 - 7x^3 + x^4$.

2. $a^3y^2 = x^5$.

3. $y^2 = 4x^3 - 3x^4$.

4. $y^2 = 35x^2 + 2x^3 - x^4$.

5. $a^2y^2 = x^2(a^2 - x^2)$.

6. $a^2y^2 = x^2(x^2 - a^2)$.

7. $y^2 = x^2(x + 3)$.

8. $y^2 = x^3(x + 3)$.

9. $y^2 = \dfrac{a^2x^2}{x^2 + a^2}$.

10. $y^2 = \dfrac{a^2x^2}{x^2 - a^2}$.

11. $y^2 = \dfrac{x^4}{1 - x^2}$.

12. $y^2 = \dfrac{x^3}{1 - x^2}$.

13. $y^2 = \dfrac{x^2}{x - 1}$.

14. $y^2 = \dfrac{x^2}{(1 - x)^3}$.

15. $y^2 = \dfrac{x^2}{x^2 + 3x - 4}$.

16. $y^2 = \dfrac{x^2}{(x - 1)^2(x + 4)}$.

17. $y^2 = \dfrac{x^2}{(x - 1)(x - 2)}$.

18. $y^2 = \dfrac{x^2}{(x - 1)^2(x - 2)}$.

19. $y^2 = x^6 - 4x^4 + 3x^2$.

20. $y^2 = 20x^2 - x^5$.

21. $y^2 = \dfrac{x^3}{a - x}$, the cissoid.

22. $y^2 = \dfrac{x^2(3a - x)}{a + x}$, the trisectrix of Maclaurin.

23. $y^2 = \dfrac{x^2(x - 1)}{x - 2}$.

24. $y^2 = \dfrac{x^2(1 - x)}{x - 2}$.

25. $y^2 = \dfrac{x^2(x + 1)}{x - 2}$.

26. $y^2 = \dfrac{x^2(x + 1)}{2 - x}$.

27. $y^3 = x^2(8 - x^2)$.

28. $y^3 = 4x^5 - 5x^4$.

29. $y^3 = \dfrac{a^3 x^2}{(x - a)^2}$.

30. $y^3 = \dfrac{x^2}{1 - x^2}$.

31. $y^4 = \dfrac{x^4}{x^2 - 7x + 10}$.

32. $y^2 = \dfrac{x^2(x^2 + 4ax + 3a^2)}{(x - a)^2}$.

Prove the theorems in Exs. 33–37.

33. The graph of a one-valued algebraic function $y = f(x)$ cannot have a singular point.

34. A line tangent to a cubic at a double point cannot intersect the curve elsewhere.

35. If a quartic curve has a triple point, it can have no other singularity.

36. A quartic cannot have more than three double points. (Assume four; then consider the conic through these four points and a fifth point of the curve.)

37. A straight line through two double points of a quartic cannot intersect the curve elsewhere.

160. *Singular Points Not at the Origin*

To locate singular points not at the origin, we must look for values of x and y satisfying the three equations (1) of § 157. Of course no rules can be given; we try to solve the simplest-looking pair, then substitute the coordinates of the points thus found in the other equation. The algebra may conceivably be very difficult. But when a curve has only one singularity, if that point is not taken as origin, it is, at least in most cases, placed on a coordinate axis; if there are two, the line joining them is likely to be taken as one of the axes.

THEOREM 38. *Given the curve*

(1) $$y^k = \frac{P(x)}{Q(x)}, \qquad (k \geq 2)$$

where $P(x)$, $Q(x)$ are polynomials, if $(x - c)^r (r \geq 2)$ is a factor of $P(x)$, the point $(c, 0)$ is a singular point of the curve.

Further, if $k = 2$, $r = 2$, the point is a node or isolated point; if $k = 2$, $r \geq 3$, or if $k \geq 3$, $r = 2$, the point is a cusp with horizontal or vertical tangent respectively, or an isolated point.

To prove the theorem, merely write $P(x)$ in the form

$$P(x) = (x - c)^r R(x),$$

and find y' from (1). Translation of the origin to $(c, 0)$ easily proves the succeeding statements,

Example.   Graph the radius of curvature of the hyperbola

(2) $$x^2 - y^2 = a^2$$

as a function of x.

   In Example (b), § 142 (page 254), we found

(3) $$\rho = \frac{(2x^2 - a^2)^{\frac{3}{2}}}{a^2}.$$

First rationalize the equation:

$$a^4\rho^2 = (2x^2 - a^2)^3.$$

1. Symmetric with respect to both axes.
2. $\rho = 0$, $x = \pm\frac{1}{2}\sqrt{2}\,a$.
3. x large positive or negative, ρ large positive and negative.
4. No vertical asymptotes.
5. ρ is imaginary for $|x| < \frac{1}{2}\sqrt{2}\,a$.
6. $2a^4\rho\rho' = 12x(2x^2 - a^2)^2$, $\rho' = \dfrac{6x(2x^2 - a^2)^2}{a^4\rho}$.   There are no critical

points, since ρ' is indeterminate for $x = \pm\frac{1}{2}\sqrt{2}\,a$, and ρ is imaginary for $x = 0$.

7. By Theorem 38 above, and remarks following, the points $(\pm\frac{1}{2}\sqrt{2}\,a, 0)$ are cusps with the x-axis as cuspidal tangent.

   Since we must have $|x| \geqq a$, by (2), and ρ is limited to positive values, the graph of (3) is the part of the curve drawn full.   See Figure 184.

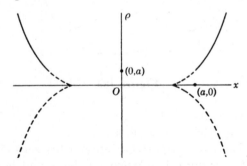

Figure 184

EXERCISES

In Exs. 1–16, trace the curve.

1. $y^2 = x(x - 4)^2$.
2. $y^2 = x(x + 2)^2$.
3. $y^2 = x^3(x - 1)^2$.
4. $y^2 = x^3(x + 2)^2$.
5. $y^2 = x(x - 1)^3$.
6. $a^3y^2 = x(a^2 - x^2)^2$.
7. $ay^4 = x(a^2 - x^2)^2$.
8. $ay^3 = (x^2 - a^2)^2$.

9. $y^2 = \dfrac{(x-4)^2}{x}.$

10. $y^2 = \dfrac{(x-4)^2}{x^3}.$

11. $y^2 = \dfrac{(x^2-4a^2)^2}{x^2-a^2}.$

12. $y^2 = \dfrac{a^4(x^2-4a^2)^2}{(x^2-a^2)^3}.$

13. $y^2 = \dfrac{a^3(x^2-a^2)^2}{x^5}.$

14. $y^2 = \dfrac{x(x+1)^2}{(x^2+1)^2}.$

15. $y^2 = \dfrac{x^3(x-1)^2}{(x^2+1)^4}.$

16. $y^2 = \dfrac{a^4(x^2-a^2)}{(x^2-4a^2)^2}.$

17. Graph the curvature of the parabola $y^2 = 4ax$ as a function of x.

18. Rationalize the equation $x^{\frac{2}{3}} + y^{\frac{2}{3}} = a^{\frac{2}{3}}$, and trace the curve.

$$Ans. \ (x^2 + y^2 - a^2)^3 + 27a^2x^2y^2 = 0.$$

161. *Transcendental Curves*

We have already had from time to time considerable practice in tracing the graphs of transcendental functions; but many curves were excluded by the fact that, at one or more points, the function or its derivative takes an "indeterminate" form. A few simple cases of this sort will now be studied.

Example (a).   Trace the curve $y = xe^x$.   The curve is shown in Figure 185 below.

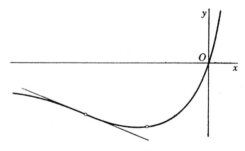

Figure 185

1. There is no symmetry.

2. The curve crosses the axes at $(0, 0)$.

3. As x becomes large and negative, y approaches zero (§ 147); hence the negative x-axis is an asymptote. When x is large and positive, y is large and positive.

4. There are no vertical asymptotes.

5. Since e^x is always positive, y has the same sign as x; the curve lies in the first and third quadrants.

6. Since $y' = xe^x + e^x$, the only critical point is $(-1, -e^{-1})$. This is a minimum point.

7. Putting $y'' = xe^x + 2e^x = 0$, we find the point of inflection $x = -2$, $y = -2e^{-2}$, with $y' = -e^{-2}$.

In Figure 185, the y-scale is three times as large as the x-scale.

Example (*b*). Trace the curve

$y = x^2 \ln x$.

1. No symmetry.
2. As $x \to 0^+$, $y \to 0^-$. When

$$y = 0, \ x = 1.$$

3. As $x \to \infty$, $y \to \infty$.
4. There are no asymptotes.
5. For $x > 1$, $y > 0$;

for $0 < x < 1$, $y < 0$;

for $x < 0$, y is imaginary.

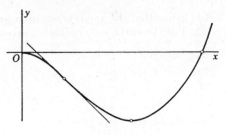

Figure 186

6. $y' = 2x \ln x + x = x(1 + 2 \ln x)$. Because y does not exist for $x = 0$, the only critical value is $x = e^{-\frac{1}{2}}$. Since $x < 0$ leads to imaginary y, the curve exists only to the right of the origin. But, $\underset{x \to 0^+}{\text{Lim}} \, y' = 0$, so the slope is small for small positive x. The curve drops to a minimum at $(e^{-\frac{1}{2}}, -\frac{1}{2}e^{-1})$, then rises as shown in Figure 186. The y-scale in the figure is twice the x-scale.

EXERCISES

In Exs. 1–30, trace the curve.

1. $y = x \ln x$.

2. $y = x^2 e^{-x}$.

3. $y = e^{-x^2}$.

4. $y = xe^{-x^2}$.

5. $y = \dfrac{\ln x}{x}$.

6. $y = xe^{-x}$.

7. $y = \dfrac{e^{-x}}{x}$.

8. $y = \dfrac{1 - \ln x}{x}$.

9. $y = \dfrac{1 + \ln x}{x}$.

10. $y = \dfrac{x}{\ln x}$.

11. $y = x \ln^2 x$.

12. $y = \dfrac{\ln x}{x^3}$.

13. $y = \dfrac{\ln^2 x}{x^2}$.

14. $y = \dfrac{x}{\ln^2 x}$.

15. $y = \dfrac{e^x}{x^2 - 3}$.

16. $y = \dfrac{e^x}{x^2}$.

17. $y = \dfrac{1 + \sin x}{\cos x}$.

18. $y = e^{-x} \sin x$.

19. $y = \dfrac{1 + \tan x}{\cos 2x}$.

20. $y^2 = xe^{-x}$.

21. $y^2 = -xe^{-x}$.

22. $y^2 = e^{-x}(8 - x^2)$.

23. $y^2 = x \ln x$.

24. $y^2 = \ln x$.

25. $y = e^{-\frac{1}{x}}$.

26. $y = e^{\frac{1}{4 - x^2}}$.

27. $y = e^{\frac{1}{x^2 - 4}}$.

28. $y = \dfrac{1}{1 + e^{-\frac{1}{x}}}$.

29. $y = \dfrac{1}{4 - e^{\frac{1}{x}}}$.

30. $y = \dfrac{1}{1 + e^{\frac{1}{x^2 - 1}}}$.

31. For the curve $y = \dfrac{\sin x^2}{x}$, show that $\underset{x \to \infty}{\text{Lim}}\, y = 0$, but that $\underset{x \to \infty}{\text{Lim}}\, y'$ does not exist; hence that the x-axis is not an asymptote.

32. For the curve $y = e^{-x} \sin e^x$, investigate $\underset{x \to \infty}{\text{Lim}}\, y$, $\underset{x \to \infty}{\text{Lim}}\, y'$.

33. Sketch $y^2 = -\ln x$.

34. Sketch the curve

$$y^2 = \frac{1 - \ln x}{x}.$$

35. Sketch the curve

$$y^2 = \frac{1 + \ln x}{x}.$$

36. Sketch the curve

$$y^2 = \frac{1}{1 + e^{-\frac{1}{x}}}.$$

162. *Curve Tracing in Polar Coordinates*

In § 24, page 35, we sketched some simple curves from polar coordinate equations. In the next few sections we shall extend that work to slightly more elaborate curves.

To each equation corresponds a single curve, but due to the fact that a given point may be represented by different pairs of coordinates, a curve may be represented in the polar system by more than one equation. Thus the equations $r = 2$, $r = -2$ both represent a circle of radius 2 with center at O. Since (r, θ) and $(-r, \pi + \theta)$ represent the same point, the equations

$$r = \cos \theta - 1$$

and

$$r = \cos \theta + 1$$

have the same locus. In obtaining intersections of curves given by polar equations, it is often vital that this phenomenon be kept in mind. See Example (*b*) of § 164.

163. *Polar Equations: Tests for Symmetry*

Although in polar coordinates there is, of course, no x or y, for brevity we shall refer to the polar axis and the perpendicular to this line through O as x-axis and y-axis, respectively.

The following results are readily demonstrated and should be verified by the reader.

If the equation is unchanged when we change

(*a*) θ *to* $-\theta$, *or* $\left.\begin{array}{l}\textit{the curve is symmetric with}\\ \textit{respect to the}\end{array}\right\}$ $\left.\begin{array}{l}\\ \\\end{array}\right\}$ *x-axis;*
(*b*) θ *to* $\pi - \theta$ *and* r *to* $-r$,

(c) θ to $\pi - \theta$, or $\left\{\begin{array}{l}\textit{the curve is symmetric with} \\ \quad \textit{respect to the}\end{array}\right\}$ *y-axis;*

(d) θ to $-\theta$ and r to $-r$,

(e) r to $-r$, or $\left\{\begin{array}{l}\textit{the curve is symmetric with} \\ \quad \textit{respect to the}\end{array}\right\}$ *origin.*

(f) θ to $\pi + \theta$,

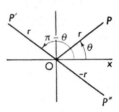

Figure 187

Instead of memorizing the above tests, the student should become thoroughly familiar with the geometric meaning of each one, whereupon they will come readily to mind as needed. For instance, test (b) operates as follows: Changing θ to $\pi - \theta$ reflects a point P to the position P'; then, changing r to $-r$ reflects P' to P'', the image of P with respect to Ox.

As a result of the fact that a point may be represented by more than one pair of coordinates, the converse theorems are not true. For instance, if the equation is changed when r is replaced by $-r$, the curve still may be symmetric with respect to O, by test (f): as an illustration, see Example (a), § 164.

The tests for symmetry afford a check on the remainder of our analysis, and also act as timesavers, often enabling us to obtain the remainder of the curve by reflection after a limited portion has been plotted. Thus, if a curve is symmetric with respect to both axes, then in most cases we may draw the curve for values of θ between 0° and 90° and deduce the rest of the curve by reflection in both axes.

However, the qualification "in most cases" must not be overlooked. The above procedure does not always give the entire curve, for various reasons. For instance, values of θ in the first quadrant may give points in the third quadrant not corresponding to third-quadrant values of θ; see, for example, Exs. 1–2, page 294. If due care is exercised, such cases are easily recognized.

164. *Polar Equations: One-valued Functions*

We consider first the case in which there is one value of r for each value of θ. *Example (a).* Trace the *four-leaved rose* $r = a \cos 2\theta$.

Since $\cos(-2\theta) = \cos 2\theta$, the curve is symmetric with respect to Ox by (a), § 163. Since $\cos 2(\pi - \theta) = \cos 2\theta$, it follows that the curve is symmetric with respect to Oy by (c). Plotting the points found below,* we

θ	0°	15°	$22\frac{1}{2}°$	30°	45°
2θ	0°	30°	45°	60°	90°
r	a	$\frac{1}{2}\sqrt{3}\,a$	$\frac{1}{2}\sqrt{2}\,a$	$\frac{1}{2}a$	0

* It is, of course, the values of r and θ, not r and 2θ, that are plotted. Thus the second point is $(\frac{1}{2}\sqrt{3}\,a, 15°)$, etc.

obtain the half-loop numbered 1. As θ ranges from $45°$ to $90°$, 2θ ranges

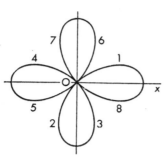

from $90°$ to $180°$; thus the values of $\cos 2\theta$ are numerically the same as those found above, but in reverse order and negative. Since r is negative, the corresponding portion of the curve lies not in the first but in the third quadrant, the half-loop 2. Reflecting in Oy, we obtain the arcs 3, 4; reflecting in Ox, the balance of the curve. Since this covers a complete period of the function $\cos 2\theta$, we have the entire curve.

Figure 188

Example (b). Find the intersections of the curves

(1)
$$r = \sin \theta + 1,$$

and

(2)
$$r = \cos \theta - 1.$$

First we sketch the two curves carefully, employing the technique of Example (a). Each turns out to be a heart-shaped figure, called a *cardioid*. The curves are shown in Figure 189.

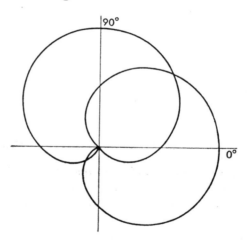

Figure 189

One intersection is at the origin, $r = 0$. To find the others, it is natural to solve (1) and (2) as simultaneous equations. Elimination of r yields

$$\sin \theta + 1 = \cos \theta - 1,$$

or

(3)
$$2 + \sin \theta = \cos \theta.$$

In equation (3) the left member is never less than unity; the right member never greater than unity. Hence (3) has no solutions unless $\sin \theta = -1$ and $\cos \theta = +1$ for the same θ, which is impossible. Equations (1) and (2) have no common solutions. The curves (1) and (2) do, however, have intersections.

Let us, then, in equation (2) replace θ by $(\pi + \theta)$ and r by $(-r)$, thus obtaining

$$(4) \qquad\qquad r = \cos \theta + 1.$$

Equation (4) represents the same curve as does (2). Now solve (1) and (4) together, obtaining

$$\sin \theta + 1 = \cos \theta + 1,$$

or

$$\tan \theta = 1,$$

from which $\theta = 45°, 225°$. The corresponding points of intersection are thus found to be $(1 + \tfrac{1}{2}\sqrt{2}, 45°)$ and $(1 - \tfrac{1}{2}\sqrt{2}, 225°)$.

EXERCISES

In Exs. 1–30, trace the curve on polar coordinate paper.

1. $r = a \sin^2 \theta$.
2. $r = a \cos^2 \theta$.
3. $r = a \sin 2\theta$.
4. $r = a(\cos \theta - \sin \theta)$.
5. $r = a(1 + \cos^2 \theta)$.
6. $r = a(2 - \cos^2 \theta)$.
7. $r = a(1 - \sin \theta)$.
8. $r = a(1 - \cos \theta)$.
9. The limaçon $r = a(4 + \cos \theta)$.
10. The limaçon $r = a(3 - \sin \theta)$.
11. The limaçon $r = a(2 \sin \theta - 1)$.
12. The limaçon $r = a(1 + 2 \cos \theta)$.
13. $r(2 - \cos \theta) = a$.
14. $r(2 + \sin \theta) = a$.
15. $r = a \sin 3\theta$.
16. $r = a \cos 3\theta$.
17. $r = a \cos 4\theta$.
18. $r = a \sin 4\theta$.
19. $r = a \cos^2 2\theta$.
20. $r = a \sin^2 2\theta$.
21. $r = a(4 \cos^2 \theta - 3)$.
22. $r = a(1 - 4 \sin^2 \theta)$.
23. $r = a \sec^2 \theta$.
24. $r = a \csc^2 \theta$.
25. $r = a \sin \theta(1 - \sin \theta)$.
26. $r = a \sin \theta(2 - \cos \theta)$.
27. The trisectrix $r = a(4 \cos \theta - \sec \theta)$.

In Exs. 28–30, express θ in radians.

28. The *Spiral of Archimedes* $r = a\theta$. Take $a = \dfrac{1}{\pi}$.

29. The spiral $r = a\theta^2$. Take $a = \dfrac{1}{\pi^2}$.

30. The *hyperbolic spiral* $r\theta = a$. Take $a = \pi$.

In Exs. 31–34, show that the two equations represent the same curve.

31. $r = a \sec \theta + b, r = a \sec \theta - b.$ (*Conchoid.*)
32. $r = a(\sec \theta - \tan \theta), r = a(\sec \theta + \tan \theta).$ (*Strophoid.*)
33. $r = a \cos \theta - b, r = a \cos \theta + b.$ (*Limaçon.*)
34. $r = a(\sec \theta - \cos \theta), r = a \sin \theta \tan \theta.$ (*Cissoid.*)

165. *Polar Equations: Two-valued Functions*

Consider the case in which r^2 is expressed as a function of θ.

Since r occurs only in an even power, all curves of this class are symmetric with respect to the pole, by (e), § 163.   Hence, if a curve of this class is symmetric with respect to one axis, it is symmetric with respect to the other also (Ex. 36, page 23).

Example.   Trace the *lemniscate* $r^2 = a^2 \cos 2\theta.$

θ	$0°$	$15°$	$22\frac{1}{2}°$	$30°$	$45°$
2θ	$0°$	$30°$	$45°$	$60°$	$90°$
r^2	a^2	$0.87a^2$	$0.71a^2$	$0.5a^2$	0
r	$\pm a$	$\pm 0.93a$	$\pm 0.84a$	$\pm 0.71a$	0

Since $\cos(-2\theta) = \cos 2\theta$, the curve is symmetric with respect to Ox;

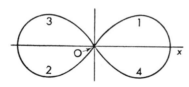

hence also to Oy, by the preceding remark. Plotting the above points, we get the arcs 1, 2.   As θ varies from $45°$ to $90°$, 2θ ranges from $90°$ to $180°$, $\cos 2\theta$ is negative, and r is imaginary.   Having examined r through the first quadrant, we obtain the balance of the curve by reflection.

Figure 190

EXERCISES

In Exs. 1–24, trace the curve.

1. $r^2 = a^2 \cos \theta.$
2. $r^2 = a^2 \sin \theta.$
3. $r^2 = 1 + \cos^2 \theta.$
4. $r^2(1 + \sin^2 \theta) = 2.$
5. $r^2(1 + 4 \sin^2 \theta) = 5.$
6. $r^2 = a^2 \sin 2\theta.$
7. $r^2 \cos 2\theta = a^2.$
8. $r^2 \sin 2\theta = a^2.$
9. $r^2 = 3 - 4 \cos^2 \theta.$
10. $r^2 = 1 - 4 \sin^2 \theta.$
11. $r^2 = a^2(1 + \cos \theta)^3.$
12. $r^2 = a^2(1 - 2 \sin \theta)^3.$
13. $r^2 = a^2(2 - \cos \theta).$
14. $r^2 = a^2(\sin \theta + 4).$
15. $r^2 = a^2(1 + \sin \theta).$
16. $r^2 = a^2(2 \cos \theta - 1).$
17. $r^2 = a^2 \sin \theta(1 + \sin \theta).$
18. $r^2 = a^2 \cos \theta(1 + \cos \theta).$
19. $r^2 = a^2(\sin \theta + \cos \theta).$
20. $r^2 = a^2 \sin \theta(1 - 2 \sin \theta).$

21. $r^2 = a^2 \sin \theta \sin 2\theta$.   **22.** $r^2 = a^2 \cos \theta \cos 2\theta$.
23. $r^2 = a^2 \cos 3\theta$.   **24.** $r^2 = a^2 \sin 3\theta$.

In Exs. 25–35, transform the equation to one in polar coordinates. Sketch the curve. See § 26, page 38, for the pertinent formulas.

25. $(x^2 + y^2)^2 = 2a^2xy$.   *Ans.* $r^2 = a^2 \sin 2\theta$.
26. $(x^2 + y^2)^3 = 4a^2x^2y^2$ *Ans.* $r = a \sin 2\theta$.
27. $(x^2 + y^2)^3 = a^4x^2$.   *Ans.* $r^2 = a^2 \cos \theta$.
28. $(x^2 + y^2 + ax)^2 = a^2(x^2 + y^2)$.   *Ans.* $r = a(1 - \cos \theta)$.
29. $(x^2 + y^2)(x^2 + y^2 - a^2)^2 = a^4y^2$.   *Ans.* $r^2 = a^2(1 + \sin \theta)$.
30. $(x^2 + y^2 - 2ax)^2 = a^2(x^2 + y^2)$.   *Ans.* $r = a(1 + 2 \cos \theta)$.
31. $(x^2 + y^2)^3 = 4a^2xy(x^2 - y^2)$.   *Ans.* $r^2 = a^2 \sin 4\theta$.
32. $(x^2 + y^2)^5 = 16a^2x^2y^2(x^2 - y^2)^2$. *Ans.* $r = a \sin 4\theta$.
33. $y^4 - 2axy^2 = x^4$.   *Ans.* $r = a \sin \theta \tan 2\theta$.
34. $y^4 + 2a^2xy = x^4$.   *Ans.* $r^2 = a^2 \tan 2\theta$.
35. $(x^2 + y^2 - 1)(x^2 + y^2) = x^2$.   (Ex. 3.)

In Exs. 36–44, transform the equation to rectangular form.

36. Ex. 4.   **37.** Ex. 5.   **38.** Ex. 7.
39. Ex. 8.   **40.** Ex. 9.   **41.** Ex. 10.
42. Ex. 15.   **43.** Ex. 21.   **44.** Ex. 22.

166. *Inequalities and Plane Curves*

It can be shown that an algebraic curve

$$f(x, y) = 0$$

divides the plane into two regions such that the function $f(x, y)$ takes on only positive values in one of the regions, only negative values in the other region. Proof of the statement can be based on the concept of continuity of a function of two variables (§ 248) but is omitted here.

As an example, consider the circle

$$x^2 + y^2 - a^2 = 0.$$

For any point (x, y) outside the circle, the distance to the origin is greater than the radius a,

$$\sqrt{x^2 + y^2} > a$$

so that for such points

$$x^2 + y^2 - a^2 > 0.$$

For points inside the circle,

$$x^2 + y^2 - a^2 < 0.$$

It is amusing to see how the above ideas can help us determine some of the shapes which can be assumed by curves of degree greater than two.

Consider the cubic

(1) $$(x + y - 1)(x^2 + y^2 - 1) = 0,$$

which, since its left member is factorable, degenerates into the line

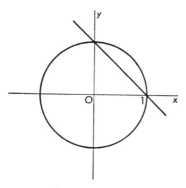

(2) $$x + y = 1$$

and the circle

(3) $$x^2 + y^2 = 1.$$

Associate with (1) the cubic

(4) $$(x + y - 1)(x^2 + y^2 - 1) = \epsilon,$$

where ϵ is to be taken constant, not zero, but as small as we wish.

By taking ϵ sufficiently small, we may make the curve (4) approximate the curve (1) as closely as desired. But the cubics (1) and (4) have no intersections, since ϵ is being

Figure 191

chosen different from zero. It follows that the cubic (4) has one of the two shapes exhibited in Figures 192–193.

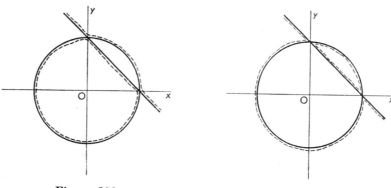

Figure 192   **Figure 193**

For our purpose it is unessential, though easily determined, that Figure 192 corresponds to small positive ϵ, Figure 193 to small negative ϵ. To see this, use $x = 0$, $y = 1.1$ in the left member of (4) and thus determine that with $\epsilon = 0.021$, the cubic (4) passes through $(0, 1.1)$.

The algebraic curve

(5) $$f(x, y) = 0$$

divides the plane into two regions, one in which f is negative, one in which f is positive. Each time a moving point (x, y) crosses the curve (5), $f(x, y)$ changes sign. Thus, for any negative ϵ, small or not, the locus of equation

(4) is restricted to the same "side" of the cubic (1) as is the dotted curve in Figure 193.   If ϵ is not small, however, the present argument gives no hint as to the shape of the cubic (4).

In Ex. 11 below, for instance, a logical first step in treating

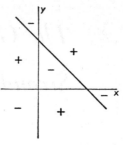

(6) $$xy(x + y - 1) = \epsilon$$

is first to determine the regions corresponding to $\epsilon > 0$ and to $\epsilon < 0$.   Choose a random point, say, $(-1, -1)$.   For this point, ϵ is negative.   At once we conclude that the various portions of the plane have associated with them the signs (of ϵ) indicated in Figure 194.

Figure 194

The following exercises are meant to be instructive and amusing but by no means exhaustive (or exhausting).

EXERCISES

In each exercise, draw the degenerate curve for $\epsilon = 0$, then draw approximate curves yielded by sufficiently small nonzero ϵ.

1. $xy = \epsilon$.
2. $(x - y)(x + y) = \epsilon$.
3. $(x - 1)(y^2 - 4x) = \epsilon$.
4. $(y - 1)(4x^2 + y^2 - 4) = \epsilon$.
5. $(x - 2)(x^2 + y^2 - 1) = \epsilon$.
6. $(x - 2)(x^2 - y^2 - 1) = \epsilon$.
7. $(x - 1)(x - 2)(y - 2) = \epsilon$.
8. $(x^2 + y^2 - 1)(x^2 + y^2 - 2x) = \epsilon$.
9. $(x^2 - 4y)(x^2 + y^2 - 5) = \epsilon$.
10. $(y^2 - x)(x^2 - y) = \epsilon$.
11. $xy(x + y - 1) = \epsilon$.
12. $(x^2 + y^2 - 1)(y^2 - 4x + 8) = \epsilon$.
13. $(x^2 + 4y^2 - 4)(x^2 - y^2 - 1) = \epsilon$.
14. $(4x^2 + y^2 - 1)(x^2 - y^2 - 1) = \epsilon$.
15. $(x^2 + y^2 - 4)[(x - 2)^2 + y^2 - 1][(x + 2)^2 + y^2 - 1] = \epsilon$.
16. $xy(x^2 + y^2 - 1) = \epsilon$.
17. $(x - 1)(x - 2)(x^2 + y^2 - 16) = \epsilon$.
18. $(x - 1)(y - 2)(y^2 - 4x) = \epsilon$.
19. $(y^2 - 4x)(x^2 - y^2 - 4) = \epsilon$.
20. $(x - 1)(x^2 + y^2 - 1) = \epsilon$.
21. $(r - a)(r - a + a \cos \theta) = \epsilon$.
22. $(r - a)(r^2 - a^2 \cos 2\theta) = \epsilon$.

The General Equation of Second Degree

167. Rotation of Axes

Before taking up the problem of this chapter, we must develop formulas for *rotation of axes*.

Let Ox, Oy and Ox_1, Oy_1 be two pairs of rectangular axes with the same origin, and denote by φ the angle through which the first pair must be rotated to come to coincidence with the second, the angle φ being considered *positive* when measured *counterclockwise*. Let P have the coordinates x, y in the first system and x_1, y_1 in the second, so that

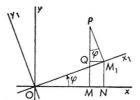

Figure 195

$$OM = x, \qquad MP = y,$$
$$OM_1 = x_1, \qquad M_1P = y_1.$$

Now

$$OM = ON - MN = ON - QM_1;$$
$$MP = MQ + QP = NM_1 + QP.$$

We thus have the formulas

(1)
$$\begin{cases} x = x_1 \cos\varphi - y_1 \sin\varphi, \\ y = x_1 \sin\varphi + y_1 \cos\varphi. \end{cases}$$

168. Removal of the Product Term

The most general equation of the second degree has the form

(1)
$$Ax^2 + Bxy + Cy^2 + Dx + Ey + F = 0.$$

If $B = 0$, then (1) is the equation of a conic as treated in Chapter 14 and §§ 63–65. If $B \neq 0$, we shall show that equation (1) can be transformed by rotation of axes into an equation of the form

(2)
$$A_1x_1^2 + C_1y_1^2 + D_1x_1 + E_1y_1 + F_1 = 0,$$

which has no x_1y_1 term and is therefore the equation of a conic.

298

Let us substitute for x and y in (1) the values given by (1), § 167:

(3)
$$
\begin{aligned}
&A(x_1 \cos \varphi - y_1 \sin \varphi)^2 \\
&+ B(x_1 \cos \varphi - y_1 \sin \varphi)(x_1 \sin \varphi + y_1 \cos \varphi) \\
&+ C(x_1 \sin \varphi + y_1 \cos \varphi)^2 + D(x_1 \cos \varphi - y_1 \sin \varphi) \\
&+ E(x_1 \sin \varphi + y_1 \cos \varphi) + F = 0.
\end{aligned}
$$

In equation (3), we wish to choose φ so that the term involving x_1y_1 will drop out. The x_1y_1 term in (3) is

(4) $\quad [-2A \sin \varphi \cos \varphi + B \cos^2 \varphi - B \sin^2 \varphi + 2C \sin \varphi \cos \varphi]x_1y_1.$

Now $2 \sin \varphi \cos \varphi = \sin 2\varphi$ and $\cos^2 \varphi - \sin^2 \varphi = \cos 2\varphi$, so that (4) becomes

(5) $\qquad\qquad [B \cos 2\varphi - (A - C) \sin 2\varphi]x_1y_1.$

To make the x_1y_1 term drop out of equation (3), we must set

(6) $\qquad\qquad (A - C) \sin 2\varphi = B \cos 2\varphi.$

If $A = C$, this equation gives*

$$\cos 2\varphi = 0, \qquad \varphi = 45°.$$

If $A \neq C$, equation (6) gives

(7) $\qquad\qquad \mathbf{\tan 2\varphi = \dfrac{B}{A - C}}.$

Now for every value of $\tan 2\varphi$, from $-\infty$ to $+\infty$, there is a value of 2φ between 0 and π; hence a value of φ between 0 and $\frac{1}{2}\pi$, so that it is always possible to determine a positive acute angle φ satisfying (6). If the curve (1) be referred to axes making this angle with the original ones, the resulting equation will be free of the product term, and its locus must be a conic.

THEOREM 39. *Every equation of the second degree (if it has a locus) repre- sents a conic section whose axes are inclined to the coordinate axes at the positive acute angle φ given by formula (7), or, if $A = C$, $B \neq 0$, at an angle of 45°.*

Thus, to trace the locus of an equation of the second degree ($B \neq 0$), for instance as in Figure 196, the first step is to determine $\tan 2\varphi$ by (7), and then use the formulas

(8)
$$
\begin{cases}
\cos \varphi = \sqrt{\dfrac{1 + \cos 2\varphi}{2}}, \\[2ex]
\sin \varphi = \sqrt{\dfrac{1 - \cos 2\varphi}{2}}.
\end{cases}
$$

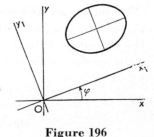

Figure 196

* Unless also $B = 0$; in that case (6) is true for all values of φ, which is to be expected. Why?

The values of cos φ and sin φ, when substituted in (1), § 167, give us the expressions for x and y in terms of the new coordinates. By substituting these expressions in the original equation, we obtain the equation of the curve referred to the new axes. This equation will contain no x_1y_1-term, so that the curve may be traced by our earlier methods.

Example. Trace the curve

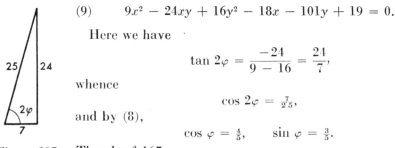

(9) $9x^2 - 24xy + 16y^2 - 18x - 101y + 19 = 0.$

Here we have

$$\tan 2\varphi = \frac{-24}{9 - 16} = \frac{24}{7},$$

whence

$$\cos 2\varphi = \tfrac{7}{25},$$

and by (8),

$$\cos \varphi = \tfrac{4}{5}, \qquad \sin \varphi = \tfrac{3}{5}.$$

Figure 197   Thus by § 167,

$$x = \tfrac{1}{5}(4x_1 - 3y_1), \qquad y = \tfrac{1}{5}(3x_1 + 4y_1).$$

In terms of the new coordinates, equation (9) reduces to

$$25y_1{}^2 - 75x_1 - 70y_1 + 19 = 0,$$

or, in the standard form,

$$(y_1 - \tfrac{7}{5})^2 = 3(x_1 + \tfrac{2}{5}).$$

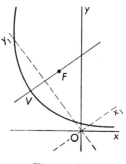

This is a parabola with axis parallel to Ox_1, opening in the positive direction, with its vertex at the point $(-\tfrac{2}{5}, \tfrac{7}{5})$ referred to the new axes. The x_1-axis has a slope $\tan \varphi = \tfrac{3}{4}$; after the new axes are drawn, the curve is traced as in Figure 198.

Figure 198

169. Test for Species of a Conic

We sometimes wish merely to determine what kind of conic is represented by a given equation, without going to the trouble of removing the xy-term. For this purpose the following test may be used.

An equation of the second degree represents:

(a) *if* $B^2 - 4AC < 0$, *an ellipse;*
(b) *if* $B^2 - 4AC = 0$, *a parabola;*
(c) *if* $B^2 - 4AC > 0$, *a hyperbola.*

The exceptional forms listed in § 108 are included under (a), (b), and (c). Proof of this test can be accomplished by doing Exs. 34–38 on page 302.

The condition $B^2 - 4AC = 0$ means that $Ax^2 + Bxy + Cy^2$ is a perfect square.

THEOREM 40. *An equation of second degree represents a parabola (exceptionally, two parallel or coincident lines, or no locus) if and only if the terms of second degree form a perfect square.*

EXERCISES

In Exs. 1–21, determine the species of conic represented by the given equation; remove the product term by rotation of axes, reduce the resulting equation to a standard form, and trace the curve on the new axes.

1. $xy = 8$.

2. $2xy + 1 = 0$.

3. $x^2 - 4xy + y^2 = -9$.

4. $5x^2 - 8xy + 5y^2 = 9$.
    Ans. $4x_1^2 + 9y_1^2 = 36$.

5. $13x^2 - 10xy + 13y^2 = 72$.
    Ans. $x_1^2 + 4y_1^2 = 16$.

6. $8x^2 - 12xy + 17y^2 = 80$.
    Ans. $x_1^2 - 2y_1^2 = 9$.

7. $2x^2 + 12xy - 7y^2 = 45$.
    Ans. $x_1^2 - y_1^2 = 4$.

8. $2x^2 - 3xy - 2y^2 = -10$.
    Ans. $2x_1^2 + y_1^2 = 8$.

9. $11x^2 + 6xy + 19y^2 = 80$.
    Ans. $9x_1^2 - y_1^2 = 1$.

10. $x^2 + 8xy + 7y^2 = 1$.
    Ans. $9x_1^2 - 4y_1^2 = 4$.

11. $5x^2 + 12xy = 4$.
    Ans. $4x_1^2 - y_1^2 = 1$.

12. $4xy + 3y^2 = 1$.
    Ans. $y_1^2 - x_1^2 = 1$.

13. $5x^2 + 24xy - 5y^2 = -13$.
    Ans. $2y_1^2 - 3x_1^2 = 6$.

14. $x^2 - 4xy - 2y^2 = 6$.
    Ans. $x_1^2 + 3y_1^2 = 9$.

15. $13x^2 - 8xy + 7y^2 = 45$.
    Ans. $3y_1^2 - x_1^2 = 24$.

16. $3x^2 + 12xy - 13y^2 = -120$.
    Ans. $2x_1^2 - y_1^2 = 8$.

17. $17x^2 + 18xy - 7y^2 = 80$.
    Ans. $y_1^2 = 2x_1$.

18. $16x^2 - 24xy + 9y^2 = 30x + 40y$.
    Ans. $y_1^2 = 4(x_1 - 1)$.

19. $16x^2 - 24xy + 9y^2 - 60x - 80y + 100 = 0$.
    Ans. $(x_1 - 1)^2 - 4y_1^2 = 4$.

20. $11x^2 - 24xy + 4y^2 + 6x + 8y = -15$.
    Ans. $x_1^2 = -6(y_1 - 1)$.

21. $3x^2 + 2\sqrt{3}\,xy + y^2 = 12x - 12\sqrt{3}\,y + 24$.

22. By rationalizing each equation, show that the three equations $x^{\frac{1}{2}} + y^{\frac{1}{2}} = a^{\frac{1}{2}}$, $x^{\frac{1}{2}} - y^{\frac{1}{2}} = a^{\frac{1}{2}}$, $y^{\frac{1}{2}} - x^{\frac{1}{2}} = a^{\frac{1}{2}}$ collectively represent a parabola, and trace the curve. What part of the curve is represented by each equation?

23. Show that if the terms of first degree are missing, the equation of second degree cannot represent a parabola.

24. Prove that if A and C have opposite signs, the equation of the second degree always represents a hyperbola. Is the converse true?

25. Prove that if the xy-term is present and either or both square terms are missing, the equation of second degree always represents a hyperbola.

26. It follows from Theorem 40 that the equation of every parabola can be put in the form $(ax + by)^2 + Dx + Ey + F = 0$. Show that the axis of the parabola is parallel to the line $ax + by = 0$. (Ex. 33, page 107.)

27. Show that if the terms of first degree are missing, an equation of second degree represents a conic with center at the origin; and conversely.

28. Prove that a straight line can intersect a conic in not more than two points.

29. Prove that two conics can intersect in not more than four points.

30. Show that a conic is determined by five points.

31. Show that a parabola is determined by four points.   (Note the equation in Ex. 26.)

32. Show that if the equations of a hyperbola and a straight line, when solved as simultaneous, have no solution real or imaginary, the line must be an asymptote to the curve. $\left(\text{Use the equations } \dfrac{x^2}{a^2} - \dfrac{y^2}{b^2} = 1, y = mx + c.\right)$

33. If in the equation of a hyperbola the terms of first degree are missing, show that the equations of the asymptotes may be found by equating to 0 the group of terms of second degree and factoring.   [Take the equation in the form

$$(a_1x + b_1y)(a_2x + b_2y) + c = 0;$$

see Ex. 32.]

34. In § 168, equation (1) was transformed by rotation of axes into equation (3). Let the coefficients in (3) be designated by A_1, B_1, etc., so that (3) may be written

(10) $A_1x_1{}^2 + B_1x_1y_1 + C_1y_1{}^2 + D_1x_1 + E_1y_1 + F_1 = 0.$

By identifying (3) and (10), show that

(11) $A_1 = A \cos^2 \varphi + B \cos \varphi \sin \varphi + C \sin^2 \varphi,$

$B_1 = B \cos 2\varphi - (A - C) \sin 2\varphi,$

$C_1 = A \sin^2 \varphi - B \cos \varphi \sin \varphi + C \cos^2 \varphi.$

35. Use the formulas (11) of Ex. 34 to show that

(12) $A_1 + C_1 = A + C,$

which is expressed in advanced mathematics by saying that $(A + C)$ is *invariant* (unchanged) under the transformation (rotation) employed.

36. Formulas (11), Ex. 34, yield

(13) $A_1 - C_1 = B \sin 2\varphi + (A - C) \cos 2\varphi.$

From (13) and the expression for B_1 in terms of A, B, C, show that

$$B_1{}^2 + (A_1 - C_1)^2 = B^2 + (A - C)^2.$$

37. Since $B^2 - 4AC = B^2 + (A - C)^2 - (A + C)^2$, conclude from the results of Exs. 35–36 that

(14) $B_1{}^2 - 4A_1C_1 = B^2 - 4AC,$

another invariant under rotation of axes.

38. Let φ be chosen as in § 168 so that $B_1 = 0$, and use (14) of Ex. 37 to prove the validity of the test in § 169.

170. *Rectangular Hyperbola*

The equation

(1) $Bxy + Dx + Ey + F = 0,$ $B \neq 0,$

if not factorable, represents a hyperbola, since

$$B^2 - 4AC = B^2 > 0.$$

Let us solve the equation for y and for x in turn:

$$y = -\frac{Dx + F}{Bx + E}, \qquad x = -\frac{Ey + F}{By + D}.$$

From the above equations we see that if $(Bx + E) = 0$, y does not exist; if $(By + D) = 0$, x does not exist. As

$$(Bx + E) \to 0, \; y \to \pm \infty ;$$

as

$$(By + D) \to 0, \; x \to \pm \infty.$$

This shows that the asymptotes are the lines

$$Bx + E = 0,$$
$$By + D = 0.$$

Thus equation (1) represents *a rectangular hyperbola with its asymptotes parallel to the coordinate axes.*

An important special case of (1) is the following: *The equation*

(2) $$2xy = a^2$$

represents a rectangular hyperbola whose asymptotes are the coordinate axes.

Since x and y must have the same sign, the curve lies in the first and third quadrants. The constant a is the semiaxis: this may be shown by rotation of axes, or by noting that the curve intersects the line $y = x$ at $(\pm \tfrac{1}{2}\sqrt{2}\,a, \pm \tfrac{1}{2}\sqrt{2}\,a)$.

Of course the equation

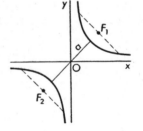

Figure 199

(3) $$2xy = -a^2$$

represents the hyperbola lying in the second and fourth quadrants (since x and y must now have opposite signs).

Both (2) and (3) are included in the single formula

(4) $$xy = k, \qquad k \neq 0,$$

where k is unrestricted as to sign. This equation, written in the form

$$y = \frac{k}{x},$$

shows that y is *inversely proportional to x.* This type of variation occurs frequently in science; as examples, see Exs. 13–14 below.

171. *Composition of Ordinates*

Given two functions of x

(1) $$y = u(x), \qquad y = v(x),$$

let it be required to trace the curve

(2) $$y = u(x) + v(x).$$

It may happen that the curve (2) is difficult to trace by our usual methods but that the curves (1) are simple and easily handled. In such a case we may make use of the fact that, for any given value of x, the ordinate of (2) is the *sum of the ordinates* of the separate curves (1). If these two curves are traced on the same axes, any number of points of (2) are easily plotted. We have already used this technique in simple specific examples in Exs. 30–31, page 248, and Ex. 21, page 251.

That we may compound abscissas instead of ordinates, when more convenient, should be clear without argument.

172. *Conics Traced by Composition*

Given an equation of second degree in which the xy-term and one or both square terms are present, the conic may be traced by composition as follows: If the term in y^2 is present, we *solve the equation as a quadratic in y*, which exhibits y as the sum of the ordinates of two curves, one of which is a straight line, while the other is a conic with axes parallel to the coordinate axes and thus amenable to our earlier methods.

Of course if the term in y^2 is missing, we solve for x instead. When both square terms are present, so that a choice is possible, there is sometimes a definite advantage in one alternative over the other (Exs. 36–37 below).

Example. Trace the parabola

$$x^2 - 2xy + y^2 + x - 1 = 0.$$

Solving for y, we find

$$y = x \pm \tfrac{1}{2}\sqrt{4x^2 - 4x^2 - 4x + 4}$$
$$= x \pm \sqrt{1 - x}.$$

The ordinates of this curve are found by adding the ordinates of the straight line

(1) $$y = x$$

and the curve

$$y = \pm \sqrt{1 - x}.$$

This equation reduces to

(2) $$y^2 = -(x - 1),$$

a parabola with vertex at $(1, 0)$, opening to the left. We now trace the curves (1) and (2) and locate points on the required curve by adding (algebraically) the ordinates of these two curves. For a given value of x, there are two points on the required curve, with ordinates

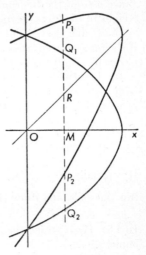

$$y = x + \sqrt{1 - x},$$
$$y = x - \sqrt{1 - x}.$$

For instance, when $x = OM$, the two ordinates are

$$MP_1 = MR + MQ_1,$$
$$MP_2 = MR + MQ_2.$$

Due regard must, of course, be paid to the sign of each segment.

Although this curve can be traced by use of § 168, the present method is definitely easier.

Figure 200

EXERCISES

In Exs. 1–4, find the asymptotes and the intercepts, plot a few other points, and draw the curve.

    1. $xy + 4x - 2y + 6 = 0.$ **2.** $xy - 3x + 2y = 0.$

    3. $xy - 5y + 5 = 0.$ **4.** $6xy - 3x - 2y + 3 = 0.$

In Exs. 5–8, locate the vertices, plot a few points, and draw the curve.

    5. $xy = 18.$ **6.** $xy = -2.$

    7. $2xy = -3.$ **8.** $6xy = 1.$

    9. As the number of terms increases indefinitely, the sum of a geometric progression of first term a and ratio r approaches the limiting value

$$S = \frac{a}{1 - r}, \qquad -1 < r < 1.$$

Graph S as a function of r.

    10. Represent $\tan (\theta + 45°)$ as a function of $\tan \theta$. [Expand by the addition formula; put $\tan \theta = x$, $\tan (\theta + 45°) = y$.]

    11. A man wishes to drive a specified distance at constant speed. Draw a curve from which he can read off the time needed to cover the distance at any given speed; show how to read from the same curve the speed required to cover the distance in a given time.

    12. Two cars drive from A to B, 200 mi. The second car starts one hour later than the first but drives 10 mi. per hr. faster. If both reach B at the same time, find analytically and graphically the time and average speed for each car.

    13. Boyle's law for "perfect gases" states that volume is inversely proportional to pressure. Draw the graph (a) of volume as a function of pressure; (b) of pressure as a function of volume.

14. A lever of length l, with the fulcrum at one end, is to lift a weight W at distance a from the fulcrum, by means of a force F at the free end. Neglecting the weight of the lever, graph F as a function of l.

15. Graph the current I from a battery as a function of the external resistance R, if the internal resistance r and electromotive force E are constant. (Current equals electromotive force divided by total resistance.)

16. In Atwood's machine (§ 127) two masses, m_1, m_2, are joined by a cord hung over a pulley. If the masses of the cord and pulley are negligible, the acceleration of gravity is reduced in the ratio

$$r = \frac{m_1 - m_2}{m_1 + m_2}, \qquad m_1 > m_2.$$

If originally $m_1 = 7$, $m_2 = 5$, and each is changed by an amount x, express r as a function of x, and draw the curve.
$Ans.\ r = \dfrac{1}{x + 6}, x > -5.$

In Exs. 17–32, trace the curve by composition, first determining the species of the conic.

17. $5x^2 - 4xy + y^2 = 1.$
18. $2x^2 - 2xy + y^2 = 4.$
19. $x^2 - 2xy + y^2 - x = 0.$
20. $x^2 - 2xy + y^2 = 4x - 4.$
21. $xy - y^2 - 4 = 0.$
22. $4xy - y^2 + 8 = 0.$
23. $2x^2 - 2xy + 3y = 0.$
24. $2x^2 - xy = 29 - 4y.$
25. $x^2 - 2xy + y^2 + 4x - 2y - 1 = 0.$
26. $x^2 - 6xy + 8y^2 + 2x - 6y = 0.$
27. $5x^2 - 2xy + y^2 = 4.$
28. $x^2 - 2xy + 10y^2 - 4x + 4y - 5 = 0.$
29. $x^2 - 6xy + 10y^2 + 8x - 23y + 10 = 0.$
30. $x^2 - 4xy + 5y^2 - 20x + 42y + 100 = 0.$
31. $x^2 - 2xy + 2y^2 - 2x + 2y + 1 = 0.$ $Ans.$ The point $(1, 0)$.
32. $4x^2 + 4xy + 5y^2 + 8x + 4y + 5 = 0.$ $Ans.$ No locus.
33. Trace the curve of Ex. **22**, page 301, by composition of ordinates.

34. Show that the conic $Ax^2 + Bxy + Dx + F = 0$ can be traced by compounding ordinates of a straight line and a rectangular hyperbola referred to its asymptotes [equation (4), § 170]. Obtain an analogous result for the conic $Bxy + Cy^2 + Ey + F = 0.$

35. The following statements (§ 172) have not been proved: (a) when the equation of a conic is solved for y, y appears as the sum of the ordinates of a straight line and a conic; (b) the axes of this conic are parallel to the coordinate axes; (c) the equations of the component line and conic have rational coefficients whenever the original coefficients are rational. By solving the general equation of second degree for y, prove these statements ($C \neq 0$).

36. By solving the general equation of second degree for y ($C \neq 0$), show that when $B^2 - 4AC = -4C^2$, the ordinates of the conic are the sum of ordinates of a straight line and a circle.

37. Obtain a theorem like that of Ex. 36, when abscissas are compounded.

Solution of Equations: Newton's Method

173. *Newton's Method*

A problem of first importance in engineering, physics, and the other mathematical sciences is to find, to any desired degree of approximation, the root or roots of an equation which cannot be solved by elementary methods. This problem can be solved by *Newton's method*, which we shall now develop.

The method exhibited in this chapter is useful in obtaining approximations to imaginary roots, as well as real roots, of equations. Only approximations to real roots are treated here.

Let the equation whose root is desired be

(1) $$f(x) = 0.$$

Consider the curve

(2) $$y = f(x).$$

A root of equation (1) is the x-coordinate of a point at which the curve (2) crosses the x-axis.

For the moment, suppose that a first approximation to the desired root has been obtained by some device, such as one of those to be discussed soon. Newton's method is essentially one for improving an approximation already obtained. With skilled application, it can be made to yield a root to any desired degree of accuracy.

In following the discussion on page 308, it is helpful to carry out the details for an equation whose solution is known. The equation

$$f(x) = x^2 - 2x - 1 = 0$$

has roots $x = 1 \pm \sqrt{2}$. Therefore, the parabola

$$y = x^2 - 2x - 1$$

crosses Ox near $x = 2.4$ and $x = -0.4$. For this equation choose as the first approximation $x_1 = 2.4$, compute $f(x_1)$, $f'(x_1)$, and the second approximation x_2 by employing equation (3) below.

Let the first approximation to the root be $x = x_1$, as shown in Figure 201. The point B, where the ordinate AB intersects the curve, has the coordinates $x = x_1$, $y = f(x_1)$. The tangent line at B will intersect the x-axis at C, whose coordinate x_2 may be a better approximation to the desired root than is x_1.

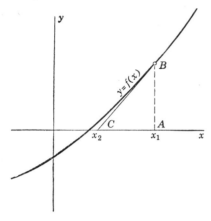

Figure 201

To find x_2, knowing x_1, note that $\overline{BA} = f(x_1)$, $\overline{CA} = x_1 - x_2$, and

$$\frac{\overline{BA}}{\overline{CA}} = f'(x_1).$$

Thus

$$\frac{f(x_1)}{x_1 - x_2} = f'(x_1),$$

which yields

$$(3) \qquad x_2 = x_1 - \frac{f(x_1)}{f'(x_1)}.$$

If we have one approximation x_1, to a root of $f(x) = 0$, equation (3) gives us another approximation, x_2, to that root. From x_2 still another approximation, x_3, is obtained in the same way by using

$$x_3 = x_2 - \frac{f(x_2)}{f'(x_2)},$$

and the process can be repeated as many times as we wish.

The term $\left[-\dfrac{f(x_1)}{f'(x_1)} \right]$ in equation (3) may be called the *correction*; it is the difference between the successive approximations x_1 and x_2. Newton's method is to iterate this process until the correction has vanished to the number of decimal places required in the root.

Examples of the use of the method will follow after a short discussion of the difficulties to be avoided and of some common procedures for obtaining a first approximation to get the wheels of Newton's method rolling.

174. *Difficulties Present in Newton's Method*

In the basic formula

$$x_2 = x_1 - \frac{f(x_1)}{f'(x_1)}$$

of Newton's method, the correction term will usually be large if its denominator $f'(x_1)$ is small. Since $f'(x)$ will vanish at a critical point of $y = f(x)$, it is highly desirable to avoid such a point in using Newton's method.   Figure 202 emphasizes that, if x_1 is unwisely chosen, the slope of the tangent line is small and the next approximation x_2 is distressingly far from the desired root.

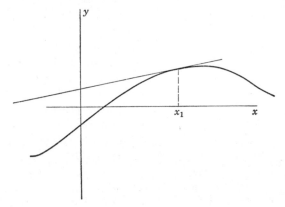

Figure 202

When two roots of the equation $f(x) = 0$ are close together, it can become quite a problem to avoid the nearby critical point.   When the root is a repeated root, both $f(x)$ and $f'(x)$ vanish there.   In theory, no difficulty arises because $\dfrac{f(x)}{f'(x)} \to 0$ as x approaches the desired root; in practice, plenty of difficulty arises because we lose significant figures rapidly in computing the small values of $f(x)$ and $f'(x)$ near the root.   The cure is usually effected by solving $f'(x) = 0$ for a double root, or $f''(x) = 0$ for a triple root, etc.

Since the solution of equations is a minor, not a major, portion of this course, the difficulties discussed here will be avoided by careful selection of problems to be solved.

175. *The First Approximation*

Three simple methods for obtaining a first approximation will now be explained.

First method.   Plot points on the curve $y = f(x)$ until the root is pinned in between two values of x, one yielding a positive y, the other a negative y. Then approximate the root by interpolation, call that approximation x_1, and proceed with Newton's method.   See Example (a) in the next section.

Second method.   If the equation $f(x) = 0$ can be written, by transferring terms from one side to the other, as $g(x) = h(x)$, where $g(x)$ and $h(x)$ are simple functions, then plot $y_1 = g(x)$ and $y_2 = h(x)$.   The x-coordinate of a point of intersection of these curves is a root of the equation $f(x) = 0$.

Example.   The equation $x^2 - \sin x = 0$ can be written $x^2 = \sin x$.   By sketching $y_1 = x^2$ and $y_2 = \sin x$ on the same figure (Figure 203), we obtain a first rough approximation, $x_1 = 0.9$.

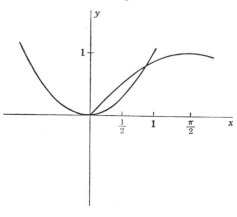

Figure 203

Third method.   If the equation is so simple that its component parts can be obtained readily from a single table, then a first approximation may be obtained from that table by inspection.   For example, to start on the solution of the equation $e^{-x} = x$, we may well consult a table of exponentials, pages 701–706, and look down the appropriate columns until we find where e^{-x} and x are about equal.   Thus we soon find that $x_1 = 0.57$ is a good first approximation.

Summary.   Any of the three methods may be employed or combinations of them can be particularly useful.   The first method has many advantages in that the more we know about the curve $y = f(x)$, the more effective will be our use of Newton's method.

176. *Solution of Equations*

In applying the technique described in this chapter, it should be kept in mind that any approximation x_n is considered exact, once chosen, and that $f(x_n)$ and $f'(x_n)$ are computed on that basis.   If tables are used, the precision of the result is restrained by the limited accuracy of the tables.   The root can then be approximated more closely only by computing the functions $f(x_n)$ and $f'(x_n)$ to a greater degree of accuracy than that present in the tables.

For a smooth curve, Newton's method yields the root as closely as desired; it "converges" to the correct value of x.   In practice, once we get fairly close to the root, the method converges quite rapidly.   Often two or three additional significant figures are picked up in a single step.

Example (a).   Find to four decimal places the smaller positive root of the equation

(1) $$x^3 - 4x + 2 = 0.$$

Here $$f(x) = x^3 - 4x + 2,$$
$$f'(x) = 3x^2 - 4.$$

Put $$y = x^3 - 4x + 2.$$

When $x = 0$, $y = 2$; when $x = 1$, $y = -1$. A root lies between $x = 0$ and $x = 1$, Figure 204. The chord joining $(0, 2)$ and $(1, -1)$ crosses Ox at $x = \frac{2}{3}$; but since $y'' = 6x$, the curve is concave upward (§ 59) in this interval and will cross Ox to the left of the chord; try $x_1 = 0.5$. By direct substitution, we find

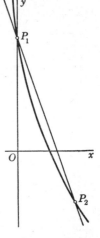

$$f(x_1) = 0.125, \qquad f'(x_1) = -3.25,$$

so that

$$x_2 = 0.5 - \frac{0.125}{-3.25} = 0.5 + 0.04,$$

$$x_2 = 0.54.$$

Next we use x_2 in a similar manner to find

$$f(x_2) = -0.0025, \qquad f'(x_2) = -3.13,$$

and

Figure 204

$$x_3 = 0.54 - \frac{-0.0025}{-3.13} = 0.54 - 0.0008,$$

$$= 0.5392.$$

Finally, from x_3 we obtain

$$x_4 = 0.5392 - \frac{-0.00003}{-3.13} = 0.5392 - 0.00001,$$

$$= 0.5392,$$

so that the desired root, to four decimal places, is $x = 0.5392$.

The work is conveniently arranged in tabular form. Let $y_n = f(x_n)$, $y'_n = f'(x_n)$.

n	x_n	y_n	y'_n	$-y_n/y'_n$
1	0.5	0.125	-3.25	0.04
2	0.54	-0.0025	-3.13	-0.0008
3	0.5392	-0.00003	-3.13	-0.00001

Example (b). Solve the equation $\cos x = x$.

A rough sketch (Figure 205) of the curve $y = \cos x$ and the line $y = x$ shows that they intersect at only one point, somewhere near $x = \frac{1}{4}\pi$. Until we learn (in Chapter 40) how to compute the cosine function to any desired degree of accuracy, we are forced to use trigonometric tables in this problem. The number of significant figures in our answer is therefore dictated by the table used.

Let us turn to the table on page 712 and hunt for the place where "radian" and "cosine" are nearly equal.   We thus obtain, as a first approximation, $x_1 = 0.74$.

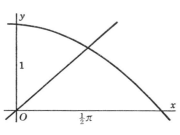

Figure 205

Put
$$f(x) = x - \cos x.$$
Then
$$f'(x) = 1 + \sin x.$$
For $x_1 = 0.74$, we find that
$$\cos x_1 = 0.738\ 47,$$
$$\sin x_1 = 0.674\ 29.$$
Then $f(x_1) = +0.001\ 53, f'(x_1) = +1.67$, so that

$$x_2 = 0.74 - \frac{0.001\ 53}{1.67} = 0.74 - 0.001 = 0.739.$$

We use interpolation in the table to obtain
$$\cos x_2 = 0.739\ 14,$$
$$\sin x_2 = 0.673\ 55.$$

Then $f(x_2) = -0.000\ 14, f'(x_2) = 1.67$.   Hence

$$x_3 = 0.739 - \frac{-0.000\ 14}{1.67} = 0.739.$$

Since we dare not interpolate to a hundredth of the interval in the table, the root we sought is $x = 0.739$, as accurately as it can be obtained without a more extensive trigonometric table.

EXERCISES

1. Find the cube root of 6 without using tables.   (Solve $x^3 = 6$.)   *Ans.* 1.817·
2. Find the cube root of 3 without tables.   *Ans.* 1.442·
3. Find the cube root of 441, without tables.   *Ans.* 7.61·
4. Find, to three decimal places, the real root of $x^3 + 3x - 2 = 0$.   *Ans.* 0.596.
5. In Example (*a*) above, find the larger positive root.   *Ans.* 1.675.
6. In Example (*a*) above, find the negative root.   Add the answers to Example (*a*), Ex. 5, and Ex. 6.   What should be the sum, and why?   *Ans.* $x = -2.214$.
7. Find the smaller positive root of $x^3 - x^2 - 2x + 1 = 0$.   *Ans.* 0.445.
8. Find the numerically smallest root of $x^3 + 9x^2 + 23x + 14 = 0$.
9. In Ex. 8, find the intermediate root.
10. Find, in inches, the radius of a sphere of volume $\frac{1}{8}$ cu. ft.   *Ans.* 3.72.
11. Find, in inches, the radius of a sphere of volume 1 cu. ft.   *Ans.* 7.44.
12. The base of a box is a square; the height is 1 ft. less than the side of the base. If the volume is 5 cu. ft., find the dimensions.   *Ans.* One side $= 2.12$ ft.
13. A hollow sphere of outer radius 10 in. weighs $\frac{1}{5}$ as much as a solid sphere of the same size and material.   Find the inner radius.   *Ans.* 9.28 in.

14. Find the edge of a cube if the volume is tripled when the edge is increased 1 in.   *Ans.* 2.26 in.

15. Find the radius of a sphere if the volume is halved when the radius is decreased by 2 in.

16. A metal sphere of radius 2 in. is recast in the form of a cone of height 2 in. surmounted by a hemisphere of the same radius as the cone.   Find the radius of the cone.   *Ans.* 2.23 in.

17. A torpedo has the longitudinal section shown in Figure 206.   When submerged, it displaces a volume of water equal to a sphere of radius 1 ft.   Find r in feet.

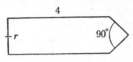

Figure 206

18. A cylinder is inscribed in a sphere of radius a.   Find the half-altitude of the cylinder if the volume of the cylinder is half that of the sphere.
Ans. $0.395a$, $0.742a$.

19. A cylinder is inscribed in a cone whose diameter and height are equal.   Find the radius of the cylinder, if its volume is $\frac{3}{20}$ that of the cone.   (Two answers.)

20. A metal hemisphere of radius 2 is recast as a circular cylinder of base radius r and height 8, surmounted by a hemisphere of radius r.   Find r.   *Ans.* 0.791.

In Exs. 21–36, solve the given equation.

21. $\sin \alpha = \frac{1}{3}\alpha^2$.   **22.** $x^2 e^x = 1$.   **23.** $\sin \theta = 1 - \theta$.

24. $\tan x = e^x$, $0 \leq x \leq \frac{1}{2}\pi$.   **25.** $x + \ln x = 0$.

26. $e^x \cos x = 1$, $0 \leq x \leq \frac{1}{2}\pi$.   **27.** $\tan \theta = 2\theta$, $0 \leq \theta \leq \frac{1}{2}\pi$.

28. $x + e^x = 0$.   **29.** $e^x = 3x$.

30. $e^x \sin x = 1$, $0 \leq x \leq \frac{1}{2}\pi$.   **31.** $(x + 2)e^{-x} = 1$.

32. $2 \tan \theta = \theta$, the smallest positive root.

33. $\cosh x = 3x$.   **34.** $\sinh x = 2x$.

35. $\cos \alpha = \alpha^2$.   **36.** $\sinh x = \cos x$.

37. A piece of wire 18 in. long is bent in the form of a circular arc, with the ends 1 ft. apart.   Find the angle subtended at the center.   *Ans.* 171.5°.

38. Solve Ex. 25 by first passing to the exponential form.

39. Solve Ex. 22 by first passing to the logarithmic form.

40. Solve Ex. 31 by first passing to the logarithmic form.

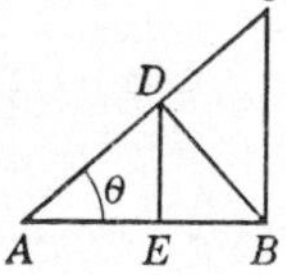

41. The triangular frame ABC is to be strengthened by braces BD perpendicular to AC, and DE perpendicular to AB.   If AE must equal DC, find θ.   *Ans.* 40° 59'.

Figure 207

42. Solve Ex. 41 if AE is to equal BC.   *Ans.* 34° 18.5'.

43. From the corners of a piece of tin 16 by 10 in. equal squares are cut out and the flaps are bent up to form an open box, as in Example (a), § 66.   If the box is to contain 100 cu. in., find the size of the squares. (Two answers.)

44. Find the eccentricity of an ellipse if the latus rectum is one-fourth the distance between the directrices.   (Two answers.)

45. A circular cone is inscribed in a sphere in such a manner that the volume of the cone is one-eighth the volume of the sphere.   Find the altitude of the cone.

46. A top, consisting of a cone of radius a and height a surmounted by a hemisphere of the same radius, is whittled down to a cylinder with axis coinciding with that of the top.   How much of the material can be saved?   *Ans.* 51.5%.

Curve Fitting

177. *Empirical Equations*

In many applications we are concerned with a set of pairs of values of two variables as determined by observation or experiment. A few examples follow:

(1) Ballistics: The range of a projectile, as a function of the initial velocity.

(2) Chemistry: The amount of a given element present during a chemical reaction, as a function of the time.

(3) Mechanical Engineering: The gasoline consumption of an automobile, as a function of the speed.

(4) Biology: The rate of growth of a culture of bacteria as a function of time.

By plotting the observed pairs of values on rectangular coordinate paper and drawing a smooth curve through the points, we obtain a more or less accurate graphic representation. The problem of this chapter is to obtain an analytic representation, an equation that corresponds to the empirically determined curve. Such an equation is called an *empirical equation*, or *empirical formula*, and the process of finding that equation is called *curve fitting*.

We shall find that different methods produce different equations for the same data. An empirical formula is merely an approximation to the true relation between the variables. Frequently a close correspondence can be found; but if important extraneous factors enter, only a rough approximation is obtainable. Even then, however, the method may yield useful results.

178. *The Method of Selected Points*

Example. A set of eight cylindrical bars, all of the same radius and material but of different lengths, are weighed, with results as tabulated* (L in feet, W in pounds). Express W as a function of L.

* By intention, the data given are quite inaccurate; for, if not, in the small-scaled drawing to which we are limited in the text, all the points would appear to lie on the line. In this chapter, the student should make all his drawings on a very generous scale.

L	1	2	3	4	5	6	7	8
W	0.38	0.68	1.13	1.47	1.78	2.18	2.60	2.84

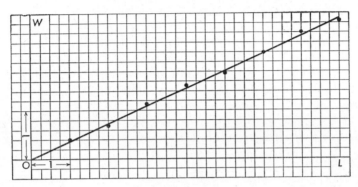

Figure 208

Plotting the points (1, 0.38), (2, 0.68), etc., with four spaces as the horizontal and five as the vertical unit, we find that the points follow more or less closely a straight line through the origin. In this example, we know beforehand that the weight is proportional to the length:

$$W = bL.$$

Now, laying a transparent ruler on the paper, we draw the straight line (through the origin) which, on the average, according to our best judgment, most closely follows the set of points. The ordinate of the last point on the line segment drawn is about 14.4 spaces, or 2.88 units; the equation of the line through (0, 0), (8, 2.88) is, by § 22,

$$W = 0.360L.$$

This is known as the *method of selected points*. That is, we select two points on our estimated "best-fitting line"—in the example, the points (0, 0), (8, 2.88)—and find the equation of the line through those points by § 22.

179. *Residuals*

The difference between the observed value of the function and the computed value, the vertical distance from the plotted point to the curve as drawn, is called the *residual* corresponding to that point. In the example above, for $L = 1$, the observed value of W is 0.38, the formula gives 0.36, the residual is 0.02; for $L = 2$, the respective values are 0.68, 0.72, -0.04.

180. *The Method of Averages*

Although the method of selected points in many cases gives good enough results for practical purposes, it is open to the serious objection that the choice of the "best-fitting" line depends solely on the judgment of the operator, and hence is to some extent a matter of guesswork. We shall therefore study two other methods, each an explicit mathematical procedure for fitting a curve of specified form to a given set of data. The first of these procedures is called the *method of averages*.

To fit an empirical equation containing one undetermined constant to given data by the method of averages, we determine the constant so that *the algebraic sum of the residuals is zero.*

181. *Linear Equation with One Constant*

In the equation

$$(1) \qquad\qquad y = a + bx,$$

assume that a is known and b is to be determined from a set of observations. The discussion applies without essential change to problems where b is known and a to be found.

Let the given pairs of values be (x_1, y_1), (x_2, y_2), (x_3, y_3), $\cdots$, (x_n, y_n). At the first point the observed value is y_1, the value computed by (1) is $a + bx_1$, the residual r_1 is

$$r_1 = y_1 - a - bx_1.$$

The succeeding residuals are

$$r_2 = y_2 - a - bx_2,$$
$$r_3 = y_3 - a - bx_3,$$
$$\cdots\cdots\cdots\cdots$$
$$r_n = y_n - a - bx_n.$$

By the method of averages the sum of the residuals must be zero:

$$(2) \qquad\qquad r_1 + r_2 + r_3 + \cdots + r_n = 0.$$

For compactness, we shall use the summation sign to indicate a sum over all the terms of which a representative one is written; for instance,

$$\Sigma r_i = r_1 + r_2 + \cdots + r_n,$$
$$\Sigma x_i = x_1 + x_2 + \cdots + x_n,$$

etc. Then (2) may be written

$$(3) \qquad\qquad \Sigma r_i = 0.$$

Since $r_i = y_i - a - bx_i$ for each of $i = 1, 2, 3, \cdots, n$, equation (3) yields

(4) $$\Sigma y_i - na - b\Sigma x_i = 0,$$

an equation from which b is to be found.

RULE I. *To make the line $y = a + bx$ fit the n points (x_1, y_1), (x_2, y_2), · · · , (x_n, y_n) by the method of averages, determine the unknown constant b from the equation*

(5) $$\boldsymbol{\Sigma y_i = na + b\Sigma x_i.}$$

This rule is easily modified to apply to an equation of any form containing a single unknown constant.

Example. Solve the example of § 178 by the method of averages.

We are to fit the line $W = bL$ to the data in the following table.

L	1	2	3	4	5	6	7	8
W	0.38	0.68	1.13	1.47	1.78	2.18	2.60	2.84

By Rule I, b is to be determined so that

$$\Sigma W_i = b\Sigma L_i.$$

From the given data,

$$\Sigma L_i = 36, \qquad \Sigma W_i = 13.06.$$

Hence

$$13.06 = 36b,$$

so that $b = 0.363$, and the fitted formula is

$$W = 0.363L.$$

EXERCISES

In Exs. 1–6, by plotting, verify the existence of an approximate linear relation. Assuming that the first point is exactly on the line, determine the equation (a) by selected points; (b) by the method of averages.

1.

x	0	1	2	3	4	5
y	0	3	5	8	10	13

Ans. (b) $y = 2.6x.$

2.

x	0	1	2	3	4	5
y	0	0.5	1.1	1.7	2.3	2.9

Ans. (b) $y = 0.57x.$

3.

x	0	1	2	3	4	5	6
y	5	4.4	4.3	3.8	3.6	3.4	2.6

Ans. (b) $y = 5 - 0.376x$.

4.

x	0	1	2	3	4	5	6
y	-3	-1.0	0.0	1.8	3.6	5.4	6.6

Ans. (b) $y = 1.64x - 3$.

5.

x	0	2	5	10	20	30	50
y	10	9.6	9.3	8.9	7.6	7.1	4.8

Ans. (b) $y = 10 - 0.109x$.

6.

x	0	5	10	20	30	50	100
y	100	95.7	92.1	81.6	74.0	56.3	10.2

Ans. (b) $y = 100 - 0.884x$.

Solve Exs. 7–10 by the method of averages.

7. A small private plane flies at practically constant speed. By landmarks, the pilot estimates his distance (in miles) from the starting point at the end of each hour as shown. Find (a) the speed; (b) the distance after $6\frac{1}{2}$ hr.

t	1	2	3	4	5	6	7
d	100	205	300	450	550	640	720

Ans. (a) 106 mi. per hr.

8. As a means of computing π, a class of high school students were required to measure the circumferences of a set of circular disks of known radii. The measurements, averaged for the whole class for each disk, were as shown. Find the error in the computed value of π.

r	3	4	5	10
c	18.829	25.092	31.390	62.853

Ans. -0.0015.

9. When a body slides from rest down a smooth inclined plane, the velocity acquired in t seconds is approximately

$$v = gt \sin \alpha,$$

where g is the acceleration of gravity (32.16 ft. per sec. per sec.) and α is the angle of inclination of the plane. For the plane on which the given observations were made, compute b in the formula $v = bt$, and find α.

t	1	2	3	4	5	6	7	8
v	1.31	2.52	3.52	4.72	5.87	7.02	8.17	9.42

Ans. $\alpha = 2°6'$.

10. A steel spring 8 in. long is suspended vertically and a weight is attached. The length of the spring for various weights is measured. By Hooke's law, L is a linear function of W; determine the function.

W	0.5	2	5	10	15	17.5
L	8.37	9.46	11.68	14.90	18.52	20.02

Ans. $L = 0.70W + 8$.

182. *Nonlinear Equations*

When the points do not follow a straight line, no linear relation exists, and we must try to represent the data by an equation of some other form.

As an example, suppose we have some reason to believe that the variables satisfy the relation

(1) $$\log_{10} y = a + bx^2.$$

Let us introduce two new variables, u, v, such that

$$u = x^2, \qquad v = \log_{10} y.$$

Equation (1) then becomes

$$v = a + bu,$$

which is linear in u and v. For each pair of values of x and y we compute x^2 and $\log_{10} y$, and plot these as abscissa and ordinate—briefly, we plot $(x^2, \log_{10} y)$ instead of (x, y). If the points plotted follow a straight line, the data given may be represented by an empirical equation of the form (1). If they do not follow a straight line, no equation of the form (1) can be made to fit the data.

RULE II: *To test a formula*

(2) $$v = a + bu,$$

where u and v are functions of x and y:

1. *For each pair of values x and y given, compute the corresponding values of u and v.*

2. *Plot the values thus obtained as abscissa and ordinate, respectively; i.e., plot the points* (u, v).

3. *Determine whether the points* (u, v) *follow a straight line.* *If they do, the data can be represented by an equation of the form* (2).

By changing the form of the equation, we may be able to discover other pairs of coordinates by which (2) can be tested. For examples, see the last paragraph of § 183. We try, naturally, to choose a pair of coordinates whose use involves the least numerical work.

The straight line is of no importance except as a means to an end. The only thing of final interest is the equation of the curve fitting the data given.

183. *Nonlinear Equation with One Constant*

First let us consider equations of the form

$$v = a + bu$$

where either a or b (usually a) is known.

Example. When a body slides from rest down a smooth inclined plane (cf. Ex. 9, page 318), it travels in time t a distance

$$(1) \qquad\qquad x = \tfrac{1}{2}gt^2 \sin \alpha.$$

Represent x as a function of t, and find α, for the plane yielding the results given in the first two lines of the table.

t	1	2	3	4	5
x	1.10	4.35	10.05	17.15	26.25
t^2	1	4	9	16	25

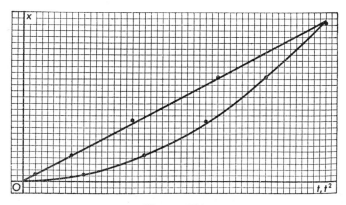

Figure 209

According to (1), we must expect the data to satisfy an equation of the form

(2) $$x = bt^2.$$

This formula can evidently be tested by plotting (t^2, x). Thus the first step is to compute the values of t^2 as shown in the third line of the table. Plotting t^2 as abscissa with two spaces as the unit, and x as ordinate with one space as the unit, we find that the points follow a straight line quite closely. By the method of averages we find

$$58.90 = 55b, \quad b = 1.071, \quad x = 1.071t^2.$$

Computing values of x from this equation, we draw the curve, with ten spaces as the t-unit and 1 as the x-unit. The points given in the table are shown by dots on Figure 209. Finally,

$$\frac{1}{2} g \sin \alpha = b = \frac{58.90}{55}, \quad \sin \alpha = \frac{2(58.90)}{55(32.16)},$$
$$\log_{10} \sin \alpha = 8.82347 - 10, \quad \alpha = 3°49'.$$

Other coordinates by which (2) may be tested are easily found: Divide through by t, plot $\left(t, \dfrac{x}{t}\right)$; take the square root of both members, plot $(t, \sqrt{x})$; take the logarithm of both members, plot $(\log_{10} t, \log_{10} x)$.

EXERCISES

1. Solve the example of § 183 by plotting $\left(t, \dfrac{x}{t}\right)$.

2. Discover by plotting that the following data suggest a relation of the form $y = bx^3$; verify this by plotting (x^3, y); determine the constant and plot the curve.

x	0.6	0.8	1.0	1.2	1.4
y	0.161	0.374	0.806	1.302	2.150

Ans. $y = 0.773x^3$.

3. Discover by plotting that the data suggest an equilateral hyperbola; verify this assumption and determine the constant.

x	0.5	0.8	1.0	1.5	2.0
y	7.11	4.23	3.69	2.20	1.64

4. The kinetic energy of a body of mass m moving with velocity v is

$$E = \tfrac{1}{2}mv^2.$$

Find a value of m to fit the following data, and plot the curve:

v	0.8	1.2	1.5	1.7	2.2
E	2.17	4.92	7.95	10.22	17.80

Ans. 7.14.

5. In Ex. 8, page 318, the disks were made of sheet metal weighing 11.03 oz. per sq. ft. The disks were weighed, and the results averaged over the whole class, as follows (r in inches, W in ounces). What was the error in the computed value of π?

r	3	4	5	10
W	2.167	3.853	6.022	24.080

Ans. +0.0023.

6. In the inclined-plane experiment (Ex. 9, page 318), the body acquires at a distance x from the starting point a velocity given by the formula

$$v^2 = 2g\, x \sin \alpha.$$

For the following experiment, verify the formula by plotting (x, v^2); find v in terms of x; plot the curve and determine α.

x	2	4	6	8	10
v	3.4	4.8	5.9	6.9	7.8

Ans. $v^2 = 5.93x$; $\alpha = 5°17'$.

7. Solve Ex. 6 by using the coordinates $(\sqrt{x}, v)$.   *Ans.* $v^2 = 5.90x$; $\alpha = 5°16'$.

8. Discover by plotting that the data suggest an equilateral hyperbola; verify this assumption and find the equation.

x	0.20	0.40	0.81	1.15	1.45
y	0.63	0.73	1.01	1.31	1.57

9. It is known from physics that the attraction between two magnetic poles is inversely proportional to the square of the distance between them: $A = \dfrac{k}{d^2}$. Find k for the following experiment, and plot the curve.

d	0.5	0.6	0.75	1.0	1.5	2.0
A	0.0352	0.0243	0.0162	0.0087	0.0041	0.0022

10. Solve Ex. 9 by plotting $\left(\dfrac{1}{d}, dA\right)$.

11. Plot the curve $y^2 = x$ accurately in the interval $0 < x < 4$. By counting squares, determine the area bounded by the curve, the x-axis, and the line $x = h$ for $h = 1, 2, 3, 4$. Show that the data fit a formula $A = kh^{\frac{3}{2}}$, and find k to four decimal places.

12. Discover by plotting that the data suggest an equilateral hyperbola with asymptotes $x = 0$, $y = 1$. Verify the assumption $y = \dfrac{x + b}{x}$ by plotting $\left(\dfrac{1}{x}, y\right)$, if a table of reciprocals is at hand; otherwise, by plotting (x, xy). Determine b and plot the curve.

x	0.23	0.51	1.04	2.52	4.10	6.20	8.02
y	8.91	5.20	2.97	1.80	1.48	1.30	1.24

In Exs. 13–19, find a pair of coordinates to test the given formula.

13. $y = ax^b$.   *Ans.** (log x, log y).

14. $y = ae^{bx}$.   *Ans.*† (x, log y).

15. A projectile is thrown with initial velocity v_0 against a wall h feet distant:

$$y = h \tan \alpha - \frac{gh^2}{2v_0{}^2} \sec^2 \alpha.$$

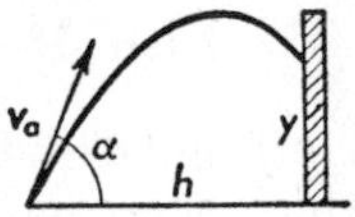

Assume the data collected with h and α constant, varying v_0.

16. Ex. 15 by another pair of coordinates.

17. Ex. 15 with v_0 and α constant, h varying.

18. Ex. 15 with h and v_0 constant, α varying.

   Ans. (sin 2α, y cos^2 α).

19. Cantilever beam bearing a load at the free end: $y = ax^2 + bx^3$.

Figure 210

184. *Equations Containing Two Constants*

Consider such equations as

$$y = a + bx, \qquad x = a + bt^2, \qquad S = ar^2 + br,$$

where both a and b are unknown. If we apply the method of averages, Rule I, § 181, we obtain only one equation. We need two equations to solve for a and b. Hence we divide the data into two groups and apply the method of averages to each group separately. Usually the best result is obtained if the two groups are of equal size or nearly so.

---

* These curves appear so often that specially ruled paper, called *logarithmic paper*, has been constructed and is obtainable on the market. When this paper is used, the data are plotted directly. If the formula is applicable, the points will follow a straight line, no matter what logarithmic base is used.

† These data may be plotted directly on the kind of specially ruled paper called *semilogarithmic paper*.

When the assumed formula involves three constants, we divide the data into three groups, and so on.

Example. Fit the equation $y = a + bx$ to the given data.

x	1	2	3	4	5	6
y	11.6	11.1	10.1	9.6	9.0	8.1

The student should plot the points on a large scale, verifying the existence of an approximate linear relation. By the method of averages:

Step 1. Divide the data into two groups (as indicated in the table).

Step 2. For the first group, form $\Sigma x_i = 6$, $\Sigma y_i = 32.8$. Then a and b must satisfy (by Rule I, § 181) the equation

(1) $$3a + 6b = 32.8.$$

Step 3. For the second group, form $\Sigma x_i = 15$, $\Sigma y_i = 26.7$. Then a and b must satisfy the equation

(2) $$3a + 15b = 26.7.$$

Step 4. Solve for a and b: $b = -0.678$, $a = 12.29$. The desired line is $y = 12.29 - 0.678x$.

185. *The Method of Least Squares: Derivation*

An important method for curve fitting is the *method of least squares*, in which the constants are determined so that the *sum of the squares of the residuals is a minimum.*

Consider the problem of fitting the equation

(1) $$y = a + bx$$

to the set of n points (x_1, y_1), (x_2, y_2), $\cdots$, (x_n, y_n) by the method of least squares. For any point (x_i, y_i), the residual is

$$r_i = y_i - a - bx_i$$

and its square is

(2) $$r_i{}^2 = y_i{}^2 + a^2 + b^2 x_i{}^2 - 2ay_i - 2bx_i y_i + 2abx_i,$$

for each of $i = 1, 2, \cdots, n$.

Let R be the sum of the squares of the residuals,

(3) $$R = \Sigma r_i{}^2 = r_1{}^2 + r_2{}^2 + \cdots + r_n{}^2,$$

the expression to be minimized. Using the n equations (2) to form R, we obtain

(4) $$R = \Sigma y_i{}^2 + na^2 + b^2 \Sigma x_i{}^2 - 2a\Sigma y_i - 2b\Sigma x_i y_i + 2ab\Sigma x_i.$$

Equation (4) gives R as a quadratic in a,

(5) $$R = na^2 + 2a(b\Sigma x_i - \Sigma y_i) + \Sigma(y_i - bx_i)^2.$$

By § 62, R takes on its minimum value when

$$a = -\frac{2(b\Sigma x_i - \Sigma y_i)}{2n};$$

i.e., when

(6) $$na + b\Sigma x_i = \Sigma y_i.$$

Equation (4) also gives R as a quadratic in b,

(7) $$R = b^2\Sigma x_i^2 + 2b(a\Sigma x_i - \Sigma x_i y_i) + \Sigma(y_i - a)^2.$$

By § 62, R takes on its minimum value when

$$b = -\frac{2(a\Sigma x_i - \Sigma x_i y_i)}{2\Sigma x_i^2};$$

i.e., when

(8) $$a\Sigma x_i + b\Sigma x_i^2 = \Sigma x_i y_i.$$

Equations (6) and (8) are two linear equations for the determination of a and b. For the a and b which satisfy equations (6) and (8), the sum of the squares of the residuals will be less than for any other values of a and b.

186. *The Method of Least Squares: Application*

The derivation in the preceding section leads us to the technique described below.

RULE III.   *To make the line $y = a + bx$ fit the n points*

$$(x_i, y_i); \qquad i = 1, 2, \cdots, n,$$

in the sense of least squares, solve for a and b in the equations

(1) $$na + b\Sigma x_i = \Sigma y_i,$$
(2) $$a\Sigma x_i + b\Sigma x_i^2 = \Sigma x_i y_i.$$

Example.   Use the method of least squares to fit the line $y = a + bx$ to the given data (Example, § 184).

x	1	2	3	4	5	6
y	11.6	11.1	10.1	9.6	9.0	8.1

Here $n = 6$. We first form the sums involved:

$$\Sigma x_i = 21, \qquad \Sigma y_i = 59.5, \qquad \Sigma x_i^2 = 91, \qquad \Sigma x_i y_i = 196.1,$$

and then solve the equations

$$6a + 21b = 59.5,$$
$$21a + 91b = 196.1,$$

for a and b. The solution is $a = 12.35$, $b = -0.694$. The required line is $y = 12.35 - 0.694x$.

EXERCISES

In Exs. 1–8, fit a linear equation to the given data (a) by selected points; (b) by the method of averages. In (b) use groups of equal size when the number of points given is even.

1.

x	1	2	3	4	5	6
y	8	6	5	3	2	0

Ans. (b) $y = 9.44 - 1.56x$.

2.

x	1	2	3	4	5	6
y	1.0	2.0	3.0	3.5	4.5	5.5

Ans. (b) $y = 0.33 + 0.83x$.

3.

x	2	3	4	6	7	8
y	0.5	1.5	2.5	4.1	5.0	6.0

Ans. (b) $y = -1.15 + 0.88x$.

4.

x	1	2	3	4	5	6
y	2.4	3.1	3.4	4.5	5.2	5.5

Ans. (b) $y = 1.57 + 0.70x$.

5.

x	0	1	2	3	4	5
y	2.6	4.2	5.7	7.4	8.9	10.4

Ans. (b) $y = 2.59 + 1.58x$.

6.

x	1	3	4	6	7	9
y	8	7	6	5	4	3

Ans. (b) $y = 8.71 - 0.64x$.

7. Group the first four and the last three pairs.

x	1	2	3	4	5	6	7
y	1.82	4.19	6.90	9.21	11.65	14.36	16.72

Ans. (b) $y = 2.49x - 0.69$.

8. Solve Ex. 7, grouping the first three and the last four pairs.

Ans. (b) $y = 2.48x - 0.66$.

9. The force necessary to lift a weight by means of a pulley was measured as shown. Find F in terms of W, and tabulate the values of F at intervals of 5 lb. from $W = 5$ to $W = 30$.

W	5	8	12	20	25	30
F	1.65	2.15	2.65	4.20	5.10	5.90

10. The work done in changing the velocity of a moving body is

$$W = \tfrac{1}{2}mv^2 - \tfrac{1}{2}mv_0^2,$$

where m is the mass of the body, v_0 the initial velocity, and v the final velocity. For the data given, verify that there exists a relation $W = a + bv^2$; determine the constants and plot the curve; find m and v_0.

v	8	10	12	14	16	18	20
W	26	115	227	358	515	684	880

Ans. $m = 5.10$; $v_0 = 7.41$.

In Exs. 11–16, use the method of least squares.

11. Ex. 1.	*Ans.* $y = 9.40 - 1.54x$.
12. Ex. 2.	*Ans.* $y = 0.20 + 0.87x$.
13. Ex. 3.	*Ans.* $y = -1.22 + 0.90x$.
14. Ex. 4.	*Ans.* $y = 1.73 + 0.65x$.
15. Ex. 5.	*Ans.* $y = 2.62 + 1.57x$.
16. Ex. 6.	*Ans.* $y = 8.71 - 0.64x$.

23

Fundamental

Integration Formulas

187. Standard Formulas

In this chapter we shall learn how to apply the following basic formulas:

$$(1) \quad \int u^n \, du = \frac{u^{n+1}}{n+1} + C, \qquad n \neq -1$$

$$(2) \quad \int \frac{du}{u} = \ln u + C, \qquad u > 0,$$

$$(2') \quad \int \frac{du}{u} = \ln(-u) + C_1, \qquad u < 0,$$

$$(2'') \quad \int \frac{du}{u} = \ln|u| + C_2, \qquad u \neq 0,$$

$$(3) \quad \int e^u \, du = e^u + C,$$

$$(3') \quad \int a^u \, du = \frac{a^u}{\ln a} + C,$$

$$(4) \quad \int \cos u \, du = \sin u + C,$$

$$(5) \quad \int \sin u \, du = -\cos u + C,$$

$$(6) \quad \int \sec^2 u \, du = \tan u + C,$$

$$(7) \quad \int \csc^2 u \, du = -\cot u + C,$$

$$(8) \quad \int \sec u \tan u \, du = \sec u + C,$$

$$(9) \quad \int \csc u \cot u \, du = -\csc u + C,$$

328

$$\text{(10)} \quad \int \frac{du}{\sqrt{a^2 - u^2}} = \text{Arcsin } \frac{u}{a} + C, \qquad a > 0,$$

$$\text{(11)} \quad \int \frac{du}{a^2 + u^2} = \frac{1}{a} \text{Arctan } \frac{u}{a} + C,$$

$$\text{(12)} \quad \int u \, dv = uv - \int v \, du.$$

The test of the correctness of an integral is that its derivative must be the given integrand. The above formulas are easily verified by differentiation.

188. *Formula (1): Powers*

Although the power formula was studied in § 76 (which should be thoroughly reviewed), our attention there was necessarily confined to algebraic integrands, so that further work with this formula is needed. The power formula is

$$\text{(1)} \qquad \int u^n \, du = \frac{u^{n+1}}{n + 1} + C, \qquad n \neq -1.$$

Example. Evaluate $\int \sqrt{\cos 2\theta} \sin 2\theta \, d\theta$.

Since

$$d(\cos 2\theta) = -2 \sin 2\theta \, d\theta,$$

we insert the factor -2 and apply (1) with $u = \cos 2\theta$:

$$\int \sqrt{\cos 2\theta} \sin 2\theta \, d\theta = -\tfrac{1}{2} \int (\cos 2\theta)^{\frac{1}{2}} (-2 \sin 2\theta) \, d\theta$$

$$= -\frac{1}{2} \cdot \frac{(\cos 2\theta)^{\frac{3}{2}}}{\frac{3}{2}} + C$$

$$= -\tfrac{1}{3}(\cos 2\theta)^{\frac{3}{2}} + C.$$

EXERCISES

Evaluate the following integrals; check by differentiation.

1. $\int \sin^4 y \cos y \, dy$.

2. $\int \cos^3 \theta \sin \theta \, d\theta$.

3. $\int \frac{\sin x}{\cos^3 x} \, dx$.

4. $\int \frac{\cos x \, dx}{(1 + 3 \sin x)^{\frac{3}{2}}}$.

5. $\int \sin 3x \sqrt{1 + 4 \cos 3x} \, dx$.

6. $\int (3 - 2 \sin 7\beta)^4 \cos 7\beta \, d\beta$.

In Exs. 7–10, evaluate each integral in two ways.

7. $\int \sin 3x \cos 3x \, dx$.

8. $\int \sin \tfrac{1}{4}u \cos \tfrac{1}{4}u \, du$.

9. $\int \tan y \sec^2 y \, dy.$

10. $\int \cot z \csc^2 z \, dz.$

11. $\int \dfrac{\csc^2 3x \, dx}{(4 + \cot 3x)^3}.$

$Ans.\ \dfrac{1}{6(4 + \cot 3x)^2} + C.$

12. $\int (1 - \sec^3 y)^{\frac{1}{2}} \sec^3 y \tan y \, dy.$

13. $\int \tan^4 2x \sec^2 2x \, dx.$

14. $\int \csc^2 x(1 + 4 \cot x)^2 \, dx.$

15. $\int \sec^3 \alpha \tan \alpha \, d\alpha.$

16. $\int \sqrt{1 - 3 \tan \varphi} \sec^2 \varphi \, d\varphi.$

17. $\int (4 + 3e^x)^2 e^x \, dx.$

18. $\int e^t (1 - 4e^t)^{\frac{1}{2}} \, dt.$

19. $\int \sin^3 (e^{2x}) \cos (e^{2x}) e^{2x} \, dx.$

20. $\int t^2 \cos^2 (t^3) \sin (t^3) \, dt.$

21. $\int \dfrac{\ln x}{x} \, dx.$

22. $\int (1 + \ln x)^3 \dfrac{dx}{x}.$

23. $\int \dfrac{du}{u \ln^3 u}.$

24. $\int \dfrac{e^{3t} \, dt}{(1 + e^{3t})^2}.$

25. $\int \dfrac{y \ln (1 + y^2)}{1 + y^2} \, dy.$

$Ans.\ \frac{1}{4} \ln^2 (1 + y^2) + C.$

26. $\int \cot x \ln \sin x \, dx.$

$Ans.\ \frac{1}{2} \ln^2 \sin x + C.$

27. $\int \tan \varphi \ln \cos \varphi \, d\varphi.$

28. $\int \sqrt{2 - \ln \sec \varphi} \tan \varphi \, d\varphi.$

29. $\int \dfrac{(x - 3) \, dx}{(x - 1)^2 (x - 5)^2}.$

$Ans.\ \dfrac{-1}{2(x^2 - 6x + 5)} + C.$

30. $\int (6 \cos^2 \varphi + \sin^2 \varphi)^{\frac{1}{2}} \sin \varphi \cos \varphi \, d\varphi.$

31. $\int (3 \sin^2 \varphi - \cos^2 \varphi)^{-\frac{1}{2}} \sin \varphi \cos \varphi \, d\varphi.$

32. $\int \dfrac{\sqrt{x + 1}}{x^{\frac{5}{2}}} \, dx.$

$Ans.\ -\dfrac{2}{3} \left(1 + \dfrac{1}{x}\right)^{\frac{3}{2}} + C.$

33. $\int \cosh^2 x \sinh x \, dx.$

34. $\int \sinh^3 (1 - 2x) \cosh (1 - 2x) \, dx.$

35. $\int \dfrac{\cosh t \, dt}{(1 + 2 \sinh t)^4}.$

36. $\int \dfrac{\sinh 3u \, du}{(1 - 2 \cosh 3u)^3}.$

189. *Formula (2): Logarithms*

Next we shall apply the formula

(2) $$\int \frac{du}{u} = \ln u + C, \qquad u > 0,$$

together with its associated forms

(2′) $$\int \frac{du}{u} = \ln(-u) + C_1, \qquad u < 0,$$

(2″) $$\int \frac{du}{u} = \ln|u| + C_2, \qquad u \neq 0.$$

Example (a). Evaluate $\int \dfrac{x\,dx}{1 - x^2}$.

Formula (2) says, in words: The integral of any quotient *whose numerator is the differential of the denominator* is the logarithm of the denominator. Therefore we insert the factor -2:

$$\int \frac{x\,dx}{1 - x^2} = -\frac{1}{2}\int \frac{-2x\,dx}{1 - x^2} = -\frac{1}{2}\ln(1 - x^2) + C, \qquad |x| < 1.$$

The integral in this example can equally well be evaluated in the following manner:

$$\int \frac{x\,dx}{1 - x^2} = -\int \frac{x\,dx}{x^2 - 1} = -\frac{1}{2}\int \frac{2x\,dx}{x^2 - 1}$$
$$= -\tfrac{1}{2}\ln(x^2 - 1) + C_1, \qquad |x| > 1,$$

a result which can also be obtained by employing (2′) directly.

Application of (2″) yields

$$\int \frac{x\,dx}{1 - x^2} = -\tfrac{1}{2}\ln|1 - x^2| + C_2, \qquad x \neq 1, x \neq -1.$$

Each of the above three evaluations of the integral in this example has its own restrictions, its own range of validity. In practice, specific problems usually dictate the form to be used because the variables involved range over known intervals.

In this book we shall ordinarily leave answers in the form to which (2) leads us. It is assumed that the reader can convert the result to the form given by (2′) or (2″) whenever such a conversion is necessary.

Example (b). Evaluate $\int \dfrac{x^2 - x}{x + 1}\,dx$.

By division we find

$$\frac{x^2 - x}{x + 1} = x - 2 + \frac{2}{x + 1}.$$

Therefore

$$\int \frac{x^2 - x}{x + 1}\, dx = \int \left(x - 2 + \frac{2}{x + 1} \right) dx$$
$$= \tfrac{1}{2}x^2 - 2x + 2 \ln (x + 1) + C.$$

RULE.   *As the first step toward integrating a rational fraction, carry out the indicated division until the numerator is of lower degree than the denominator.*

EXERCISES

Evaluate each integral; check by differentiation.

1. $\displaystyle \int \frac{3dt}{4t + 1}.$

2. $\displaystyle \int \frac{5dx}{1 - 2x}.$

3. $\displaystyle \int \frac{v\, dv}{3v^2 - 4}.$

4. $\displaystyle \int \frac{y^2\, dy}{y^3 - 1}.$

5. $\displaystyle \int \frac{(2x + 1)\, dx}{x^2 + x + 1}.$

6. $\displaystyle \int \frac{(3y^2 + 2)\, dy}{y^3 + 2y - 7}.$

7. $\displaystyle \int \frac{(1 + x)^2}{x}\, dx.$

8. $\displaystyle \int \frac{(t^2 - 1)^2}{t^3}\, dt.$

9. $\displaystyle \int \frac{y\, dy}{(1 + y^2)^3}.$

10. $\displaystyle \int \frac{x^2\, dx}{(x^3 + 8)^2}.$

11. $\displaystyle \int \frac{u + 2}{u - 1}\, du.$

12. $\displaystyle \int \frac{x(x^2 + 1)}{x^2 - 1}\, dx.$

13. $\displaystyle \int \tan x\, dx.$

14. $\displaystyle \int \cot y\, dy.$

15. $\displaystyle \int \frac{\sin \theta\, d\theta}{3 + 2 \cos \theta}.$

16. $\displaystyle \int \frac{\cos 2t\, dt}{4 - 3 \sin 2t}.$

17. $\displaystyle \int \frac{\sec^2 x\, dx}{\tan x + 1}.$

18. $\displaystyle \int \frac{\csc^2 2x\, dx}{\sqrt{2 + \cot 2x}}.$

19. $\displaystyle \int \frac{(t^2 + 4)\, dt}{t^3 + 12t + 2}.$

20. $\displaystyle \int \frac{dy}{(1 + y)^{\frac{2}{3}}}.$

21. $\displaystyle \int \frac{x^3}{x + 1}\, dx.$

22. $\displaystyle \int \frac{x^3 + x - 4}{x - 1}\, dx.$

23. $\displaystyle \int \frac{\sec \theta \tan \theta\, d\theta}{2 + 3 \sec \theta}.$

24. $\displaystyle \int \frac{\csc x \cot x\, dx}{1 + \csc x}.$

25. $\displaystyle \int \frac{e^x\, dx}{1 + e^x}.$

26. $\displaystyle \int \frac{e^{2t}\, dt}{e^{2t} - 4}.$

27. $\displaystyle \int \frac{e^{2x}\, dx}{1 + e^x}.$

28. $\displaystyle \int \frac{e^{2y} - e^{-2y}}{e^{2y} + e^{-2y}}\, dy.$

29. $\displaystyle \int \frac{dv}{v \ln v}.$

30. $\displaystyle \int \frac{dt}{t(1 + \ln t)}.$

31. $\displaystyle\int \frac{\sin 2\theta\, d\theta}{1 + \sin^2 \theta}.$

32. $\displaystyle\int \frac{\sec^2 x \tan x\, dx}{4 + \tan^2 x}.$

33. $\displaystyle\int \frac{(x + 6)\, dx}{(x + 2)^2}.$

Hint: $\dfrac{x + 6}{(x + 2)^2} = \dfrac{(x + 2) + 4}{(x + 2)^2}.$

Ans. $2 \ln (1 + \sqrt{x}) + C.$

34. $\displaystyle\int \frac{dx}{\sqrt{x}\,(1 + \sqrt{x})}.$

35. $\displaystyle\int \frac{dx}{x(1 + x^2)}.$ $\left[\dfrac{1}{x(1 + x^2)} = \dfrac{(1 + x^2) - x^2}{x(1 + x^2)}. \right]$ *Ans.* $\dfrac{1}{2} \ln \dfrac{x^2}{1 + x^2} + C.$

36. $\displaystyle\int \sec \theta\, d\theta.$ (Multiply and divide by sec θ + tan θ.)

Ans. $\ln (\sec \theta + \tan \theta) + C.$

37. Ex. 36 by a second method.   (Multiply and divide by sec θ − tan θ.)

38. $\displaystyle\int \csc \theta\, d\theta$ by two methods.   (Cf. Exs. 36–37.)

Ans. $\ln (\csc \theta - \cot \theta) + C.$

39. $\displaystyle\int \frac{d\varphi}{\cos 5\varphi}.$

40. $\displaystyle\int \frac{dx}{\sin 3x}.$

41. $\displaystyle\int \frac{1 - \cos t}{\cos t}\, dt.$

42. $\displaystyle\int \frac{4 + \sin 3x}{\sin 3x}\, dx.$

43. $\displaystyle\int \frac{\sin x - \cot x}{\sin^2 x}\, dx.$

44. $\displaystyle\int \frac{\cos y + \tan y}{\cos^2 y}\, dy.$

45. $\displaystyle\int \tanh 3x\, dx.$

46. $\displaystyle\int \coth \tfrac{1}{4}x\, dx.$

190. Formulas (3)–(3′): Exponential Functions

There are two basic formulas for the integration of exponential functions:

(3)
$$\int e^u\, du = e^u + C,$$

(3′)
$$\int a^u\, du = \frac{a^u}{\ln a} + C.$$

Equation (3′) includes (3) as a special case, but (3) is used much more frequently than the general (3′).

Example (a).   Evaluate $\int \sin 2x\, e^{\cos 2x}\, dx.$

If we insert the factor −2, this can be evaluated by (3), with $u = \cos 2x$, $du = -2 \sin 2x\, dx$:

$$\int \sin 2x\, e^{\cos 2x}\, dx = -\tfrac{1}{2} \int e^{\cos 2x}\, (-2 \sin 2x)\, dx = -\tfrac{1}{2} e^{\cos 2x} + C.$$

Example (b).   Evaluate $\displaystyle\int \frac{dx}{3^{2x}}$.

Since

$$\frac{d}{dx}\, a^u = a^u (\ln a)\, \frac{du}{dx},$$

we proceed as follows:

$$\int \frac{dx}{3^{2x}} = \int 3^{-2x}\, dx = -\frac{1}{2}\frac{3^{-2x}}{\ln 3} + C.$$

EXERCISES

Evaluate the following integrals.

1. $\displaystyle\int e^{-2t}\, dt.$

2. $\displaystyle\int e^{4x}\, dx.$

3. $\displaystyle\int \frac{dy}{e^y}.$

4. $\displaystyle\int xe^{-x^2}\, dx.$

5. $\displaystyle\int 2^x\, dx.$

6. $\displaystyle\int 10^{-2x}\, dx.$

7. $\displaystyle\int (e^x + e^{-x})^2\, dx.$

8. $\displaystyle\int e^{3y}(1 + e^{3y})^4\, dy.$

9. $\displaystyle\int t^2 e^{2t^3}\, dt.$

10. $\displaystyle\int ue^{4u^2+3}\, du.$

11. $\displaystyle\int \frac{e^\theta\, d\theta}{(4e^\theta + 3)^2}.$

12. $\displaystyle\int e^{2x}\sqrt{1 - e^{2x}}\, dx.$

13. $\displaystyle\int \frac{(e^y - 1)^2}{e^y}\, dy.$

14. $\displaystyle\int \frac{e^{2t}\, dt}{1 + 4e^{2t} + 4e^{4t}}.$

15. $\displaystyle\int \cos 3x\, e^{\sin 3x}\, dx.$

16. $\displaystyle\int (1 + e^{\tan x})\sec^2 x\, dx.$

17. $\displaystyle\int \frac{e^{\cot \theta}\, d\theta}{\sin^2 \theta}.$

18. $\displaystyle\int \frac{e^{-\frac{1}{x}}}{x^2}\, dx.$

19. $\displaystyle\int 3e^{2\ln x}\, dx.$

20. $\displaystyle\int \ln e^{2x}\, dx.$

21. $\displaystyle\int \sinh u\, du = \cosh u + C.$

22. $\displaystyle\int \cosh u\, du = \sinh u + C.$

23. $\displaystyle\int 4 \sinh 3y\, dy.$

24. $\displaystyle\int 3 \cosh 2t\, dt.$

25. $\displaystyle\int \tanh u\, du.$

26. $\displaystyle\int e^{-x} \cosh x\, dx.$

27. $\displaystyle\int t \cosh (3t^2)\, dt.$

28. $\displaystyle\int \coth v\, dv.$

29. $\displaystyle\int (\cosh^2 t - \sinh^2 t)\, dt.$

30. $\displaystyle\int (\cosh^2 t + \sinh^2 t)\, dt.$

191. *Formulas (4)–(9): Trigonometric Functions*

The basic formulas for integrations involving trigonometric functions are

(4)
$$\int \cos u \; du = \sin u + C,$$

(5)
$$\int \sin u \; du = - \cos u + C,$$

(6)
$$\int \sec^2 u \; du = \tan u + C,$$

(7)
$$\int \csc^2 u \; du = - \cot u + C,$$

(8)
$$\int \sec u \tan u \; du = \sec u + C,$$

(9)
$$\int \csc u \cot u \; du = - \csc u + C.$$

Notice the way in which the functions pair off for purposes of integration. The pairs $\sin u$ and $\cos u$, $\sec u$ and $\tan u$, $\csc u$ and $\cot u$ fit well together. An integral involving, for instance, $\sin x$ and $\tan x$ is not in appropriate form for application of simple integration formulas. Upon meeting such an integral, we first put the integrand entirely in terms of $\sin x$ and $\cos x$ or in terms of $\tan x$ and $\sec x$.

Example (a). Evaluate $\int \sin x \tan x \; dx$.
We proceed as follows:

$$\int \sin x \tan x \; dx = \int \frac{\sin^2 x \; dx}{\cos x} = \int \frac{1 - \cos^2 x}{\cos x} \; dx$$

$$= \int \sec x \; dx - \int \cos x \; dx$$

$$= \ln(\sec x + \tan x) + \sin x + C,$$

in which we have used the result in Ex. 36, page 333.

Because of the situation described above, the exercises are usually stated in terms of appropriate pairs of functions. Such pairing permits the student to do more exercises (and thus acquire more skill) in a specified time than would otherwise be possible. There is, of course, no guarantee of corresponding simplicity in the integrals encountered in the normal course of events in engineering or other scientific work.

Example (b).
$$\int x \sin x^2 \; dx = \tfrac{1}{2} \int \sin x^2 \cdot 2x \; dx$$
$$= - \tfrac{1}{2} \cos x^2 + C.$$

Example (c).
$$\int \tan^2 \theta \; d\theta = \int (\sec^2 \theta - 1) \; d\theta = \tan \theta - \theta + C.$$

EXERCISES

Evaluate the integrals below.

1. $\int \cos 3\beta \, d\beta.$

2. $\int \sin \tfrac{1}{2}t \, dt.$

3. $\int \csc^2 4x \, dx.$

4. $\int \sec^2 3x \, dx.$

5. $\int \sec 2y \tan 2y \, dy.$

6. $\int \csc 4x \cot 4x \, dx.$

7. $\int \dfrac{\cos 4x \, dx}{3 - 2 \sin 4x}.$

8. $\int \dfrac{\sin t \cos t \, dt}{1 + 3 \cos 2t}.$

9. $\int \tan 2u \sec^2 2u \, du.$

10. $\int \dfrac{\cos \varphi \, d\varphi}{\sin^4 \varphi}.$

11. $\int \dfrac{\sin \ln x}{x} \, dx.$

12. $\int \dfrac{dy}{e^y \cos^2 (e^{-y})}.$

13. $\int \tan \left(\theta - \dfrac{\pi}{6} \right) d\theta.$

14. $\int \cot \left(\varphi - \dfrac{\pi}{4} \right) d\varphi.$

15. $\int \cot^2 z \, dz.$

16. $\int \tan^2 ky \, dy.$

17. $\int (1 - \tan \theta)^2 \, d\theta.$

18. $\int (1 + \cot x)^2 \, dx.$

19. $\int \dfrac{\sin t + \cos t}{\sin t} \, dt.$

20. $\int \dfrac{y \cos (y^2) \, dy}{\sin (y^2)}.$

21. $\int \sec^2 \beta \tan^2 \beta \, d\beta.$

22. $\int \dfrac{\sin^2 x \, dx}{1 - \cos x}.$

23. $\int \dfrac{\cos^2 \alpha}{1 + \sin \alpha} \, d\alpha.$

24. $\int \dfrac{\cos^3 \theta}{1 + \sin \theta} \, d\theta.$

25. $\int \dfrac{\sin^3 u}{1 - \cos u} \, du.$

26. $\int \dfrac{\cos^2 x \, dx}{\sin^4 x}.$

27. $\int \sin 3y \sin 6y \, dy.$

28. $\int (\cos^4 t - \sin^4 t) \, dt.$

29. $\int \dfrac{\sec^2 3u \, du}{1 - \tan 3u}.$

30. $\int \dfrac{\csc^2 x \, dx}{\cot x - 1}.$

31. $\int (\cos C + 1) \, dC.$

$Ans.$ $\sin C + C + x.$

32. $\int \cot (C - \tfrac{1}{4}\pi) \, dC.$

$Ans.$ $\ln \sin (C - \tfrac{1}{4}\pi) + y.$

Use the "double angle" formulas of trigonometry in Exs. 33–36.

—33. $\displaystyle\int \frac{1 + \cos 2y}{1 - \cos 2y}\, dy.$ 34. $\displaystyle\int \frac{\tan w}{1 - \tan^2 w}\, dw.$

35. $\displaystyle\int \sin \beta (1 + \cos 2\beta)^3\, d\beta.$ —36. $\displaystyle\int \frac{(1 - \cos 4x)\, dx}{(1 + \cos 4x)^2}.$

192. *Transformation by Trigonometric Formulas*

Many trigonometric integrals can be evaluated after transformations of the integrand, requiring only the most familiar trigonometric formulas.   If instead of memorizing the types listed below, the student will observe the character of the transformations employed, he can easily pick the requisite method in any given case.

Type I. $\int \sin^m x \cos^n x\, dx$, *where either m or n is a positive odd integer.*

For definiteness, let n be a positive odd integer.   Writing the integral in the form $\int \sin^m x \cos^{n-1} x \cdot \cos x\, dx$, and putting

$$\cos^2 x = 1 - \sin^2 x,$$

we obtain a series of powers of $\sin x$ each multiplied by $\cos x\, dx$.   We proceed in a similar manner when m is odd and positive.

Example (a).

$$\begin{aligned}
\int \sin^2 x \cos^3 x\, dx &= \int \sin^2 x \cos^2 x \cdot \cos x\, dx \\
&= \int \sin^2 x (1 - \sin^2 x) \cos x\, dx \\
&= \int \sin^2 x \cos x\, dx - \int \sin^4 x \cos x\, dx \\
&= \tfrac{1}{3} \sin^3 x - \tfrac{1}{5} \sin^5 x + C.
\end{aligned}$$

Type II. $\int \tan^n x\, dx$, or $\int \cot^n x\, dx$, *where n is an integer.*
By use of the formulas

$$\tan^2 x = \sec^2 x - 1, \qquad \cot^2 x = \csc^2 x - 1,$$

these integrals reduce to forms that can be evaluated.

Example (b).

$$\begin{aligned}
\int \tan^4 x\, dx &= \int \tan^2 x (\sec^2 x - 1)\, dx \\
&= \int \tan^2 x \sec^2 x\, dx - \int \tan^2 x\, dx \\
&= \tfrac{1}{3} \tan^3 x - \int (\sec^2 x - 1)\, dx \\
&= \tfrac{1}{3} \tan^3 x - \tan x + x + C.
\end{aligned}$$

Type III. $\int \tan^m x \sec^n x \, dx$, or $\int \cot^m x \csc^n x \, dx$, *where n is a positive even integer.*

Example (c).

$$\int \tan^2 x \sec^4 x \, dx = \int \tan^2 x \sec^2 x (1 + \tan^2 x) \, dx$$

$$= \int \tan^2 x \sec^2 x \, dx + \int \tan^4 x \sec^2 x \, dx$$

$$= \tfrac{1}{3} \tan^3 x + \tfrac{1}{5} \tan^5 x + C.$$

Type IV. $\int \sin^m x \cos^n x \, dx$, *where both m and n are positive even integers.* When m and n are *both* even, it is easily seen that the method used for Type I is useless. Instead, we use the formulas

$$\sin^2 x = \tfrac{1}{2}(1 - \cos 2x), \qquad \cos^2 x = \tfrac{1}{2}(1 + \cos 2x),$$
$$\sin x \cos x = \tfrac{1}{2} \sin 2x,$$

repeatedly if necessary.

Example (d).

$$\int \sin^4 \theta \cos^2 \theta \, d\theta = \int (\sin^2 \theta \cos^2 \theta) \sin^2 \theta \, d\theta$$

$$= \tfrac{1}{8} \int \sin^2 2\theta (1 - \cos 2\theta) \, d\theta$$

$$= \tfrac{1}{8} \int \sin^2 2\theta \, d\theta - \tfrac{1}{8} \int \sin^2 2\theta \cos 2\theta \, d\theta$$

$$= \tfrac{1}{16} \int (1 - \cos 4\theta) \, d\theta - \tfrac{1}{48} \sin^3 2\theta$$

$$= \tfrac{1}{16}\theta - \tfrac{1}{64} \sin 4\theta - \tfrac{1}{48} \sin^3 2\theta + C.$$

EXERCISES

Evaluate each of the following integrals.

1. $\int \sin^3 x \, dx$.

               Ans. $\tfrac{1}{3} \cos^3 x - \cos x + C$.

2. $\int \cos^3 x \, dx$.

               Ans. $\sin x - \tfrac{1}{3} \sin^3 x + C$.

3. $\int \cos^3 y \sin^3 y \, dy$.

               Ans. $\tfrac{1}{4} \sin^4 y - \tfrac{1}{6} \sin^6 y + C_1$,
                 or $\tfrac{1}{6} \cos^6 y - \tfrac{1}{4} \cos^4 y + C_2$.

4. Do Ex. 3 with the aid of the formula: $\sin y \cos y = \tfrac{1}{2} \sin 2y$.

               Ans. $\tfrac{1}{48} \cos^3 2y - \tfrac{1}{16} \cos 2y + C_3$.

5. $\int \cos^2 t \sin^5 t \, dt$.

         Ans. $-\tfrac{1}{3} \cos^3 t + \tfrac{2}{5} \cos^5 t - \tfrac{1}{7} \cos^7 t + C$.

6. $\int \sin^2 u \cos^5 u \, du$.

         Ans. $\tfrac{1}{3} \sin^3 u - \tfrac{2}{5} \sin^5 u + \tfrac{1}{7} \sin^7 u + C$.

7. $\int \cos^5 2\theta \, d\theta.$ *Ans.* $\frac{1}{2} \sin 2\theta - \frac{1}{3} \sin^3 2\theta + \frac{1}{10} \sin^5 2\theta + C.$

8. $\int \sin^5 3\theta \, d\theta.$ *Ans.* $-\frac{1}{3} \cos 3\theta + \frac{2}{9} \cos^3 3\theta - \frac{1}{15} \cos^5 3\theta + C.$

9. $\int \dfrac{\sin^3 v \, dv}{\cos^2 v}.$ 10. $\int \dfrac{\cos^3 v \, dv}{\sin^4 v}.$

11. $\int \dfrac{\sin^5 2y \, dy}{\cos^2 2y}.$ 12. $\int \dfrac{\cos^5 t \, dt}{\sin^2 t}.$

13. $\int \sin^7 x \, dx.$ 14. $\int \cos x (1 - \sin x)^4 \, dx.$

15. $\int \sin^2 x \, dx.$ *Ans.* $\frac{1}{2} x - \frac{1}{4} \sin 2x + C.$

16. $\int \cos^2 y \, dy.$ *Ans.* $\frac{1}{2} y + \frac{1}{4} \sin 2y + C.$

17. $\int \sin^2 \beta \cos^2 \beta \, d\beta.$ (See Ex. 4.)   *Ans.* $\frac{1}{8} \beta - \frac{1}{32} \sin 4\beta + C.$

18. $\int \cos^4 2\theta \, d\theta.$ *Ans.* $\frac{3}{8} \theta + \frac{1}{8} \sin 4\theta + \frac{1}{64} \sin 8\theta + C.$

19. $\int \sin x \sqrt{1 + 4 \cos x} \, dx.$

20. $\int \dfrac{\cos^3 \theta \, d\theta}{\sin \theta}.$ 21. $\int \dfrac{t \sin^3 (t^2) \, dt}{\cos (t^2)}.$

22. $\int \sin^2 z \sin^3 2z \, dz.$ 23. $\int \cos^3 y \sin^3 2y \, dy.$

24. $\int \sin^5 u \cos^5 u \, du.$ 25. $\int \sin^4 x \cos^4 x \, dx.$

26. $\int \sin^6 \varphi \cos^6 \varphi \, d\varphi.$ 27. $\int \sin^2 \theta \cos^4 \theta \, d\theta.$

28. $\int \dfrac{\sin^2 y}{\cot y} \, dy.$

29. $\int \tan^3 \theta \, d\theta.$ *Ans.* $\frac{1}{2} \sec^2 \theta - \ln \sec \theta + C_1$
$= \frac{1}{2} \tan^2 \theta - \ln \sec \theta + C_2$
$= \frac{1}{2} \sec^2 \theta + \ln \cos \theta + C_3,$ etc.

30. $\int \cot^4 y \, dy.$ *Ans.* $-\frac{1}{3} \cot^3 y + \cot y + y + C.$

31. $\int \tan^2 4x \, dx.$ 32. $\int \cot^3 y \, dy.$

33. $\int \tan^5 x \, dx.$ *Ans.* $\frac{1}{4} \tan^4 x - \frac{1}{2} \tan^2 x - \ln \cos x + C.$

— 34. $\displaystyle\int \tan^6 x\,dx.$ *Ans.* $\frac{1}{5}\tan^5 x - \frac{1}{3}\tan^3 x + \tan x - x + C.$

— 35. $\displaystyle\int \sec^4 \alpha\,d\alpha.$ — 36. $\displaystyle\int \csc^4 \alpha\,d\alpha.$

— 37. $\displaystyle\int \tan^4 z \sec^2 z\,dz.$ — 38. $\displaystyle\int \cot^3 z \csc^2 z\,dz.$

— 39. $\displaystyle\int \sec^4 y \tan^4 y\,dy.$ — 40. $\displaystyle\int \csc^6 u\,du.$

193. *Formulas (10)–(11): Inverse Trigonometric Functions*

Consider next the two formulas

(10) $$\int \frac{du}{\sqrt{a^2 - u^2}} = \text{Arcsin }\frac{u}{a} + C, \qquad a > 0,$$

(11) $$\int \frac{du}{a^2 + u^2} = \frac{1}{a}\text{ Arctan }\frac{u}{a} + C.$$

In applying (10) it is important to note that the numerator du is the differential of the variable quantity u which appears squared inside the square root symbol.

Example (a). Evaluate $\displaystyle\int \frac{dx}{\sqrt{9 - 4x^2}}.$

The presence of a constant minus the square of a variable under the square root sign is what suggests the use of formula (10). Therefore we mentally put the quantity under the radical into the form of the square of a constant minus the square of a variable. That is, we think of $\sqrt{9 - 4x^2}$ as $\sqrt{3^2 - (2x)^2}$. This shows that the u in formula (10) is to be $2x$. Hence $du = 2dx$, and we need to insert the constant 2 into the numerator before we can employ (10). To insert the constant legitimately, we must compensate for it by putting its reciprocal as a factor outside the integral:

$$\int \frac{dx}{\sqrt{9 - 4x^2}} = \frac{1}{2}\int \frac{2\,dx}{\sqrt{9 - (2x)^2}}$$

$$= \frac{1}{2}\text{ Arcsin }\frac{2x}{3} + C.$$

Example (b). $\displaystyle\int \frac{dy}{9y^2 + 6y + 5} = \int \frac{dy}{(3y + 1)^2 + 4}$

$$= \frac{1}{3}\int \frac{3dy}{(3y + 1)^2 + 4}$$

$$= \frac{1}{3}\cdot\frac{1}{2}\text{ Arctan }\frac{3y + 1}{2} + C$$

$$= \frac{1}{6}\text{ Arctan }\frac{3y + 1}{2} + C.$$

Example (c). $\displaystyle\int \frac{dx}{x\sqrt{1-4\ln^2 x}} = \int \frac{\dfrac{dx}{x}}{\sqrt{1-4\ln^2 x}}$

$$= \frac{1}{2}\int \frac{2\,\dfrac{dx}{x}}{\sqrt{1-4\ln^2 x}}$$

$$= \frac{1}{2}\,\text{Arcsin}\,(2\ln x) + C.$$

EXERCISES

1. $\displaystyle\int \frac{dx}{9+x^2}.$ **2.** $\displaystyle\int \frac{dy}{\sqrt{16-y^2}}.$ **3.** $\displaystyle\int \frac{dv}{4+9v^2}.$

4. $\displaystyle\int \frac{dt}{\sqrt{3-4t^2}}.$ **5.** $\displaystyle\int \frac{y\,dy}{4+y^2}.$ **6.** $\displaystyle\int \frac{x\,dx}{\sqrt{16-25x^2}}.$

7. $\displaystyle\int \frac{y\,dy}{4+y^4}.$ **8.** $\displaystyle\int \frac{x\,dx}{\sqrt{16-25x^4}}.$ **9.** $\displaystyle\int \frac{dx}{x^2+2x+10}.$

10. $\displaystyle\int \frac{dt}{4t^2+4t+5}.$ **11.** $\displaystyle\int \frac{dy}{\sqrt{3+4y-4y^2}}.$ **12.** $\displaystyle\int \frac{dy}{4y-25-4y^2}.$

13. $\displaystyle\int \frac{x+4}{x^2+9}\,dx.$ **14.** $\displaystyle\int \frac{(4\beta+1)\,d\beta}{16\beta^2+8\beta+37}.$ **15.** $\displaystyle\int \frac{\cos\varphi\,d\varphi}{3+\sin^2\varphi}.$

16. $\displaystyle\int \frac{e^{2x}\,dx}{\sqrt{7-e^{4x}}}.$ **17.** $\displaystyle\int \frac{x^2-3}{x^2+1}\,dx.$ **18.** $\displaystyle\int \frac{y^3\,dy}{4+y^2}.$

19. $\displaystyle\int \frac{\sec^2\theta\,d\theta}{\sqrt{5-\sec^2\theta}}.$ *Ans.* $\text{Arcsin}\,(\tfrac{1}{2}\tan\theta) + C.$

20. $\displaystyle\int \frac{du}{\sqrt{9e^{-2u}-1}}.$ *Ans.* $\text{Arcsin}\,(\tfrac{1}{3}e^u) + C.$

21. $\displaystyle\int \sin(\text{Arctan}\,x)\,dx.$ *Ans.* $\sqrt{1+x^2} + C.$

22. $\displaystyle\int \frac{\csc^2\varphi\cot\varphi\,d\varphi}{4-\csc^2\varphi}.$

23. $\displaystyle\int \frac{(3x-2)\,dx}{x^2+2x+17}.$ Write as $\displaystyle\int \frac{3(x+1)-5}{(x+1)^2+16}\,dx.$

Ans. $\dfrac{3}{2}\ln(x^2+2x+17) - \dfrac{5}{4}\,\text{Arctan}\,\dfrac{x+1}{4} + C.$

24. $\displaystyle\int \frac{(4x-15)\,dx}{x^2-4x+13}.$ See Ex. 23.

25. $\displaystyle\int \frac{(10y+11)\,dy}{4y^2-4y+5}.$ **26.** $\displaystyle\int \frac{x\,dx}{\sqrt{-7-8x-x^2}}.$

27. $\displaystyle\int \frac{(x+2)\,dx}{\sqrt{3+2x-x^2}}.$

28. $\displaystyle\int \frac{(2x-1)\,dx}{16x^2+8x+37}.$

29. $\displaystyle\int \frac{u(u^2+4)\,du}{u^4+9}.$

30. $\displaystyle\int \frac{\sin\theta(\cos\theta+4)\,d\theta}{1+\cos^2\theta}.$

31. $\displaystyle\int \frac{x^4\,dx}{x^2+1}.$

32. $\displaystyle\int \frac{x^3\,dx}{x^2+1}.$

33. $\displaystyle\int \frac{e^{4x}\,dx}{\sqrt{9-e^{4x}}}.$

34. $\displaystyle\int \frac{e^{2t}\,dt}{9+25e^{4t}}.$

35. $\displaystyle\int \frac{(3\sin\theta-7)\cos\theta\,d\theta}{4\sin^2\theta+9}.$

36. $\displaystyle\int \frac{(1+\tan x)\,dx}{\cos^2 x\,\sqrt{5-3\tan^2 x}}.$

37. $\displaystyle\int \frac{dt}{t\sqrt{t^2-a^2}}.$
    $\qquad\qquad\qquad\qquad$ *Ans.* $-\dfrac{1}{a}\operatorname{Arcsin}\dfrac{a}{t}+C.$

38. $\displaystyle\int \frac{\tan\theta\,d\theta}{\sec\theta+4\cos\theta}.$

39. $\displaystyle\int \frac{\cot\theta\,d\theta}{\csc\theta+4\sin\theta}.$

194. Formula (12): Integration by Parts

From the formula for the differential of a product,

$$d(uv) = u\,dv + v\,du,$$

we find, integrating both sides,

$$uv = \int u\,dv + \int v\,du.$$

By transposing, we obtain the formula

(12) $$\int u\,dv = uv - \int v\,du.$$

Integration by this formula is called *integration by parts*.

Example (a). Evaluate $\displaystyle\int x\sin 2x\,dx.$

Let

$$u = x, \qquad dv = \sin 2x\,dx,$$

$$du = dx, \qquad v = \int \sin 2x\,dx = -\tfrac{1}{2}\cos 2x.$$

(It is a fact, which should be verified by the student, that in evaluating $\int dv = v$, the constant of integration may be omitted, since the final result is the same with or without it.)   Hence

$$\int x\sin 2x\,dx = -\tfrac{1}{2}x\cos 2x + \tfrac{1}{2}\int \cos 2x\,dx$$

$$= -\tfrac{1}{2}x\cos 2x + \tfrac{1}{4}\sin 2x + C.$$

Only by experience and practice can one develop skill in telling when integration by parts is indicated.   Further, when it has been decided to try the method, no rules can be laid down telling how to choose u and dv (except that dv must be so chosen that $\int dv$ can be evaluated).   However, in integrating a product, this method gives us a chance to differentiate one of the factors. In Example (a), differentiating x, we replace it by 1; differentiating $\sin x$, we replace it by $\cos x$.   The former change, being more drastic, seems more promising.   By looking ahead a bit in this way, we can usually make the right choice in the first instance.

Example (b).   Evaluate $\int \sec^3 \theta \, d\theta$.

Take

$$u = \sec \theta, \qquad\qquad dv = \sec^2 \theta \, d\theta,$$
$$du = \sec \theta \tan \theta \, d\theta, \qquad v = \tan \theta;$$

$$\int \sec^3 \theta \, d\theta = \sec \theta \tan \theta - \int \sec \theta \tan^2 \theta \, d\theta$$

$$= \sec \theta \tan \theta - \int \sec^3 \theta \, d\theta + \int \sec \theta \, d\theta.$$

Evaluate the last integral (Ex. 36, p. 333) and transpose the next-to-last to the other side:

$$2 \int \sec^3 \theta \, d\theta = \sec \theta \tan \theta + \ln (\sec \theta + \tan \theta) + C,$$

$$\int \sec^3 \theta \, d\theta = \tfrac{1}{2} \sec \theta \tan \theta + \tfrac{1}{2} \ln (\sec \theta + \tan \theta) + C_1.$$

Example (c).   Evaluate $\int e^x \sin 2x \, dx$.

Take

$$u = e^x, \qquad\qquad dv = \sin 2x \, dx,$$
$$du = e^x \, dx, \qquad v = -\tfrac{1}{2} \cos 2x:$$

(1) $$\int e^x \sin 2x \, dx = -\tfrac{1}{2} e^x \cos 2x + \tfrac{1}{2} \int e^x \cos 2x \, dx.$$

Since this new integral is no simpler than the original, let us return to the given integral and take

$$u = \sin 2x, \qquad\qquad dv = e^x \, dx,$$
$$du = 2 \cos 2x \, dx, \qquad v = e^x;$$

(2) $$\int e^x \sin 2x \, dx = e^x \sin 2x - 2 \int e^x \cos 2x \, dx.$$

Here again we have failed temporarily, but since the troublesome integral is exactly the same one that appeared in (1), it may be *eliminated from the two equations*: Multiplying each member of (1) by 4 and adding to the corresponding members of (2), we find that

$$5 \int e^x \sin 2x \, dx = -2e^x \cos 2x + e^x \sin 2x + C,$$

$$\int e^x \sin 2x \, dx = -\tfrac{2}{5}e^x \cos 2x + \tfrac{1}{5}e^x \sin 2x + C_1.$$

Before considering himself skilled in the use of integration by parts, the student should learn to disassociate the technique from the letters employed in formula (12). The original integrand is always split into two factors, one of which involves a differential. Let us place those factors beside one another; beneath the factor with the differential put its integral; beneath the factor with no differential put its differential. Thus, in attacking the integral

$$\int \text{Arcsin } u \, du$$

we form the array shown below.

The components of the lower line are the factors in the new integrand. The integrated portion in formula (12) is the product of the two components which contain no differential. Therefore we write

$$\begin{array}{c|c}
\text{Arcsin } u & du \\
\hline
\dfrac{du}{\sqrt{1-u^2}} & u
\end{array}$$

$$\int \text{Arcsin } u \, du = u \text{ Arcsin } u - \int \frac{u \, du}{\sqrt{1-u^2}}$$

$$= u \text{ Arcsin } u + (1 - u^2)^{\frac{1}{2}} + C.$$

EXERCISES

Evaluate each of the following integrals.

1. $\displaystyle\int xe^{-x} \, dx.$

2. $\displaystyle\int ye^{3y} \, dy.$

3. $\displaystyle\int \ln u \, du.$

4. $\displaystyle\int x \ln x \, dx.$

5. $\displaystyle\int x \cos 3x \, dx.$

6. $\displaystyle\int x \sin 2x \, dx.$

7. $\displaystyle\int t^2 \sin t \, dt.$

8. $\displaystyle\int v^2 \cos 2v \, dv.$

9. $\displaystyle\int t^2 \sin (t^3) \, dt.$

10. $\displaystyle\int v \sin (v^2) \, dv.$

11. $\displaystyle\int x^2 e^{3x} \, dx.$

12. $\displaystyle\int y^2 e^{-y} \, dy.$

13. $\displaystyle\int \text{Arctan } u \, du.$

14. $\displaystyle\int u \text{ Arctan } u \, du.$

15. $\displaystyle\int x(3x + 1)^7 \, dx$, by parts.

16. $\int x(3x + 1)^7 \, dx$, by using $x = \frac{1}{3}(3x + 1) - \frac{1}{3}$.

17. $\int \dfrac{\theta \, d\theta}{(\theta + 1)^3}$, in two ways.   See Exs. 15, 16.

18. $\int x \sqrt{x - 2} \, dx$, in two ways.   See Exs. 15, 16.

19. $\int x^3 e^{-x^2} \, dx$.

20. $\int x e^{-x^2} \, dx$.

21. $\int x^3 (a^2 + x^2)^{\frac{1}{2}} \, dx$.

22. $\int y^3 (a^2 - y^2)^{\frac{1}{2}} \, dy$.

23. $\int v \sin 3v \cos 3v \, dv$.

24. $\int x \cos^2 x \, dx$.

25. $\int \varphi \csc^2 \varphi \, d\varphi$.

26. $\int \varphi \sec^2 \varphi \tan \varphi \, d\varphi$.

27. $\int x \cosh \dfrac{x}{a} \, dx$.

28. $\int y \sinh \dfrac{y}{a} \, dy$.

29. $\int y \cos y \sin^2 y \, dy$.

Ans. $\frac{1}{3}y \sin^3 y + \frac{1}{3} \cos y - \frac{1}{9} \cos^3 y + C$.

30. $\int x \cos^3 x \, dx$.

Ans. $x \sin x - \frac{1}{3}x \sin^3 x + \frac{2}{3} \cos x + \frac{1}{9} \cos^3 x + C$.

In Exs. 31–36, employ integration by parts twice to evaluate the indicated integral.

31. $\int \sin x \sin 4x \, dx$.

Ans. $\frac{1}{15}(\cos x \sin 4x - 4 \sin x \cos 4x) + C$.

32. $\int \cos 2x \sin 3x \, dx$.

Ans. $-\frac{1}{5}(3 \cos 2x \cos 3x + 2 \sin 2x \sin 3x) + C$.

33. $\int e^{ax} \cos mx \, dx$.

Ans. $\dfrac{e^{ax}(a \cos mx + m \sin mx)}{a^2 + m^2} + C$.

34. $\int e^{ax} \sin mx \, dx$.

Ans. $\dfrac{e^{ax}(a \sin mx - m \cos mx)}{a^2 + m^2} + C$.

35. $\int \ln^2 x \, dx$.

Ans. $x \ln^2 x - 2x \ln x + 2x + C$.

36. $\int \cos (\ln x) \, dx$.

Ans. $\frac{1}{2}x[\cos (\ln x) + \sin (\ln x)] + C$.

In Exs. 37–38, combine integration by parts with other appropriate devices, as in Example (b) above, to evaluate the indicated integral.

37. $\int \csc^3 y \, dy$.

Ans. $-\frac{1}{2} \csc y \cot y + \frac{1}{2} \ln (\csc y - \cot y) + C$.

38. $\int \sqrt{a^2 - x^2} \, dx$.

Ans. $\frac{1}{2}x \sqrt{a^2 - x^2} + \frac{1}{2}a^2 \operatorname{Arcsin} \dfrac{x}{a} + C$.

MISCELLANEOUS EXERCISES

Evaluate the integrals in Exs. 1–60.

1. $\int \tan 3\theta \, d\theta.$

2. $\int z e^z \, dz.$

3. $\int x \ln (x + 1) \, dx.$

4. $\int \csc^2 5\varphi \, d\varphi.$

5. $\int x(1 + x^2)^3 \, dx.$

6. $\int x^2(1 + x^2)^3 \, dx.$

7. $\int e^{-2x} \cos 5x \, dx.$

8. $\int e^{3x} \sin 4x \, dx.$

9. $\int \frac{2(y + 6) \, dy}{y^2 + 9}.$

10. $\int \frac{3(y - 8) \, dy}{4y^2 + 1}.$

11. $\int \sec^2 2\theta \tan^2 2\theta \, d\theta.$

12. $\int \sec^2 2\theta \tan 2\theta \, d\theta.$

13. $\int \frac{dx}{e^{3x} + 4}.$

14. $\int \frac{\tan \theta \, d\theta}{2 + \sec \theta}.$

15. $\int \cos \theta \sin 3\theta \, d\theta.$

16. $\int \cos 2\theta \sin 4\theta \, d\theta.$

17. $\int \frac{y^3 \, dy}{y^4 - 1}.$

18. $\int \frac{y^3 \, dy}{y^2 - 1}.$

19. $\int \frac{(3t - 2) \, dt}{t^2 - 4t + 5}.$

20. $\int \frac{(t - 2) \, dt}{t^2 - 4t + 5}.$

21. $\int \cos^7 \alpha \, d\alpha.$

22. $\int \sin^4 y \cos^3 y \, dy.$

23. $\int \cos^2 6\theta \, d\theta.$

24. $\int \tan^2 3y \, dy.$

25. $\int \text{Arcsin } 2x \, dx.$

26. $\int \sin (\ln u) \, du.$

27. $\int x \cos 7x \, dx.$

28. $\int \sec^3 2z \tan 2z \, dz.$

29. $\int \frac{(x - 1)^2 \, dx}{x + 3}.$

30. $\int \frac{e^{3y} \, dy}{e^{2y} + 9}.$

31. $\int \cos^4 \frac{x}{2} \, dx.$

32. $\int \frac{dy}{\sqrt{2ay - y^2}}.$

33. $\int \frac{y \, dy}{\sqrt{2ay - y^2}}.$

34. $\int \frac{(2t^3 - 5t) \, dt}{9t^4 + 4}.$

35. $\int \csc^3 4\beta \cot 4\beta \, d\beta.$

36. $\int \csc^6 2\varphi \, d\varphi.$

37. $\displaystyle\int \sin^2 x \csc^2 2x \, dx.$

38. $\displaystyle\int x^3 \ln x \, dx.$

39. $\displaystyle\int \frac{dz}{(2z-1)^4}.$

40. $\displaystyle\int \frac{dv}{\sqrt{3-4v^2}}.$

41. $\displaystyle\int y \ln (3y+1) \, dy.$

42. $\displaystyle\int \cosh^3 \frac{x}{a} \sinh \frac{x}{a} \, dx.$

43. $\displaystyle\int \sin^2 \tfrac{1}{4}x \cos^2 \tfrac{1}{4}x \, dx.$

44. $\displaystyle\int \frac{y^3 \, dy}{(y-1)^2}.$

45. $\displaystyle\int t^2 \cos \tfrac{1}{2}t \, dt.$

46. $\displaystyle\int \frac{u \ln (u^2+4)}{u^2+4} \, du.$

47. $\displaystyle\int \frac{d\varphi}{\sqrt{\varphi}\,\sqrt{1-\varphi}}.$

48. $\displaystyle\int (10)^{-3x} \, dx.$

49. $\displaystyle\int x(10)^{-3x} \, dx.$

50. $\displaystyle\int \sec^4 3\varphi \, d\varphi.$

51. $\displaystyle\int \beta \tan^3 (\beta^2) \, d\beta.$

52. $\displaystyle\int \frac{\sin^3 2x}{\cos^5 2x} \, dx.$

53. $\displaystyle\int \frac{(6v+1) \, dv}{v^2-v+1}.$

54. $\displaystyle\int (x+1)e^{2\ln x} \, dx.$

55. $\displaystyle\int (\sin^4 2z - \cos^4 2z) \, dz.$

56. $\displaystyle\int \sec^4 u \tan^3 u \, du.$

57. $\displaystyle\int \frac{(1+x)^5}{x^7} \, dx.$

58. $\displaystyle\int \frac{dx}{x \ln \sqrt{x}}.$

59. $\displaystyle\int (x^2 + 2x - 3)(x-1)^2 \, dx.$

60. $\displaystyle\int \frac{dx}{\sin x \cos x}.$ Solve in two ways: (a) by using $\sin x \cos x = \tfrac{1}{2} \sin 2x$; and (b) by first dividing numerator and denominator by $\sin^2 x$.

Exs. 61–69 concern the motion of a particle in a straight line; the distance x from a specified origin is dependent upon the time t. For the given acceleration a, and the given "boundary conditions," determine in each instance the velocity v, and the distance x, in terms of t.

61. $a = 3 \sin 2t$; when $t = 0$, $x = 4$ and $v = 0$.   *Ans.* $x = 4 + \tfrac{3}{2}t - \tfrac{3}{4} \sin 2t$.

62. $a = 4e^{-2t} - e^{-t}$; when $t = 0$, $x = 2$ and $v = -1$.

63. $a = (t-2)e^{-t}$; when $t = 0$, $x = 0$ and $v = 1$.

64. $a = -3 \cos 3t$; when $t = 0$, $x = 0$ and $v = 0$.

65. $a = 4(e^{-2t} - 2e^{-4t})$; when $t = 0$, $x = \tfrac{1}{2}$ and $v = 0$.

66. $a = 4(t+2)e^{-2t}$; when $t = 0$, $x = 3$ and $v = -7$.   *Ans.* $x = (t+3)e^{-2t} - 2t$.

67. $a = -32$; when $t = 0$, $x = 100$, and when $t = 2$, $x = 30$.

68. $a = -\tfrac{3}{4}(2 \cos \tfrac{1}{2}t + \sin \tfrac{1}{2}t)$; when $t = 0$, $x = -6$, and $v = 1.5$.

69. $a = 8 \sin 4t$; when $t = 0$, $x = 0$, and when $t = \dfrac{4\pi}{3}$, $v = 0$.

Integration by Substitution

195. *Integration by Substitution*

Many integrals may be evaluated by introducing a new variable of integration (say, z) in place of the original variable x, the two variables being connected by some suitable formula. The change of variable is usually brought about by means of an explicit substitution:

$$x = \varphi(z), \qquad dx = \varphi'(z)\, dz.$$

This process, called *integration by substitution*, is highly important. It is to be remembered that *not merely x, but dx as well*, must be replaced by the proper expression in terms of the new variable.

The substitution to be made must be determined by inspection of the integrand. No general rules can be given; skill in the choice of substitutions comes only with practice. There is, however, one rather crude rule of thumb which succeeds often enough to make it worth consideration. Determine, if possible, what quantity seems to be causing the trouble (keeping you from performing the integration by the simple devices of Chapter 23), and then introduce a new variable for that quantity. In many cases, several different substitutions may be found, any one of which will succeed.

Example (a). Evaluate $\displaystyle\int \frac{\sqrt{x}\, dx}{1 + x}$.

Put $\sqrt{x} = z$. Then $x = z^2$ and $dx = 2z\, dz$. Hence

$$\int \frac{\sqrt{x}\, dx}{1 + x} = 2 \int \frac{z^2\, dz}{1 + z^2} = 2 \int \left(1 - \frac{1}{1 + z^2}\right) dz$$

$$= 2z - 2 \operatorname{Arctan} z + C$$

$$= 2\sqrt{x} - 2 \operatorname{Arctan} \sqrt{x} + C.$$

Example (b). Evaluate $\displaystyle\int \frac{z^3\, dz}{\sqrt{z^2 - a^2}}$.

348

Put $\sqrt{z^2 - a^2} = v$. Then $z^2 = v^2 + a^2$ and $z\,dz = v\,dv$. Since $z\,dz$ is expressed simply (as $v\,dv$) in terms of the new variable, it is wise to exhibit $z\,dz$ explicitly before proceeding with the substitution. Therefore we write

$$\int \frac{z^3\,dz}{\sqrt{z^2 - a^2}} = \int \frac{z^2 \cdot z\,dz}{\sqrt{z^2 - a^2}} = \int \frac{(v^2 + a^2)v\,dv}{v}$$

$$= \tfrac{1}{3}v^3 + a^2 v + C$$

$$= \tfrac{1}{3}(z^2 - a^2)^{\frac{3}{2}} + a^2(z^2 - a^2)^{\frac{1}{2}} + C.$$

At times it is desirable to put the result in other forms. From the above we obtain

$$\int \frac{z^3\,dz}{\sqrt{z^2 - a^2}} = \tfrac{1}{3}(z^2 - a^2)^{\frac{1}{2}}(z^2 - a^2 + 3a^2) + C$$

$$= \tfrac{1}{3}(z^2 + 2a^2)(z^2 - a^2)^{\frac{1}{2}} + C.$$

Integrals involving $\sqrt{a^2 - x^2}$, $\sqrt{a^2 + x^2}$, $\sqrt{x^2 - a^2}$ occur very often. It should be noted that substitution of a new variable for the radical, as in Example (*b*), is indicated whenever the integrand contains, as a factor, an *odd* positive or negative integral power of x; but if not, the radical will reappear after the substitution.

It will be found that some of the integrals in this chapter can be solved directly by the methods of Chapter 23. Although substitutions are frequently necessary, the student should be alert for opportunities to avoid them by exercise of a little ingenuity. For instance, the integral in Example (*b*) above is easily evaluated without recourse to a substitution. Write

$$\int \frac{z^3\,dz}{\sqrt{z^2 - a^2}} = \int \frac{(z^2 - a^2 + a^2)z\,dz}{\sqrt{z^2 - a^2}}$$

$$= \int (z^2 - a^2)^{\frac{1}{2}}z\,dz + a^2 \int (z^2 - a^2)^{-\frac{1}{2}}z\,dz, \text{ etc.}$$

EXERCISES

Evaluate the integrals in Exs. 1–30.

1. $\displaystyle\int \frac{(6x - 1)\,dx}{\sqrt{3x + 1}}.$ Ans. $\tfrac{4}{9}(3x + 1)^{\frac{3}{2}} - 2(3x + 1)^{\frac{1}{2}} + C.$

2. $\displaystyle\int \frac{dx}{1 - \sqrt{x}}.$ Ans. $2(1 - \sqrt{x}) - 2 \ln (1 - \sqrt{x}) + C.$

3. $\displaystyle\int (2v - 1)\sqrt{v + 3}\,dv.$ Ans. $\tfrac{4}{5}(v + 3)^{\frac{5}{2}} - \tfrac{14}{3}(v + 3)^{\frac{3}{2}} + C.$

4. $\displaystyle\int \frac{2(x - 7)\,dx}{(2x + 1)^{\frac{3}{2}}}.$ Ans. $(2x + 1)^{\frac{1}{2}} + 15(2x + 1)^{-\frac{1}{2}} + C.$

5. $\displaystyle\int \cos \sqrt{t}\,dt.$ Ans. $2(\sqrt{t} \sin \sqrt{t} + \cos \sqrt{t}) + C.$

6. $\displaystyle \int \frac{dx}{\sqrt{x+2}-4}.$ *Ans.* $2(\sqrt{x+2}-4)+8\ln(\sqrt{x+2}-4)+C$

$$= 2\sqrt{x+2}+8\ln(\sqrt{x+2}-4)+C_1.$$

7. $\displaystyle \int \frac{u\,du}{\sqrt{u}-1}.$

Ans. $\frac{2}{3}(\sqrt{u}-1)^3+3(\sqrt{u}-1)^2+6(\sqrt{u}-1)+2\ln(\sqrt{u}-1)+C.$

8. $\displaystyle \int (x+2)\sqrt{3x-1}\,dx.$ *Ans.* $\frac{2}{45}(3x-1)^{\frac{5}{2}}+\frac{14}{27}(3x-1)^{\frac{3}{2}}+C.$

9. $\displaystyle \int v^3(a^2-v^2)^{\frac{1}{2}}\,dv.$ *Ans.* $\frac{1}{5}(a^2-v^2)^{\frac{5}{2}}-\frac{1}{3}a^2(a^2-v^2)^{\frac{3}{2}}+C$

$$= -\tfrac{1}{15}(3v^2+2a^2)(a^2-v^2)^{\frac{3}{2}}+C.$$

10. $\displaystyle \int x^3\sqrt{a^2+x^2}\,dx.$ *Ans.* $\frac{1}{5}(a^2+x^2)^{\frac{5}{2}}-\dfrac{a^2}{3}(a^2+x^2)^{\frac{3}{2}}+C$

$$= \tfrac{1}{15}(3x^2-2a^2)(a^2+x^2)^{\frac{3}{2}}+C.$$

11. $\displaystyle \int \frac{x^3}{(4-x^2)^2}\,dx.$ *Ans.* $\dfrac{2}{4-x^2}+\frac{1}{2}\ln(4-x^2)+C.$

12. $\displaystyle \int \frac{\sqrt{y^5-1}}{y}\,dy.$ *Ans.* $\frac{2}{5}\sqrt{y^5-1}-\frac{2}{5}\operatorname{Arctan}\sqrt{y^5-1}+C.$

13. $\displaystyle \int \frac{\sqrt{x^2-a^2}}{x}\,dx.$ *Ans.* $\sqrt{x^2-a^2}+a\operatorname{Arcsin}\dfrac{a}{x}+C.$

14. $\displaystyle \int \sqrt{1-\sqrt{x}}\,dx.$ **15.** $\displaystyle \int \frac{x\,dx}{(x^2-a^2)^{\frac{3}{2}}}.$

16. $\displaystyle \int y^2(1+y^3)^4\,dy.$ **17.** $\displaystyle \int \frac{e^{3v}\,dv}{\sqrt{e^v-1}}.$

18. $\displaystyle \int \sqrt{e^y-4}\,dy.$ **19.** $\displaystyle \int \frac{\cos\theta\,\sin^2\theta\,d\theta}{\sqrt{1+\sin\theta}}.$

20. $\displaystyle \int \sec^2\theta\,\tan\theta(1+3\tan\theta)^{\frac{1}{2}}\,d\theta.$

21. $\displaystyle \int \frac{dx}{1-x^{\frac{1}{2}}}.$ **22.** $\displaystyle \int \frac{(x^3+4x)\,dx}{\sqrt{1-x^4}}.$

23. $\displaystyle \int \frac{dt}{\sqrt{1+t^{\frac{1}{2}}}}.$ **24.** $\displaystyle \int \frac{dy}{y^{\frac{1}{2}}+y^{\frac{1}{4}}}.$

25. $\displaystyle \int \frac{z^5\,dz}{(z^2-a^2)^2}.$ **26.** $\displaystyle \int \frac{dt}{(1-\sqrt{t})^{\frac{2}{3}}}.$

27. $\displaystyle \int \frac{(x^2-1)^{\frac{3}{2}}\,dx}{x}.$ **28.** $\displaystyle \int \frac{(x^2-1)^{\frac{2}{3}}\,dx}{x}.$

29. $\displaystyle \int \frac{(1+\ln x)\,dx}{x^2}.$ **30.** $\displaystyle \int \ln(\sqrt{x}+4)\,dx.$

In Exs. 31–38, evaluate by using the reciprocal substitution $x = \dfrac{a^2}{v}$.

31. $\displaystyle\int \frac{x^3\, dx}{(x^2 + a^2)^3}.$ $\qquad$ *Ans.* $\dfrac{x^4}{4a^2(x^2 + a^2)^2} + C.$

32. $\displaystyle\int \frac{dx}{x^2\sqrt{a^2 - x^2}}.$ $\qquad$ *Ans.* $-\dfrac{\sqrt{a^2 - x^2}}{a^2 x} + C.$

33. $\displaystyle\int \frac{\sqrt{a^2 + x^2}\, dx}{x^4}.$ $\qquad$ *Ans.* $\dfrac{-(a^2 + x^2)^{\frac{3}{2}}}{3a^2 x^3} + C.$

34. $\displaystyle\int \frac{dx}{x^2(a^2 + x^2)}.$ $\qquad$ *Ans.* $-\dfrac{1}{a^2 x} + \dfrac{1}{a^3}\,\text{Arctan}\,\dfrac{a}{x} + C.$

35. $\displaystyle\int \frac{x^3\, dx}{(x^2 - a^2)^3}.$ $\qquad$ **36.** $\displaystyle\int \frac{dx}{(a^2 - x^2)^{\frac{3}{2}}}.$

37. $\displaystyle\int \frac{dx}{x(x^2 - a^2)}.$ $\qquad$ **38.** $\displaystyle\int \frac{dx}{(a^2 + x^2)^{\frac{3}{2}}}.$

39. Evaluate the integral of Ex. 31 by first writing

$$\int \frac{x^3\, dx}{(x^2 + a^2)^3} = \int \frac{x(x^2 + a^2 - a^2)\, dx}{(x^2 + a^2)^3} = \int \frac{x\, dx}{(x^2 + a^2)^2} - \int \frac{a^2 x\, dx}{(x^2 + a^2)^3}.$$

Ans. $-\tfrac{1}{2}(x^2 + a^2)^{-1} + \tfrac{1}{4}a^2(x^2 + a^2)^{-2} + C_1.$

40. Compare the answers to Exs. 31 and 39 and show that $C_1 = C + \dfrac{1}{4a^2}.$

41. Evaluate the integral in Ex. 34 by first writing

$$\int \frac{dx}{x^2(a^2 + x^2)} = \frac{1}{a^2}\int \frac{(x^2 + a^2) - x^2}{x^2(a^2 + x^2)}\, dx.$$

42. Evaluate the integral of Ex. 35 by the technique used in Exs. 39 and 41.

43. Evaluate the integral of Ex. 37 by the technique used in Exs. 39 and 41.

44. Evaluate $\displaystyle\int x^3(a^2 + x^2)^k\, dx.$ Note the special treatment necessary for $k = -1$ and $k = -2$.

196. *Trigonometric Substitutions*

Many integrals can be evaluated by substituting a trigonometric function for x. The following substitutions are especially promising:

(1) *When the integrand involves* $a^2 - x^2$, *try* $x = a \sin \theta$.

(2) *When the integrand involves* $a^2 + x^2$, *try* $x = a \tan \theta$.

(3) *When the integrand involves* $x^2 - a^2$, *try* $x = a \sec \theta$.

However, it will be found that these combinations by no means exhaust the usefulness of trigonometric substitutions.

Let us examine the reasons underlying the choice (1) above. We know that

$$1 - \sin^2 \theta = \cos^2 \theta.$$

Therefore, if x is chosen to be $a \sin \theta$,

$$a^2 - x^2 = a^2 - a^2 \sin^2 \theta = a^2 \cos^2 \theta.$$

We thus replace $(a^2 - x^2)$ by a single term $a^2 \cos^2 \theta$. Furthermore, that single term is a perfect square, which is particularly effective when the quantity $(a^2 - x^2)$ appears under a square root symbol. Corresponding analyses of the choices (2) and (3) above should be made by the student.

Example (a). Evaluate $\displaystyle\int \frac{dx}{(a^2 - x^2)^{\frac{3}{2}}}.$

Putting $x = a \sin \theta$, $dx = a \cos \theta \, d\theta$, we get

$$\int \frac{a \cos \theta \, d\theta}{(a^2 - a^2 \sin^2 \theta)^{\frac{3}{2}}} = \frac{1}{a^2} \int \frac{\cos \theta \, d\theta}{(1 - \sin^2 \theta)^{\frac{3}{2}}} = \frac{1}{a^2} \int \frac{\cos \theta \, d\theta}{\cos^3 \theta}$$

$$= \frac{1}{a^2} \int \sec^2 \theta \, d\theta = \frac{1}{a^2} \tan \theta + C.$$

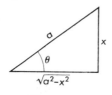

Figure 211

From the triangle,

$$\tan \theta = \frac{x}{\sqrt{a^2 - x^2}},$$

whence

$$\int \frac{dx}{(a^2 - x^2)^{\frac{3}{2}}} = \frac{x}{a^2 \sqrt{a^2 - x^2}} + C.$$

The triangle in Figure 211 was constructed, of course, to permit easy return to the original variable x. Note that the quantity $\sqrt{a^2 - x^2}$, which originally suggested the substitution used, appears in the triangle. This brings in a mild check on the work. Unless the quantity which suggests a trigonometric substitution appears in the associated triangle relating new and old variables, there is probably an error in the work.

Example (b). Evaluate $\displaystyle\int \frac{\sqrt{x - a}}{x^{\frac{5}{2}}} \, dx.$

Here there are two troublesome elements; both $(x - a)$ and x appear with fractional exponents. If we put $x = u^2$, the disturbing element $(u^2 - a)$ would appear under a square root sign. The choice $x - a = v^2$ would introduce $(v^2 + a)$ for x, which is undesirable in the same way.

Now $(x - a)$ may be thought of as $(\sqrt{x})^2 - (\sqrt{a})^2$, thus suggesting the substitution in (3) above. Hence we try

$$\sqrt{x} = \sqrt{a} \sec \theta$$

from which

$$x = a \sec^2 \theta, \qquad dx = 2a \sec^2 \theta \tan \theta \, d\theta.$$

Then

$$\int \frac{\sqrt{x-a}}{x^{\frac{5}{2}}}\,dx = \int \frac{\sqrt{a\sec^2\theta - a}\cdot 2a\sec^2\theta\tan\theta\,d\theta}{a^{\frac{5}{2}}\sec^5\theta}$$

$$= \frac{2}{a}\int \frac{\sqrt{\sec^2\theta - 1}\cdot\tan\theta\,d\theta}{\sec^3\theta}$$

$$= \frac{2}{a}\int \tan^2\theta\cos^3\theta\,d\theta$$

$$= \frac{2}{a}\int \sin^2\theta\cos\theta\,d\theta$$

$$= \frac{2}{3a}\sin^3\theta + C = \frac{2}{3a}\frac{(x-a)^{\frac{3}{2}}}{x^{\frac{3}{2}}} + C.$$

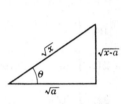

Figure 212

EXERCISES

Evaluate the integrals in Exs. 1–36, making use of trigonometric substitutions.

1. $\displaystyle\int \frac{dx}{(a^2 + x^2)^{\frac{3}{2}}}.$ *Ans.* $\displaystyle\frac{x}{a^2\sqrt{a^2+x^2}} + C.$

2. $\displaystyle\int \frac{dx}{(a^2 + x^2)^{\frac{5}{2}}}.$ *Ans.* $\displaystyle\frac{x(3a^2 + 2x^2)}{3a^4(a^2+x^2)^{\frac{3}{2}}} + C.$

3. $\displaystyle\int \frac{dx}{x^2\sqrt{a^2 - x^2}}.$ *Ans.* $\displaystyle\frac{-\sqrt{a^2 - x^2}}{a^2 x} + C.$

4. $\displaystyle\int \sqrt{a^2 - x^2}\,dx.$ *Ans.* $\frac{1}{2}x\sqrt{a^2 - x^2} + \frac{1}{2}a^2\,\text{Arcsin}\,\frac{x}{a} + C.$

5. $\displaystyle\int \frac{\sqrt{a^2 - x^2}}{x^2}\,dx.$ *Ans.* $\displaystyle\frac{-\sqrt{a^2 - x^2}}{x} - \text{Arcsin}\,\frac{x}{a} + C.$

6. $\displaystyle\int \frac{dx}{(x^2 - a^2)^{\frac{3}{2}}}.$ *Ans.* $\displaystyle\frac{-x}{a^2\sqrt{x^2 - a^2}} + C.$

7. $\displaystyle\int \frac{v^2\,dv}{(a^2 - v^2)^{\frac{3}{2}}}.$ *Ans.* $\displaystyle\frac{v}{\sqrt{a^2 - v^2}} - \text{Arcsin}\,\frac{v}{a} + C.$

8. $\displaystyle\int \frac{dw}{w^2\sqrt{w^2 + a^2}}.$ *Ans.* $\displaystyle\frac{-\sqrt{w^2 + a^2}}{a^2 w} + C.$

9. $\displaystyle\int \frac{dy}{\sqrt{y^2 + a^2}}.$ *Ans.* $\ln\left(y + \sqrt{y^2 + a^2}\right) + C.$

10. $\displaystyle\int \frac{du}{(u^2 + a^2)^2}.$ *Ans.* $\displaystyle\frac{1}{2a^3}\left(\frac{au}{u^2 + a^2} + \text{Arctan}\,\frac{u}{a}\right) + C.$

11. $\displaystyle\int \frac{\sqrt{9x^2 - 4}}{x}\,dx.$ **12.** $\displaystyle\int \frac{\sqrt{16 - x^2}}{x}\,dx.$

13. $\displaystyle\int \frac{dy}{y(y^2 + 1)}.$ **14.** $\displaystyle\int \frac{dy}{y^3(y^2 + 1)}.$

15. $\displaystyle\int \frac{du}{u^2 \sqrt{4u^2-1}}.$

16. $\displaystyle\int \frac{du}{u^4 \sqrt{4u^2-1}}.$

17. $\displaystyle\int \frac{dx}{x^4 \sqrt{9-x^2}}.$

18. $\displaystyle\int \frac{y^2\, dy}{(16y^2+9)^{\frac{3}{2}}}.$

19. $\displaystyle\int \frac{\sqrt{x}\, dx}{(1+x)^2}.$

20. $\displaystyle\int \frac{\sqrt{x}\, dx}{(1+x)^3}.$

21. $\displaystyle\int (a^2-x^2)^{\frac{3}{2}}\, dx.$ *Ans.* $\displaystyle\frac{x}{4}(a^2-x^2)^{\frac{3}{2}} + \frac{3a^2x}{8}(a^2-x^2)^{\frac{1}{2}} + \frac{3a^4}{8}\operatorname{Arcsin}\frac{x}{a} + C.$

22. $\displaystyle\int \sqrt{a^2+x^2}\, dx.$ *Ans.* $\displaystyle\frac{x}{2}\sqrt{a^2+x^2} + \frac{a^2}{2}\ln(x+\sqrt{a^2+x^2}) + C.$

23. $\displaystyle\int \frac{x^2\, dx}{\sqrt{a^2+x^2}}.$ *Ans.* $\displaystyle\frac{x}{2}\sqrt{a^2+x^2} - \frac{a^2}{2}\ln(x+\sqrt{a^2+x^2}) + C.$

24. $\displaystyle\int \frac{dx}{(a^2-x^2)^{\frac{5}{2}}}.$ *Ans.* $\displaystyle\frac{x(3a^2-2x^2)}{3a^4(a^2-x^2)^{\frac{3}{2}}} + C$

25. $\displaystyle\int \frac{\sqrt{a-y}}{\sqrt{y}}\, dy.$

26. $\displaystyle\int \frac{\sqrt{y}}{\sqrt{a-y}}\, dy.$

27. $\displaystyle\int \frac{dx}{\sqrt{1+\sqrt{x}}}.$

28. $\displaystyle\int \sqrt{1-\sqrt{x}}\, dx.$

29. $\displaystyle\int \frac{\cos\varphi\sin\varphi\, d\varphi}{(1-\cos\varphi)^2}.$

30. $\displaystyle\int \frac{\cos\beta\, d\beta}{(1+\sin^2\beta)^{\frac{3}{2}}}.$

31. $\displaystyle\int \frac{dx}{x\sqrt{2ax-x^2}}.$ (Put $x = 2a\sin^2\theta$.)   *Ans.* $-\dfrac{\sqrt{2ax-x^2}}{ax} + C.$

32. $\displaystyle\int \frac{dx}{x\sqrt{2ax+x^2}}.$ (Put $x = 2a\tan^2\theta$.)   *Ans.* $-\dfrac{\sqrt{2ax+x^2}}{ax} + C.$

33. $\displaystyle\int \frac{dx}{x\sqrt{x^2-2ax}}.$ (Put $x = 2a\sec^2\theta$.)   *Ans.* $\dfrac{\sqrt{x^2-2ax}}{ax} + C.$

34. Solve Ex. 31 by a second method.   Put $x - a = a\sin\theta$.
35. Solve Ex. 32 by a second method.
36. Solve Ex. 33 by a second method.

37. Evaluate $\displaystyle\int \frac{dx}{x(x^4-1)}$ in several ways.

In Exs. 38–49, evaluate the integral with, or without, the aid of trigonometric substitutions, using whatever method seems best adapted to the problem.

38. $\displaystyle\int \frac{dy}{1-e^y}.$

39. $\displaystyle\int \frac{du}{e^{2u}+1}.$

40. $\displaystyle\int \frac{dx}{\sqrt{4-9x^2}}.$

41. $\displaystyle\int \frac{d\varphi}{16\varphi^2+1}.$

42. $\displaystyle\int \frac{dx}{x(x+a)}.$

43. $\displaystyle\int \frac{dy}{y(y-9)}.$

44. $\displaystyle\int \frac{dy}{y(y-4)^2}.$ 45. $\displaystyle\int \frac{x^2\,dx}{(x^2+a^2)^2}.$ 46. $\displaystyle\int \frac{y^3\,dy}{(y^2+a^2)^3}.$

47. $\displaystyle\int \frac{dx}{x(x+k)^2}.$ 48. $\displaystyle\int \frac{dx}{\sqrt{4e^{2x}-9}}.$ 49. $\displaystyle\int \frac{dx}{x(a^2+x^2)^{\frac{3}{2}}}.$

197. *Limitations on Certain Formulas*

To verify (**10**), page 329, the work is as follows:

$$\frac{d}{du}\,\mathrm{Arcsin}\,\frac{u}{a} = \frac{\dfrac{1}{a}}{\sqrt{1-\dfrac{u^2}{a^2}}} = \frac{1}{a}\cdot\frac{1}{\sqrt{\dfrac{a^2-u^2}{a^2}}} = \frac{1}{a}\cdot\frac{\sqrt{a^2}}{\sqrt{a^2-u^2}}.$$

This proves the formula for the case $a > 0$; but if $a < 0$, then $\sqrt{a^2} = -a$, and *the formula must be changed* to read

(1) $$\int \frac{du}{\sqrt{a^2-u^2}} = -\,\mathrm{Arcsin}\,\frac{u}{a} + C, \qquad a < 0.$$

The above is typical of a phenomenon that occurs many times in integration. A formula, valid within certain ranges, is incorrect in other ranges, even though all the functions occurring are well defined there. The commonest region of failure is for negative values of the variable of integration x, or of some constant.

With the limitation $a > 0$ on (**10**), the standard formulas (page 328) are valid wherever the functions are defined. But the exercises of this and the preceding chapter contain a number of formulas to which the above remarks apply.

Example. Find the area in the second quadrant bounded by the curve $y^2 = \dfrac{x^2-1}{x^2}$, the x-axis, and the line $x = -2$.

In the second quadrant

$$y = -\frac{\sqrt{x^2-1}}{x},$$

(2) $$A = \int_{-2}^{-1} y\,dx = -\int_{-2}^{-1} \frac{\sqrt{x^2-1}\,dx}{x}.$$

An attempt to evaluate the above integral by using the result of Ex. 13, page 350,

(3) $$\int \frac{\sqrt{x^2-a^2}}{x}\,dx = \sqrt{x^2-a^2} + a\,\mathrm{Arcsin}\,\frac{a}{x} + C.$$

is doomed to failure because (3) is based on the assumption that x is positive. [In the derivation of (3), $\sqrt{x^2}$ is replaced by x.]   Indeed,

$$- \left[\sqrt{x^2 - 1} + \text{Arcsin } \frac{1}{x} \right]_{-2}^{-1}$$

$$= - \text{Arcsin } (-1) - \left[- \sqrt{3} - \text{Arcsin } (-\tfrac{1}{2}) \right]$$

$$= \sqrt{3} + \frac{\pi}{3} = 1.73 + 1.05 = 2.78.$$

But the area A, shaded in Figure 213, is less than $\frac{1}{2} \sqrt{3} = 0.87$.

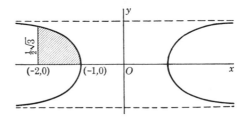

Figure 213

Evaluation of the integral in (3) for negative x, replacing $\sqrt{x^2}$ by $(-x)$ in the derivation, yields

$$(4) \quad \int \frac{\sqrt{x^2 - a^2}}{x} \, dx = \sqrt{x^2 - a^2} - a \text{ Arcsin } \frac{a}{x} + C; \quad x \leq -a < 0.$$

The integral in (2) may now be evaluated with the aid of (4), which produces the correct answer,

$$A = \sqrt{3} - \frac{\pi}{3} = 0.68.$$

Although, of course, such situations are not the most usual thing, they occur far too often to be considered freakish.   But it would be wearisome and time consuming to keep constant track of such matters in our daily work; thus we have ignored them and must continue to do so.   We leave the subject with the following injunction (applying not so much to the work of this course, where these difficulties will be largely avoided, as to activities in applied mathematics, in which the student may now or subsequently be interested):

In an integration involving a square root or other many-valued function, particularly when some of the quantities are negative, watch every detail closely to make sure that in each transformation the right branch is taken.

25

Integration of

Rational Fractions

198. *Introduction*

We take up next the problem of integrating a *rational algebraic fraction*—i.e., the quotient of two polynomials.

As noted in § 189, the first step in dealing with an integral of this type is to *carry out the indicated division until the numerator is of lower degree than the denominator.* In developing our theory, we shall suppose always that this preliminary step has been taken.

In this chapter, whenever the quantity $ax^2 + bx + c$ occurs, it will be assumed that $b^2 - 4ac < 0$. If $b^2 - 4ac \geqq 0$, the quantity $ax^2 + bx + c$ can be factored into real linear factors.

By methods already familiar, we can immediately integrate fractions of the forms

$$\frac{A}{(ax + b)^n}, \qquad \frac{A(2ax + b)}{(ax^2 + bx + c)^n}, \qquad \frac{A}{ax^2 + bx + c}.$$

The first two lead to powers (if $n > 1$) or to logarithms (if $n = 1$); the third leads to an arctangent. We can also integrate

$$\frac{A}{(ax^2 + bx + c)^n}, \qquad n > 1,$$

by a trigonometric substitution.

199. *Partial Fractions*

It is shown in algebra that every rational fraction whose numerator is of lower degree than the denominator can be broken up into so-called *partial fractions* of the exact forms listed above. It follows that *every rational fraction can be integrated* in elementary terms. In the next few pages we show how to effect the breakup into partial fractions.

357

In order to apply the results, it is necessary that the operator actually be able to find the linear and quadratic factors of the denominator—conceivably a formidable task.   Fortunately most cases that arise are relatively simple.

200. *Distinct Linear Factors*

The simplest case is that in which the denominator can be broken up into real linear factors, none of which are repeated.   In this case we may always rewrite the given fraction (provided the numerator is of lower degree than the denominator) as a sum of fractions whose numerators are constants and whose respective denominators are the factors of the original denominator.

Example (a).   Evaluate $\int \dfrac{x^3 + 2}{x^3 - x} \, dx$.

By division,

$$\frac{x^3 + 2}{x^3 - x} = 1 + \frac{x + 2}{x^3 - x}.$$

The factors of the denominator are $x, x + 1, x - 1$.   Assume

$$\frac{x + 2}{x^3 - x} = \frac{A}{x} + \frac{B}{x + 1} + \frac{C}{x - 1},$$

where A, B, C are constants to be determined.   Clearing of fractions, we find

$$x + 2 = A(x^2 - 1) + Bx(x - 1) + Cx(x + 1).$$

This relation must hold for *all values* of x.   Hence, assigning to x any three values whatever, we must obtain three simultaneous equations to determine A, B, C.   But the most convenient values to use are $0, -1, 1$ (the zeros of the original denominator), for each of these causes two terms to drop out:

$$x = 0, \qquad A = -2;$$
$$x = -1, \qquad B = \tfrac{1}{2};$$
$$x = 1, \qquad C = \tfrac{3}{2}.$$

Thus

$$\int \frac{x^3 + 2}{x(x^2 - 1)} \, dx = \int \left(1 - \frac{2}{x} + \frac{1}{2} \cdot \frac{1}{x + 1} + \frac{3}{2} \cdot \frac{1}{x - 1} \right) dx$$

$$= x - 2 \ln x + \frac{1}{2} \ln (x + 1) + \frac{3}{2} \ln (x - 1) + C.$$

The student is urgently warned not to forget the preliminary division (when necessary).   Without that, the above process will determine values of A, B, C; but the sum of partial fractions thus found will be equal to the given fraction for no values of x except the three that were assigned.

Careful scrutiny of the method used in Example (a) shows that the expansion is easily obtained mentally.   Let us develop the idea in detail.

Consider any rational fraction with numerator of lower degree than the denominator, and with denominator consisting of distinct linear factors only. Let $(x - a)$ be a representative factor of the denominator.   Then the fraction may be written $\dfrac{f(x)}{(x - a)g(x)}$, where $g(a) \neq 0$.   The theory of rational fractions shows that

(1)
$$\frac{f(x)}{(x - a)g(x)} = \frac{A}{x - a} + \varphi(x),$$

where $\varphi(x)$ is the sum of the other terms in the desired expansion into rational fractions.   Multiply each term of (1) by $(x - a)$, thus getting

$$\frac{f(x)}{g(x)} = A + (x - a)\,\varphi(x),$$

from which

$$A = \frac{f(a)}{g(a)}.$$

Thus the numerator of the representative term $\dfrac{A}{x - a}$ can be obtained from the original fraction by (mentally) removing the factor $(x - a)$ and evaluating what remains at $x = a$.

Example (b).   Expand $\dfrac{x^2 + 1}{(x - 2)(x - 1)(2x + 1)}$ into rational fractions.

We know that

$$\frac{x^2 + 1}{(x - 2)(x - 1)(2x + 1)} = \frac{A}{x - 2} + \frac{B}{x - 1} + \frac{C}{2x + 1},$$

from which

$$A = \left[\frac{x^2 + 1}{(x - 1)(2x + 1)}\right]_{x=2} = \frac{5}{(1)(5)} = 1,$$

$$B = \left[\frac{x^2 + 1}{(x - 2)(2x + 1)}\right]_{x=1} = \frac{2}{(-1)(3)} = -\frac{2}{3},$$

$$C = \left[\frac{x^2 + 1}{(x - 2)(x - 1)}\right]_{x=-\frac{1}{2}} = \frac{\frac{5}{4}}{(-\frac{5}{2})(-\frac{3}{2})} = \frac{1}{3}.$$

Therefore,

$$\frac{x^2 + 1}{(x - 2)(x - 1)(2x + 1)} = \frac{1}{x - 2} + \frac{-\frac{2}{3}}{x - 1} + \frac{\frac{1}{3}}{2x + 1},$$

all of which should be accomplished mentally.

201. *An Important Logarithmic Formula*

Under the heading of § 200, one particular integral occurs so often that it is worth listing for reference.

To evaluate $\int \dfrac{dx}{a^2 - x^2}$, assume

$$\frac{1}{a^2 - x^2} = \frac{A}{a + x} + \frac{B}{a - x},$$

$$1 = A(a - x) + B(a + x),$$

$$x = -a, \qquad A = \frac{1}{2a};$$

$$x = a, \qquad B = \frac{1}{2a};$$

$$\int \frac{dx}{a^2 - x^2} = \frac{1}{2a} \int \frac{dx}{a + x} + \frac{1}{2a} \int \frac{dx}{a - x}$$

$$= \frac{1}{2a} \ln (a + x) - \frac{1}{2a} \ln (a - x) + C,$$

or

$$\int \frac{dx}{a^2 - x^2} = \frac{1}{2a} \ln \frac{a + x}{a - x} + C = \frac{1}{2a} \ln \frac{x + a}{x - a} + C'.$$

As a corollary, by changing signs we get

$$\int \frac{dx}{x^2 - a^2} = \frac{1}{2a} \ln \frac{a - x}{a + x} + C_1 = \frac{1}{2a} \ln \frac{x - a}{x + a} + C_1'.$$

EXERCISES

Evaluate each of the following integrals.

1. $\int \dfrac{(3x + 7)\, dx}{x^2 - 2x - 3}.$ *Ans.* $4 \ln (x - 3) - \ln (x + 1) + C.$

2. $\int \dfrac{(x + 2)\, dx}{x^2 - 6x + 8}.$ *Ans.* $3 \ln (x - 4) - 2 \ln (x - 2) + C.$

3. $\int \dfrac{dx}{x^2 + ax}.$ *Ans.* $\dfrac{1}{a} \ln \dfrac{x}{x + a} + C.$

4. Do Ex. 3 by using the reciprocal substitution, $x = \dfrac{a^2}{v}.$

5. $\int \dfrac{(2x^2 + 5x - 4)\, dx}{x^3 + x^2 - 2x}.$ *Ans.* $2 \ln x + \ln (x - 1) - \ln (x + 2) + C.$

6. $\int \dfrac{(2x^2 + 5x + 5)\, dx}{x^3 + 7x^2 + 10x}.$ *Ans.* $\frac{1}{2} \ln x + 2 \ln (x + 5) - \frac{1}{2} \ln (x + 2) + C.$

7. $\int \dfrac{(7x + 1)\, dx}{x^3 + 2x^2 - 5x - 6}.$

8. $\int \dfrac{(x + 1)\, dx}{x^3 - 7x^2 + 14x - 8}.$

9. $\int \dfrac{(2x^2 + x - 5)\, dx}{x^2 + x - 2}.$

10. $\int \dfrac{5x^2\, dx}{x^2 - x - 6}.$

11. $\int \dfrac{(x + 12)\, dx}{x(x + 2)(x - 3)}.$

12. $\int \dfrac{dx}{(x - 1)(x + 2)(x - 4)}.$

13. $\int \dfrac{(x^2 - 16x - 12)\, dx}{x(x - 4)(x + 1)}.$

14. $\int \dfrac{x^2\, dx}{(x - 1)(x - 2)(x - 3)}.$

15. $\int \dfrac{x^3\, dx}{x^2 - 4}.$

16. $\int \dfrac{x^3\, dx}{x^4 - 16}.$

17. $\int \dfrac{15y^4\, dy}{y^{10} - 4y^5 - 5}.$

18. $\int \dfrac{(2 \sin \theta - 1) \cos \theta\, d\theta}{\sin^2 \theta + 3 \sin \theta - 10}.$

19. $\int \dfrac{3t^2\, dt}{t^4 + 5t^2 - 14}.$

20. $\int \dfrac{(3u^3 - u)\, du}{u^4 + 16}.$

21. $\int \dfrac{e^{3y}\, dy}{e^{2y} - 4}.$

22. $\int \dfrac{dz}{(4 - z)\sqrt{z}}.$

23. $\int \dfrac{d\theta}{\theta(\theta^3 + 2)}.$

24. $\int \dfrac{dx}{x(1 - x^5)}.$

25. $\int \dfrac{dv}{\sqrt{4e^v + 1}}.$

26. $\int \dfrac{dy}{\sqrt{1 - e^{2y}}}.$

27. $\int \dfrac{4dx}{e^x + 4}.$ Use the substitution $e^x + 4 = v$.

28. $\int \dfrac{4dx}{e^x + 4}.$ Use the fact that $\dfrac{4}{e^x + 4} = \dfrac{4e^{-x}}{1 + 4e^{-x}}.$

29. $\int \dfrac{4dx}{e^x + 4}.$ Use the substitution $e^x = 4 \tan^2 \varphi$.

30. $\int \dfrac{4dx}{e^x + 4}.$ Use the fact that $\dfrac{4}{e^x + 4} = 1 - \dfrac{e^x}{e^x + 4}.$

31. $\int \dfrac{dx}{e^x - 1}.$ See the suggestions in Exs. 27–30.

32. $\int \dfrac{dx}{x\sqrt{a^2 + x^2}}.$ (Put $a^2 + x^2 = v^2$.)   *Ans.* $-\dfrac{1}{a} \ln \dfrac{a + \sqrt{a^2 + x^2}}{x} + C.$

33. $\int \dfrac{dx}{x\sqrt{a^2 - x^2}}.$ (Put $a^2 - x^2 = y^2$.)   *Ans.* $-\dfrac{1}{a} \ln \dfrac{a + \sqrt{a^2 - x^2}}{x} + C.$

34. $\int \dfrac{\sqrt{a^2 - x^2}}{x}\, dx.$ (Put $a^2 - x^2 = y^2$.)

202. *Repeated Linear Factors*

If the denominator contains a factor $(x - \alpha)^r$, the above method fails, since there would be r partial fractions with denominator $x - \alpha$, and these could be combined into a single fraction with denominator $x - \alpha$. In this case, corresponding to the factor $(x - \alpha)^r$, we *assume r partial fractions of the form*

$$\frac{A}{x-\alpha} + \frac{B}{(x-\alpha)^2} + \cdots + \frac{D}{(x-\alpha)^r}.$$

Example.   Evaluate $\displaystyle\int \frac{x^3 - 1}{x(x+1)^3}\, dx.$

Assume

(1) $$\frac{x^3 - 1}{x(x+1)^3} = \frac{A}{x} + \frac{B}{x+1} + \frac{C}{(x+1)^2} + \frac{D}{(x+1)^3},$$

(2) $$x^3 - 1 = A(x+1)^3 + Bx(x+1)^2 + Cx(x+1) + Dx.$$

To get the necessary four equations for the determination of A, B, C, D, two methods are at once available.   Specific values of x can be used in the identity (2), or the coefficients of like powers of x in the two members of (2) can be equated.

We naturally employ whatever combination of these methods yields simple equations to be solved for the unknowns A, B, etc.

From (2) we obtain equations as follows:

$$
\begin{aligned}
x = 0: \quad & -1 = A, \\
x = -1: \quad & -2 = -D, \\
\text{Coefficients of } x^3: \quad & 1 = A + B, \\
\text{Coefficients of } x^2: \quad & 0 = 3A + 2B + C.
\end{aligned}
$$

These equations yield $A = -1$, $B = 2$, $C = -1$, $D = 2$, whence

$$\int \frac{(x^3 - 1)\, dx}{x(x+1)^3} = \int \left(-\frac{1}{x} + \frac{2}{x+1} - \frac{1}{(x+1)^2} + \frac{2}{(x+1)^3} \right) dx$$

$$= -\ln x + 2 \ln (x+1) + \frac{1}{x+1} - \frac{1}{(x+1)^2} + C.$$

The algebra may be checked by obtaining an additional equation from the identity (2).   For instance,

$$x = 1: \quad 0 = 8A + 4B + 2C + D,$$

which must also be satisfied by the A, B, C, D, if they are correct.

EXERCISES

Evaluate each of the following integrals.

1. $\displaystyle\int \frac{dx}{x^3 - x^2}.$ *Ans.* $\dfrac{1}{x} - \ln x + \ln (x - 1) + C.$

2. $\displaystyle\int \frac{(5u + 2)\, du}{u^3 + 2u^2}.$ *Ans.* $\dfrac{-1}{u} + 2 \ln u - 2 \ln (u + 2) + C.$

3. $\displaystyle\int \frac{(7x - 4)\, dx}{x^3 - 3x + 2}.$ *Ans.* $2 \ln (x - 1) - 2 \ln (x + 2) - \dfrac{1}{x - 1} + C.$

4. $\int \dfrac{(5x - 1)\,dx}{x^3 - 3x - 2}.$ *Ans.* $\ln(x - 2) - \ln(x + 1) - \dfrac{2}{x + 1} + C.$

5. $\int \dfrac{(2x^3 - 1)\,dx}{x^4 + 2x^3 + x^2}.$ *Ans.* $2\ln x + \dfrac{1}{x} + \dfrac{3}{x + 1} + C.$

6. $\int \dfrac{dy}{y^2(y + 2)^2}.$ *Ans.* $\dfrac{1}{4}\ln\dfrac{y + 2}{y} - \dfrac{y + 1}{2y(y + 2)} + C.$

7. $\int \dfrac{(9v^2 + 4v - 12)\,dv}{v^2(v^2 - 4)}.$ *Ans.* $2\ln(v - 2) - \ln v - \ln(v + 2) - \dfrac{3}{v} + C.$

8. $\int \dfrac{(11u - 14)\,du}{u^4 + u^3 - 2u^2}.$ *Ans.* $3\ln(u + 2) - 2\ln u - \ln(u - 1) - \dfrac{7}{u} + C.$

9. $\int \dfrac{(3x^4 - 2x^2 + 2)\,dx}{x^3(x - 1)}.$ *Ans.* $3x + \dfrac{2}{x} + \dfrac{1}{x^2} + 3\ln(x - 1) + C.$

10. $\int \dfrac{(3x^2 - 2x - 4)\,dx}{x^3(x + 2)}.$ *Ans.* $\dfrac{1}{x^2} + \dfrac{3}{2}\ln\dfrac{x}{x + 2} + C.$

11. $\int \dfrac{(13x - 12)\,dx}{x^3 - 3x^2}.$ **12.** $\int \dfrac{(2y^2 + 1)\,dy}{y^3 + 2y^2 + y}.$

13. $\int \dfrac{dv}{(4 + v)^3}.$ **14.** $\int \dfrac{v\,dv}{(4 + v)^3}.$

15. $\int \dfrac{z\,dz}{(z^2 - 1)^2}.$ **16.** $\int \dfrac{(y^4 + 1)\,dy}{y^2(y - 1)^2}.$

17. $\int \dfrac{d\theta}{\sin\theta\cos^2\theta}.$ Introduce a new variable, $\alpha = \cos\theta.$

18. $\int \dfrac{dx}{(a^2 - x^2)^2}.$ *Ans.* $\dfrac{x}{2a^2(a^2 - x^2)} + \dfrac{1}{4a^3}\ln\dfrac{a + x}{a - x} + C.$

19. $\int \sec^3\theta\,d\theta.$ $\left[\sec^3\theta = \dfrac{1}{\cos^3\theta} = \dfrac{\cos\theta}{\cos^4\theta} = \dfrac{\cos\theta}{(1 - \sin^2\theta)^2};\text{ Ex. 18.}\right]$

20. $\int \csc^3\theta\,d\theta.$ (Cf. Ex. 19.)   *Ans.* $-\dfrac{\cos\theta}{2\sin^2\theta} + \dfrac{1}{4}\ln\dfrac{1 - \cos\theta}{1 + \cos\theta} + C.$

21. $\int \dfrac{dx}{x(x^2 - 1)^2}.$ *Ans.* $\dfrac{1}{2(1 - x^2)} + \dfrac{1}{2}\ln\dfrac{x^2}{x^2 - 1} + C.$

22. Do Ex. 21 in another way.

23. $\int \dfrac{dx}{e^x(e^x + 1)}.$ Use $v = e^x.$ *Ans.* $\ln(1 + e^x) - x - e^{-x} + C.$

24. Do Ex. 23 in two other ways.

25. $\int \dfrac{dx}{(1 - e^x)^2}.$ Use $e^x = \beta.$

26. Do Ex. 25, using $e^{-x} = v.$
27. Do Ex. 25, using $e^x = \sin^2\varphi.$

28. $\int \dfrac{dx}{x(1 - \sqrt{x})^2}.$ *Ans.* $\dfrac{2}{1 - \sqrt{x}} + \ln\dfrac{x}{(1 - \sqrt{x})^2} + C.$

203. *Quadratic Factors*

Corresponding to a factor in the denominator of the form $ax^2 + bx + c$ with $b^2 - 4ac < 0$, we assume the partial fraction* $\dfrac{A(2ax + b) + B}{ax^2 + bx + c}$, where A and B are to be determined.

Example (a). Evaluate $\displaystyle \int \frac{x^2 + 4x + 10}{x^3 + 2x^2 + 5x}\, dx.$

Assume

$$\frac{x^2 + 4x + 10}{x^3 + 2x^2 + 5x} = \frac{A}{x} + \frac{B(2x + 2)}{x^2 + 2x + 5} + \frac{C}{x^2 + 2x + 5},$$

$$x^2 + 4x + 10 = A(x^2 + 2x + 5) + Bx(2x + 2) + Cx.$$

Put $x = 0$: $5A = 10,\ A = 2.$

Equate coefficients of x^2: $A + 2B = 1,\ B = -\tfrac{1}{2}.$

Equate coefficients of x: $2A + 2B + C = 4,\ C = 1.$

Therefore

$$\int \frac{x^2 + 4x + 10}{x^3 + 2x^2 + 5x}\, dx = \int \left(\frac{2}{x} - \frac{1}{2} \cdot \frac{2x + 2}{x^2 + 2x + 5} + \frac{1}{x^2 + 2x + 5} \right) dx$$

$$= 2 \ln x - \frac{1}{2} \ln (x^2 + 2x + 5) + \frac{1}{2} \operatorname{Arctan} \frac{x + 1}{2} + C.$$

The case of repeated quadratic factors occurs less often, and may be dismissed very briefly. Corresponding to a factor $(ax^2 + bx + c)^r$, we assume r partial fractions with linear numerators as above, and successive denominators building up the exponents step-by-step just as in § 202.

Example (b). Evaluate $\displaystyle \int \frac{x^2\, dx}{(x^2 + 4x + 5)^2}.$

Assume

$$\frac{x^2}{(x^2 + 4x + 5)^2} = \frac{A(2x + 4) + B}{(x^2 + 4x + 5)} + \frac{C(2x + 4) + D}{(x^2 + 4x + 5)^2};$$

etc. The last integral may be evaluated as suggested in § 198.

EXERCISES

Evaluate the following integrals.

1. $\displaystyle \int \frac{(4x - 7)\, dx}{x^2 - 6x + 13}.$ *Ans.* $2 \ln (x^2 - 6x + 13) + \dfrac{5}{2} \operatorname{Arctan} \dfrac{x - 3}{2} + C.$

2. $\displaystyle \int \frac{(6x + 1)\, dx}{x^2 + 4x + 20}.$ *Ans.* $3 \ln (x^2 + 4x + 20) - \dfrac{11}{4} \operatorname{Arctan} \dfrac{x + 2}{4} + C.$

* This form rather than the equivalent form $\dfrac{Ax + B}{ax^2 + bx + c}$, in order that the new integrals shall be in form to evaluate at once.

3. $\int \dfrac{dx}{x^3 + 2x^2 + 5x}.$

$Ans.\ \dfrac{1}{5}\ln x - \dfrac{1}{10}\ln (x^2 + 2x + 5) - \dfrac{1}{10}\text{Arctan}\dfrac{x+1}{2} + C.$

4. $\int \dfrac{(7x - 58)\,dx}{x^3 - 4x^2 + 29x}.$

5. $\int \dfrac{dy}{(y - 1)(y^2 + 1)}.$

6. $\int \dfrac{(9y + 14)\,dy}{(y - 2)(y^2 + 4)}.$

7. $\int \dfrac{u\,du}{9u^4 + 1}.$

8. $\int \dfrac{dv}{v^3(1 + v^2)}.$

9. $\int \dfrac{dy}{y(9 + y^2)^2}.$

10. $\int \dfrac{y\,dy}{(4 + y^2)^3}.$

11. $\int \dfrac{\cos \varphi\,d\varphi}{\sin^3 \varphi + 9 \sin \varphi}.$

$Ans.\ \dfrac{1}{18}\ln \dfrac{\sin^2 \varphi}{9 + \sin^2 \varphi} + C.$

12. $\int \dfrac{\sec^2 \theta\,d\theta}{4 \tan^3 \theta + \tan \theta}.$

$Ans.\ \dfrac{1}{2}\ln \dfrac{\tan^2 \theta}{4 \tan^2 \theta + 1} + C.$

13. $\int \dfrac{(x^3 - 4)\,dx}{x^3 + 2x^2 + 2x}.$

$Ans.\ x - 2 \ln x + 2\,\text{Arctan}\,(x + 1) + C.$

14. $\int \dfrac{(x^3 + 10)\,dx}{x^3 - 2x^2 + 5x}.$

$Ans.\ x + 2 \ln x - \dfrac{1}{2}\text{Arctan}\dfrac{x-1}{2} + C.$

15. $\int \dfrac{v \ln v\,dv}{(1 + v^2)^2}.$

$Ans.\ \dfrac{1}{2}\ln v - \dfrac{1}{4}\ln (1 + v^2) - \dfrac{1}{2}\dfrac{\ln v}{1 + v^2} + C.$

16. $\int \dfrac{\text{Arctan}\,y\,dy}{y^3}.$

$Ans.\ -\dfrac{1}{2y} - \dfrac{1 + y^2}{2y^2}\text{Arctan}\,y + C.$

17. $\int \dfrac{dx}{x^3 - 2x^2 + 9x - 18}.$

$Ans.\ \dfrac{1}{13}\ln (x - 2) - \dfrac{1}{26}\ln (x^2 + 9) - \dfrac{2}{39}\text{Arctan}\dfrac{x}{3} + C.$

18. $\int \dfrac{(2x + 7)\,dx}{x^3 + x^2 + 4x + 4}.$ $Ans.\ \ln (x + 1) - \dfrac{1}{2}\ln (x^2 + 4) + \dfrac{3}{2}\text{Arctan}\dfrac{x}{2} + C.$

19. $\int \dfrac{(\theta + 65)\,d\theta}{\theta^3 + \theta^2 + \theta - 39}.$

$Ans.\ 2 \ln (\theta - 3) - \ln (\theta^2 + 4\theta + 13) - 3\,\text{Arctan}\dfrac{\theta + 2}{3} + C.$

20. $\int \dfrac{(y - 1)(y - 5)\,dy}{y^3 - y^2 + 3y - 5}.$

21. $\int \dfrac{dx}{(x^2 + 2x + 10)^2}.$ $Ans.\ \dfrac{x + 1}{18(x^2 + 2x + 10)} + \dfrac{1}{54}\text{Arctan}\dfrac{x+1}{3} + C.$

22. $\int \dfrac{(x^3 - 2x^2 + 1)\,dx}{(x^2 - 2x + 5)^2}.$

$Ans.\ \dfrac{1}{2}\ln (x^2 - 2x + 5) + \dfrac{1}{4}\text{Arctan}\dfrac{x-1}{2} - \dfrac{x - 6}{2(x^2 - 2x + 5)} + C.$

Definite Integrals.
Wallis' Formula

204. Definite Integrals

Now that we have acquired some facility in integration, it is feasible to start seriously on the many applications of the definite integral. Before taking up the applications, let us review the technique of definite integration, and in § 206, add one more tool to our kit.

Example (a). Evaluate $\int_0^{\frac{\pi}{3}} x \sin x \, dx$.

We employ integration by parts to obtain

$$\int_0^{\frac{\pi}{3}} x \sin x \, dx = \left[-x \cos x \right]_0^{\frac{\pi}{3}} + \int_0^{\frac{\pi}{3}} \cos x \, dx$$

$$= -\frac{\pi}{3} \cos \frac{\pi}{3} + 0 + \left[\sin x \right]_0^{\frac{\pi}{3}}$$

$$= -\frac{\pi}{6} + \sin \frac{\pi}{3} - 0$$

$$= \frac{\sqrt{3}}{2} - \frac{\pi}{6} = 0.342.$$

Example (b). Evaluate $\int_0^1 \frac{dy}{3 + 4y^2}$.

One of our standard formulas yields

$$\int_0^1 \frac{dy}{3 + 4y^2} = \frac{1}{2} \int_0^1 \frac{2dy}{3 + 4y^2} = \frac{1}{2\sqrt{3}} \left[\text{Arctan} \frac{2y}{\sqrt{3}} \right]_0^1$$

$$= \frac{1}{2\sqrt{3}} \text{Arctan} \frac{2}{\sqrt{3}} = 0.289 \, \text{Arctan} \, (1.155)$$

$$= (0.289)(0.86) = 0.25.$$

205. *Change of Variable with Change of Limits*

In the definite integral $\int_a^b f(x)\, dx$, it is always implied that a and b are *the limiting values of the variable of integration x.* If we change the variable by a substitution

$$(1) \qquad\qquad x = \varphi(z),$$

we must either return to the original variable before substituting the limits or *change the limits to correspond with the change of variable.* The latter method is usually preferable. The new limits are found, of course, from the equation of substitution (1).

Example. Evaluate $\displaystyle\int_0^a \frac{x^3\, dx}{(a^2 + x^2)^{\frac{3}{2}}}$.

Put $x = a \tan \varphi$. Then $dx = a \sec^2 \varphi\, d\varphi$; when $x = 0$, $\varphi = 0$, and when $x = a$, $\varphi = \frac{1}{4}\pi$. Thus we proceed as follows:

$$\int_0^a \frac{x^3\, dx}{(a^2 + x^2)^{\frac{3}{2}}} = \int_0^{\frac{\pi}{4}} \frac{a^3 \tan^3 \varphi\, a \sec^2 \varphi\, d\varphi}{(a^2 \sec^2 \varphi)^{\frac{3}{2}}}$$

$$= \frac{1}{a} \int_0^{\frac{\pi}{4}} \frac{\tan^3 \varphi\, d\varphi}{\sec^3 \varphi} = \frac{1}{a} \int_0^{\frac{\pi}{4}} \sin^3 \varphi\, d\varphi$$

$$= \frac{1}{a} \int_0^{\frac{\pi}{4}} \sin \varphi\, (1 - \cos^2 \varphi)\, d\varphi$$

$$= \frac{1}{a} \left[- \cos \varphi + \frac{\cos^3 \varphi}{3} \right]_0^{\frac{\pi}{4}}$$

$$= \frac{1}{a} \left[- \frac{1}{\sqrt{2}} + \frac{1}{6\sqrt{2}} - \left(-1 + \frac{1}{3} \right) \right]$$

$$= \frac{1}{a} \left[\frac{2}{3} - \frac{5}{6\sqrt{2}} \right] = \frac{4\sqrt{2} - 5}{6a\sqrt{2}}.$$

206. *Wallis' Formula*

The integral

$$(1) \qquad\qquad \int_0^{\frac{\pi}{2}} \sin^m x \cos^n x\, dx,$$

in which m and n are integers ≥ 0, arises over and over again in elementary applications. Fortunately the integral (1) can be evaluated simply, with a formula which is easy to remember in words, though bulky-looking in symbols.

We prove in the next section that, if *m* and *n* are integers > 1 [for exponents 0 and 1, see the rule following Example (*c*) below], then

(2) $\displaystyle\int_0^{\frac{\pi}{2}} \sin^m x \cos^n x\, dx$

$$= \frac{\left[(m-1)(m-3)\cdots\begin{smallmatrix}2\\\text{or}\\1\end{smallmatrix}\right]\left[(n-1)(n-3)\cdots\begin{smallmatrix}2\\\text{or}\\1\end{smallmatrix}\right]}{(m+n)(m+n-2)\cdots\begin{smallmatrix}2\\\text{or}\\1\end{smallmatrix}}\cdot\alpha,$$

in which

$$\alpha = \frac{\pi}{2}, \qquad \text{if } m \text{ and } n \text{ are both even,}$$

$$\alpha = 1, \qquad \text{otherwise.}$$

In words, the value of the integral (1) is $\dfrac{A\cdot B}{C}\cdot\alpha$, in which

A = the product, starting with one less than the exponent *m*, going down 2 at a time, until 2 or 1 is reached,
B = a similar product, starting with one less than the other exponent,
C = a similar product, starting with the sum of the exponents,
$\alpha = \dfrac{\pi}{2}$, if *m* and *n* are both even,
$\alpha = 1$, otherwise.

Example (a).   Evaluate $\displaystyle\int_0^{\frac{\pi}{2}} \sin^8 x \cos^4 x\, dx$.

By Wallis' formula, we obtain

$$\int_0^{\frac{\pi}{2}} \sin^8 x \cos^4 x\, dx = \frac{(7\cdot5\cdot3\cdot1)(3\cdot1)}{12\cdot10\cdot8\cdot6\cdot4\cdot2}\cdot\frac{\pi}{2} = \frac{7\pi}{2^{11}} = \frac{7\pi}{2048}.$$

Example (b).   Evaluate $\displaystyle\int_0^{\frac{\pi}{2}} \sin^5 \beta \cos^6 \beta\, d\beta$.

By Wallis' formula,

$$\int_0^{\frac{\pi}{2}} \sin^5 \beta \cos^6 \beta\, d\beta = \frac{(4\cdot2)(5\cdot3\cdot1)}{11\cdot9\cdot7\cdot5\cdot3\cdot1}\cdot1$$

$$= \frac{2^3}{11\cdot9\cdot7} = \frac{8}{693}.$$

Example (c).   Evaluate $\displaystyle\int_0^{\frac{\pi}{2}} \cos^3 \varphi \sin^5 \varphi \, d\varphi$.

At once,

$$\int_0^{\frac{\pi}{2}} \cos^3 \varphi \sin^5 \varphi \, d\varphi = \frac{(2)(4 \cdot 2)}{8 \cdot 6 \cdot 4 \cdot 2} \cdot 1 = \frac{1}{8 \cdot 3} = \frac{1}{24}.$$

If either m or n is unity, the integral (1) can be evaluated at once by the power formula. If either m or n is zero, the result is not so simple, but one added device permits us to include that result in the forumla (2).

RULE. *If the first factor in any of the products to be formed in applying Wallis' formula, for m, $n \geq 0$, is less than one, replace that product by unity.*

Example (d).   Evaluate $\displaystyle\int_0^{\frac{\pi}{2}} \cos^7 \varphi \sin \varphi \, d\varphi$.

Here, in forming the product associated with the exponent of the sine, we would normally start with one less than one, namely with zero. Hence, by the rule above, we replace that product by unity, and write

$$\int_0^{\frac{\pi}{2}} \cos^7 \varphi \sin \varphi \, d\varphi = \frac{(6 \cdot 4 \cdot 2)(1)}{8 \cdot 6 \cdot 4 \cdot 2} = \frac{1}{8},$$

a result readily verified by direct integration. Since this integration is so easily performed by the power formula of § 188, the student should realize that the example is included only *because* it permits such simple verification. In practice we do not use Wallis' formula when one of the exponents is unity; such a procedure would be somewhat like using an atom bomb to remove a tree stump.

Example (e).   Evaluate $\displaystyle\int_0^{\frac{\pi}{2}} \sin^6 y \, dy$.

Here one exponent is zero. Now $6 + 0 = 6$, to start the denominator product. Also, 6 and 0 are both even. Hence,

$$\int_0^{\frac{\pi}{2}} \sin^6 y \, dy = \frac{(5 \cdot 3 \cdot 1)(1)}{6 \cdot 4 \cdot 2} \cdot \frac{\pi}{2} = \frac{5\pi}{2^5} = \frac{5\pi}{32}.$$

207. *Derivation of Wallis' Formula*

First, consider the integral

(1) $$T = \int_0^{\frac{\pi}{2}} \cos^n x \, dx.$$

Use integration by parts, with $u = \cos^{n-1} x$, $dv = \cos x\, dx$, to obtain

$$T = \left[\cos^{n-1} x \sin x \right]_0^{\frac{\pi}{2}} + (n-1) \int_0^{\frac{\pi}{2}} \cos^{n-2} x \sin^2 x\, dx$$

$$= 0 + (n-1) \int_0^{\frac{\pi}{2}} \cos^{n-2} x\, (1 - \cos^2 x)\, dx$$

$$= (n-1) \int_0^{\frac{\pi}{2}} \cos^{n-2} x\, dx - (n-1)\, T,$$

from which

(2) $$T = \frac{n-1}{n} \int_0^{\frac{\pi}{2}} \cos^{n-2} x\, dx.$$

In a like manner, replacing n by $(n-2)$ in (2), we find that

$$\int_0^{\frac{\pi}{2}} \cos^{n-2} x\, dx = \frac{n-3}{n-2} \int_0^{\frac{\pi}{2}} \cos^{n-4} x\, dx,$$

and the process can be iterated, beating down the exponent of the cosine two at a time, until the exponent is one or zero.

Thus, if n is even,

$$T = \frac{n-1}{n} \cdot \frac{n-3}{n-2} \cdots \frac{3}{4} \cdot \frac{1}{2} \int_0^{\frac{\pi}{2}} \cos^0 x\, dx$$

$$= \frac{(n-1)(n-3) \cdots 3 \cdot 1}{n(n-2) \cdots 4 \cdot 2} \cdot \frac{\pi}{2},$$

as described in the rule of the preceding section.

If n is odd, iteration of (2) yields

$$T = \frac{n-1}{n} \cdot \frac{n-3}{n-2} \cdots \frac{4}{5} \cdot \frac{2}{3} \int_0^{\frac{\pi}{2}} \cos x\, dx$$

$$= \frac{(n-1)(n-3) \cdots 4 \cdot 2}{n(n-2) \cdots 5 \cdot 3} \cdot 1,$$

also as described in the rule of the preceding section.

In order to evaluate $\int_0^{\frac{\pi}{2}} \sin^n x\, dx$, put $x = \frac{1}{2}\pi - y$, and thus obtain

$$\int_0^{\frac{\pi}{2}} \sin^n x\, dx = - \int_{\frac{\pi}{2}}^0 \cos^n y\, dy = \int_0^{\frac{\pi}{2}} \cos^n y\, dy,$$

the integral already treated above.

Finally, consider

(3) $$W = \int_0^{\frac{\pi}{2}} \sin^m x \cos^n x \, dx.$$

Use integration by parts, with $u = \sin^{m-1} x$, $dv = \cos^n x \sin x \, dx$, to find that

$$W = \frac{-1}{n+1} \left[\sin^{m-1} x \cos^{n+1} x \right]_0^{\frac{\pi}{2}} + \frac{m-1}{n+1} \int_0^{\frac{\pi}{2}} \sin^{m-2} x \cos^{n+2} x \, dx$$

$$= 0 + \frac{m-1}{n+1} \int_0^{\frac{\pi}{2}} \sin^{m-2} x \cos^n x (1 - \sin^2 x) \, dx,$$

or

$$W = \frac{m-1}{n+1} \int_0^{\frac{\pi}{2}} \sin^{m-2} x \cos^n x \, dx - \frac{m-1}{n+1} W.$$

This last equation is easily solved for W, yielding

(4) $$W = \frac{m-1}{m+n} \int_0^{\frac{\pi}{2}} \sin^{m-2} x \cos^n x \, dx.$$

Formula (4) can be used to reduce the exponent on the sine two at a time, until that exponent is one or zero.

If m is odd in (3), then iteration of (4) gives

$$W = \frac{(m-1)(m-3) \cdots 4 \cdot 2}{(m+n)(m+n-2) \cdots (n+5)(n+3)} \int_0^{\frac{\pi}{2}} \sin x \cos^n x \, dx$$

$$= \frac{(m-1)(m-3) \cdots 4 \cdot 2}{(m+n)(m+n-2) \cdots (n+5)(n+3)(n+1)},$$

from which the result stated in Wallis' formula follows by inserting the factors $\left[(n-1)(n-3) \cdots \begin{array}{c} 2 \\ \text{or} \\ 1 \end{array} \right]$ in numerator and denominator.

If m is even in (3), then iteration of (4) gives

$$W = \frac{(m-1)(m-3) \cdots 3 \cdot 1}{(m+n)(m+n-2) \cdots (n+4)(n+2)} \int_0^{\frac{\pi}{2}} \cos^n x \, dx.$$

As the last step in obtaining the desired expression for W, we insert the value of the integral T, of equation (1), as determined at the beginning of this section, and we thus arrive at the formula

$$W = \frac{\left[(m-1)(m-3) \cdots 3 \cdot 1\right]\left[(n-1)(n-3) \cdots \begin{array}{c} 2 \\ \text{or} \\ 1 \end{array}\right]}{\left[(m+n)(m+n-2) \cdots (n+4)(n+2)\right]\left[n(n-2) \cdots \begin{array}{c} 2 \\ \text{or} \\ 1 \end{array}\right]} \cdot \alpha,$$

which is the result stated in Wallis' formula.

EXERCISES

In Exs. 1–18, use Wallis' formula.

1. $\int_0^{\frac{\pi}{2}} \sin^2 x \, dx.$ *Ans.* $\frac{\pi}{4}$. 2. $\int_0^{\frac{\pi}{2}} \cos^2 x \, dx.$ *Ans.* $\frac{\pi}{4}$.

3. $\int_0^{\frac{\pi}{2}} \cos^5 y \, dy.$ *Ans.* $\frac{8}{15}$. 4. $\int_0^{\frac{\pi}{2}} \sin^7 y \, dy.$ *Ans.* $\frac{16}{35}$

5. $\int_0^{\frac{\pi}{2}} \cos^3 \varphi \sin^4 \varphi \, d\varphi.$ *Ans.* $\frac{2}{35}$.

6. $\int_0^{\frac{\pi}{2}} \sin^6 \varphi \cos^4 \varphi \, d\varphi.$ *Ans.* $\frac{3\pi}{512}$.

7. $\int_0^{\frac{\pi}{2}} \sin^2 \alpha \cos^2 \alpha \, d\alpha.$ 8. $\int_0^{\frac{\pi}{2}} \sin^4 x \cos^5 x \, dx.$

9. $\int_0^{\frac{\pi}{2}} \cos^6 y \sin^7 y \, dy.$ 10. $\int_0^{\frac{\pi}{2}} \cos^{10} \theta \sin^4 \theta \, d\theta.$

11. $\int_0^{\frac{\pi}{2}} \sin^8 \theta \, d\theta.$ 12. $\int_0^{\frac{\pi}{2}} \sin^5 \theta \cos^5 \theta \, d\theta.$

13. $\int_0^1 (1 - x^2)^{\frac{3}{2}} \, dx.$ Put $x = \sin \varphi.$ *Ans.* $\frac{5\pi}{32}$.

14. $\int_0^a x^2(a^2 - x^2)^{\frac{3}{2}} \, dx.$ Put $x = a \sin \varphi.$ *Ans.* $\frac{\pi a^6}{32}$.

15. $\int_0^a x^5(a^2 - x^2)^6 \, dx.$ 16. $\int_0^1 x^4 \sqrt{1 - x^2} \, dx.$

17. $\int_0^{\frac{\pi}{6}} \cos^8 3\theta \, d\theta.$ Put $3\theta = x.$ *Ans.* $\frac{35\pi}{768}$.

18. $\int_0^{\pi} \sin^3 \tfrac{1}{2}y \cos^4 \tfrac{1}{2}y \, dy.$ Put $y = 2\varphi.$ *Ans.* $\frac{4}{35}$.

In Exs. 19–43, evaluate the given definite integral by any available device.

19. $\displaystyle\int_0^1 \frac{dx}{\sqrt{1 + 8x}}.$ *Ans.* $\frac{1}{2}$.

20. $\displaystyle\int_{-1}^0 \frac{x^2 \, dx}{(1 - x^3)^{\frac{3}{2}}}.$ *Ans.* $\dfrac{2 - \sqrt{2}}{3}.$

21. $\displaystyle\int_0^{\frac{\pi}{3}} \sin^3 y \, dy.$ *Ans.* $\frac{5}{24}$.

22. $\displaystyle\int_0^{\frac{\pi}{2}} \sin^3 y \, dy.$ *Ans.* $\frac{2}{3}$.

23. $\displaystyle\int_0^{\frac{\pi}{3}} \sin^2 x \, dx.$ *Ans.* $\dfrac{4\pi - 3\sqrt{3}}{24}.$

24. $\displaystyle\int_0^{\ln 2} x e^{-x} \, dx.$ *Ans.* $\frac{1}{2}(1 - \ln 2).$

25. $\displaystyle\int_1^2 \frac{x \, dx}{x + 1}.$ *Ans.* $1 - \ln \frac{3}{2}.$

26. $\displaystyle\int_0^{\frac{1}{2}} \frac{(5 - x) \, dx}{4x^2 + 1}.$ *Ans.* $\dfrac{5\pi - \ln 2}{8}.$

27. $\displaystyle\int_1^{\sqrt{3}} \text{Arctan } x \, dx.$ *Ans.* $-\dfrac{1}{2} \ln 2 + \dfrac{\pi}{12}(4\sqrt{3} - 3).$

28. $\displaystyle\int_0^1 \frac{y \, dy}{(1 + y)^4}.$ *Ans.* $\frac{1}{12}$.

29. $\displaystyle\int_0^1 x \sin (2x^2) \, dx.$ *Ans.* $\frac{1}{4}(1 - \cos 2).$

30. $\displaystyle\int_2^3 \frac{x^3 - 2x}{x - 1} \, dx.$

31. $\displaystyle\int_3^4 \frac{dv}{(2 - v)^3}.$

32. $\displaystyle\int_{-2}^2 \frac{dv}{v^2 + 4}.$

33. $\displaystyle\int_{\frac{\pi}{3}}^{\frac{2\pi}{3}} \csc x \cot x \, dx.$

34. $\displaystyle\int_0^a \frac{x^2 \, dx}{(a^2 + x^2)^2}.$ *Ans.* $\dfrac{\pi - 2}{8a}.$

35. $\displaystyle\int_0^1 \frac{x^3 \, dx}{(1 + x^2)^3}.$ *Ans.* $\frac{1}{16}$.

36. $\displaystyle\int_{-1}^1 \frac{dz}{\sqrt{4 - z^2}}.$ *Ans.* $\dfrac{\pi}{3}.$

37. $\displaystyle\int_0^{\frac{\pi}{6}} \tan 2\theta \, d\theta.$ *Ans.* 0.347.

38. $\displaystyle\int_0^{\ln 2} \frac{e^x \, dx}{2e^x - 1}.$ *Ans.* 0.549.

39. $\displaystyle\int_2^3 \frac{dx}{x^2 - 6x + 10}.$ *Ans.* $\dfrac{\pi}{4}.$

40. $\displaystyle\int_0^{\frac{\pi}{2}} \alpha \sin 3\alpha \, d\alpha.$ *Ans.* $-\frac{1}{9}$.

41. $\displaystyle\int_1^2 \frac{\ln x}{x} \, dx.$ *Ans.* 0.240.

42. $\displaystyle\int_0^1 y e^{-y^2} \, dy.$ *Ans.* $\frac{1}{2}(1 - e^{-1}).$

43. $\displaystyle\int_0^2 \frac{u \, du}{u^4 + 1}.$ *Ans.* 0.663.

44. $\displaystyle\int_0^1 \sqrt{1 - \sqrt{u}} \, du.$ Put $u = \sin^4 x.$ *Ans.* $\frac{8}{15}$.

Plane Areas.

Improper Integrals

208. *Plane Areas*

In our first attack on the problem of plane area, we were greatly handicapped by limited facility in integration. We therefore return briefly to this topic.

Example. Find the area of the loop of the curve

$$y^2 = 4x^2(1 - x).$$

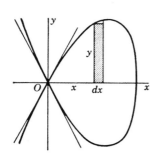

Figure 214

We have

$$A = 2 \int_0^1 y \, dx = 4 \int_0^1 x \sqrt{1 - x} \, dx.$$

Integrate by parts, with $u = x$:

$$A = -\tfrac{8}{3} \left[x(1 - x)^{\frac{3}{2}} \right]_0^1 + \tfrac{8}{3} \int_0^1 (1 - x)^{\frac{3}{2}} \, dx$$

$$= 0 - \tfrac{16}{15} \left[(1 - x)^{\frac{5}{2}} \right]_0^1 = \tfrac{16}{15}.$$

Let us obtain a check by evaluating the integral in another way. Put $\sqrt{1 - x} = v$. Then

$$x = 1 - v^2,$$

$$dx = -2v \, dv.$$

When $x = 0$, $v = 1$, and when $x = 1$, $v = 0$. Therefore

$$A = 4 \int_1^0 (1 - v^2)v(-2v \, dv) = 8 \int_0^1 v^2(1 - v^2) \, dv$$

$$= 8 \left[\frac{v^3}{3} - \frac{v^5}{5} \right]_0^1 = 8 \left(\frac{1}{3} - \frac{1}{5} \right) = \frac{16}{15}.$$

209. *Substitution Suggested by the Problem*

In Chapter 10, when finding plane areas by the formula

(1)
$$A = \int_a^b y\, dx,$$

we invariably substituted for y.   But it is equally proper, and frequently more convenient, to *substitute for dx and change to y-limits*.   That is, we take, as the substitution formula, *the equation of the curve itself.*

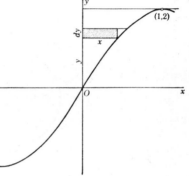

Of course similar remarks will apply in all the other applications that we shall take up.

Example. Find, in two ways, the area in the first quadrant bounded by the cubic $y = 3x - x^3$, and the lines $x = 0$, $y = 2$.   The curve is shown in Figure 215.

First method. Using a vertical element (not shown) and the technique of Chapter 10, we find that

Figure 215

$$A = \int_0^1 (2 - y)\, dx = \int_0^1 (2 - 3x + x^3)\, dx$$

$$= \left[2x - \frac{3x^2}{2} + \frac{x^4}{4} \right]_0^1$$

$$= 2 - \frac{3}{2} + \frac{1}{4} = \frac{3}{4}.$$

Second method. As a check we find the same area using the horizontal element shown in Figure 215:

$$A = \int_0^2 x\, dy.$$

It is not feasible to substitute for x, but we may easily substitute for dy and change limits:

$$dy = (3 - 3x^2)\, dx; \qquad x = 0 \text{ when } y = 0,\ x = 1 \text{ when } y = 2;$$

$$A = \int_0^2 x\, dy = 3 \int_0^1 (x - x^3)\, dx$$

$$= \left[\tfrac{3}{2}x^2 - \tfrac{3}{4}x^4 \right]_0^1 = \tfrac{3}{4}.$$

To evaluate an integral such as (1) when x and y are given in terms of a parameter, we *substitute for both y and dx*, taking as new limits the values of the parameter corresponding to the given limits.

Example (b).   Find the area of the ellipse (Figure 216)

$$x = a \cos \varphi, \qquad y = b \sin \varphi.$$

At once

$$A = 4 \int_0^a y \, dx.$$

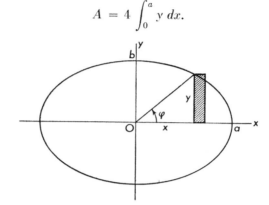

Figure 216

When $x = 0$, $\varphi = \frac{1}{2}\pi$, and when $x = a$, $\varphi = 0$.   Therefore

$$A = 4 \int_{\frac{1}{2}\pi}^0 (b \sin \varphi)(-a \sin \varphi \, d\varphi)$$

$$= 4ab \int_0^{\frac{1}{2}\pi} \sin^2 \varphi \, d\varphi$$

$$= 4ab \cdot \frac{1}{2} \cdot \frac{\pi}{2} = \pi ab.$$

The transformations suggested in this section are intuitively reasonable. Rigorous justification of them belongs to a course in advanced calculus.

EXERCISES

1. Find the area under one arch of the curve $y = \sin \frac{1}{2}x$.   *Ans.* 4.

2. Find the area under one arch of the curve $y = a \cos \dfrac{x}{a}$.   *Ans.* $2a^2$.

3. Find the area bounded by the curve $y = \ln x$ and the lines $y = 0$ and $x = e$. Solve in two ways.   *Ans.* 1.

4. Find the area bounded by the curve $y^2 = \dfrac{1}{(1 - x)^3}$ and the lines $x = -1$, $x = 0$.   *Ans.* 1.17.

5. Find the area in the first quadrant bounded by the x-axis, the line $x = a$, and the curve with parametric equations $x = a \sin^2 \varphi$, $y = 2a \sin \varphi$. Check your answer with that of Example (a), page 155.

6. Find the area bounded by the hyperbola $xy = a^2$ and the lines $y = 0$, $x = a$, $x = 2a$.   *Ans.* $a^2 \ln 2$.

7. Solve Ex. 6, using the equations $x = a \sec \varphi$, $y = a \cos \varphi$.

8. Find the area bounded by the curve $y = (1 - x^2)^2$ and the x-axis.   *Ans.* $\frac{16}{15}$.

9. Solve Ex. 8, using the horizontal element. Evaluate the integral in two ways.

10. Find the area bounded by the curve $y = \dfrac{\ln x}{x}$, the x-axis, and the maximum ordinate.   *Ans.* $\frac{1}{2}$.

11. Find the area bounded by the curve $y = \dfrac{\ln x - 1}{x}$, the x-axis, and the maximum ordinate.   *Ans.* $\frac{1}{2}$.

12. Find the area under the catenary $y = a \cosh \dfrac{x}{a}$ from $x = -a$ to $x = a$.

Ans. $2.35a^2$.

13. Find the area bounded by the curve $y = xe^{-x^2}$, the x-axis, and the maximum ordinate.   *Ans.* $\frac{1}{2}(1 - e^{-\frac{1}{2}})$.

14. Find the area bounded by the curve $y = \dfrac{x}{(x^2 + 3)^2}$, the x-axis, and the extreme ordinates.   *Ans.* $\frac{1}{12}$

15. Find the area of the first arch of the curve $y = x \sin x$.

16. Find the area of the first arch of the curve $y = e^{-x} \sin x$.   *Ans.* $\frac{1}{2}(1 + e^{-\pi})$.

17. Find the area of one arch of the cycloid (Figure 217)

$$x = a(\theta - \sin \theta), \quad y = a(1 - \cos \theta).$$
Ans. $3\pi a^2$.

Figure 217

18. Find the area of a circular sector of radius r and angle α. Check the result for specific values of α.   *Ans.* $\frac{1}{2}r^2\alpha$.

19. Find the area of the four-cusped hypocycloid $x^{\frac{2}{3}} + y^{\frac{2}{3}} = a^{\frac{2}{3}}$. (Figure 169, page 257.)   *Ans.* $\frac{3}{8}\pi a^2$.

20. Solve Ex. 19, using the parametric equations $x = a \cos^3 t$, $y = a \sin^3 t$.

21. Find the area bounded by the curve $y = \dfrac{1 + x^2}{2x^2}$ and the lines $y = 0$, $y = x$, $x = 2$.   *Ans.* $\frac{5}{4}$.

22. Find the area bounded by the curve $y^3 = x^3 + x^4$ and the x-axis.   *Ans.* $\frac{9}{28}$.

23. Find the area bounded by the curve $y = \dfrac{2x - 3}{x^2 + 4}$, the axes, and the minimum ordinate.   *Ans.* 0.92.

24. Find the area in the first quadrant under the curve $y^2 = \dfrac{x^2}{x-1}$ between the minimum ordinate and the line $x = 3$. *Ans.* 2.05.

25. Find the area bounded by the curve $2y^2 + 2y - x - 2 = 0$ and the line $x = 2y$. *Ans.* $\frac{8}{3}$.

26. Find the area bounded by the parabolas $y^2 = 4x$ and $y^2 + 12x = 36$. *Ans.* 12.

27. Find the area of the loop of the curve $y^2 = x(1 - x^2)^2$. *Ans.* $\frac{16}{21}$.

28. Find the area of the loop of the curve $y^2 = x^3(1 - x^2)^2$. *Ans.* $\frac{16}{45}$.

29. Find the area of the loop of the curve $a^7y^2 = x^5(a^2 - x^2)^2$. *Ans.* $\frac{16}{77}a^2$.

30. Find the area enclosed by the curve $a^2y^2 = x^2(a^2 - x^2)$. *Ans.* $\frac{4}{3}a^2$.

In solving Exs. 31–41, it will be found that Wallis' formula is particularly useful.

31. Find the area enclosed by the curve $y^2 = x^4(1 - x^2)$. *Ans.* $\frac{1}{4}\pi$.

32. Find the area enclosed by the curve $y^2 = x^6(1 - x^2)^3$. *Ans.* $\frac{8}{35}$.

33. Find the area enclosed by the curve $y^2 = x^3(1 - x)$. *Ans.* $\frac{1}{8}\pi$.

34. Find the area enclosed by the curve $y^2 = x(1 - x)^5$. *Ans.* $\frac{5}{64}\pi$.

35. Find the area enclosed by the curve $a^6y^2 = x^5(a - x)^3$. *Ans.* $\frac{3}{128}\pi a^2$.

36. Find the area of the loop of the curve $y^2 = x^4(1 - x)^5$. *Ans.* $\frac{32}{693}$.

37. Find the area of the loop of the curve $a^3y^2 = x^2(a - x)^3$. *Ans.* $\frac{8}{35}a^2$.

38. Find the area of the loop of the curve $y^2 = x^4(1 - x)^3$. *Ans.* $\frac{32}{315}$.

39. Find the area of the loop of the curve $y^2 = x^3(1 - x)^6$. *Ans.* $\frac{64}{1155}$.

40. Find the area of the loop of the curve $y^2 = x(1 - x)^6$. *Ans.* $\frac{64}{315}$.

41. Find the area enclosed by the curve $y^2 = (1 - x^2)^9$. *Ans.* $\frac{63}{128}\pi$.

42. Find the area enclosed by the curve $y^2 = (x + 1)^2(4 - x^2)$. *Ans.* $6\sqrt{3} + \frac{4}{3}\pi$.

210. *Plane Areas in Polar Coordinates*

Given the equation

$$r = f(\theta)$$

of a plane curve in polar coordinates, let us try to find the area bounded by the curve and two fixed radius vectors $\theta = \alpha$, $\theta = \beta$, as shown in Figure 218, page 379.

Inscribe in the area n *circular sectors* of radius r_i and angle $\Delta\theta$. By elementary geometry (or Ex. 18, page 377), the area of each sector is $\frac{1}{2}r_i^2\,\Delta\theta$.

Now add up the areas of all the sectors: $\displaystyle\sum_{i=1}^{n} \frac{1}{2}r_i^2\,\Delta\theta$. As n increases and the sectors become narrower and narrower, this sum *approaches as its limit the area under the curve.* Hence, by Theorem 29, § 81,

$$A = \lim_{n\to\infty} \sum_{i=1}^{n} \frac{1}{2}r_i^2\,\Delta\theta = \frac{1}{2}\int_{\alpha}^{\beta} r^2\,d\theta.$$

For the present, we must rely upon geometric intuition to assure us that the limit of this sum (i.e., the area) is the same as the one appearing in the definition (§ 81). From a formulation to be set up in § 308, this fact will appear clearly.

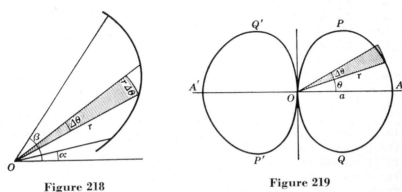

Figure 218   Figure 219

Example. Find the area within the curve $r^2 = a^2 \cos \theta$. (Figure 219.)

As θ varies from 0 to $\frac{1}{2}\pi$, we get positive and negative values of r, giving rise to the arcs APO, $A'P'O$. For $\frac{1}{2}\pi < \theta < \frac{3}{2}\pi$, r is imaginary. For $\frac{3}{2}\pi < \theta < 2\pi$, we get the arcs OQA, $OQ'A'$. Integrate through the first quadrant and multiply by* 4:

$$A = 4 \cdot \frac{1}{2} \int_0^{\frac{1}{2}\pi} r^2 \, d\theta = 2a^2 \int_0^{\frac{1}{2}\pi} \cos \theta \, d\theta = 2a^2 \left[\sin \theta \right]_0^{\frac{1}{2}\pi} = 2a^2.$$

In this example, since the curve is symmetric in all four quadrants, it might seem that we could equally well have integrated from 0 to 2π. Trying this, we find

$$\frac{1}{2} \int_0^{2\pi} r^2 \, d\theta = \frac{1}{2}a^2 \int_0^{2\pi} \cos \theta \, d\theta = \frac{1}{2}a^2 \left[\sin \theta \right]_0^{2\pi} = 0.$$

This result, puzzling at first, is due to a peculiarity of the polar coordinate system. Although the curve appears in the second and third quadrants, these arcs, as noted above, correspond not to values of θ in those quadrants but to values of θ in the first and fourth quadrants with negative r: when $\frac{1}{2}\pi < \theta < \frac{3}{2}\pi$, r^2 becomes negative and r imaginary. When we integrate across a region in which this occurs, each of the elements $\frac{1}{2}r^2 \, d\theta$ is negative, and the same is true of the limit of their sum. This illustrates the fact that in polar coordinates, *it is not safe to choose the limits merely from the appearance of the curve.* Here, even more than in rectangular coordinates, it is best to *keep the limits of integration as narrow as possible* by using considerations of symmetry to the fullest extent.

* The answer may be checked by comparing the area of the curve with that of a rectangle of sides $2a$, a with center at O.

EXERCISES

In Exs. 1–19, find the area enclosed by the given curve.

1. $r = 2a \sin \theta$.　　　　　　　　　　　　　　　　　　　　*Ans.* πa^2.
2. $r = 2a \sin^2 \theta$.　　　　　　　　　　　　　　　　　　*Ans.* $\frac{3}{2}\pi a^2$.
3. $r = 2a \cos^2 \theta$.　　　　　　　　　　　　　　　　　　*Ans.* $\frac{3}{2}\pi a^2$.
4. $r = 2a \cos \theta$.　　　　　　　　　　　　　　　　　　　*Ans.* πa^2.
5. $r = a \cos 2\theta$.　　　　　　　　　　　　　　　　　　　*Ans.* $\frac{1}{2}\pi a^2$.
6. $r = a \sin 2\theta$.　　　　　　　　　　　　　　　　　　　*Ans.* $\frac{1}{2}\pi a^2$.
7. $r = a \cos 3\theta$.　　　　　　　　　　　　　　　　　　　*Ans.* $\frac{1}{4}\pi a^2$.
8. $r = a \sin 3\theta$.　　　　　　　　　　　　　　　　　　　*Ans.* $\frac{1}{4}\pi a^2$.
9. $r = a(1 - \sin \theta)$.　　　　　　　　　　　　　　　　*Ans.* $\frac{3}{2}\pi a^2$.
10. $r = a(2 + \cos \theta)$.　　　　　　　　　　　　　　　*Ans.* $\frac{9}{2}\pi a^2$.
11. $r = a(3 - 2 \sin \theta)$.　　　　　　　　　　　　　*Ans.* $11\pi a^2$.
12. $r^2 = a^2 \sin 2\theta$.　　　　　　　　　　　　　　　*Ans.* a^2.
13. $r^2 = a^2 \cos 2\theta$.　　　　　　　　　　　　　　　*Ans.* a^2.
14. $r^2 = a^2(2 \cos \theta - 1)$.　　　　　　　　　　*Ans.* $1.37a^2$.
15. $r = a(1 + \cos \theta)$.　　　　　　　　　　　　　　*Ans.* $\frac{3}{2}\pi a^2$.
16. $r^2 = a^2 \cos \theta(1 - \cos \theta)$.　　　　　*Ans.* $0.43a^2$.
17. $r^2 = a^2 \sin \theta(1 + \sin \theta)$.　　　　　*Ans.* $3.57a^2$.
18. $r^2 = a^2 \sin \theta(1 - 2 \sin \theta)$.　　　*Ans.* $0.09a^2$.
19. $r^2 = a^2(\sin \theta + \cos \theta)$.　　　　　　*Ans.* $2 \sqrt{2}\, a^2$.

20. Find the area of the inner loop of the curve $r = a(1 + 2 \cos \theta)$.　*Ans.* $0.54a^2$.
21. Find the area between the inner and outer ovals of the curve $r^2 = a^2(1 + \sin \theta)$.
　　　　　　　　　　　　　　　　　　　　　　　　　　　　　　　　Ans. $4a^2$.
22. Find the area between the ovals of the curve $r^2 = a^2(2 - \cos \theta)$.　*Ans.* $4a^2$.
23. Find the area of the curve $r^2 = a^2 \sin \theta(1 - \cos \theta)$.　　*Ans.* $2a^2$.
24. Find the area of the curve $r^2 = a^2 \cos \theta(2 - \cos^2 \theta)$.　　*Ans.* $\dfrac{8a^2}{3}$.

25. Find the area of the curve $r^2 = a^2 \cos \theta \cos 2\theta$.

　　　　　　　　　Ans. $\frac{1}{3}(4 \sqrt{2} - 2)a^2 = 1.22a^2$.
26. Find the area inside the *spiral of Archimedes* $r = a\theta$, from $\theta = 0$ to $\theta = 2\pi$.
　　　　　　　　　　　　　　　　　　　　　　　　　　　　Ans. $\frac{4}{3}\pi^3 a^2$.
27. Find the area inside the *logarithmic spiral* $r = ae^{k\theta}$, from $\theta = 0$ to $\theta = 2\pi$.

　　　　　　　　　Ans. $\dfrac{a^2}{4k}(e^{4k\pi} - 1)$.

Solve Exs. 28–35 in polar coordinates.

28. Find the area cut off from the parabola $y^2 = 4ax$ by a chord through the vertex making an angle α with the axis.　　　　　*Ans.* $\frac{8}{3}a^2 \cot^3 \alpha$.
29. A chord of a circle makes an angle α with the tangents at its ends. Find the area of the segment cut off.　　　　　*Ans.* $(\alpha - \sin \alpha \cos \alpha)a^2$.
30. Find the area in the first quadrant bounded by the curves $y = x^3$, $y = 2x$.
31. Find the area bounded by the curves $y^2 = 4ax$, $y = 2x$, $y = 4x$.　*Ans.* $\frac{7}{24}a^2$.
32. Find the area of the loop of the folium $x^3 + y^3 = 3axy$.　　*Ans.* $\frac{3}{2}a^2$.

33. Find the area in the first quadrant bounded by the straight line $y = x$ and
the curve $(x^2 + a^2)y^2 = 4a^2x^2$.   Ans. $\frac{1}{2}a^2$.

34. Find the area between the curve $(a^2 - x^2)y^2 = x^4$ and its asymptotes.

Ans. πa^2.

35. Find the area of the loop of the curve $(y^2 - x^2)^2 = x^5$.   Ans. $\frac{128}{315}$.

36. Solve Ex. 33 in rectangular coordinates.

37. Solve Ex. 35 in rectangular coordinates.

211. *Integrable Functions*

A function $f(x)$ is said to be *integrable* in the interval $a \leqq x \leqq b$ if the
definite integral

$$A = \int_a^b f(x)\, dx$$

has a meaning.

We have spoken from time to time of being "able to evaluate" an integral,
meaning by this, able to express it in terms of elementary functions.   But
we know (§ 81) that the area "under" any continuous curve *exists*; hence
every continuous function is integrable.   Whether or not we can express the

integral in elementary terms is imma-
terial: if not, it will still be possible by
more advanced methods to evaluate
it in the strict sense of the term—i.e.,
to find its value, to any degree of approximation, for given values of
a and b.

Furthermore, if the function has a
finite number of finite discontinuities
in the interval, as in Figure 220, the
area still exists, and the function is
integrable.

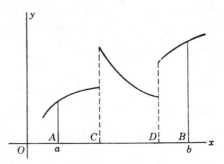

Figure 220

DEFINITION.   *If $f(x)$ has a finite discontinuity at $x = b$, then*

$$\int_a^b f(x)\, dx = \operatorname*{Lim}_{c \to b^-} \int_a^c f(x)\, dx;$$

if there is a finite discontinuity at $x = a$, then

$$\int_a^b f(x)\, dx = \operatorname*{Lim}_{c \to a^+} \int_c^b f(x)\, dx.$$

Applying this definition, repeatedly if necessary, we integrate over the
separate segments and add the results.   In this connection, missing-point
discontinuities (§ 36) may be ignored, since the value of the function, or
lack of any value, at a single point cannot affect the value of the area.

We proceed to extend the list of integrable functions still further.

212. *Improper Integrals*

In certain instances, a meaning may be assigned to the function

$$A = \int_a^b f(x)\, dx$$

under either or both of the following circumstances:

(a) Either a or b, or both, increase numerically without limit; or

(b) The integrand $f(x)$ has an infinite discontinuity at an end point or one or more interior points of the interval.

In either case, the integral is called an *improper integral*.

213. *Integrals with Infinite Limits*

If we keep a fixed, the integral

$$A = \int_a^b f(x)\, dx$$

becomes a function of b only.   It may happen that, as b increases without bound, the function A approaches a limit.   If so, this limit is denoted by the symbol $\int_a^\infty f(x)\, dx$:

$$\int_a^\infty f(x)\, dx = \operatorname*{Lim}_{b \to \infty} \int_a^b f(x)\, dx.$$

Similarly,

$$\int_{-\infty}^b f(x)\, dx = \operatorname*{Lim}_{a \to -\infty} \int_a^b f(x)\, dx;$$

(1)
$$\int_{-\infty}^\infty f(x)\, dx = \operatorname*{Lim}_{a \to -\infty} \int_a^c f(x)\, dx + \operatorname*{Lim}_{b \to \infty} \int_c^b f(x)\, dx,$$

where c may have any fixed value.   If the limits occurring in the right members do not exist, the integrals on the left have no meaning.

It should be noted that $\int_{-\infty}^\infty f(x)\, dx$ does not mean $\operatorname*{Lim}_{b \to \infty} \int_{-b}^b f(x)\, dx$.   If the former exists, then the latter also exists, and the two limits are equal; but the latter may exist when the former does not.   For example,

$$\operatorname*{Lim}_{b \to \infty} \int_{-b}^b x\, dx = \operatorname*{Lim}_{b \to \infty} \left[\frac{x^2}{2} \right]_{-b}^b = \operatorname*{Lim}_{b \to \infty} \left(\frac{b^2}{2} - \frac{b^2}{2} \right) = 0;$$

but $\int_{-\infty}^\infty x\, dx$ has no meaning, since neither limit in (1) exists.

Example (a). $\displaystyle \int_1^\infty \frac{dx}{x^2} = \operatorname*{Lim}_{b \to \infty} \int_1^b \frac{dx}{x^2} = \operatorname*{Lim}_{b \to \infty} \left[-\frac{1}{x} \right]_1^b = 1.$

The curve $y = \dfrac{1}{x^2}$ is shown in Figure 221. Geometrically the above integral means the limit of the shaded area as b becomes infinite. This limit

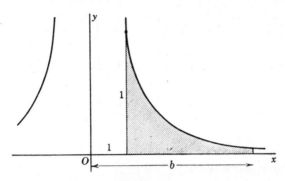

Figure 221

we *define* as the "area bounded by" the curve, the x-axis, and the line $x = 1$, although it is not properly a bounded area in the literal sense. It is evident that a similar argument holds in general; an integral with an infinite limit may be interpreted as the area under a curve which approaches the x-axis, usually without ever reaching it. In ordinary cases, the x-axis is an asymptote of the curve. However, even though the curve is asymptotic to Ox, the integral does not necessarily have a meaning (see, for example, Exs. 24–25 below).

Example (*b*). Find the area between the curve $y = \dfrac{x^2 - 1}{x^2 + 1}$ and its asymptote.

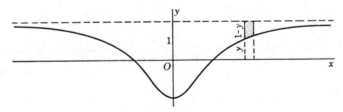

Figure 222

Since the curve is symmetric with respect to Oy, we may write

$$A = 2 \int_0^\infty \left(1 - \frac{x^2 - 1}{x^2 + 1} \right) dx.$$

Reduce the integrand to a common denominator:

$$A = 4 \int_0^\infty \frac{dx}{1 + x^2} = \lim_{b \to \infty} 4 \int_0^b \frac{dx}{1 + x^2} = \lim_{b \to \infty} \left[4 \operatorname{Arctan} x \right]_0^b = 2\pi.$$

EXERCISES

Evaluate the integrals in Exs. 1–13.

1. $\displaystyle\int_1^\infty \frac{dx}{x^4}.$　　Ans. $\frac{1}{3}.$　　2. $\displaystyle\int_0^\infty e^{-4y}\,dy.$　　Ans. $\frac{1}{4}.$

3. $\displaystyle\int_{-\infty}^0 e^{3x}\,dx.$　　Ans. $\frac{1}{3}.$　　4. $\displaystyle\int_0^\infty xe^{-x^2}\,dx.$　　Ans. $\frac{1}{2}.$

5. $\displaystyle\int_0^\infty \frac{x\,dx}{(x^2+9)^2}.$　　Ans. $\frac{1}{18}.$　　6. $\displaystyle\int_{-\infty}^\infty \frac{x\,dx}{(x^2+9)^2}.$　　Ans. $0.$

7. $\displaystyle\int_1^\infty \frac{dx}{x\sqrt{4x^2-1}}.$　　Ans. $\dfrac{\pi}{6}.$

8. Do Ex. 7 a second way.

9. Do Ex. 7 a third way.

10. $\displaystyle\int_1^\infty \frac{dx}{x(x^2+1)}.$　　Ans. $0.347.$

11. $\displaystyle\int_1^\infty \frac{dx}{x\sqrt{x^2+1}}.$　　Ans. $0.881.$

12. $\displaystyle\int_0^\infty e^{-st}\,dt.$　　Ans. $\dfrac{1}{s}$, for $s>0$; meaningless, for $s \leqq 0.$

13. $\displaystyle\int_0^\infty te^{-st}\,dt;\ s>0.$　　Ans. $\dfrac{1}{s^2}.$

14. Find the area between the curve $y = xe^{-\frac{1}{2}x^2}$ and its asymptote.　　Ans. $2.$

15. Find the area bounded by the curve $y = xe^x$ and its asymptote.　　Ans. $1.$

16. Find the area between the curve $y = \dfrac{a^3}{x^2+a^2}$ and its asymptote.　　Ans. $\pi a^2.$

17. Find the area under the curve $y = \dfrac{1}{x^2-1}$ to the right of the line $x = 2.$

Ans. $\frac{1}{2}\ln 3.$

18. Find the area under the curve $y = \dfrac{1}{x(x+1)^2}$ to the right of the line $x = 1.$

Ans. $\ln 2 - \frac{1}{2} = 0.193.$

19. Find the area between the curve $y = \dfrac{x}{(1+x^2)^2}$ and its asymptote.　　Ans. $1.$

20. Find the area bounded by the curve $y^2 = \dfrac{a^3}{(a^2+x^2)^3}$ and the lines $x = \pm\frac{1}{3}\sqrt{3}\,a.$

Ans. $2a^2.$

21. Find the entire area enclosed by the curve $y^2 = \dfrac{a^8}{(a^2+x^2)^3}.$　　Ans. $4a^2.$

22. Solve Ex. 21 by another method.

23. Find the area bounded by the curve $y = \dfrac{1}{(x^2 + 4)^2}$ and its asymptote.

$$Ans. \ \frac{\pi}{16}.$$

24. Find the area under the hyperbola $xy = a^2$ to the right of the line $x = a$.

Ans. Meaningless.

25. Find the area under the curve $y = \dfrac{1}{x \ln x}$ to the right of the line $x = e$.

Ans. Meaningless.

26. In § 140, find the area bounded by the path of the man, the path of the weight, and the original position of the rope. (Set up the integral with vertical element; see Ex. 19, page 251.)

$$Ans. \ \tfrac{1}{4}\pi a^2.$$

214. *Infinite Discontinuities of the Integrand*

Consider now the second class of improper integrals mentioned in § 212, those in which the limits are finite but the integrand has an infinite discontinuity at an end point or an interior point of the interval.

DEFINITIONS.   *If $f(x)$ increases numerically without limit as $x \rightarrow b^-$,*

$$\int_a^b f(x)\, dx = \operatorname*{Lim}_{c \to b^-} \int_a^c f(x)\, dx;$$

if $f(x)$ increases numerically without limit as $x \rightarrow a^+$,

$$\int_a^b f(x)\, dx = \operatorname*{Lim}_{c \to a^+} \int_c^b f(x)\, dx.$$

Example (a). Find the area bounded by the curve $xy^2 = 1$, the axes, and the line $x = 1$.

We write

$$A = \int_0^1 y\, dx = \operatorname*{Lim}_{c \to 0^+} \int_c^1 \frac{dx}{\sqrt{x}}$$

$$= \operatorname*{Lim}_{c \to 0^+} \left[2\sqrt{x} \right]_c^1 = \operatorname*{Lim}_{c \to 0^+} (2 - 2\sqrt{c})$$

$$= 2.$$

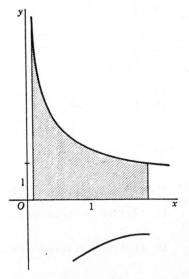

Figure 223

When the integrand $f(x)$ has an infinite discontinuity at an interior point of the interval—say, at $x = c$, where $a < c < b$—we merely subdivide the interval.

Example (b).   Find the area under the curve $x^2 y = 1$ from

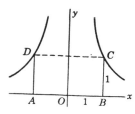

Figure 224

$x = -1$ to $x = 1$.

Since y becomes infinite at the interior point $x = 0$, we write

$$A = \int_{-1}^{1} y\, dx = \operatorname*{Lim}_{c_1 \to 0^-} \int_{-1}^{c_1} \frac{dx}{x^2} + \operatorname*{Lim}_{c_2 \to 0^+} \int_{c_2}^{1} \frac{dx}{x^2}$$

$$= \operatorname*{Lim}_{c_1 \to 0} \left[-\frac{1}{x} \right]_{-1}^{c_1} + \operatorname*{Lim}_{c_2 \to 0^+} \left[-\frac{1}{x} \right]_{c_2}^{1}.$$

Since these limits do not exist, the integral has no meaning.

EXERCISES

Evaluate the integrals in Exs. 1–10.

1. $\displaystyle\int_{0}^{1} \frac{dx}{x^{\frac{1}{3}}}.$ *Ans.* $\frac{3}{2}$.   **2.** $\displaystyle\int_{0}^{1} \frac{dx}{x^{\frac{4}{3}}}.$ *Ans.* Meaningless.

3. $\displaystyle\int_{-1}^{1} \frac{dx}{x^{\frac{1}{3}}}.$ *Ans.* 0.   **4.** $\displaystyle\int_{-1}^{1} \frac{dy}{y^{\frac{4}{3}}}.$ *Ans.* Meaningless.

5. $\displaystyle\int_{-1}^{3} \frac{du}{u+1}.$ *Ans.* Meaningless.

6. $\displaystyle\int_{\frac{1}{e}}^{e} \frac{dx}{x(\ln x)^{\frac{1}{3}}}.$ *Ans.* 0.

7. $\displaystyle\int_{-a}^{a} \frac{dx}{\sqrt{a^2 - x^2}}.$ *Ans.* π.   **8.** $\displaystyle\int_{-a}^{a} \frac{x^4\, dx}{\sqrt{a^2 - x^2}}.$ *Ans.* $\dfrac{3\pi a^4}{8}$.

9. $\displaystyle\int_{0}^{\frac{\pi}{2}} \sec^2 2\theta\, d\theta.$ *Ans.* Meaningless.

10. $\displaystyle\int_{-\frac{\pi}{4}}^{\frac{\pi}{4}} \csc\theta \cot\theta\, d\theta.$ *Ans.* Meaningless.

11. Find the area between the curve $xy^2 = (x-1)^2$ and the y-axis.   *Ans.* $\frac{8}{3}$.

12. Find the area between the curve $y^2 = \dfrac{1}{x(4-x)}$ and its asymptotes.   *Ans.* 2π.

13. Find the area between the curve $y^2 = \dfrac{x^4}{a^2 - x^2}$ and its asymptotes.   *Ans.* πa^2.

14. Find the area between the curve $y^2 = \dfrac{1}{x(1+x)^2}$ and the y-axis.   *Ans.* 2π.

15. Find the area in the fourth quadrant bounded by $y = \ln x$ and the axes. Solve in two ways.

16. Find the area between the curve $xy^2 = 1 - x$ and its asymptote. Solve in two ways.   *Ans.* π.

17. Find the area in the second quadrant under the curve $x^2y = e^{\frac{1}{x}}$.   *Ans.* 1.

18. Find the area between the curves $y = \dfrac{1}{x}$, $y = \dfrac{1}{x + x^2}$, from $x = 0$ to $x = 2$.

Ans. $\ln 3 = 1.099$.

19. Find the area between the curves $y = \csc x$, $y = \cot x$, from $x = -\dfrac{\pi}{2}$ to $x = \dfrac{\pi}{2}$.

Ans. $2 \ln 2 = 1.386$.

20. Find the area between the cissoid $y^2 = \dfrac{x^3}{2a - x}$ and its asymptote.   *Ans.* $3\pi a^2$.

21. Find the area between the curve $y = \dfrac{1}{x(1 + x^2)}$ and the x-axis.

Ans. Meaningless.

22. Find the area under the curve $y = \dfrac{1}{x^2 - 1}$.   *Ans.* Meaningless.

Three-dimensional Geometry

215. *Rectangular Coordinates*

To determine the position of a point in three-dimensional space, three magnitudes must be given. Thus to locate a point in the interior of a room, we may give its height above the floor and its distances from two adjacent walls; the position of a point in the interior of the earth may be fixed by its depth below the surface, together with the latitude and longitude of the point on the surface above it.

Usually the most convenient way of fixing the position of a point in space is by means of its *distances from three mutually perpendicular planes,* as in the first example cited. These distances are the *rectangular coordinates* of the point: the three planes are the *coordinate planes,* their three lines of intersection are the *coordinate axes,* and their point of intersection is the *origin.* The coordinates are denoted by the letters x, y, z and are written $P: (x, y, z)$, or merely (x, y, z). The three axes are called the x-axis, the y-axis, and the z-axis; the three planes are the xy-plane (containing the x- and y-axes), the yz-plane, and the zx-plane. Of course a definite positive sense must be chosen for each coordinate; i.e., the coordinates are *directed segments.*

Space is divided by the coordinate planes into eight compartments, or *octants.* The region in which all three coordinates are positive is called the *first octant;* there will be no occasion to refer to the others by number.

216. *Figures*

In the system of drawing adopted in this and most books, *parallel lines are represented by parallel lines;* i.e., if two lines in space are parallel, they are shown in the figure by lines that are actually parallel.

Two of the axes are represented by perpendicular lines, while the third (which, of course, is supposed to be perpendicular to the other two) is shown by a line drawn in any suitable direction. The axes will be placed as in Figure 225 (except when some other arrangement is more convenient), the positive half of each axis being the part drawn in full. Figures in the yz-plane, or in a plane parallel to that plane, are drawn in their true form and proportions; all others are distorted, due to foreshortening.

217. *Distance Between Two Points*

Given any two points P_1: (x_1, y_1, z_1), P_2: (x_2, y_2, z_2), as in Figure 226,

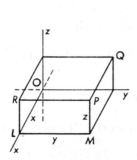

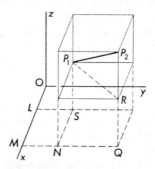

Figure 225   Figure 226

$$LM = x_2 - x_1,$$
$$NQ = y_2 - y_1,$$
$$RP_2 = z_2 - z_1.$$

Since

$$\overline{P_1P_2} = \sqrt{\overline{P_1R}^2 + \overline{RP_2}^2} = \sqrt{\overline{SN}^2 + \overline{NQ}^2 + \overline{RP_2}^2},$$

the length of the segment P_1P_2 is

(1) $$d = \sqrt{(x_2 - x_1)^2 + (y_2 - y_1)^2 + (z_2 - z_1)^2}.$$

218. *Mid-point of a Line Segment*

To find the point P: (x, y, z) bisecting the line segment joining P_1: (x_1, y_1, z_1) and P_2: (x_2, y_2, z_2), let us drop perpendiculars PL, P_1L_1, P_2L_2 from these points to Ox.   Then

$$OL = OL_1 + \tfrac{1}{2}L_1L_2;$$

that is,

$$x = x_1 + \tfrac{1}{2}(x_2 - x_1) = \tfrac{1}{2}(x_1 + x_2).$$

In this way we obtain the formulas

(1) $$\begin{cases} x = \tfrac{1}{2}(x_1 + x_2), \\ y = \tfrac{1}{2}(y_1 + y_2), \\ z = \tfrac{1}{2}(z_1 + z_2). \end{cases}$$

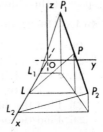

Figure 227

EXERCISES

1. Plot the points $(3, 4, 1)$, $(-3, 4, 1)$, $(-3, -4, 1)$.
2. Plot the points $(2, 3, 4)$, $(2, 3, -4)$, $(-2, 3, -4)$.
3. From the point $(2, 3, 4)$ draw perpendiculars to each coordinate axis; find the length of each perpendicular segment.

4. From the point (3, 2, 3) draw perpendiculars to each coordinate axis; find the length of each perpendicular segment.

5. In each coordinate plane, draw a line through O making an angle of 45° with each of the axes, and (a) a parallel, (b) a perpendicular to this line through an arbitrary point in that plane.

6. Draw a box with its edges parallel to the axes, having the points (0, 0, 0), (3, 4, 2) as ends of a diagonal.

7. In each coordinate plane, plot by points a circular quadrant of radius 5 with its center at the origin.

8. In the xy-plane, sketch the parabola $y^2 = 4x$.

9. In the yz-plane, sketch the parabola $y^2 = 16z$.

10. In the xz-plane, sketch the ellipse $x^2 + 4z^2 = 4$.

11. What is the distance of the point (x, y, z) from Ox? From Oy? From Oz? From O?

12. Where is a point situated if

(a) $x = 0$?	(b) $z = 0$?	(c) $x = y = 0$?
(d) $y = z = 0$?	(e) $x = 2$?	(f) $x = 2, y = 1$?
(g) $x = z$?	(h) $y = z, x = 0$?	(i) $x = y = z$?

13. (a) Show that the triangle with vertices (2, 4, 1), (1, 2, −2), (5, 0, −2) is right-angled; (b) find its area. *Ans.* (b) $\sqrt{70}$.

14. (a) Show that the triangle with vertices (5, 9, 11), (0, −1, −4), (5, −11, 1) is right-angled; (b) find its area. *Ans.* (b) $25\sqrt{21}$.

15. (a) Show that the triangle with vertices (2, 0, 8), (8, −4, 6), (−4, −2, 4) is isosceles; (b) find its area. *Ans.* (b) $6\sqrt{19}$.

16. (a) Show that the triangle with vertices (6, 2, 3), (1, −3, 2), (0, −2, −5) is isosceles; (b) find its area. *Ans.* (b) $\sqrt{638}$.

17. (a) Show that the triangle with vertices (1, 3, 3), (2, 2, 1), (3, 4, 2) is equilateral; (b) find its area. *Ans.* (b) $\frac{3}{2}\sqrt{3}$.

18. Show, by counterexamples, that the theorem of Ex. 21, pages 29, is false in space of three dimensions.

In Exs. 19–22, do the points lie on a straight line?

19. (−2, −4, 7), (2, 2, 3), (4, 5, 1).
20. (−5, 4, −3), (1, 1, 3), (−9, 6, −7).
21. (−1, −1, 1), (7, 11, 9), (−6, −9, −4).
22. (−5, −10, 9), (−1, −5, 5), (11, 10, −9).
23. Find the mid-point between (2, −1, 6), (−4, 9, 1).
24. Find the mid-point between (4, 0, −3), (−1, 8, 13).

In Exs. 25–28, solve by another method (§ 218).

25. Ex. 13 (a).   **26.** Ex. 14 (a).
27. Ex. 15 (a).   **28.** Ex. 16 (a).
29. Show that the quadrilateral with vertices (5, 1, 1), (3, 1, 0), (4, 3, −2), (6, 3, −1) is a rectangle.

30. Show that the quadrilateral with vertices (3, 2, 5), (1, 1, 1), (4, 0, 3), (6, 1, 7) is a parallelogram.

31. Show that the quadrilateral with vertices $(3, -3, 5)$, $(1, 3, 4)$, $(-5, 4, 6)$, $(-1, 1, 2)$ is not a parallelogram.

32. Show that the quadrilateral with vertices $(3, 5, 1)$, $(2, 4, 6)$, $(3, -1, 7)$, $(0, 2, 4)$ is not a parallelogram.

33. Find the fourth vertex of the parallelogram having as consecutive vertices the first three points of Ex. 31.   *Ans.* $(-3, -2, 7)$.

34. Prove that the straight lines joining the mid-points of adjacent sides of any quadrilateral (not necessarily plane) form a parallelogram.

219. *Direction Cosines; Radius Vector*

Given a directed line L passing through the origin, the angles α, β, γ formed by this line with the positive x-, y-, and z-axes are called the *direction angles* of the line, and the cosines of these angles are the *direction cosines* of the line. Direction cosines are denoted by l, m, n: that is,

$$l = \cos \alpha, \qquad m = \cos \beta, \qquad n = \cos \gamma.$$

More generally, if the given line does not pass through the origin, its direction angles and direction cosines are defined as *equal to those of the parallel line through the origin.*

Let $P: (x, y, z)$ be any point on the line L. The segment OP, denoted by ρ, is called the *radius vector* of P. By the distance formula it follows that

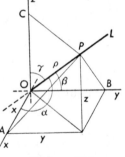

Figure 228

$$(1) \qquad \rho = \sqrt{x^2 + y^2 + z^2}.$$

From the triangles OAP, OBP, OCP we read off

$$(2) \qquad \cos \alpha = l = \frac{x}{\rho}, \qquad m = \frac{y}{\rho}, \qquad n = \frac{z}{\rho}.$$

Hence:

The direction cosines of the radius vector of a point are proportional to the coordinates of the point.

Clearing of fractions in (2), we see that

$$(3) \qquad x = l\rho, \qquad y = m\rho, \qquad z = n\rho.$$

Square both members of (1) and substitute the values (3):

$$l^2\rho^2 + m^2\rho^2 + n^2\rho^2 = \rho^2.$$

The direction cosines of any line satisfy the relation

$$(4) \qquad l^2 + m^2 + n^2 = 1.$$

By (1) and (4), the radius vector of the point (l, m, n) is

$$\rho = \sqrt{l^2 + m^2 + n^2} = 1.$$

Hence, given any set of numbers l, m, n satisfying (4), there will always be a line having those numbers as direction cosines, the line through $(0, 0, 0)$ and (l, m, n).

If the positive sense on the line be reversed, its direction angles are replaced by their supplements, and the signs of the direction cosines are changed.

220. *Direction Components*

Consider any line (not necessarily through the origin) whose direction cosines are *proportional to three numbers a, b, c*:

$$l = ka, \qquad m = kb, \qquad n = kc.$$

To determine the proportionality constant k, substitute in (4), § 219:

$$k^2(a^2 + b^2 + c^2) = 1, \qquad k = \frac{1}{\sqrt{a^2 + b^2 + c^2}}.$$

If the direction cosines of a line are proportional to three numbers a, b, c, their actual values are

(1) $$l = \frac{a}{\sqrt{a^2 + b^2 + c^2}}, \qquad m = \frac{b}{\sqrt{a^2 + b^2 + c^2}},$$
$$n = \frac{c}{\sqrt{a^2 + b^2 + c^2}}.$$

The ambiguity of sign mentioned in § 219 appears here in the fact that we might equally well have chosen the negative sign before each radical.

Given a line with direction cosines l, m, n, any set of numbers a, b, c proportional to l, m, n are called *direction components* for that line. We shall hereafter enclose each set of direction components in square brackets, thus: $[a, b, c]$. The student must exercise particular care to distinguish between the coordinates of a point $(2, 4, 3)$ enclosed in parentheses and the direction components of a line $[4, -1, 2]$ enclosed in square brackets.

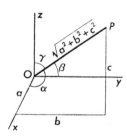

Figure 229

Although the direction cosines of a given line are definite, fixed numbers (except that all the signs may be changed), it is clear that every line has infinitely many sets of direction components; viz., any set of numbers proportional to l, m, n.

Given any three numbers a, b, c (not all zero), the formulas (1) produce values of l, m, n, no matter what a, b, c may be; thus there will always be a line through the origin having a, b, c as direction components. In fact this, of course, is the line through $(0, 0, 0)$ and $P: (a, b, c)$, as shown in Figure 229.

221. *Direction Components of the Line Through Two Points*

Let d be the distance between the two points P_1: (x_1, y_1, z_1), P_2: (x_2, y_2, z_2). Then the direction cosines of the line P_1P_2 are

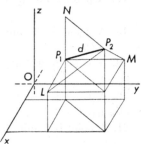

$$l = \frac{P_1L}{d} = \frac{x_2 - x_1}{d},$$

$$m = \frac{P_1M}{d} = \frac{y_2 - y_1}{d},$$

$$n = \frac{P_1N}{d} = \frac{z_2 - z_1}{d}.$$

Hence:

Figure 230

A set of direction components of the line joining the points (x_1, y_1, z_1) *and* (x_2, y_2, z_2) *is* $[x_2 - x_1, y_2 - y_1, z_2 - z_1]$.

EXERCISES

1. A line makes an angle of 45° with Oy and 60° with Oz. What angle does it make with Ox?

2. A line has the direction cosines $l = \frac{3}{10}$, $m = \frac{2}{5}$. What angle does it make with Oz?   *Ans.* 30°.

3. A line has direction cosines $l = \frac{7}{10}$, $n = \frac{1}{10}$. What angle does it make with Oy?   *Ans.* 45°.

4. In Fig. 228, if the point P lies in the xy-plane, show that the relation $l^2 + m^2 + n^2 = 1$ reduces to $\cos^2 \alpha + \sin^2 \alpha = 1$.

5. For each of the following points, find the length and direction cosines of the radius vector: (a) $(2, 1, 3)$; (b) $(-3, 2, 4)$; (c) $(-1, 4, 0)$.

6. Where must a point lie if its radius vector has (a) $m = 0$? (b) $m = \frac{1}{2}$? (c) $l = n = 0$? (d) $m = 1$? (e) $m = n = \frac{1}{2}\sqrt{2}$?

7. Can a line be drawn at an angle of 30° with Ox and 45° with Oz?

8. Show that it is impossible to draw a line, two of whose direction angles shall be less than 45°.

In Exs. 9–12, draw the line:

9. Through O, with direction components $[2, 3, 1]$.

10. Through O, with direction components $[4, 2, 5]$.

11. Through $(1, 3, 2)$, with direction components $[4, 2, 1]$.

12. Through $(5, 4, 6)$, with direction components $[2, 2, 3]$.

In Exs. 13–26, find the coordinates of the points satisfying the given conditions.

13. A point is at a distance 6 from O, and its radius vector makes an angle of 45° with Ox and 60° with Oz.

14. A point is at a distance 12 from O, and its radius vector has $m = \frac{1}{3}$, $n = \frac{5}{6}$.   *Ans.* $(\pm 2\sqrt{7}, 4, 10)$.

15. A point is at a distance 21 from O, and its radius vector has direction components [6, -2, 3]. *Ans.* (18, -6, 9); $(-18, 6, -9)$.

16. A point is 18 units from O, and its radius vector has direction components [4, 8, -1]. *Ans.* (8, 16, -2); $(-8, -16, 2)$.

17. A point is 8 units from O, $2\sqrt{5}$ from Ox, and its radius vector has $m = \frac{1}{2}$. *Ans.* $(\pm 2\sqrt{11}, 4, 2)$; $(\pm 2\sqrt{11}, 4, -2)$.

18. A point is 3 units from the xz-plane, and its radius vector has $l = \frac{1}{4}$, $n = \frac{1}{2}\sqrt{3}$. *Ans.* $(\sqrt{3}, 3, 6)$.

19. A point is 2 units from the xz-plane, 6 from the yz-plane, and its radius vector has $n = \frac{1}{3}$. *Ans.* $(6, 2, \sqrt{5})$.

20. A point is 6 units from the xy-plane, 3 from the xz-plane, and its radius vector has $l = -\frac{1}{2}$. *Ans.* $(-\sqrt{15}, 3, 6)$.

21. A point is 2 units from O, and its radius vector has $\beta = 60°$, $\gamma = 45°$. *Ans.* $(\pm 1, 1, \sqrt{2})$.

22. A point is at distance 5 from O, 4 from the yz-plane, and its radius vector has $n = \frac{1}{5}$. *Ans.* $(4, \pm 2\sqrt{2}, 1)$.

23. A point is distant $4\sqrt{10}$ from Ox, and its radius vector has direction components [3, 2, 6].

24. A point is at the distance $\sqrt{5}$ from the z-axis, 1 from the xy-plane, and its radius vector makes an angle $\frac{1}{4}\pi$ with Ox.

25. A point is at the distance $\sqrt{2}$ from Oz, $\sqrt{3}$ from Ox, and its radius vector makes an angle of 45° with Oz.

26. A point is at the distance $2\sqrt{10}$ from Oz, $2\sqrt{7}$ from Oy, and its radius vector has $l = \frac{1}{4}$.

In Exs. 27–32, solve by a new method.

27. Ex. 19, p. 390.   **28.** Ex. 20, p. 390.
29. Ex. 21, p. 390.   **30.** Ex. 22, p. 390.
31. Ex. 31, p. 391.   **32.** Ex. 32, p. 391.

33. Show that it is impossible to draw a line so that the sum of any two (positive) direction angles is less than 90°. (Show that if $0° < \alpha + \beta < 90°$, then $\cos \alpha > \sin \beta$, from which it follows that $\cos^2 \alpha + \cos^2 \beta > 1$.)

222. *Projections*

The *projection* of a point P upon any line is defined as the *foot of the perpendicular* from P to that line. The projection of a line segment P_1P_2 upon any line is the segment joining the projections of the endpoints P_1, P_2 upon that line.

The projection of a broken line upon any line is the sum of the projections of the segments forming the broken line. *The projection of a broken line $P_1P_2 \cdots P_n$ upon any line is equal to the projection of the closing line P_1P_n upon that line.* Thus, in Figure 231,

$$L_1L_2 + L_2L_3 + L_3L_4 = L_1L_4.$$

Note that the segments need not all lie in the same plane.

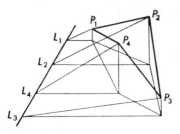

Figure 231

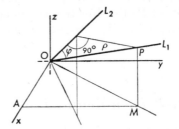

Figure 232

223. *Angle Between Two Lines*

To find the angle φ between any two lines L_1, L_2 intersecting at the origin, let us denote the direction cosines of L_1 by $[l_1, m_1, n_1]$, those of L_2 by $[l_2, m_2, n_2]$, and choose on L_1 any point $P: (x, y, z)$ with radius vector ρ. Then, in Figure 232,

$$OA = x = l_1\rho, \qquad AM = y = m_1\rho, \qquad MP = z = n_1\rho.$$

Now the projection on L_2 of the broken line $OAMP$ equals the projection on L_2 of the closing line OP:

$$OP \cos \varphi = OA \cdot l_2 + AM \cdot m_2 + MP \cdot n_2,$$

$$\rho \cos \varphi = l_1\rho l_2 + m_1\rho m_2 + n_1\rho n_2;$$

i.e.,

$$(1) \qquad \cos \varphi = l_1 l_2 + m_1 m_2 + n_1 n_2.$$

If the two lines have direction components $[a_1, b_1, c_1]$ and $[a_2, b_2, c_2]$, the direction cosines may be found by § 220. Substituting in formula (1), we find

$$(2) \qquad \cos \varphi = \frac{a_1 a_2 + b_1 b_2 + c_1 c_2}{\sqrt{a_1{}^2 + b_1{}^2 + c_1{}^2} \cdot \sqrt{a_2{}^2 + b_2{}^2 + c_2{}^2}}.$$

Of course these results apply at once (§ 219, second paragraph) to any two intersecting lines. Further, the angle between two nonintersecting lines is defined as *equal to the angle between two intersecting lines that are respectively parallel to the given lines.* With this convention the formulas give the angle between any two lines in space.

On account of the ambiguity of sign mentioned in §§ 219–220, each of the above formulas will give either a positive or a negative result, according to the way we happen to choose the signs. This corresponds to the fact that there are two angles "between two lines," one the supplement of the other.

Example. Find the angle between the lines joining the points $(3, 1, 2)$, $(4, 0, 4)$ and $(-2, 4, 4)$, $(0, -1, 3)$.

By § 221, the direction components of the lines are respectively $[1, -1, 2]$ and $[2, -5, -1]$. By (2), we find

$$\cos \varphi = \frac{2 + 5 - 2}{\sqrt{6} \cdot \sqrt{30}} = \frac{1}{6} \sqrt{5}.$$

224. *Perpendicular Lines*

In formula (1), § 223, if $\cos \varphi = 0$, $\varphi = 90°$, and vice versa.

THEOREM 41. *Two lines having the direction cosines* $[l_1, m_1, n_1]$ *and* $[l_2, m_2, n_2]$ *are perpendicular if and only if*

(1) $$l_1 l_2 + m_1 m_2 + n_1 n_2 = 0.$$

COROLLARY. *Two lines having direction components* $[a_1, b_1, c_1]$ *and* $[a_2, b_2, c_2]$ *are perpendicular if and only if*

(2) $$a_1 a_2 + b_1 b_2 + c_1 c_2 = 0.$$

EXERCISES

1. Find the angle between two lines whose direction components are $[2, 1, 1]$ and $[1, -1, -2]$. *Ans.* 60°.

2. Find the angle between two lines whose direction components are $[1, 4, 8]$ and $[1, -2, 2]$. *Ans.* $\cos \varphi = \frac{1}{3}$.

3. Find the angle between the radius vectors of the points $(1, 1, 0)$ and $(3, 4, -5)$. *Ans.* $\cos \varphi = \frac{7}{10}$.

4. Find the angle between the radius vectors of the points $(1, 1, -2)$ and $(1, 1, 0)$. *Ans.* $\cos \varphi = \frac{1}{3} \sqrt{3}$.

In Exs. 5–8, find the angle between the line joining the first pair of points and the line joining the second pair of points.

5. $(6, 4, 3)$, $(4, 3, 5)$ and $(3, -1, 4)$, $(2, -2, 4)$. *Ans.* 45°.
6. $(-1, 9, 4)$, $(-3, 2, 5)$ and $(6, 3, 2)$, $(1, 4, -1)$.
7. $(6, 4, 2)$, $(2, 3, -1)$ and $(-3, 7, 4)$, $(-1, 2, 3)$.
8. $(4, 4, 4)$, $(2, 5, 2)$ and $(3, 1, 2)$, $(2, 2, 2)$. *Ans.* 45°.

In Exs. 9–14, show that the quadrilateral with vertices P_1, P_2, P_3, P_4, as given, has the shape indicated. Find the area. (Figures not drawn to scale.)

9. $(4, 5, 4)$, $(7, 8, 4)$, $(-1, 0, -4)$, $(0, 1, 0)$: isosceles trapezoid. (Figure 233.) *Ans.* $18 \sqrt{2}$.

10. $(4, 0, 7)$, $(5, 1, -1)$, $(0, -4, 3)$, $(1, -3, 7)$: kite. (Figure 234.) *Ans.* $24 \sqrt{2}$.

11. (2, 2, 2), (4, 4, −8), (−2, −2, −2), (3, 3, −6): arrowhead.   (Figure 235.)

    Ans. $6\sqrt{2}$.

12. (0, 0, 0), (4, 2, −4), (6, 6, 0), (2, 4, 4): square.   *Ans.* 36.

13. (7, 1, 3), (5, 0, 0), (4, −2, 3), (6, −1, 6): rhombus.   *Ans.* $3\sqrt{19}$.

    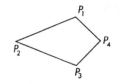

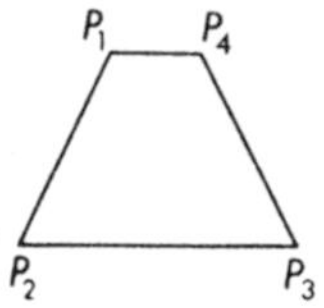

Figure 233   Figure 234 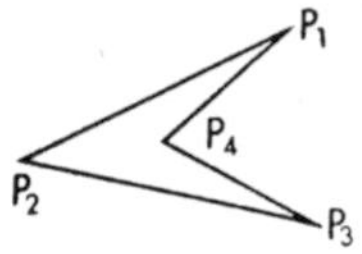   Figure 235 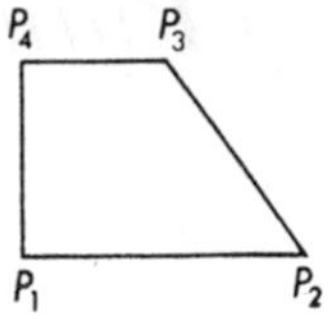   Figure 236

14. (1, 3, 5), (−3, −3, 3), (3, −2, 2), (5, 1, 3): right-angled trapezoid.   (Figure 236.)

    Ans. $6\sqrt{21}$.

In Exs. 15–17, find the area of the triangle with the given vertices, using the formula $A = \frac{1}{2}S_1S_2 \sin \varphi$.   (Figure 237.)

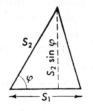

15. (2, 2, −1), (3, 1, 2), (4, 2, −2).   *Ans.* $\frac{3}{2}\sqrt{6}$.

16. (3, 1, 0), (6, 4, −1), (5, 2, 2).   *Ans.* $\frac{1}{2}\sqrt{122}$.

17. (0, 0, 0), (x_1, y_1, z_1), (x_2, y_2, z_2).

$$Ans.\ A = \frac{1}{2}\left\{ \begin{vmatrix} x_1 & x_2 \\ y_1 & y_2 \end{vmatrix}^2 + \begin{vmatrix} z_1 & z_2 \\ x_1 & x_2 \end{vmatrix}^2 + \begin{vmatrix} y_1 & y_2 \\ z_1 & z_2 \end{vmatrix}^2 \right\}^{\frac{1}{2}}.$$

Figure 237

18. Find the area of a triangle with vertices (0, 0, 0), $(x_1, y_1, 0)$, $(x_2, y_2, 0)$, (a) by Ex. 17; (b) by § 21.

19. Show, with the aid of a figure, that when the axes are translated to a point $O_1: (h, k, l)$ as new origin, the old and new coordinates are connected by the following formulas.   Compare with § 64.

$$x = x_1 + h, \qquad y = y_1 + k, \qquad z = z_1 + l.$$

20. In Ex. 15, find the coordinates of the vertices referred to (2, 2, −1) as new origin; find the area by Ex. 17.   *Ans.* (0, 0, 0), (1, −1, 3), (2, 0, −1).

21. In Ex. 16, find the coordinates of the vertices referred to (3, 1, 0) as new origin; find the area by Ex. 17.   *Ans.* (0, 0, 0), (3, 3, −1), (2, 1, 2).

Planes and Lines

225. *Equation of a Plane; the Normal Form*

Given a plane RST (Figure 238), let P: (x, y, z) be any point of that plane, and N the foot of the perpendicular from O upon the plane. Denote the length of the normal ON by p, and its direction cosines by $[l, m, n]$. We shall consider the segment p as *directed*: positive if the given plane has a positive z-intercept, so that ON slopes upward, negative if ON slopes downward. With this convention, the plane is determined when $[l, m, n]$, and p are given.

By (3), § 219, the coordinates of N are (lp, mp, np), so that by § 221 the direction components of NP are $[x - lp, y - mp, z - np]$. By § 224 (corollary), the lines ON and NP are perpendicular if and only if

$$l(x - lp) + m(y - mp) + n(z - np) = 0;$$

this is therefore the equation of the plane. Simplifying, we get

$$lx + my + nz = l^2p + m^2p + n^2p,$$

or by (4), § 219,

(1) $$lx + my + nz = p.$$

This is the *normal form* of the equation of the plane.

Our convention as to the sign of p fails if the plane is perpendicular to the xy-plane (no z-intercept) or passes through the origin (z-intercept zero). In the former case (Figure 239), let us say that p shall have the same sign as the y-intercept. The above derivation goes through unchanged, except that now $\gamma = 90°$ and $n = 0$; the result, of course, is

$$lx + my = p.$$

This does not cover the case in which the plane is parallel to the yz-plane (no z- or y-intercept). In this case, let p have the same sign as the x-intercept. Now, $m = n = 0$, $l = 1$, and the equation is

$$x = p.$$

398

Finally, given a plane through the origin, let [l, m, n] be the direction cosines of the perpendicular line through O. Since this line is perpendicular

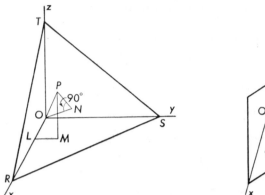

Figure 238

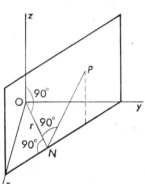

Figure 239

to every line OP in the plane, and since the direction components of OP, by § 219, are [x, y, z], the equation of the plane is (§ 224, corollary)

$$lx + my + nz = 0.$$

But this is the form to which (1) reduces when, as here,

$$p = 0.$$

Thus, formula (1) applies to any plane.

THEOREM 42. *A plane always has an equation of the first degree.*

226. General Form; Reduction to Normal Form

Every equation of the first degree can be written in the form

(1) $$Ax + By + Cz + D = 0.$$

Let us transpose the constant term to the right member and then divide through by $\pm \sqrt{A^2 + B^2 + C^2}$, leaving the sign (for a moment) ambiguous:

(2) $$\pm \frac{A}{\sqrt{A^2 + B^2 + C^2}} x \pm \frac{B}{\sqrt{A^2 + B^2 + C^2}} y$$
$$\pm \frac{C}{\sqrt{A^2 + B^2 + C^2}} z = \frac{\mp D}{\sqrt{A^2 + B^2 + C^2}}.$$

Now the coefficients of x, y, and z are the direction cosines of a certain line, since the sum of their squares is unity; it follows that (2) is, apart from the ambiguity of sign, the equation of a plane in the normal form. This reduction can always be carried out because $\sqrt{A^2 + B^2 + C^2}$ cannot be zero.

THEOREM 43.   *Every equation of the first degree represents a plane.*

Further, the conventions laid down in § 225, as to the sign of p, yield a systematic procedure for reduction to normal form.

RULE.   *To reduce to the normal form the equation*

(a) $Ax + By + Cz + D = 0,$ $C \neq 0,$

divide by $\sqrt{A^2 + B^2 + C^2}$ *and choose signs so that the coefficient of z is positive;*

(b) $Ax + By + D = 0,$ $B \neq 0,$

divide by $\sqrt{A^2 + B^2}$ *and choose signs so that the coefficient of y is positive;*

(c) $Ax + D = 0,$

divide by A.

The student is now in a position, by specializing the work of this and the preceding section, to discuss the normal form of the equation of a line in plane geometry.   By using that normal form, it is possible to obtain the distance from a point to a line (in plane geometry) and thus circumvent the use of calculus made in § 68.   Naturally we prefer to use, not circumvent the use of, calculus in this book.

227. *Perpendicular Line and Plane*

The coefficients A, B, C in the general equation of the plane are, by (2), § 226, proportional to the direction cosines of the normal.

THEOREM 44.   *If a line and plane are perpendicular, the direction components of the line may be taken as coefficients of x, y, z in the equation of the plane, and vice versa.*

Thus, if a line has direction components $[a, b, c]$, a plane is perpendicular to the line if and only if the equation of the plane can be written in the form

$$ax + by + cz = k.$$

Example.   Write the equation of a plane through $(0, 4, 5)$, and perpendicular to the line joining $(2, -3, 5)$ to $(-1, -4, 3)$.

The numbers $[3, 1, 2]$ are direction components of the line; by the above theorem, these numbers may be taken as coefficients in the equation of the plane.   The result is

$$3x + y + 2z = 14,$$

the right member being necessarily the value assumed by the left member when the coordinates $(0, 4, 5)$ are substituted for x, y, and z.

EXERCISES

In Exs. 1–12, reduce the equation to normal form; determine the direction cosines of the normal and the distance of the plane from the origin.

1. $4x + y + 8z = 36$.   Draw the figure.
2. $x + 2y + 2z = 6$.   Draw the figure.
3. $2x + y - 2z = -12$.
4. $2x - 3y + 6z = -21$.
5. $3x - 4y - 5z = 30$.
6. $x - y - 2z = 24$.
7. $x + y + z = 0$.
8. $x - 2y + 2z = 0$.
9. $2y + 7 = 0$.
10. $7x - y + 10 = 0$.
11. $4y + 3z = 30$.   Draw the figure.
12. $x + z = 6$.   Draw the figure.

In Exs. 13–24, find the equation of the plane:

13. At a distance 4 from O, with normal having direction components $[1, 2, -2]$.
    Ans. $x + 2y - 2z = \pm 12$.

14. At a distance 2 from O, with normal having direction components $[8, -1, 4]$.
    Ans. $8x - y + 4z = \pm 18$.

15. Through $(1, 2, 3)$ perpendicular to the radius vector of that point.
    Ans. $x + 2y + 3z = 14$.

16. Through $(-2, 1, 4)$ perpendicular to the radius vector of that point.
    Ans. $2x - y - 4z = -21$.

17. With the point $(5, 3, -1)$ as the foot of the normal from O.

18. With the point $(4, -3, -2)$ as the foot of the normal from O.

19. Through $(1, 7, -4)$ perpendicular to the radius vector of the point $(2, 1, -2)$.
    Ans. $2x + y - 2z = 17$.

20. Through $(4, -3, 2)$ perpendicular to the radius vector of the point $(1, 0, 3)$.
    Ans. $x + 3z = 10$.

21. Through $(2, 0, -1)$ perpendicular to the line joining $(3, 4, 4)$, $(-1, 2, 1)$.
    Ans. $4x + 2y + 3z = 5$.

22. Through $(2, -2, 1)$ perpendicular to the line joining $(7, -3, 2)$, $(4, -2, 3)$.
    Ans. $3x - y - z = 7$.

23. At a distance 4 from O perpendicular to the line joining $(-2, 3, 1)$, $(-5, 1, -5)$.
    Ans. $3x + 2y + 6z = \pm 28$.

24. At a distance 3 from O perpendicular to the line joining $(6, 4, 1)$, $(4, 5, 0)$.
    Ans. $2x - y + z = \pm 3\sqrt{6}$.

25. One side of a right triangle joins the points $(2, 4, -3)$, $(1, 0, 5)$, with the right angle at the latter point.   Find the locus of the third vertex.
    Ans. $x + 4y - 8z = -39$.

26. One side of a right triangle joins the points $(7, -2, 4)$, $(1, 1, -1)$, with the right angle at the latter point.   Find the locus of the third vertex.
    Ans. $6x - 3y + 5z = -2$.

27. Solve Ex. 25 by another method.

28. Solve Ex. 26 by another method.

29. The base of an isosceles triangle joins the points $(4, 3, 7)$, $(-2, 1, 5)$.   Find the locus of the third vertex by § 227.   *Ans.* $3x + y + z = 11$.

30. The base of an isosceles triangle joins the points $(4, 3, 0)$, $(2, 1, 1)$.   Find the locus of the third vertex by § 227.   *Ans.* $4x + 4y - 2z = 19$.

31. Solve Ex. 29 by another method (§ 217).

32. Solve Ex. 30 by another method (§ 217).

33. Derive the normal form from the fact that, in Figure 238, the projection of the broken line $OLMPN$ upon the normal must equal ON.

34. Derive the normal form from the fact that the mid-point of OP is equidistant from O and N. Does the derivation hold in all cases?

35. Derive the normal form by applying the Theorem of Pythagoras to the triangle ONP. Does the derivation hold in all cases?

228. Parallel Planes

If the equations of two planes differ only in the constant term, the same must be true after reduction to the normal form. Hence the normals to the two planes have the same direction cosines and are parallel, from which it follows that *the planes are parallel.*

Conversely, *if two planes are parallel, their equations can be made to differ only in the constant term.*

Example. Write the equation of a plane through (3, 1, 4) and parallel to the plane

$$2x - 5y + 6z = 7.$$

The answer is

$$2x - 5y + 6z = 25,$$

the right member being written at once from the fact that it must be the value assumed by the left member when the coordinates (3, 1, 4) are used for x, y, z, respectively.

229. Plane Through a Given Point

If the plane

$$Ax + By + Cz + D = 0$$

is to pass through the point (x_1, y_1, z_1), we must have

$$Ax_1 + By_1 + Cz_1 + D = 0.$$

By subtraction, we find that:

The equation of any plane through the point (x_1, y_1, z_1) may be written in the form

(1) $$A(x - x_1) + B(y - y_1) + C(z - z_1) = 0.$$

230. Plane Determined by Three Points

The general equation of the plane contains three essential constants, since at least one of the quantities A, B, C, D must not be zero and can therefore be divided out. We conclude that a plane is determined by three points (not in a straight line) or by any set of three independent conditions which, when expressed analytically, give three consistent equations to determine the essential constants.

A direct method of finding the equation of a plane determined by three points is to substitute the coordinates of the points in turn in the equation

$$Ax + By + Cz + D = 0,$$

thus obtaining three equations to solve for three of the constants in terms of the fourth. The solution may, however, be expedited by use of (1), § 229.

Example. Find the equation of the plane through the points $(2, 4, 3)$, $(1, 3, 1)$, $(-1, -1, -4)$.

The equation of any plane through $(2, 4, 3)$ is

(1) $$A(x - 2) + B(y - 4) + C(z - 3) = 0.$$

Substitute the coordinates of the other points in (1):

$$-A - B - 2C = 0,$$
$$-3A - 5B - 7C = 0.$$

Solving for A and C in terms of B, we find

$$A = 3B, \qquad C = -2B.$$

Using these expressions for A and C in (1), we find the equation of the desired plane to be

$$3B(x - 2) + B(y - 4) - 2B(z - 3) = 0,$$

or

$$3x + y - 2z = 4.$$

231. *Perpendicular Planes*

Two planes
$$A_1x + B_1y + C_1z + D_1 = 0,$$
$$A_2x + B_2y + C_2z + D_2 = 0$$

are perpendicular if and only if their normals are perpendicular to each other. The direction cosines of the normals are proportional to $[A_1, B_1, C_1]$ and $[A_2, B_2, C_2]$, respectively. We can now apply the condition of perpendicularity (§ 224) to these lines.

THEOREM 45. *Two planes,*

$$A_1x + B_1y + C_1z + D_1 = 0,$$
$$A_2x + B_2y + C_2z + D_2 = 0,$$

are perpendicular if and only if

(1) $$A_1A_2 + B_1B_2 + C_1C_2 = 0.$$

Example. Find the equation of a plane through the points (1, 1, 2), (2, 4, 3), and perpendicular to the plane

(2) $$x - 3y + 7z + 5 = 0.$$

The equation of any plane through (1, 1, 2) is (§ 229)

(3) $$A(x - 1) + B(y - 1) + C(z - 2) = 0.$$

Substituting the coordinates (2, 4, 3) in (3), we get

(4) $$A + 3B + C = 0.$$

The condition of perpendicularity (1) applied to the planes (2) and (3) gives

(5) $$A - 3B + 7C = 0.$$

From (4) and (5) we find

$$A = -4C, \qquad B = C,$$

whence the equation of the plane is

$$-4C(x - 1) + C(y - 1) + C(z - 2) = 0,$$

or

$$4x - y - z = 1.$$

EXERCISES

In Exs. 1–12, find the equation of the plane.

1. Through (2, 1, −3) parallel to the plane $3x + 4y + z = 4$.

$Ans.\ 3x + 4y + z = 7.$

2. Through (1, 0, 4) parallel to the plane $2x - 5y + 3z = 6$.

3. Through (−1, −2, 3) parallel to the plane $x + y + 4z = 5$.

4. Through (4, 3, 1) parallel to the plane $x + 3z = 8$.

5. Parallel to the plane $x + 4y - 8z = 18$ and (a) half as far from the origin; (b) at a distance 4 from the origin; (c) at the same distance from the origin.

$Ans.\ (a)\ x + 4y - 8z = \pm 9.$

6. Parallel to the plane $6x - 3y + 2z = 21$ and (a) twice as far from the origin; (b) one unit nearer the origin; (c) at a distance 4 from the origin.

$Ans.\ (b)\ 6x - 3y + 2z = \pm 14.$

7. Parallel to the plane $2x + y + 2z = 15$ and (a) 2 units nearer the origin; (b) 2 units farther from the origin; (c) at a distance 4 from the given plane.

$Ans.\ (c)\ 2x + y + 2z = 15 \pm 12.$

8. Parallel to the plane $x + y - 2z = 12$ and (a) 3 units nearer the origin; (b) 3 units farther from the origin; (c) at a distance 2 from the given plane.

$Ans.\ (c)\ x + y - 2z = 12 \pm 2\sqrt{6}.$

9. Parallel to the plane $4x + y + 8z = 11$ and passing at a distance 2 from (1, 5, −3).

$Ans.\ 4x + y + 8z = -15 \pm 18.$

10. Parallel to the plane $x - 2y + 2z = 7$ and passing at a distance 4 from (4, 1, 3).

$Ans.\ x - 2y + 2z = 8 \pm 12.$

11. Parallel to the plane $4x - 3y + 5z = 8$ and (a) twice as far from $(1, 2, 1)$; (b) half as far from $(1, 2, 1)$; (c) at a distance 6 from $(1, 2, 1)$.

12. Parallel to the plane $4x + 4y - 2z = 11$ and (a) twice as far from $(1, -1, -3)$; (b) half as far from $(1, -1, -3)$; at a distance unity from $(1, -1, -3)$.

In Exs. 13–16, find the distance between the planes.

13. $x + y - 2z = 5$, $x + y - 2z = 17$.
14. $8x - y - 4z = -4$, $8x - y - 4z = 23$.
15. $2x + 2y + z + 11 = 0$, $4x + 4y + 2z = 11$.
16. $3x + y + z + 4 = 0$, $6x + 2y + 2z = 1$.
17. Show that the planes $x + y - z + 1 = 0$, $x + y - z - 1 = 0$, $3x - 2y + z + 3 = 0$, $3x - 2y + z + 2 = 0$, $x + 4y + 5z + 20 = 0$, $x + 4y + 5z = 1$ form a box; find its volume.   *Ans.* $V = 1$.

18. Show that *the directed distance from the plane*

$$Ax + By + Cz + D = 0$$

to the point (x_1, y_1, z_1) is

$$d = \frac{Ax_1 + By_1 + Cz_1 + D}{\pm \sqrt{A^2 + B^2 + C^2}},$$

where the ambiguous sign is chosen like the sign of C if $C \neq 0$, or like the sign of B if $C = 0$, $B \neq 0$, or like the sign of A if $B = C = 0$.

In Exs. 19–22, find the distance from the plane to the point.   (Ex. 18.)

19. $x + y + 2z = 4$, $(2, 0, -5)$.   *Ans.* $-2\sqrt{6}$.
20. $3x + y - z = -23$, $(2, 5, 1)$.   *Ans.* $-3\sqrt{11}$.
21. $6x - 3y - 2z = -4$, $(4, 1, 2)$.   *Ans.* -3.
22. $8x + 4y + z = -9$, $(4, -3, 7)$.   *Ans.* 4.

In Exs. 23–24, find the equations of the planes bisecting the angles between the given planes.

23. $x + 2y + 2z = 0$, $6x - 2y + 3z = 14$.
                    Ans. $11x - 20y - 5z = 42$, $25x + 8y + 23z = 42$.
24. $x + y + z = 2$, $5x - y + z + 4 = 0$.
                    Ans. $x - 2y - z + 5 = 0$, $4x + y + 2z = 1$.

In Exs. 25–30, find the equation of the plane through the given points.

25. $(3, 2, 1)$, $(1, -3, -2)$, $(3, 11, 4)$.   *Ans.* $2x + y - 3z = 5$.
26. $(6, 6, 1)$, $(-6, 3, -1)$, $(1, 3, 0)$.   *Ans.* $3x + 2y - 21z = 9$.
27. $(4, 3, -1)$, $(0, 4, 5)$, $(6, -3, 7)$.   *Ans.* $2x + 2y + z = 13$.
28. $(2, 0, 3)$, $(5, 6, -1)$, $(-1, 4, -3)$.   *Ans.* $2x - 3y - 3z = -5$.
29. $(3, 2, -2)$, $(4, 1, 3)$, $(-1, 6, 1)$.   *Ans.* $x + y = 5$.
30. $(a, 0, 0)$, $(0, b, 0)$, $(0, 0, c)$.

                                        Ans. $\dfrac{x}{a} + \dfrac{y}{b} + \dfrac{z}{c} = 1$.

In Exs. 31–38, find the equation of the plane.

31. Through the points $(1, 3, 1)$, $(4, 6, -2)$ perpendicular to $x + y - z = 3$.
Ans. $2x + y + 3z = 8$.

32. Through the points $(-2, 1, 2)$, $(-2, -3, -1)$ perpendicular to the plane $x - 3y - 2z = 4$.   *Ans.* $x + 3y - 4z = -7$.

33. Through $(8, 3, 1)$, $(1, \frac{1}{2}, -1)$ perpendicular to the yz-plane.

34. Through $(1, 4, 1)$, $(-8, 3, 7)$ perpendicular to the xz-plane.

35. Through $(3, 0, -1)$ perpendicular to the planes $2x - y - 4z - 9 = 0$, $x + y + 2z = -1$.   *Ans.* $2x - 8y + 3z = 3$.

36. Through $(2, 2, 3)$ perpendicular to the planes $2x - 2y - 4z + 1 = 0$, $3x + y + 6z = 14$.   *Ans.* $x + 3y - z = 5$.

37. Perpendicular to the planes $y = 3x + z$, $x + 5y + 3z = 0$ and passing at a distance $\sqrt{6}$ from the origin.   *Ans.* $x + y - 2z = \pm 6$.

38. Perpendicular to the planes $z = 4y - x$, $3x + 4y + z = 2$, and passing at a distance 1 from the origin.   *Ans.* $4x - y - 8z = \pm 9$.

39. Prove that the equation

$$\begin{vmatrix} x & y & z & 1 \\ x_1 & y_1 & z_1 & 1 \\ x_2 & y_2 & z_2 & 1 \\ x_3 & y_3 & z_3 & 1 \end{vmatrix} = 0$$

represents the plane determined by the points (x_1, y_1, z_1), (x_2, y_2, z_2), (x_3, y_3, z_3).

40. In Ex. 39, what happens if the minors of all the elements in the first row are zero? Explain geometrically.

41. Solve Ex. 25, using Ex. 39.

42. Solve Ex. 26, using Ex. 39.

43. Solve Ex. 27, using Ex. 39.

232. *Planes Through a Given Line*

Every first-degree equation represents a plane and two intersecting planes determine a line.

THEOREM 46. *The locus of two different consistent simultaneous equations of the first degree is a straight line.*

If the two equations are inconsistent, the planes represented are parallel and do not intersect; the two equations, taken together, then represent no locus.

Given the equations

(1) $\qquad \begin{cases} A_1x + B_1y + C_1z + D_1 = 0, \\ A_2x + B_2y + C_2z + D_2 = 0 \end{cases}$

of a straight line, consider the equation formed by multiplying one of the given equations by an *arbitrary constant c* and adding:

(2) $\qquad A_1x + B_1y + C_1z + D_1 + c(A_2x + B_2y + C_2z + D_2) = 0$.

Since this equation is of first degree, it represents, as c ranges through all real values, a *family of planes*. All these planes have one property in common: they pass through the line (1). To see this, let $P: (x_1, y_1, z_1)$ be any point of that line. Since the coordinates of P satisfy both of the equations (1), we have the relations

$$(3) \qquad \begin{cases} A_1x_1 + B_1y_1 + C_1z_1 + D_1 = 0, \\ A_2x_1 + B_2y_1 + C_2z_1 + D_2 = 0. \end{cases}$$

Now substitute the coordinates of P in (2); the result is

$$A_1x_1 + B_1y_1 + C_1z_1 + D_1 + c(A_2x_1 + B_2y_1 + C_2z_1 + D_2) = 0,$$

which is true, for all values of c, by virtue of (3). Thus all the planes (2) pass through P, and by the same argument, through all points of the line (1).

THEOREM 47. *If*

$$(4) \qquad A_1x + B_1y + C_1z + D_1 = 0, \qquad A_2x + B_2y + C_2z + D_2 = 0$$

are the equations of any line, the equation

$$(5) \qquad A_1x + B_1y + C_1z + D_1 + c(A_2x + B_2y + C_2z + D_2) = 0$$

represents a family of planes through the given line.

Although there is no value of c that will produce the plane

$$(6) \qquad A_2x + B_2y + C_2z + D_2 = 0,$$

we could equally well have written, instead of (5), the equation

$$(7) \qquad k(A_1x + B_1y + C_1z + D_1) + A_2x + B_2y + C_2z + D_2 = 0,$$

which includes (6) as the case $k = 0$. In this sense we shall say that we include (6) in the family (5) by special agreement.

Given any plane through the line (4), excepting (6), let Q be any point of that plane, not in the line (4). The coordinates of Q, substituted in (5), determine a value of c, which means that our plane belongs to the family (5). Since (6) is already included, we have proved that the family (5) *includes all planes through the line* (4).

Example. Find the equation of the plane through the line

$$2x - 2y + 3z = 1, \qquad x - 5y - z = 2$$

and perpendicular to the plane

$$(8) \qquad 2x + y + 4z = 5.$$

The required equation must be of the form

$$2x - 2y + 3z - 1 + c(x - 5y - z - 2) = 0,$$

or

(9) $(2 + c)x - (2 + 5c)y + (3 - c)z - 1 - 2c = 0.$

By § 231, planes (8) and (9) will be perpendicular if

$$2(2 + c) - 1(2 + 5c) + 4(3 - c) = 0.$$

This gives $c = 2$; substituting in (9), we have the answer

$$4x - 12y + z - 5 = 0.$$

233. *Projecting Planes*

Consider the line in Theorem 47 above. For the plane in equation (5) of that theorem, choose c so as to eliminate the z-term. The resulting equation will have the form

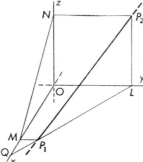

(1) $A_3x + B_3y + D_3 = 0.$

The plane (1) is perpendicular to the xy-plane

(2) $z = 0$

by Theorem 45, page 403. Then (1) is called the xy-*projecting plane* of the line. By eliminating x or y from two equations of a line, we obtain respectively the yz-projecting plane or the xz-projecting plane.

Figure 240

Example. Draw the line

$$4x + 4y + 3z = 14,$$
$$x - 2y + 3z = 2.$$

Eliminating z and y in turn, we find the xy- and zx- projecting planes:

$$x + 2y = 4, \qquad 2x + 3z = 6.$$

The xy cross-sections of these planes are the lines LQ, MP_1, intersecting at P_1; the yz cross-sections are the lines LP_2, NP_2, intersecting at P_2. Thus the line P_1P_2 is the given line.

EXERCISES

In Exs. 1–14, find the equation of the plane.

1. Through the line $x + 2z = 1$, $y = 5$ and the point $(1, 2, 3)$.
2. Through the line $3x + y = 2$, $z = 1$ and the point $(2, -1, 4)$.
3. Through the line $x + 3y - 2z = 3$, $2x + y + 5z = -3$ and the point $(1, 0, -2)$.
4. Through the line $4x = y + 2z - 5$, $x + y = 7z + 2$ and the point $(-2, 1, 0)$.

5. Through the line $x + y + z = 0$, $2x - y + 3z = 4$ and perpendicular to the plane $3x + y - 2z = 6$.   *Ans.* $5x - y + 7z = 8$.

6. Through the line $y + 2z = 8$, $2x - y = 4$ and perpendicular to the plane $x + 3y + 4z = 6$.   *Ans.* $11x - 5y + z = 26$.

7. Through the line of Ex. 5, perpendicular to the yz-plane.

8. Through the line of Ex. 6, perpendicular to the xz-plane.

9. Through the line $x - y + z = 0$, $2x + y + z = 2$ and perpendicular to the plane $x + 2y + 2z = 4$.

10. Through the line $3x + y - z = 4$, $x + 2y + z = 1$ and perpendicular to the plane $2x - y - z = 5$.

11. Through the line $x - 5z = 6$, $y = z$ and passing at a distance $\sqrt{2}$ from the origin.   *Ans.* $x - 4y - z = 6$, $x - y - 4z = 6$.

12. Through the line $y - 5z + 1 = 0$, $x + y = 2$ and passing at a distance $\frac{1}{2}\sqrt{2}$ from O.   *Ans.* $3x + 4y - 5z = 5$, $4x + y + 15z = 11$.

13. Through the line $x + 2z = -10$, $y - 2z = 8$ and passing at a distance 2 from the origin.   *Ans.* $x + 2y - 2z = 6$; $11x + 10y + 2z = -30$.

14. Through the line $y - 2z = 7$, $x + y = 3$ and passing at a distance 2 from $(2, 1, 0)$.   *Ans.* $x + 2y - 2z = 10$; $2x + y + 2z = -1$.

15. Show that the line $3x + y - z = 4$, $2x + y + 3z = 7$ lies in the plane $5x + y - 9z = -2$.

16. Show that the line $x + 7y - 3z = 2$, $2x + 4y + z = 5$ lies in the plane $8x + 6y + 11z = 21$.

17. Solve Ex. 15 by another method.

18. Solve Ex. 16 by another method.

In Exs. 19–22, write equations of the line.

19. Through $(2, -3, -2)$ parallel to the line $3x - 2y + 3z + 3 = 0$, $x + y - 2z = 4$.   *Ans.* $3x - 2y + 3z = 6$, $x + y - 2z = 3$.

20. Through $(-3, 1, -2)$ parallel to the line $x + 2y - 3z - 4 = 0$, $x - y - 4z = 0$.   *Ans.* $x + 2y - 3z = 5$, $x - y - 4z = 4$.

21. Through $(0, -5, -1)$ parallel to the line $12x - y + 3z + 2 = 0$, $3x + y + z = 4$.

22. Through $(2, 7, 3)$ parallel to the line $15x - 2y + 4z - 7 = 0$, $x + y - z = 0$.

23. What is represented by (5), § 232, when the given planes are parallel?

234. *Parametric Equations of a Line*

Consider the parametric equations

(1)
$$x = x_1 + at,$$
$$y = y_1 + bt,$$
$$z = z_1 + ct,$$

with t as a parameter and a, b, c, x_1, y_1, z_1 as specified constants. Equations (1) represent a straight line because the elimination of t from them yields two linear equations in x, y, and z. Furthermore, the point (x_1, y_1, z_1)

lies on the line, since for $t = 0$: $x = x_1$, $y = y_1$, $z = z_1$. The numbers $[a, b, c]$ form a set of direction components for the line (1), since a, b, c are proportional to $[x - x_1, y - y_1, z - z_1]$.

Example (a). For the line

(2)
$$x = 2 + t,$$
$$y = 5 - 3t,$$
$$z = -1 + 4t,$$

find the direction cosines, and locate three points on the line.

A set of direction components for (2) is $[1, -3, 4]$, so that direction cosines for (2) are $\left[\dfrac{1}{\sqrt{26}}, \dfrac{-3}{\sqrt{26}}, \dfrac{4}{\sqrt{26}}\right]$. Using $t = 0$, 1, $-\frac{1}{2}$, we immediately compute coordinates of three points on the line: $(2, 5, -1)$, $(3, 2, 3)$, and $(\frac{3}{2}, \frac{13}{2}, -3)$.

Example (b). Write parametric equations for the line through the points $(4, 3, 5)$, $(2, 3, 8)$.

A set of direction components for the line is $[2, 0, -3]$. The equations

(3)
$$x = 4 + 2t,$$
$$y = 3,$$
$$z = 5 - 3t$$

are, therefore, parametric equations of the line. We can equally well use the point $(2, 3, 8)$ in the parametric form and write, instead of (3), the equations

(4)
$$x = 2 + 2w,$$
$$y = 3,$$
$$z = 8 - 3w,$$

with parameter w.

235. *Symmetric Equations of a Line*

Elimination of the parameter t from equations (1), § 234, yields the equations

(1)
$$\frac{x - x_1}{a} = \frac{y - y_1}{b} = \frac{z - z_1}{c},$$

called the *symmetric form* of the equations of a line.* Equations (1) may be

---

* It may be objected that in (1) there are three equations:

$$\frac{x - x_1}{a} = \frac{y - y_1}{b}, \qquad \frac{x - x_1}{a} = \frac{z - z_1}{c}, \qquad \frac{y - y_1}{b} = \frac{z - z_1}{c}.$$

These equations, however, are not independent, since any one follows from the other two. These equations, of course, represent three planes through the line; they are in fact the projecting planes.

obtained at once, without recourse to the parametric form, as follows: Given a point (x_1, y_1, z_1) on the line, and direction components $[a, b, c]$ for the line, let (x, y, z) be any point on the line. Then $[x - x_1, y - y_1, z - z_1]$ are also direction components of the line, and must be proportional to $[a, b, c]$, thus yielding (1).

Example. Write the equations of the line joining the points $(2, 3, 1)$, $(1, -3, -1)$.

By § 221, the direction components are $[1, 6, 2]$; hence the equations of the line are

$$(2) \qquad \frac{x - 2}{1} = \frac{y - 3}{6} = \frac{z - 1}{2}.$$

Given the equations of a line in the symmetric form, it is frequently necessary to obtain two equations in the ordinary or general form. As an example, we shall do this for the line (2). Disregarding the third member and clearing of fractions, we get

$$(3) \qquad 6x - y = 9.$$

Disregarding the second member, we find

$$(4) \qquad 2x - z = 3.$$

Equations (3) and (4) represent the line; if more equations are needed, combinations of these may be made by use of formula (5), § 232.

236. *Line Parallel to a Coordinate Plane*

If a line is parallel to the yz-plane, the parallel line through the origin intersects the x-axis at right angles, so that $\alpha = 90°$, and $l = 0$; thus any set of direction components must be of the form $[0, b, c]$. Difficulty therefore arises in using the symmetric form, since one of the denominators is zero. The same trouble appears, of course, if the line is parallel to the zx- or xy-plane. No such difficulty arises if the parametric equations of § 234 are employed.

Consider the line L (Figure 241) through P_1: (x_1, y_1, z_1), with direction components $[0, b, c]$. The xy-projecting plane is

$$x = x_1;$$

the yz-projecting plane,

$$\frac{y - y_1}{b} = \frac{z - z_1}{c}.$$

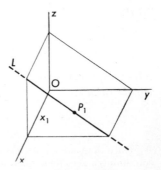

Figure 241

Thus the equations of the line are

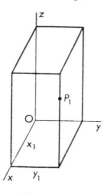

Figure 242

$$(1) \qquad x - x_1 = 0, \qquad \frac{y - y_1}{b} = \frac{z - z_1}{c}.$$

However, the symmetric form is so useful that we should like to have it always available. Formal substitution in (1), § 235, produces the result

$$(2) \qquad \frac{x - x_1}{0} = \frac{y - y_1}{b} = \frac{z - z_1}{c}.$$

If we agree to consider this as merely a conventional way of writing the equations* of the line—that is, if we consider (2) as *equivalent to* (1)—the symmetric form is preserved when the line is parallel to a coordinate plane.

If the line is parallel to Oz (Figure 242), its equations are

$$(3) \qquad x - x_1 = 0, \qquad y - y_1 = 0.$$

By a further convention, we shall agree to write

$$\frac{x - x_1}{0} = \frac{y - y_1}{0} = \frac{z - z_1}{1}$$

as *equivalent to* (3). Thus the symmetric form becomes available for all lines.

237. *Reduction to the Symmetric Form*

Being given the equations of a line in the general form, it is often necessary to reduce them to the symmetric form, or at least to find a set of direction components.

Example (a). Reduce the equations of the line

$$4x + 4y + 3z = 14,$$
$$x - 2y + 3z = 2$$

to the symmetric form.

Find any two of the projecting planes: for instance,

$$x + 2y = 4, \qquad 2x + 3z = 6.$$

These equations contain one variable in common; *solve for that variable and equate values:*

$$x = -2y + 4 = \frac{-3z + 6}{2}.$$

---

* Once more we emphasize that division by zero is never permitted. An "equation" containing a zero denominator is not a true equation at all and can only be interpreted and used in accordance with some special convention, as in the present instance.

Divide through by such a number as to reduce the coefficient of each variable to unity, in this case by -6:

$$\frac{x}{-6} = \frac{y-2}{3} = \frac{z-2}{4}.$$

Comparing these equations with (1), § 235, we see that the line passes through $(0, 2, 2)$ and has direction components $[-6, 3, 4]$.

If the line is parallel to a coordinate plane, the above process fails, since the equations of the projecting planes will not contain one variable in common.

Example (b). Reduce the equations of the line

$$2x + 2y + 3z = 8,$$
$$x + 4y + 6z = 10$$

to the symmetric form.

The projecting planes, found by the usual method, are

(1) $x = 2,$
(2) $2y + 3z = 4.$

Equation (1) shows that the line is parallel to the *yz*-plane. Equation (2) may be written in the form

$$2y - 4 = -3z,$$

or

(3) $\dfrac{y-2}{3} = \dfrac{z}{-2}.$

By the convention of § 236, (1) and (3) may be put in the form

$$\frac{x-2}{0} = \frac{y-2}{3} = \frac{z}{-2}.$$

This is the line L of Figure 241.

EXERCISES

In Exs. 1–8, write parametric equations of the line through the given points.

1. $(3, 4, -1), (1, 1, 4).$ 2. $(6, 3, 2), (4, 0, 1).$
3. $(2, 1, 3), (0, -3, 1).$ 4. $(-7, 1, 4), (3, -4, -1).$
5. $(3, 1, 2), (3, -1, 5).$ 6. $(2, 4, -1), (-1, 4, -2).$
7. $(6, -2, 3), (4, -2, 3).$ 8. $(5, 4, 3), (5, 1, 3).$

In Exs. 9–16, write symmetric equations of the line through the given points.

9. Ex. 1.   10. Ex. 2.   11. Ex. 5.
12. Ex. 6.   13. Ex. 7.   14. Ex. 8.
15. $(2, 2, 1), (1, 3, -2).$ 16. $(4, 1, 4), (3, -4, 1).$

In Exs. 17–22, reduce the equations to symmetric form.

17. $5x + 2y - 2z = 9$, $4x + 4y - z = 3$.
18. $x + 4y + 8z = 0$, $2x - 2y + z = -5$.
19. $2x + 4y + z = 14$, $x + 2y + 3z = 2$.
20. $6x - y + 2z = 4$, $3x + 2y + z = 7$.

21. $3x - 4z + 6 = 0$, $4x + 3z = 17$.   *Ans.* $\dfrac{x-2}{0} = \dfrac{y}{1} = \dfrac{z-3}{0}$.

22. $2y + 3z = 9$, $3y - 5z = 4$.   *Ans.* $\dfrac{x}{1} = \dfrac{y-3}{0} = \dfrac{z-1}{0}$.

In Exs. 23–28, find the angle between the given lines.

23. $\dfrac{x+1}{1} = \dfrac{y}{2} = \dfrac{z-7}{2}$; $\dfrac{x-6}{-3} = \dfrac{y-2}{4} = \dfrac{z}{5}$.   *Ans.* 45°.

24. $\dfrac{x}{2} = \dfrac{y}{3} = \dfrac{z+6}{4}$; $\dfrac{x-3}{1} = \dfrac{y+4}{-2} = \dfrac{z}{1}$.   *Ans.* 90°.

25. $\dfrac{x-4}{1} = \dfrac{y+2}{2} = \dfrac{z-4}{3}$; $\dfrac{x}{3} = \dfrac{y+8}{2} = \dfrac{z}{-1}$.   *Ans.* $\cos \varphi = \frac{2}{7}$.

26. $\dfrac{x+5}{3} = \dfrac{y-1}{2} = \dfrac{z-4}{-2}$; $\dfrac{x}{2} = \dfrac{y}{1} = \dfrac{z-5}{4}$.

27. $x + y - z = 2$, $2x + 2y - z = 7$; $2x + y - 2z = 2$, $3x + y - z = -2$.   *Ans.* $\cos \varphi = \frac{5}{6}$.

28. $x + 3y - z = 5$, $z = x$; $x + y + 3z = 1$, $2x + 3y + 6z = 3$.
29. Write symmetric equations of the line through $(4, 1, 2)$ parallel to the line
$$\frac{x-1}{3} = \frac{y}{5} = \frac{z-7}{-1}.$$

30. Write symmetric equations of the line through $(2, 0, -4)$ parallel to the line
$$\frac{x}{4} = \frac{y+6}{-7} = \frac{z-2}{3}.$$

31. Show that the lines $3x - 5y - z = 1$, $4x - 3y + 6z = 5$, and $x - y + z = 0$, $4x - 7y - 2z = 6$ are parallel.
32. Show that the lines $2x + y - z - 1 = 0$, $x - y + 3z - 10 = 0$ and $5x - 2y + 8z = 44$, $x + 5y - 11z = -38$ are parallel.
33. Show that for the line
$$a_1 x + b_1 y + c_1 z = d_1$$
$$a_2 x + b_2 y + c_2 z = d_2,$$

a set of direction components is

$$\left[\begin{vmatrix} b_1 & c_1 \\ b_2 & c_2 \end{vmatrix}, \quad -\begin{vmatrix} a_1 & c_1 \\ a_2 & c_2 \end{vmatrix}, \quad \begin{vmatrix} a_1 & b_1 \\ a_2 & b_2 \end{vmatrix} \right].$$

In Exs. 34–36, use the result proved in Ex. 33.

34. Ex. 27.   **35.** Ex. 31.   **36.** Ex. 32.

37. Find the equation of the plane determined by the parallel lines of Ex. 31.

Ans. $3x - 4y + z = 2$.

38. Find the equation of the plane determined by the parallel lines of Ex. 32.

Ans. $7x + 5y - 7z = -6$.

39. Find the point of intersection of the intersecting lines $2x + y + 2z = 2$, $y = 2x$, and $2x - y + 2z + 2 = 0$, $3x + y + z = 4$.

40. Find the point of intersection of the intersecting lines $x + y - z = 0$, $2x - y - 3z = 1$, and $x + 2y + z = 3$, $3x + 3y - 2z = 2$.

41. Find the equation of the plane determined by the lines of Ex. 39.

Ans. $18x + y + 10z = 10$.

42. Find the equation of the plane through the lines of Ex. 40.

Ans. $12x + 9y - 13z = 1$.

43. Find the distance from the point $(4, 0, 1)$ to the line $2x - y - z = 4$, $x - y = 1$. (Pass a plane through the point and the line, then a plane through the line perpendicular to the plane just determined.) *Ans.* $\sqrt{6}$

44. Find the distance from the point $(2, 4, 1)$ to the line $2x = 3y + 2z - 7$, $y + z = 2$. (Note the suggestion in Ex. 43.) *Ans.* 3.

238. *Perpendicular Line and Plane*

From Theorem 44, page 400, we obtain at once a condition that a line and a plane be perpendicular.

THEOREM 48. *The plane*

$$Ax + By + Cz + D = 0$$

and the line

$$\frac{x - x_1}{a} = \frac{y - y_1}{b} = \frac{z - z_1}{c}$$

are perpendicular if and only if the quantities A, B, C and a, b, c are proportional.

Example. The equation of the plane through the point $(3, 2, -1)$ perpendicular to the line

$$\frac{x - 2}{2} = \frac{y - 1}{1} = \frac{z + 3}{4}$$

is

$$2x + y + 4z = 4.$$

239. *Parallel Line and Plane*

If a line is parallel to a plane, it is perpendicular to a normal of the plane. The normal has as direction components the coefficients A, B, C in the equation of the plane. Thus the condition that two lines be perpendicular yields a condition that a line and plane be parallel.

THEOREM 49. *The plane*

$$Ax + By + Cz + D = 0$$

and the line

$$\frac{x - x_1}{a} = \frac{y - y_1}{b} = \frac{z - z_1}{c}$$

are parallel if and only if

$$aA + bB + cC = 0.$$

EXERCISES

In Exs. 1–6, write the equations of the line:

1. Through $(2, 4, -3)$ perpendicular to the plane $5x - y + 7z = 8$.
2. Through $(-1, 0, 5)$ perpendicular to the plane $2x + 3y - z = 4$.
3. Through $(7, 1, 0)$ perpendicular to the plane $4x + 3z = 8$.
4. Through $(4, 0, -3)$ perpendicular to the plane $2y + 5z = -1$.
5. Through $(2, 1, 4)$ perpendicular to the xy-plane.
6. Through $(2, 1, 4)$ perpendicular to the yz-plane.
7. Find the foot of the perpendicular from the origin upon the plane

$$x + 2y + z = 12.$$

Draw the figure.   *Ans.* $(2, 4, 2)$.

8. Find the foot of the perpendicular from the point $(2, 4, 3)$ upon the plane $x + 2y + 3z = 5$.   *Ans.* $(1, 2, 0)$.

In Exs. 9–18, find the equation of the plane.

9. Through $(2, -1, 4)$ perpendicular to the line

$$\frac{x - 1}{5} = \frac{y}{-3} = \frac{z + 2}{1}.$$

10. Through $(0, 4, 3)$ perpendicular to the line

$$\frac{x + 3}{1} = \frac{y - 2}{4} = \frac{z - 5}{-2}.$$

11. Through $(3, 1, -2)$ perpendicular to the line $2x = y = 3z + 3$.
12. Through $(4, 0, 1)$ perpendicular to the line $x - 2 = y = 2z - 3$.
13. Perpendicular to the line $x + 1 = y = 2z$ and passing at a distance 2 from the origin.   *Ans.* $2x + 2y + z = \pm 6$.
14. Perpendicular to the line $x = y - 3 = 2(z - 1)$ and passing at a distance 1 from $(1, 2, -4)$.   *Ans.* $2x + 2y + z = 2 \pm 3$.
15. Through $(2, 1, 1)$, $(3, 4, -2)$ and parallel to the line $7x + y - z = 15$, $x - y - z = 6$.   *Ans.* $3x - 7y - 6z = -7$.
16. Through $(1, 2, 0)$, $(2, 0, -4)$ and parallel to the line $x + 2y = 8$, $y + z = 2$.   *Ans.* $2x + 3y - z = 8$.
17. Through the line $x + 2y + z = 0$, $2x - 3y + 3z = 2$ and parallel to the line $2y - z = -1$, $2x + 3z = 2$.   *Ans.* $5x + 3y + 6z = 2$.

18. Through the line $y = x + 3z$, $2y = 2x + z - 1$ and parallel to the line $2x = y = 2z$.   *Ans.* $5x - 5y + 5z = 2$.

19. Find the distance of the point $(4, 2, 3)$ from the line $y = x + 1$, $y + 2z = 5$. Solve in two ways.   *Ans.* 3.

20. Find the distance of the point $(1, 3, 0)$ from the line

$$y = 2x + z, \qquad 4x - y + 3z = 4.$$

Solve in two ways.   *Ans.* $\frac{1}{3}\sqrt{6}$.

21. Find symmetric equations of the line through $(3, 1, 5)$ intersecting the line

$$\frac{x + 2}{4} = \frac{y + 3}{2} = \frac{z + 2}{-1}$$

at right angles.   *Ans.* $\dfrac{x - 3}{1} = \dfrac{y - 1}{2} = \dfrac{z - 5}{8}$.

22. Find symmetric equations of the line through $(3, 1, -2)$ intersecting the line $3x - y - 3z = -6$, $3x + 2y - 12z = 3$ at right angles.

$$\textit{Ans. } \frac{x - 3}{2} = \frac{y - 1}{-1} = \frac{z + 2}{-1}.$$

23. Solve Ex. 21 by another method.

24. Solve Ex. 22 by another method.

25. Show that the line $4x - y = 2$, $y - 4z = 18$ and the plane $4x + y - 8z = 2$ are parallel; find the distance between them.   *Ans.* 4.

26. Show that the line $x = 4y + 1 = 19 - 4z$ and the plane $x - 2y + 2z = -8$ are parallel; find the distance between them.   *Ans.* 6.

27. Find the distance between the parallel lines $x = y - 1 = -z + 4$ and $x = y = -z$.   *Ans.* $\sqrt{11}$.

28. Find the distance between the parallel lines $2x + z = -1$, $y - 3x = 2$, and $3x + y + 3z = 28$, $9x - y + 3z = 44$.   *Ans.* $3\sqrt{5}$.

29. Find the locus of points equidistant from the parallel lines of Ex. 27.
                                                          Ans. $x + 2y + 3z = 7$.

30. Find the locus of points equidistant from the parallel lines of Ex. 28.
                                                          Ans. $8x + 4y + 10z = 43$.

31. Find the shortest distance between the skew lines

$$\frac{x}{1} = \frac{y + 3}{1} = \frac{z - 2}{1}; \qquad \frac{x}{1} = \frac{y + 1}{2} = \frac{z}{-1}.$$

(Pass a plane through each line parallel to the other line.)   *Ans.* $\frac{1}{7}\sqrt{14}$.

32. Find the shortest distance between the skew lines $x + y = 2$, $y + 2z = 3$, and $x + y - 3z = 3$, $x + z = -8$. (Note the suggestion in Ex. 31.)   *Ans.* 2.

30

Surfaces.

Partial Differentiation

240. Surfaces

The locus of the points whose coordinates satisfy a single equation in the three rectangular coordinates x, y, z is called a *surface*. The equation may yield z as an explicit function of x and y, as in

(1)
$$z = f(x, y),$$

or as an implicit function of x and y, as in

(2)
$$F(x, y, z) = 0.$$

241. Intercepts; Traces

To find the intercepts of a surface on the axes, we *equate two of the variables to zero and solve for the third*: to find the x-intercepts, set $y = z = 0$.

A plane and a surface intersect in general in a curve, called the *section* of the surface by the plane. The sections by the coordinate planes will be called the *traces* of the surface.

If in the equation of the surface we substitute $z = k$, the resulting equation in x and y, considered as the equation of a curve in the plane $z = k$, represents the section of the surface by that plane. In particular, *to obtain the xy-trace, we set $z = 0$.* Similarly for the other traces.

Example. For the plane

$$3x + 6y + 2z = 6,$$

the x-intercept is 2, y-intercept 1, z-intercept 3. The traces are,

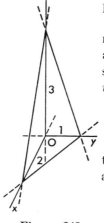

Figure 243

in the xy-plane, the line $x + 2y = 2$;
in the yz-plane, the line $3y + z = 3$;
in the zx-plane, the line $3x + 2z = 6$.

418

242. *Symmetry*

To reduce the mechanical difficulties of draftsmanship, we shall confine our sketches chiefly to the first octant. Fortunately, in many applications involving three variables, all the variables are restricted to positive values. If not, considerations of symmetry may be helpful.

Two points P_1, P_2 are said to be *symmetric with respect to a plane* if the plane is perpendicular to the line P_1P_2 at its mid-point; i.e., if P_2 is the image, or reflection, of P_1 in that plane. A geometric figure is symmetric with respect to a plane if corresponding to every point P_1 of the figure the image P_2 also belongs to the figure.

The definitions of line and center of symmetry laid down in § 18 apply without change to figures in space.

The principal tests for symmetry follow.

THEOREM 50. *A surface is symmetric with respect to the yz-plane if x can be replaced by $-x$ without changing the equation; and conversely.* A similar statement is true for symmetry with respect to the zx- and xy-planes.

THEOREM 51. *A surface is symmetric with respect to the x-axis if y and z can be replaced by $-y$ and $-z$ simultaneously without changing the equation; and conversely.* A similar statement holds for symmetry with respect to the y- and z-axes.

243. *Sketching by Parallel Plane Sections*

One of the simplest methods of sketching a surface is by means of a series of plane sections parallel to a coordinate plane. It often happens that one particular set of sections will form a clearer picture of the surface than any other set, so that care should be taken to make the best choice.

It is well to begin by carrying out the following steps:

1. *Test the surface for symmetry.*
2. *Find the intercepts on the axes.*
3. *Determine the traces on the coordinate planes.*
4. *Examine the sections parallel to each coordinate plane.*

Example (a). Discuss the surface

$$x^2 = 1 - yz,$$

and make a first-octant sketch.

1. The surface is symmetric with respect to the yz-plane, the x-axis, and the origin.

2. The x-intercepts are ± 1; no y- or z-intercept.

3. The xy-trace is the pair of lines $x = \pm 1$; yz-trace, the equilateral hyperbola $yz = 1$; zx-trace, the lines $x = \pm 1$.

4. Sections $x = k$ are hyperbolas; $y = k$, parabolas; $z = k$, parabolas.

In Figure 244 the surface is pictured by means of the sections $y = k$. The construction is as follows: On the axis that is *perpendicular to the cutting planes*—here, the y-axis—mark the total interval OA that is to be included and divide this into a suitable number of (preferably equal) subintervals. At each point of division, such as M, draw the traces MP, MQ of the cutting plane, intersecting the traces of the surface at P and Q.   The parabolic arc PQ is the required section.

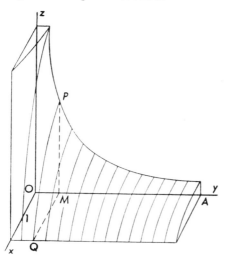

| Figure 244 | Figure 245 |

In the drawing of Figure 244, the xy- and yz-traces play a vital role; in any plane $y = k$, we have merely to draw a parabolic arc terminated by those traces.   It may happen that two such useful traces are not present. Then, as a guide curve, we may take a section of the surface by any convenient plane parallel to a coordinate plane (or two such sections if necessary).

Example (b).   Discuss and sketch the surface

$$x^2 = yz.$$

The general discussion will be left to the reader.   The only traces are the y- and z-axes.   Take a section in a horizontal plane—say, the plane $z = 1$ (the curve AQB in Figure 245).   Then, in each plane $y = k$, draw a parabolic arc such as the arc PQ from the y-axis to the section AQB.

EXERCISES

In Exs. 1–8, mark the intercepts; draw the traces, and any other lines that may be needed to show the position of the plane.

1. $2x + 3y + z = 12$.

3. $x + y - 3z = 3$.

2. $x + y + 3z = 6$.

4. $x - 2y + z = 4$.

5. $2x + y = 6.$ **6.** $2y + 9z = 18.$
7. $y - z = 1.$ **8.** $y = x + z.$

In Exs. 9–30, discuss the surface and make a first octant sketch.

9. $4x^2 + y^2 + z^2 = 4.$ **10.** $x^2 + 4y^2 + 16z^2 = 16.$
11. $y^2 + z^2 = 2x.$ **12.** $x^2 + z^2 = 6y.$
13. $x^2 - y^2 + z^2 = 9.$ **14.** $z^2 - 4x^2 - y^2 = 4.$
15. $z^2 = 9x^2 + y^2.$ **16.** $x^2 = y^2 + z^2.$
17. $z = x^2.$ **18.** $y^2 + z^2 = 4y.$
19. $x^2 + z^2 = 8 - y.$ **20.** $y^2 + z^2 = 4 - x.$
21. $z = 1 - x - y^2.$ **22.** $z = 1 - xy.$
23. $z = y - xy.$ **24.** $z = y^2 - xy.$
25. $z^2 = y - xy.$ **26.** $z^2 = y^2 - xy.$
27. $z = x^2y.$ **28.** $z^2 = x^2y.$
29. $z = y^2(1 - x).$ **30.** $z^2 = (1 - x^2)(1 - y^2).$

In Exs. 31–34, discuss the locus.

31. $y^2 + z^2 = 0.$ **32.** $x^2 + y^2 + z^2 = 0.$
33. $y^2 + z^2 + a^2 = 0.$ **34.** $x^2y^2 + z^2 = 0.$

244. *Surfaces of Revolution*

A *surface of revolution* is a surface that can be generated by rotating a curve about a straight line. Sections by planes perpendicular to the axis of revolution are *right sections*, or *parallels*; evidently these are circles with centers on the axis of revolution. Sections by planes through the axis are *meridians*; since these are merely the generating curve in its successive positions, they are all equal curves.

Example. Discuss the surface $x^2 + z^2 = ay.$

The sections $y = k$ are circles with centers on the y-axis; thus the surface is one of revolution around the y-axis. A meridian section is the parabola $x^2 = ay$ in the xy-plane; the surface is a "paraboloid of revolution." (Figure 246.)

The equation of a surface of revolution around the x-axis must contain y and z only in the combination $(y^2 + z^2)$ because any cross-section $x = k$ must be a circle with center on the x-axis. Therefore the surface must have an equation of the form

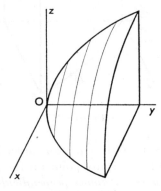

Figure 246

(1) $$y^2 + z^2 = f(x)$$

or of the form

(2) $$F(x, y^2 + z^2) = 0.$$

A similar result holds, of course, for surfaces of revolution around Oy or Oz. Hence, whenever the surface is one of revolution around a coordinate axis, that fact should be apparent from a glance at the equation.

245. *Cylinders*

A *cylinder* is the surface described by a moving line which remains parallel to its original position and always intersects a fixed curve, called the *directing curve*. Thus the cylinder is completely covered by straight lines, called *generators*, all of which are parallel.

The section by any plane perpendicular to the generators is a *right section*; all right sections, and in fact all parallel plane sections, are equal curves. If the right section has a center, the line through this center parallel to the generators is the *axis* of the cylinder.

Consider an equation of the form

(1) $$f(x, y) = 0;$$

that is, an equation not containing z. In the xy-plane this equation repre-

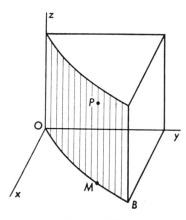

Figure 247

sents, of course, a curve of some kind; say, the curve OMB in Figure 247. At any point M of this curve erect a perpendicular to the xy-plane, and let $P: (x, y, z)$ be any point of the perpendicular. Now the coordinates of M satisfy (1), and those of P must do the same, since its x- and y-coordinates are the same as those of M and z does not occur in the equation. Thus P is on the surface, and since P is any point of the perpendicular at M, that entire line must lie in the surface. Further, since M is any point of the curve, the surface includes all lines perpendicular to the xy-plane through points of the curve. On the other hand, if a point does not lie in one of these lines, its coordinates cannot satisfy the equation, since its x- and y-coordinates cannot be identical with those of any point on the curve. Thus the equation represents a *cylinder with generators perpendicular to the xy-plane*, the directing curve being the curve represented by the given equation in that plane.

A similar result holds for equations involving y and z only, or x and z only.

THEOREM 52. *An equation in two variables represents a cylinder whose generators are perpendicular to the plane of the two variables and whose directing curve is the curve represented by the given equation in that plane.*

COROLLARY. *An equation of the first degree in two variables represents a plane perpendicular to the plane of the two variables.*

The corollary, of course, is merely that case of the theorem in which the directing curve is a straight line.

Example. Discuss the surface

(2) $$y^2 = 4 - 3x.$$

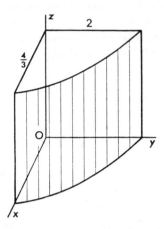

Figure 248

Since z is missing, we know at once that the surface is a cylinder with generators perpendicular to the xy-plane, whose base is the parabola represented by (2) in that plane. Sections $x = k$ are pairs of straight lines; $y = k$, straight lines; $z = k$, parabolas.

Another easily recognized case is that in which the equation represents a cylinder with generators *parallel* to a coordinate plane. For, in the process of examining the three sets of sections, we are bound to uncover a family of straight lines all parallel to each other and to one of the coordinate planes.

EXERCISES

In Exs. 1–12, show that the equation represents a surface of revolution. Sketch the surface.

1. $x^2 + y^2 + 4z^2 = 4a^2$.
2. $4x^2 + y^2 + 4z^2 = 4a^2$.
3. $x^2 + z^2 = y^2$.
4. $x^2 + y^2 = (1 - z)^2$.
5. $x^2 + y^2 - z^2 = a^2$.
6. $x^2 - 4y^2 - 4z^2 = 4a^2$.
7. $x^2 + y^2 + z^2 = 2ay$.
8. $y^4 = x^2 + z^2$.
9. $y^3 + x^2 + z^2 = y$.
10. $x^2y^2 + y^2z^2 = (1 - y)^2$.
11. $x^2y + yz^2 = 1 - y$.
12. $(x^2 + y^2 - 1)z = 2x^2 + 2y^2$.

In Exs. 13–18, discuss and sketch the surface.

13. $x^2 + y^2 = 4x$.
14. $4y = 1 - x^2$.
15. $2yz = a^2$.
16. $y^2 - z^2 = a^2$.
17. $x^2z = (1 - x)^2$.
18. $x^2z - x^2 + z = 0$.

In Exs. 19–24, show that the surface is a cylinder with generators parallel to a coordinate plane. Sketch the surface.

19. $y^2 = 1 - x - z$.
20. $z^2 = 6 - y - 2x$.
21. $xy + yz = 1$.
22. $y^2 + xy + zy = 1$.
23. $(x + y)^2 = 1 - z$.
24. $y^2 + (x + z)^2 = 1$.

246. Cylindrical Coordinates

Given a point P (Figure 249), let us drop a perpendicular from P to a point M in the xy-plane. The position of P is evidently determined if we know the polar coordinates r, θ of M together with the z-coordinate MP. This combination of polar coordinates in the xy-plane with the rectangular z

is the so-called *cylindrical* system.   The coordinates are written in the order (r, θ, z).

The only formulas required for transformation from cylindrical to rectangular coordinates, or vice versa, are those of § 26.

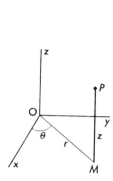

Figure 249

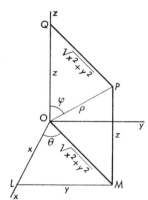

Figure 250

247. *Spherical Coordinates*

The position of a point P is fixed if we know the length ρ of its radius vector, the angle θ from the x-axis to the horizontal projection OM of the radius vector, and the angle φ from the z-axis to the radius vector.   The coordinates (ρ, θ, φ) are the *spherical coordinates* of P.

In Figure 250,

$$OL = OM \cos \theta, \qquad OM = QP = OP \sin \varphi,$$
$$LM = OM \sin \theta, \qquad MP = OQ = OP \cos \varphi.$$

That is,

$$x = \rho \cos \theta \sin \varphi, \qquad y = \rho \sin \theta \sin \varphi, \qquad z = \rho \cos \varphi;$$

$$\rho = \sqrt{x^2 + y^2 + z^2}, \qquad \tan \theta = \frac{y}{x}, \qquad \tan \varphi = \frac{\sqrt{x^2 + y^2}}{z}.$$

A moment's thought shows that the system of coordinates used in geography is merely a slight modification of the system just described.   The "longitude" of a point, measured from some standard meridian, is our angle θ; the "latitude," in the northern hemisphere, is the complement of φ.

EXERCISES

In Exs. 1–14, discuss the surface (cylindrical coordinates) either directly or after transforming the equation to rectangular coordinates.

1. $\theta = \frac{1}{3}\pi$.

3. $r \sin \theta = 2$.

2. $r = 3$.

4. $r \cos \theta = 2$.

5. $r = 2a \cos \theta$.

6. $r = 2a \sin \theta$.

7. $r \cos \theta = z$.

8. $r^2 \sin 2\theta = z$.

9. $r^2 = z$.

10. $r^2 = 4(1 - z^2)$.

11. $r^2 + z^2 = 2az$.

12. $r^2 + z^2 = 2ar$.

13. $z = a \cot \theta$.

14. $z = a(1 - \tan \theta)$.

15. Show that every equation in r and z (i.e., not involving θ) represents a surface of revolution around Oz.

16. Show that every equation in r and θ (not containing z) represents a vertical cylinder.

In Exs. 17–28, discuss the surface (spherical coordinates) either directly or after transforming the equation to rectangular coordinates.

17. $\varphi = \frac{1}{4}\pi$.

18. $\rho = a$.

19. $\rho \cos \varphi = a$.

20. $\rho \sin \varphi = a$.

21. $\rho = 2a \sin \varphi$.

22. $\rho \sin \varphi = 2a \sin \theta$.

23. $\rho^2 \sin 2\varphi \sin \theta = a^2$.

24. $\cot \varphi = \cos \theta$.

25. $\rho^2 \cos 2\varphi = a^2$.

26. $\rho^2 \sin 2\varphi = a^2$.

27. $\rho \cos \varphi = a \tan \theta$.

28. $\rho \sin \varphi = a \tan \theta$.

29. Show that an equation in ρ and φ (not containing θ) represents a surface of revolution about Oz.

30. If the equation of a surface involves only ρ and θ, show that sections by planes through the z-axis are circles with centers at O.

31. Sketch the surface $\rho = 2a \cos \theta$. (Ex. 30.)

248. *Limits; Continuity*

Consider a function

(1) $$z = f(x, y)$$

representing a surface in space. When x and y approach the respective values x_1, y_1, the function z is said to *approach a limit* z_1 if the point (x, y, z) of the surface (1) approaches a limiting point (x_1, y_1, z_1). In other words, if the difference between the variable z and the fixed value z_1 can be made as small as desired by taking x sufficiently near the fixed x_1, and y sufficiently near the fixed y_1, then z is said to approach z_1; in symbols,

$$\lim_{\substack{x \to x_1 \\ y \to y_1}} f(x, y) = z_1.$$

A function $f(x, y)$ is *continuous* at the point (x_1, y_1) (compare with § 35) if $f(x_1, y_1)$ exists, and

$$\lim_{\substack{x \to x_1 \\ y \to y_1}} f(x, y) = f(x_1, y_1).$$

Similar definitions are laid down for functions of more than two variables.

In what follows, it is assumed that all functions occurring are continuous at all points under consideration.

249. *Partial Derivatives*

If y be kept *fixed*, the function

$$z = f(x, y)$$

becomes a function of x alone, and its derivative may be found by the ordinary rules. This derivative is called the *partial derivative of z with respect to x*, and is denoted by

$$\frac{\partial z}{\partial x}, \quad \frac{\partial f}{\partial x}, \quad \text{or} \quad f_x(x, y).$$

The partial derivative with respect to y has a similar meaning.

When z is defined implicitly as a function of x and y by the equation

$$F(x, y, z) = 0,$$

the partial derivatives may still be found by the rule of § 55.

The idea of partial differentiation may be extended at once to functions of any number of variables. We have only to remember that in differentiating with respect to any one variable, *all the other variables are treated as constants*.

Applications of partial differentiation will be found in Chapter 32.

Example (a). If $V = \pi r^2 h$, then

$$\frac{\partial V}{\partial r} = 2\pi rh, \qquad \frac{\partial V}{\partial h} = \pi r^2.$$

Thus, if the altitude of a circular cylinder is kept fixed, the volume changes at a rate equal to the lateral area; etc.

Example (b). If $z^2 + 2zx = x^2 - y^2$, then

$$2z \frac{\partial z}{\partial x} + 2z + 2x \frac{\partial z}{\partial x} = 2x, \qquad \frac{\partial z}{\partial x} = \frac{x - z}{x + z},$$

$$2z \frac{\partial z}{\partial y} + 2x \frac{\partial z}{\partial y} = -2y, \qquad \frac{\partial z}{\partial y} = \frac{-y}{x + z}.$$

It is basic that before any partial differentiations can be performed, the independent and dependent variables must be stipulated. As an example, consider the system of equations

(1) $\qquad\qquad v^2 + x^2 + uxy - t^2 = 0,$

(2) $\qquad\qquad u^2 + v^2 + y^2 - 3xt = 0.$

Equations (1) and (2) determine two of the five variables present as functions of the other three. There are therefore two dependent variables and three independent variables in the system.

Suppose that we seek $\dfrac{\partial u}{\partial x}$. Then surely u is one of the dependent variables and x is one of the independent variables. Before we can proceed to perform any differentiation, we must know what to hold constant during that differentiation. The solution is not unique until the character of each of the variables has been stipulated.

If in (1) and (2) we decide to use u and v as the two dependent variables, then x, y, and t are the independent ones. We must then hold y and t constant while differentiating (1) and (2) with respect to x. We thus obtain

$$(3) \qquad 2v\,\frac{\partial v}{\partial x} + 2x + xy\,\frac{\partial u}{\partial x} + uy = 0,$$

$$(4) \qquad 2u\,\frac{\partial u}{\partial x} + 2v\,\frac{\partial v}{\partial x} - 3t = 0.$$

From (3) and (4) it follows, by elimination of $\dfrac{\partial v}{\partial x}$, that

$$(5) \qquad \frac{\partial u}{\partial x} = \frac{2x + 3t + uy}{2u - xy}.$$

Instead of $\dfrac{\partial u}{\partial x}$ in (5) it is much safer to write

$$\left(\frac{\partial u}{\partial x}\right)_{y,t}$$

in which the subscripts indicate what variables were held constant during the manipulations performed.

Next let us return to equations (1) and (2) and consider u and y to be the dependent variables. Then x, v, and t are to be independent variables and, in any differentiation with respect to x, we must hold v and t constant. Then (1) and (2) yield

$$(6) \qquad 2x + xy\,\frac{\partial u}{\partial x} + uy + ux\,\frac{\partial y}{\partial x} = 0,$$

$$(7) \qquad 2u\,\frac{\partial u}{\partial x} + 2y\,\frac{\partial y}{\partial x} - 3t = 0,$$

from which it follows that

$$(8) \qquad \left(\frac{\partial u}{\partial x}\right)_{v,t} = \frac{4xy + 2uy^2 + 3xut}{2x(u^2 - y^2)}$$

in contrast to (5) above.

In physical problems the ambiguity discussed here should not arise. The purpose to which the partial derivative is to be put, together with other details of the problem, must dictate which are to be the independent and the dependent variables. The study of an artificial system such as (1) and (2) above should clarify the student's feeling for the meaning of partial differentiation. In thermodynamics and physical chemistry the ideas discussed in this section play a useful role.

250. *Geometric Interpretation*

To keep y constant ($y = y_1$) in the equation $z = f(x, y)$ means geometrically that we cut the surface by the plane $y = y_1$. The partial derivative $\dfrac{\partial z}{\partial x}$ is therefore the *slope of the curve of intersection* of the surface and the plane $y = y_1$; i.e., the slope of the tangent PT. The partial derivative $\dfrac{\partial z}{\partial y}$ may be interpreted similarly.

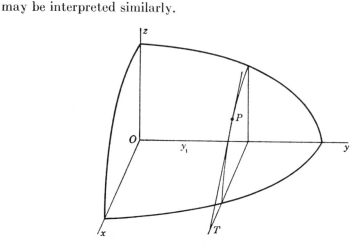

Figure 251

Example.   Find the equations of the tangent to the parabola

$$(x + y)^2 + 32z = 256, \qquad x = 5$$

at $P: (5, 3, 6)$.

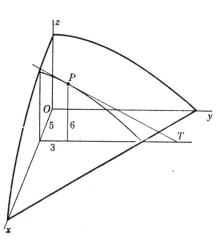

Figure 252

Since x is constant, we differentiate partially with respect to y:

$$2(x + y) + 32 \frac{\partial z}{\partial y} = 0,$$

$$\frac{\partial z}{\partial y} = -\frac{1}{16} (x + y),$$

$$\left[\frac{\partial z}{\partial y} \right]_P = -\frac{1}{2}.$$

Thus the equations of the tangent PT are

$$z - 6 = -\tfrac{1}{2}(y - 3), \qquad x = 5,$$

or

$$y + 2z = 15, \qquad x = 5.$$

251. *Higher Derivatives*

The derivatives $\dfrac{\partial z}{\partial x}, \dfrac{\partial z}{\partial y}$ are themselves functions of x and y, and their partial derivatives can in turn be found. They are denoted by the following symbols:

$$\frac{\partial}{\partial x}\left(\frac{\partial z}{\partial x}\right) = \frac{\partial^2 z}{\partial x^2} = f_{xx}(x,\, y),$$

$$\frac{\partial}{\partial y}\left(\frac{\partial z}{\partial x}\right) = \frac{\partial^2 z}{\partial y\, \partial x} = f_{xy}(x,\, y),$$

$$\frac{\partial}{\partial x}\left(\frac{\partial z}{\partial y}\right) = \frac{\partial^2 z}{\partial x\, \partial y} = f_{yx}(x,\, y),$$

$$\frac{\partial}{\partial y}\left(\frac{\partial z}{\partial y}\right) = \frac{\partial^2 z}{\partial y^2} = f_{yy}(x,\, y).$$

The process can, of course, be repeated to find still higher derivatives.

It can be shown that the two "cross-derivatives" $\dfrac{\partial^2 z}{\partial y\, \partial x},\ \dfrac{\partial^2 z}{\partial x\, \partial y}$ are identical, provided they are continuous:

$$\frac{\partial^2 z}{\partial y\, \partial x} \equiv \frac{\partial^2 z}{\partial x\, \partial y}.$$

EXERCISES

In Exs. 1–16, find the first partial derivatives of the given function.

1. $z = x^3 - x^2 y + 4y^2$.   *Ans.* $\dfrac{\partial z}{\partial x} = 3x^2 - 2xy;\ \dfrac{\partial z}{\partial y} = 8y - x^2$.

2. $z = 4x^2 y - y^2 + 3x - 1$.   *Ans.* $\dfrac{\partial z}{\partial x} = 8xy + 3;\ \dfrac{\partial z}{\partial y} = 4x^2 - 2y$.

3. $z = \sin(xy)$.   **4.** $z = \cot(xy)$.

5. $u = \sqrt{x^2 - v^2}$.   **6.** $v = (x^2 + w^2)^{-\frac{1}{2}}$.

7. $x = \dfrac{u - v}{u^2 + v^2}$.   **8.** $s = \left(\dfrac{t + 3y}{t}\right)^2$.

9. $r = \cos^2(\theta - 3\varphi)$.   **10.** $r = \sec^2(2\theta - 3\varphi)$.

11. $y = \ln(z^2 + x^2)$.   **12.** $u = \ln[z^2(x^2 - y^2)]$.

13. $v = e^{-xy}$.   **14.** $u = ze^{-x^2 - y^2}$.

15. $w = \tan(x + 2y - z^2)$.   **16.** $\alpha = \ln[xy(2t - 1)^2]$.

17. If (x, y) and (r, θ) are the rectangular and polar coordinates of a point, find the partial derivatives of x and y with respect to r and θ.   *Ans.* $\dfrac{\partial x}{\partial \theta} = -r\sin\theta$.

18. In Ex. 17, find the partial derivatives of r and θ with respect to x and y.

$$\textit{Ans.}\ \frac{\partial \theta}{\partial x} = -\frac{y}{x^2 + y^2}.$$

In Exs. 19–24, find $\dfrac{\partial z}{\partial x}, \dfrac{\partial z}{\partial y}$.

19. $x^2 - y^2 + z^2 = a^2$.　　　　　　Ans. $\dfrac{\partial z}{\partial x} = \dfrac{-x}{z}; \dfrac{\partial z}{\partial y} = \dfrac{y}{z}$.

20. $z^2 - 4xz + y^2 = 4$.　　　　Ans. $\dfrac{\partial z}{\partial x} = \dfrac{2z}{z - 2x}; \dfrac{\partial z}{\partial y} = \dfrac{y}{2x - z}$.

21. $xy + xz + yz = 3$.　　　　　　22. $x^2 + z^2 = 4yz$.

23. $xyz = x + y + z$.　　　　　　24. $2x^2z - z^3y = x$.

In Exs. 25–30, find the equations of the tangent line in the given plane.

25. Tangent to the parabola $z = x^2 + 4y^2$, $x = 2$, at the point (2, 1, 8).

　　　　　　　　　　　　Ans. $x = 2$, $z = 8y$.

26. Tangent to the parabola $z = y^2 - 4x^2 - 1$, $y = 4$, at the point $(-2, 4, -1)$.

　　　　　　　　　　Ans. $y = 4$, $16x - z = -31$.

27. Tangent to the circle $x^2 + 3y^2 + z^2 = 13$, $y = -1$, at the point $(1, -1, 3)$.

　　　　　　　　　　Ans. $y = -1$, $x + 3z = 10$.

28. Tangent to the ellipse $x^2 + 3y^2 + z^2 = 13$, $x = 1$, at the point $(1, -1, 3)$.

　　　　　　　　　　Ans. $x = 1$, $z = y + 4$.

29. Tangent to the curve $z^2 = xy + x^2$, $z = 4$, at (2, 6, 4). What kind of curve
is this?　　　　　　　Ans. $z = 4$, $5x + y = 16$.

30. Tangent to the curve $xy + xz + yz = 0$, $x = 6$, at $(6, -2, 3)$. What kind
of curve is this?　　　　　　Ans. $x = 6$, $9y + 4z = -6$.

31. Given $z = (x - 2y^2)^3$, find $\dfrac{\partial^2 z}{\partial x^2}, \dfrac{\partial^2 z}{\partial x\, \partial y}, \dfrac{\partial^2 z}{\partial y\, \partial x}, \dfrac{\partial^2 z}{\partial y^2}$.

32. Given $v = (t - 3x)e^{-t}$, find $\dfrac{\partial^2 v}{\partial t^2}, \dfrac{\partial^2 v}{\partial x^2}, \dfrac{\partial^2 v}{\partial x\, \partial t}, \dfrac{\partial^2 v}{\partial t\, \partial x}$.

33. Given $u = \sin(x + 2y)$, verify that $\dfrac{\partial^3 u}{\partial y\, \partial x^2} = \dfrac{\partial^3 u}{\partial x\, \partial y\, \partial x} = \dfrac{\partial^3 u}{\partial x^2\, \partial y}$.

34. For the u of Ex. 33, obtain $\dfrac{\partial^3 u}{\partial x^3}, \dfrac{\partial^3 u}{\partial y^2\, \partial x}$, and $\dfrac{\partial^3 u}{\partial y\, \partial x\, \partial y}$.

35. If $w = x^3 - 7xy^2$, show that $x\dfrac{\partial w}{\partial x} + y\dfrac{\partial w}{\partial y} = 3w$.

36. If $u = 3x^2 + 2xz - y^2$, show that $x\dfrac{\partial u}{\partial x} + y\dfrac{\partial u}{\partial y} + z\dfrac{\partial u}{\partial z} = 2u$.

37. If $z = \dfrac{xy}{x^2 + y^2}$, show that $x\dfrac{\partial z}{\partial x} + y\dfrac{\partial z}{\partial y} = 0$.

38. If $u = \sqrt{x^3 - 2y^3}$, show that $x\dfrac{\partial u}{\partial x} + y\dfrac{\partial u}{\partial y} = \dfrac{3}{2}u$.

39. If $u = \ln(x^2 + y^2)$, show that $\dfrac{\partial^2 u}{\partial x^2} + \dfrac{\partial^2 u}{\partial y^2} = 0$.

40. If $\theta = \operatorname{Arctan}\dfrac{y}{x}$, show that $\dfrac{\partial^2 \theta}{\partial x^2} + \dfrac{\partial^2 \theta}{\partial y^2} = 0$.

41. Show that $u = e^{-\alpha^2 t} \sin \alpha x$ satisfies the simple heat equation $\dfrac{\partial u}{\partial t} = \dfrac{\partial^2 u}{\partial x^2}$ for all values of α.

42. Determine the relation that must hold between α and β if $u = e^{\alpha x} \sin \beta y$ is to satisfy Laplace's equation $\dfrac{\partial^2 u}{\partial x^2} + \dfrac{\partial^2 u}{\partial y^2} = 0.$ *Ans.* $\beta = \pm \alpha.$

43. If $u = e^{\sqrt{m^2 + n^2}\, x} \cos my \sin nz$, show that $\dfrac{\partial^2 u}{\partial x^2} + \dfrac{\partial^2 u}{\partial y^2} + \dfrac{\partial^2 u}{\partial z^2} = 0.$

44. Find the relation connecting α, β, γ if $u = e^{\alpha t} \cos \beta x \sin \gamma y$ is to satisfy the heat equation $\dfrac{\partial^2 u}{\partial x^2} + \dfrac{\partial^2 u}{\partial y^2} = \dfrac{\partial u}{\partial t}.$

45. For the function $z = x^2 y^2 + y^{\frac{1}{2}}$, show that $\dfrac{\partial^2 z}{\partial y\, \partial x} \neq \dfrac{\partial^2 z}{\partial x\, \partial y}$ at $(0, 0, 0)$.

46. Find all the possible values of $\dfrac{\partial v}{\partial t}$ from the system

$$uv + xyt = 0,$$
$$x^2 + v^2 - 2ut = 0.$$

47. Find the different possible values of $\dfrac{\partial y}{\partial u}$ from the system of equations in Ex. 46.

48. Let $f_1(z)$ and $f_2(z)$ be functions whose second derivatives are continuous, and let a be a constant. Show that

$$y = f_1(x - at) + f_2(x + at)$$

satisfies the wave equation

$$\frac{\partial^2 y}{\partial t^2} = a^2 \frac{\partial^2 y}{\partial x^2}.$$

252. *Curves*

Two surfaces intersect in general in a curve. If the equations of the two surfaces be considered as simultaneous, their locus consists of all points lying on both surfaces.

The locus of two simultaneous equations is a curve, the curve of intersection of the surfaces represented by the two equations separately.

Of course the curve of intersection may be a plane curve, but ordinarily its points do not all lie in a plane, in which case it is called a *twisted curve*, or *skew curve*.

An infinite number of surfaces may evidently be passed through a given curve. Thus, while there is only one equation representing a given surface, *a curve may be represented by an infinite number of different pairs of equations,* by the equations of any two surfaces having that curve as their intersection. From the given pair of equations it is often possible to derive a simpler pair from which the form and properties of the curve are more readily seen.

Indeed, if $u = 0$, $v = 0$ is any curve C and if k is constant, then the locus of the equation $u + kv = 0$ is a surface containing the curve C.

253. *Projecting Cylinders*

If a perpendicular be dropped from a point P to a plane, the foot P' of the

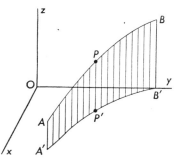

Figure 253

perpendicular is the *projection* of P upon the plane, and the line PP' is the *projecting line*. If all the points of a curve in space be projected upon any plane, their projections form a certain curve in that plane. This curve is called the *projection* of the given curve, and the cylinder whose generators are the projecting lines is the *projecting cylinder* of the curve upon the plane. Figure 253 shows the projection $A'P'B'$ of a curve APB upon the xy-plane, together with that portion of the projecting cylinder that lies between the curve and its projection.

Upon eliminating z between the equations of a curve, we obtain a third equation which is satisfied whenever both the original equations are satisfied, and therefore represents a surface through the given curve. Furthermore, since the new equation does not contain z, it represents a cylinder perpendicular to the xy-plane, i.e., the xy-projecting cylinder of the curve.

To obtain the xy-projecting cylinder of a given curve, eliminate z between the equations of the curve; similarly for the other projecting cylinders.

An especially useful method of drawing a curve in space is to exhibit it as the intersection of two of its projecting cylinders.

Example. Draw the curve

$$4x^2 + y^2 + 3z^2 = 5,$$
$$2x^2 + y^2 + z^2 = 3.$$

Eliminating x, y, and z in turn, we get the three projecting cylinders

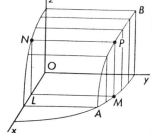

(1) $y^2 - z^2 = 1,$
(2) $x^2 + z^2 = 1,$
(3) $x^2 + y^2 = 2.$

Figure 254

Thus one projection of the curve is an arc of a hyperbola, while the other two are circular arcs. In Figure 254 the curve APB is shown as the intersection of the circular cylinders (2) and (3). The construction is as follows: Through any point L on Ox, draw lines parallel to Oy and Oz intersecting the directing curves of the cylinders at M and N. Through M and N draw the generators of the cylinders respectively parallel to Oz and Oy; their point of intersection P is a point of the curve.

254. *Solid with Composite Boundary*

In Chapter 33 it will frequently be necessary to picture a portion of space bounded by two or more surfaces, in addition (usually) to the coordinate planes. As a rule the best plan is to cut through the whole figure by a set of planes parallel to a coordinate plane, exactly as in § 243. But now, instead of picking out the sections that are simplest for some one surface, we try to select those that are simplest, on the average, for all the surfaces involved.

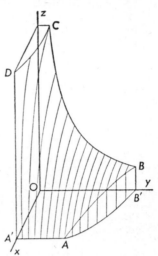

Figure 255

Example. Sketch the solid that is common to those shown in Figures 244 and 248.

The bounding surfaces are the coordinate planes and the surfaces

(1) $$x^2 + yz = 1,$$
(2) $$y^2 = 4 - 3x.$$

The xy-traces ($z = 0$) of these surfaces intersect at $A: (1, 1, 0)$, $(1, -1, 0)$, and at $(-1, \pm \sqrt{7}, 0)$, the last three of which are outside the first octant. The yz-traces intersect at $B: (0, 2, \frac{1}{2})$ and, outside the first octant, at $(0, -2, -\frac{1}{2})$. The xz-traces do not intersect.

The respective sections are:

$x = k$, hyperbolas and straight lines;
$y = k$, parabolas and straight lines;
$z = k$, parabolas and parabolas.

We begin by drawing the relevant portions of the traces of the two surfaces: in the xy-plane, the arcs $A'A$, AB'; in the yz-plane, the arcs $B'B$, BC; in the xz-plane, the arc $A'D$. Choosing sections $y = k$, we reproduce Figure 244 in the interval $0 < y < 1$ (out to A). In the interval $1 < y < 2$, the sections of the surface (1) are cut off by the curve of intersection AB; from the points of that curve, generators of the cylinder (2) are dropped to the xy-plane.

EXERCISES

In Exs. 1–14, draw the curve.

1. $x^2 + z^2 = a^2$, $y = x$.
2. $x^2 + y^2 = a^2$, $y^2 + z^2 = 2a^2$.
3. $y^2 + z^2 = a^2$, $x + y = a$.
4. $x^2 + z^2 = 2a^2$, $y = a$.

5. $x^2 + y^2 + 3z^2 = 4,\ 2x^2 - y^2 + 9z^2 = 8.$

6. $x^2 + y^2 + 2z^2 = 2a^2,\ 3x^2 - y^2 + 2z^2 = 2a^2.$

7. $x^2 + 2y^2 + z^2 = 5,\ x^2 - y^2 - 2z^2 = 2.$

8. $3x^2 + 3y^2 + 2z^2 = 8,\ 3x^2 = y^2 + 6z^2.$

9. $x^2 - 3y^2 + z^2 = 9a^2,\ x^2 + 9y^2 + 4z^2 = 9a^2.$ *Ans.* ($\pm 3a$, 0, 0).

10. $x^2 + y^2 + z^2 = 1,\ x^2 + 2y^2 + z^2 = 5.$ *Ans.* No intersection.

11. $z = x^2 + y^2,\ z^2 = x^2 + y^2.$

12. $z = xy,\ z^2 = y.$

13. $xyz = 1 - y^2,\ xy = z.$

14. $y = xz,\ xyz = 1.$

15. If $u = 0$ and $v = 0$ are any two equations in x, y, and z, what is the locus of the equation $u^2 + v^2 = 0$?

16. Sketch the surface $x^2 + y^2 + z^2 = 2xy.$ (Ex. 15.)

In Exs. 17–20, draw the straight line.

17. $x + 3y + z = 3,\ 2x + 4y + z = 4.$

18. $x + y + 4z = 4,\ 2x + 3y + 3z = 6.$

19. $x + 2y - z = 0,\ 3x - y - 2z = 0.$

20. $6x - y - 2z = 0,\ y = 3x.$

In Exs. 21–34, draw the solid in the first octant bounded by the given surfaces.

21. $x^2 + y^2 = a^2,\ y^2 = az.$

22. $y^2 + z^2 = a^2,\ x^2 + y^2 = a^2.$

23. $x^2 = ay,\ z = y,\ y = a.$

24. $y^2 + z^2 = a^2,\ y = x,\ 2y = x.$

25. $x^2 = y,\ z = x + y,\ y = 1.$

26. $x + y + z = 2,\ z = 1 - x^2.$

27. $z^2 + ay = a^2,\ y^2 + z^2 = ax.$

28. $z = 1 - x^2,\ y = 1 - xz.$

29. $y = x^2z,\ z^2 = x,\ z = x^2.$

30. $z = x^2y^2,\ x = 2y,\ x = 2.$

31. $y + z = 1,\ x = y - zy.$

32. $az = xy,\ x^2 + ay = 4a^2.$

33. $xy = az,\ z = x,\ x = a.$

34. $x^2 + z^2 = a^2,\ y = x + z.$

From a sheet of paper 1 ft. square, portions are removed as indicated in Exs. 35–38. Exhibit graphically the remaining area as a function of x and y, drawing only the portion of the surface that has a meaning in the problem.

35. Fig. 256.   **36.** Fig. 257.

37. Fig. 258.   **38.** Fig. 259.

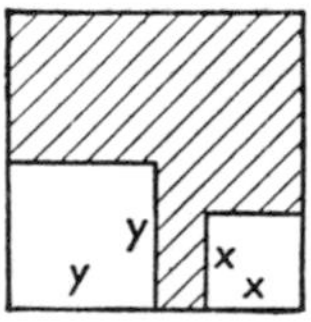

Figure 256 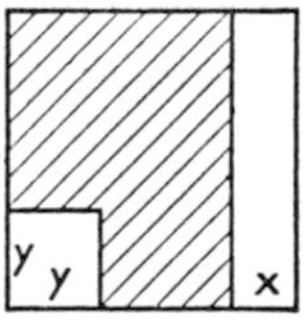   Figure 257 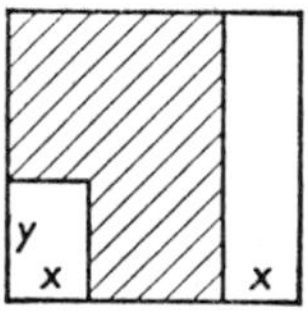   Figure 258 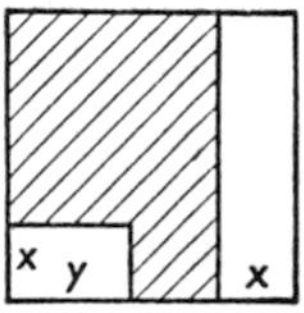   Figure 259

39. A box, of volume 1 cu. ft., is to be placed in a cubical container of edge 2 ft. Show graphically the depth of the box as a function of its other two dimensions.

Quadric Surfaces

255. *Definition*

A surface whose equation is of the second degree is called a *quadric surface*. In this chapter we shall discuss a number of surfaces of particular importance, confining our attention chiefly to quadrics with equations in the simplest standard form.

The quadrics proper are of nine species: the ellipsoid (of which the sphere is a special case), the hyperboloids (two species), the paraboloids (two species), the quadric cylinders (three species), and the quadric cone. In addition there are the degenerate forms: two parallel, coincident, or intersecting planes, a single straight line, or a point.

256. *The Sphere*

A *sphere* is the locus of a moving point that remains at a constant distance from a fixed point. The constant distance is the *radius* and the fixed point the *center*.

The equation of a sphere of given center and radius can be written down at once by the distance formula. The equation of a sphere of radius a is, if the center is the origin,

$$(1) \qquad x^2 + y^2 + z^2 = a^2;$$

if the center is the point (h, k, l),

$$(2) \qquad (x - h)^2 + (y - k)^2 + (z - l)^2 = a^2.$$

Every equation of the form

$$(3) \qquad Ax^2 + Ay^2 + Az^2 + Gx + Hy + Iz + K = 0, \qquad A \neq 0$$

can be reduced to the form (2) by completing the squares in x, y, and z; hence *every equation of the form* (3) *represents a sphere* (exceptionally, a point, or no locus).

Example. Find the center and radius of the sphere

$$(4) \qquad x^2 + y^2 + z^2 + 2x - 6z - 6 = 0.$$

First we complete the squares in x, y, z. We get

$$x^2 + 2x + 1 + y^2 + z^2 - 6z + 9 = 6 + 1 + 9,$$

or

(5) $$(x + 1)^2 + y^2 + (z - 3)^2 = 16.$$

By comparing equation (5) with the standard form (2), we may conclude that the sphere (4) has its center at $(-1, 0, 3)$ and its radius equal to 4.

EXERCISES

In Exs. 1–6, find the center and radius of the sphere.

1. $x^2 + y^2 + z^2 - 4x - 6y + 2z - 11 = 0$.
2. $x^2 + y^2 + z^2 + 8x - 2y + 1 = 0$.
3. $x^2 + y^2 + z^2 = 6y - 8z$.
4. $x^2 + y^2 + z^2 = 12x$.
5. $2x^2 + 2y^2 + 2z^2 + 14x - 6y = 1$.
6. $3x^2 + 3y^2 + 3z^2 - x + 2y + 4z - 2 = 0$.

In Exs. 7–13, find the equation of the sphere.

7. Of radius 4 with center at $(1, -2, 3)$.
8. Of radius 3 with center at $(0, 4, -1)$.
9. With center at O tangent to the plane $x + 2y - 3z = 28$.
10. With center at O tangent to the plane $x + 2y - 2z = 15$.
11. With center at $(-2, 3, 5)$ tangent to the plane $4x + 8y = z - 7$.
12. With center at $(1, 2, 3)$ tangent to the plane $3x + 4z = 5y - 15$.
13. With center on the line $x = y = z$ and passing through $(5, 3, 0)$, $(-1, 4, 1)$.
    Ans. $(x - 2)^2 + (y - 2)^2 + (z - 2)^2 = 14$.
14. Find the tangent plane to the sphere $x^2 + y^2 + z^2 = 9$ at $(1, 2, -2)$.
    Ans. $x + 2y - 2z = 9$.
15. Find the tangent plane to the sphere of Ex. 13 at $(5, 3, 0)$.
    Ans. $3x + y - 2z = 18$.
16. Find the tangent plane to the sphere $x^2 + y^2 + z^2 - 2x + 4y = 76$ at $(0, 2, 8)$.
    Ans. $x - 4y - 8z = -72$.
17. Find the tangent plane to the sphere $x^2 + y^2 + z^2 = a^2$ at any point (x_1, y_1, z_1) on it.
    Ans. $x_1 x + y_1 y + z_1 z = a^2$.
18. Prove that a sphere is determined by four points not in a plane.
19. Find the equation of a sphere through $(0, 0, 0)$, $(1, 0, 0)$, $(0, 4, 0)$, $(-1, 2, 1)$.
    Ans. $x^2 + y^2 + z^2 - x - 4y + z = 0$.
20. A point moves so that the sum of the squares of its distances from two fixed points is constant. Show that its locus is a sphere.
21. A point moves so that the square of its distance from a fixed point is proportional to its distance from a fixed plane. Show that its locus is a sphere.
22. Find the equation of a sphere of radius 9 touching the plane $x + 8y - 4z = 9$ at $(1, 1, 0)$.
23. Find the equation of a sphere touching the plane $x + y + 2z = 1$ at $(0, -1, 1)$ and passing through $(-2, 0, 0)$.   *Ans.* $(x + 1)^2 + (y + 2)^2 + (z + 1)^2 = 6$.

257. *The Ellipsoid*

The locus of the equation

$$\frac{x^2}{a^2} + \frac{y^2}{b^2} + \frac{z^2}{c^2} = 1$$

is an *ellipsoid*. This surface is symmetric with respect to all three coordinate planes and lies within the box

$$-a \leqq x \leqq a, \qquad -b \leqq y \leqq b, \qquad -c \leqq z \leqq c.$$

The segments of length $2a$, $2b$, $2c$ cut off on the coordinate axes are the *axes* of the ellipsoid; the point O is the *center*.

When two of the semiaxes a, b, c are equal, so that the sections by planes perpendicular to the third axis are circles, the surface becomes an *ellipsoid of revolution*: if the equal axes are shorter than the third, a *prolate spheroid*; if longer, an *oblate spheroid*. When $a = b = c$, the surface is a sphere.

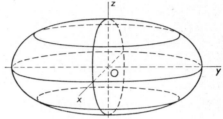

Figure 260

Example. An equation such as

$$x^2 + 4y^2 + 9z^2 - 2x + 16y - 19 = 0$$

can be rewritten as

$$(x - 1)^2 + 4(y + 2)^2 + 9z^2 = 36,$$

in which form it is readily recognized as the equation of an ellipsoid with center at $(1, -2, 0)$, and with semiaxes of lengths 6, 3, 2.

258. *The Hyperboloid of One Sheet*

The equation

(1) $$\frac{x^2}{a^2} + \frac{y^2}{b^2} - \frac{z^2}{c^2} = 1$$

represents a *hyperboloid of one sheet* (Figure 261). The sections parallel to the yz- and zx-planes are hyperbolas; parallel to the xy-plane, ellipses. The intercepts on Ox are $\pm a$; on Oy, $\pm b$; on Oz, imaginary. The surface is a connected, open surface extending to infinity in both directions along the z-axis.

If $a = b$, the elliptic sections become circular and the surface is the *hyperboloid of revolution of one sheet*. If $a = c$ or $b = c$, but $a \neq b$, the surface is not one of revolution; the result merely means that the sections $y = k$ or $x = k$ are equilateral hyperbolas.

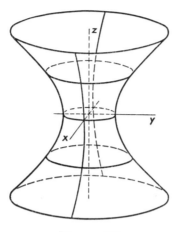

Figure 261

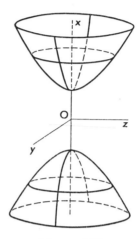

Figure 262

259. *The Hyperboloid of Two Sheets*

The equation

(1)
$$\frac{x^2}{a^2} - \frac{y^2}{b^2} - \frac{z^2}{c^2} = 1$$

represents a *hyperboloid of two sheets* (Figure 262). A study of the sections shows that the surface consists of two disconnected sheets, one in the region $x \geqq a$, the other in the region $x \leqq -a$, each opening out larger along Ox as x increases numerically. Note the unconventional arrangement of the axes in Figure 262.

When $b = c$, the elliptic sections become circles, and the surface becomes the *hyperboloid of revolution of two sheets*.

EXERCISES

In Exs. 1–16, classify the surface, state whether it is a surface of revolution, and make a sketch.

1. $\dfrac{x^2}{4} + \dfrac{y^2}{1} + \dfrac{z^2}{9} = 1.$

2. $\dfrac{x^2}{1} + \dfrac{y^2}{16} + \dfrac{z^2}{9} = 1.$

3. $\dfrac{x^2}{9} - \dfrac{y^2}{4} + \dfrac{z^2}{4} = 1.$

4. $\dfrac{z^2}{2} + \dfrac{y^2}{2} - \dfrac{x^2}{16} = 1.$

5. $\dfrac{x^2}{9} - \dfrac{y^2}{4} - \dfrac{z^2}{4} = 1.$

6. $\dfrac{y^2}{4} - \dfrac{x^2}{1} - \dfrac{z^2}{1} = 1.$

7. $x^2 - y^2 + z^2 = 1.$

8. $z^2 = 1 - 4x^2 + 4y^2.$

9. $x^2 - y^2 + z^2 + 1 = 0.$ 10. $z^2 = 1 + 4x^2 + 4y^2.$
11. $2x^2 + 2y^2 = 4 - z^2.$ 12. $3z^2 + 3x^2 = y^2 + 27.$
13. $z^2 = 9 + x^2 + 4y^2.$ 14. $y^2 = 4(4 - x^2 - z^2).$
15. $x^2 + 5y^2 + 8z^2 = 0.$ 16. $4x^2 + y^2 + z^2 = -4.$

In Exs. 17–24, by completing squares in x, y, z, show that the equation represents an ellipsoid or hyperboloid with axes parallel to the coordinate axes; locate the center and identify the surface. (Example, page 437.)

17. $x^2 - y^2 + z^2 + 2x + 4y - 4z - 3 = 0.$
18. $x^2 - y^2 - z^2 - 6x + 2z - 8 = 0.$
19. $2x^2 + 4y^2 + z^2 + 4y - 4z + 1 = 0.$
20. $4x^2 + y^2 + z^2 - 4y + 2z - 4 = 0.$
21. $9x^2 - 2y^2 - z^2 - 18x + y - 4z + 15 = 0.$
22. $4x^2 + y^2 - 4z^2 + 12x - 8y + 4z + 8 = 0.$
23. $16x^2 + y^2 - z^2 - 8x - 2y - 30 = 0.$
24. $x^2 + 3y^2 + z^2 + x + 3y + 4z - 4 = 0.$

25. A point moves so that the sum of its distances from two fixed points is constant. Show that its locus is a prolate spheroid. Take the fixed points as $(\pm c, 0, 0)$. Compare with § 110.

26. A point moves so that the difference of its distances from two fixed points is constant. Show that its locus is a hyperboloid of revolution of two sheets. Compare with § 115.

260. *The Elliptic Paraboloid*

The locus of the equation

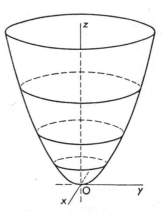

Figure 263

$$(1) \qquad \frac{x^2}{a^2} + \frac{y^2}{b^2} = \frac{z}{c}$$

for either positive or negative values of c is an *elliptic paraboloid*.

From equation (1) we find that the elliptic paraboloid has two planes of symmetry; it also has one line of symmetry, called the *axis* of the surface. The axis intersects the surface in a single point, called the *vertex*. The surface lies entirely on one side of the xy-plane, and extends to infinity along Oz.

When $a = b$, the surface is the *paraboloid of revolution*.

Example. The equation

$$(1) \qquad 4x^2 + y^2 = 8(2x + z + 1)$$

may be put in the form

$$4(x^2 - 4x + 4) + y^2 = 8(z + 3),$$

or

$$\frac{(x-2)^2}{1} + \frac{y^2}{4} = \frac{z+3}{\frac{1}{2}}.$$

Therefore equation (1) represents an elliptic paraboloid with vertex at $(2, 0, -3)$. Since $a = 1$ and $b = 2$, the surface is not one of revolution. For $k < -3$, sections $z = k$ yield imaginary curves. For $k > -3$, the sections $z = k$ are real ellipses.

261. *The Hyperbolic Paraboloid*

The surface

(1)
$$\frac{x^2}{a^2} - \frac{y^2}{b^2} = \frac{z}{c}$$

is a *hyperbolic paraboloid*. The sections $y = k$ are parabolas opening upward or downward, according to the sign of c; sections $x = k$ are parabolas opening

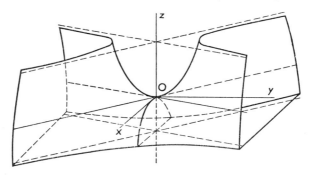

Figure 264

in the opposite direction. Thus the surface is "saddle-shaped," as shown in Figure 264.

The hyperbolic paraboloid cannot be a surface of revolution. The case $a = b$ is merely the case in which the sections $z = k$ are equilateral hyperbolas.

EXERCISES

In Exs. 1–12, classify the surface; state whether it is a surface of revolution, and make a sketch.

1. $x^2 + y^2 = z$.
2. $x^2 + z^2 - 9y = 0$.
3. $z^2 = 4x - 9y^2$.
4. $y^2 = 9x - 16z^2$.
5. $z^2 = 4x + 9y^2$.
6. $y^2 = 9x + 16z^2$.
7. $y - 3x^2 - 3z^2 = 0$.
8. $4z + x^2 = 9y^2$.
9. $y - 3x^2 + 3z^2 = 0$.
10. $x^2 + 4y + 4z^2 = 0$.
11. $x^2 + 9y^2 - 9z^2 + 4 = 0$.
12. $4x^2 + y^2 + z^2 = 16$.

In Exs. 13–18, by completing squares, determine whether the given equation represents an elliptic or hyperbolic paraboloid, and locate the vertex or saddle point, whichever is pertinent.

13. $x^2 + 4y^2 - 4x - 8y - 2z + 14 = 0.$ *Ans. V*: $(2, 1, 3)$.

14. $4y^2 - z^2 + x - 4y + 6z - 9 = 0.$ *Ans. SP*: $(1, \frac{1}{2}, 3)$.

15. $x^2 - 3z^2 - x + 4y - 3z - 2 = 0.$

16. $y^2 + 4z^2 - x + 4y - 8z + 10 = 0.$

17. $x^2 + z^2 + y - 6z = 0.$

18. $x^2 - 2z^2 + 4x - y - 4z + 2 = 0.$

19. In Figures 263–264, is the constant c positive or negative?

20. Find the equation of a paraboloid with vertex at O, axis Oy, and passing through $(1, -2, 1)$, $(-3, -3, 2)$.   *Ans.* $x^2 - 3z^2 = y$.

21. Find the equation of a paraboloid with vertex at O, axis Ox, and passing through $(3, 1, 2)$, $(3, 3, 0)$.   *Ans.* $y^2 + 2z^2 = 3x$.

22. Discuss the locus of a point moving so that its distance from a fixed point is equal to its distance from a fixed plane.

In Exs. 23–28, classify the surface (cylindrical coordinates, § 246).

23. $z^2 - r^2 = a^2.$ 24. $r^2 - z^2 = a^2.$

25. $r^2 = az.$ 26. $r^2 + z^2 = 2az.$

27. $2r^2 + z^2 = 2a^2.$ 28. $r^2 \cos 2\theta = az.$

In Exs. 29–32, classify the surface (spherical coordinates, § 247).

29. $\rho \sin^2 \varphi = a \cos \varphi.$ 30. $\rho = 2a \cos \varphi.$

31. $\rho^2 \cos 2\varphi + a^2 = 0.$ 32. $\rho^2 \cos 2\varphi = a^2.$

262. *Quadric Cylinders*

If a cylinder has its generators perpendicular to one of the coordinate planes, its equation has only two variables in it; for example,

$$f(x, z) = 0.$$

Then, by examining sections $y = k$, we see that the cylinder will have an equation of second degree if and only if its right section is a conic. This situation is a special case of the following theorem, which can be proved with the aid of rotation of axes in three dimensions.

THEOREM 53. *A cylinder is a quadric surface if and only if its right section is a conic.*

A quadric cylinder is called *elliptic*, *parabolic*, or *hyperbolic*, according to the nature of its right section.

A parabolic cylinder with generators parallel to the z-axis is shown in Figure 248, page 423. Two circular cylinders were employed in drawing a skew curve in Figure 254, page 432.

263. *Cones*

A *cone* is the surface generated by a moving line that always passes through a fixed point, called the *vertex*, and intersects a fixed curve, called the *directing curve*. Thus the surface is completely covered by straight lines, or *generators*, all passing through a fixed point. Like the cylinder, a cone may or may not be a quadric surface.

264. *The Elliptic Cone*

The locus of the equation

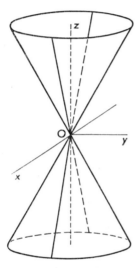

Figure 265

(1) $$\frac{x^2}{a^2} + \frac{y^2}{b^2} - \frac{z^2}{c^2} = 0$$

is a cone with vertex at the origin. To see this, let $P: (x_1, y_1, z_1)$ be any point of the surface (except O), so that

(2) $$\frac{x_1^2}{a^2} + \frac{y_1^2}{b^2} - \frac{z_1^2}{c^2} = 0.$$

Let Q be any other point of the straight line OP. Then the coordinates of Q must be proportional to those of P; i.e., they must have the form (kx_1, ky_1, kz_1). Substituting these coordinates in (1), we get

$$k^2 \left(\frac{x_1^2}{a^2} + \frac{y_1^2}{b^2} - \frac{z_1^2}{c^2} \right) = 0,$$

which is true by (2). Thus the entire line OP lies in the surface.

A study of the sections shows that the surface consists of two open sheets extending to infinity along the z-axis.

By suitable coordinate transformations, the equation of every quadric cone can be reduced to the form (1). Hence there is only a single species of quadric cone. Since the surface is most clearly visualized by means of its elliptic sections, it is usually called the *elliptic cone*. The line through the centers of the elliptic sections is the *axis* of the cone, and sections by planes perpendicular to the axis are *right sections*.

When $a = b$, the right sections are circles, and the surface is the *circular cone*, or *cone of revolution*.

265. *Ruled Surfaces*

A surface that can be generated by a moving straight line is called a *ruled surface*. The straight lines are called *rulings* or *generators*.

A cylinder is a ruled surface all of whose rulings are parallel, and a cone is a ruled surface all of whose rulings are concurrent.

The hyperboloid of one sheet and the hyperbolic paraboloid are doubly ruled; i.e., each is covered by two distinct families of straight lines. Proof of these statements is omitted to save space; no advanced methods are

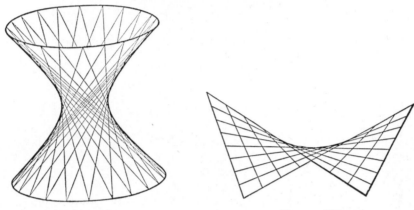

| Figure 266 | Figure 267 |

needed. Figures 266–267 exhibit rulings on these surfaces. More striking verification can be obtained by placing a straightedge in appropriate positions on the plaster models of such surfaces, models which are usually in the possession of the mathematics department.

Except for the four surfaces mentioned above, the quadric surfaces are not ruled.

266. *Transformation of Coordinates*

We have seen (Ex. 19, page 397) that a pure translation of axes in space may be effected by formulas analogous to those of § 64. Rotation of axes in three dimensions is not as simple as in two dimensions and is omitted in this book.

Rotation of axes in one of the three coordinate planes, holding the third axis fixed, is precisely a two-dimensional rotation accomplished by the method of § 167.

Example. Show that the surface (Figure 245, page 420)

$$(1) \qquad\qquad x^2 = yz$$

is an elliptic cone.

We know by § 170 that rotation of the axes through 45° replaces the product term by the difference of two squares. Hence, taking $\varphi = 45°$ in § 167, put

$$x = x_1, \qquad y = \tfrac{1}{2}\sqrt{2}\,(y_1 - z_1), \qquad z = \tfrac{1}{2}\sqrt{2}\,(y_1 + z_1).$$

This reduces (1) to the form

$$2x_1^2 + z_1^2 - y_1^2 = 0.$$

From the above equation we see that the surface (1) is an elliptic cone, the axis being the line whose equations (in the original system) are

$$x = 0, \qquad y = z.$$

Thus the (elliptic) sections by planes $y + z = k$ would give a clear picture of the surface.

EXERCISES

In Exs. 1–12, classify and draw the surface.

1. $x^2 + z^2 = a^2$.

2. $z^2 = 4ay$.

3. $\dfrac{x^2}{a^2} - \dfrac{y^2}{b^2} = 1$.

4. $\dfrac{x^2}{a^2} + \dfrac{z^2}{b^2} = 1$.

5. $2zy = a^2$.

6. $x^2 - z^2 = 0$.

7. $x^2 - 4y^2 + z^2 = 0$.

8. $9x^2 - 4y^2 - 36z^2 = 0$.

9. $4x^2 - y^2 - 4z^2 = 0$.

10. $3y^2 - 2x^2 + 3z^2 = 0$.

11. $4z^2 = 9x^2 - 9y^2$.

12. $25z^2 = 4x^2 + 4y^2$.

13. A moving point is equidistant from the point $(a, 0, 0)$ and the line $x + a = 0$, $y = 0$. Find the equation of its locus.   *Ans.* $z^2 = 4ax$.

14. A fixed line and fixed plane are perpendicular to each other; a point moves so that its distance from the line bears a constant ratio to its distance from the plane. Find the equation of its locus.   (Take the line as x-axis, the plane as yz-plane.)

15. Show that the surface $Ax^2 + By^2 + Cz^2 + Dyz + Ezx + Fxy = 0$ is a cone with vertex at the origin.   (Compare with § 264.)   Discuss exceptions.

In Exs. 16–19, classify the surface (cylindrical coordinates, § 246).

16. $r = z$.

17. $r^2 \cos 2\theta = z^2$.

18. $r^2 \sin 2\theta = z^2$.

19. $z = a \tan \theta$.

20. Show that an equation in φ and θ (spherical coordinates, § 247) represents a cone with vertex at the origin.   Discuss exceptions.

In Exs. 21–23, show that the surface (spherical coordinates) is a circular cone.

21. $\varphi = \tfrac{1}{3}\pi$.

22. $\cot^2 \varphi = \cos 2\theta$.

23. $\cot^2 \varphi = \sin 2\theta$.

In Exs. 24–26, prove the statement by rotating one of the coordinate planes through 45°.   (Adapt the formulas of § 167.)

24. The surface $z^2 = 2xy$ is a circular cone.

25. The surface $az = 2xy$ is a hyperbolic paraboloid.

26. The surface $x^2 + yz = 1$ is a hyperboloid of one sheet.   (Figure 244.)

27. The cost of a freight haul is roughly proportional to weight and distance: $C = kwd$.   Draw the graph of C.   (Ex. 25.)

28. The time required to pave a highway is (roughly) proportional to the length and inversely proportional to the number of men employed; $t = \dfrac{kl}{n}$. Show that the graph of t is a hyperbolic paraboloid. (Ex. 25.)

267. *Generation of Surfaces of Revolution*

The equation of a surface of revolution is easily derived when the axis and the generating curve are given, if the axis is parallel to a coordinate axis and the generating curve lies in a plane parallel to a coordinate plane.

Example. Derive the equation of the surface generated by revolving the parabola

$$(1) \qquad\qquad y^2 = -8(x - 2), \qquad z = 0$$

about the x-axis. See Figure 268.

In the rotation, every point of the generating curve describes a circle parallel to the yz-plane, with its center on the x-axis. Let Q be any point on the generating curve, and P any point of the circle described by Q, so that P is a general point on the surface. If the coordinates of P are denoted by (x, y, z), those of Q are $(x, k, 0)$, where k is the y-coordinate of Q, the distance LQ in Figure 268. We must obtain an equation containing x, y, z but not involving k.

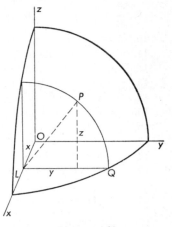

Since Q lies on the generating curve, the coordinates of Q must satisfy the equations of that curve. Thus we obtain the relation

$$(2) \qquad\qquad k^2 = -8(x - 2),$$

Figure 268

and note as a check that the z-coordinate of Q must be zero.

We need another equation involving k so that we can eliminate k with the aid of the relation (2). Since P and Q lie on a circle with center at L, the radii LP and LQ must be equal. Since L has the same x-coordinate as P, and since L is on the x-axis, the coordinates of L are $(x, 0, 0)$. Then $LQ = k$ and $LP = \sqrt{y^2 + z^2}$, from which it follows that

$$(3) \qquad\qquad k^2 = y^2 + z^2.$$

The elimination of k from equations (2) and (3) yields the desired equation of the surface of revolution

$$(4) \qquad\qquad y^2 + z^2 = -8(x - 2).$$

As a check, note that sections $x = \text{constant}$ yield circles, and that the xy-trace of the surface (4) is the generating parabola (1).

EXERCISES

In each exercise, derive the equation of the surface generated by revolving the given curve about the designated axes or other lines, drawing the pertinent figure similar to Figure 268.　Check your results.

1. $x + y = 1$, $z = 0$ about (a) Ox; (b) Oy.

　　　　　　　Ans. (a) $y^2 + z^2 = (1 - x)^2$; (b) $x^2 + z^2 = (1 - y)^2$.

2. $y = 3x$, $z = 0$ about (a) Ox; (b) Oy.

　　　　　　　Ans. (a) $9x^2 - y^2 - z^2 = 0$; (b) $9x^2 - y^2 + 9z^2 = 0$.

3. $z = 2y$, $x = 0$ about (a) Oy; (b) Oz.

4. $z = x + 4$, $y = 0$ about (a) Ox; (b) Oz.

5. $x^2 + y^2 = a^2$, $z = 0$ about Oy.

6. $x^2 + z^2 = 2ax$, $y = 0$ about Ox.

7. $y^2 = 4az$, $x = 0$ about (a) its axis; (b) the tangent at the vertex.

8. $y^2 = 4(x - 1)$, $z = 0$ about (a) its axis; (b) its directrix.

　　　　　　　Ans. (b) $y^4 - 16x^2 + 8y^2 - 16z^2 + 16 = 0$.

9. $\dfrac{x^2}{a^2} + \dfrac{z^2}{b^2} = 1$, $y = 0$ about each of its axes in turn.

10. $z^2 - y^2 = a^2$, $x = 0$ about each of its axes in turn.

11. $x = 4$, $z = 0$ about Oy.

12. $z = 6$, $y = 0$ about Ox.

13. $z = y^3$, $x = 0$ about Oz.

14. $xy^2 = 4$, $z = 0$ about Oy.

15. $z = y^3$, $x = 0$ about Oy.

16. $xy^2 = 4$, $z = 0$ about Ox.

17. $y = z = 4$ about Ox.

18. $x = 3$, $y = 4$ about Oz.

19. $z = x + 4$, $y = 4$ about the line $y = 4$, $z = 0$.

　　　　　　　Ans. $(y - 4)^2 + z^2 = (x + 4)^2$.

20. $(x - 4)^2 + z^2 = 4$, $y = 2$ about the line $x = 4$, $y = 2$.

　　　　　　　Ans. $(x - 4)^2 + (y - 2)^2 + z^2 = 4$.

21. $z^2 = y - 1$, $x = 2$ about its axis.　　　　　*Ans.* $(x - 2)^2 + z^2 = y - 1$.

22. $x = 3$, $z = 1$ about the line $x = 4$, $z = 2$.

23. $x = 4$, $y = 3$ about the line $x = 2$, $y = 4$.

24. $x = 3y$, $y = z$ about (a) Ox; (b) Oy; (c) Oz.　　*Ans.* (a) $9y^2 + 9z^2 = 2x^2$.

25. The line through $(0, 0, 0)$ and $(1, 2, 3)$ about each of the axes in turn.

　　　　　　　Ans. About Oy, $2x^2 + 2z^2 = 5y^2$.

26. $x + y = a$, $z = a$ about Oy.　　　　　*Ans.* $x^2 + z^2 - y^2 = 2a(a - y)$.

Applications of Partial Differentiation

268. *The Total Differential*

In studying functions of one variable,

$$y = f(x),$$

we found much use for the differential

$$dy = f'(x)\, dx = \frac{dy}{dx}\, dx.$$

We shall now set up the corresponding quantity for functions of more than one variable.

Let u be a function of the two independent variables x and y. Consider

(1)
$$u = f(x, y).$$

If we change x by the amount Δx and y by the amount Δy, u will change by an amount Δu. Then, from (1),

(2)
$$u + \Delta u = f(x + \Delta x, y + \Delta y)$$

so that

(3)
$$\Delta u = f(x + \Delta x, y + \Delta y) - f(x, y).$$

For a function $g(x)$ of one variable, the first law of the mean, Theorem 35, § 145, is

(4)
$$g(b) - g(a) = (b - a)g'(x_1), \qquad a < x_1 < b.$$

If in (4) we put $a = x$ and $b = x + \Delta x$, we may write

$$x_1 = x + \alpha\, \Delta x, \qquad 0 < \alpha < 1.$$

Then (4) assumes the form

(5)
$$g(x + \Delta x) - g(x) = g'(x + \alpha\, \Delta x)\, \Delta x, \qquad 0 < \alpha < 1.$$

In order to employ (5) in (3) we first rewrite (3) in the form

(6) $\Delta u = f(x + \Delta x, y + \Delta y) - f(x + \Delta x, y) + [f(x + \Delta x, y) - f(x, y)].$

Consider the last two terms in (6). If y is held fixed, we may use $g(x) = f(x, y)$ in (5) to obtain

(7) $f(x + \Delta x, y) - f(x, y) = \Delta x \, f_x(x + \alpha \, \Delta x, y),$ $0 < \alpha < 1.$

In (7) the subscript x indicates partial differentiation with respect to x (y being held fixed).

For the first two terms on the right in (6), we use (5) applied to the function $f(x + \Delta x, y)$ with x and Δx being held fixed. Thus we write from (5)

(8) $f(x + \Delta x, y + \Delta y) - f(x + \Delta x, y)$
$$= \Delta y \, f_y(x + \Delta x, y + \beta \, \Delta y),   0 < \beta < 1.$$

By employing (7) and (8), we may now write equation (6) in the form

(9) $\Delta u = \Delta x \, f_x(x + \alpha \, \Delta x, y) + \Delta y \, f_y(x + \Delta x, y + \beta \, \Delta y),$
$$0 < \alpha < 1, \, 0 < \beta < 1.$$

In using (5) to obtain (7) and (8), we assumed that the first partial derivatives of f, i.e., of u, exist. If we also assume that those partial derivatives are continuous functions of their arguments, we may rewrite (9) as

(10) $\Delta u = \Delta x[f_x(x, y) + \epsilon] + \Delta y[f_y(x, y) + \eta],$

in which $\epsilon \to 0$ and $\eta \to 0$ as $\Delta x \to 0$ and $\Delta y \to 0$. Since $u = f(x, y)$, we may put (10) in the form

(11) $\Delta u = \dfrac{\partial u}{\partial x} \, \Delta x + \dfrac{\partial u}{\partial y} \, \Delta y + \epsilon \, \Delta x + \eta \, \Delta y.$

As Δx and $\Delta y \to 0$ independently, the first two terms on the right in (11) yield an approximation to Δu, the change in u. Therefore we proceed to use those terms in defining a differential for a function of two variables in much the same way that we laid down the corresponding definition in the one variable case in § 71.

We define the *total differential du* of a function u of two independent variables x and y by

(12) $du = \dfrac{\partial u}{\partial x} \, \Delta x + \dfrac{\partial u}{\partial y} \, \Delta y.$

For the particular function $u = x$, we obtain

$$\frac{\partial u}{\partial x} = 1, \qquad \frac{\partial u}{\partial y} = 0,$$

so (12) yields

(13)
$$dx = \Delta x.$$

In the same way the function $u = y$ leads us to write

(14)
$$dy = \Delta y.$$

Therefore we define the differentials dx and dy of the independent variables by (13) and (14). This also permits us to rewrite the definition (12) as

(15)
$$du = \frac{\partial u}{\partial x} dx + \frac{\partial u}{\partial y} dy.$$

If x and y are functions of a third variable t, then u becomes a function of t alone, and its differential has been defined in § 71. It can be shown that the value of du as given by (15) agrees with the earlier definition.

For functions of more than two arguments, a similar definition is used. Thus, if

(16)
$$u = f(x, y, z),$$

the total differential of u is

(17)
$$du = \frac{\partial u}{\partial x} dx + \frac{\partial u}{\partial y} dy + \frac{\partial u}{\partial z} dz.$$

Example. If $u = x^3 - xy^2 + yt - t^3$,
$$du = 3x^2 \, dx - y^2 \, dx - 2xy \, dy + y \, dt + t \, dy - 3t^2 \, dt.$$

269. *Approximate Formulas*

It follows from the discussion in the preceding section that when Δx and Δy are small, du and Δu are *nearly equal.* Hence the differential can be used as an approximation to the increment, for functions of two (or more) variables, exactly as in § 73.

Example (a). Find the error in the value of a fraction produced by small errors in the numerator and denominator.

Let the fraction be

(1)
$$f = \frac{y}{x}.$$

Then the change in f due to small changes in y and x is approximately, if Δx and Δy are small compared with x,

$$df = \frac{x \, \Delta y - y \, \Delta x}{x^2}.$$

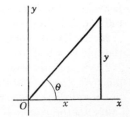

Figure 269

Example (b). In Figure 269, if $x = 9.986$, $y = 7.013$, find $\tan \theta$.

In Example (a), take $y = 7$, $\Delta y = 0.013$; $x = 10$, $\Delta x = -0.014$. Then

$$\tan \theta = \frac{7.013}{9.986} = 0.7 + \frac{10(0.013) - 7(-0.014)}{100}$$

$$= 0.7 + \frac{0.13 + 0.098}{100} = 0.7023.$$

EXERCISES

In Exs. 1–15, find the total differential.

1. $z = y^4 - 4xy^3$.   *Ans.* $dz = 4(y^3 - 3xy^2)\,dy - 4y^3\,dx$.

2. $z = x^2y - u^2 + x$.   *Ans.* $dz = (2xy + 1)\,dx + x^2\,dy - 2u\,du$.

3. $z = \sqrt{x^2 + y^2}$.   *Ans.* $dz = \dfrac{x\,dx + y\,dy}{\sqrt{x^2 + y^2}}$.

4. $\theta = \operatorname{Arctan} \dfrac{y}{x}$.   *Ans.* $d\theta = \dfrac{x\,dy - y\,dx}{x^2 + y^2}$.

5. $\theta = \operatorname{Arcsin} \dfrac{y}{r}$.   *Ans.* $d\theta = \dfrac{r\,dy - y\,dr}{r\sqrt{r^2 - y^2}}$.

6. $z = \dfrac{y}{\sqrt{x^2 + y^2}}$.   *Ans.* $dz = \dfrac{x(x\,dy - y\,dx)}{(x^2 + y^2)^{\frac{3}{2}}}$.

7. $V = \pi r^2 h$.   **8.** $S = 2\pi rh + 2\pi r^2$.

9. $x = \dfrac{u^2}{v}$.   **10.** $w = \ln \sqrt{x^2 + y^2 + z^2}$.

11. $y = e^{-zt^2}$.   **12.** $r = \cos \theta \sin \varphi \sin \psi$.

13. $v = \ln (xyz)$.   **14.** $r = \sqrt{x^2 + y^2 + z^2}$.

15. $u = e^{-\alpha^2 t} \sin \alpha x$; α constant.

16. In the product xy, find the error due to small errors in x and y.

     Ans. $x\,\Delta y + y\,\Delta x$.

17. Compute the product 0.5102 by 0.6303 to four decimal places. (Ex. 16.)

18. A lot is approximately 60 by 140 ft. If each of the measurements is uncertain by 3 in., find the maximum uncertainty in the area.

19. A certain giant saguaro in the Arizona desert has no protruding limbs, and is roughly a circular cylinder in shape. At the present time, its rate of growth is found to be an increase in height of 0.8 in. per year and an increase in diameter of 0.1 in. per year. Find the rate of increase of its volume, given that the saguaro is 40 ft. tall and 2 ft. in diameter.   *Ans.* 1.26 cu. ft. per year.

20. In Ex. 19, compute the rate of change of the lateral surface area (disregarding the spines, which is not always advisable).   *Ans.* 1.47 sq. ft. per year.

21. A sprinter runs 100 yd. in about 10 sec. If the time may be in error by as much as $\frac{1}{10}$ sec., and the distance by as much as 6 in., find the greatest possible error in the velocity.   *Ans.* 0.35 ft. per sec.

22. In the common logarithm of the product of two numbers x and y, find the error due to small errors in the numbers.

$$\text{*Ans.* } M\left(\frac{\Delta x}{x} + \frac{\Delta y}{y}\right).$$

23. A box is approximately 3 by 4 by 5 ft. If each dimension is in excess by 0.1 in., find the excess volume. *Ans.* 677 cu. in.

24. In Ex. 23, find the length of a diagonal. (Ex. 14.)

25. A right triangle is constructed and the tangent of one of the acute angles is found by measuring the opposite side y and the adjacent side x. If $y = 2.5 \pm 0.1$, $x = 1.5 \pm 0.1$, what is the greatest possible error in the tangent? [Example (*a*), § 269.] *Ans.* About 0.18.

26. In Ex. 25, find the greatest possible error in the angle. (Ex. 4.)
Ans. About 2° 42′.

27. In Ex. 25, find the greatest possible error in the sine of the angle.

28. It is desired to draw a line through the points (0, 0), (3, 4). If the line is actually drawn through $(-0.04, 0.11)$ and $(3.01, 3.94)$, find the error in the slope of the line. *Ans.* -0.08.

29. Find approximately the error in the function $x^2 y$ due to small errors in x and y.

30. The base of a box is a square of side 6.005; the depth is 8.997. Find the volume. (Ex. 29.)

31. Find the hypotenuse of a right triangle whose sides are 6.03, 7.96.

32. The cosine of an angle is measured: $\cos \theta = \dfrac{x}{r}$. Find the error in $\cos 2\theta$ due to errors in x and r.

33. Find an approximate formula for the change in volume of a right circular cylinder if small changes are made in the base radius r and the height h.
Ans. $dV = \pi(2rh\,dr + r^2\,dh)$.

34. Find an approximate formula for the change in total surface area for the cylinder of Ex. 33. *Ans.* $dA = 2\pi(2r\,dr + h\,dr + r\,dh)$.

35. Do Ex. 34 for lateral surface area only.

36. Parallel Ex. 33 for a right circular cone.

37. Parallel Ex. 34 for a right circular cone.

270. *Differentiation of Implicit Functions*

Let z be defined implicitly as a function of the two independent variables x and y by the equation

(1) $$F(x, y, z) = 0.$$

We already know how to obtain the derivatives of z with respect to x, and with respect to y, in an efficient manner; see Example (*b*), § 249. There are times, as in the next section, when it is expedient to have a formula for each of these derivatives.

For the function in equation (1), put

$$u = F(x, y, z);$$

then

$$du = \frac{\partial F}{\partial x}\,dx + \frac{\partial F}{\partial y}\,dy + \frac{\partial F}{\partial z}\,dz.$$

But since $u = 0$, $du = 0$ likewise, and

$$\frac{\partial F}{\partial x}\, dx + \frac{\partial F}{\partial y}\, dy + \frac{\partial F}{\partial z}\, dz = 0.$$

Further, since z is a function of x and y, we may write

$$dz = \frac{\partial z}{\partial x}\, dx + \frac{\partial z}{\partial y}\, dy.$$

Eliminating dz between these two equations, we find

$$\left(\frac{\partial F}{\partial x} + \frac{\partial F}{\partial z}\frac{\partial z}{\partial x}\right) dx + \left(\frac{\partial F}{\partial y} + \frac{\partial F}{\partial z}\frac{\partial z}{\partial y}\right) dy = 0.$$

To find $\dfrac{\partial z}{\partial x}$, keep y fixed, so that $dy = 0$.   Then

$$\frac{\partial F}{\partial x} + \frac{\partial F}{\partial z}\frac{\partial z}{\partial x} = 0,$$

whence

(2)
$$\frac{\partial z}{\partial x} = -\frac{\dfrac{\partial F}{\partial x}}{\dfrac{\partial F}{\partial z}}, \qquad \frac{\partial F}{\partial z} \neq 0.$$

Similarly

(3)
$$\frac{\partial z}{\partial y} = -\frac{\dfrac{\partial F}{\partial y}}{\dfrac{\partial F}{\partial z}}, \qquad \frac{\partial F}{\partial z} \neq 0.$$

271. Tangent Plane to a Surface

It can be shown that all the lines tangent to a surface

(1)
$$z = f(x,\, y)$$

at a point P: (x_1, y_1, z_1) lie in a plane, the *tangent plane* to the surface at that point.   (It is assumed that z, $\dfrac{\partial z}{\partial x}$, and $\dfrac{\partial z}{\partial y}$ are continuous at P.)   This plane is determined by any two tangent lines.

Let us assume the equation of the tangent plane in the form

$$z - z_1 = m_1(x - x_1) + m_2(y - y_1),$$

where m_1 and m_2 are to be determined.   Now the line of intersection of this plane with the plane $y = y_1$ has the slope m_1.   But this line is the tangent lying in the plane $y = y_1$, and, by § 250, its slope is the value of $\dfrac{\partial z}{\partial x}$ at P:

$$m_1 = \left[\frac{\partial z}{\partial x}\right]_P.$$

Similarly we find

$$m_2 = \left[\frac{\partial z}{\partial y}\right]_P.$$

Thus the equation of the plane tangent to the surface (1) at (x_1, y_1, z_1) is

(2) $$z - z_1 = \left[\frac{\partial z}{\partial x}\right]_P (x - x_1) + \left[\frac{\partial z}{\partial y}\right]_P (y - y_1).$$

More generally, let the equation of the surface be given in the implicit form

(3) $$F(x, y, z) = 0.$$

We may imagine equation (3) solved for z and may then write the equation of the tangent plane by (2). Substituting for $\frac{\partial z}{\partial x}$ and $\frac{\partial z}{\partial y}$ the values given by (2) and (3) of § 270, and clearing of fractions, we find

(4) $$\left[\frac{\partial F}{\partial x}\right]_P (x - x_1) + \left[\frac{\partial F}{\partial y}\right]_P (y - y_1) + \left[\frac{\partial F}{\partial z}\right]_P (z - z_1) = 0.$$

272. *Normal Line*

The *normal* to a surface at a point P is the line through P perpendicular to the tangent plane.

It will be recalled from solid analytic geometry that the direction cosines of any line perpendicular to the plane

$$Ax + By + Cz + D = 0$$

are *proportional to the coefficients* A, B, C. Hence, since the normal is perpendicular to the tangent plane (4), § 271, we have at once the following theorem.

THEOREM 54. *The direction cosines of the normal to the surface*

$$F(x, y, z) = 0$$

at a point are proportional to the values of $\frac{\partial F}{\partial x}, \frac{\partial F}{\partial y}, \frac{\partial F}{\partial z}$ *at that point.*

This theorem is fundamental in the geometry of surfaces.

The equations of a line through (x_1, y_1, z_1) with direction cosines proportional to $[a, b, c]$ are

(1) $$\frac{x - x_1}{a} = \frac{y - y_1}{b} = \frac{z - z_1}{c}.$$

From this the equations of the normal at any point may be written down at once.

Example. Find the tangent plane and normal line to the sphere

$$(2) \qquad x^2 + y^2 + z^2 = a^2$$

at any point $P: (x_1, y_1, z_1)$ on the surface.

With

$$F(x, y, z) = x^2 + y^2 + z^2 - a^2 = 0,$$

we have

$$\frac{\partial F}{\partial x} = 2x, \qquad \frac{\partial F}{\partial y} = 2y, \qquad \frac{\partial F}{\partial z} = 2z,$$

or at P,

$$\left[\frac{\partial F}{\partial x}\right]_P = 2x_1, \qquad \left[\frac{\partial F}{\partial y}\right]_P = 2y_1, \qquad \left[\frac{\partial F}{\partial z}\right]_P = 2z_1.$$

Substituting in (4), § 271, and simplifying the result, we find

$$x_1 x + y_1 y + z_1 z = x_1^2 + y_1^2 + z_1^2,$$

or, since the coordinates of P satisfy (2),

$$x_1 x + y_1 y + z_1 z = a^2.$$

By the theorem and equations (1) above, the equations of the normal are

$$\frac{x - x_1}{x_1} = \frac{y - y_1}{y_1} = \frac{z - z_1}{z_1}.$$

These equations may be simplified (Ex. 20 below).

EXERCISES

In Exs. 1–13, find the equation of the tangent plane and the equations of the normal line at the given point.

1. The ellipsoid $x^2 + 4y^2 + z^2 = 36$ at $(2, -2, 4)$.   Draw the figure.

$$\text{Ans. } x - 4y + 2z = 18; \frac{x - 2}{1} = \frac{y + 2}{-4} = \frac{z - 4}{2}.$$

2. The cone $x^2 + 2z^2 = y^2$ at $(1, 3, -2)$.   *Ans.* Tangent plane: $x = 3y + 4z$.

3. The paraboloid $z = xy$ at $(3, 4, 12)$.

$$\text{Ans. Normal: } \frac{x - 3}{4} = \frac{y - 4}{3} = \frac{z - 12}{-1}.$$

4. The paraboloid $z = x^2 - y^2$ at $(3, 3, 0)$.   *Ans.* Tangent plane: $z = 6(x - y)$.

5. The hyperboloid $x^2 - 3y^2 - z^2 + 3 = 0$ at $(2, 1, -2)$.

$$\text{Ans. Normal: } \frac{x - 2}{2} = \frac{y - 1}{-3} = \frac{z + 2}{2}.$$

6. The paraboloid $4z = x^2 + 4y^2$ at $(2, 1, 2)$.   Draw the figure.

$$\text{Ans. Tangent plane: } x + 2y - 2z = 0.$$

7. The cylinder $y^2 = 4ax$ at $(a, 2a, a)$.   Draw the figure.

$$\text{Ans. } x - y + a = 0; \frac{x - a}{1} = \frac{y - 2a}{-1} = \frac{z - a}{0}.$$

8. The paraboloid $yz = x$ at the origin.   *Ans.* $x = 0; y = z = 0.$

9. The cubic surface $xy^2 + 3x - z^2 = 4$ at $(2, 1, -2)$.

10. The surface $y = x(2z - 1)$ at $(4, 4, 1)$.

11. The paraboloid $Ax^2 + Cz^2 = 2Gy$ at (x_1, y_1, z_1).

Ans. Tangent plane: $Ax_1x + Cz_1z = G(y + y_1)$.

12. The cylinder $Ax^2 + Cz^2 = 1$ at (x_1, y_1, z_1).

13. The quadric surface $Ax^2 + By^2 + Cz^2 = K$ at (x_1, y_1, z_1).

Ans. Tangent plane: $Ax_1x + By_1y + Cz_1z = K$.

14. Find the equations of the tangent at the point $(1, 2, 2)$ to the circle $x^2 + y^2 + z^2 = 9$, $x + y + z = 5$; draw the figure.

15. Find the equations of the tangent at the point $(1, 1, 1)$ to the ellipse $x^2 + y^2 = 2z^2$, $x + y + 2z = 4$.

16. Show that the surfaces $x^2 - y^2 + 4z^2 = 1$ and $x^2 - y^2 + 2(z + 1)^2 = 5$ are tangent at the point $(1, 2, 1)$.

17. Show that the sphere $x^2 + y^2 + z^2 = 2a^2$ and the hyperbolic cylinder $xy = a^2$ are tangent to each other at the point $(a, a, 0)$. Draw the figure.

18. Show that the surfaces $2x^2 + 2y^2 - z^2 = 25$, $x^2 + y^2 = 5z$ are tangent to each other at $(4, 3, 5)$. Draw the figure.

19. Prove that the tetrahedron formed by the coordinate planes and a tangent plane to the surface $xyz = a^3$ is of constant volume.

20. Prove that every normal to a sphere passes through the center.

21. State and prove a converse of the theorem of Ex. 20.

22. Two surfaces are said to intersect at right angles (or be perpendicular to each other) at a common point P if their normals at P intersect at right angles. Prove that two surfaces,

$$F(x, y, z) = 0, \qquad G(x, y, z) = 0,$$

intersect at right angles at P if

$$\left[\frac{\partial F}{\partial x}\right]_P \cdot \left[\frac{\partial G}{\partial x}\right]_P + \left[\frac{\partial F}{\partial y}\right]_P \cdot \left[\frac{\partial G}{\partial y}\right]_P + \left[\frac{\partial F}{\partial z}\right]_P \cdot \left[\frac{\partial G}{\partial z}\right]_P = 0.$$

23. Prove that the ellipsoid $2x^2 + y^2 + z^2 = 7$ and the cylinder $y^2 = 4x$ are perpendicular to each other at $(1, 2, 1)$. (Ex. 22.)

24. Prove that the paraboloid $2x^2 + y^2 = 6az + 6a^2$ and the cone $z^2 = xy$ intersect at right angles at $(a, 4a, 2a)$.

25. Determine a and b so as to make the paraboloid $y = ax^2 + bz^2$ perpendicular to the ellipsoid $x^2 + y^2 + 2z^2 = 7$ at the point $(1, 2, 1)$.   *Ans.* $a = 3, b = -1$.

26. Determine b and c so as to make the surfaces $x^2 = by + cz$ and $x^2 + y^2 = 2z(y - 4) + 25$ perpendicular at the point $(3, -2, 1)$.

27. Find the angle between the sphere $x^2 + y^2 + z^2 = 14$ and the ellipsoid $3x^2 + 2y^2 + z^2 = 20$ at the point $(1, 2, 3)$.   *Ans.* $23° 33'$.

273. *The Chain Rule; Change of Variables*

The useful chain rule

$$\frac{dy}{dx} = \frac{dy}{du}\frac{du}{dx}$$

of § 51 can be extended to involve any number of independent variables.

As an example, consider F a function of two independent variables x and y:

$$(1) \qquad\qquad F = g_1(x, y).$$

Let x and y be functions of two other independent variables u and v. Then

$$(2) \qquad\qquad x = x(u, v), \qquad y = y(u, v),$$

or, equivalently,

$$(2)' \qquad\qquad u = u(x, y), \qquad v = v(x, y).$$

It follows that F is a function of u and v:

$$(3) \qquad\qquad F = g_2(u, v).$$

Of course g_2 is neither necessarily nor usually the same function as g_1. In simple instances g_2 may be found by direct substitution of the x and y of (2) into the g_1 of equation (1).

From (3) we obtain, as in § 268,

$$(4) \qquad\qquad \Delta F = \frac{\partial F}{\partial u} \Delta u + \frac{\partial F}{\partial v} \Delta v + \epsilon \, \Delta u + \eta \, \Delta v$$

in which ϵ and $\eta \to 0$ as Δu and $\Delta v \to 0$. As usual, we postulate the existence and (if need be) the continuity of any derivatives which enter our work.

From (4) it follows that

$$(5) \qquad\qquad \frac{\Delta F}{\Delta x} = \frac{\partial F}{\partial u} \frac{\Delta u}{\Delta x} + \frac{\partial F}{\partial v} \frac{\Delta v}{\Delta x} + \epsilon \frac{\Delta u}{\Delta x} + \eta \frac{\Delta v}{\Delta x}.$$

Now, if we let Δx and $\Delta y \to 0$, Δu and Δv will also approach 0, and (5) leads us to the chain rule

$$(6) \qquad\qquad \frac{\partial F}{\partial x} = \frac{\partial F}{\partial u} \frac{\partial u}{\partial x} + \frac{\partial F}{\partial v} \frac{\partial v}{\partial x}.$$

In the same way we obtain

$$(7) \qquad\qquad \frac{\partial F}{\partial y} = \frac{\partial F}{\partial u} \frac{\partial u}{\partial y} + \frac{\partial F}{\partial v} \frac{\partial v}{\partial y}.$$

The student should find it easy to remember (6) if he thinks of it in the following way: The derivative of a function F with respect to an old variable x is the sum of terms, each of which is the product of the derivative of F with respect to a new variable by the derivative of that new variable with respect to x. The sum includes one such product term for each new variable.

It is true that the chain rule also applies in the other direction; that is,

$$(8) \qquad\qquad \frac{\partial F}{\partial u} = \frac{\partial F}{\partial x} \frac{\partial x}{\partial u} + \frac{\partial F}{\partial y} \frac{\partial y}{\partial u},$$

but most often we wish to move from the old variables to the new ones, so that (6) is the basic formula needed.

Iteration of (6) leads easily to formulas for change of variables in higher derivatives.

One frequent use of the chain rule in more advanced mathematics is in changing independent variables in partial differential equations. We choose as an example the change from rectangular to polar coordinates in what are called the *Cauchy–Riemann equations*, which are equations (9) and (10) below.

It is vital that in performing partial differentiations the operator keep in mind what independent variables go together so that he will know what variables to hold constant during a specific operation.

Example. In the following equations,

$$(9) \qquad\qquad \frac{\partial u}{\partial x} = \frac{\partial v}{\partial y},$$

$$(10) \qquad\qquad \frac{\partial u}{\partial y} = -\frac{\partial v}{\partial x},$$

change independent variables from the rectangular coordinates x, y to a polar coordinate system r, θ given by

$$(11) \qquad\qquad x = r\cos\theta, \qquad y = r\sin\theta.$$

Note that in (9) and (10) u and v are dependent variables.

In order to use the chain rule (6) efficiently, we prefer to have the new variables expressed in terms of the old ones. From (11), or our previous knowledge, we write

$$(12) \qquad\qquad r^2 = x^2 + y^2, \qquad \theta = \text{Arctan}\,\frac{y}{x}.$$

Because of (6) we have

$$(13) \qquad\qquad \frac{\partial u}{\partial x} = \frac{\partial u}{\partial r}\frac{\partial r}{\partial x} + \frac{\partial u}{\partial \theta}\frac{\partial \theta}{\partial x}$$

together with corresponding formulas involving u and y, v and x, v and y.

In seeking $\dfrac{\partial r}{\partial x}$ and $\dfrac{\partial \theta}{\partial x}$ from (12), or from (11), we must differentiate throughout with respect to x holding y constant. From (12) we obtain

$$r\,\frac{\partial r}{\partial x} = x, \qquad \frac{\partial \theta}{\partial x} = \frac{-\dfrac{y}{x^2}}{1 + \dfrac{y^2}{x^2}} = \frac{-y}{x^2 + y^2}.$$

We need these derivatives in terms of the new variables r and θ. Hence we proceed as follows:

$$\frac{\partial r}{\partial x} = \frac{x}{r} = \frac{r \cos \theta}{r} = \cos \theta,$$

$$\frac{\partial \theta}{\partial x} = \frac{-r \sin \theta}{r^2} = \frac{-\sin \theta}{r}.$$

We are now able to employ equation (13) to get

(14)
$$\frac{\partial u}{\partial x} = \cos \theta \frac{\partial u}{\partial r} - \frac{\sin \theta}{r} \frac{\partial u}{\partial \theta}.$$

The student should use a similar procedure to obtain

(15)
$$\frac{\partial u}{\partial y} = \sin \theta \frac{\partial u}{\partial r} + \frac{\cos \theta}{r} \frac{\partial u}{\partial \theta}.$$

Naturally equations (14) and (15) may be rewritten with v replacing u throughout. Then the original system of equations (9) and (10) becomes the system

(16)
$$\cos \theta \frac{\partial u}{\partial r} - \frac{\sin \theta}{r} \frac{\partial u}{\partial \theta} = \sin \theta \frac{\partial v}{\partial r} + \frac{\cos \theta}{r} \frac{\partial v}{\partial \theta},$$

(17)
$$\sin \theta \frac{\partial u}{\partial r} + \frac{\cos \theta}{r} \frac{\partial u}{\partial \theta} = - \cos \theta \frac{\partial v}{\partial r} + \frac{\sin \theta}{r} \frac{\partial v}{\partial \theta}.$$

Multiply each member of (16) by $\cos \theta$, each member of (17) by $\sin \theta$, and add the results to arrive at

(18)
$$\frac{\partial u}{\partial r} = \frac{1}{r} \frac{\partial v}{\partial \theta}.$$

Multiply each member of (16) by $\sin \theta$, each member of (17) by $\cos \theta$, and subtract to get

(19)
$$\frac{1}{r} \frac{\partial u}{\partial \theta} = - \frac{\partial v}{\partial r}.$$

We have shown that a change from rectangular coordinates x, y to polar coordinates r, θ transforms the system of equations (9) and (10) into the system (18) and (19).

EXERCISES

1. Obtain $\dfrac{\partial r}{\partial x}$ and $\dfrac{\partial \theta}{\partial x}$ directly from equations (11) above.

2. Obtain $\dfrac{\partial r}{\partial y}$ and $\dfrac{\partial \theta}{\partial y}$ directly from equations (11) above.

3. Let x and y be rectangular coordinates. Convert the expression

$$\left(\frac{\partial F}{\partial x} \right)^2 + \left(\frac{\partial F}{\partial y} \right)^2$$

into polar coordinates r and θ.   *Ans.* $\left(\dfrac{\partial F}{\partial r}\right)^2 + \dfrac{1}{r^2}\left(\dfrac{\partial F}{\partial \theta}\right)^2.$

4. Let F be a function of the independent variables x, y, z. Introduce new variables u, v, w by

$$u = \tfrac{1}{2}(y + z),$$
$$v = \tfrac{1}{2}(2x - y - z),$$
$$w = \tfrac{1}{2}(z - y).$$

Convert the first partial derivatives of F with respect to the old variables x, y, z into expressions involving only the new variables. Obtain a check on your answers by using a specific function; for instance,

$$F = x^2 - y^2 + z^2.$$

Ans. $\dfrac{\partial F}{\partial x} = \dfrac{\partial F}{\partial v}, \dfrac{\partial F}{\partial y} = \dfrac{1}{2}\left(\dfrac{\partial F}{\partial u} - \dfrac{\partial F}{\partial v} - \dfrac{\partial F}{\partial w}\right),$ etc.

5. Let F be a function of x, y, and z. Introduce new variables u, v, w by

$$u = \tfrac{1}{2}(x + y - z), \qquad v = \tfrac{1}{2}(x - y - z), \qquad w = z.$$

Obtain the first partial derivatives of F with respect to x, y, z in terms of the new variables. Thus show, among other things, that $\dfrac{\partial F}{\partial z} \neq \dfrac{\partial F}{\partial w}$ even though $w = z$.

Applications of Integration

274. The General Method

From the mode of development of Theorem 29, page 150, it might be thought that the theorem applies only in the computation of plane areas. But *any function of one variable may be represented graphically as a plane curve.* It follows that the theorem may be used to evaluate

$$\operatorname*{Lim}_{\Delta x \to 0} \sum_{i=1}^{n} f(x_i)\, \Delta x$$

regardless of the physical meaning of the function $f(x)$. For if the graph of the function were to be drawn (it is not necessary actually to do this), we could see that the quantity $f(x_i)\, \Delta x$ would represent a rectangular element of area, so that the theorem becomes applicable at once.

In this and succeeding chapters we shall develop a considerable variety of applications of integral calculus. In every case, the quantity to be computed will appear in the first instance as the limit of a sum; this limit will then be evaluated by application of Theorem 29—i.e., by a definite integration. This general method is one of the most important and far-reaching in the whole field of science because it solves, directly or indirectly, a large proportion of the mathematical problems arising in engineering, physics, chemistry, astronomy, and biology.

275. Solids of Revolution: Circular Disks

Let a solid be generated by rotating the area OAB about the x-axis (the figure shows one quadrant of the solid). Imagine this solid cut into thin slices by *planes perpendicular to the axis of revolution* (a typical slice being formed by rotation of the area $PQRS$). Trim off the irregular outer edge (generated by revolving the area $S'RS$), to leave a thin *circular disk* (generated by revolving the rectangle $PQRS'$). The radius of this element is y_i, the thickness Δx, the volume $\pi y_i^2\, \Delta x$. Now as the disks are taken thinner and thinner, the aggregate volume of trimmings approaches zero, and the
460

sum of all the elementary volumes $\pi y_i{}^2 \, \Delta x$ approaches as its limit *the volume of the solid*:

$$(1) \qquad V = \operatorname*{Lim}_{n \to \infty} \sum_{i=1}^{n} \pi y_i{}^2 \, \Delta x = \pi \int_a^b y^2 \, dx.$$

In formula (1) we have resorted to equal divisions Δx in our use of Theorem 29.   This simplification will be used regularly so as to avoid an unnecessary appearance of complexity in the setting up of the many definite integrals to be encountered in our later work.   Formula (1) may be viewed as a definition of the volume under consideration.

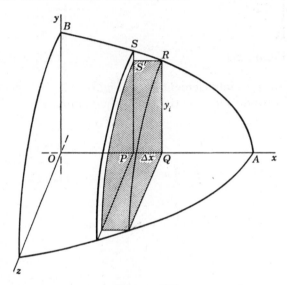

Figure 270

The student is strongly advised not to memorize this or any similar formulas but to make sure that he fully understands the argument.   Then, only the simplest elementary geometry is required to make up the correct integral in any given case.

Example (*a*).   The area bounded by a parabola, its axis, and its latus rectum revolves about the axis.   Find the volume generated.   See Figure 271, page 462.

Let the equation of the parabola be $y^2 = 4ax$.   Dividing the area into elements as in Figure 271, we see that each rectangle generates a cylindrical volume element of radius y, altitude dx, and volume $\pi y^2 \, dx$.   Hence

$$V = \pi \int_0^a y^2 \, dx = 4\pi a \int_0^a x \, dx = 2\pi a^3.$$

Example (*b*).   The above area rotates about the latus rectum.   Find
the volume generated.

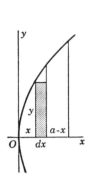

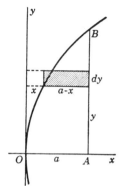

Figure 271   Figure 272

If we divide the area into elements as in Figure 272, each element generates
a circular disk of radius $a - x$, thickness dy, volume $\pi(a - x)^2 \, dy$.   Hence

$$V = \pi \int_0^{2a} (a - x)^2 \, dy$$

$$= \pi \int_0^{2a} \left(a - \frac{y^2}{4a} \right)^2 dy$$

$$= \pi \int_0^{2a} \left(a^2 - \frac{y^2}{2} + \frac{y^4}{16a^2} \right) dy$$

$$= \frac{16}{15} \pi a^3.$$

276. *Solids of Revolution: Circular Rings*

In the general argument and examples of § 275, the axis of rotation formed
part of the boundary of the rotating area; but the method works equally well
when this is not the case.   If, say, the area in Figure 273 is to revolve about
the x-axis, we may use as element the *circular ring*, or *washer*, formed by
revolution of the rectangle* *PQRS*.

Example.   Find the volume generated by revolving a circle about one of
its tangents.   (Figure 274.)

Let the circle

$$x^2 + y^2 = a^2$$

---

* Instead, we might find separately the volumes generated by rotating the areas
AMNBSA, *AMNBPA* (using as elements the disks generated by the rectangles *P'Q'RS*,
P'Q'QP), and subtract the latter from the former.   But the method of circular rings
gives us a chance to *simplify before integrating*, as is beautifully illustrated by the example
in this section.

revolve about the line $x = a$. The volume-element is a circular ring of outer radius $SP' = a + x$, inner radius $PP' = a - x$, thickness dy:

$$V = \pi \int_{-a}^{a} [(a + x)^2 - (a - x)^2] \, dy,$$

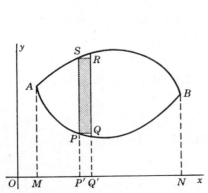

Figure 273   Figure 274

which reduces to

$$V = 8\pi a \int_{0}^{a} x \, dy.$$

Since this integral represents the area of the circular quadrant, we know its value:

$$V = 8\pi a \cdot \tfrac{1}{4}\pi a^2 = 2\pi^2 a^3.$$

EXERCISES

1. The area bounded by the curve $y = e^{-x}$, the axes, and the line $x = 1$ is revolved about the x-axis. Find the volume generated.   *Ans.* $\tfrac{1}{2}\pi(1 - e^{-2})$.

2. The area bounded by the parabola $ay = x^2$, the x-axis, and the line $x = b$ is revolved about the x-axis. Find the volume generated.

$$Ans. \frac{\pi b^5}{5a^2}.$$

3. The area of Ex. 2 is revolved about the y-axis. Find the volume generated.

$$Ans. \frac{\pi b^4}{2a}.$$

4. The area bounded by the parabola $ay = x^2$ and the line $y = b$ is revolved about the x-axis. Find the volume generated.   *Ans.* $\tfrac{8}{5}\pi b^2 \sqrt{ab}$.

5. The area bounded by the curve $a^2y = x^3$, the x-axis, and the line $x = a$ revolves about Ox. Find the volume generated.   *Ans.* $\tfrac{1}{7}\pi a^3$.

6. The area bounded by the hyperbola $x^2 - y^2 = a^2$, the x-axis, and the line $x = 2a$ revolves about Ox. Find the volume.   *Ans.* $\tfrac{4}{3}\pi a^3$.

APPLICATIONS OF INTEGRATION

7. Find the volume generated by revolving about Ox the area in the second quadrant under the curve $y = e^x$. *Ans.* $\frac{1}{2}\pi$.

8. Find the volume of a sphere. *Ans.* $\frac{4}{3}\pi a^3$.

9. Find the volume of a circular cone. *Ans.* $\frac{1}{3}\pi a^2 h$.

10. Find the volume of a prolate spheroid. *Ans.* $\frac{4}{3}\pi ab^2$.

11. Find the volume of an oblate spheroid, using the equations $x = a \cos \varphi$, $y = b \sin \varphi$. *Ans.* $\frac{4}{3}\pi a^2 b$.

12. The area enclosed by the loop of the curve $y^2 = x(x - 2)^2$ is revolved about the x-axis. Find the volume generated.

Ans. $\dfrac{4\pi}{3}$.

13. Find the volume formed by revolving about the y-axis the area bounded by the parabola $x^2 = 4ay$, the line $x = a$ and the x-axis.

Ans. $\dfrac{\pi a^3}{8}$.

14. Find the volume formed by revolving the area of Ex. 13 about the line $x = a$.

Ans. $\dfrac{\pi a^3}{24}$.

15. Find the volume generated by revolving about Ox the area bounded by the hyperbola $xy = a^2$, the line $x = a$, and the x-axis. *Ans.* πa^3.

16. Solve Ex. 15, using for the hyperbola the equations $x = a \cot \varphi$, $y = a \tan \varphi$.

17. Solve Ex. 15, using the equations $x = a \sec \psi$, $y = a \cos \psi$.

18. Find the volume generated by revolving about the y-axis the area bounded by the curve $x^2 = 4(x - y)$, the y-axis, and the line $y = 1$. *Ans.* $\frac{2}{3}\pi$.

19. Find the volume formed by revolving the area of Ex. 18 about the line $y = 1$.

Ans. $\frac{2}{5}\pi$.

20. Find the volume formed by revolving the area of Ex. 18 about the x-axis.

Ans. $\dfrac{14\pi}{15}$.

21. The area bounded by the curve $y = (x^2 - 4)^2$ and the x-axis revolves about the y-axis. Find the volume. *Ans.* $\frac{64}{3}\pi$.

22. Find the volume generated by revolving one arch of the cycloid $x = a(\theta - \sin \theta)$, $y = a(1 - \cos \theta)$ (Figure 217, page 377) about Ox. *Ans.* $5\pi^2 a^3$.

23. The area bounded by the curve $y = 3 - 2x + x^2$ and the line $y = 3$ is revolved about the line $y = 3$. Find the volume generated.

Ans. $\dfrac{16\pi}{15}$.

24. Find the volume formed by revolving about the line $y = 4$ the area of Ex. 23.

Ans. $\dfrac{56\pi}{15}$.

25. Find the volume generated by revolving about the line $x = 2a$ the area bounded by that line, the x-axis, and the curve $a^2 y = x^3$. *Ans.* $\frac{16}{5}\pi a^3$.

26. The area bounded by the parabola $y^2 = 4ax$, the y-axis, and the line $y = 2a$ revolves about the line $y = 2a$. Find the volume obtained. *Ans.* $\frac{2}{3}\pi a^3$.

27. The area bounded by the parabola $x^2 - 2x + y = 3$, the y-axis, and the line $y = 4$ revolves about the line $y = 4$. Find the volume generated. *Ans.* $\frac{1}{5}\pi$.

28. The area of Ex. 27 revolves about the line $x = 2$. Find the volume.

29. Find the volume formed by revolving the ellipse $\dfrac{x^2}{a^2} + \dfrac{y^2}{b^2} = 1$ about the line $y = b$.   *Ans.* $2\pi^2 ab^2$.

30. The area under one arch of the sine-curve revolves about the x-axis. Find the volume generated.   *Ans.* $\frac{1}{2}\pi^2$.

31. Find the volume generated by revolving about Oy the area in the fourth quadrant bounded by the curve $y = \ln x$.   *Ans.* $\frac{1}{2}\pi$.

32. The area in the first quadrant between the curve $y(1 + x) = x$ and its horizontal asymptote revolves about the asymptote. Find the volume.   *Ans.* π.

33. Find the volume of a spherical segment of height h.   *Ans.* $\frac{1}{3}\pi h^2(3a - h)$.

34. Find the volume generated by revolving about the y-axis the area bounded by the curve $y = \dfrac{\sin x}{x}$ and the coordinate axes.   *Ans.* 4π.

35. Find the volume generated by revolving about Ox the area under the curve $xy = e^{\frac{1}{x}}$, to the right of $x = 1$.   *Ans.* $\frac{1}{2}\pi(e^2 - 1)$.

36. In Ex. 35, find the volume generated by revolving the area in the third quadrant about Ox.   *Ans.* $\frac{1}{2}\pi$.

37. Find the volume of the torus formed by revolving the circle $x^2 + y^2 = a^2$ about the line $x = b$ $(b > a)$.   *Ans.* $2\pi^2 a^2 b$.

38. Solve Ex. 37, using the equations $x = a \sin \theta$, $y = a \cos \theta$.

39. Find the volume formed by revolving the area enclosed by the curve $y^2 = (x + 1)^2(4 - x^2)$ about Ox.   *Ans.* $\frac{96}{5}\pi$.

40. Find the volume formed by revolving about the x-axis the area enclosed by the four-cusped hypocycloid $x^{\frac{2}{3}} + y^{\frac{2}{3}} = a^{\frac{2}{3}}$.

$$\text{*Ans.* } \frac{32\pi a^3}{105}.$$

41. Solve Ex. 40, using the parametric equations $x = a \sin^3 \theta$, $y = a \cos^3 \theta$.

42. Find the volume formed by revolving about the y-axis the area bounded by the curve $y^2 = 4(x - y - 1)$ and the line $x = 1$.   *Ans.* $\frac{16}{5}\pi$.

In Exs. 43–46, transform to rectangular coordinates.

43. Find the volume generated by revolving the curve $r^2 = a^2 \sin \theta$ about Oy.   *Ans.* $\frac{8}{15}\pi a^3$.

44. Find the volume generated by revolving the curve $r = a \sin^2 \theta$ about Oy.   *Ans.* $\frac{4}{21}\pi a^3$.

45. Find the volume generated by revolving the curve $r = a \cos^3 \theta$ about Ox.

46. Find the volume generated by rotating the curve $r^2 = a^2 \cos^3 \theta$ about Ox.   *Ans.* $\frac{8}{33}\pi a^3$.

277. *Solids of Revolution: Cylindrical Shells*

The following method for computing volume of a solid of revolution frequently works out more simply than those of §§ 275–276; also, when two methods are feasible, solution both ways gives a valuable check.

Let a solid be formed by revolving the area OAB about Ox (Figure 275 exhibits one quadrant). Divide the solid into thin shells, each with its axis in the axis of revolution: a typical shell is formed by rotation of the strip *PQRS*. Trim the outer end, leaving the *cylindrical shell* formed by rotation of the rectangle *PQRS'*. The inner radius is y_i, outer radius $y_i + \Delta y$, height x_i, volume

(1) $$\Delta V_i = \pi (y_i + \Delta y)^2 x_i - \pi y_i^2 x_i = 2\pi y_i x_i \, \Delta y + \pi x_i \, \overline{\Delta y}^2.$$

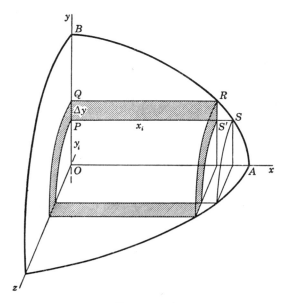

Figure 275

Hence the volume of the solid is

$$V = \operatorname*{Lim}_{\Delta y \to 0} \sum_{i=1}^{n} (2\pi y_i x_i \, \Delta y + \pi x_i \, \overline{\Delta y}^2)$$

$$= \operatorname*{Lim}_{\Delta y \to 0} \sum_{i=1}^{n} 2\pi y_i x_i \, \Delta y + \operatorname*{Lim}_{\Delta y \to 0} \sum_{i=1}^{n} \pi x_i \, \overline{\Delta y}^2.$$

Now, in regard to the second summation, we may write*

$$\operatorname*{Lim}_{\Delta y \to 0} \sum_{i=1}^{n} \pi x_i \, \overline{\Delta y}^2 = \pi \operatorname*{Lim}_{\Delta y \to 0} \sum_{i=1}^{n} x_i \, \Delta y \cdot \operatorname*{Lim}_{\Delta y \to 0} \Delta y = 0,$$

since

$$\operatorname*{Lim}_{\Delta y \to 0} \sum_{i=1}^{n} x_i \, \Delta y = A,$$

---

* This particular method of proof requires that all the Δy's be taken equal. The result is true, however, without this restriction.

where A is the rotating area. It follows that, in the expression for the volume element, we may write

$$(2) \qquad V = \operatorname*{Lim}_{\Delta y \to 0} \sum_{i=1}^{n} 2\pi y_i x_i \, \Delta y = 2\pi \int_{a}^{b} yx \, dy.$$

In § 304 we shall lay down a definition for volume in general and show that both the present formula and that of § 275 fall out as special cases when the solid is one of revolution.

In equation (2) the roles of x and y are in a sense accidental, being due to the particular position of the volume and axis of revolution in Figure 275. The important conclusion to be drawn from (2) is that a volume of revolution may be obtained by taking the limit of the sum of (integrating) cylindrical shell elements, each of which is equal in volume to the *circumference times the height times the thickness.* This is the only formula to be remembered in connection with the present method.

Example (a). The area bounded by a parabola, its axis, and the latus rectum rotates about the latus rectum. Find the volume generated. (Figure 276.)

With the shell as element,

$$V = 2\pi \int_{0}^{a} (a - x)y \, dx = 4\pi \sqrt{a} \int_{0}^{a} (ax^{\frac{1}{2}} - x^{\frac{3}{2}}) \, dx$$

$$= 4\pi \sqrt{a} \left[\tfrac{2}{3}ax^{\frac{3}{2}} - \tfrac{2}{5}x^{\frac{5}{2}} \right]_{0}^{a} = \tfrac{16}{15}\pi a^{3}.$$

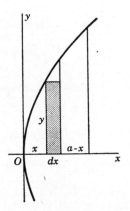

Figure 276

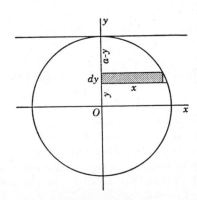

Figure 277

Example (b). Find the volume generated by revolving a circle about one of its tangents. (Figure 277.)

Let the circle

$$x^2 + y^2 = a^2$$

rotate around the line $y = a$. The volume, with the shell as element, is

$$V = 2 \cdot 2\pi \int_{-a}^{a} (a - y)x \, dy$$

or

(1) $$V = 4\pi a \int_{-a}^{a} x \, dy - 4\pi \int_{-a}^{a} yx \, dy.$$

The first integral in (1) represents the area of the semicircle; the second, being the integral of an odd function between limits equally spaced from the origin, vanishes. Hence

$$V = 4\pi a \cdot \tfrac{1}{2}\pi a^2 = 2\pi^2 a^3.$$

EXERCISES

In Exs. 1–28, solve by the method of cylindrical shells.

1. Find the volume generated by revolving about Oy the area in the first quadrant bounded by the curve $y = 4 - x^2$ and the axes. *Ans.* 8π.

2. Find the volume formed by revolving the area of Ex. 1 about the line $x = 2$.

Ans. $\dfrac{40\pi}{3}$.

3. Find the volume of a sphere.

4. Find the volume of a prolate spheroid. *Ans.* $\tfrac{4}{3}\pi ab^2$.

5. Find the volume of an oblate spheroid, using the equations $x = a \cos \varphi$, $y = b \sin \varphi$. *Ans.* $\tfrac{4}{3}\pi a^2 b$.

6. Find the volume of a circular cone.

7. The area enclosed by the loop of the curve $y^2 = x(1 - x)^2$ is revolved about the y-axis. Find the volume generated.

Ans. $\dfrac{16\pi}{35}$.

8. The area of Ex. 7 is revolved about the line $x = 1$. Find the volume formed.

Ans. $\dfrac{64\pi}{105}$.

9. Find the volume generated by revolving about the line $x = 2a$ the area bounded by that line, the x-axis, and the curve $a^2 y = x^3$. *Ans.* $\tfrac{16}{5}\pi a^3$.

10. Find the volume formed by revolving about the line $y = 2a$ the area bounded by that line, the y-axis, and the parabola $y^2 = 4ax$. *Ans.* $\tfrac{2}{3}\pi a^3$.

11. The area bounded by the parabola $x^2 - 2x + y = 3$, the y-axis, and the line $y = 4$ revolves about the line $y = 4$. Find the volume. *Ans.* $\tfrac{1}{5}\pi$.

12. The area bounded by the parabola $y^2 + x - 2y = 1$, the x-axis, and the line $x = 2$ revolves about Ox. Find the volume.

Ans. $\tfrac{1}{5}\pi$.

13. The area of Ex. 12 revolves about the line $x = 2$. Find the volume.

Ans. $\tfrac{1}{5}\pi$.

14. The area in the first quadrant between the curve $y(1 + x) = x$ and its horizontal asymptote revolves about the asymptote. Find the volume. *Ans.* π.

15. Find the volume of a spherical segment of height h.   *Ans.* $\frac{1}{3}\pi h^2(3a - h)$

16. The area enclosed by the hypocycloid of four cusps, $x^{\frac{2}{3}} + y^{\frac{2}{3}} = a^{\frac{2}{3}}$, is revolved about Oy. Use the parametric equations $x = a \sin^3 \varphi$, $y = a \cos^3 \varphi$, in finding the volume formed.

$$Ans. \frac{32\pi a^3}{105}.$$

17. Find the volume generated by revolving about Oy the area under that arch of the curve $y = \sin x$ for which x varies from 0 to π.   *Ans.* $2\pi^2$.

18. Find the volume generated by revolving about Oy the left-hand half of the area of Ex. 17.   *Ans.* 2π.

19. Find the volume formed by revolving about Oy the area in the first quadrant bounded by $y = \cos x$ and the two axes.   *Ans.* $\pi(\pi - 2)$.

20. Find the volume formed by revolving about the line $x = 1$ the area bounded by $x = 1$, $y = e^{-x}$, and the axes.

$$Ans. \frac{2\pi}{e}.$$

21. Find the volume generated by revolving about the y-axis the area enclosed by the curve $a^2y^2 = x^2(a^2 - x^2)$.   *Ans.* $\frac{1}{4}\pi^2 a^3$.

22. The area bounded by the curve $y = (x^2 - 4)^2$ and the x-axis revoves about the y-axis. Find the volume.   *Ans.* $\frac{64}{3}\pi$.

23. A round hole of radius a is bored through the center of a sphere of radius $2a$. Find the volume cut out.   *Ans.* $\frac{4}{3}\pi(8 - 3\sqrt{3})a^3$.

24. Find the volume of the torus formed by revolving the circle $x^2 + y^2 = a^2$ about the line $x = b$.   *Ans.* $2\pi^2 a^2 b$.

25. Solve Ex. 24, using the equations $x = a \sin \theta$, $y = a \cos \theta$.

26. Find the volume formed by revolving about Oy the area bounded by the curve $y = \dfrac{\sin x}{x}$ and the coordinate axes.   *Ans.* 4π.

27. Find the volume formed by revolving the area of Ex. 18, page 464, about the line $x = 4$.

$$Ans. \frac{14\pi}{3}.$$

28. Find the volume formed by revolving about the line $x = 1$ the area bounded by the curve $y = (x^2 - 1)^2$ and the x-axis.   *Ans.* $\frac{32}{15}\pi$.

In Exs. 29–49, use any legitimate method.

29. Find the volume generated by revolving the area under the curve $y = e^x$, from $x = 0$ to $x = 1$, about the line $x = 1$.   *Ans.* $2\pi(e - 2)$.

30. Find the volume generated by revolving about Oy the area in the second quadrant under the curve $y = e^x$.   *Ans.* 2π.

31. The area bounded by the parabola $y^2 = 4ax$ and its latus rectum revolves about the directrix. Find the volume generated.   *Ans.* $\frac{128}{15}\pi a^3$.

32. The area enclosed by $y^2 = x^4(1 - x^2)$ is revolved about the x-axis. Find the volume generated.

$$Ans. \frac{4\pi}{35}.$$

33. The area of Ex. 32 is revolved about Oy. Find the volume formed.

34. The area under the curve $y = \ln x$ from $x = 1$ to $x = e$ is revolved about the y-axis. Find the volume generated.   *Ans.* $\frac{1}{2}\pi(1 + e^2)$.

35. Find the volume formed by revolving about Ox the area in the first quadrant bounded by the curves $y = 3x - x^3$, $x = 0$, $y = 2$.   *Ans.* $\frac{72}{35}\pi$.

36. Find the volume formed by revolving about Ox the area between the curves $x^2 = 2ay$, $x^2 = 4ay - a^2$.   *Ans.* $\frac{2}{15}\pi a^3$.

37. Find the volume formed by revolving the area of Ex. 36 about Oy.
          Ans. $\frac{1}{8}\pi a^3$.

38. Find the voulme generated by revolving the first arch of the cycloid $x = a(\theta - \sin\theta)$, $y = a(1 - \cos\theta)$ about Oy. (Figure 217, page 377.)
          Ans. $6\pi^3 a^3$.

39. Find the volume formed by revolving one arch of the cycloid (Ex. 38) about the tangent at the vertex.   *Ans.* $\pi^2 a^3$.

40. Find the volume formed by revolving about Oy the area bounded by the curve $x^2 y^2 = a^2(a^2 - x^2)$.   *Ans.* $\pi^2 a^3$.

41. Find the volume obtained by revolving about Ox the area under the curve $x^3 y = a^4$ to the right of the line $x = a$.   *Ans.* $\frac{1}{5}\pi a^3$.

42. Find the volume generated by revolving about Oy the area bounded by the curve $ay^3 = (x^2 - a^2)^2$ and the x-axis.   *Ans.* $\frac{3}{5}\pi a^3$.

43. Find the volume bounded by the cylinder $x^2 + y^2 = 2a^2$ and the hyperboloid $x^2 + y^2 - z^2 = a^2$.   *Ans.* $\frac{4}{3}\pi a^3$.

44. Find the volume bounded by the surfaces $x^2 + y^2 = 4az$, $x^2 + y^2 = z^2$.
          Ans. $\frac{32}{3}\pi a^3$.

45. Find the volume bounded by the hyperboloid $x^2 + y^2 - z^2 = a^2$ and the cone $x^2 + y^2 = 2z^2$.   *Ans.* $\frac{4}{3}\pi a^3$.

46. Find the volume enclosed by the surfaces $x^2 + y^2 - z^2 + 2a^2 = 0$, $x^2 + y^2 = az$.   *Ans.* $\frac{2}{3}\pi a^3(5 - 2\sqrt{2})$.

47. Find the volume common to the sphere $x^2 + y^2 + z^2 = a^2$ and the cone $x^2 + y^2 = z^2$.   *Ans.* $\frac{4}{3}\pi a^3(1 - \frac{1}{2}\sqrt{2})$.

48. Find the volume inside the cone $x^2 + y^2 = z^2$ and the paraboloid $x^2 + y^2 + az = 2a^2$.   *Ans.* $\frac{5}{6}\pi a^3$.

49. Find the volume formed by revolving about Ox the area under the tractrix. See § 140, and particularly Ex. 19, page 251. $\frac{1}{3}\pi a^3$.

278. *Miscellaneous Solids*

The volume of any solid can be expressed as a definite integral, provided we know the *area of every plane section parallel to some fixed plane*. We divide the solid into thin slices by means of n planes parallel to the fixed plane, trim off the outer edge exactly as in § 275 (which is merely a special case of the present problem), and take as element the slab remaining. The volume of this slab, of course, is the thickness times the area of the face, which by hypothesis is known.

The only plane figures whose area we are supposed to know offhand are the rectangle, the triangle, the trapezoid, the circle, the circular sector ($\frac{1}{2}r^2\alpha$), and the ellipse (πab). Thus the only solids whose volumes we can find at this time are those that can be divided into parallel slices of one of these shapes. More complicated volumes are found by iterated integration (Chapter 37).

Example (a). A woodsman chops halfway through a tree of diameter $2a$, one face of the cut being horizontal, the other inclined at $45°$. Find the volume of wood cut out.

Figure 278 shows one-half of the required solid. If we pass cutting planes parallel to the yz-plane, the element is a *triangular plate* of width y, altitude z, and thickness dx. Hence

$$V = 2 \int_0^a \tfrac{1}{2} yz \, dx.$$

But $z = y$, and $y^2 = a^2 - x^2$, so that

$$V = \int_0^a (a^2 - x^2) \, dx = \tfrac{2}{3} a^3.$$

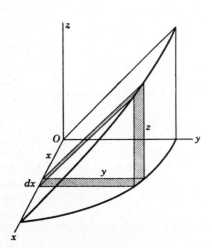

Figure 278

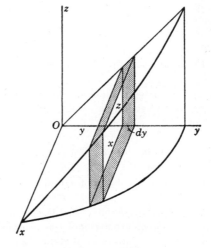

Figure 279

Example (b). Solve Example (a) by another method.

Planes parallel to the zx-plane cut the solid into *rectangular plates* of length x, height z, thickness dy (Figure 279). Hence

$$V = 2 \int_0^a xz \, dy.$$

But $z = y$, $x^2 + y^2 = a^2$, $y \, dy = -x \, dx$, $x = a$ when $y = 0$, $x = 0$ when $y = a$, so that

$$V = 2 \int_0^a xy \, dy = -2 \int_a^0 x^2 \, dx = \tfrac{2}{3} a^3.$$

EXERCISES

1. Find the volume in the first octant under the plane $z = y$ and inside the cylinder $y^2 = 4 - x$. Solve in two ways.   *Ans.* 4.

2. Find the volume cut from the paraboloid $\dfrac{x^2}{a^2} + \dfrac{y^2}{b^2} = \dfrac{4z}{c}$ by the plane $z = c$.

Ans. $2\pi abc$.

3. Find the volume of an ellipsoid.   *Ans.* $\frac{4}{3}\pi abc$.

4. Find the volume of an elliptic cone bounded by a right section.   *Ans.* $\frac{1}{3}\pi abh$.

5. Find the volume in the first octant inside the cylinder $\dfrac{x^2}{a^2} + \dfrac{y^2}{b^2} = 1$, under the

plane $z = mx$. Solve in two ways.   *Ans.* $\frac{1}{3}ma^2 b$.

6. Find the volume of a tetrahedron with three mutually perpendicular faces.

Ans. $\frac{1}{6}abc$.

7. Find the volume in the first octant enclosed by the cylinder $y^2 = ax$ and the planes $x = a$, $z = x$.   *Ans.* $\frac{2}{5}a^3$.

8. Find the volume in the first octant bounded by the cylinder $y^2 - x^2 = a^2$ and the planes $x = a$, $z = y$.   *Ans.* $\frac{2}{3}a^3$.

9. Find the volume in the first octant bounded by the surfaces $x = 1$, $x^2 = y + 2z$.   *Ans.* $\frac{1}{20}$.

10. Find the volume in the first octant inside the cylinder $y^2 + z^2 = a^2$ and outside the cylinder $y^2 = ax$.   *Ans.* $\frac{1}{16}\pi a^3$.

11. Find the volume in the first octant bounded by the surfaces $x + y = a$, $z^2 = 4ay$. Solve in two ways.   *Ans.* $\frac{8}{15}a^3$.

12. Find the volume in the first octant bounded by the surfaces $y + z = a$, $z^2 = ax$.   *Ans.* $\frac{1}{12}a^3$.

13. Find the volume of a right pyramid with a square base of side $2a$. Solve in two ways.   *Ans.* $\frac{4}{3}a^2 h$.

14. Find the volume of a wedge cut from a circular cone by two planes through the axis.   *Ans.* $\frac{1}{6}\alpha a^2 h$.

15. Find the volume of a spherical wedge.   *Ans.* $\frac{2}{3}\alpha a^3$.

16. By two methods, find the volume common to two equal cylinders of revolution whose axes intersect at right angles.   *Ans.* $\frac{16}{3}a^3$.

17. Find the volume in the first octant bounded by the surfaces $az = xy$, $y^2 + ax = 4a^2$. Solve in two ways.   *Ans.* $\frac{16}{3}a^3$.

18. Find the volume in the first octant under the surface $az = xy$, bounded by the cylinder $y^2 = ax$ and the plane $x = a$.   *Ans.* $\frac{1}{6}a^3$.

19. A carpenter chisels a square hole of side 2 in. through a round post of radius 2 in., the axis of the hole intersecting that of the post at right angles. Find the volume of wood cut out.   *Ans.* $4\sqrt{3} + \frac{8}{3}\pi = 15.3$ cu. in.

20. A hyperbolic paraboloid is generated by a line moving parallel to the zx-plane intersecting the lines $x = a$, $z = 0$ and $z = y$, $x = 0$. Find the volume enclosed by this surface, the coordinate planes, and the plane $y = b$.   *Ans.* $\frac{1}{4}ab^2$.

21. A hyperbolic paraboloid is generated by a line moving parallel to the zx-plane and intersecting the lines $x = y = z$ and $x = a$, $z = 0$. Find the volume bounded by this surface, the xy-plane, and the plane $y = x$.   *Ans.* $\frac{1}{12}a^3$.

22. A surface is generated by a line parallel to the xy-plane intersecting the parabolas $z^2 = ax$, $y = 0$ and $y^2 = a^2 - az$, $x = 0$. Find the volume in the first octant bounded by this surface and the planes $x = 0$, $y = 0$. *Ans.* $\frac{8}{105}a^3$.

23. A surface is generated by a line parallel to the zx-plane intersecting the parabola $y^2 = 4ax$, $z = 0$ and the line $z = b$, $x = 0$. Find the volume in the first octant bounded by this surface and the plane $y = a$. *Ans.* $\frac{1}{24}a^2b$.

24. Find the volume in the first octant bounded by the hyperbolic paraboloid generated by a straight line moving always parallel to the xy-plane and passing through the lines $y + z = a$ in the yz-plane and $x = b$ in the xz-plane. *Ans.* $\frac{1}{4}a^2b$.

25. In Ex. 24, derive the equation of the paraboloid; then find the volume by a second method. *Ans.* $xz - ax - by - bz + ab = 0$.

26. Find the volume in the first octant bounded by the surfaces $y + z = a$, $x^2 + ay = a^2$. Solve in two ways. *Ans.* $\frac{2}{5}a^3$.

27. Find the volume bounded by the cylinder $x^2 + y^2 = 2a^2$ and the planes $z = 0$, $x = 0$, $y = x$, $y = z$. *Ans.* $\frac{2}{3}a^3$.

28. Find the volume bounded by the cylinder $x^2 = ay$ and the planes $z = 0$, $y = x$, $y = z$. *Ans.* $\frac{1}{15}a^3$.

29. A circular conoid is generated by a straight line which moves always parallel to the xy-plane and passes through the line $y = h$ in the yz-plane and the circle $x^2 + z^2 = a^2$ in the xz-plane. Find the volume of the conoid. *Ans.* $\frac{1}{2}\pi a^2 h$.

30. In Ex. 29, derive the equation of the conoid; then find the volume by a second method. *Ans.* $h^2x^2 = (a^2 - z^2)(h - y)^2$.

31. Solve Ex. 29 if the line $y = h$ is replaced by the line $y + z = h(h > a)$. *Ans.* $\frac{1}{2}\pi a^2 h$.

32. A cylinder is generated by a line moving always parallel to the line $y + z = a$, $x = 0$ and following the circle $x^2 + y^2 = a^2$, $z = 0$. Find the volume in the first octant inside the cylinder. *Ans.* $\frac{1}{3}a^3$.

33. A cylinder is generated by a line moving always parallel to the line $x + z = a$, $y = 0$, and following the curve $y^2 + az = a^2$, $x = 0$. Find the volume in the first octant inside the cylinder. *Ans.* $\frac{4}{15}a^3$.

34. Find the volume in the first octant bounded by the surfaces $yz = z - x$, $z = 1$. Solve in two ways. *Ans.* $\frac{1}{4}$.

35. Find the volume in the first octant bounded by the surfaces $yz = z^2 - x$, $z = 1$. *Ans.* $\frac{1}{8}$.

36. Find the volume in the first octant bounded by the surfaces $z = y - xy$, $x + y = 1$. Solve in two ways. *Ans.* $\frac{1}{8}$.

37. The vertex of a cone is at $(a, 0, 0)$; the base is the curve $y^2 + z^2 = 2by$, $x = 0$. Find the volume of the cone. *Ans.* $\frac{1}{3}\pi ab^2$.

279. Length of a Curve

In § 72, page 132, we defined the differential ds of arc length by

(1) $$ds = \sqrt{(dx)^2 + (dy)^2}.$$

Instead of (1) it is sometimes convenient to use the equivalent forms

(2) $$ds = \left[1 + \left(\frac{dy}{dx}\right)^2\right]^{\frac{1}{2}} dx = \left[1 + \left(\frac{dx}{dy}\right)^2\right]^{\frac{1}{2}} dy$$

or, if x and y are known in terms of a parameter t, the form

$$(3) \qquad ds = \left[\left(\frac{dx}{dt} \right)^2 + \left(\frac{dy}{dt} \right)^2 \right]^{\frac{1}{2}} dt.$$

In agreement with (1) we now define the length s of a curve along an arc C by

$$(4) \qquad s = \int_C ds = \int_a^b \sqrt{1 + \left(\frac{dy}{dx} \right)^2}\, dx,$$

where a and b are the abscissas of the end points of C, and where $\dfrac{dy}{dx}$ must be replaced by its value in terms of x from the equation of the curve.

If it is more convenient to integrate with respect to y, we put

$$(5) \qquad s = \int_c^d \sqrt{\left(\frac{dx}{dy} \right)^2 + 1}\, dy.$$

If x and y are given in terms of a parameter t,

$$(6) \qquad s = \int_{t_1}^{t_2} \sqrt{\left(\frac{dx}{dt} \right)^2 + \left(\frac{dy}{dt} \right)^2}\, dt.$$

We assume, of course, that in any instance the integrand is a single-valued function of the variable of integration. If this condition is not satisfied, C must consist of several portions for each of which the condition holds, and each portion may be considered separately.

The equation of the curve may be known in polar, rather than in rectangular, coordinates. From $x = r \cos \theta$, $y = r \sin \theta$, we obtain the total differentials

$$dx = \cos \theta\, dr - r \sin \theta\, d\theta, \qquad dy = \sin \theta\, dr + r \cos \theta\, d\theta.$$

Then (1) yields

$$(7) \qquad ds = \sqrt{(dr)^2 + r^2 (d\theta)^2} = \left[\left(\frac{dr}{d\theta} \right)^2 + r^2 \right]^{\frac{1}{2}} d\theta.$$

The student should verify (Ex. 1, below) that formula (4) yields the desired result for the distance between any two points (x_1, y_1), (x_2, y_2) along the straight line joining them. See also Ex. 2 below.

Example (a). Find the length of the curve $y = \ln \sin x$ from $x = \frac{1}{4}\pi$ to $x = \frac{1}{2}\pi$.

From $y = \ln \sin x$, we obtain $y' = \cot x$, so that the desired length is given by

$$s = \int_{\frac{1}{4}\pi}^{\frac{1}{2}\pi} \sqrt{1 + \cot^2 x}\, dx.$$

Then

$$s = \int_{\frac{1}{4}\pi}^{\frac{1}{2}\pi} \csc x \, dx = \Big[\ln (\csc x - \cot x) \Big]_{\frac{1}{4}\pi}^{\frac{1}{2}\pi}$$

$$= \ln (1 - 0) - \ln (\sqrt{2} - 1) = - \ln (\sqrt{2} - 1)$$

$$= - \ln \frac{2 - 1}{\sqrt{2} + 1} = \ln (1 + \sqrt{2}).$$

Example (b).   Find the length of one arch of the cycloid $x = a(\theta - \sin \theta)$, $y = a(1 - \cos \theta)$.   See Figure 217, page 377.

Here the θ is a parameter; we use formula (6) above.   From

$$dx = a(1 - \cos \theta) \, d\theta$$

and $dy = a \sin \theta \, d\theta$, we obtain

$$ds = \sqrt{a^2(1 - \cos \theta)^2 + a^2 \sin^2 \theta} \, d\theta.$$

Because of symmetry, we can integrate from $x = 0$ to $x = \pi a$ (from $\theta = 0$ to $\theta = \pi$) and double the result.   Hence,

$$s = 2 \int_0^\pi a \sqrt{1 - 2 \cos \theta + \cos^2 \theta + \sin^2 \theta} \, d\theta$$

$$= 2a \int_0^\pi \sqrt{2 - 2 \cos \theta} \, d\theta.$$

Now $1 - \cos \theta = 2 \sin^2 \frac{1}{2}\theta$, so

$$s = 2a \int_0^\pi \sqrt{4 \sin^2 \tfrac{1}{2}\theta} \, d\theta = 4a \int_0^\pi \sin \tfrac{1}{2}\theta \, d\theta$$

$$= -8a \Big[\cos \tfrac{1}{2}\theta \Big]_0^\pi = 8a.$$

EXERCISES

1. Verify that equation (4) of this section yields the desired result for the distance between two points (x_1, y_1), (x_2, y_2) along the straight line joining those points.

2. Use the polar equation $r = a$ and equation (7) of this section to compute the length of arc of one quadrant of a circle.

In Exs. 3–22, find the length of the curve over the given interval.

3. One branch of the curve $9y^2 = 4x^3$ from $x = 0$ to $x = 3$.   *Ans.* $\frac{14}{3}$.

4. The curve $y = \ln x$ from $x = \sqrt{3}$ to $x = 2\sqrt{2}$.   *Ans.* $1 + \frac{1}{2} \ln \frac{3}{2}$.

5. The curve $y = \ln \cos x$ from $x = 0$ to $x = \frac{1}{4}\pi$.   Use x as the variable of integration.   *Ans.* $\ln (1 + \sqrt{2})$.

6. Solve Ex. 5, using y as the variable of integration.

7. One branch of the curve $ay^2 = x^3$ from $x = 0$ to $x = 5a$.   *Ans.* $\frac{335}{27} a$.

8. Solve Ex. 7, using the parametric equations $x = at^2$, $y = at^3$.

9. The four-cusped hypocycloid $x^{\frac{2}{3}} + y^{\frac{2}{3}} = a^{\frac{2}{3}}$.   *Ans.* $6a$.

10. Solve Ex. 9, using the parametric equations $x = a \sin^3 t$, $y = a \cos^3 t$.

11. One branch of the parabola $y^2 = 4ax$ from the vertex to the end of the latus rectum, integrating with respect to x.　　　*Ans.* $2.295a$.

12. Solve Ex. 11, using y as the variable of integration.

13. Solve Ex. 11, using the equations $x = a \tan^2 \psi$, $y = 2a \tan \psi$.

14. The curve $y = e^x$ from $x = 0$ to $x = 1$, using x as the variable of integration.

15. The catenary $y = a \cosh \dfrac{x}{a}$ from $x = 0$ to $x = x_1$.　　　*Ans.* $a \sinh \dfrac{x_1}{a}$.

16. The curve $y = \frac{4}{5}x^{\frac{5}{4}}$, from $x = 0$ to $x = 9$.　　Evaluate the integral in two ways.　　　*Ans.* $\frac{232}{15}$.

17. One branch of the curve $9y^2 = 4(1 + x^2)^3$, from $x = 0$ to $x = 2$.　　*Ans.* $\frac{22}{3}$.

18. The curve $y = \text{Arcsin } e^{-x}$, from $x = 0$ to $x = \ln \frac{5}{4}$.　　　*Ans.* $\ln 2$.

19. One branch of the curve $25y^2 = (x + 2)^2(2x - 1)^3$, from $x = \frac{1}{2}$ to $x = 3$.　　　*Ans.* $\frac{58}{5}$.

20. One branch of the curve $3y^2 = (2x + 3)^3$, from $x = -1$ to $x = 1$.　　*Ans.* $\frac{56}{9}$.

21. The curve $y = e^x$ from $x = 0$ to $x = 1$, using y as the variable of integration.

22. The curve $6xy = x^4 + 3$ from the minimum point to $x = 2$.　　*Ans.* $\frac{17}{12}$.

23. Find the perimeter of the loop of the curve $9ay^2 = x(x - 3a)^2$.　　　*Ans.* $4\sqrt{3}\,a$.

24. Find the perimeter of the loop of the curve $9y^2 = x^2(2x + 3)$.　　*Ans.* $2\sqrt{3}$.

25. Find the length of the tractrix (§ 140) from the starting point to $y = h$. (See Ex. 19, page 251.)　　　*Ans.* $a \ln (a/h)$.

26. A point moves in a plane curve according to the law $x = 1 - \cos 2t$, $y = 2 \cos t$.　　Find the length of the path.　　*Ans.* $2\sqrt{5} + \ln (2 + \sqrt{5}) = 5.92$ ft.

27. A point moves according to the law $x = e^{-3t}$, $y = e^{-2t}$.　　Find the entire distance traveled $(t > 0)$.　　　*Ans.* $\frac{1}{27}(13^{\frac{3}{2}} - 8) = 1.44$ ft.

28. A point moves according to the law $x = e^{-t}$, $y = e^{-t} - e^{-2t}$.　　Find the length of its path $(t > 0)$.　　　*Ans.* 1.15 ft.

29. Find the length of the cycloid $x = a(\theta - \sin \theta)$, $y = a(1 - \cos \theta)$ from $(0, 0)$ to any point (x_1, y_1) on the curve $(0 \leq \theta \leq \pi)$.　　Check the answer against Example (b).　　　*Ans.* $4a - \sqrt{4a^2 - 2ay_1}$.

In Exs. 30–34, the equation of the curve is given in polar coordinates.　　Find the length of the arc described.

30. The total length of the cardioid $r = a(1 + \cos \theta)$.　　　*Ans.* $8a$.

31. The total length of the cardioid $r = a(1 - \sin \theta)$.

32. The total length of the curve $r = a \cos^2 \theta$.　　*Ans.* $\dfrac{2a}{3}[6 + \sqrt{3} \ln (2 + \sqrt{3})]$.

33. The logarithmic spiral $r = ae^{k\theta}$ from $\theta = 0$ to $\theta = \pi$.　　　*Ans.* $k^{-1}a(1 + k^2)^{\frac{1}{2}}[e^{k\pi} - 1]$.

34. The spiral of Archimedes $r = a\theta$ from $\theta = 0$ to $\theta = \pi$.　　　*Ans.* $\frac{1}{2}a[\pi(1 + \pi^2)^{\frac{1}{2}} + \ln \{\pi + (1 + \pi^2)^{\frac{1}{2}}\}]$.

35. Show that for the curve $r = \sin^{2k} \theta$ for k any positive integer, the integral encountered in applying formula (7) of this section is an elementary integral.　　That is, show that the integration can be performed by the techniques studied earlier in this course.

280. *Surfaces of Revolution*

The problem of this section is to find the area of the surface generated by rotating a plane curve C about a line in its plane (say, for definiteness about the x-axis). For variety, let us revert to fundamentals to obtain the desired formula. In Figure 280 we cut the pertinent section along the axis of revolution into equal segments Δx which project onto elements Δs_i along the curve C. Next inscribe in C a broken line of n segments $\Delta s_i'$. In the rotation, each segment $\Delta s_i'$ generates the frustum of a circular cone, the radii of whose bases are $y_i, y_i + \Delta y_i$. By elementary geometry, the surface area of this conical frustum is *the circumference of the middle section multiplied by the slant height*, or $2\pi(y_i + \frac{1}{2}\Delta y_i)\,\Delta s_i'$. It can be shown that

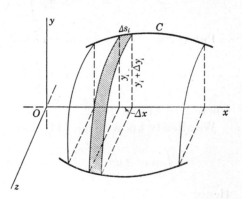

Figure 280

$$\operatorname*{Lim}_{n\to\infty} \sum_{i=1}^{n} 2\pi(\tfrac{1}{2}\Delta y_i)\,\Delta s_i' = 0.$$

Therefore

$$A = \operatorname*{Lim}_{n\to\infty} \sum_{i=1}^{n} 2\pi y_i\,\Delta s_i' = 2\pi \int_C y\,ds.$$

Example. Find the surface area generated by revolving about the y-axis the hyperbola

$$x^2 - y^2 = a^2$$

from $y = 0$ to $y = 2a$.

At once

$$A = 2\pi \int_{y=0}^{y=2a} x\,ds.$$

From the equation $x^2 - y^2 = a^2$, we obtain $x\,dx - y\,dy = 0$, so that

$$ds = \sqrt{1 + \left(\frac{dx}{dy}\right)^2}\,dy$$

$$= \sqrt{1 + \frac{y^2}{x^2}}\,dy.$$

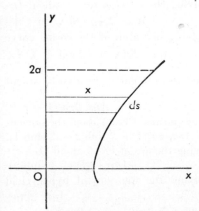

Figure 281

Thus we have

$$A = 2\pi \int_0^{2a} x \sqrt{1 + \frac{y^2}{x^2}}\, dy$$

$$= 2\pi \int_0^{2a} \sqrt{x^2 + y^2}\, dy$$

$$= 2\pi \int_0^{2a} \sqrt{a^2 + 2y^2}\, dy.$$

Put $\sqrt{2}\, y = a \tan \theta$, which yields

$$A = \frac{2\pi a^2}{\sqrt{2}} \int_0^{\beta} \sec^3 \theta\, d\theta,$$

where $\beta = \text{Arctan } 2\sqrt{2}$.

We already know (page 343) that

$$\int \sec^3 \theta\, d\theta = \tfrac{1}{2}\left[\sec \theta \tan \theta + \ln (\sec \theta + \tan \theta) \right] + C.$$

Hence

$$A = \frac{\pi a^2}{\sqrt{2}} \left[\sec \theta \tan \theta + \ln (\sec \theta + \tan \theta) \right]_0^{\beta}.$$

But $\tan \beta = 2\sqrt{2}$, $\sec \beta = 3$, $\tan 0 = 0$, and $\sec 0 = 1$.　Therefore

$$A = \frac{\pi a^2}{\sqrt{2}} [6\sqrt{2} + \ln (3 + 2\sqrt{2})].$$

EXERCISES

1. Find the surface area of a sphere of radius a.　　　　　　*Ans.* $4\pi a^2$.

2. Solve Ex. 1, using the equations $x = a \cos \theta$, $y = a \sin \theta$.

3. Find the surface area generated by revolving the curve $a^2 y = x^3$ about Ox, from $x = 0$ to $x = a$.　　　　　　*Ans.* $\frac{1}{27}\pi a^2(10\sqrt{10} - 1)$.

4. Find the surface area generated by revolving one arch of the cosine curve about Ox.　　　　　*Ans.* $2\pi[\sqrt{2} + \ln (1 + \sqrt{2})]$.

5. Find the surface area formed by revolving the catenary $y = a \cosh \dfrac{x}{a}$ about Oy, from $x = 0$ to $x = a$.　　　　　*Ans.* $2\pi a^2(1 - e^{-1})$.

6. Find the surface area generated by revolving the arc of Ex. 5 about the tangent at the vertex.　　　　　*Ans.* $\pi a^2(1 + \tfrac{1}{2} \sinh 2 - 2 \sinh 1)$.

7. Find the surface area generated by revolving the arc of Ex. 5 about Ox.　　　　　*Ans.* $\pi a^2(1 + \tfrac{1}{2} \sinh 2)$.

8. Find the surface area formed by revolving the four-cusped hypocycloid $x^{\frac{2}{3}} + y^{\frac{2}{3}} = a^{\frac{2}{3}}$ about Ox.　　　　　*Ans.* $\frac{12}{5}\pi a^2$.

9. Solve Ex. 8, using the parametric equations $x = a \sin^3 t$, $y = a \cos^3 t$.

10. Find the surface area of a torus.　　　　　*Ans.* $4\pi^2 ab$.

11. Find the surface area generated by revolving an arch of the cycloid $x = a(\theta - \sin \theta)$, $y = a(1 - \cos \theta)$ about its base. *Ans.* $\frac{64}{3}\pi a^2$.

12. Find the surface area of a zone cut from a sphere by two parallel planes at a distance h apart. *Ans.* $2\pi ah$.

13. Find the surface area cut from a sphere by a circular cone of half-angle α with its vertex at the center of the sphere. (Use $x = a \cos \theta$, $y = a \sin \theta$.)
Ans. $2\pi a^2(1 - \cos \alpha)$.

14. Find the surface area generated by revolving about Oy that part of the curve $y = \ln x$ lying in the fourth quadrant, using x as the variable of integration.
Ans. $\pi[\sqrt{2} + \ln(1 + \sqrt{2})]$.

15. Solve Ex. 14, using y as the variable of integration.

16. Find the surface area generated by revolving about Ox the arc of the curve $6xy = x^4 + 3$, from the minimum point to $x = 2$. *Ans.* $\frac{47}{16}\pi$.

17. In Ex. 16, revolve the arc about Oy. *Ans.* $(\frac{15}{4} + \ln 2)\pi$.

18. Find the surface area generated by revolving about Ox the curve $8a^2y^2 = x^2(a^2 - x^2)$. *Ans.* $\frac{1}{2}\pi a^2$.

19. Find the area cut off from the paraboloid $x^2 + y^2 = 4az$ by the plane $z = a$, using z as the variable of integration. *Ans.* $\frac{8}{3}\pi a^2(2\sqrt{2} - 1)$.

20. Solve Ex. 19, using x or y as the variable.

21. Solve Ex. 19, using the equations $x = 2a \cot \psi$, $z = a \cot^2 \psi$.

22. Find the surface area generated by revolving about the y-axis that arc of the curve $a^2y = x^3$ from $x = 0$ to $x = a$.
Ans. $\frac{\pi a^2}{12} [3\sqrt{10} + \ln(3 + \sqrt{10})]$.

Centroids

281. *Density*

A mass is said to be *homogeneous* if the masses contained in any two equal volumes are equal. In all other cases the mass is *heterogeneous*. In the present chapter we confine our attention to homogeneous masses.

The *density* of a homogeneous mass is the ratio of the mass M to the volume V that it occupies. That is, the density is the mass per unit volume.

A *mass point* may be imagined as the limiting form approached by a body whose dimensions approach zero, while the density increases in such a way that the mass remains finite. Similarly we may think of masses of one dimension and of two dimensions—i.e., of material curves and surfaces. Such masses are represented approximately, for example, by slender wires and thin sheets of metal. In these cases we define the density as "linear density," or mass per unit length, and "surface density," or mass per unit area.

282. *First Moment of Mass*

The product of a mass m, concentrated at a point P, by the distance l of P from a given point, line, or plane, is called the *first moment* of m with respect to the point, line, or plane (also called *simple moment*, or *mass moment*). Denoting this moment by G, we have

$$G = ml.$$

Second moments, those involving the square of the distance from P to a point, line, or plane, will be considered in Chapter 35.

If a system of points $P_1, P_2, \cdots, P_n$, having masses $m_1, m_2, \cdots, m_n$, respectively, be referred to rectangular coordinate axes, the first moments of the system with respect to the three coordinate planes are

$$(1) \qquad G_{yz} = \sum_{i=1}^{n} m_i x_i, \qquad G_{zx} = \sum_{i=1}^{n} m_i y_i, \qquad G_{xy} = \sum_{i=1}^{n} m_i z_i.$$

If the particles all lie in one of the coordinate planes, the moments with respect to coordinate planes reduce to moments with respect to the axes.

The idea of mass moment may be extended to the case of a continuous mass by thinking of the body as composed of an indefinitely large number of particles. (A definition will be laid down in § 319.) The actual computation of such a moment is usually effected by means of definite integrals; we return to this question presently.

283. *Centroid*

Given any mass M, let G_{yz}, G_{zx}, G_{xy} denote the first moments of the mass with respect to the coordinate planes. The point C whose coordinates $\bar{x}$, $\bar{y}$, $\bar{z}$ are given by the formulas

$$(1) \qquad M\bar{x} = G_{yz}, \qquad M\bar{y} = G_{zx}, \qquad M\bar{z} = G_{xy}$$

has the property that the moment of the mass with respect to each coordinate plane is the same as if the whole mass were concentrated at that point. For, the moments for a particle of mass M at the point C are $M\bar{x}$, $M\bar{y}$, $M\bar{z}$; and by (1), these are equal to the moments for the original distribution.

It can be shown that this property holds for first moments with respect to any other plane. For a system of mass particles the proof is as follows: Let

$$(2) \qquad x \cos \alpha + y \cos \beta + z \cos \gamma = p$$

be the equation of any plane in the normal form; let $\bar{p}$, p_1, $\cdots$, p_n be the distances of the points C, P_1, $\cdots$, P_n from this plane. Then

$$p_1 = x_1 \cos \alpha + y_1 \cos \beta + z_1 \cos \gamma - p,$$
$$\cdots \cdots \cdots \cdots \cdots \cdots \cdots \cdots \cdots$$
$$\cdots \cdots \cdots \cdots \cdots \cdots \cdots \cdots \cdots$$
$$\cdots \cdots \cdots \cdots \cdots \cdots \cdots \cdots \cdots$$
$$p_n = x_n \cos \alpha + y_n \cos \beta + z_n \cos \gamma - p,$$

so that by simple addition

$$\sum_{i=1}^{n} m_i p_i = \left(\sum_{i=1}^{n} m_i x_i \right) \cos \alpha + \left(\sum_{i=1}^{n} m_i y_i \right) \cos \beta + \left(\sum_{i=1}^{n} m_i z_i \right) \cos \gamma - \left(\sum_{i=1}^{n} m_i \right) p$$
$$= M\bar{x} \cos \alpha + M\bar{y} \cos \beta + M\bar{z} \cos \gamma - Mp$$
$$= M(\bar{x} \cos \alpha + \bar{y} \cos \beta + \bar{z} \cos \gamma - p) = M\bar{p}.$$

The point C is called the *centroid* (also called *center of mass*, or *center of gravity*). Hence:

The centroid of a mass is a point such that the first moment of the mass with respect to any plane is the same as if the whole mass were concentrated at that point.

The first moment of a mass with respect to any plane through the centroid is zero.

In the determination of centroids, the following considerations are often useful (the first two apply only to homogeneous masses):

(a) *If the body has a geometrical center, that point is the centroid.*

(b) *Any plane or line of symmetry must contain the centroid.*

(c) *If the body consists of several portions for each of which the centroid can be found, each portion may be imagined concentrated at its centroid for the sole purpose of computing first moments.*

In many applications, we are concerned with centroids of purely geometric figures (volumes, areas, lines), *no idea of mass being involved.* However, it is unnecessary to write out a separate theory for such cases; the above discussion applies to plane areas, for instance, if we merely replace the word "mass" throughout by "area." To see this, note that for a homogeneous body of given size and shape, both the mass and its moment with respect to any plane are proportional to the density δ. Hence, in the formulas for $\bar{x}$, $\bar{y}$, $\bar{z}$, the factor δ cancels out from both members, leaving the coordinates of the centroid independent of the density. We may therefore take $\delta = 1$, so that the "mass" is numerically equal to the area.

284. *Centroid of a System of Particles*

Combining (1), § 282, with (1), § 283, we see that the coordinates of the centroid of a *system of particles* are given by the formulas

$$M\bar{x} = \sum_{i=1}^{n} m_i x_i, \qquad M\bar{y} = \sum_{i=1}^{n} m_i y_i, \qquad M\bar{z} = \sum_{i=1}^{n} m_i z_i.$$

By use of (c), § 283, problems involving distributed masses may frequently be reduced to consideration of a set of particles, as in the following examples.

Example (a). Find the centroid of a metal plate having the shape shown in Figure 282 (or, what amounts to the same thing, the centroid of the area itself).

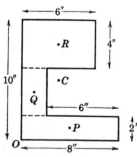

Figure 282

Dividing the area into rectangles by the dotted lines, we have 16 units at P: (4, 1), 8 units at Q: (1, 4), and 24 units at R: (3, 8). Hence

$$M\bar{x} = 16 \cdot 4 + 8 \cdot 1 + 24 \cdot 3 = 144,$$
$$\bar{x} = \tfrac{144}{48} = 3,$$

$$M\bar{y} = 16 \cdot 1 + 8 \cdot 4 + 24 \cdot 8 = 240,$$
$$\bar{y} = \tfrac{240}{48} = 5.$$

In problems of this type, mistakes are easy to make. The danger is greatly reduced if we draw the figure to scale on coordinate paper. In most cases, the centroid can be fairly accurately located by estimate. A very valuable rough check is obtained if in each problem we *compare our answer with the estimate*; if a mistake of any great magnitude has been made, it will certainly be evident.

It is frequently convenient to adopt the fiction of *negative mass*. That this is allowable is clear; for, our theory nowhere requires that M be positive.

Example (*b*). Find the centroid of a square plate with a square cut out of one corner.

Place the axes as shown. We might consider the figure as composed of two rectangles $C'B'DC$, $A'ABD$; but the algebra is much simpler if we consider it as a square plate $OABC$, together with a plate $OA'B'C'$ of numerically equal but negative density:

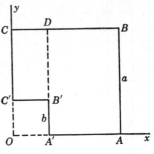

Figure 283

$$M\bar{x} = M\bar{y} = a^2 \cdot \tfrac{1}{2}a - b^2 \cdot \tfrac{1}{2}b,$$
$$\bar{x} = \bar{y} = \frac{a^3 - b^3}{2(a^2 - b^2)} = \frac{a^2 + ab + b^2}{2(a + b)}.$$

EXERCISES

In Exs. 1–6, find the centroid of the given system.

1. Equal masses at $(3, 0)$, $(1, 2)$, $(4, 1)$, $(-3, -3)$.   *Ans.* $(\tfrac{5}{4}, 0)$.
2. Equal masses at $(0, 0)$, $(0, 3)$, $(2, 1)$, $(-4, -5)$.   *Ans.* $(-\tfrac{1}{2}, -\tfrac{1}{4})$.
3. Masses of 1, 2, 4, 5 units at $(-3, 2)$, $(2, 0)$, $(2, 4)$, $(-1, -2)$ respectively.   *Ans.* $(\tfrac{1}{3}, \tfrac{2}{3})$.
4. Masses of 2, 3, 3, 4 units at $(2, -1)$, $(-1, 1)$, $(3, -3)$, $(-1, 5)$ respectively.   *Ans.* $(\tfrac{1}{2}, 1)$.
5. Masses of 1, 3, 4 units at $(0, -3, -1)$, $(4, 5, 3)$, $(1, -3, -4)$ respectively.   *Ans.* $(2, 0, -1)$.
6. Masses of 2, 3, 4 units at $(4, \tfrac{1}{2}, 1)$, $(3, 4, 0)$, $(-2, -1, 4)$ respectively.   *Ans.* $(1, 1, 2)$.

7. Two posts of equal radius, 6 ft. and 4 ft. tall, stand upright 5 ft. apart. Find the centroid.   *Ans.* 2 ft. from taller post, 2.6 ft. above the ground.
8. Two posts of equal radius, 7 ft. and 3 ft. tall, stand upright 20 ft. apart. Find the centroid.   *Ans.* 6 ft. from taller post, 2.9 ft. above the ground.
9. Show that the centroid of two particles divides the line joining them into segments inversely proportional to the masses.
10. Show that the centroid of three equal particles lies at the intersection of the medians of the triangle having the three points as vertices. (Deduce from Ex. 9.)
11. A slender rod 40 in. long is bent so as to form a right angle. If the segments are 8 in. and 32 in. long, find the centroid.   *Ans.* Coordinates in inches relative to the corner: $(12.8, 0.8)$.
12. Three rods, of lengths 10, 10, 16 ft., form a triangle. Find the centroid.   *Ans.* On the altitude to the longest side, $\tfrac{5}{3}$ ft. from that side.

13. Weights of 2, 3, 7, and 8 lb. rest on the four corners of a table 5 ft. square. Find the centroid of the four weights.

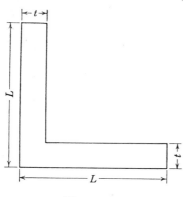

Figure 284

14. Find the centroid of a cross-section of an angle-iron (Figure 284), the outside flange width L being 3 in. and the thickness $\frac{1}{2}$ in.

15. Solve Ex. 14, if the flange width remains 3 in., and the thickness is increased to 1 in.

16. For the angle-iron of Figure 284, for what proportions does the centroid lie at the inner corner?   *Ans.* $L = 2.62t$.

17. Find the centroid of a nonsymmetrical angle-iron, like that of Figure 284, except that one flange is 3 in. wide and $\frac{1}{2}$ in. thick, the other 4 in. wide and $\frac{3}{4}$ in. thick.

18. The legs of a table are 2 ft. 6 in. long; the legs weigh 5 lb. each, the top 10 lb. Find the centroid.   *Ans.* 20 in. above the floor.

19. If in Ex. 18, the top of the table is taken as 1 in. thick, how much does the centroid rise?   *Ans.* $\frac{1}{6}$ in.

20. From a square of side $2a$ a circle of radius $b(b < a)$ is stamped out. If the circle is tangent to two sides of the square, find the centroid (tangents as axes).

$$Ans. \ \bar{x} = \bar{y} = \frac{4a^3 - \pi b^3}{4a^2 - \pi b^2}.$$

21. Check the answer to Example (*a*) by solving in another way (different subdivision).

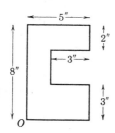

Figure 285

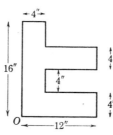

Figure 286

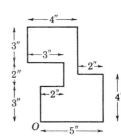

Figure 287

22. Find the centroid of the area in Figure 285. Check by solving in two ways.

23. Find in two ways the centroid of the area in Figure 286.

24. In Figure 287, find the centroid.   *Ans.* $(\frac{125}{62}, \frac{231}{62})$.

25. The base of a box is 4 by 3 ft.; the depth is 2 ft. If there is no top, find the centroid.   *Ans.* 0.7 ft. from the base.

26. Solve Ex. 25 if the bottom is twice as heavy, per unit area, as the sides.   *Ans.* 0.54 ft. from the base.

27. A sphere of radius 3 in. rests on a cylinder of radius 4 in. and height 8 in. Find the height of the centroid.   *Ans.* 5.54 in.

28. Find the centroid of a cylindrical basin of radius 4 in. and depth 3 in.

29. Solve Ex. 28 if the bottom is twice as heavy, per unit area, as the sides.   *Ans.* $\frac{9}{14}$ in. above the base.

30. A circular disk of radius b, density k, is inset in a disk of radius a, density 1. If the two circles are tangent, find the centroid.

$$Ans. \text{ From point of tangency, } \bar{x} = \frac{a^3 + (k-1)b^3}{a^2 + (k-1)b^2}.$$

31. Solve Ex. 30 if the circumference of the smaller passes through the center of the larger ($2b < a$).

$$Ans. \text{ From center, } \bar{x} = \frac{(k-1)b^3}{a^2 + (k-1)b^2}.$$

32. A sphere of radius a and density 2 is imbedded in a sphere of radius $2a$ and density 3, the two spheres being tangent (internally). Find the centroid.

285. *Determination of Centroids by Integration*

To find the centroid of a continuous mass, we must as a rule resort to integration. In the most general case, multiple integrals (Chapters 37–38) must be used, but in many cases of practical importance the result may be obtained by methods analogous to those of Chapter 33.

In the following discussion we restrict ourselves to one-, two-, or three-dimensional bodies of the forms considered in Chapter 33. Nevertheless the formulas obtained are applicable, with proper interpretation, to *all* masses. Let us choose, as in that chapter, a suitable geometrical element (of volume, area, or length), and denote the mass contained in this element by Δm_i. Let x_i, y_i, z_i be the *coordinates of the centroid of* Δm_i. Then the product $x_i \, \Delta m_i$ is the simple mass moment of Δm_i with respect to the yz-plane (or the y-axis, for a plane mass in the xy-plane), and the limit of the sum of all such moments is the moment of the whole mass. In this way we obtain the following formulas:

$$(1) \qquad M\bar{x} = \lim_{n\to\infty} \sum_{i=1}^{n} x_i \, \Delta m_i = \int x_c \, dm,$$

$$(2) \qquad M\bar{y} = \lim_{n\to\infty} \sum_{i=1}^{n} y_i \, \Delta m_i = \int y_c \, dm,$$

$$(3) \qquad M\bar{z} = \lim_{n\to\infty} \sum_{i=1}^{n} z_i \, \Delta m_i = \int z_c \, dm,$$

where x_c, y_c, z_c are the *coordinates of the centroid of the element.*

The subscript is inserted to make sure that we never forget the meaning of the multipliers x_c, y_c, z_c. Of course in any problem these variables, as well as the mass element, must be expressed in terms of some one variable.

As usual, we have omitted writing, in equations (1)–(3), those terms which will drop out in the limit as $n \to \infty$. For instance, it often happens that the x-coordinate is, exactly, $x_i + \frac{1}{2}\Delta x$, so that the first limit above is

$$M\bar{x} = \operatorname*{Lim}_{n\to\infty} \sum_{i=1}^{n} (x_i + \tfrac{1}{2}\Delta x)\, \Delta m_i.$$

But

$$\operatorname*{Lim}_{n\to\infty} \sum_{i=1}^{n} \Delta m_i = \int dm = M$$

and $\Delta x \to 0$ as $n \to \infty$, so that

$$\operatorname*{Lim}_{n\to\infty} \sum_{i=1}^{n} \tfrac{1}{2}\Delta x\, \Delta m_i = 0.$$

286. *Centroid of a Plane Area: Rectangular Coordinates*

In any system of coordinates, formulas (1) and (2) above become, for a plane area,

(1) $$A\bar{x} = \int x_c\, dA, \qquad A\bar{y} = \int y_c\, dA.$$

In rectangular coordinates, the area element dA is, of course, the usual rectangular element.

Example. Find the centroid of the area in the first quadrant bounded by the parabola $y^2 = 4ax$ and its latus rectum.

Figure 288

With the vertical element, the area is

$$A = \int_0^a y\, dx = 2\sqrt{a} \int_0^a \sqrt{x}\, dx = \tfrac{4}{3}a^2.$$

The centroid C of the element is $(x, \tfrac{1}{2}y)$: by (1),

$$A\bar{x} = \int_0^a xy\, dx = 2\sqrt{a} \int_0^a x^{\frac{3}{2}}\, dx = \tfrac{4}{5}a^3,$$

$$A\bar{y} = \int_0^a \tfrac{1}{2}y \cdot y\, dx = 2a \int_0^a x\, dx = a^3.$$

Thus the coordinates of the centroid K are

$$\bar{x} = \tfrac{3}{5}a, \qquad \bar{y} = \tfrac{3}{4}a,$$

which checks very well by estimate.*

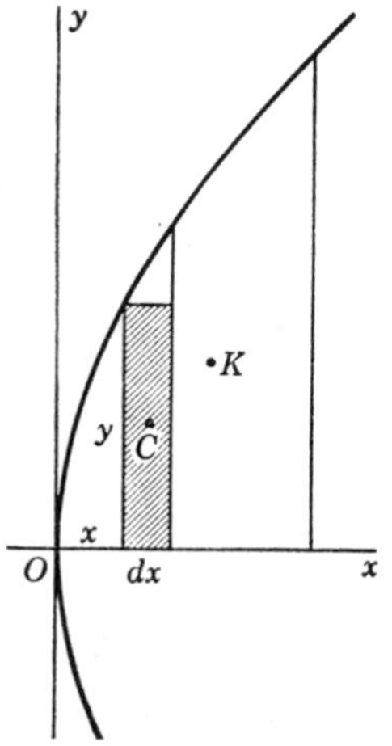

* The student is strongly advised not to write out formulas for $\bar{x}$, $\bar{y}$, as quotients of integrals. Aside from clumsiness of form, the continual turning back and forth from one integral to the other wastes time and increases the likelihood of mistake. The best technique is to take up in turn the three tasks (of finding A, $A\bar{x}$, $A\bar{y}$) and complete each before the next is started.

Anyone who thoroughly understands this simple example should have little difficulty, either here or later, with the subject of centroids. One has not fully mastered it, however, until he sees clearly that this example is exactly the same, in kind, as Example (*a*), § 284. There, we replaced three rectangles by equivalent particles at the respective centroids, and found the total moment by simple arithmetic; here, we replace *n* rectangles by particles in exactly the same way and find the limit of the sum of elementary moments by integration.

We shall have occasion to use the following theorem.

THEOREM 56.   *The centroid of a triangular area is at the intersection of the medians.*

The proof of this theorem is a very easy problem in integration (Ex. 9 below). Also, a special device may be noted. Divide the triangle into strips parallel to the base. The centroid of each strip is in the median, so that the same must be true for the centroid of the whole. And by symmetry of argument, if the centroid lies in one median, it must lie in all three.

Figure 289

EXERCISES

In Exs. 1–31, find the centroid of the area. (Where *A* is given, it has been found in a previous exercise.) In each case, draw a figure and estimate the coordinates of the centroid.

1. A semicircular area.   Solve in two ways.
$$Ans. \ \bar{x} = \frac{4a}{3\pi}.$$

2. An elliptic quadrant.   Solve in two ways.
$$Ans. \ \left(\frac{4a}{3\pi}, \frac{4b}{3\pi}\right).$$

3. Ex. 2, using the equations $x = a \cos \varphi$, $y = b \sin \varphi$.

4. The area in the first quadrant under that arch of $y = \sin \frac{1}{2}x$ nearest the *y*-axis. ($A = 4$.)
$$Ans. \ (\pi, \tfrac{1}{8}\pi).$$

5. The area in the first quadrant under the curve $y = 4 - x^2$.   Find each coordinate in two ways.

6. The area bounded by the curve $y = 2(1 + x^3)$ and the coordinate axes.
$$Ans. \ (-\tfrac{2}{5}, \tfrac{6}{7}).$$

7. The area bounded by the curve $y^2 = 4ax$, the *x*-axis, and the line $x = x_1$. ($A = \frac{2}{3}x_1y_1.$)
$$Ans. \ (\tfrac{3}{5}x_1, \tfrac{3}{8}y_1).$$

8. The area bounded by the curve $x^2 = 4ay$, the *x*-axis, and the line $x = x_1$. Find each coordinate in two ways.
$$Ans. \ (\tfrac{3}{4}x_1, \tfrac{3}{10}y_1).$$

9. A triangle. (Solve for a right triangle by integration; deduce the general answer.)

10. The area in the first quadrant bounded by the curve $y = e^{-x}$, the axes, and the ordinate $x = \ln 5$.
$$Ans. \ (1 - \tfrac{1}{4}\ln 5, \tfrac{3}{10}).$$

11. The whole area in the first quadrant between the curve $y = e^{-x}$ and the axes.
$$Ans. \ (1, \tfrac{1}{4}).$$

12. The area bounded by the curve $2y^2 + 2y - x - 2 = 0$ and the line $x = 2y$. $(A = \frac{8}{3}.)$ *Ans.* $(-\frac{4}{5}, 0)$.

13. The area bounded by the curve $y = \ln x$, the x-axis, and the line $x = e$. $(A = 1.)$

$$Ans. \left(\frac{e^2 + 1}{4}, \frac{e - 2}{2}\right).$$

14. The area bounded by the curve $y^2 = \dfrac{1}{(1 - x)^3}$, the y-axis, and the line $x = -1$. $A = 2(2 - \sqrt{2})$.   *Ans.* $(1 - \sqrt{2}, 0)$.

15. One arch of the cycloid $x = a(\theta - \sin \theta)$, $y = a(1 - \cos \theta)$. $(A = 3\pi a^2.)$ *Ans.* $(\pi a, \frac{5}{6}a)$.

16. The area between the curves $2y = x^2$, $y = x^3$.   *Ans.* $(\frac{3}{10}, \frac{3}{70})$.

17. The area in the first quadrant under the curve $y = \dfrac{a^3}{x^2 + a^2}$. $(A = \frac{1}{2}\pi a^2.)$

                                                   Ans. Nonexistent.

18. The area in the first quadrant under the curve $y = \dfrac{x}{(1 + x^2)^2}$. $(A = \frac{1}{2}.)$

19. The area bounded by the parabola $y^2 = 4ax$, its axis prolonged, and the tangent at the upper end of the latus rectum.   *Ans.* $(-\frac{1}{5}a, \frac{1}{2}a)$.

20. The area bounded by the parabola $x^2 - 4x + y = 5$ and the lines $x = 0$, $y = 9$.   *Ans.* $(\frac{1}{2}, \frac{39}{5})$.

21. The fourth-quadrant area bounded by the parabola $y^2 + 2x - 2y = 3$. Obtain each coordinate in two ways.   *Ans.* $(0.53, -0.35)$.

22. The area bounded by the curve $xy^3 = 1$ and the lines $x = 0$, $y = 1$.

                                                   Ans. $(\frac{1}{5}, 2)$.

23. The area between the curve $y = xe^z$ and its asymptote.   *Ans.* $(-2, -\frac{1}{8})$.

24. The area in the first quadrant bounded by the hypocycloid $x = a \cos^3 t$, $y = a \sin^3 t$. $(A = \frac{3}{32}\pi a^2.)$

$$Ans. \; \bar{x} = \bar{y} = \frac{256a}{315\pi}.$$

25. The area in the first quadrant between the two parabolas $x^2 - 4ay + a^2 = 0$, $x^2 = 2ay$.   *Ans.* $(\frac{3}{8}a, \frac{1}{5}a)$.

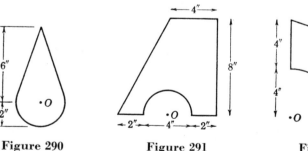 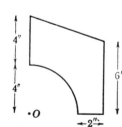

Figure 290   Figure 291   Figure 292

26. The area in Figure 290.

27. The area in Figure 291.

28. The area in Figure 292.

29. The area of the loop of the curve $y^2 = x(1 - x^2)^2$. $(A = \frac{16}{21}.)$ *Ans.* $(\frac{7}{15}, 0)$.

30. The area in the first quadrant enclosed by the curve $a^2y^2 = x^2(a^2 - x^2)$ and the axes. $\left(A = \dfrac{a^2}{3}. \right)$ *Ans.* $\left(\dfrac{3\pi a}{16}, \dfrac{a}{5} \right)$.

31. The area of the loop of the curve $y^2 = x^2(1 - x)$. $(A = \frac{8}{15}.)$ *Ans.* $(\frac{4}{7}, 0)$.

32. Devise a method for finding graphically the centroid of any quadrilateral.

287. *Centroid of a Plane Area: Polar Coordinates*

In a definite integration, if we always make sure that the *limit of the sum of elements* represents the quantity required, nothing else matters.   In two different problems using the same coordinates and dealing with the same kind of physical entity (e.g., a plane area), or even at different stages of the same problem, we may at any time shift from one type of element to another, according to convenience.

Figure 293 represents an enlargement of a single element of polar area. The area of the *sector* is $\frac{1}{2}r_i^2 \, \Delta\theta$.   We may adjust the technique of § 286 to the use of polar coordinates once we have the location of the centroid of the sector in Figure 293.   Actually, we shall first obtain the centroid of the sector in Figure 294 and then find the centroid in Figure 293 by rotation of axes.

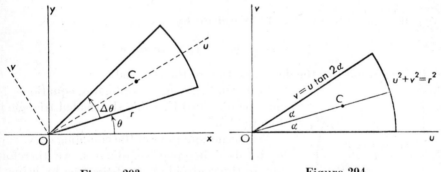

Figure 293   **Figure 294**

In Figure 294 the area is $A = \alpha r^2$, and we know that the centroid of the sector lies on the line of symmetry.   Hence $\bar{u} = \bar{v} \cot \alpha$.   By the methods of § 286,

(1) $$A\bar{v} = \int_0^{r \sin 2\alpha} v[(r^2 - v^2)^{\frac{1}{2}} - v \cot 2\alpha] \, dv.$$

The integrations to be performed in (1) are simple.   The student should show that

$$\bar{v} = \frac{r}{3\alpha} [1 - \cos^3 2\alpha - \sin^2 2\alpha \cos 2\alpha]$$

$$= \frac{r(1 - \cos 2\alpha)}{3\alpha} = \frac{2r \sin^2 \alpha}{3\alpha}.$$

Since $\bar{u} = \bar{v} \cot \alpha$, we may now write the coordinates of the centroid in Figure 294:

(2) $$\bar{u} = \frac{2}{3} r \cos \alpha \, \frac{\sin \alpha}{\alpha}, \qquad \bar{v} = \frac{2}{3} r \sin \alpha \, \frac{\sin \alpha}{\alpha}.$$

To obtain Figure 294 from Figure 293, choose $\alpha = \frac{1}{2}\Delta\theta$ and rotate the axes through the angle $(\theta + \frac{1}{2}\Delta\theta)$. By the rotation formulas of § 167, it follows that the centroid of the sector in Figure 293 has the coordinates

(3) $$\bar{x} = \bar{u} \cos (\theta + \tfrac{1}{2}\Delta\theta) - \bar{v} \sin (\theta + \tfrac{1}{2}\Delta\theta),$$
(4) $$\bar{y} = \bar{u} \sin (\theta + \tfrac{1}{2}\Delta\theta) + \bar{v} \cos (\theta + \tfrac{1}{2}\Delta\theta).$$

Because of (2) with $\alpha = \frac{1}{2}\Delta\theta$, equations (3) and (4) lead to

(5) $$\bar{x} = \frac{2}{3} r \cos (\theta + \Delta\theta) \, \frac{\sin \frac{1}{2}\Delta\theta}{\frac{1}{2}\Delta\theta},$$

(6) $$\bar{y} = \frac{2}{3} r \sin (\theta + \Delta\theta) \, \frac{\sin \frac{1}{2}\Delta\theta}{\frac{1}{2}\Delta\theta}.$$

Since

$$\lim_{\Delta\theta\to0} \frac{\sin \frac{1}{2}\Delta\theta}{\frac{1}{2}\Delta\theta} = 1,$$

we can replace the $\bar{x}$ and $\bar{y}$ of (5) and (6) by

(7) $$x_c = \tfrac{2}{3} r \cos \theta, \qquad y_c = \tfrac{2}{3} r \sin \theta$$

in the integrands for the determination of the centroid.

Note that the same coordinates, equations (7), may be obtained by using the shaded triangle in Figure 295.

When the equations of the bounding curves are to be used in polar coordinates, we therefore obtain the centroid $(\bar{x}, \bar{y})$ of the area by using

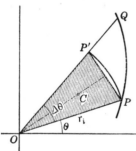

(8) $$A = \tfrac{1}{2} \int_\alpha^\beta r^2 \, d\theta,$$

$$A\bar{x} = \tfrac{1}{2} \int_\alpha^\beta \tfrac{2}{3} r \cos \theta \cdot r^2 \, d\theta,$$

Figure 295

$$A\bar{y} = \tfrac{1}{2} \int_\alpha^\beta \tfrac{2}{3} r \sin \theta \cdot r^2 \, d\theta.$$

Example. Using polar coordinates, find the centroid of the area between the curves $x^2 = ay$, $y = x$.

In polar coordinates, the equation of the parabola is

$$r^2 \cos^2 \theta = ar \sin \theta, \qquad r = a \tan \theta \sec \theta :$$

$$A = \tfrac{1}{2} \int_0^{\frac{\pi}{4}} r^2 \, d\theta = \tfrac{1}{2}a^2 \int_0^{\frac{\pi}{4}} \tan^2 \theta \, \sec^2 \theta \, d\theta = \tfrac{1}{6}a^2 \left[\tan^3 \theta \right]_0^{\frac{\pi}{4}} = \tfrac{1}{6}a^2;$$

$$A\bar{x} = \tfrac{1}{2} \int_0^{\frac{\pi}{4}} \tfrac{2}{3}r \cos \theta \cdot r^2 \, d\theta$$

$$A\bar{x} = \tfrac{1}{3}a^3 \int_0^{\frac{\pi}{4}} \tan^3 \theta \, \sec^2 \theta \, d\theta$$

$$= \tfrac{1}{12}a^3,$$

$$\bar{x} = \tfrac{1}{2}a;$$

$$A\bar{y} = \tfrac{1}{2} \int_0^{\frac{\pi}{4}} \tfrac{2}{3}r \sin \theta \cdot r^2 \, d\theta$$

$$= \tfrac{1}{3}a^3 \int_0^{\frac{\pi}{4}} \tan^4 \theta \, \sec^2 \theta \, d\theta$$

$$= \tfrac{1}{15}a^3,$$

$$\bar{y} = \tfrac{2}{5}a.$$

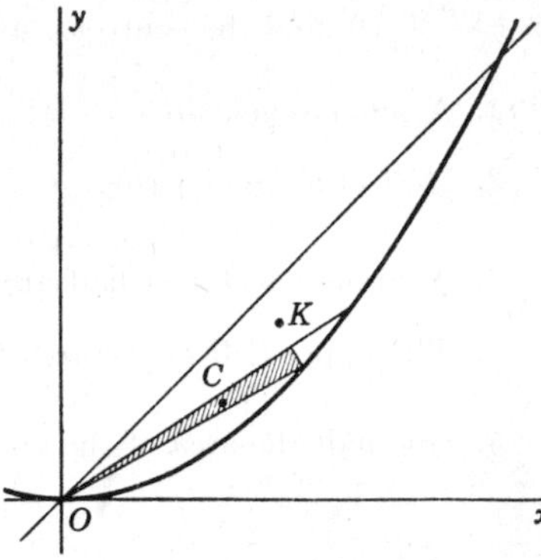

Figure 296

288. *A Theorem of Pappus*

The following theorem, known as the *Second Proposition of Pappus*, is useful in a variety of ways (see also Ex. 20, page 499):

THEOREM 57. *The volume of any solid of revolution is equal to the generating area times the circumference of the circle described by the centroid of the area.**

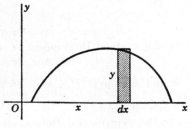

Figure 297

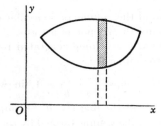

Figure 298

For definiteness, take the axis of revolution as x-axis, and suppose first that this forms part of the boundary of the rotating area (Figure 297). The proof is very easy. By §§ 275, 286,

$$V = \pi \int_a^b y^2 \, dx, \qquad A\bar{y} = \int_a^b \tfrac{1}{2}y \cdot y \, dx,$$

so that

$$V = 2\pi A\bar{y} = A \cdot 2\pi\bar{y}.$$

* The case in which the axis of revolution crosses the generating area is excluded.

But this last formula, translated into words, is the theorem. The proof is readily extended to cover the situation shown in Figure 298.

EXERCISES

In Exs. 1–10, find the centroid, using polar coordinates.

1. A semicircular area.

2. Half of a circular ring. $\qquad$ *Ans.* $\bar{x} = \dfrac{4}{3\pi} \cdot \dfrac{a^2 + ab + b^2}{a + b}$.

3. A circular sector of half-angle α. $\qquad$ *Ans.* $\bar{x} = \dfrac{2}{3} r \dfrac{\sin \alpha}{\alpha}$.

4. The upper half of the area bounded by the curve $r^2 = a^2 \cos \theta$. $(A = a^2.)$

Ans. $\bar{y} = \frac{4}{15} a$.

5. One-half the area of the curve $r = a(1 - \sin \theta)$. $(A = \frac{3}{4}\pi a^2.)$

Ans. $\left(\dfrac{16a}{9\pi}, \dfrac{-5a}{6} \right)$.

6. One quadrant of the area of the curve $r = 2a \cos^2 \theta$. $(A = \frac{3}{8}\pi a^2.)$

Ans. $\left(\dfrac{1024a}{315\pi}, \dfrac{64a}{21\pi} \right)$.

7. The area bounded by the curves $y = 2x$, $y^2 = 4ax$. $\qquad$ *Ans.* $(\frac{2}{5}a, a)$.

8. The area in the first quadrant bounded by the curves $y = x^3$, $y = 2x$. $(A = 1.)$

9. One loop of the curve $r = a \cos 2\theta$. $(A = \frac{1}{8}\pi a^2.)$

10. The area between the curves $x^2 = ay$, $y^2 = ax$. (Deduce from the example directly above these exercises.)

In Exs. 11–21, use the Second Proposition of Pappus.

11. Find the volume of a circular cylinder.

12. Find the volume of a torus. $\qquad$ *Ans.* $2\pi^2 a^2 b$.

13. Find the volume generated by rotating an ellipse about the tangent at one end of the minor axis. $\qquad$ *Ans.* $2\pi^2 ab^2$.

14. The ellipse $\dfrac{x^2}{a^2} + \dfrac{y^2}{b^2} = 1$, in which $a \geqq b$, and the circle $x^2 + y^2 = ab$ are rotated about the line $x = a$. Compare the volumes obtained.

15. Find the volume formed by rotating about Oy the quadrilateral whose vertices are $(1, 4)$, $(13, 9)$, $(18, -3)$, $(6, -8)$. $\qquad$ *Ans.* 3211π.

16. Find the volume formed by rotating about Ox the area bounded by the lines $3x + 5y + 14 = 0$, $2y = x + 1$, $3x + 5y + 25 = 0$, $x - 2y = 10$. (Do not find the vertices.) $\qquad$ *Ans.* 66π.

17. Find the centroid of a right triangle.

18. Find the centroid of a semicircular area.

19. Find the centroid of half of a circular ring. (Cf. Ex. 2.)

20. Find the centroid of the area in Figure 291.

21. Find the centroid of the area in Figure 292.

22. Prove the Second Proposition of Pappus by another method.

23. Prove the Second Proposition for the case shown in Figure 298.

289. *Centroid of a Solid of Revolution*

Since the centroid of a solid of revolution lies on the axis, a single coordinate determines its position. If, say, the revolution takes place around the x-axis, the general formulas of § 285 reduce to

$$V \bar{x} = \int x_c \, dV,$$

where dV is a disk, ring, or shell, according to convenience, and x_c is the x-coordinate of the centroid of the volume element.

Example (a). The area bounded by the parabola $y^2 = 4ax$, the x-axis, and the latus rectum revolves about the x-axis. Find the centroid of the solid generated.

Cutting the generating area into rectangles as shown, we have as the element a circular disk of volume $\pi y^2 \, dx$. The centroid C of the element is at its center, i.e., on the x-axis at a distance x from O. Hence

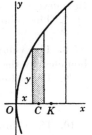

$$V\bar{x} = \pi \int_0^a xy^2 \, dx = 4\pi a \int_0^a x^2 \, dx = \tfrac{4}{3}\pi a^4.$$

By Example (a), § 275, $V = 2\pi a^3$, so that

$$\bar{x} = \frac{\tfrac{4}{3}\pi a^4}{2\pi a^3} = \frac{2}{3}\, a.$$

Figure 299

Example (b). Solve Example (a) by another method.

With the cylindrical shell as element,

$$dV = 2\pi y(a - x) \, dy.$$

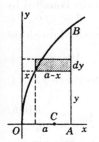

By the mid-point formula of analytic geometry,

$$x_c = \tfrac{1}{2}(a + x).$$

Thus

$$V\bar{x} = 2\pi \cdot \tfrac{1}{2} \int_0^{2a} y(a^2 - x^2) \, dy.$$

Figure 300   Putting $y \, dy = 2a \, dx$ and changing limits, we get

$$V\bar{x} = 2\pi a \int_0^a (a^2 - x^2) \, dx = 2\pi a \left[a^2 x - \tfrac{1}{3}x^3 \right]_0^a = \tfrac{4}{3}\pi a^4,$$

so that

$$\bar{x} = \frac{\tfrac{4}{3}\pi a^4}{2\pi a^3} = \frac{2}{3}\, a,$$

as before.

EXERCISES

In Exs. 1–28, find the centroid.

1. A hemisphere of radius R. Solve in two ways.

Ans. At distance $\frac{3}{8}R$ from the center.

2. The volume formed by revolving about Oy the area in the first quadrant bounded by $y^2 = 4ax$, $y = 0$, $x = a$. Solve in two ways.   *Ans.* $(0, \frac{5}{6}a, 0)$.

3. The volume formed by rotating the area of Ex. 2 about the latus rectum. Solve in two ways.   *Ans.* $(a, \frac{5}{8}a, 0)$.

4. The upper half of the oblate spheroid formed by revolving the ellipse $\dfrac{x^2}{a^2} + \dfrac{y^2}{b^2} = 1$ about Oy. Solve in two ways.   *Ans.* $(0, \frac{3}{8}b, 0)$.

5. A circular cone. Solve in two ways.   *Ans. At distance $\frac{1}{4}h$ from the base.*

6. The volume formed by revolving about Ox the area enclosed by the loop of the curve $y^2 = x^2(1 - x)$.   *Ans.* $(\frac{3}{5}, 0, 0)$.

7. The volume formed by revolving about Oy the top half of the loop of Ex. 6.

Ans. $(0, \frac{21}{128}, 0)$.

8. The volume formed by revolving about Ox the area in the first quadrant bounded by the curve $y^2 = x^2(1 - x^2)$ and the x-axis.   *Ans.* $(\frac{5}{8}, 0, 0)$.

9. The volume formed by revolving about Oy the area of Ex. 8.

$$\textit{Ans.}\ \left(0, \frac{2}{3\pi}, 0\right).$$

10. The volume formed by revolving about the line $x = -1$ the area bounded by $y = x^3$, $y = 0$, $x = 1$.   *Ans.* $(-1, \frac{25}{84}, 0)$.

11. The volume generated by revolving about Ox the area in the second quadrant under the curve $y = e^x$. ($V = \frac{1}{2}\pi$.)   *Ans.* $\bar{x} = -\frac{1}{2}$.

12. The volume generated by revolving about Oy the area in the second quadrant under the curve $y = e^x$. ($V = 2\pi$.)   *Ans.* $\bar{y} = \frac{1}{8}$.

13. The volume formed by revolving about the line $x = 2a$ the area bounded by that line, the x-axis, and the curve $a^2y = x^3$. ($V = \frac{16}{5}\pi a^3$.)   *Ans.* $\bar{y} = \frac{10}{7}a$.

14. The volume generated by revolving about Ox the area in the third quadrant under the curve $y^2 = \dfrac{1}{(1 - x)^3}$.   *Ans.* $\bar{x} = -1$.

15. The volume formed by revolving about Ox the area under the curve $xy = 1$, from $x = 1$ to $x = b$. What happens as b increases?

$$\textit{Ans.}\ \bar{x} = \frac{b \ln b}{b - 1}.$$

16. One-half of a torus (cut by a plane perpendicular to the axis). Solve in two ways. ($V = \pi^2 a^2 b$.)

$$\textit{Ans.}\ \bar{y} = \frac{4a}{3\pi}.$$

17. The volume formed by rotating about Oy the area in the third quadrant bounded by the curve $y^2 = x + 1$. Solve in two ways.   *Ans.* $\bar{y} = -\frac{5}{16}$.

18. The volume formed by rotating the area of Ex. 17 about Ox. Solve in two ways.   *Ans.* $\bar{x} = -\frac{1}{3}$.

19. The volume generated by revolving about the directrix the area in the first

quadrant bounded by the parabola $y^2 = 4ax$, its axis, and its latus rectum.
($V = \frac{64}{15}\pi a^3$.)   *Ans.* $\bar{y} = \frac{25}{32}a$.

20. The volume generated by revolving about Ox the area bounded by $y = \ln x$, $y = 0$, $x = e$.

$$Ans.\ \bar{x} = \frac{e^2 - 1}{4(e - 2)}.$$

21. The volume generated by revolving the area of Ex. 20 about Oy.

$$Ans.\ \bar{y} = \frac{e^2 - 1}{2(e^2 + 1)}.$$

22. The volume cut off from the hyperboloid $x^2 + y^2 - z^2 + a^2 = 0$ by the plane $z = 2a$.   *Ans.* $\bar{z} = \frac{27}{16}a$.

23. The upper half of the solid bounded by the surfaces $x^2 + y^2 = 2a^2$, $x^2 + y^2 - z^2 = a^2$.   ($V = \frac{2}{3}\pi a^3$.)   *Ans.* $\bar{z} = \frac{3}{8}a$.

24. The upper half of the solid bounded by the surfaces $x^2 + y^2 - z^2 = a^2$, $x^2 + y^2 = 2z^2$.   ($V = \frac{2}{3}\pi a^3$.)

$$Ans.\ \bar{z} = \frac{3a}{8}.$$

25. The volume inside the surfaces $x^2 + y^2 = z^2$, $x^2 + y^2 + az = 2a^2$. ($V = \frac{5}{6}\pi a^3$.)   *Ans.* $\bar{z} = \frac{11}{10}a$.

26. The volume bounded by the surfaces $x^2 + y^2 = 3a^2 - 2az$, $x^2 + y^2 = az$.
                                                               Ans. $\bar{z} = \frac{5}{6}a$.

27. The volume formed by revolving about Ox the area in the first quadrant between the parabolas $x^2 = 2ay$, $x^2 = 4ay - a^2$. ($V = \frac{1}{15}\pi a^3$.)

$$Ans.\ \bar{x} = \frac{15a}{32}.$$

28. The volume formed by revolving the area of Ex. 27 about Oy. ($V = \frac{1}{8}\pi a^3$.)
                                              Ans. $\bar{y} = \frac{1}{4}a$.

29. A top consists of a cone of radius 2 in. and height 2 in., surmounted by a cylinder of radius $\frac{1}{4}$ in. and height 2 in.   Find the centroid.
                                     Ans. 1.57 in. from vertex of cone.

30. A wooden buoy consists of a cone and hemisphere placed base to base; the common radius is 2 ft., the height of the cone 6 ft.   Find the centroid.
                                        Ans. 5.4 ft. from vertex.

31. Find the centroid of the volume formed by rotating about Oy the area under the curve $y = e^{-\frac{1}{2}x^2}$.   *Ans.* $\bar{y} = \frac{1}{4}$.

32. Solve Ex. 31 by inspection.   (In $V\bar{y}$, put $x^2 = \frac{1}{2}z^2$; compare $V\bar{y}$ and V.)

33. If a plane area, *symmetric with respect to* Oy, rotates about an external line parallel to Oy, show that $\bar{y}$ for the solid thus formed is equal to $\bar{y}$ for the area.   State the result as a general theorem.   Check Ex. 16 above with Ex. 1, page 487.

34. Find the centroid of the solid formed by rotating an isosceles triangle about an external line perpendicular to the base.   (Ex. 33.)

35. Find graphically the centroid of the solid formed by rotating an isosceles trapezoid about an external line perpendicular to the base.   (Ex. 32, page 489, and Ex. 33 above.)

36. If V_x, V_y denote the volumes formed by revolving a plane area (lying all in one quadrant) about Ox and Oy in turn, show that the mass moments $V_x\bar{x}$, $V_y\bar{y}$ are equal.   Check Ex. 16.

290. *Centroids of Miscellaneous Solids*

Example (a). Find the centroid of one-half of the solid in the examples of § 278.

With the triangular element (Figure 278, page 471), we know by § 286 that the centroid of the element is $(x_c, y_c, z_c) \equiv (x, \frac{2}{3}y, \frac{1}{3}z)$. Thus

$$V\bar{x} = \int_0^a x \cdot \tfrac{1}{2}yz \, dx.$$

But $z = y$, $x \, dx = -y \, dy$:

$$V\bar{x} = \tfrac{1}{2}\int_0^a xy^2 \, dx$$

$$= -\tfrac{1}{2}\int_a^0 y^3 \, dy = \tfrac{1}{8}a^4.$$

In § 278 we found $V = \tfrac{1}{3}a^3$, so that

$$\bar{x} = \frac{\tfrac{1}{8}a^4}{\tfrac{1}{3}a^3} = \tfrac{3}{8}a.$$

Next,

$$V\bar{y} = \int_0^a \tfrac{2}{3}y \cdot \tfrac{1}{2}yz \, dx$$

$$= \tfrac{1}{3}\int_0^a y^3 \, dx = \tfrac{1}{3}\int_0^a (a^2 - x^2)^{\frac{3}{2}} \, dx.$$

Putting $x = a \sin \theta$, we find

$$V\bar{y} = \tfrac{1}{16}\pi a^4,$$

$$\bar{y} = \frac{\tfrac{1}{16}\pi a^4}{\tfrac{1}{3}a^3} = \tfrac{3}{16}\pi a.$$

Since for all the elements $z_c = \tfrac{1}{3}z = \tfrac{1}{3}y = \tfrac{1}{2}y_c$,

$$\bar{z} = \tfrac{1}{2}\bar{y} = \tfrac{3}{32}\pi a.$$

Example (b). Solve Example (a) by another method.

For the rectangular element (Figure 279, page 471), the centroid is easily seen to be $(x_c, y_c, z_c) \equiv (\tfrac{1}{2}x, y, \tfrac{1}{2}z)$. Thus

$$V\bar{x} = \int_0^a \tfrac{1}{2}x \cdot xz \, dy = \tfrac{1}{2}\int_0^a x^2y \, dy = -\tfrac{1}{2}\int_a^0 x^3 \, dx,$$

as before. Next,

$$V\bar{y} = \int_0^a y \cdot xz \, dy = \int_0^a y^2x \, dy = \int_0^a y^2 \sqrt{a^2 - y^2} \, dy.$$

Putting $y = a \sin \theta$, we obtain the same result as above.

EXERCISES

Find the centroid of the given solid.

1. An elliptic cone cut off by a right section. $(V = \frac{1}{3}\pi abh.)$ *Ans.* $\bar{z} = \frac{1}{4}h.$

2. The volume cut from the paraboloid $\dfrac{x^2}{a^2} + \dfrac{y^2}{b^2} = \dfrac{z}{c}$ by the plane $z = c$.

$$Ans. \; \bar{z} = \tfrac{2}{3}c.$$

3. The volume in the first octant under the plane $z = y$ and inside the parabolic cylinder $y^2 = 4 - x$. Solve in two ways. $(V = 4.)$ *Ans.* $(\frac{4}{3}, \frac{16}{15}, \frac{8}{15}).$

4. A pyramid with a square base, whose apex lies vertically above one corner of the base.   *Ans.* $(\frac{3}{8}a, \frac{3}{8}a, \frac{1}{4}h).$

5. The volume in the first octant enclosed by the cylinder $y^2 = ax$ and the planes $x = a$, $z = x$. $(V = \frac{2}{5}a^3.)$ *Ans.* $(\frac{5}{7}a, \frac{5}{12}a, \frac{5}{14}a).$

6. The volume in the first octant bounded by the surfaces $y + z = a$, $z^2 = ax$. $(V = \frac{1}{12}a^3.)$

7. The volume in the first octant bounded by the surfaces $x^2 = y + 2z$, $x = 1$. $(V = \frac{1}{20}.)$

8. The volume in the first octant inside the cylinder $y^2 + z^2 = a^2$ and outside the cylinder $y^2 = ax$. $(V = \frac{1}{16}\pi a^3.)$

$$Ans. \; \left(\frac{a}{4}, \frac{32a}{15\pi}, \frac{16a}{15\pi}\right).$$

9. One-eighth of the solid bounded by two equal circular cylinders whose axes intersect at right angles. $(V = \frac{2}{3}a^3.)$ *Ans.* $(\frac{9}{64}\pi a, \frac{9}{64}\pi a, \frac{3}{8}a).$

10. The volume in the first octant bounded by the surfaces $y + z = a$, $x^2 + ay = a^2$. $(V = \frac{2}{5}a^3.)$

11. The volume bounded by the cylinder $x^2 = ay$ and the planes $z = 0$, $y = x$, $y = z$. $(V = \frac{1}{15}a^3.)$

12. The volume in the first octant bounded by the surfaces $yz = z - x$, $z = 1$. Solve in two ways. $(V = \frac{1}{4}.)$

13. The volume in the first octant bounded by the surfaces $y^2 = 4a^2 - ax$, $az = xy$. $(V = \frac{16}{3}a^3.)$

14. The volume in the first octant bounded by the surfaces $x + y = a$, $z^2 = 4ay$. Solve in two ways. $(V = \frac{8}{15}a^3.)$

15. The volume enclosed by the plane $y = x$, the xy-plane, and the hyperbolic paraboloid with rulings parallel to the zx-plane intersecting the lines $x = a$, $z = 0$ and $x = y = z$. $(V = \frac{1}{12}a^3.)$

16. One-quarter of the circular conoid generated by a line parallel to the xy-plane following the line $y = h$, $x = 0$ and the circle $x^2 + z^2 = a^2$, $y = 0$. $(V = \frac{1}{8}\pi a^2 h.)$

$$Ans. \; \left(\frac{8a}{9\pi}, \frac{h}{3}, \frac{4a}{3\pi}\right).$$

17. The volume of Ex. 16 by a second method. (Ex. 30, page 473, and Ex. 2, page 487.)

18. The volume in the first octant inside the cylinder formed by a line parallel to the line $y + z = a$, $x = 0$, and following the circle $x^2 + y^2 = a^2$, $z = 0$. $(V = \frac{1}{3}a^3.)$
    Ans. $(\frac{3}{8}a, \frac{3}{32}\pi a, \frac{3}{32}\pi a).$

291. *Centroid of an Arc; of a Surface of Revolution*

The centroid of a curved arc or of a surface of revolution can be found by choosing an element as in § 279 or § 280, respectively.

Example. Find the centroid of a semicircular wire.

Taking the bounding diameter as axis of y, we have $\bar{y} = 0$, and

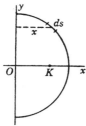

Figure 301

$$s\bar{x} = \int_C x \, ds = 2 \int_0^a x \sqrt{1 + \left(\frac{dy}{dx}\right)^2} \, dx$$

$$= 2 \int_0^a x \sqrt{1 + \frac{x^2}{y^2}} \, dx = 2a \int_0^a \frac{x \, dx}{\sqrt{a^2 - x^2}}$$

$$= -2a \left[\sqrt{a^2 - x^2} \right]_0^a = 2a^2.$$

Hence

$$\bar{x} = \frac{2a^2}{s} = \frac{2a^2}{\pi a} = \frac{2a}{\pi} = 0.63a.$$

EXERCISES

In Exs. 1–17, find the centroid.

1. The example above, using y as the variable of integration.
2. The example above, using the equations $x = a \cos \theta$, $y = a \sin \theta$.
3. A circular arc of half-angle α.   *Ans.* $\bar{x} = \dfrac{a \sin \alpha}{\alpha}.$
4. Half the arc of the hypocycloid $x^{\frac{2}{3}} + y^{\frac{2}{3}} = a^{\frac{2}{3}}$. $(s = 3a.)$ *Ans.* $\bar{x} = \frac{2}{5}a.$
5. Half the arc of the hypocycloid $x = a \cos^3 \varphi$, $y = a \sin^3 \varphi$.
6. The arc from cusp to vertex of the cycloid $x = a(\theta - \sin \theta)$, $y = a(1 - \cos \theta)$.
$(s = 4a.)$ *Ans.* $(\frac{4}{3}a, \frac{4}{3}a).$
7. The entire arc which is cut off on the curve $9y^2 = 4x^3$ by the line $x = 3$.
                                           Ans. $(\frac{58}{35}, 0)$
8. The entire arc of the loop of the curve $9ay^2 = x(x - 3a)^2$. $(s = 4\sqrt{3}\,a.)$
                                           Ans. $(\frac{7}{5}a, 0).$
9. The entire arc of the cardioid $r = a(1 + \cos \theta)$.   *Ans.* $(\frac{4}{5}a, 0).$
10. The entire arc of the loop of the curve $9y^2 = x^2(2x + 3)$. $(s = 2\sqrt{3}.)$
                                           Ans. $(-\frac{4}{5}, 0).$
11. The two arcs of the curve $9y^2 = 4(1 + x^2)^3$ between $x = 0$ and $x = 2$.
$(s = \frac{44}{3}.)$ *Ans.* $(\frac{15}{11}, 0).$
12. A hemispherical surface.   *Ans.* $\bar{x} = \dfrac{a}{2}.$
13. A hemispherical surface, using the equations $x = a \cos \theta$, $y = a \sin \theta$.
14. A spherical zone.   *Ans.* Midway between the bounding planes.
15. The lateral surface area of a circular cone.   *Ans.* $\bar{x} = \frac{1}{3}h.$
16. The surface area cut from a sphere by one sheet of a cone of half-angle $60°$.
                                           Ans. $\bar{x} = \frac{3}{4}a.$

17. One-half the surface area of a torus (cut by a plane at right angles to the axis). $(A = 2\pi^2 ab.)$

$$Ans. \; \bar{y} = \frac{2a}{\pi}.$$

18. If an arc, *symmetric with respect to Oy*, rotates about an external axis parallel to Oy, show that $\bar{y}$ for the surface area thus formed is the same as $\bar{y}$ for the arc. Formulate the result as a theorem.   Check Ex. 17.

19. One arch of the cycloid $x = a(\theta - \sin\theta)$, $y = a(1 - \cos\theta)$ rotates about Oy. Find the centroid of the surface area generated.   (Exs. 6, 18.) $Ans. \; \bar{y} = \tfrac{4}{3}a.$

20. Prove the First Proposition of Pappus:

The surface area of a solid of revolution is equal to the length of the generating arc times the circumference of the circle described by the centroid of the arc.

Solve Exs. 21–25 by the First Proposition of Pappus.

21. Find the surface area of a circular cone.
22. Find the surface area of a torus.
23. Find the centroid of a semicircular wire.
24. Find the surface area of a circular cone frustum.
25. Find the centroid of a semicircular wire plus a wire of the same density joining the ends.

$$Ans. \; \bar{x} = \frac{2a}{\pi + 2}.$$

Moments of Inertia

292. *Moment of Inertia*

The product of a mass m, concentrated at a point P, by the square of the distance r of P from a fixed line, or *axis*, is called the second moment or the *moment of inertia* of m with respect to that axis:

$$I = mr^2.$$

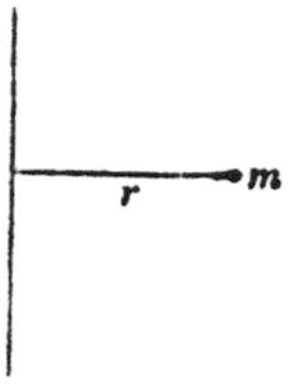

The moment of inertia of a system of such masses is, of course, the sum

(1)
$$I = \sum_{i=1}^{n} m_i r_i^2.$$

Figure 302

Moment of inertia with respect to the x-axis will be denoted by I_x; similarly I_y and I_z. Since the distance from the x-axis to a point (x, y, z) is $\sqrt{y^2 + z^2}$, we have by (1)

(2)
$$I_x = \sum_{i=1}^{n} m_i(y_i^2 + z_i^2); \quad \text{etc.}$$

It is fundamentally important to realize that the moment of inertia of a particle of given mass, with respect to a given axis, is *independent of the direction* from that axis, being dependent on the distance only. Thus for a given particle, I_z is the same whether the particle is at $(5, 0, 0)$, or $(0, 5, 2)$, or $(3, -4, 6)$, or any other point for which

$$x^2 + y^2 = 25.$$

Example. Find I_z for the following set of particles: 2 units at $(1, 3, -2)$, 3 units at $(-3, 2, 6)$, 4 units at $(0, 0, 2)$, 1 unit at $(-3, 0, 1)$.

By (2), properly adapted, we have

$$I_z = 2(1 + 9) + 3(9 + 4) + 4(0) + 1(9) = 68.$$

By thinking of a continuous mass as an aggregate of particles, we may obtain an intuitive conception of the meaning of moment on inertia for such a mass. A formal definition will be stated in § 319.

500

293. *Radius of Gyration*

Let M denote the mass of the physical object (solid, plane sheet, system of particles, etc.) under consideration. Since $M \neq 0$, we may always divide I by M; from the fact that moment of inertia is mass times square of distance, it appears that $\dfrac{I}{M}$ will be the square of a length:

$$\frac{I}{M} = R^2,$$

or

(1) $$I = MR^2.$$

The length R is called the *radius of gyration*, or *radius of inertia*, of M with respect to the given axis of moments. The radius of gyration is the distance from the axis at which a *particle* of mass M must be placed in order to have the same moment of inertia as the original mass.

We confine our attention now to *homogeneous* bodies. In this case, the mass M is proportional to the density δ. It follows from the definition of moment of inertia that I is also proportional to δ. Thus in (1) the density factor δ cancels out, so that the radius of gyration of a homogeneous body, with respect to any axis, is *independent of the density*.

Just as in the case of first moment, by taking $\delta = 1$, we may speak of "moment of inertia" of areas, volumes, etc., with no idea of mass being involved.

294. *Moment of Inertia by Integration*

The actual computation of the moment of inertia of a continuous mass is effected by integration in much the same way that the first moment (§ 285) is determined.

Choose an element (of volume, area, or length) in some suitable way, and denote the mass of this element by Δm_i. Let r_i denote the radius of gyration of the element. Then $r_i^2 \, \Delta m_i$ is the moment of inertia of the element. Add together all the elementary moments and take the limit of the sum:

(1) $$I = \operatorname*{Lim}_{n \to \infty} \sum_{i=1}^{n} r_i^2 \, \Delta m_i = \int r^2 \, dm,$$

where r is the *radius of gyration of the mass element* with respect to the axis of moments. Of course the integrand must be expressed in terms of a single variable, and the integration must be extended over the whole mass.

Just as in finding centroids, we must take an element the position of whose centroid is known; so here the essential point is to *choose an element whose radius of gyration is known*. The way in which the integral (1) is built up will be explained piecemeal, for the cases of greatest importance.

295. *Moment of Inertia of a Plane Area*

To find the moment of inertia of a plane area with respect, say, to the

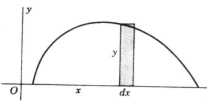

Figure 303

y-axis, let us take as element a rectangle parallel to that axis. [A second method will appear in Example (b) below.] Then, the radius of gyration r of the element is simply x, since (apart from terms which drop out in the limit) the entire element is at distance x from the axis of moments:

$$I_y = \int_a^b x^2 y \; dx.$$

It is definitely inadvisable to memorize this formula; again, the reader should concentrate on understanding the argument.

Example (a). Find the moment of inertia of the area bounded by a parabola, its axis, and its latus rectum, with respect to the axis.

Taking the horizontal element, we have

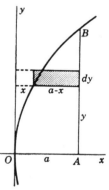

Figure 304

$$I_z = \int_0^{2a} y^2(a - x) \; dy = \int_0^{2a} y^2 \left(a - \frac{y^2}{4a} \right) dy$$

$$= \left[\frac{ay^3}{3} - \frac{y^5}{20a} \right]_0^{2a} = \frac{16}{15} a^4.$$

By Example (a), § 84, the mass, or area, is $M = \frac{4}{3}a^2$, so that

$$I_z = \frac{16}{15} a^4 \cdot \frac{M}{\frac{4}{3}a^2} = \frac{4}{5} Ma^2.$$

This shows that the square of the radius of gyration is

$$R^2 = \tfrac{4}{5}a^2.$$

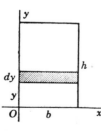

Figure 305

To find the moment of inertia of a rectangle with respect to the base, we have

$$I_x = \int_0^h y^2 x \; dy = b \int_0^h y^2 \; dy = \tfrac{1}{3}bh^3.$$

Since $M = bh$, the result may be written as

(1)
$$I_x = \frac{bh^3}{3} = \frac{1}{3} Mh^2.$$

This formula, which should be memorized, says in words:

The moment of inertia of a rectangle with respect to the base is one-third the mass, or area, times the square of the altitude.

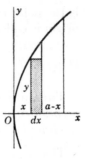

Figure 306

Example (b). Solve Example (a) by another method. Taking the vertical element, we have by (1)

$$I_x = \int_0^a \tfrac{1}{3}y^2 \cdot y \, dx = \tfrac{1}{3} \int_0^a y^3 \, dx$$

$$= \tfrac{8}{3}a^3 \int_0^a x^{\frac{3}{2}} \, dx = \tfrac{16}{15}a^4.$$

Example (c). Find the moment of inertia, with respect to the line $x = 1$, of the area enclosed by the loop of the curve $y^2 = x^2(1 - x)$. See Figure 307.

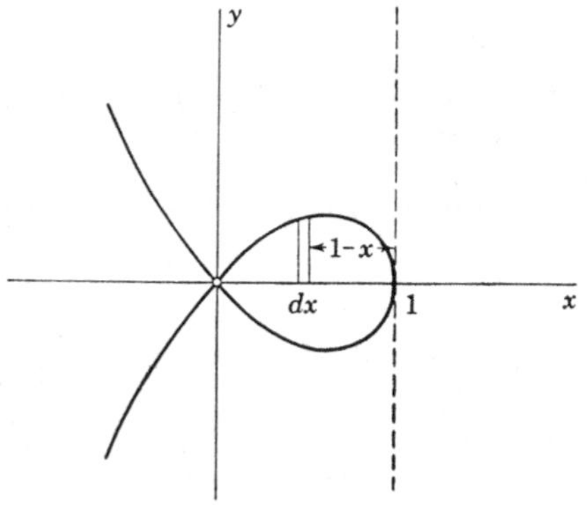

Choosing a vertical element, one parallel to the line $x = 1$, we obtain at once

$$I_{x=1} = 2 \int_0^1 (1 - x)^2 y \, dx.$$

Here $y = x \sqrt{1 - x}$, so that we have

$$I_{x=1} = 2 \int_0^1 x(1 - x)^{\frac{5}{2}} \, dx.$$

Figure 307

One of the many easy ways of evaluating this integral is to use Wallis' formula. Put $x = \sin^2 \varphi$, and thus obtain

$$I_{x=1} = 4 \int_0^{\frac{\pi}{2}} \sin^2 \varphi \cos^5 \varphi \sin \varphi \cos \varphi \, d\varphi$$

$$= 4 \int_0^{\frac{\pi}{2}} \sin^3 \varphi \cos^6 \varphi \, d\varphi$$

$$= 4 \frac{2 \cdot 5 \cdot 3 \cdot 1}{9 \cdot 7 \cdot 5 \cdot 3 \cdot 1} = \frac{8}{63}.$$

296. *Polar Moment of Inertia*

It is frequently necessary to find the moment of inertia of a plane mass, or area, with respect to a line perpendicular to the plane. Take the plane in which the area lies as xy-plane, and the perpendicular line as z-axis. The distance of each particle from the z-axis is merely its distance from the origin, so that this moment may equally well be considered as moment of inertia *with respect to the origin*. Since, for a particle at (x, y), the distance is the polar radius vector $\sqrt{x^2 + y^2}$, moment of inertia with respect to the origin is called *polar moment of inertia.*   For a system of particles,

$$(1) \qquad\qquad I_z = I_0 = \sum_{i=1}^{n} m_i(x_i^2 + y_i^2).$$

THEOREM 58.   *The moment of inertia of a plane mass with respect to a line perpendicular to its plane is equal to the sum of the moments with respect to two lines in the plane intersecting at right angles in the foot of the perpendicular.*

That is, for a mass (or area) in the xy-plane,

$$I_z = I_0 = I_x + I_y.$$

For a system of particles, the truth of this theorem follows at once from (1):

$$I_z = \sum_{i=1}^{n} m_i(x_i^2 + y_i^2) = \sum_{i=1}^{n} m_i y_i^2 + \sum_{i=1}^{n} m_i x_i^2 = I_x + I_y.$$

Later (§ 319), it will be a simple matter to complete the proof.

EXERCISES

In Exs. 1–4, find the moment of inertia with respect to each of the coordinate axes.

1. Masses of 2 units at $(0, -4)$, 2 units at $(3, 0)$, 3 units at $(1, 4)$, and 5 units at $(-2, -2)$.   *Ans.* $I_x = 100$; $I_y = 41$.
2. Masses of 2 units at $(1, 0)$, 2 units at $(1, -3)$, 3 units at $(0, -2)$, and 1 unit at $(-1, 1)$.   *Ans.* $I_x = 31$; $I_y = 5$.
3. Masses of 2 units at $(0, 3, 0)$, 3 units at $(2, -4, 1)$, and 1 unit at $(-1, -2, -3)$.   *Ans.* $I_x = 82$; $I_y = 25$; $I_z = 83$.
4. Masses of 2 units at $(1, 1, 4)$, 3 units at $(2, 0, 0)$, and 4 units at $(-2, -3, 1)$.   *Ans.* $I_x = 74$; $I_y = 66$; $I_z = 68$.

In Exs. 5–38, find the moment of inertia.   The symbol M denotes the total mass of the system.

5. Equal particles at each corner of a square, with respect to one side of the square.   *Ans.* $\frac{1}{2}Ma^2$.
6. Equal particles at three corners of a square, with respect to a side through the vacant corner.   *Ans.* $\frac{2}{3}Ma^2$.
7. Equal particles at each corner of a cube, with respect to an edge of the cube.   *Ans.* Ma^2.
8. Equal particles at seven corners of a cube, with respect to an edge through the vacant corner.   *Ans.* $\frac{8}{7}Ma^2$.
9. A straight rod or wire, with respect to a perpendicular through one end.   *Ans.* $\frac{1}{3}Ml^2$.
10. A straight rod, with respect to a perpendicular through a trisection point. Solve by integration; check by Ex. 9.

11. A wire bent in the form of a square, with respect to one side.　*Ans.* $\frac{5}{12}Ma^2$.

12. A circular wire, with respect to its axis (line through the center perpendicular to the plane).

13. The area bounded by the parabola $y^2 = 4ax$ and the latus rectum, with respect to Oy.　　　　　　　　　　　*Ans.* $\frac{3}{7}Ma^2$.

14. The area bounded by $y^2 = 4ax$ and its latus rectum, with respect to the latus rectum.

$$Ans. \quad \frac{64a^4}{105}.$$

15. The area of the loop of $y^2 = x^2(1 - x)$, Figure 307, with respect to Oy.

$$Ans. \ \tfrac{64}{315}.$$

16. The area of the loop of $y^2 = x^4(1 - x)$, with respect to Oy.

$$Ans. \quad \frac{2^9}{11 \cdot 9 \cdot 7 \cdot 5} = \frac{512}{3465}.$$

17. The area of Ex. 16, with respect to the line $x = 1$.　　*Ans.* $\frac{32}{693}$.

18. The area enclosed by the curve $y^2 = x^5(1 - x)^3$, with respect to Oy.

$$Ans. \quad \frac{9\pi}{1024}.$$

19. The area of Ex. 18, with respect to the line $x = 1$.　　*Ans.* $\frac{5\pi}{1024}$.

20. The area bounded by $y^2 = 4ax$ and its latus rectum, with respect to the line $y = 2a$.

$$Ans. \quad \frac{64a^4}{5}.$$

21. The area bounded by the curve $2x^2 + 2x - y - 2 = 0$ and the line $y = 2x$, with respect to the line $x = 1$.　　　　　　　*Ans.* $\frac{16}{5}$.

22. A triangle, with respect to the line through the vertex parallel to the base. (Solve for the right triangle and deduce the general answer.)　　*Ans.* $\frac{1}{2}Mh^2$.

23. A triangle, with respect to the base.　　　　　　*Ans.* $\frac{1}{6}Mh^2$.

24. Ex. 23 another way.

25. A circular area, with respect to a diameter.　　　*Ans.* $\frac{1}{4}Ma^2$.

26. Solve Ex. 25 by inspection.　(Set up I_y and I_x, each with vertical element; add the former to three times the latter and note that $I_z = I_y$.)

27. An ellipse, with respect to each of its axes.　　*Ans.* $\frac{1}{4}Ma^2$, $\frac{1}{4}Mb^2$.

28. The area in the fourth quadrant bounded by the curve $y = \ln x$, with respect to Oy.　　　　　　　　　　　　　*Ans.* $\frac{1}{9}$.

29. A rectangle of sides b, h, with respect to the line bisecting the sides of length h.　　　　　　　　　　　　*Ans.* $\frac{1}{12}bh^3$.

30. The area bounded by the curve $y = 1 + x^3$ and the axes, with respect to Oy.

31. The area in Figure 287, page 484, with respect to the right side.　*Ans.* 348.3.

32. The area in Figure 282, page 482, with respect to the base.　　*Ans.* 1728.

33. The area in Figure 282, with respect to the left side.　　　*Ans.* 640.

34. The area in Figure 282, with respect to O.　(Exs. 32–33.)

35. The area in Figure 284, page 484, with respect to the base.

36. The area in Figure 290, page 488, with respect to the line of symmetry.

37. The area in Figure 292, page 488, with respect to the left side.　*Ans.* 417.7.

38. A circular area with respect to a perpendicular to the plane through the center. (Ex. 25 and § 296.)   *Ans.* $\frac{1}{2}Ma^2$.

39. Solve Ex. 38 by integration. (Take as element a circular ring.)

40. Find the moment of inertia of a circular sector of angle α, with respect to a line through the center perpendicular to the plane. (Deduce the answer from Ex. 38.)   *Ans.* $\frac{1}{2}Ma^2$.

41. Using the answer to Ex. 40, show that the polar moment of inertia of an area bounded by a polar curve and two radius vectors is

$$I_0 = \tfrac{1}{4} \int_\alpha^\beta r^4 \, d\theta.$$

In Exs. 42–46, find the moment of inertia with respect to the origin. (Ex. 41.)

42. The area of the curve $r^2 = a^2 \cos \theta$.   *Ans.* $\frac{1}{4}\pi a^4$.

43. The area of the curve $r^2 = a^2 \cos 2\theta$.   *Ans.* $\frac{1}{8}\pi a^4$.

44. The triangle bounded by the lines $y = 0$, $x = b$, $y = \dfrac{h}{b}x$. Check by § 296 (Exs. 22–23).   *Ans.* $\frac{1}{12}bh(h^2 + 3b^2)$.

45. The area bounded by the parabola $y^2 = ax$ and the line $y = x$.

46. The area bounded by the curve $a^2y = x^3$ and the line $y = x$.

47. Find the moment of inertia of a circular area with respect to a point on the circumference.   *Ans.* $\frac{3}{2}Ma^2$.

48. Find the moment of inertia of a rectangle with respect to one corner.   *Ans.* $\frac{1}{3}bh(b^2 + h^2)$.

297. *Moment of Inertia of a Solid of Revolution*

No additional theory is needed to find the moment of inertia of a solid of revolution with respect to its axis, but other solids are out of reach at present (§ 319).

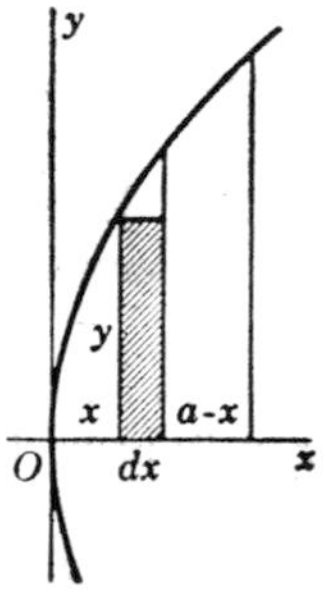

Example (*a*). A solid is generated by revolving about Oy the area bounded by the parabola $y^2 = 4ax$, the x-axis, and the latus rectum. Find the moment of inertia of the solid with respect to Oy.

Take as volume element the cylindrical shell $2\pi xy \, dx$. The radius of gyration of this shell is evidently x:

$$I_y = 2\pi \int_0^a x^2 \cdot xy \, dx = 4\pi \sqrt{a} \int_0^a x^{\frac{5}{2}} \, dx = \tfrac{8}{9}\pi a^5.$$

Figure 308   The mass, or volume, is

$$M = 2\pi \int_0^a xy \, dx = \tfrac{8}{5}\pi a^3,$$

whence

$$I_y = \tfrac{5}{9}Ma^2.$$

To find the moment of inertia of a circular cylinder with respect to its axis, divide the cylinder into shells:

$$I_y = 2\pi \int_0^r x^2 \cdot xy \, dx = 2\pi h \int_0^r x^3 \, dx,$$

or

(1)
$$I_y = \frac{\pi r^4 h}{2} = \frac{1}{2} M r^2.$$

That is, *the moment of inertia of a cylinder with respect to its axis is one-half the mass times the square of the radius.*

Since the circular disk is merely a cylinder of small altitude, this gives us a valuable second method for moment of inertia of a solid of revolution with respect to its axis.

Example (b). Find I_x for the solid formed by revolving about Ox the area of Figure 308.

Take as volume element the disk $\pi y^2 \, dx$. Then by (1),

$$I_x = \pi \int_0^a \frac{1}{2} y^2 \cdot y^2 \, dx = \frac{\pi}{2} \cdot 16a^2 \int_0^a x^2 \, dx$$

$$= \frac{8}{3} \pi a^5.$$

298. The Translation Theorem

Let the term *centroidal line* be used to denote a line through the centroid.

THEOREM 59. *The moment of inertia of a mass, with respect to any line, equals the moment with respect to the parallel centroidal line plus the mass times the square of the distance between the lines.*

That is, if l is any line, $\bar{l}$ the parallel centroidal line, h the distance between them, then

$$I_l = I_{\bar{l}} + Mh^2.$$

This theorem applies to *all* masses. For brevity, the proof will be deferred to § 320, at which time the general proof can be given.

Example. Find the moment of inertia of a right triangle with respect to its centroid (i.e., with respect to a line through the centroid perpendicular to the plane).

By Ex. 23, page 505,

$$I_y = \tfrac{1}{6}Ma^2, \qquad I_x = \tfrac{1}{6}Mb^2,$$

so that

$$I_0 = \tfrac{1}{6}M(a^2 + b^2),$$
$$I_c = I_0 - M \cdot \overline{OC}^2 = I_0 - M \cdot \tfrac{1}{9}(a^2 + b^2)$$
$$= \tfrac{1}{18}M(a^2 + b^2).$$

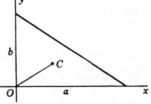

Figure 309

EXERCISES

In Exs. 1–18, find the moment of inertia with respect to the axis of revolution.

1. A sphere. *Ans.* $\frac{2}{5}Ma^2$.
2. A circular cone. *Ans.* $\frac{3}{10}Ma^2$.
3. An oblate spheroid.   Solve by two methods. *Ans.* $\frac{2}{5}Ma^2$.
4. A prolate spheroid, using the equations $x = a \cos \varphi$, $y = b \sin \varphi$.   *Ans.* $\frac{2}{5}Mb^2$.
5. A torus. *Ans.* $(b^2 + \frac{3}{4}a^2)M$.
6. The volume formed by revolving about Ox the area bounded by $y^2 = 4ax$, $x = 0$, $y = 2a$.
7. The volume formed by revolving the area of Ex. 6 about the line $y = 2a$.

$$Ans. \ \frac{8\pi a^5}{15}.$$

8. The volume formed by revolving about Ox the area in the first quadrant under the curve $y = e^{-x}$. *Ans.* $\frac{1}{8}\pi$.
9. The volume formed by revolving about Ox the area bounded by the curve $y = \ln x$ and the lines $x = e$, $y = 0$. *Ans.* $\frac{3}{2}\pi(3e - 8)$.
10. The volume generated by revolving the area of Ex. 9 about Oy.

$$Ans. \ \frac{\pi(3e^4 + 1)}{8}.$$

11. The volume formed by revolving the area of Figure 282, page 482, about the left side.
12. The volume formed by revolving the area of Figure 282 about the base.
13. The volume formed by revolving the area of Figure 285, page 484, about the base.
14. The volume generated by revolving the area of Figure 284, page 484, about its base.
15. The volume bounded by the surfaces $x^2 + y^2 = 4az$, $x^2 + y^2 = 4z^2$.

Ans. $\frac{16}{15}\pi a^5$.

16. The volume bounded by the quadric surfaces $x^2 + y^2 - z^2 = a^2$, $x^2 + y^2 = 2a^2$.

Ans. $\frac{32}{15}\pi a^5$.

17. The volume bounded by the quadric surfaces $x^2 + y^2 - z^2 = a^2$, $x^2 + y^2 = 2z^2$.

Ans. $\frac{16}{15}\pi a^5$.

18. The volume inside the surfaces $x^2 + y^2 = 3z^2$, $x^2 + y^2 + az = 4a^2$.

In Exs. 19–23, find the moment of inertia.

19. A circular wire with respect to a diameter, using rectangular coordinates.

Ans. $\frac{1}{2}Ma^2$.

20. The wire of Ex. 19, using the equations $x = a \cos \theta$, $y = a \sin \theta$.
21. A circular wire with respect to a tangent.   (Use $x = a \cos \theta$, $y = a \sin \theta$.)

Ans. $\frac{3}{2}Ma^2$.

22. Solve Ex. 21 in rectangular coordinates.

23. The arc of the catenary $y = a \cosh \dfrac{x}{a}$, from the vertex to the point (x_1, y_1), with respect to Ox. $\left(s = a \sinh \dfrac{x_1}{a}. \right)$ *Ans.* $a^2 s + \frac{1}{3}s^3$.

In Exs. 24–28, find the moment of inertia with respect to the axis of revolution.

24. A spherical surface area, using rectangular coordinates.   *Ans.* $\frac{2}{3}Ma^2$.

25. A spherical surface area, using the parametric equations $x = a \cos \theta$, $y = a \sin \theta$.

26. The lateral surface area of a cone of revolution.   *Ans.* $\frac{1}{2}Ma^2$.

27. The surface area of a torus.   *Ans.* $(b^2 + \frac{3}{2}a^2)M$.

28. A cylindrical drum.   *Ans.* $\pi r^4 + 2\pi r^3 h$.

In Exs. 29–39, obtain the required moment of inertia by using the theorem of § 298, with reference to previous exercises.

29. A square plate with respect to (a) a line through the center parallel to a side; (b) a perpendicular through the center; (c) a line trisecting two opposite sides (two cases); (d) a diagonal.   *Ans.* (a) $\frac{1}{12}Ma^2$; (b) $\frac{1}{6}Ma^2$; (d) $\frac{1}{12}Ma^2$.

30. An isosceles triangle with respect to a line (a) parallel to the base bisecting the altitude; (b) through the vertex perpendicular to the plane.
    Ans. (a) $\frac{1}{12}Mh^2$; (b) $\frac{1}{2}M(h^2 + \frac{1}{3}a^2)$.

31. A circular wire with respect to (a) a tangent; (b) any line perpendicular to the plane.   *Ans.* (a) $\frac{3}{2}Ma^2$; (b) $M(a^2 + h^2)$.

32. A circular area with respect to (a) a tangent; (b) a perpendicular through a point in the circumference.

33. The volume of a sphere with respect to a tangent.

34. A spherical surface area with respect to a tangent.

35. The volume of a torus with respect to a tangent parallel to the axis.

36. The area of Figure 282, page 482, with respect to a line through the centroid parallel to the base.   *Ans.* 528.

37. The area of Figure 282, with respect to a line through the centroid parallel to the sides.   *Ans.* 208.

38. The area of Figure 282, with respect to the centroid. (Exs. 36–37.)

39. The area of Figure 282, with respect to a line through P perpendicular to the plane. (Ex. 38.)   *Ans.* 1552.

Fluid Pressure.   Work

299. Distributed Force

We have frequently to consider a force not acting at a single point but distributed over an area or throughout a volume. Examples are the pressure of a carload of sand against the sides of the car, the attraction between two electrified plates, the gravitational attraction between two spheres or other solids. If the mass upon which the force acts be thought of as composed ultimately of particles, such a distributed force may be regarded as comprising the totality of forces acting on the separate particles.

300. Fluid Pressure

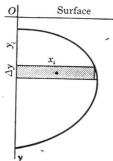

Figure 310

Given a plane area submerged vertically in a homogeneous fluid, let us for definiteness take the x-axis in the surface with the y-axis *positive downward*. (Of course, in any particular problem, the axes should be so chosen as to make the analytic geometry simple.) Divide the area into rectangles of length x_i, width Δy, and depth y_i below the surface. Now the force on any submerged *horizontal* area is equal to the weight of the column of fluid standing on this area. Hence the force on our elementary rectangle is, apart from terms which will drop out when the limit (the definite integral) is taken,*

$$\Delta F_i = w y_i x_i \, \Delta y,$$

where w is the weight of the fluid per unit volume. Therefore

$$F = \operatorname*{Lim}_{n \to \infty} \sum_{i=1}^{n} w y_i x_i \, \Delta y = w \int_c^d yx \, dy,$$

where c and d are the least and greatest depths below the surface.

* The reasoning is as follows: If the rectangle were rotated about its upper side through 90° into a horizontal position at depth y_i, the force would be $w y_i x_i \, \Delta y$; if it were rotated about the lower side to a horizontal position at depth $y_i + \Delta y$, the force would be $w(y_i + \Delta y)x_i \, \Delta y$. The actual force is greater than the former and less than the latter.

Under the integral sign, we have multiplied the area $x \, dy$ of the element by its depth y below the surface, so that the integral represents the first moment of the submerged area with respect to the axis in the surface.

THEOREM 60. *The force on a submerged vertical plane area equals the product of the weight per unit volume, the submerged area, and the depth of the centroid of the area below the surface:*

(1)
$$F = wA\bar{y}.$$

Example. Find the force on one face of the submerged triangle of Figure 311.

The equation of the line through $(0, 3)$, $(2, 1)$ is

$$x + y = 3.$$

Thus the force is

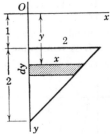

$$F = w \int_1^3 yx \, dy = w \int_1^3 y(3 - y) \, dy$$

$$= w \left[\tfrac{3}{2}y^2 - \tfrac{1}{3}y^3 \right]_1^3 = \tfrac{10}{3}w.$$

Figure 311

Check: The area is $A = \tfrac{1}{2} \cdot 2 \cdot 2 = 2$, the depth of the centroid is $1 + \tfrac{2}{3} = \tfrac{5}{3}$; the force, by (1), is $F = w \cdot 2 \cdot \tfrac{5}{3} = \tfrac{10}{3}w$.

EXERCISES

In Exs. 1–17, solve by direct integration. When the position of the centroid is already known, check by Theorem 60.

1. Find the force on one face of a plank 12 ft. by 6 in., submerged vertically with its upper end in the surface.

2. Solve Ex. 1, if the upper end is 6 ft. below the surface.

3. Find the force on one face of a right triangle of sides $AB = 3$ ft., $AC = 4$ ft., submerged with AC vertical and AB in the surface. *Ans.* $8w$.

4. Solve Ex. 3 if AB is 4 ft., C 8 ft., below the surface.

5. Solve Ex. 3 if AB is 8 ft., C 4 ft., below the surface.

6. What force must be withstood by a vertical dam 100 ft. long and 20 ft. deep? *Ans.* 620 tons.

7. What force must be withstood by a trapezoidal dam 100 ft. long at the top, 80 ft. long at the bottom, and 20 ft. deep? *Ans.* $17,333w$.

8. A horizontal cylindrical boiler 4 ft. in diameter is half full of water. Find the force on one end. *Ans.* 330 lb.

9. Solve Ex. 8 if the boiler is full of water. *Ans.* $8\pi w$.

10. Find the force that must be withstood by a bulkhead closing a water main 4 ft. in diameter, if the surface of the water in the reservoir is 40 ft. above the center of the bulkhead. *Ans.* 16 tons.

11. Find the force on one end of a parabolic trough full of water, if the depth is 2 ft. and the width across the top 2 ft.   *Ans.* $\frac{32}{15}w$.

12. The ends of a trough have the shape of an inverted arch of the curve $y = a \cos \frac{x}{a}$. If the trough is filled with a liquid weighing w lb. per cu. ft., find the force on one end.   *Ans.* $\frac{1}{4}\pi w a^3$.

13. The vertical face of a dam is in the shape of an inverted arch of the cycloid $x = a(\theta - \sin \theta)$, $y = a(1 - \cos \theta)$. Find the maximum force that the dam must withstand.   *Ans.* $\frac{5}{2}\pi w a^3$.

14. A trough 4 ft. deep and 6 ft. wide has semielliptical ends. If the trough is full of water, find the force on one end.   *Ans.* $32w$.

15. Solve Ex. 14, using the equations $x = 3 \cos \varphi$, $y = 4 \sin \varphi$.

16. Find the force on one face of a square 2 ft. on a side, submerged with one diagonal vertical and one corner in the surface.   *Ans.* $4\sqrt{2}\,w$.

17. A triangular trough of width $2a$ and depth $2a$ is filled to depth a with a liquid of unit weight $2w$, which is overlaid with a stratum of depth a and unit weight w. (a) Find the force on one end; (b) find the force if the liquids were thoroughly mixed.   *Ans.* (a) $\frac{3}{2}w a^3$; (b) $\frac{5}{3}w a^3$.

18. Show that for an area submerged as in Figure 312, the force is

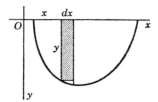

Figure 312

$$F = \tfrac{1}{2}w \int_a^b y^2 \, dx.$$

Solve Exs. 19–24 by the method of Ex. 18.

19. Ex. 3.   **20.** Example, § 300.   **21.** Ex. 8.
22. Ex. 11.   **23.** Ex. 12.   **24.** Ex. 13.

301. *Resultant of Parallel Forces*

Given a set of parallel forces $f_1, f_2, \cdots, f_n$ whose resultant (algebraic sum) is not 0, the problem of finding the line of action of the resultant is analogous to that of finding the centroid of a set of mass particles.

The simplest case arises when all the forces lie in one plane; for concreteness, consider a straight beam bearing concentrated loads. Take the line of the beam as x-axis, and mark an origin; say, at the left end. Multiply each force by its distance (i.e., the distance of its line of action) from the origin. *The sum of these first moments must equal the moment of the resultant;* i.e.,

$$F\bar{x} = \sum_{i=1}^{n} f_i x_i.$$

Example (a). A straight beam bears concentrated loads as shown. Find the position of the resultant and the reactions at the ends.

Taking moments about A, we have

$$F\bar{x} = 4 \cdot 60 + 8 \cdot 40 + 16 \cdot 100 = 2160, \qquad \bar{x} = \tfrac{2160}{200} = 10.8 \text{ ft.}$$

The moment, about A, of the reaction R_2 must balance the moments of the forces, so that $20R_2 = 2160$, $R_2 = 108$ lb. We could find R_1 from the fact that

$$R_1 + R_2 = 200,$$

but as a check, let us find it independently by taking moments about B:

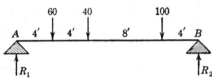

Figure 313

$$20R_1 = 16 \cdot 60 + 12 \cdot 40 + 4 \cdot 100 = 1840, \qquad R_1 = 92 \text{ lb.}$$

If the parallel forces do not all lie in the same plane, take the xy-plane perpendicular to the forces. Let (x_i, y_i) be the point where the line of action of f_i pierces the xy-plane. Taking moments first with respect to the y-axis, then with respect to the x-axis, we obtain the equations

$$F\bar{x} = \sum_{i=1}^{n} f_i x_i, \qquad F\bar{y} = \sum_{i=1}^{n} f_i y_i,$$

where $(\bar{x}, \bar{y})$ is the point where the line of action of the resultant F pierces the xy-plane.

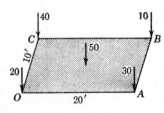

Figure 314

Example (*b*). A table 20 by 10 ft., weighing 4 oz. per sq. ft., bears loads at the corners as shown. Find the point of application of the resultant.

The weight of the table top may be replaced by a force of 50 lb. at the center. Taking moments about OC as y-axis and about OA as x-axis, we find

$$F\bar{x} = 10 \cdot 50 + 20 \cdot 30 + 20 \cdot 10 = 1300,$$
$$\bar{x} = \tfrac{1300}{150} = \tfrac{26}{3} \text{ ft.};$$
$$F\bar{y} = 5 \cdot 50 + 10 \cdot 40 + 10 \cdot 10 = 750,$$
$$\bar{y} = \tfrac{750}{150} = 5 \text{ ft.}$$

302. *Center of Pressure*

Let us return to the problem of fluid pressure. In taking moments, we may replace the force

$$\Delta F_i = w y_i x_i \, \Delta y,$$

acting on the elementary rectangle, by a concentrated force of the same

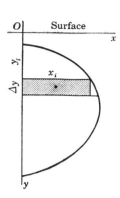

Figure 315

magnitude at the center of the rectangle (just as, in the example above, we replaced the weight of the table by a force at its center). The moments of this force with respect to Oy and Ox are respectively $wy_ix_i \Delta y \cdot \frac{1}{2}x_i$, $wy_ix_i \Delta y \cdot y_i$. Adding all these elementary moments and taking the limits of the sums, we obtain the formulas

$$F\bar{x} = \underset{n \to \infty}{\text{Lim}} \sum_{i=1}^{n} \tfrac{1}{2}wy_ix_i^2 \, \Delta y = \tfrac{1}{2}w \int_c^d yx^2 \, dy,$$

$$F\bar{y} = \underset{n \to \infty}{\text{Lim}} \sum_{i=1}^{n} wy_i^2x_i \, \Delta y = w \int_c^d y^2x \, dy,$$

where $(\bar{x}, \bar{y})$ is the point of application of a single force F that would balance the distributed force. This point is called the *center of pressure*.

Once more the student is advised not to memorize these formulas but to concentrate on understanding the mechanics of the problem.

Example. Find the center of pressure on the submerged triangle of Figure 311. (Example, § 300.)

We have

$$F\bar{x} = \frac{1}{2} w \int_1^3 yx^2 \, dy = \frac{1}{2} w \int_1^3 y(3 - y)^2 \, dy$$

$$= \frac{1}{2} w \left[\frac{9y^2}{2} - 2y^3 + \frac{1}{4} y^4 \right]_1^3 = 2w,$$

$$\bar{x} = \frac{2w}{\frac{10}{3}w} = \frac{3}{5};$$

$$F\bar{y} = w \int_1^3 y^2x \, dy = w \int_1^3 y^2(3 - y) \, dy$$

$$= w \left[y^3 - \frac{1}{4} y^4 \right]_1^3 = 6w,$$

$$\bar{y} = \frac{6w}{\frac{10}{3}w} = \frac{9}{5}.$$

EXERCISES

1. A man weighing 200 lb. stands on the end of a plank supported as shown in Figure 316. If the plank weighs 4 lb. per ft., what weight W must be applied at A to hold the plank in position?
Ans. 40 lb. (critical value).

2. In Ex. 1, what must be the weight of the plank per foot, if it is to remain in position due to its own weight?

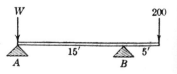

Figure 316

3. In Ex. 1, with W removed, a child weighing 60 lb. walks from A toward B. How far can he go? *Ans.* 5 ft.

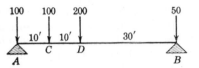

Figure 317

4. A straight beam is loaded as shown in Figure 317. If the weight of the beam is negligible, find (a) the point of application of the resultant; (b) the reactions at the supports. *Ans.* (a) $\bar{x} = 16$ ft. 8 in.; (b) 300 lb., 150 lb.

5. Solve Ex. 4 if the beam weighs 2 lb. per ft.

6. Solve Ex. 4 if the segment AD bears a uniformly distributed load of 5 lb. per ft.

7. Solve Ex. 4 if the segment AD bears a uniformly distributed load of 5 lb. per ft., and the segment DB bears a distributed load increasing uniformly from 5 lb. per ft. at D to 15 lb. per ft. at B. *Ans.* $\bar{x} = 23$ ft. 3 in.

8. A platform 20 ft. square, weighing $1\frac{1}{2}$ lb. per sq. ft., bears loads of 100 lb. at (5, 4), 200 lb. at (15, 5), 50 lb. at (8, 12), 50 lb. at (20, 0). At what point would a single support hold the platform in place? *Ans.* (10.9, 8).

9. A weight W is to be raised by a lever with the force F at one end and the fulcrum A at the other. If the weight is a ft. from the fulcrum, and the lever

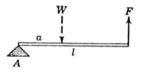

Figure 318

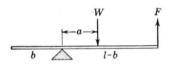

Figure 319

weighs w lb. per ft., what should be the length of the lever to lift the weight most easily? (Figure 318.)

$$Ans.\ l = \sqrt{\frac{2Wa}{w}}.$$

10. Solve Ex. 9 if the lever projects a distance b beyond the fulcrum (Figure 319).

Ans. If $\sqrt{\dfrac{2Wa - b^2w}{w}} > a,\ l = b + \sqrt{\dfrac{2Wa - b^2w}{w}}$; otherwise, $l = a + b$.

11. A platform 20 ft. square, of negligible weight, bears a single concentrated load. The reactions are: at (0, 0), 50 lb.; at (20, 0), 80 lb.; at (20, 20), 100 lb.; at (0, 20), 70 lb. Where is the load?

12. Solve Ex. 11 if the platform weighs 4 oz. per sq. ft. *Ans.* (13, 12).

In Exs. 13–18, find the depth of the center of pressure.

13. A rectangle submerged vertically with one edge in the surface. *Ans.* $\frac{2}{3}a$.

14. A rectangle submerged vertically with its upper edge at depth c.

15. An isosceles triangle submerged with the line of symmetry vertical and the vertex in the surface. *Ans.* $\frac{3}{4}h$.

16. An isosceles triangle submerged with the line of symmetry vertical and the base in the surface. *Ans.* $\frac{1}{2}h$.

17. One end of a horizontal cylindrical tank, half filled.

18. One end of the parabolic trough of Ex. 11, page 512.

19. Find the center of pressure in Ex. 3, page 511.

20. Find the center of pressure in Ex. 4, page 511.

21. Find the center of pressure in Ex. 5, page 511.

22. Find the center of pressure on the right half of the square of Ex. 16, page 512.

23. Find integrals for the center of pressure on the submerged area of Ex. 18, page 512.   (Ex. 13.)

303. *Work*

Let a constant force act continuously upon a body so as to move it through a distance d.   The product of the magnitude F of the force and the distance d is called the work done in moving the body through the distance d:

Work = (magnitude of force)(distance over which it acts),
$$\mathbf{W = F \cdot d.}$$

If, for instance, you use a constant 20-lb. force to push a block 10 ft., then the work you do is

$$W = (20 \text{ lb.})(10 \text{ ft.})$$
$$= 200 \text{ ft-lb.}$$

The above basic concept of work is readily extended to the determination of the work done by a variable force, as is illustrated in the example below.

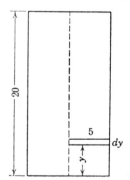

Figure 320

Example.   A cylindrical tank, with a base radius of 5 ft. and a height of 20 ft., is filled with water. Find the work done in pumping all the water out the top of the tank.

A cross-section of the tank is exhibited in Figure 320. Consider a representative element, as shown, at a distance y from the base of the tank.   The circular disk, formed by revolving that element about the axis of the tank, has a volume $\pi(5^2)\, dy$ cu. ft.   Water weighs about 62.5 lb. per cu. ft.   Therefore the circular disk of water weighs $62.5(25\pi)\, dy$ lb., and it is to be raised a distance of $(20 - y)$ ft.

The work to be done in raising the circular disk of water to the top of the tank is $62.5(25\pi)(20 - y)\, dy$.

To empty the whole tank, the work required is

(1) $$W = 62.5(25\pi) \int_0^{20} (20 - y)\, dy.$$

From (1) it follows that

$$W = \frac{3125\pi}{2}\left[-\frac{(20 - y)^2}{2} \right]_0^{20}$$
$$= 9.82(10)^5 \text{ ft-lb.}$$

EXERCISES

In order to simplify the numerical work, let w denote the weight in pounds per cubic foot of the liquid in Exs. 1–13.

1. Suppose the tank of the example above is only half full (the bottom half!); find the work done in pumping the water out the top of the tank.   *Ans.* $3750\pi w$ ft-lb.

2. A hemispherical tank of diameter 6 ft. is full of liquid.   Find the work done in pumping the liquid out the top of the tank.

$$Ans.\ \frac{81\pi w}{4}\ \text{ft-lb.}$$

3. For the tank of Ex. 2, suppose the surface of the liquid is 1 ft. from the top of the tank.   Find the work done in pumping the liquid out the top.

$$Ans.\ 16\pi w\ \text{ft-lb.}$$

4. A cistern is built in the form of a hemisphere of radius r, surmounted by a right circular cylinder with base radius r and height h.   If the cistern is full of water, find the work done in pumping the water out the top of the cistern.

$$Ans.\ \tfrac{1}{12}\pi wr^2(3r^2 + 8rh + 6h^2).$$

5. Let a cistern of the shape of that in Ex. 4 have its cylinder height equal its hemisphere radius, $h = r$.   If the cistern is half full, 50% of capacity volume, find the work done in pumping the water out the top of the cistern.

$$Ans.\ \frac{77\pi wr^4}{72}.$$

6. Let the cistern of Ex. 5 be three-fourths full.   Find the work done in pumping the water out the top.

$$Ans.\ \frac{383\pi wr^4}{288}.$$

7. If the cistern of Ex. 4 is filled only to the top of the hemisphere, find the work done in pumping the water out the top.   *Ans.* $\tfrac{1}{12}\pi wr^3(3r + 8h).$

8. A tank is made in the shape of a right circular cylinder surmounted by a frustum of a cone, a vertical cross-section being shown in Figure 321.   The tank is full of water.   Find the work needed to pump all the water out the top.

$$Ans.\ \frac{314\pi w}{3}\ \text{ft-lb.}$$

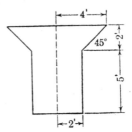

Figure 321

9. A conical reservoir of top radius r and height h is filled with oil.   Find the work needed to pump the oil out the top of the reservoir.   *Ans.* $\tfrac{1}{12}\pi wr^2h^2.$

10. If the reservoir of Ex. 9 is filled only to one-eighth of its capacity, find the work needed.   *Ans.* $\tfrac{5}{192}\pi wr^2h^2.$

11. A tank is made in the form of a cone, of base radius r and height h, surmounted by a right circular cylinder of base radius r and height H.   The tank is full of water.   Find the work done in pumping all the water out the top of the tank.   *Ans.* $\tfrac{1}{12}\pi wr^2(h^2 + 4hH + 6H^2).$

12. If the tank of Ex. 11 is filled only to a distance c units ($c < H$) from the top of the tank, find the work done.   *Ans.* $\tfrac{1}{12}\pi wr^2(h^2 + 4hH + 6H^2 - 6c^2).$

13. Solve Ex. 12, if $H < c < H + h$.   *Ans.* $\dfrac{\pi w r^2}{12h^2} (h + H - c)^3 (h + H + 3c)$.

It is known empirically that (within the so-called elastic limit) for an elastic spring, the force f needed to stretch it beyond its natural length is proportional to the elongation s; $f = k \cdot s$. The number k is called the spring constant.

14. A spring of natural length 10 in. is such that a force of 6 lb. will stretch it 2 in. Show that the spring constant is 3 lb. per in., and find the work done in stretching the spring from its natural length to a length of 14 in.   *Ans.* 24 in.-lb.

15. Find the work necessary to stretch the spring of Ex. 14 an additional 4 in., from a length of 14 in. to one of 18 in.   *Ans.* 72 in.-lb.

16. It takes twice as much work to stretch a certain spring from 9 to 10 in. as it does to stretch it from 8 to 9 in. Find the natural length of the spring.

Ans. 7.5 in.

Double Integrals

304. *Volume under a Surface*

The method employed in § 278 for finding the volume of a solid succeeds only when the solid can be cut into slices such that the area of the face of each slice is known. We proceed to develop a method that is free of this restriction.

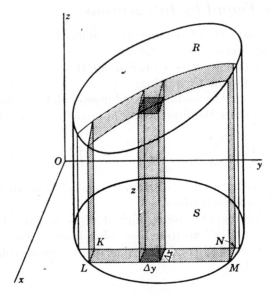

Figure 322

Consider the solid bounded by a portion R of the surface

$$z = f(x, y), \qquad z \geq 0,$$

the area S into which R projects in the xy-plane, and the vertical cylinder through the boundaries of S and R. We may compute the volume V of this solid as follows:

Draw in S a set of n lines parallel to the y-axis and a set of m lines parallel to the x-axis, thus dividing S into rectangles of area $\Delta y\, \Delta x$, together with a number of irregular portions around the boundary. By passing through each line of the two sets a plane perpendicular to the xy-plane, we divide V into vertical rectangular columns, together with smaller irregular columns. The upper boundary of each rectangular column is a portion of the surface R.

Through that point of the upper boundary of each column which is nearest the xy-plane, pass a horizontal plane, thus forming a set of rectangular prisms lying wholly within V. As Δx and Δy both approach 0, the *limit of the sum* of all these prisms is the volume under the surface:*

$$(1) \qquad V = \operatorname*{Lim}_{\substack{\Delta x \to 0 \\ \Delta y \to 0}} \sum_{i=1}^{n} \sum_{j=1}^{m} f(x_i, y_j) \, \Delta y \, \Delta x.$$

From the critical standpoint this formula, based directly on our intuitive conception of volume, may be regarded as a *definition* analogous to the definition of area in § 81. The definition is valid whenever the limit exists. If z is a continuous function, existence of the limit can be proved.

305. *Volume Found by Integration*

The "double limit" (1) above may be evaluated by two successive applications of the theorem of § 81, as follows:

Let us fix our attention on the rectangle *KLMN* in S (Figure 322), keeping x and Δx constant for the time being. The volume $\Delta V'_i$, whose base is this rectangle, may be found by adding the volumes of all the included elementary prisms and then taking the limit as Δy approaches zero. Hence, by § 81,

$$\Delta V'_i = \operatorname*{Lim}_{m \to \infty} \sum_{j=1}^{m} f(x_i, y_j) \, \Delta y \, \Delta x = \left[\int_{y_i'}^{y_i''} f(x_i, y) \, dy \right] \Delta x.$$

Here primes are being used to distinguish one y_i from another, etc. The primes do not denote derivatives.

In the expression for $\Delta V'_i$ the coefficient of Δx is a function of x_i alone, since the limits y_i' and y_i'' are functions of x_i alone. Thus we may apply again the theorem of § 81, and find that the required volume under the surface $z = f(x, y)$ is

$$V = \operatorname*{Lim}_{n \to \infty} \sum_{i=1}^{n} \left[\int_{y_i'}^{y_i''} f(x_i, y) \, dy \right] \Delta x = \int_{a}^{b} \left[\int_{y'}^{y''} f(x, y) \, dy \right] dx,$$

where a and b are the extreme values of x on the boundary of S.

The quantity just found is usually written without the brackets:

$$(1) \qquad V = \int_{a}^{b} \int_{y'}^{y''} f(x, y) \, dy \, dx.$$

---

* This is illustrated by the common sawmill practice of cutting slabs and edgings into lath or other thin, narrow boards. By reducing the width and thickness of the product the volume of waste is reduced toward the ideal limit zero.

It is called an *iterated integral*, being merely an integral of an integral. It is to be noted that *the inner integral sign belongs with the inner differential*, and that *during the integration with respect to y, x remains constant.* Further, the first or inner limits of integration are in general variables, but the outer limits are always constants.

Of course we could integrate first with respect to x, then with respect to y. The same reasoning as before would lead to the formula

$$(2) \qquad V = \int_c^d \int_{x'}^{x''} f(x,\ y)\ dx\ dy,$$

y remaining constant during the first integration. The change from (1) to (2) is called *inverting the order* of integration.

In the foregoing argument, we have assumed our solid to be divided into rectangular columns perpendicular to the xy-plane. Sometimes, however, it is more convenient to erect columns perpendicular to one of the other coordinate planes. Such variations offer no difficulty, provided the geometric meaning of the successive integrations be kept clearly in mind. In every problem, a sketch of the required volume should be made, and the iterated integral built up by inspection of the figure.

Any function $f(x,\ y)$ of two independent variables may be interpreted as the z-coordinate of a variable point on a surface. If, then, in any problem, we can express the required quantity as a double limit of the form (1), § 304, *no matter what may be the geometric or physical meaning of the given function* $f(x,\ y)$, the limit may be evaluated by an iterated integration (1) or (2). Thus the method described above is by no means confined to the determination of volumes—it applies to a great variety of problems.

Example (a). Find the volume in the first octant bounded by the plane $z = 2 - x - y$ and the cylinder $y = 1 - x^2$. (Figure 323, page 522.)

By means of planes parallel to the yz-plane, cut the solid into thin slabs. Then, by planes parallel to the zx-plane, cross-cut the slabs into slender vertical columns of base $dy\ dx$, height z, volume $z\ dy\ dx$. (Since we are intending to integrate first with respect to y, we write $z\ dy\ dx$ rather than $z\ dx\ dy$.) In the first integration adding up all the columns in the slab, x remains constant, and y varies from 0 (at P) to $1 - x^2$ (at Q). The second integration adds up all the slabs, from $x = 0$ (at O) to $x = 1$ (at A):

$$V = \int_0^1 \int_0^{1-x^2} z\ dy\ dx$$

$$= \int_0^1 \int_0^{1-x^2} (2 - x - y)\ dy\ dx.$$

Therefore the volume V shown in Figure 323 is given by

$$V = -\tfrac{1}{2} \int_0^1 \Bigg[(2 - x - y)^2 \Bigg]_0^{1-x^2} dx$$

$$= -\tfrac{1}{2} \int_0^1 \Bigg[(1 - x + x^2)^2 - (2 - x)^2 \Bigg] dx = \tfrac{49}{60}.$$

Example (*b*). Solve Example (*a*) by a second method.

Cut the solid into slabs by planes parallel to the zx-plane, the slabs into

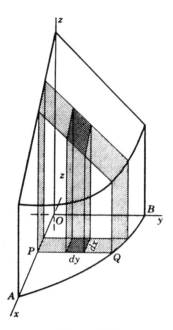

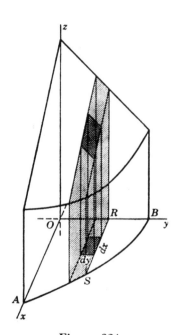

| Figure 323 | Figure 324 |

columns by planes parallel to the yz-plane (Figure 324).   In the first integration, x varies from 0 (at R) to $\sqrt{1-y}$ (at S); then y varies from 0 (at O) to 1 (at B):

$$V = \int_0^1 \int_0^{\sqrt{1-y}} z \, dx \, dy = \int_0^1 \int_0^{\sqrt{1-y}} (2 - x - y) \, dx \, dy$$

$$= -\tfrac{1}{2} \int_0^1 \Bigg[(2 - x - y)^2 \Bigg]_0^{\sqrt{1-y}} dy$$

$$= -\tfrac{1}{2} \int_0^1 \Bigg[(2 - \sqrt{1-y} - y)^2 - (2 - y)^2 \Bigg] dy = \tfrac{49}{60}.$$

EXERCISES

In each of the following exercises, the limits of integration should be obtained directly from a figure.

1. Find the volume in the first octant bounded by the planes $x = 1$, $z = 2x + y$, and the cylinder $y^2 = x$. Solve in two ways, integrating once in the order x, y, then in the order y, x.   *Ans.* $\frac{21}{20}$.

2. Find the volume in the first octant bounded by the surfaces $z = 1 + xy$, $y = 1 - x^2$. Solve in two ways.   *Ans.* $\frac{3}{4}$.

3. Find the volume in the first octant bounded by the surfaces $z = xy^2$, $y = 2x$, $y = 2$. Solve in two ways.   *Ans.* $\frac{4}{5}$.

4. Find in two ways the volume in the first octant bounded by the surfaces $az = x^2 + 2ay$, $y = x$, $x = a$.   *Ans.* $\frac{7}{12}a^3$.

5. Find the volume of a cylindrical column having as its base the area between the curves $y = x$, $y = x^2$, and cut off by the plane $x - y - z + 1 = 0$.   *Ans.* $\frac{11}{60}$.

6. Find the volume of a sphere by iterated integration.

7. Find by iterated integration the volume of a segment of an elliptic paraboloid.

8. Find in two ways the volume in the first octant bounded by the surfaces $yz = ax$, $y^2 = az$, $z = a$.   *Ans.* $\frac{1}{6}a^3$.

9. Find the volume in the first octant bounded by the surfaces $y^2 + z^2 = ax$, $2y + z = 2a$.   *Ans.* $\frac{5}{6}a^3$.

10. Find in two ways the volume in the first octant bounded by the surfaces $z = x^2y$, $y^2 = x$, $y = x^2$.   *Ans.* $\frac{3}{56}$.

11. Find the volume in the first octant bounded by the surfaces $az = xy$, $x^2 = 4ay$, $x - y = a$.   *Ans.* $\frac{1}{24}a^3$.

12. Find the volume under the surface $az = xy$, whose base is the area in the xy-plane bounded by the curves $y^2 = ax$, $x + y = 2a$, $y = 0$.

13. Find in two ways the volume in the first octant under the plane $x + z = 1$, cut off by the surface $x^2 + y + z = 4$.   *Ans.* $\frac{7}{4}$.

14. Find the volume in the first octant bounded by the surfaces $y^2 + az = a^2$, $y^2 + z^2 = ax$. Solve in two ways.   *Ans.* $\frac{2}{7}a^3$.

15. Find the volume enclosed by the surfaces $az = y^2 + ax$, $y = x$, $x + y = 2a$, $y = 0$, $z = 0$.   *Ans.* $\frac{7}{6}a^3$.

16. Find the volume enclosed by the surfaces $az = y^2 + ax$, $x + y = 2a$, $y = x$, $x = 0$, $z = 0$.   *Ans.* $\frac{3}{2}a^3$.

17. Find the volume bounded by the coordinate planes and the surface $x^{\frac{1}{2}} + y^{\frac{1}{2}} + z^{\frac{1}{2}} = a^{\frac{1}{2}}$.   *Ans.* $\frac{1}{90}a^3$.

18. Find the entire volume inside the surface $x^{\frac{2}{3}} + y^{\frac{2}{3}} + z^{\frac{2}{3}} = a^{\frac{2}{3}}$.   *Ans.* $\frac{4}{35}\pi a^3$.

19. Find the centroid of the solid in the first octant bounded by the surfaces $az = x^2 + y^2$, $y = x$, $x = a$.   *Ans.* $(\frac{4}{5}a, \frac{9}{20}a, \frac{7}{15}a)$.

20. Find the centroid of the solid in Ex. 2.

21. Find the centroid of the solid in Ex. 3.

22. Solve each part of Ex. 21 by a second method.

23. In Ex. 3, find the moment of inertia with respect to the z-axis.

24. Find the centroid of the solid in Ex. 10.

25. Find the centroid of the solid bounded by the surfaces $z = 0$, $z = x$, $y = x$, $x^2 = ay$.   *Ans.* $(\frac{3}{5}a, \frac{1}{2}a, \frac{3}{10}a)$.

26. Solve each part of Ex. 25 by a second method.

27. In Ex. 25, find the moment of inertia with respect to the *z*-axis.

28. Show that when an area in the *xy*-plane rotates about the *x*-axis, the volume generated is

$$V = 2\pi \int_a^b \int_{y'}^{y''} y \, dy \, dx.$$

29. In Ex. 28, show that the result of the first integration is either the circular disk or the cylindrical shell, depending on the order of integration.

306. *The Double Integral*

Being given a function *f* of two independent variables, defined at all points of a plane region *S*, let us divide *S* into *k* elements ΔS_i $(i = 1, 2, \cdots, k)$ in such a way that as *k* increases and ΔS_i approaches zero, the maximum distance between any two points on the boundary of ΔS_i approaches zero. Multiply the area ΔS_i of each element by the value f_i of the function at some point of ΔS_i; add all these products together and take the limit of the sum. This limit is called the *double integral of f over the region S*, and is denoted by the symbol $\iint_S f \, dS$:

$$(1) \qquad \operatorname*{Lim}_{k \to \infty} \sum_{i=1}^k f_i \, \Delta S_i = \iint_S f \, dS.$$

Let us take a moment to tie this up with the argument of § 304. There, the independent variables were the rectangular coordinates (x, y) of any point in *S*; the equation

$$z = f(x, y)$$

Figure 325

represented a surface in space; the elements of area ΔS were rectangles $\Delta y \, \Delta x$; and since we took *m* cutting planes in one direction and *n* in the other, the number of elements was $k = mn$.

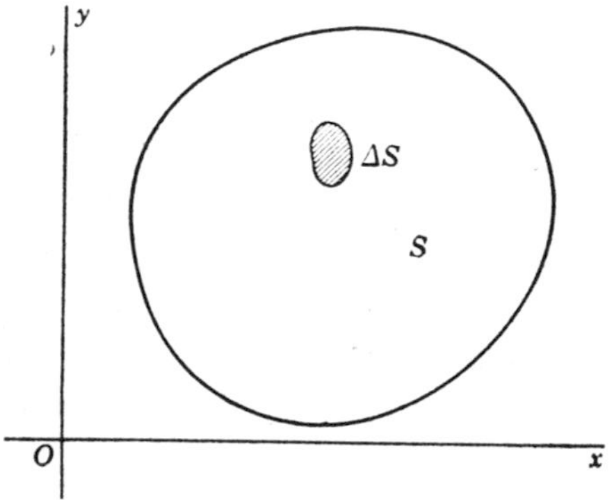

The double integral, like the "iterated" integral $\int_a^b \int_{y'}^{y''} f(x, y) \, dy \, dx$, may always be interpreted as the volume under a surface. Since this volume, for a given surface and given base *S*, is a definite fixed quantity, the value of a double integral is *independent of the mode of division* of *S* into elements, as long as the longest chord in every ΔS approaches zero.

Whenever the double integral exists, the iterated integral also exists, and gives us one means of evaluating the double integral. However, the double integral does not tie us down to a particular coordinate system or to any particular mode of division of S. We shall take advantage of this in the next section.

307. *The Double Integral in Polar Coordinates*

Let S be a plane area bounded by a curve whose equation is given in polar coordinates. We may divide S into elements ΔS by means of concentric circular arcs and radial lines, as in the figure. Then ΔS is the difference between two circular sectors of angle $\Delta \theta$ and radii r and $r + \Delta r$, respectively; i.e.,

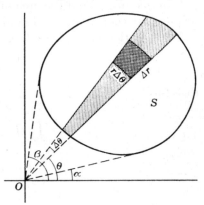

$$\Delta S = \tfrac{1}{2}(r + \Delta r)^2 \, \Delta \theta - \tfrac{1}{2} r^2 \, \Delta \theta$$

$$= r \, \Delta r \, \Delta \theta + \tfrac{1}{2}\overline{\Delta r}^2 \, \Delta \theta.$$

Let $f(r, \theta)$ be a function of the polar coordinates defined at all points of S. Then, since $\tfrac{1}{2}\overline{\Delta r}^2 \, \Delta \theta$ may be neglected, the double integral of § 306 appears as

Figure 326

$$\iint_S f \, dS = \lim_{\substack{\Delta r \to 0 \\ \Delta \theta \to 0}} \sum \sum f(r, \theta) r \, \Delta r \, \Delta \theta.$$

This double limit can be evaluated by two successive applications of Theorem 29, just as in § 304; the result is

$$\lim_{\substack{\Delta r \to 0 \\ \Delta \theta \to 0}} \sum \sum f(r, \theta) r \, \Delta r \, \Delta \theta = \int_\alpha^\beta \int_{r'}^{r''} f(r, \theta) r \, dr \, d\theta,$$

where α, β are the least and greatest values of θ (Figure 326), and r', r'' are the least and greatest values of r in the typical sector—α and β constant, r' and r'' functions of θ, in general.

308. *Plane Area as a Double Integral*

If in § 306 we take the function f as unity everywhere in S, the double integral $\iint_S f \, dS$ reduces to $\iint_S dS$. Since this is merely the limit of the sum of all the elements ΔS, the result is the area A of the region S itself:

$$A = \iint_S dS.$$

In rectangular coordinates,

$$A = \int_a^b \int_{y'}^{y''} dy\, dx = \int_c^d \int_{x'}^{x''} dx\, dy;$$

in polar coordinates,

$$A = \int_\alpha^\beta \int_{r'}^{r''} r\, dr\, d\theta.$$

Example (a).   Find the area of a right triangle by iterated integration in rectangular coordinates.   (Figure 327.)

The equation of the bounding line is

$$y = \frac{b}{a} x;$$

therefore

$$A = \int_0^a \int_0^{\frac{b}{a}x} dy\, dx = \int_0^a \left[y \right]_0^{\frac{b}{a}x} dx$$

$$= \frac{b}{a} \int_0^a x\, dx = \frac{1}{2}\, ab.$$

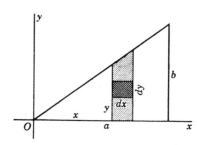

Figure 327

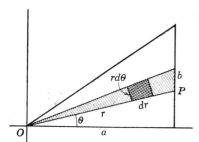

Figure 328

Example (b).   Solve Example (a) in polar coordinates.

The upper limit for *r* is seen from Figure 328 to be*

$$OP = a \sec \theta,$$

so that

$$A = \int_0^{\operatorname{Arctan}\frac{b}{a}} \int_0^{a\sec\theta} r\, dr\, d\theta$$

$$= \frac{1}{2}\, a^2 \int_0^{\operatorname{Arctan}\frac{b}{a}} \sec^2 \theta\, d\theta$$

$$= \frac{1}{2}\, a^2 \left[\tan\theta \right]_0^{\operatorname{Arctan}\frac{b}{a}} = \frac{1}{2}\, a^2 \cdot \frac{b}{a} = \frac{1}{2}\, ab.$$

* Or, we may transform the equation $x = a$ to polar coordinates: $x = r \cos\theta = a$, $r = a \sec\theta$.

309. *Volume in Cylindrical Coordinates*

Let (Figure 329)

$$z = f(r, \theta)$$

be the equation of a surface in cylindrical coordinates (polar coordinates in the xy-plane with the rectangular z). To find the volume under any portion of this surface, divide the base into polar elements $r\, dr\, d\theta$ and erect on each element a column of height z, volume $zr\, dr\, d\theta$. Then the volume desired is the double integral over S:

$$V = \operatorname*{Lim}_{\substack{\Delta r \to 0 \\ \Delta\theta \to 0}} \sum\sum zr\, \Delta r\, \Delta\theta = \int_\alpha^\beta \int_{r'}^{r''} zr\, dr\, d\theta.$$

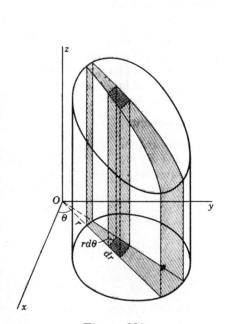

Figure 329

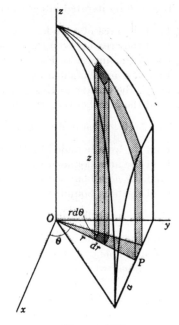

Figure 330

Example. Find the volume lying above the triangle bounded by the lines $x = 0$, $y = x$, $y = a$, and cut off by the surface

(1) $$x^2 + y^2 + az = 2a^2.$$

In cylindrical coordinates (1) becomes

$$r^2 + az = 2a^2;$$

the upper limit OP for r is found from

$$y = r\sin\theta = a,$$

so that

$$V = \frac{1}{a} \int_{\frac{\pi}{4}}^{\frac{\pi}{2}} \int_{0}^{a\,\csc\,\theta} (2a^2 - r^2) r \, dr \, d\theta$$

$$= \frac{1}{a} \int_{\frac{\pi}{4}}^{\frac{\pi}{2}} \left[a^2 r^2 - \frac{1}{4} r^4 \right]_{0}^{a\,\csc\,\theta} d\theta$$

$$= a^3 \int_{\frac{\pi}{4}}^{\frac{\pi}{2}} (\csc^2\,\theta - \tfrac{1}{4}\csc^4\,\theta) \, d\theta = \tfrac{2}{3}a^3.$$

EXERCISES

Solve Exs. 1–6 by iterated integration in rectangular coordinates.

1. Find the area of a circle.
2. Find the area between the cubic $xy^2 = a^3$ and the lines $y = a$ and $x = 0$.
3. Check the answer to Ex. 2 by inverting the order of integration.
4. Find the area bounded by the parabola $y^2 = 4ax$ and its latus rectum.
5. Check the answer to Ex. 3 by inverting the order of integration.
6. Find the area between the curves $x^2 = 2ay$, $x^2 = 4ay - a^2$.   *Ans.* $\tfrac{1}{3}a^2.$

Solve Exs. 7–10 by iterated integration in polar coordinates.

7. Find the area bounded by the curve $r = a(1 - \cos\,\theta)$.   *Ans.* $\tfrac{3}{2}\pi a^2.$
8. Find the area bounded by the curve $r = a(2 - \sin\,\theta)$.   *Ans.* $\tfrac{9}{2}\pi a^2.$
9. Find the area bounded by the curve $r = 2a \cos^2\,\theta$.   *Ans.* $\tfrac{3}{2}\pi a^2.$
10. Find the area bounded by the curve $r^2 = a^2 \sin 2\theta$.   *Ans.* $a^2.$

In Exs. 11–34, use cylindrical coordinates.

11. Find the volume of a sphere.
12. A round hole of radius b is bored through the center of a sphere of radius a. Find the volume cut out.

$$\textit{Ans.} \ \frac{4\pi}{3} \left[a^3 - (a^2 - b^2)^{\frac{3}{2}} \right].$$

13. Find the volume above the xy-plane, inside the cylinder $x^2 + y^2 = a^2$ and below the paraboloid $x^2 + y^2 = az$.   *Ans.* $\tfrac{1}{2}\pi a^3.$

14. Find the volume above the xy-plane common to the paraboloid $x^2 + y^2 + az = 4a^2$ and the cylinder $x^2 + y^2 = a^2$.   *Ans.* $\tfrac{7}{2}\pi a^3.$

15. Find the volume inside the cylinder $x^2 + y^2 = a^2$ and outside the cone $x^2 + y^2 = z^2$.   *Ans.* $\tfrac{4}{3}\pi a^3.$

16. Find the volume above the xy-plane bounded by the surfaces $x^2 + y^2 = a^2$, $z = y$, $z = 0$.   (Examples, § 278.)   *Ans.* $\tfrac{2}{3}a^3.$

17. Find the volume in the first octant inside the cylinder $y^2 + z^2 = a^2$ and outside the cylinder $y^2 = ax$.   *Ans.* $\tfrac{1}{16}\pi a^3.$

18. Find the volume in the first octant bounded by the surfaces $y = x$, $x = a$, $xy = az$.   *Ans.* $\tfrac{1}{8}a^3.$

19. Find the volume in the first octant bounded by the surfaces $y = x$, $x = a$, $2az = x^2 + y^2$.   *Ans.* $\tfrac{1}{6}a^3.$

20. Find the volume in the first octant bounded by the surfaces $y = x$, $z = x$, $ay = x^2$.   Ans. $\frac{1}{12}a^3$.

21. Find the volume in the first octant bounded by the cylinder $x^2 + z^2 = a^2$ and the plane $x - y + z = 0$.   Ans. $\frac{2}{3}a^3$.

22. Find the volume inside the cylinder $x^2 + z^2 = 4a^2$ and outside the hyperboloid $x^2 + z^2 - y^2 = a^2$.   Ans. $4\sqrt{3}\,\pi a^3$.

23. Find the volume inside the cylinder $y^2 + z^2 = a^2$ and outside the hyperboloid $x^2 - y^2 - z^2 = a^2$.   Ans. $\frac{4}{3}\pi(2\sqrt{2} - 1)a^3$.

24. A square hole of side $2a$ whose axis is the z-axis is cut through the paraboloid of Ex. 14. Find the volume cut out.   Ans. $\frac{40}{3}a^3$.

25. A vertical cylinder is passed through the circle $r = a\cos\theta$. Find the volume of the cylinder inside a sphere of radius a with center at the origin.
                                                                            Ans. $\frac{2}{3}(\pi - \frac{4}{3})a^3$.

26. Find the volume bounded by the surfaces $z = 0$, $x = 0$, $y = x$, $y = a$, $y^2 = a(z - x)$.   Ans. $\frac{5}{12}a^3$.

27. In Ex. 13, find the centroid of that part of the solid that lies in the first octant.

$$Ans. \left(\frac{8a}{5\pi}, \frac{8a}{5\pi}, \frac{a}{3}\right).$$

28. In Ex. 13, find the moment of inertia with respect to the z-axis.   Ans. $\frac{2}{3}Ma^2$.

29. Find the centroid of half of a circular cone. $Ans. \left(\dfrac{a}{\pi}, 0, \dfrac{h}{4}\right).$

30. Find the moment of inertia of the volume of a sphere with respect to a diameter.

31. Find the centroid of one octant of a sphere.   Ans. $(\frac{3}{8}a, \frac{3}{8}a, \frac{3}{8}a)$.

32. In Ex. 15, find the centroid of the volume lying in the first octant.

$$Ans. \left(\frac{3a}{2\pi}, \frac{3a}{2\pi}, \frac{3a}{8}\right).$$

33. Find the centroid of the volume in the first octant bounded by the surfaces $y = x$, $x = a$, $zx = ay$.   Ans. $(\frac{2}{3}a, \frac{4}{9}a, \frac{1}{3}a)$.

34. In Ex. 33, find the moment of inertia with respect to the z-axis.   Ans. $\frac{3}{16}a^5$.

35. Show that when an area bounded by the curve $r = f(\theta)$ rotates about the polar axis, the volume generated is

$$V = 2\pi \int_\alpha^\beta \int_{r'}^{r''} r^2 \sin\theta\, dr\, d\theta.$$

In Exs. 36–42, use the method of Ex. 35.

36. Find the volume of a sphere.

37. Find the volume of a circular cone.

38. Find the volume generated by revolving the cardioid $r = a(1 - \sin\theta)$ about its line of symmetry.   Ans. $\frac{8}{3}\pi a^3$.

39. The curve $r^2 = a^2 \sin\theta$ revolves about the y-axis. Find the volume generated.   Ans. $\frac{8}{15}\pi a^3$.

40. Find the volume of a torus.

41. Find the volume cut from a sphere by one sheet of a cone of half-angle α with its vertex at the center of the sphere.   Ans. $\frac{2}{3}\pi a^3(1 - \cos\alpha)$.

42. Find the centroid of a circular cone.

310. *Evaluation by Inversion of Order*

We have seen that inversion of the order of integration frequently affords a useful check on the value of an iterated integral. There are important integrals which cannot be evaluated in terms of elementary functions, as they stand, but which yield to elementary methods when the order of integration is inverted.

Example. Evaluate $\int_0^1 \int_x^1 e^{y^2}\, dy\, dx$.

Here the first integration is impossible by elementary methods. We shall invert the order of integration. The inner integration runs from $y = x$ to $y = 1$; the outer one from $x = 0$ to $x = 1$. Therefore the integration covers the triangle bounded by $x = 0$, $y = x$, $y = 1$ (Figure 331). The integrand is unaffected by a change of order of integration. Hence,

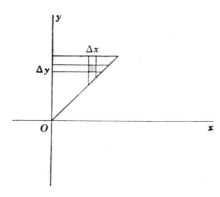

Figure 331

$$\int_0^1 \int_x^1 e^{y^2}\, dy\, dx = \int_0^1 \int_0^y e^{y^2}\, dx\, dy$$

$$= \int_0^1 \left[x e^{y^2} \right]_0^y dy$$

$$= \int_0^1 y e^{y^2}\, dy$$

$$= \left[\tfrac{1}{2} e^{y^2} \right]_0^1$$

$$= \tfrac{1}{2}(e - 1).$$

311. *Evaluation by Change of Coordinate System*

An integration impossible by elementary methods in rectangular coordinates may become possible (even simple) in polar coordinates, or vice versa. We shall use two examples, of which the second is of vital importance in many advanced applications of mathematics to engineering and physics.

Example (a). Evaluate

$$\int_0^a \int_0^{\sqrt{a^2 - x^2}} \sqrt{x^2 + y^2}\, dy\, dx.$$

Here we can perform the first integration, but not the second one, by elementary means. The integration runs from $y = 0$ to $y = \sqrt{a^2 - x^2}$, then from $x = 0$ to $x = a$; i.e., over the first quadrant of a circle of radius a, center at the origin. This suggests polar coordinates. The

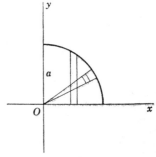

Figure 332

new element of area is $r\,dr\,d\theta$, and $\sqrt{x^2 + y^2}$ becomes r.   Therefore

$$\int_0^a \int_0^{\sqrt{a^2-x^2}} \sqrt{x^2 + y^2}\,dy\,dx = \int_0^{\frac{\pi}{2}} \int_0^a r \cdot r\,dr\,d\theta$$

$$= \int_0^{\frac{\pi}{2}} \tfrac{1}{3}a^3\,d\theta = \frac{\pi a^3}{6}.$$

Example (b).   Evaluate $\int_0^\infty e^{-x^2}\,dx$.

This involves only a single integration but a nonelementary one.   Put

$$B = \int_0^\infty e^{-x^2}\,dx.$$

Then, of course, it is also true that

$$B = \int_0^\infty e^{-y^2}\,dy.$$

Now, consider the iterated integral

$$\int_0^\infty \int_0^\infty e^{-x^2-y^2}\,dx\,dy.$$

Since $e^{-x^2-y^2} = e^{-x^2} \cdot e^{-y^2}$, we may write

$$\int_0^\infty \int_0^\infty e^{-x^2-y^2}\,dx\,dy = \int_0^\infty \left[\int_0^\infty e^{-x^2}\,dx \right] e^{-y^2}\,dy$$

$$= B \int_0^\infty e^{-y^2}\,dy = B^2.$$

Hence

$$B^2 = \int_0^\infty \int_0^\infty e^{-x^2-y^2}\,dx\,dy.$$

The region of integration in this last integral is the entire first quadrant.
Turning to polar coordinates, we find that the element of area is $r\,dr\,d\theta$
and the integrand is e^{-r^2}.   Therefore

$$B^2 = \int_0^{\frac{\pi}{2}} \int_0^\infty e^{-r^2} r\,dr\,d\theta$$

$$= \int_0^{\frac{\pi}{2}} \left[-\tfrac{1}{2}e^{-r^2} \right]_0^\infty d\theta$$

$$= \int_0^{\frac{\pi}{2}} \tfrac{1}{2}d\theta = \tfrac{1}{4}\pi.$$

Since $B^2 = \tfrac{1}{4}\pi$, and $B > 0$, $B = \tfrac{1}{2}\sqrt{\pi}$.   That is,

$$\int_0^\infty e^{-x^2}\,dx = \frac{\sqrt{\pi}}{2}.$$

EXERCISES

In Exs. 1–9, evaluate the integrals by inverting the order of integration.

1. $\displaystyle\int_0^1 \int_y^1 \frac{y\,dx\,dy}{\sqrt{x^2+y^2}}.$ Ans. $\frac{1}{2}(\sqrt{2}-1).$

2. $\displaystyle\int_0^1 \int_{2y}^2 y\sqrt{x^2+y^2}\,dx\,dy.$ Ans. $\frac{1}{6}(5\sqrt{5}-8).$

3. $\displaystyle\int_0^1 \int_x^1 x(x^2+y^2)^{\frac{1}{2}}\,dy\,dx.$ Ans. $\frac{1}{30}(4\sqrt{2}-1).$

4. $\displaystyle\int_0^1 \int_x^1 x\sin y^3\,dy\,dx.$ Ans. $0.077.$

5. $\displaystyle\int_0^1 \int_y^1 \frac{\sqrt{y}\sin x}{x}\,dx\,dy.$ Ans. $0.159.$

6. $\displaystyle\int_{-1}^0 \int_{-x}^1 \frac{x^2\,dy\,dx}{1+y^4}.$ Ans. $0.058.$

7. $\displaystyle\int_0^2 \int_{\frac{1}{2}y}^1 \frac{dx\,dy}{(1+x^2)^3}.$ Ans. $\frac{3}{8}.$

8. $\displaystyle\int_0^1 \int_{\sqrt{x}}^1 \sqrt{1+y^3}\,dy\,dx.$ Ans. $0.406.$

9. $\displaystyle\int_0^4 \int_{\sqrt{y}}^2 \frac{y\,dx\,dy}{\sqrt{1+x^5}}.$ Ans. $0.949.$

In Exs. 10–18, evaluate by transforming to polar coordinates.

10. $\displaystyle\int_0^1 \int_0^{\sqrt{1-x^2}} e^{-x^2-y^2}\,dy\,dx.$ Ans. $\dfrac{\pi(e-1)}{4e}.$

11. $\displaystyle\int_0^1 \int_0^{\sqrt{1-x^2}} e^{x^2+y^2}\,dy\,dx.$ Ans. $\frac{1}{4}\pi(e-1).$

12. Ex. 1.   13. Ex. 2.

14. Ex. 3.   15. Ex. 4.

16. The example of § 310.

17. $\displaystyle\int_0^a \int_0^{\sqrt{a^2-x^2}} x^2\sqrt{x^2+y^2}\,dy\,dx.$ Ans. $\dfrac{\pi a^5}{20}.$

18. $\displaystyle\int_0^a \int_0^x \frac{x^2\,dy\,dx}{\sqrt{x^2+y^2}}.$ Ans. $\dfrac{a^3}{3}\ln(1+\sqrt{2}).$

19. Evaluate $\displaystyle\int_0^{\frac{\pi}{2}} \int_0^{\sec\theta} \frac{r\,dr\,d\theta}{1+r^2\sin^2\theta}$ by transforming to rectangular coordinates.

                                                       Ans. $\frac{1}{2}\pi.$

20. Use the result in Example (b), § 311, to evaluate

$$\int_0^\infty e^{-a^2x^2}\,dx, \qquad \text{for } a>0.$$ Ans. $\dfrac{\sqrt{\pi}}{2a}.$

21. Evaluate the integral in Ex. 20 for $a < 0$.

Ans. $\dfrac{-\sqrt{\pi}}{2a}$.

22. Find the volume generated by revolving about the x-axis the area between $y = e^{-x^2}$ and its asymptote.

Ans. $2\left(\dfrac{\pi}{2}\right)^{\frac{3}{2}}$.

23. For the area of Ex. 22, find the moment of inertia with respect to Oy.

24. For the area of Ex. 22, find the moment of inertia with respect to Ox.

25. Evaluate $\displaystyle\int_0^\infty x^{-\frac{1}{2}}e^{-ax}\,dx$, for $a > 0$. Put $x = v^2$.

Ans. $\sqrt{\dfrac{\pi}{a}}$.

26. Evaluate $\displaystyle\int_0^\infty x^{\frac{1}{2}}e^{-ax}\,dx$, for $a > 0$.

Ans. $\frac{1}{2}\sqrt{\dfrac{\pi}{a^3}}$.

27. Evaluate $\displaystyle\int_0^1 \left(\ln\dfrac{1}{x}\right)^{\frac{1}{2}}\,dx$.

Ans. $\frac{1}{2}\sqrt{\pi}$.

312. *Area of a Surface*

We have seen (§ 280) that the area of a surface of revolution may be found by simple integration. To find areas of curved surfaces in general, double integration is required.

Consider a region R on the surface

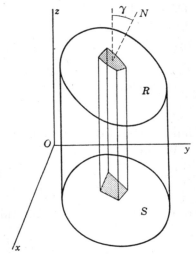

Figure 333

(1) $$z = f(x, y).$$

Let us pass through the boundary of R a vertical cylinder, cutting from the xy-plane a region S; i.e., S is the horizontal projection of R. Divide S into elements ΔS_i in any convenient way (§ 306), and denote by ΔR_i the portion of R lying above the ith element. Draw the tangent plane at some point (any point) of ΔR_i, and denote by $\Delta R_i'$ the element of area (above ΔS_i) on on the tangent plane. Now the two elements ΔR_i and $\Delta R_i'$, on the surface and on the tangent plane respectively, are essentially equal in the sense that in taking the limit of the sum, we may *substitute the latter for the former*.

It is known from geometry (or if not known, is easily established—Ex. 30 below) that if two planes intersect at an acute angle, an area in one plane may be projected into the other by multiplying by the cosine of the included angle. The angle between the xy-plane and the tangent plane equals the angle between their normals; i.e., it is the angle between the z-axis and the normal to the surface at the point of contact of the tangent plane. Thus, if γ_i is the z-direction angle of the normal N_i,

$$\Delta R'_i \cos \gamma_i = \Delta S_i,$$
$$\Delta R'_i = \sec \gamma_i \, \Delta S_i.$$

Adding all the elements and taking the limit of the sum, we define the area R as

(2)
$$R = \iint_S \sec \gamma \, dS.$$

Of course if it is more convenient to project the area into the yz- or zx-plane, the same formula holds with α or β in place of γ.

By § 272, the direction cosines of the normal to the surface (1) are proportional to $-\dfrac{\partial z}{\partial x}, -\dfrac{\partial z}{\partial y}, 1$, so that

$$\cos \gamma = \frac{1}{\sqrt{\left(\dfrac{\partial z}{\partial x}\right)^2 + \left(\dfrac{\partial z}{\partial y}\right)^2 + 1}}.$$

Thus (2) becomes in rectangular coordinates

(3)
$$R = \int_a^b \int_{y'}^{y''} \sqrt{\left(\frac{\partial z}{\partial x}\right)^2 + \left(\frac{\partial z}{\partial y}\right)^2 + 1} \; dy \, dx.$$

Example (a). Find the area of the cylinder* (Figure 334)

$$2az = 2a^2 - ax - y^2$$

intercepted in the first octant by the planes $y = x$, $y = a$.
We find

$$\frac{\partial z}{\partial x} = -\frac{1}{2}, \qquad \frac{\partial z}{\partial y} = -\frac{y}{a}.$$

In the order x, y (which is in this case much the simpler),

$$R = \int_0^a \int_0^y \sqrt{\frac{1}{4} + \frac{y^2}{a^2} + 1} \; dx \, dy$$
$$= \frac{1}{2a} \int_0^a \int_0^y \sqrt{5a^2 + 4y^2} \; dx \, dy$$
$$= \frac{1}{2a} \int_0^a \sqrt{5a^2 + 4y^2} \; y \, dy,$$

so that

$$R = \frac{1}{16a} \cdot \frac{2}{3} \left[(5a^2 + 4y^2)^{\frac{3}{2}} \right]_0^a = \frac{1}{24} (27 - 5^{\frac{3}{2}})a^2.$$

* Sections by planes $y = k$ are easily seen to be parallel straight lines, the yz-trace is a parabola, so that the surface is a parabolic cylinder with generators parallel to the zx-plane.

To use (2) in polar coordinates, we would usually work out sec γ in rectangular coordinates and transform the result to the polar system.

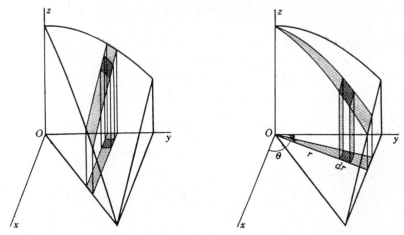

Figure 334   **Figure 335**

Example (b).   Solve the problem above in polar coordinates.

Using the value of sec γ from Example (a), we have (Figure 335)

$$R = \frac{1}{2a} \iint_{S} \sqrt{5a^2 + 4y^2}\, dS$$

$$= \frac{1}{2a} \int_{\frac{\pi}{4}}^{\frac{\pi}{2}} \int_{0}^{a \csc \theta} \sqrt{5a^2 + 4r^2 \sin^2 \theta}\; r\, dr\, d\theta$$

$$= \frac{1}{16a} \cdot \frac{2}{3} \int_{\frac{\pi}{4}}^{\frac{\pi}{2}} \frac{(5a^2 + 4r^2 \sin^2 \theta)^{\frac{3}{2}} \Big]_{0}^{a \csc \theta}}{\sin^2 \theta}\, d\theta$$

$$= \frac{(27 - 5^{\frac{3}{2}})a^2}{24} \int_{\frac{\pi}{4}}^{\frac{\pi}{2}} \csc^2 \theta\, d\theta = \frac{(27 - 5^{\frac{3}{2}})a^2}{24}.$$

313. *Surfaces of Revolution*

In § 280 we defined the area of a surface of revolution; in § 312 we defined curved area in general, including the former as a special case.   Thus for the surface of revolution, area has been defined in two ways; this is allowable only if the two definitions are equivalent.   It is interesting and not difficult to see how the general formula works out in the special case.

Let a surface of revolution be formed by revolving about Ox, from $x = a$ to $x = b$, the curve

$$y = u, \qquad z = 0,$$

where u is a function of x. By § 280, the area generated is

$$S = 2\pi \int_C y \, ds = 2\pi \int_a^b u \sqrt{1 + \left(\frac{du}{dx}\right)^2} \, dx.$$

Any point Q of the given curve describes, in the rotation, a circle of radius $MQ = u$. Let $P: (x, y, z)$ be a random point of that circle. Then, directly from the figure,

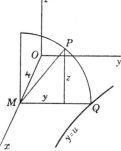

$$y^2 + z^2 = \overline{MP}^2 = \overline{MQ}^2 = u^2,$$

or, above the xy-plane,

$$z = \sqrt{u^2 - y^2}.$$

This gives

Figure 336

$$\frac{\partial z}{\partial x} = \frac{u \dfrac{du}{dx}}{\sqrt{u^2 - y^2}}, \qquad \frac{\partial z}{\partial y} = \frac{-y}{\sqrt{u^2 - y^2}}.$$

Substituting in (3), § 312, and remembering that the first octant contains only one-fourth of the surface, we find after a trifle of simplifying

$$R = 4 \int_a^b \int_0^u \frac{u \sqrt{1 + \left(\dfrac{du}{dx}\right)^2}}{\sqrt{u^2 - y^2}} \, dy \, dx$$

$$= 4 \int_a^b u \sqrt{1 + \left(\frac{du}{dx}\right)^2} \left[\operatorname{Arcsin} \frac{y}{u} \right]_0^u dx$$

$$= 2\pi \int_a^b u \sqrt{1 + \left(\frac{du}{dx}\right)^2} \, dx = S.$$

EXERCISES

In Exs. 1–12, use rectangular coordinates.

1. Find the surface area of a sphere.

2. Find the area on the cylinder $y^2 + z^2 = a^2$ included between the planes $y = x$, $y = 3x$.   *Ans.* $\frac{8}{3}a^2$.

3. Find the area of that part of the surface $az = ay + x^2$ lying above the xy-triangle bounded by the lines $y = 0$, $y = x$, $x = a$.   *Ans.* $\frac{1}{12}(6^{\frac{3}{2}} - 2^{\frac{3}{2}})a^2$.

4. Find the area on the cylinder $x^2 + z^2 = a^2$ included between the planes $y = 0$, $y = mx$.   *Ans.* $4ma^2$.

5. Solve Ex. 4, integrating in the other order.

6. Find the area of that part of the surface $9(z - y)^2 = 4x^3$ whose projection in the xy-plane is the triangle bounded by the lines $y = 0$, $y = x$, $x = 2$.

     Ans. $\frac{16}{15}(2 + \sqrt{2})$.

7. Solve Ex. 6, integrating in the other order.

8. Find the area cut off on the cylinder $y^2 + z^2 = a^2$ by the circular paraboloid $y^2 + z^2 = bx$.

$$Ans. \ \frac{2\pi a^3}{b}.$$

9. Find the area on the cylinder $z^2 = 4ax$ and inside the cylinder $y^2 = 4ax$, from $x = 0$ to $x = 3a$.

$$Ans. \ \frac{112a^2}{3}.$$

10. How much of the conical surface $z^2 = x^2 + y^2$ lies above a square of side $2a$ in the xy-plane whose center is the origin?

11. Find the area of that part of the surface $a^2z = a^2x + y^3$ intercepted in the first quadrant by the cylinder $y^3 = a^2x$ and the plane $y = a$.　　*Ans.* $\frac{1}{54}(11^{\frac{3}{2}} - 2^{\frac{3}{2}})a^2$.

12. A square hole of side $\sqrt{2}\,a$ is cut centrally through a sphere of radius a. Find the area cut from the surface of the sphere.　　　*Ans.* $4\pi(\sqrt{2} - 1)a^2$.

In Exs. 13–20, use polar coordinates.

13. Ex. 1.	**14.** Ex. 2.	**15.** Ex. 3.
16. Ex. 4.	**17.** Ex. 8.	**18.** Ex. 9.

19. How much of the surface area of the hyperbolic paraboloid $az = xy$ lies within the cylinder $x^2 + y^2 = a^2$, in the first octant?

20. The center of a sphere of radius a is on the surface of a cylinder of diameter a.　　Find the surface area on the sphere cut out by the cylinder.　　　*Ans.* $2(\pi - 2)a^2$.

21. A vertical cylinder is cut by a surface $z = f(x, y)$. Show that the area of the cylinder intercepted between the xy-plane and the cutting surface is

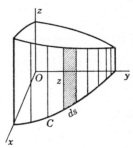

$$R = \int_C z \ ds,$$

where C is the horizontal projection of the curve of intersection.

Figure 337

In Exs. 22–29, use (or adapt) the formula of Ex. 21.

22. A woodsman chops halfway through a tree, the lower face of the cut being horizontal, the upper inclined at 45°.　Find the area of bark cut out.　(Examples, § 278.)　　　　　　　　　　　　　　　　　　　*Ans.* $2a^2$.

23. Solve Ex. 22, integrating in the other order.

24. Solve Ex. 22 in polar coordinates.

25. Ex. 2.　　　　　　　**26.** Ex. 8.　　　　　　　**27.** Ex. 9.

28. In Ex. 20, find the surface area cut from the cylinder by the sphere.

29. A solid is bounded by two equal circular cylinders of radius a whose axes intersect at right angles.　Find the total surface area of the solid.　　　*Ans.* $16a^2$.

30. Two planes intersect at an angle α.　(a) Given, in one plane, a rectangle of area A with its base parallel to the line of intersection, show that the projection of this area in the other plane is $A \cos \alpha$.　(b) Show that this formula holds for an area of any shape.　(Divide into rectangular strips, with their ends parallel to the line of intersection, and integrate.)

Triple Integrals

314. *The Triple Integral in Rectangular Coordinates*

Suppose we have given a continuous function $f(x, y, z)$ defined at all points of a three-dimensional region V. Let us pass through V three sets of planes parallel to the coordinate planes, thus dividing V into elementary boxes of

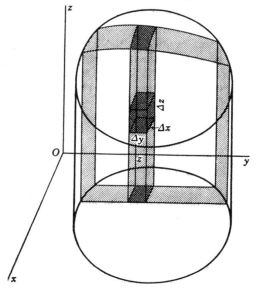

Figure 338

volume $\Delta x \, \Delta y \, \Delta z$, together with smaller irregular portions around the boundary. Now multiply the volume of each element by the value of the function at some point of the element and form the sum of these products. The triple limit

$$\text{Lim}_{\substack{\Delta z \to 0 \\ \Delta y \to 0 \\ \Delta x \to 0}} \Sigma\Sigma\Sigma f(x, y, z) \, \Delta z \, \Delta y \, \Delta x$$

is defined as the value of the *triple integral*, or *volume integral*, of $f(x, y, z)$ throughout the region V.

This limit may be evaluated by three successive integrations (cf. § 305):

$$T = \lim_{\substack{\Delta z \to 0 \\ \Delta y \to 0 \\ \Delta x \to 0}} \Sigma\Sigma\Sigma \, f(x, y, z) \, \Delta z \, \Delta y \, \Delta x$$

(1)
$$= \int_a^b \int_{y'}^{y''} \int_{z'}^{z''} f(x, y, z) \, dz \, dy \, dx.$$

The first integration extends over a vertical column of base $\Delta y \, \Delta x$; the limits z', z'' are the extreme values of z in this column and in general are functions of both x and y. The integration with respect to y is extended over a slice parallel to the yz-plane; the limits y' and y'' are the extreme values of y in this slice and are functions of x alone. In the final integration the limits are, of course, the extreme values of x in the whole region.

Since there are six permutations of the three letters x, y, z, five other orders of integration are possible, in addition to (1).

315. *Volume as a Triple Integral*

If in § 314 the given function be taken as unity, the integrand becomes merely the volume element, so that the result of integration is the volume itself:

$$V = \int_a^b \int_{y'}^{y''} \int_{z'}^{z''} dz \, dy \, dx.$$

Example. Find the volume sliced off the paraboloid $x^2 + z^2 = ay$ by the plane $y = a$. (Figure 339.)

We read directly from the figure

$$V = 4 \int_0^a \int_{\frac{x^2}{a}}^a \int_0^{\sqrt{ay - x^2}} dz \, dy \, dx$$

$$= 4 \int_0^a \int_{\frac{x^2}{a}}^a \left[z \right]_0^{\sqrt{ay - x^2}} dy \, dx$$

$$= 4 \int_0^a \int_{\frac{x^2}{a}}^a \sqrt{ay - x^2} \, dy \, dx$$

$$= \frac{8}{3a} \int_0^a \left[(ay - x^2)^{\frac{3}{2}} \right]_{\frac{x^2}{a}}^a dx = \frac{\pi}{2} a^3.$$

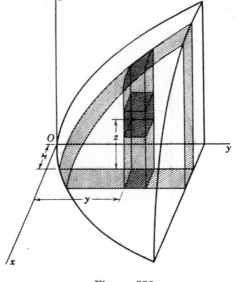

Figure 339

For practice in reading limits, the student should verify the following integrals for the same volume:

$$V = 4 \int_0^a \int_0^{\sqrt{ay}} \int_0^{\sqrt{ay - x^2}} dz \, dx \, dy;$$

$$V = 4 \int_0^a \int_0^{\sqrt{a^2 - x^2}} \int_{\frac{x^2+z^2}{a}}^a dy \, dz \, dx.$$

A figure should be drawn for each case.

316. *The Triple Integral: General Formulation*

We may generalize the setup of § 314 in two ways. First, let the given function f be a function not necessarily of x, y, z but of any three independent variables. Second, let the region of integration be divided into k volume-elements ΔV_i, of any shape whatever, subject to the single condition that as k increases, *the maximum distance between any two points of ΔV_i approaches zero.*

Now, multiply each ΔV_i by the value of f at some point of the element, and add all these products. The *limit of this sum* as k approaches infinity (always provided the limit exists) is the triple integral of f throughout V:

(1)
$$\operatorname*{Lim}_{k \to \infty} \sum_{i=1}^k f_i \, \Delta V_i = \iiint_V f \, dV.$$

317. *The Triple Integral in Cylindrical Coordinates*

Divide the volume into elements by planes through the z-axis, cylinders around the z-axis, and planes perpendicular to the z-axis (Figure 340). Then the base of the element (apart from terms which drop out in the limit) is $r \, \Delta r \, \Delta \theta$, the altitude Δz, volume $r \, \Delta z \, \Delta r \, \Delta \theta$, so that

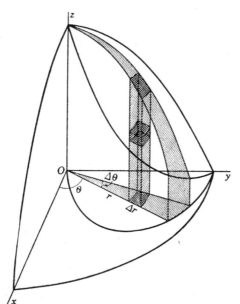

Figure 340

$$\operatorname*{Lim}_{\substack{\Delta z \to 0 \\ \Delta r \to 0 \\ \Delta \theta \to 0}} \sum \sum \sum f(r, \theta, z) r \, \Delta z \, \Delta r \, \Delta \theta$$

$$= \int_\alpha^\beta \int_{r'}^{r''} \int_{z'}^{z''} f(r, \theta, z) r \, dz \, dr \, d\theta.$$

In particular, if

$$f(r, \theta, z) = 1,$$

the integral represents the volume of the region in question:

$$V = \int_\alpha^\beta \int_{r'}^{r''} \int_{z'}^{z''} r \, dz \, dr \, d\theta.$$

Example. Find the volume in the first octant inside the cylinder $x^2 + y^2 = ay$ and the paraboloid $x^2 + y^2 + az = a^2$. (Figure 340.)

In cylindrical coordinates, the given equations are

$$r = a \sin \theta, \qquad r^2 + az = a^2:$$

$$V = \int_0^{\frac{\pi}{2}} \int_0^{a \sin \theta} \int_0^{\frac{a^2-r^2}{a}} r \, dz \, dr \, d\theta$$

$$= \int_0^{\frac{\pi}{2}} \int_0^{a \sin \theta} \left[z \right]_0^{\frac{a^2-r^2}{a}} r \, dr \, d\theta = \frac{1}{a} \int_0^{\frac{\pi}{2}} \int_0^{a \sin \theta} (a^2 - r^2) r \, dr \, d\theta$$

$$= -\frac{1}{4a} \int_0^{\frac{\pi}{2}} \left[(a^2 - r^2)^2 \right]_0^{a \sin \theta} d\theta = \frac{a^3}{4} \int_0^{\frac{\pi}{2}} (1 - \cos^4 \theta) \, d\theta = \frac{5}{64} \pi a^3.$$

EXERCISES

In Exs. 1–16, use triple integration in rectangular coordinates.

1. Find the volume in the first octant bounded by the surfaces $a^2z = xy^2$, $y = x$, $x = a$, integrating in the order z, x, y.

2. Check Ex. 1, by integrating in the order z, y, x.

3. Find the volume of a sphere.

4. Find the volume in the first octant bounded by the surfaces $yz = x^2 + z^2$, $z = x$, $z = a$, integrating in order y, z, x. *Ans.* $\frac{4}{9}a^3$.

5. Ex. 4, integrating in order y, x, z.

6. Find the volume in the first octant bounded by the surfaces $z^2 = xy$, $y = x$, $x = a$, integrating in order z, y, x. *Ans.* $\frac{2}{9}a^3$.

7. Ex. 6, integrating in order z, x, y.

8. Find the volume in the first octant bounded by the surfaces $a^2z = a^3 - xy^2$, $y^2 = ax$, $y = a$, integrating in order z, y, x. *Ans.* $\frac{11}{42}a^3$.

9. Ex. 8, integrating in order z, x, y.

10. Find the volume in the first octant bounded by the surfaces $z = x + y$, $y = 1 - x^2$. *Ans.* $\frac{31}{60}$.

11. In Ex. 1, find the centroid.

12. In Ex. 4, find the centroid. *Ans.* $(\frac{27}{64}a, \frac{21}{40}a, \frac{3}{4}a)$.

13. In Ex. 6, find the centroid. *Ans.* $(\frac{3}{4}a, \frac{9}{20}a, \frac{9}{32}a)$.

14. In Ex. 8, find the centroid.   15. In Ex. 4, find I_x, I_y, I_z.

16. In Ex. 6, find I_x, I_y, I_z. *Ans.* $I_y = \frac{18}{25}Ma^2$

In Exs. 17–25, use triple integration with cylindrical coordinates.

17. Ex. 1.   18. Ex. 4.   19. Ex. 6.   20. Ex. 8.

21. Find the volume of a sphere.

22. Find the volume bounded by the xy-plane, the cylinder $x^2 + y^2 = ay$, and the paraboloid, $x^2 + y^2 = az$ *Ans.* $\frac{3}{32}\pi a^3$.

23. Find the volume in the first octant bounded by the cylinder $x^2 + y^2 = ay$ and the cone $a^2z^2 = h^2(x^2 + y^2)$. *Ans.* $\frac{2}{9}a^2h$.

24. In Ex. 22, find the centroid. *Ans.* $(0, \frac{2}{3}a, \frac{5}{18}a)$.

25. In Ex. 22, find I_x, I_y, I_z. *Ans.* $I_x = \frac{175}{288}Ma^2$.

318. *Heterogeneous Masses*

The density of a homogeneous mass has been defined in § 281 as the ratio of the mass to the volume it occupies:

$$\delta = \frac{M}{V}.$$

For a *heterogeneous* mass, i.e., one whose density varies from point to point, we must introduce the idea of *density at a point.*

Consider an element of volume ΔV including a point P, and let ΔM denote the mass contained in ΔV. Then the ratio $\dfrac{\Delta M}{\Delta V}$ is the *average density* of ΔV.

If ΔV approaches zero in such a way that P is always included, the ratio $\dfrac{\Delta M}{\Delta V}$ in general approaches a limit δ, called the *density at the point* P:

$$\delta = \operatorname*{Lim}_{\Delta V \to 0} \frac{\Delta M}{\Delta V} = \frac{dM}{dV}.$$

If the density at any point is given as a function of the coordinates, the mass can be found by integration. In the most general case we divide the space occupied by the body into volume-elements ΔV_i as in § 316, multiply each element by the density δ_i at one of its points, and add all these products. The limit of this sum is the mass:

$$M = \iiint_V \delta dV.$$

We shall use the term *homogeneous element* to mean that the density δ is essentially constant throughout the element in the sense that $\delta = \delta_i + \Delta\delta_i$ and

$$\operatorname*{Lim}_{\Delta V_i \to 0} \Sigma\Sigma\Sigma \, \Delta\delta_i \, \Delta V_i = 0.$$

That is, the variation in δ throughout the *element* makes a zero contribution to the mass integral. It is important to see two points clearly:

(*a*) The element must always be homogeneous, since otherwise, in building up the integral, we would not know what value to use for δ.

(*b*) Homogeneity of the element is the only requisite; the volume element may be of any character whatever, provided the mass contained in it is homogeneous, since then we know the values of both δ and dV.

If δ varies in some simple manner, it is possible in many cases to find a homogeneous element of one of the shapes used in Chapters 33 and 37; if so, we may find the volume by simple or at worst by iterated integration. See Examples (*a*) and (*b*).

Example (a). Find the mass of a circular cone whose density varies as the distance from the axis. (Figure 341.)

Let the cone be generated by revolving the line

$$\frac{x}{h} + \frac{y}{a} = 1$$

about Ox. If we divide the mass into cylindrical shells about the axis, each element will be homogeneous of density $\delta = ky$:

$$M = \int \delta \, dV = 2\pi k \int_0^a y \cdot yx \, dy$$

$$= 2\pi k \int_0^a y^2 \left(h - \frac{hy}{a} \right) dy = \tfrac{1}{6}\pi k a^3 h.$$

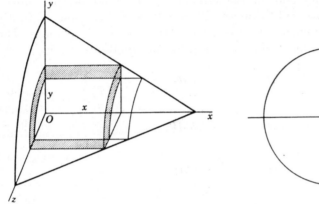

Figure 341

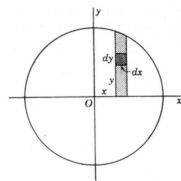

Figure 342

Example (b). Find the mass of a circular plate if the density is proportional to the sum of the distances from two perpendicular diameters. (Figure 342.)

With the two diameters as axes, $\delta = k(x + y)$, whence

$$M = 4k \int_0^a \int_0^{\sqrt{a^2 - x^2}} (x + y) \, dy \, dx, \quad \text{etc.}$$

Example (c). Find the mass of a sphere whose density is proportional to the sum of the distances from three mutually perpendicular diametral planes.

Since the density varies with all three coordinates, a triple integral is required; in rectangular coordinates,

$$M = 8k \int_0^a \int_0^{\sqrt{a^2 - x^2}} \int_0^{\sqrt{a^2 - x^2 - y^2}} (x + y + z) \, dz \, dy \, dx.$$

319. *Centroids; Moments of Inertia*

In Chapters 34–35, in order to make the ideas of centroid and moment of inertia intelligible on an intuitive basis, we adopted the rough-and-ready expedient of considering the mass as an "aggregate of particles." We are now, for the first time, in position to state analytic definitions of first and second moments of mass.

Given a three-dimensional mass M occupying a volume V, with the density δ expressed as a function of the coordinates (including as a special case the homogeneous body, δ constant), take

$$\Delta M_i = \delta_i \, \Delta V_i$$

as in § 318. Multiply each element by the distance x_i of one of its points from the yz-plane, and add all the products. The limit of this sum is defined as the *first moment* of the mass with respect to the yz-plane. Similar definitions hold for moments with respect to the zx- and xy-planes. The point $(\bar{x}, \bar{y}, \bar{z})$, whose coordinates are given by the equations

$$M\bar{x} = \iiint\limits_{V} x\delta \, dV,$$

$$M\bar{y} = \iiint\limits_{V} y\delta \, dV,$$

$$M\bar{z} = \iiint\limits_{V} z\delta \, dV$$

is the *centroid* of the mass.

In analogous fashion we arrive at a suitable definition for *moment of inertia* with respect to the x-axis:

$$I_x = \iiint\limits_{V} (y^2 + z^2)\delta \, dV,$$

with similar definitions for I_y and I_z.

For area masses or line masses, the defining formulas are the two- and one-dimensional analogues of those above.

Example (a). In Example (a), § 318,

$$M\bar{x} = 2\pi k \int_0^a \frac{x}{2} \cdot y \cdot yx \, dy = \frac{\pi k h^2}{a^2} \int_0^a y^2(a-y)^2 \, dy$$

$$= \frac{1}{30} \pi k a^4 h,$$

$$\bar{x} = \frac{\frac{1}{30}\pi k a^4 h}{\frac{1}{6}\pi k a^3 h} = \frac{1}{5} a.$$

Example (b).   In Example (b), § 318,

$$I_x = 4k \int_0^a \int_0^{\sqrt{a^2-x^2}} y^2(x+y) \, dy \, dx.$$

320. *Translation Theorem on Moments of Inertia*

We are now able to prove the theorem of § 298, that if the lines l and $\bar{l}$ are parallel at a distance h apart, and if $\bar{l}$ passes through the centroid of the mass M, then

$$I_l = I_{\bar{l}} + Mh^2.$$

Take the line $\bar{l}$ as x-axis, the line l as $y = h$, $z = 0$. With a volume element chosen in any suitable manner (the figure shows only one element), we have

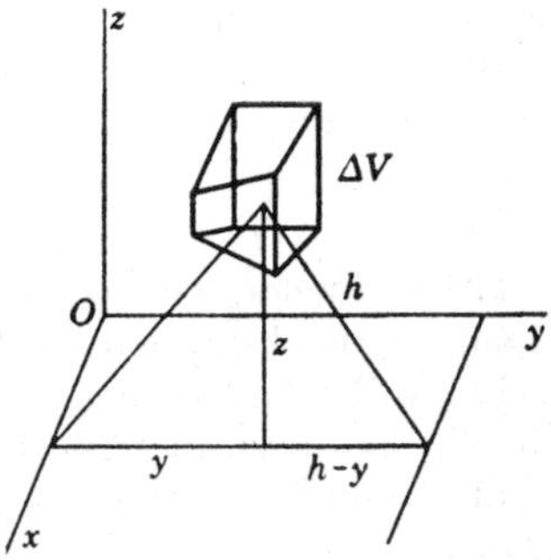

$$I_{\bar{l}} = \iiint_V (y^2 + z^2)\delta \, dV,$$

$$I_l = \iiint_V [(h-y)^2 + z^2]\delta \, dV,$$

Figure 343

$$I_l = h^2 \iiint_V \delta \, dV - 2h \iiint_V y\delta \, dV + \iiint_V (y^2 + z^2)\delta \, dV.$$

By § 318, the first of these three integrals is Mh^2; by § 319, the second is $-2hM\bar{y}$ and therefore vanishes, since the centroid is in the zx-plane; the third is $I_{\bar{l}}$.

COROLLARY.   *If two parallel lines* l_1, l_2 *are at distances* h_1, h_2 *from the centroid,*

$$I_{l_2} = I_{l_1} + M(h_2{}^2 - h_1{}^2).$$

EXERCISES

In Exs. 1–22, find the mass.

1. A straight rod of length c, whose density is proportional to the distance from one end.   *Ans.* $\frac{1}{2}kc^2$.

2. A straight rod of length c, whose density is proportional to the square of the distance from one end.   *Ans.* $\frac{1}{3}kc^3$.

3. A straight rod of length c, whose density is proportional to the square of the distance from the center.   *Ans.* $\frac{1}{12}kc^3$.

4. Four rods forming a square of side c, with the density varying as the square of the distance from one corner.   *Ans.* $\frac{10}{3}kc^3$.

5. A rectangular plate, sides a and b, with density proportional to the square of the distance from a side of length b.   *Ans.* $\frac{1}{3}ka^3b$

6. A rectangular plate, sides a and b, with density proportional to the product of the distances to two adjacent sides. *Ans.* $\frac{1}{4}ka^2b^2$.

7. A semicircular wire, radius a, whose density varies as the distance from the bounding diameter. Use polar coordinates. *Ans.* $2ka^2$.

8. A semicircular wire, radius a, whose density varies as the fourth power of the distance from the bounding diameter.

$$Ans. \; \frac{3k\pi a^5}{8}.$$

9. A circular plate, radius a, whose density varies as the square of the distance from a fixed diameter. *Ans.* $\frac{1}{4}k\pi a^4$.

10. A circular plate, radius a, with density varying as the cube of the distance from the center.

$$Ans. \; \frac{2k\pi a^5}{5}.$$

11. A circular cylinder, base radius a and height h, whose density varies as the square of the distance from the base. *Ans.* $\frac{1}{3}k\pi a^2h^3$.

12. A circular cylinder, base radius a and height h, with density proportional to the distance from the axis of the cylinder. *Ans.* $\frac{2}{3}k\pi a^3h$.

13. A sphere, radius a, whose density varies as the distance from a fixed diametral plane. *Ans.* $\frac{1}{2}k\pi a^4$.

14. A spherical surface, radius a, with density proportional to the distance from a fixed diameter. *Ans.* $k\pi^2a^3$.

15. A spherical surface, radius a, with density proportional to the distance from a fixed diametral plane. *Ans.* $2k\pi a^3$.

16. A square, side a, whose density varies as the square of the distance from one corner.

$$Ans. \; \frac{2ka^4}{3}.$$

17. A square, side a, whose density varies as the distance from one corner. Use polar coordinates. *Ans.* $\frac{1}{3}ka^3\left[\sqrt{2} + \ln\left(1 + \sqrt{2}\right)\right]$.

18. A rectangular plate, sides a and b, whose density is proportional to the sum of the distances from two adjacent sides. *Ans.* $\frac{1}{2}kab(a + b)$.

19. A circular plate, radius a, whose density is proportional to the distance from a fixed point on the circumference. Use polar coordinates, with the equation $r = 2a \cos \theta$. *Ans.* $\frac{32}{9}ka^3$.

20. Use polar coordinates to solve Example (*b*), § 318. *Ans.* $\frac{8}{3}ka^3$.

21. A cube, edge length a, with density varying as the square of the distance from one corner. *Ans.* ka^5.

22. A cube, edge length a, whose density varies as the sum of the distances from three adjacent faces. *Ans.* $\frac{3}{2}ka^4$.

23. Complete the solution in Example (*c*), § 318. *Ans.* $\frac{3}{2}k\pi a^4$.

24. Solve Example (*c*), § 318, in cylindrical coordinates.

25. Show that the problem of determining fluid pressure on a submerged vertical area (§ 300) is equivalent to that of finding the mass of a thin plate whose density is proportional to the distance from a line in the plane.

In Exs. 26–38, find the centroid.

26. Ex. 1.   *Ans.* $\frac{2}{3}$ way from the end of zero density.
27. Ex. 2.   **28.** Ex. 4.   **29.** Ex. 5.   **30.** Ex. 6.
31. A semicircular plate, radius a, whose density varies as the square of the distance from the bounding diameter.   Use polar coordinates.

Ans. On the line of symmetry, $\dfrac{32a}{15\pi}$ from the center.

32. A semicircular plate, radius a, whose density varies as the distance from the center.
33. One quadrant of a circular plate, radius a, with density proportional to the distance from one of the bounding radii.
34. One quadrant of a circular wire, radius a, with density varying as the distance from one of the bounding radii.
35. Ex. 19.

Ans. On the line of symmetry, $\dfrac{6a}{5}$ from the point of zero density.

36. A circular plate, radius a, whose density is proportional to the square of the distance from a fixed point on the circumference.

Ans. On the line of symmetry, $\dfrac{4a}{3}$ from the point of zero density.

37. Ex. 21.   *Ans.* $\left(\dfrac{7a}{12}, \dfrac{7a}{12}, \dfrac{7a}{12}\right)$.   **38.** Ex. 22.   *Ans.* $\left(\dfrac{5a}{9}, \dfrac{5a}{9}, \dfrac{5a}{9}\right)$.

In Exs. 39–48, find the indicated moment of inertia.

39. The rod of Ex. 1, with respect to the point of zero density.   *Ans.*$\frac{1}{4}kc^4$.
40. The rod of Ex. 1, with respect to the point of maximum density.   *Ans.* $\frac{1}{12}kc^4$.
41. The rod of Ex. 3, with respect to the center.   *Ans.* $\dfrac{kc^5}{80}$.

42. The rod of Ex. 3, with respect to one end point.   *Ans.* $\dfrac{kc^5}{30}$.

43. The circular plate of Ex. 9, with respect to the center.
44. The cylinder of Ex. 11, with respect to the plane of its base.   *Ans.* $\frac{3}{8}Mh^2$.
45. The cylinder of Ex. 11, with respect to the plane at the end of maximum density.   *Ans.* $\frac{1}{10}Mh^2$.
46. The sphere of Ex. 13, with respect to a diameter in the fixed plane (yz-plane).
Ans. $I_z = \frac{1}{2}Ma^2$.

47. The sphere of Ex. 13, with respect to the diameter perpendicular to the fixed plane.   *Ans.* $I_x = \frac{1}{3}Ma^2$.
48. The cube of Ex. 21, with respect to an edge through the corner of zero density.   *Ans.* $I_z = \frac{38}{45}Ma^2$.
49. Prove the theorem of § 296 for any continuous plane mass.
50. Prove the corollary, § 320.
51. Solve Example (*b*), § 319.   (Find I_0 by using polar coordinates; $I_x = \frac{1}{2}I_0$.)

Series of Constant Terms

321. *Infinite Series*

A *finite series*, or *series of n terms*, is an expression of the form

$$u_1 + u_2 + u_3 + \cdots + u_n,$$

where each term is formed by some definite rule. Familiar examples are the *arithmetic series* (also called arithmetic progression), in which each term is formed by adding a fixed amount to the preceding term; the *geometric series* (progression), in which each term bears a constant ratio to the preceding; and the expansion of $(1 + x)^m$ by the binomial theorem, where m is a positive integer.

Cases frequently arise where the generating law may be supposed to apply over and over indefinitely, so that the number of terms is unlimited. When this occurs, the series is called an *infinite series*, denoted by the symbol

$$u_1 + u_2 + u_3 + \cdots + u_n + \cdots .$$

This symbol may be more compactly expressed by a simple extension of the Σ-notation introduced in § 80:

$$u_1 + u_2 + u_3 + \cdots + u_n + \cdots = \sum_{n=1}^{\infty} u_n.$$

Example. The geometric series with first term 1 and ratio $\frac{1}{2}$ is

(1) $$1 + \frac{1}{2} + \frac{1}{4} + \frac{1}{8} + \cdots + \frac{1}{2^{n-1}} + \cdots = \sum_{n=1}^{\infty} \frac{1}{2^{n-1}}.$$

Instead, we may write either

$$1 + \sum_{n=1}^{\infty} \frac{1}{2^n} \quad \text{or} \quad \sum_{n=0}^{\infty} \frac{1}{2^n}.$$

The student should write the series in other forms equivalent to (1).

322. *Sum of an Infinite Series*

The *sum* of a finite series is merely the algebraic sum of all the terms and can always be found (theoretically at least) by direct addition.

On the other hand, an infinite series has no sum in the ordinary sense of the term, since no matter how many terms we might add together there would always be more to come.

Let us return to the example of the preceding section. Let the sum of the first n terms of the series

(1) $$1 + \frac{1}{2} + \frac{1}{2^2} + \cdots + \frac{1}{2^{n-1}} + \cdots$$

be S_n; that is,

(2) $$S_n = 1 + \frac{1}{2} + \frac{1}{2^2} + \cdots + \frac{1}{2^{n-1}}.$$

Since this is a finite geometric series, we know its sum from elementary algebra,

$$S_n = \frac{1 - (\frac{1}{2})^n}{1 - \frac{1}{2}} = 2 - \frac{1}{2^{n-1}}.$$

Note that, as n increases, $S_n \to 2$; that is,

(3) $$\operatorname*{Lim}_{n \to \infty} S_n = \operatorname*{Lim}_{n \to \infty} \left(2 - \frac{1}{2^{n-1}}\right) = 2.$$

It is only natural, then, to define as the sum of the series (1) the value of the limit in (3), a number which can be approached as closely as desired by adding a sufficient number of terms of the original series.

DEFINITION.   *The* **sum** *of an infinite series is the limit, if it exists, of the sum of a finite number of terms, as the number of terms approaches infinity:*

$$S = \operatorname*{Lim}_{n \to \infty} S_n.$$

By replacing n by $(n - 1)$, we may also write

$$S = \operatorname*{Lim}_{n \to \infty} S_{n-1}.$$

Example.   The sum of the first n terms of the infinite geometric series

$$a + ar + ar^2 + \cdots + ar^{n-1} + \cdots$$

is

$$S_n = \frac{a - ar^n}{1 - r}, \qquad r \neq 1.$$

Hence the sum of the series, if the sum exists, is

$$S = \operatorname*{Lim}_{n \to \infty} \frac{a - ar^n}{1 - r}.$$

When $|r| < 1$, the quantity ar^n approaches zero as n increases, and

$$S = \frac{a}{1-r}.$$

When $|r| > 1$, the quantity $|ar^n| \to \infty$, and the above limit does not exist; the series has no sum. The student should show that S_n does not approach a limit if $r = \pm 1$.

323. *Convergence and Divergence*

If the series has a sum S, i.e., if S_n approaches a limit when $n \to \infty$, the series is said to be *convergent*, or to *converge to the value* S; if the limit does not exist, the series is *divergent*.

For instance, the above example shows that a geometric series converges to the value $\dfrac{a}{1-r}$ if $|r| < 1$; it diverges if $|r| \geq 1$.

A series may diverge because $S_n \to \infty$ as $n \to \infty$; or it may diverge because S_n fails in some other way to approach a limit. A common type of divergence is that in which S_n increases and decreases alternately, or *oscillates*, without approaching any limit. In the latter case the series is called *oscillatory*. A very simple example of oscillatory divergence is furnished by the geometric series for which $r = -1$:

$$a - a + a - a + \cdots + (-1)^{n-1}a + \cdots.$$

Here $S_n = a$ or $S_n = 0$ alternately, according as n is odd or even.

In the elementary applications, divergent series are of no importance. Before being able to use a given series, we must determine whether it converges or diverges. If S_n can be expressed explicitly as a simple function of n, as in the case of the arithmetic and geometric series, we can usually determine the convergence or divergence of the series directly and find the sum if it exists; but S_n cannot be so expressed in most cases.

If the series $\displaystyle\sum_{n=1}^{\infty} u_n$ converges, then S_n approaches a limit S, as $n \to \infty$. But then also $S_{n-1} \to S$, as $n \to \infty$, since it is purely a matter of notation whether $(n-1)$ or n terms are taken in the finite sum. Then, if the series converges, $\underset{n \to \infty}{\text{Lim }} S_{n-1} = \underset{n \to \infty}{\text{Lim }} S_n$, so that

$$\underset{n \to \infty}{\text{Lim }} (S_n - S_{n-1}) = \underset{n \to \infty}{\text{Lim }} u_n = 0.$$

THEOREM 61. If $\displaystyle\sum_{n=1}^{\infty} u_n$ converges,

$$\underset{n \to \infty}{\text{Lim }} \boldsymbol{u_n} = 0.$$

This condition, though necessary, is not sufficient; i.e., if the nth term does not approach zero, the series diverges, but if the nth term does approach zero, the series still may diverge. This is illustrated by the "harmonic series"

$$1 + \frac{1}{2} + \frac{1}{3} + \frac{1}{4} + \cdots + \frac{1}{n} + \cdots,$$

which will be shown in § 324 to be divergent, although its nth term approaches zero as $n \to \infty$.

We shall make use of the following fundamental result without proof.

THEOREM 62. *If a variable steadily $\begin{Bmatrix} increases \\ decreases \end{Bmatrix}$ but never becomes $\begin{Bmatrix} greater \\ less \end{Bmatrix}$ than some fixed number A, the variable approaches a limit which is not $\begin{Bmatrix} greater \\ less \end{Bmatrix}$ than A.*

324. *The Harmonic Series*

The series

(1) $$1 + \frac{1}{2} + \frac{1}{3} + \frac{1}{4} + \cdots + \frac{1}{n} + \cdots = \sum_{n=1}^{\infty} \frac{1}{n}$$

is called the *harmonic series*.

A common notation for the sum of the first n terms of this important series is H_n:

$$H_n = 1 + \frac{1}{2} + \frac{1}{3} + \cdots + \frac{1}{n} = \sum_{k=1}^{n} \frac{1}{k}.$$

We shall prove that the harmonic series diverges; $H_n \to \infty$, as $n \to \infty$. Of course, $1 + \frac{1}{2} > 1 + \frac{1}{3}$, $\frac{1}{3} + \frac{1}{4} > \frac{1}{4} + \frac{1}{4}$, $\frac{1}{5} + \frac{1}{6} > \frac{1}{6} + \frac{1}{6}$, etc. That is, the following n inequalities are true:

$$1 + \tfrac{1}{2} > 1 + \tfrac{1}{3},$$

$$\tfrac{1}{3} + \tfrac{1}{4} > \tfrac{1}{2},$$

$$\tfrac{1}{5} + \tfrac{1}{6} > \tfrac{1}{3},$$

$$\cdots \cdots \cdots \cdots$$

$$\frac{1}{2n-1} + \frac{1}{2n} > \frac{1}{n}.$$

Adding the corresponding members of these inequalities, we obtain

$$H_{2n} > H_n + \tfrac{1}{3}.$$

Thus $H_{2n} - H_n > \tfrac{1}{3}$. But, if the harmonic series converges, then a limit H exists such that as $n \to \infty$, $H_n \to H$, and also $H_{2n} \to H$. Then

$$H_{2n} - H_n \to 0,$$

which contradicts the inequality $H_{2n} - H_n > \tfrac{1}{3}$. Hence, the harmonic series cannot converge; it must diverge.

325. *The Factorial Notation*

The symbol $n!$ (read *factorial n*) is used to denote the *product of all the integers from* 1 *to n inclusive*:

$$n! = 1 \cdot 2 \cdot 3 \cdots (n-2)(n-1)n.$$

By special definition (introduced to facilitate the writing of certain formulas),

$$0! = 1.$$

It will be found as we proceed that factorials occur prominently in many important series.

In manipulating the factorial symbol, we must have constant recourse to the definition. For example,

$$\frac{6!}{3!} = \frac{1 \cdot 2 \cdot 3 \cdot 4 \cdot 5 \cdot 6}{1 \cdot 2 \cdot 3} = 4 \cdot 5 \cdot 6;$$

$$\frac{n!}{3! \cdot (n-3)!} = \frac{n(n-1)(n-2)}{1 \cdot 2 \cdot 3}.$$

EXERCISES

In Exs. 1–6, write out the first five terms of each series.

1. $\displaystyle\sum_{n=1}^{\infty} \frac{1}{n^2}.$

2. $\displaystyle\sum_{n=1}^{\infty} \frac{(-1)^n}{n!}.$

3. $\displaystyle\sum_{n=1}^{\infty} \frac{2n^2 - 9n + 13}{6(n-1)!}.$ *Ans.* $1 + \tfrac{1}{2} + \tfrac{1}{3} + \tfrac{1}{4} + \tfrac{1}{8} + \cdots.$

4. $\displaystyle\sum_{n=1}^{\infty} \frac{1}{3n^4 - 30n^3 + 105n^2 - 149n + 72}.$ *Ans.* $1 + \tfrac{1}{2} + \tfrac{1}{3} + \tfrac{1}{4} + \tfrac{1}{77} + \cdots.$

5. $\displaystyle\sum_{n=2}^{\infty} \frac{1 + (-1)^n}{n^2 + 1}.$ *Ans.* $\tfrac{2}{5} + 0 + \tfrac{2}{17} + 0 + \tfrac{2}{37} + \cdots.$

6. $\displaystyle\sum_{n=0}^{\infty} \frac{(-1)^n(n+1)}{(2n+1)!}.$

Prove that the series in Exs. 7–14 are divergent.

7. $\displaystyle\sum_{n=0}^{\infty} \frac{n^2+1}{2n+5}.$

8. $1 - 2 + 3 - \cdots + (-1)^{n-1}n + \cdots.$

9. $1 + \dfrac{2}{4} + \dfrac{3}{8} + \dfrac{4}{12} + \cdots + \dfrac{n+1}{4n} + \cdots.$

10. $\dfrac{1}{3} + \dfrac{3}{5} + \dfrac{5}{7} + \cdots + \dfrac{2n-1}{2n+1} + \cdots.$

11. $1 + \dfrac{e}{2^2} + \dfrac{e^2}{3^2} + \dfrac{e^3}{4^2} + \cdots + \dfrac{e^{n-1}}{n^2} + \cdots.$

12. $\dfrac{1}{2} + \dfrac{1}{4} + \dfrac{1}{6} + \dfrac{1}{8} + \cdots + \dfrac{1}{2n} + \cdots.$

13. $\displaystyle\sum_{n=1}^{\infty} \sin\frac{n\pi}{2}.$ **14.** $\displaystyle\sum_{n=0}^{\infty} \frac{\pi^n}{e^n}.$

15. Show that every infinite arithmetic series, with terms not all zero, is divergent.

In each of Exs. 16–20, show that the given series are identical.

16. $\displaystyle\sum_{n=0}^{\infty} \frac{x^n}{n!}$ and $1 + x + \displaystyle\sum_{n=2}^{\infty} \frac{x^n}{n!}.$

17. $\displaystyle\sum_{n=0}^{\infty} \frac{x^{n+1}}{n+1}$ and $\displaystyle\sum_{n=1}^{\infty} \frac{x^n}{n}.$ In the first series replace n everywhere by $(n-1)$.

This is called a *shift in index.*

18. $\displaystyle\sum_{n=0}^{\infty} \frac{(-1)^n y^{2n+1}}{(2n+1)!}$ and $\displaystyle\sum_{n=1}^{\infty} \frac{(-1)^{n-1} y^{2n-1}}{(2n-1)!}.$

19. $\displaystyle\sum_{n=1}^{\infty} (n^2+1)z^{n+2}$ and $\displaystyle\sum_{n=3}^{\infty} (n^2-4n+5)z^n.$

20. $\displaystyle\sum_{n=1}^{\infty} \frac{(-1)^{n+1} x^n}{n}$ and $\displaystyle\sum_{n=0}^{\infty} \frac{(-1)^n x^{n+1}}{n+1}.$

326. *A Comparison Test*

Let

$$u_1 + u_2 + u_3 + \cdots + u_n + \cdots$$

be a series of *positive terms* to be tested.

(a) *If a series*

$$a_1 + a_2 + a_3 + \cdots + a_n + \cdots$$

of positive terms, known to be convergent, can be found such that

$$u_n \leqq a_n,$$

then the series to be tested is convergent.

(b) *If a series*

$$b_1 + b_2 + b_3 + \cdots + b_n + \cdots$$

of positive terms, known to be divergent, can be found such that

$$u_n \geqq b_n,$$

then the series to be tested is divergent.

To prove (a), let S_n be the sum of the first n terms of the u-series, T_n the sum of the first n terms of the a-series, and T the sum of the a-series. Since all the terms u_n and a_n are positive, both S_n and T_n increase as n increases. On the other hand, we have

$$S_n < T_n < T.$$

Therefore S_n always increases with n but never exceeds the fixed number T. Hence S_n approaches a limit, not greater than T, by the theorem quoted at the end of § 323.

The proof of (b) is left to the student.

The success of the test depends on our ability to find a *convergent* series whose terms are *greater* than the corresponding terms of the series to be tested, or a *divergent* series whose terms are *less* than those of the series to be tested. To show that the terms of the u-series are greater than those of some convergent series, or less than those of some divergent series, proves nothing.

Since the convergence of a series is not affected by discarding any finite number of terms, the conditions of the test do not need to be satisfied from the very beginning of the series but only *after a certain point*, all the terms to that point being neglected.

If we change the signs of all the terms, the sign of the sum S (if the sum exists) is changed, but its existence is not affected. Thus if all the terms are negative, we may change all the signs before testing.

Example. Test for convergence the series

$$\frac{2}{1^2} + \frac{3}{2^2} + \frac{4}{3^2} + \cdots + \frac{n+1}{n^2} + \cdots.$$

We know (§ 324) that the harmonic series

$$1 + \frac{1}{2} + \frac{1}{3} + \cdots + \frac{1}{n} + \cdots$$

is divergent. Since

$$\frac{n+1}{n^2} = \frac{1}{n} + \frac{1}{n^2} > \frac{1}{n},$$

the given series is divergent.

327. *Other Comparison Tests*

The test in the preceding section has the advantage of simplicity of concept. That test is, however, more tedious to use than the slightly more sophisticated comparison tests contained in Theorems 63–65 below.

THEOREM 63. *If $u_n > 0$ and $a_n > 0$, and if*

$$\text{(1)} \qquad \qquad \lim_{n \to \infty} \frac{u_n}{a_n} = c \neq 0,$$

the series $\displaystyle\sum_{n=1}^{\infty} u_n$ and $\displaystyle\sum_{n=1}^{\infty} a_n$ converge or diverge together.

That is, if two series satisfy the conditions of Theorem 63, then if either series converges, the other converges, and if either series diverges, the other also diverges.

A shift of index in u_n from n to $(n + k)$ for any fixed k has no effect upon the limit in (1). Hence the theorem may be applied to series whose terms are all positive from some n value onward.

Proof of Theorem 63. Because of (1) there exists a constant M_1 such that for all n

$$\text{(2)} \qquad \qquad \left| \frac{u_n}{a_n} - c \right| < M_1.$$

For n sufficiently large, M_1 can be made arbitrarily small, but that does not concern us here. From (2) and the fact that all the quantities involved are positive, it follows that

$$\text{(3)} \qquad \qquad u_n < (M_1 + c)a_n.$$

Because of (1), $\displaystyle\lim_{n \to \infty} \frac{a_n}{u_n} = c^{-1} \neq 0$, so we may also conclude that there exists a constant M_2 such that for all n

$$\text{(4)} \qquad \qquad a_n < (M_2 + c^{-1})u_n.$$

As in § 326, let the sum of the first n terms of the u-series be S_n; of the a-series be T_n. Then by (3) and (4) there exist constants M_3 and M_4 such that

$$(5) \qquad\qquad S_n < M_3 T_n, \qquad T_n < M_4 S_n,$$

from which the conclusion in Theorem 63 follows at once.

    Example.   Test for convergence:

$$(6) \qquad\qquad \sum_{n=1}^{\infty} \frac{2n - 1}{5n^2 - 31n + 8}.$$

    Note that for large n the general term in the series (6) behaves like $\dfrac{2n}{5n^2} = \dfrac{2}{5n}$. Let us compare (6) with the harmonic series

$$(7) \qquad\qquad \sum_{n=1}^{\infty} \frac{1}{n}$$

which we know to be divergent. For $n > 5$, the terms of (6) are positive. Since

$$\lim_{n \to \infty} \frac{2n - 1}{5n^2 - 31n + 8} \cdot \frac{n}{1} = \frac{2}{5} \neq 0,$$

we may conclude that (6) diverges because (7) diverges.

    THEOREM 64.   *If $u_n > 0$ and $a_n > 0$, and if*

$$(8) \qquad\qquad \lim_{n \to \infty} \frac{u_n}{a_n} = 0,$$

the series $\displaystyle\sum_{n=1}^{\infty} u_n$ *converges if* $\displaystyle\sum_{n=1}^{\infty} a_n$ *converges.*

    Theorem 64 says nothing about what happens if the a-series diverges.

    THEOREM 65.   *If $u_n > 0$ and $d_n > 0$, and if*

$$(9) \qquad\qquad \lim_{n \to \infty} \frac{u_n}{d_n} = \infty,$$

the series $\displaystyle\sum_{n=1}^{\infty} u_n$ *diverges if* $\displaystyle\sum_{n=1}^{\infty} d_n$ *diverges.*

    Theorem 65 says nothing about what happens if the d-series converges. Proof of Theorems 64 and 65 is left to the student.

    The value of the comparison tests increases as we add to our list of series which we know converge or diverge.

328. *An Integral Test*

Consider an infinite series,

$$\sum_{n=1}^{\infty} u_n,$$

of positive terms, such that the terms never increase with increasing n; i.e., $0 < u_{n+1} \leqq u_n$. For such a series the following test may* determine whether the series converges or diverges.

Integral Test. If, for $x \geqq 1$, the function $f(x)$ is positive, continuous, and never increases with increasing x, then

(a) If $\displaystyle\int_1^{\infty} f(x)\,dx$ exists, the series $\displaystyle\sum_{n=1}^{\infty} f(n)$ converges;

(b) If $\displaystyle\int_1^{\infty} f(x)\,dx$ does not exist, the series $\displaystyle\sum_{n=1}^{\infty} f(n)$ diverges.

Let us prove part (a) of the test. Put

$$S_n = f(1) + f(2) + f(3) + \cdots + f(n).$$

Now, as shown in Fig. 344, the area under the curve $y = f(x)$, from $x = 1$ to $x = n$, is

$$\int_1^n f(x)\,dx,$$

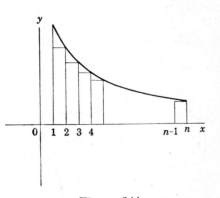

Figure 344

and the sum of the areas of the rectangles, from $x = 1$ to $x = n$, is

$$f(2) + f(3) + \cdots + f(n) = S_n - f(1).$$

Since $f(x)$ never increases with increasing x,

$$S_n - f(1) \leqq \int_1^n f(x)\,dx.$$

But $\displaystyle\int_1^{\infty} f(x)\,dx$ exists; call its value A. Then

$$S_n - f(1) \leqq A,$$

* No test for convergence is capable of effective testing of all series. At best, a test will show that certain series converge, that others diverge, but there will remain series for which it gives no answer.

or $S_n \leqq A + f(1)$, by which we have shown that S_n, always increasing, is bounded above.   Then S_n approaches a limit as $n \to \infty$; the series $\sum\limits_{n=1}^{\infty} f(n)$ converges.

The proof of part (b) is similar to the above, with rectangles formed by using horizontal lines drawn to the right where each ordinate,

$$x = 1, 2, 3, \cdots, n,$$

intersects the curve.   Completion of the proof is left as an exercise.

Since, for continuous $f(x)$, $\int_{a}^{\infty} f(x)\, dx$ and $\int_{1}^{\infty} f(x)\, dx$ exist, or do not exist together, the lower limit in the integral need not be taken as one; its value is unessential.

It is important to notice that in order to apply the integral test, it is necessary to find a continuous function $f(x)$ for which the values $f(n)$, for integral n, coincide with the terms of the series to be tested.   That is not a serious matter for elementary problems.

Example (a).   Test the series $\sum\limits_{n=0}^{\infty} \dfrac{1}{n^2 + 1}.$

The terms of this series are all positive, and they decrease steadily, since

$$\frac{1}{(n + 1)^2 + 1} < \frac{1}{n^2 + 1}.$$

Consider the function $f(x) = \dfrac{1}{x^2 + 1}.$ For $x = n$, this function yields the terms of the series.   Also, $f(x)$ decreases steadily with increasing x. Further, $f(x)$ is continuous, and

$$\int_{k}^{\infty} \frac{dx}{x^2 + 1} = \Big[\operatorname{Arctan} x \Big]_{k}^{\infty}$$

$$= \frac{\pi}{2} - \operatorname{Arctan} k,$$

so that $\int_{k}^{\infty} f(x)\, dx$ exists.   Hence the series $\sum\limits_{n=0}^{\infty} \dfrac{1}{n^2 + 1}$ converges.

Note that the lower limit k played no essential role, and also note that the fact that the series starts with the $n = 0$ term has no bearing whatever on the question of convergence.

Example (b).   Test the series $\sum\limits_{n=2}^{\infty} \dfrac{1}{n \ln n}.$

Here the series starts with $n = 2$, which does not interfere at all with the application of the integral test. We could shift the index, if we wished, to

get $\displaystyle\sum_{n=1}^{\infty} \frac{1}{(n+1)\ln(n+1)}$.

The function $f(x) = \dfrac{1}{x \ln x}$ yields the general term of our series for integral values, $x = n$. Now

$$f'(x) = -\frac{1 + \ln x}{x^2 \ln^2 x},$$

which is negative for $x \geq 2$ (even for $x > 1$), so $f(x)$ decreases steadily. Consider the appropriate integral,

$$\int_2^{\infty} \frac{dx}{x \ln x} = \Big[\ln \ln x\Big]_2^{\infty},$$

which does not exist. It follows that $\displaystyle\sum_{n=2}^{\infty} \frac{1}{n \ln n}$ is divergent.

329. The p-Series

The series

(1) $$1 + \frac{1}{2^p} + \frac{1}{3^p} + \cdots + \frac{1}{n^p} + \cdots = \sum_{n=1}^{\infty} \frac{1}{n^p}$$

is called the p-series.

If $p = 1$, this is the harmonic series, which we know is divergent. **If $p < 1$,**

$$\frac{1}{n^p} > \frac{1}{n},$$

so that the series (1) diverges for $p < 1$ by comparison with the harmonic series.

If $p > 1$, we use the integral test. From $f(x) = \dfrac{1}{x^p}$, for fixed p, we obtain

$f'(x) = -\dfrac{p}{x^{p+1}}$, which is negative, for $x \geq 1$; the function decreases with increasing x. The integral

$$\int_1^{\infty} \frac{dx}{x^p} = \left[\frac{1}{(1-p)x^{p-1}}\right]_1^{\infty} = 0 - \frac{1}{1-p}$$

exists, for $p > 1$. Hence the series (1) converges for $p > 1$.

In recapitulation, the p-series $\sum\limits_{n=1}^{\infty} \dfrac{1}{n^p}$ diverges for $p \leq 1$, converges for $p > 1$. It is quite useful in applying the comparison tests of §§ 326–327.

Example. Test the series

(2) $$\frac{1}{1 \cdot 2} + \frac{1}{2 \cdot 3} + \frac{1}{3 \cdot 4} + \cdots + \frac{1}{n(n+1)} + \cdots .$$

The series

$$\frac{1}{1^2} + \frac{1}{2^2} + \frac{1}{3^2} + \frac{1}{4^2} + \cdots + \frac{1}{n^2} + \cdots$$

is the p-series with $p = 2$ and is therefore convergent. Since

$$\frac{1}{n^2 + n} < \frac{1}{n^2}$$

for all (positive integral) values of n, the series (2) converges.

EXERCISES

In Exs. 1–6, test for convergence, employing a comparison test.

1. $\sum\limits_{n=1}^{\infty} \dfrac{1}{n^n}.$ *Ans.* Convergent.

2. $\dfrac{1}{2} + \dfrac{1}{2 \cdot 4} + \dfrac{1}{3 \cdot 8} + \dfrac{1}{4 \cdot 16} + \cdots + \dfrac{1}{n \cdot 2^n} + \cdots .$

3. $\dfrac{1}{5} + \dfrac{1}{11} + \dfrac{1}{17} + \cdots + \dfrac{1}{6n - 1} + \cdots .$

4. $\sum\limits_{n=0}^{\infty} \dfrac{1}{(2n-1)(n^2+1)}.$ *Ans.* Convergent.

5. $\sum\limits_{k=2}^{\infty} \dfrac{\sqrt{k-1}}{k}.$ *Ans.* Divergent.   6. $\sum\limits_{k=1}^{\infty} \dfrac{k^2+1}{k^3-7}.$

In Exs. 7–12, test for convergence, using the integral test.

7. $\sum\limits_{n=1}^{\infty} ne^{-n^2}.$ *Ans.* Convergent.   8. $\sum\limits_{n=1}^{\infty} \dfrac{1}{1+\sqrt{n}}.$

9. $\dfrac{1}{2\sqrt{2}} + \dfrac{1}{5\sqrt{5}} + \dfrac{1}{10\sqrt{10}} + \cdots + \dfrac{1}{(1+k^2)^{\frac{3}{2}}} + \cdots .$

10. $\displaystyle\sum_{k=2}^{\infty} \frac{1}{k(\ln k)^2}$.   *Ans.* Convergent.   11. $\displaystyle\sum_{j=2}^{\infty} \frac{\ln j}{j}$.   *Ans.* Divergent.

12. $\displaystyle\sum_{n=1}^{\infty} \frac{n}{(1 + n^2)^2}$.

13. Show that the series $\displaystyle\sum_{n=1}^{\infty} \frac{1}{an + b}$ is divergent for all values* of a and b.

$\left(\text{Compare with } \displaystyle\sum_{n=1}^{\infty} \frac{1}{2an}.\right)$

14. Show that the series $\displaystyle\sum_{n=1}^{\infty} \frac{1}{an^2 + bn + c}$ is convergent for all values* of a, b, c $(a \neq 0)$. (Adapt the suggestion in Ex. 13.)

15. Show that the series $\displaystyle\sum_{n=1}^{\infty} \frac{a_0 n + a_1}{b_0 n^2 + b_1 n + b_2}$ is divergent* $(a_0 \neq 0)$.

16. Do Ex. 13 by the integral test.

17. Complete the proof of part (b) of the integral test.

18. Using Theorem 63 with $u_n = \dfrac{P(n)}{Q(n)}$, $a_n = \dfrac{1}{n^{q-p}}$, prove the validity of the following test.

POLYNOMIAL TEST. *If $P(n)$ is a polynomial of degree p, $Q(n)$ a polynomial of degree q, the series* $\displaystyle\sum_{n=1}^{\infty} \frac{P(n)}{Q(n)}$ *converges if $q > p + 1$, otherwise diverges.*

In Exs. 19–29, test by using the polynomial test.

19. $\displaystyle\sum_{n=1}^{\infty} \frac{n^2 - 2}{(3n + 1)^3}$.

20. $\displaystyle\sum_{n=2}^{\infty} \frac{n^3 + 1}{n^4(3n + 1)}$.

21. $\displaystyle\sum_{k=0}^{\infty} \frac{1}{(2k + 1)^2}$.

22. $\dfrac{3 \cdot 4}{2 + 1} + \dfrac{4 \cdot 5}{16 + 1} + \dfrac{5 \cdot 6}{54 + 1} + \cdots + \dfrac{(n + 2)(n + 3)}{2n^3 + 1} + \cdots$.

* The case in which the denominator vanishes for a positive integral value of n is tacitly excluded, since then the series would not be defined.

23. $\displaystyle\sum_{n=0}^{\infty} \frac{2n-1}{4(n+4)(n+1)}.$

24. Ex. 3.   25. Ex. 4.   26. Ex. 6.

27. Ex. 12.   28. Ex. 13.   29. Ex. 14.

In Exs. 30–41, test by any available means.

30. $1 + \dfrac{1}{2^1} + \dfrac{1}{2^4} + \dfrac{1}{2^9} + \cdots + \dfrac{1}{2^{n^2}} + \cdots$.

31. $\displaystyle\sum_{m=0}^{\infty} \frac{\sin^2 (2m+1)}{(m+1)^2}.$ *Ans.* Convergent.

32. $\displaystyle\sum_{n=0}^{\infty} \frac{(-1)^n n^2}{n+1}.$ *Ans.* Divergent.

33. $\displaystyle\sum_{n=0}^{\infty} \frac{2n+1}{(2n-1)^3 + n^2}.$

34. $\displaystyle\sum_{n=1}^{\infty} n^2 e^{-sn}, \ s > 0.$ 35. $\displaystyle\sum_{n=1}^{\infty} n^2 e^{-sn}, \ s < 0.$

36. $\displaystyle\sum_{k=2}^{\infty} \frac{\sqrt{k}}{k^2 + 1}.$ *Ans.* Convergent.   37. $\displaystyle\sum_{n=1}^{\infty} \frac{n}{e^n}.$

38. $\dfrac{e+1}{\pi} + \dfrac{(e+1)^2}{\pi^2} + \dfrac{(e+1)^3}{\pi^3} + \cdots + \dfrac{(e+1)^n}{\pi^n} + \cdots$.

39. $\displaystyle\sum_{n=0}^{\infty} \frac{1}{2^{3n}}.$ 40. $\displaystyle\sum_{n=1}^{\infty} \frac{1}{7n+1}.$

41. $\displaystyle\sum_{n=1}^{\infty} \frac{100 n^2}{\pi^n}.$

42. Show, by using examples such as $\displaystyle\sum_{n=0}^{\infty} (-1)^n$, that you cannot, in general, test for convergence by grouping terms together before testing.

43. Show that for series of positive terms it is legitimate to group terms before testing for convergence.

44. Use the integral test on the harmonic series.

45. Show that the harmonic series is divergent by grouping the terms as follows:

$$1 + \left(\frac{1}{2}\right) + \left(\frac{1}{3} + \frac{1}{4}\right) + \left(\frac{1}{5} + \frac{1}{6} + \frac{1}{7} + \frac{1}{8}\right) + \cdots$$

$$+ \left(\frac{1}{2^k+1} + \frac{1}{2^k+2} + \cdots + \frac{1}{2^k+2^k}\right) + \cdots,$$

and proving that the sum of the terms in each group $\geq \frac{1}{2}$.

46. Adapt the suggestion of Ex. 45 to a new proof of the convergence of $\sum\limits_{n=1}^{\infty} \dfrac{1}{n^p}$ for $p > 1$.   Group the terms as follows.

$$1 + \left(\frac{1}{2^p} + \frac{1}{3^p}\right) + \left(\frac{1}{4^p} + \frac{1}{5^p} + \frac{1}{6^p} + \frac{1}{7^p}\right) + \cdots$$
$$+ \left(\frac{1}{2^{np}} + \frac{1}{(2^n + 1)^p} + \cdots + \frac{1}{(2^{n+1} - 1)^p}\right) + \cdots,$$

and show that the new series has its terms less than the corresponding terms of the convergent geometric series

$$1 + \frac{1}{2^{p-1}} + \frac{1}{(2^{p-1})^2} + \cdots + \frac{1}{(2^{p-1})^n} + \cdots.$$

330. *Absolute Convergence*

First we prove the following important result.

THEOREM 66.   *If the series* $\sum\limits_{n=1}^{\infty} |u_n|$ *converges, then* $\sum\limits_{n=1}^{\infty} u_n$ *converges.*

In the finite sum

$$S_n = u_1 + u_2 + u_3 + \cdots + u_n,$$

let the positive terms be denoted by a's, the numerical values of the negative ones by b's.   Then

$$S_n = A_k - B_m,$$

where $A_k = \sum a$'s, $B_m = \sum b$'s, and $k + m = n$.

For the series $\sum\limits_{n=1}^{\infty} |u_n|$, the corresponding finite sum is

$$|u_1| + |u_2| + |u_3| + \cdots + |u_n| = A_k + B_m.$$

The theorem states that if $(A_k + B_m)$ approaches a limit, then $(A_k - B_m)$ does also.   But, since A_k and B_m are positive and increasing, if $(A_k + B_m)$ approaches a limit, then A_k and B_m must do so separately.   Hence $(A_k - B_m)$ approaches a limit, and the proof is ended.

DEFINITION.   *A series is said to be* **absolutely convergent** *if the series formed from it by replacing all its terms by their absolute values is convergent.*

Theorem 66 above may now be reworded.

THEOREM 66a.   *If a series is absolutely convergent, it is convergent.*

A series which is convergent, but not absolutely convergent, is called *simply convergent*.

Example. Test the series $\sum\limits_{n=1}^{\infty} \dfrac{\sin \dfrac{n\pi}{4}}{n^2}$.

The numerator takes on values which are positive, negative, or zero, depending on the value of n. However, $\left| \sin \dfrac{n\pi}{4} \right| \leq 1$, so

$$\left| \frac{\sin \dfrac{n\pi}{4}}{n^2} \right| < \frac{1}{n^2}$$

and we know $\sum\limits_{n=1}^{\infty} \dfrac{1}{n^2}$ is convergent. Hence the given series is absolutely convergent by a comparison test, so it is also convergent.

331. *Ratio Test*

Given the series

(1) $$\sum_{n=1}^{\infty} u_n = u_1 + u_2 + u_3 + \cdots + u_n + \cdots ,$$

form the ratio $\dfrac{u_{n+1}}{u_n}$ of a general term to the one *preceding* it. Then,

(a) *If* $\operatorname*{Lim}\limits_{n\to\infty} \left| \dfrac{u_{n+1}}{u_n} \right| < 1$, *the series converges: indeed, converges absolutely.*

(b) *If* $\operatorname*{Lim}\limits_{n\to\infty} \left| \dfrac{u_{n+1}}{u_n} \right| > 1$, *or if* $\left| \dfrac{u_{n+1}}{u_n} \right|$ *increases without bound, the series diverges.*

(c) *If* $\operatorname*{Lim}\limits_{n\to\infty} \left| \dfrac{u_{n+1}}{u_n} \right| = 1$, *the test fails.*

(d) *If* $\left| \dfrac{u_{n+1}}{u_n} \right|$ *does not approach a limit and does not increase without bound, the test fails.*

Since the ratio test deals with absolute values, it applies to series in general, not merely to series of positive terms.

The ratio test as stated here can be refined in many ways. For example, if $|u_{n+1}/u_n|$ remains always less than some constant which is itself less than unity, the series converges whether or not the ratio approaches a limit. Such refinements are important in more advanced work, but the ratio test as stated above is sufficiently powerful for elementary work.

Proof of the validity of the ratio test:

Consider the first case: $\operatorname{Lim}_{n \to \infty} \left| \dfrac{u_{n+1}}{u_n} \right| = L < 1$. Let us choose some number r between L and 1. By the definition of limit, the difference between the ratio $\left| \dfrac{u_{n+1}}{u_n} \right|$ and its limit L can be made as small as desired by choosing n large enough; therefore a number k can be found such that for all values of $n \geq k$, we have

$$\left| \frac{u_{n+1}}{u_n} \right| < r.$$ **Figure 345**

Hence

$$|u_{k+1}| < |u_k|\, r,$$
$$|u_{k+2}| < |u_{k+1}|\, r < |u_k|\, r^2,$$
$$|u_{k+3}| < |u_{k+2}|\, r < |u_k|\, r^3,$$

$$\cdot \qquad \cdot \qquad \cdot \qquad \cdot$$

Discarding the first k terms of $\displaystyle\sum_{n=1}^{\infty} |u_n|$, we see that the remaining terms are less than the corresponding terms of the series

$$|u_k|\, r + |u_k|\, r^2 + |u_k|\, r^3 + \cdots + |u_k|\, r^m + \cdots .$$

But this last, being a geometric series with ratio $r < 1$, is convergent; hence the given series converges by a comparison test.

In case (b), it is easy to show that u_n does not approach zero.

Example (a). In the series

$$1 - \frac{1}{2} + \frac{2}{2^2} - \frac{3}{2^3} + \cdots + \frac{(-1)^n \cdot n}{2^n} + \frac{(-1)^{n+1}(n+1)}{2^{n+1}} + \cdots ,$$

$$\operatorname{Lim}_{n \to \infty} \left| \frac{u_{n+1}}{u_n} \right| = \operatorname{Lim}_{n \to \infty} \frac{\dfrac{n+1}{2^{n+1}}}{\dfrac{n}{2^n}} = \operatorname{Lim}_{n \to \infty} \frac{n+1}{2n} = \frac{1}{2}.$$

Thus the series converges.

Example (b). In the series

$$1 + 1 + \frac{1}{2!} + \frac{1}{3!} + \frac{1}{4!} + \cdots + \frac{1}{n!} + \frac{1}{(n+1)!} + \cdots ,$$

$$\operatorname{Lim}_{n \to \infty} \left| \frac{u_{n+1}}{u_n} \right| = \operatorname{Lim}_{n \to \infty} \frac{\dfrac{1}{(n+1)!}}{\dfrac{1}{n!}} = \operatorname{Lim}_{n \to \infty} \frac{n!}{(n+1)!},$$

so that

$$\operatorname*{Lim}_{n \to \infty} \left| \frac{u_{n+1}}{u_n} \right| = \operatorname*{Lim}_{n \to \infty} \frac{1 \cdot 2 \cdot 3 \cdots n}{1 \cdot 2 \cdot 3 \cdots n(n+1)} = \operatorname*{Lim}_{n \to \infty} \frac{1}{n+1} = 0.$$

Hence the series converges.

Example (c). For the *p*-series $\sum_{n=1}^{\infty} \dfrac{1}{n^p}$, we have

$$\operatorname*{Lim}_{n \to \infty} \frac{\dfrac{1}{(n+1)_p}}{\dfrac{1}{n^p}} = \operatorname*{Lim}_{n \to \infty} \frac{n^p}{(n+1)^p} = \operatorname*{Lim}_{n \to \infty} \frac{1}{\left(1 + \dfrac{1}{n}\right)^p} = 1.$$

This is sufficient to show that the test fails in case (c), for the *p*-series converges if $p > 1$, diverges if $p \leq 1$, so that there are both convergent and divergent series for which $L = 1$.

Failure of the test in case (d) follows at once, since the limit L, which is our criterion, is nonexistent. See Ex. 25 below.

EXERCISES

In Exs. 1–14, test for convergence by the ratio test.

1. $\sum_{n=1}^{\infty} \dfrac{(-1)^{n+1} n}{3^n}.$ *Ans.* Convergent.

2. $\dfrac{2^5}{\pi^2} + \dfrac{3^5}{\pi^3} + \dfrac{4^5}{\pi^4} + \cdots + \dfrac{n^5}{\pi^n} + \cdots.$

3. $\dfrac{1^2}{2^0} + \dfrac{2^2}{2^1} + \dfrac{3^2}{2^2} + \cdots + \dfrac{k^2}{2^{k-1}} + \cdots.$

4. $\sum_{n=0}^{\infty} \dfrac{(-1)^n}{(2n)!}.$ *Ans.* Convergent.

5. $\sum_{n=1}^{\infty} \dfrac{(n-2)(n+3)}{2 \cdot 4 \cdot 6 \cdots (2n)}.$ *Ans.* Convergent.

6. $\sum_{n=1}^{\infty} \dfrac{1 \cdot 4 \cdot 7 \cdots (3n+1)}{n^5}.$ *Ans.* Divergent.

7. $\sum_{n=0}^{\infty} \dfrac{(-1)^n (n+1)}{(2n+1)!}.$

8. $\displaystyle\sum_{n=2}^{\infty} \frac{4n+1}{2^n n!(2n+1)}.$

9. $\displaystyle\sum_{n=1}^{\infty} \frac{1\cdot 3\cdot 5\cdot 7\;\cdots\;(2n-1)}{3\cdot 6\cdot 9\;\cdots\;(3n)}.$ *Ans.* Convergent.

10. $\dfrac{\pi}{3} - 2\left(\dfrac{\pi}{3}\right)^2 + 3\left(\dfrac{\pi}{3}\right)^3 - \cdots + (-1)^{n+1}n\left(\dfrac{\pi}{3}\right)^n + \cdots.$

11. $\displaystyle\sum_{n=1}^{\infty} \frac{n^{100}}{e^n}.$

12. $\displaystyle\sum_{k=0}^{\infty} \frac{1}{(2k+1)\cdot 5^{2k+1}}.$

13. $\displaystyle\sum_{n=1}^{\infty} \frac{3\cdot 6\cdot 9\;\cdots\;(3n)}{1\cdot 5\cdot 9\;\cdots\;(4n+1)}.$ *Ans.* Convergent.

14. $\displaystyle\sum_{n=1}^{\infty} \frac{(-1)^{n-1}(2n+1)!}{n!}.$ *Ans.* Divergent.

15. If $P(n)$ is a polynomial of any degree in n, show that *the series* $\displaystyle\sum_{n=1}^{\infty} \frac{P(n)}{k^n}$

converges provided $|k| > 1.$

In Exs. 16–27, show that the ratio test fails; test for convergence by some other method.

16. $\displaystyle\sum_{n=1}^{\infty} \frac{n+2}{n(n+3)(2n-1)}.$

17. $\displaystyle\sum_{n=2}^{\infty} \frac{\sqrt{n-1}}{n^2(n+1)}.$

18. $\dfrac{1}{1\cdot 3} + \dfrac{1}{3\cdot 5} + \dfrac{1}{5\cdot 7} + \cdots + \dfrac{1}{(2n-1)(2n+1)} + \cdots.$

19. $\dfrac{1}{2^3} + \dfrac{2^2}{3^3} + \dfrac{3^2}{4^3} + \cdots + \dfrac{(n-1)^2}{n^3} + \cdots.$

20. $\displaystyle\sum_{n=1}^{\infty} \frac{(-1)^n 3n}{n+1}.$ *Ans.* Divergent.

21. $\displaystyle\sum_{n=1}^{\infty} \frac{\sec^2 n}{n}.$ *Ans.* Divergent.

22. $\displaystyle\sum_{n=1}^{\infty} \frac{1}{n^2} \cos \frac{2n\pi}{n+1}.$ *Ans.* Convergent.

23. $\displaystyle\sum_{n=0}^{\infty} \frac{e^{\cos \frac{n\pi}{4}}}{(n+1)(n+2)}.$

24. $\displaystyle\sum_{n=1}^{\infty} (-1)^n n^3.$ *Ans.* Divergent.

25. $\displaystyle\sum_{n=1}^{\infty} u_n,$ where $u_n = \dfrac{1}{n}$ if n is odd, $u_n = \dfrac{1}{2^n}$ if n is even.   *Ans.* Divergent.

26. $\displaystyle\sum_{n=0}^{\infty} \frac{\cos \frac{n\pi}{6}}{e^n}.$

27. $\displaystyle\sum_{n=1}^{\infty} \frac{(3 + \cos n\pi)n}{2^n}.$ *Ans.* Convergent.

332. *Alternating Series*

A series whose terms are alternately positive and negative is called an *alternating series*. We shall obtain two extremely useful results concerning such series.

ALTERNATING SERIES TEST. *If after a certain point the terms of an alternating series never increase numerically, and if the limit of the n-th term is zero, the series is convergent.*

THEOREM 67. *If a series has been shown to be convergent by the alternating series test, then the difference between the sum of the series and the sum of the first n terms is numerically less than the (n + 1)-th term:*

$$|S - S_n| < |u_{n+1}|.$$

While formal proofs of these theorems are easily written out, the situation may be shown more vividly by plotting the successive terms as distances laid off end to end on an axis. Let $OP_1 = u_1$, $P_1P_2 = u_2$, $P_2P_3 = u_3$, and for any n, $P_nP_{n+1} = u_{n+1}$. It follows from the hypotheses that the successive segments are measured alternately right and left and become shorter and shorter, approaching the limit zero. For any n, the segment OP_n represents the sum S_n of the first n terms.   Then P_n must approach some fixed limit-point Q, and OP_n, or S_n, approaches the limiting value $OQ = S$.   This proves the validity of the alternating series test.

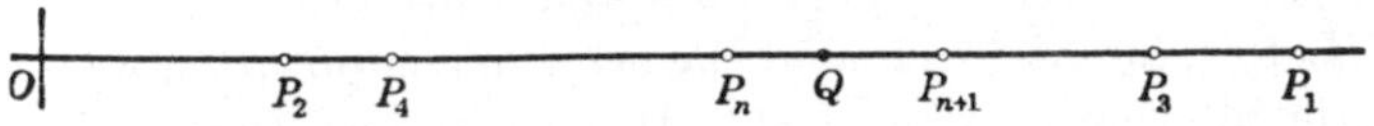

Figure 346

To prove the theorem following the test, note that any two successive points P_n, P_{n+1} must fall on opposite sides of Q.   Hence $|P_nQ| < |P_nP_{n+1}|$. But

$$P_nQ = OQ - OP_n = S - S_n, \quad P_nP_{n+1} = u_{n+1}.$$

It is important to realize that the theorem does not state a bound on the error for any convergent alternating series but only for those whose convergence can be demonstrated by the alternating series test.

Example (a).   Test the series $\sum\limits_{n=1}^{\infty} \dfrac{(-1)^{n-1}}{n}$.

This series is not absolutely convergent, since the series of absolute values is the harmonic series.

Let

$$u_n = \frac{(-1)^{n-1}}{n}.$$

Then

(1) The u_n alternate in sign;

(2) $\operatorname*{Lim}\limits_{n\to\infty} u_n = 0$;

(3) $\dfrac{1}{n+1} < \dfrac{1}{n}$, so $|u_{n+1}| < |u_n|$; the terms steadily decrease in numerical value.

Hence the series in question converges by the alternating series test. Since it is convergent, but not absolutely convergent, it is simply convergent.

Let

$$S_n = 1 - \frac{1}{2} + \frac{1}{3} - \frac{1}{4} + \cdots + \frac{(-1)^{n-1}}{n},$$

the sum to n terms of the series, and let E_n be the error made by stopping with the nth term.   Thus E_n is the difference between the sum of the series and the approximation S_n.   By the theorem of this section,

$$|E_n| < \frac{1}{n+1},$$

which in this instance is not particularly helpful, as is pointed out in Ex. 23 below.   The next example has a more cheerful ending.

Example (b). Test the series $\displaystyle\sum_{n=0}^{\infty} \frac{(-1)^n}{(2n)!}$.

We already know (Ex. 4, page 566) that this series is absolutely convergent. Let us, in order to bound the error in computation with the series, test it by the alternating series test. It is easily seen that

(1) The terms alternate in sign;

(2) $\displaystyle\lim_{n \to \infty} \frac{(-1)^n}{(2n)!} = 0;$

(3) $\displaystyle\frac{1}{(2n+2)!} < \frac{1}{(2n)!}.$

Therefore the alternating series test applies. Now consider the error made in using only the terms out to $n = 4$. Because the alternating series test worked, we know that

$$|E_4| < \frac{1}{(2 \cdot 5)!} = \frac{1}{10!} = \frac{1}{3{,}628{,}800} = 0.000\ 000\ 3.$$

That is, the approximation

$$S_4 = 1 - \frac{1}{2!} + \frac{1}{4!} - \frac{1}{6!} + \frac{1}{8!}$$

yields the sum of the series correct to six decimal places!

333. *Evaluation of the Sum of a Series*

So far we have striven merely to determine whether a given series is convergent or divergent; i.e., whether it does or does not have a sum. The existence of a sum having been established, the next problem is to determine its value. It follows from the definition of convergence that this can be done to any desired degree of approximation by merely adding together a sufficient number of terms at the beginning of the series. However, unless the series is "rapidly convergent"—i.e., unless the successive terms diminish rapidly in numerical value—the amount of computation involved in this process is likely to be prohibitive. (See Ex. 23 below.) More elaborate methods, beyond the range of this book, make it possible to sum many slowly convergent series with comparative ease.

In computing the sum of a series by addition of terms, it is necessary to know an upper limit for the error committed by stopping with any given term. In this connection the theorem of the preceding section is useful, as we saw in Example (b) of that section.

If a series converges rapidly, it is usually easy to show that, even though the succeeding terms all have the same sign, the error committed by stopping at any point is only slightly greater than the first term neglected (see the example below).

As a rule, the terms retained in the computation are replaced by decimal approximations, and care must be taken to see that the errors thus introduced do not accumulate sufficiently to affect the result. If the sum is to be correct to k decimal places, each term must be computed to $k + 1$ places at least and frequently more. The reader is warned against the very common mistake of stopping at too early a point in the series so that the terms neglected are sufficient to vitiate the result.

Example. Find the sum of the series

$$\frac{1}{5} + \frac{1}{3 \cdot 5^3} + \frac{1}{5 \cdot 5^5} + \frac{1}{7 \cdot 5^7} + \cdots + \frac{1}{(2n - 1) \cdot 5^{2n-1}} + \cdots,$$

correct to four decimal places. (Ex. 12, page 567.)

To find the sum, we have

$$\frac{1}{5} = 0.2, \qquad \frac{1}{3 \cdot 5^3} = 0.002\,67, \qquad \frac{1}{5 \cdot 5^5} = 0.000\,06.$$

The fourth term is evidently far too small in itself to affect the fifth place, and the error committed by stopping with the third term is but slightly greater than the fourth term.* Adding the three terms computed above, and discarding the fifth place as untrustworthy, we find the sum to be 0.2027.

EXERCISES

In Exs. 1–16, test the series (a) for convergence; (b) for absolute convergence.

1. $\displaystyle\sum_{n=1}^{\infty} \frac{(-1)^{n+1}}{2n + 1}.$ *Ans.* Convergent.

2. $\displaystyle\sum_{n=1}^{\infty} \frac{(-1)^{n+1}}{(2n + 1)^2}.$ *Ans.* Absolutely convergent.

3. $\displaystyle\sum_{n=2}^{\infty} \frac{(-1)^n(n + 2)}{3n - 1}.$ *Ans.* Divergent.

4. $\displaystyle\sum_{n=1}^{\infty} \frac{(-1)^{n-1}1000n^2}{3^n}.$ *Ans.* Absolutely convergent.

* The argument is as follows:

$$\frac{1}{7 \cdot 5^7} + \frac{1}{9 \cdot 5^9} + \frac{1}{11 \cdot 5^{11}} + \cdots + \frac{1}{(2n - 1)5^{2n-1}} + \cdots < \frac{1}{7 \cdot 5^7} + \frac{1}{7 \cdot 5^9} + \frac{1}{7 \cdot 5^{11}}$$

$$+ \cdots + \frac{1}{7 \cdot 5^{2n-1}} + \cdots < \frac{1}{7 \cdot 5^7}\left(1 + \frac{1}{5^2} + \frac{1}{5^4} + \cdots + \frac{1}{5^{2k}} + \cdots\right).$$

The series in parentheses is a geometric series whose sum is $\dfrac{1}{1 - \frac{1}{25}} = \dfrac{25}{24}.$ Thus the error in stopping with the third term is less than $\frac{25}{24}$ times the fourth term.

5. $\displaystyle\sum_{k=0}^{\infty} \frac{(-1)^k k!}{100^k}.$ *Ans.* Divergent.

6. $\displaystyle\sum_{k=0}^{\infty} \frac{(-1)^k (2k)!}{10^k}.$ **7.** $\displaystyle\sum_{n=0}^{\infty} \frac{(-1)^n 10^{4n}}{n!}.$

8. $\displaystyle\sum_{n=0}^{\infty} \frac{(-1)^n}{n^3 + 1}.$ **9.** $\displaystyle\sum_{n=0}^{\infty} \frac{(-1)^n (n + 1)}{n^2 + 4n + 5}.$

10. $\displaystyle\sum_{n=1}^{\infty} \frac{(-1)^{n+1} n \pi^n}{e^{2n} + 1}.$

11. $1 - \dfrac{1}{2\sqrt{1}} + \dfrac{1}{3\sqrt{2}} - \dfrac{1}{4\sqrt{3}} + \cdots + \dfrac{(-1)^{n-1}}{n\sqrt{n-1}} + \cdots .$

12. $1 - \dfrac{1}{\sqrt{2}} + \dfrac{1}{\sqrt{3}} - \dfrac{1}{\sqrt{4}} + \cdots + \dfrac{(-1)^{n-1}}{\sqrt{n}} + \cdots .$

13. $\displaystyle\sum_{n=1}^{\infty} \frac{1}{n^2} \sin n.$ **14.** $\displaystyle\sum_{n=1}^{\infty} \frac{\sin \frac{1}{4} n \pi}{n^4}.$ **15.** $\displaystyle\sum_{n=1}^{\infty} \frac{n \cos \frac{1}{4} n \pi}{n + 1}.$

16. $\displaystyle\sum_{n=1}^{\infty} u_n,$ where $u_n = \dfrac{1}{n}$ if n is odd, $u_n = -\dfrac{1}{n^{\frac{3}{2}}}$ if n is even. *Ans.* Divergent.

In Exs. 17–22, find the sum of the series, correct to the number of decimal places indicated in the respective answers.

17. $1 - \dfrac{1}{10} + \dfrac{2}{10^2} - \dfrac{3}{10^3} + \cdots + \dfrac{(-1)^n \cdot n}{10^n} + \cdots .$ *Ans.* 0.91736.

18. $1 - \dfrac{1}{3!} + \dfrac{1}{5!} - \cdots + \dfrac{(-1)^{n-1}}{(2n - 1)!} + \cdots .$ *Ans.* 0.84147.

19. $1 - \dfrac{1}{2!} + \dfrac{2}{3!} - \dfrac{3}{4!} + \cdots + \dfrac{(-1)^{n-1}(n - 1)}{n!} + \cdots .$ *Ans.* 0.736.

20. $\dfrac{1}{10} - \dfrac{1}{2 \cdot 10^2} + \dfrac{1}{3 \cdot 10^3} - \cdots + \dfrac{(-1)^{n-1}}{n \cdot 10^n} + \cdots .$ *Ans.* 0.0953.

21. $\dfrac{1}{5} + \dfrac{2}{5^2} + \dfrac{3}{5^3} + \cdots + \dfrac{n}{5^n} + \cdots .$ *Ans.* 0.3125.

22. $\dfrac{1}{1 \cdot 2} + \dfrac{1}{2 \cdot 3} \cdot \dfrac{1}{10} + \dfrac{1}{3 \cdot 4} \cdot \dfrac{1}{10^2} + \cdots + \dfrac{1}{n(n + 1)10^{n-1}} + \cdots .$

Ans. 0.5176.

23. How many terms of the series $1 - \dfrac{1}{2} + \dfrac{1}{3} - \dfrac{1}{4} + \cdots + \dfrac{(-1)^{n-1}}{n} + \cdots$

must be taken to insure correctness of the sum to four places, with an error of not more than 5 points in the fifth place? *Ans.* 20,000.

Power Series

334. *Power Series*

A series of the form

$$a_0 + a_1v + a_2v^2 + \cdots + a_nv^n + \cdots = \sum_{n=0}^{\infty} a_nv^n,$$

where v is a variable and $a_0, a_1, a_2, \cdots$ are constants, is called a *power series*. Such series will be studied in this chapter.

A power series may converge for all values of the variable v or for no values except zero, but usually it will converge for all values in some interval of length greater than zero and diverge for all values outside that interval. The interval of convergence always extends equal distances on each side of the point $v = 0$.

In simple cases, the interval of convergence can be determined by the ratio test.

Example (a). Find the interval of convergence of the series

$$1 + x + \frac{x^2}{2} + \frac{x^3}{3} + \cdots + \frac{x^n}{n} + \cdots .$$

Here

$$\lim_{n \to \infty} \left| \frac{u_{n+1}}{u_n} \right| = \lim_{n \to \infty} \left| \frac{\dfrac{x^{n+1}}{n+1}}{\dfrac{x^n}{n}} \right| = \lim_{n \to \infty} \frac{n}{n+1} \cdot |x| = |x|.$$

Therefore:

(a) The series converges when $|x| < 1$, i.e., $-1 < x < 1$.

(b) The series diverges when $|x| > 1$.

(c) The test fails when $x = \pm 1$. But when $x = 1$, the series is

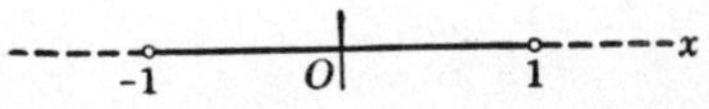

$$1 + 1 + \frac{1}{2} + \frac{1}{3} + \cdots + \frac{1}{n} + \cdots ,$$

and therefore diverges; when $x = -1$, the series is

Figure 347

573

$$1 - 1 + \frac{1}{2} - \frac{1}{3} + \frac{1}{4} - \cdots + \frac{(-1)^n}{n} + \cdots ,$$

which converges by § 332.

Hence the interval of convergence is $-1 \leqq x < 1$.

Example (b).   Find the interval of convergence of the series

$$(x - 3) + 2(x - 3)^2 + 3(x - 3)^3 + \cdots + n(x - 3)^n + \cdots .$$

In this case

$$\operatorname*{Lim}_{n \to \infty} \left| \frac{(n + 1)(x - 3)^{n+1}}{n(x - 3)^n} \right| = \operatorname*{Lim}_{n \to \infty} \frac{n + 1}{n} \cdot |x - 3| = |x - 3|.$$

(a) The series converges if $|x - 3| < 1$, or $2 < x < 4$.

(b) The series diverges if $|x - 3| > 1$, or $x > 4$, $x < 2$.

(c) By § 323, the series diverges if $x = 2$ or $x = 4$.

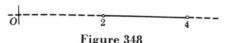

Figure 348

Thus the interval is $2 < x < 4$.

Example (c).   Find the region of convergence of the series

$$\frac{1}{x} + \frac{2}{x^3} + \frac{2^2}{x^5} + \frac{2^3}{x^7} + \cdots + \frac{2^n}{x^{2n+1}} + \cdots .$$

The test limit is

$$\operatorname*{Lim}_{n \to \infty} \frac{\dfrac{2^{n+1}}{x^{2n+3}}}{\dfrac{2^n}{x^{2n+1}}} = \operatorname*{Lim}_{n \to \infty} \frac{2}{x^2} = \frac{2}{x^2}.$$

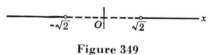

Figure 349

Thus the series converges if $\dfrac{2}{x^2} < 1$, $|x| > \sqrt{2}$; it diverges at both end points.

EXERCISES

In Exs. 1–28, find the interval of convergence and test the series at the end points of the interval.

1. $\displaystyle\sum_{n=0}^{\infty} (-1)^n x^n.$ *Ans.* $-1 < x < 1.$

2. $\displaystyle\sum_{n=1}^{\infty} \frac{x^n}{2n - 1}.$ *Ans.* $-1 \leqq x < 1.$

3. $\displaystyle\sum_{n=0}^{\infty} \frac{(-1)^n y^n}{(2n + 1)^2 3^{n+1}}.$ *Ans.* $-3 \leqq y \leqq 3.$

4. $\displaystyle\sum_{n=1}^{\infty} \frac{(n+1)y^{2n}}{5^n}.$ *Ans.* $-\sqrt{5} < y < \sqrt{5}.$

5. $\displaystyle\sum_{n=0}^{\infty} (-1)^n n! x^n.$ *Ans.* $x = 0.$

6. $\displaystyle\sum_{n=1}^{\infty} \frac{n! x^n}{2n-1}.$ *Ans.* $x = 0.$

7. $\displaystyle\sum_{n=0}^{\infty} \frac{x^n}{n!}.$ *Ans.* All values of $x.$

8. $\displaystyle\sum_{n=0}^{\infty} \frac{(-1)^n x^{2n}}{(2n)!}.$ *Ans.* All values of $x.$

9. $y + \dfrac{y^2}{1+2^2} + \dfrac{y^3}{1+3^2} + \cdots + \dfrac{y^n}{1+n^2} + \cdots .$

10. $z - \dfrac{z^3}{4} + \dfrac{z^5}{7} - \dfrac{z^7}{10} + \cdots + \dfrac{(-1)^n z^{2n+1}}{3n+1} + \cdots .$

11. $\dfrac{x}{2\cdot 3\cdot 4} - \dfrac{x^2}{5\cdot 6\cdot 7} + \dfrac{x^3}{8\cdot 9\cdot 10} - \cdots + \dfrac{(-1)^{n-1}x^n}{(3n-1)(3n)(3n+1)} + \cdots .$

12. $\dfrac{1}{1\cdot 2} - \dfrac{x^2}{2\cdot 3} + \dfrac{x^4}{3\cdot 4} - \dfrac{x^6}{4\cdot 5} + \cdots + \dfrac{(-1)^n x^{2n}}{(n+1)(n+2)} + \cdots .$

13. $\displaystyle\sum_{n=0}^{\infty} \frac{(-1)^n x^{n+2}}{(n+1)^2 2^{2n}}.$ *Ans.* $-4 \leq x \leq 4.$

14. $\displaystyle\sum_{n=1}^{\infty} \frac{n x^{2n+3}}{(n+1)^2}.$ *Ans.* $-1 < x < 1.$

15. $\displaystyle\sum_{n=0}^{\infty} \frac{(-1)^n x^{2n+1}}{(2n+1)!}.$ *Ans.* All values of $x.$

16. $\displaystyle\sum_{n=0}^{\infty} \frac{n! x^n}{(2n+1)!}.$ *Ans.* All values of $x.$

17. $\displaystyle\sum_{k=1}^{\infty} (-1)^{k-1}(3k+1)y^{2k}.$

18. $\displaystyle\sum_{k=0}^{\infty} \frac{(-1)^k(3k+1)y^{2k}}{2^k}.$

19. $\displaystyle\sum_{n=1}^{\infty} n^2(x + 1)^n.$

Ans. $-2 < x < 0.$

20. $\displaystyle\sum_{n=0}^{\infty} \frac{(-1)^n(x - 4)^{n+1}}{(n + 1)^3}.$

Ans. $3 \leqq x \leqq 5.$

21. $\displaystyle\sum_{n=1}^{\infty} n(x - 2)^n.$

22. $\displaystyle\sum_{n=1}^{\infty} \frac{n(x + 3)^n}{(2n - 1)^3}.$

23. $\displaystyle\sum_{n=0}^{\infty} \frac{(n + 2)(x - 1)^n}{n!}.$

24. $\displaystyle\sum_{n=1}^{\infty} \frac{(-1)^n(2n - 1)x^{2n-1}}{(2n)!}.$

25. $\displaystyle\sum_{n=1}^{\infty} \frac{(-1)^n}{nx^n}.$

Ans. $x \geqq 1,$ and $x < -1.$

26. $\displaystyle\sum_{n=0}^{\infty} \frac{n + 1}{2^{n+2}x^n}.$

Ans. $x > \frac{1}{2},$ and $x < -\frac{1}{2}.$

27. $\displaystyle\sum_{n=0}^{\infty} \frac{(-1)^n 5^n}{(3n + 1)x^n}.$

28. $\displaystyle\sum_{n=2}^{\infty} \frac{(-1)^n 2^{n+1}}{n^2 x^{n+2}}.$

In Exs. 29–33, find the interval of convergence, but do not test the series at the end points of the interval.

29. $\displaystyle\sum_{n=1}^{\infty} \frac{1 \cdot 3 \cdot 5 \cdot 7 \cdots (2n - 1)x^{2n}}{2^n n!}.$

30. $\displaystyle\sum_{n=1}^{\infty} \frac{n^n x^n}{n!}.$

Ans. $|x| < \dfrac{1}{e}.$

31. $\displaystyle\sum_{n=1}^{\infty} \frac{n! x^n}{n^n}.$

32. $\displaystyle\sum_{n=1}^{\infty} \frac{1 \cdot 3 \cdot 5 \cdot 7 \cdots (2n - 1)x^{2n}}{2 \cdot 4 \cdot 6 \cdot 8 \cdots (2n + 2)}.$

33. $1 + \sum_{n=1}^{\infty} \dfrac{m(m-1) \cdots (m-n+1)x^n}{n!}$.   *Ans.* $|x| < 1$.

335. *Maclaurin Series*

Being given a power series in x, if we substitute for x any value within the interval of convergence, the sum of the series is determined; i.e., the sum is a function of x. This suggests a very important problem: Being given a function of x, to determine whether it has a power series expansion, and if it has one, to find that expansion.

In § 339 we shall justify many of the power series expansions to be employed in this book. At present we proceed on a purely formal basis. That is, we first develop techniques for obtaining the desired series and afterward prove the validity of the results.

Suppose that $f(x)$ does have a power series expansion:

(1) $f(x) = c_0 + c_1 x + c_2 x^2 + \cdots + c_n x^n + \cdots$,

where the coefficients c_0, c_1, c_2, $\cdots$, are constants to be determined. Setting $x = 0$, we get

$$f(0) = c_0;$$

i.e., c_0 is the value of the given function at $x = 0$. Differentiating (1) (see Theorem 73, § 345),

$$f'(x) = c_1 + 2c_2 x + 3c_3 x^2 + \cdots,$$

and setting $x = 0$, we find

$$f'(0) = c_1.$$

Proceeding in this way, we get successively

$$f''(0) = 2 \cdot 1 c_2,$$
$$f'''(0) = 3 \cdot 2 \cdot 1 c_3,$$
$$\vdots$$
$$f^{(n)}(0) = n!\, c_n,$$
$$\vdots$$

Hence (1) takes the following form, called *Maclaurin's series*:

(2) $f(x) = f(0) + f'(0)x + \dfrac{f''(0)}{2!} x^2 + \cdots + \dfrac{f^{(n)}(0)}{n!} x^n + \cdots$.

It should be noted that we have not proved the validity of this result; we have merely proved that if there is a series of the form (1) whose sum is $f(x)$, that series is given by equation (2). The series (2) can always be formally written down whenever the function and its successive derivatives are defined at $x = 0$, but cases can be found in which the sum of the series is not the given function (see Ex. 49 below).

For all functions that we shall consider, *the interval within which the Maclaurin series is valid coincides with the interval of convergence of the series.* Within that interval the series is said to *represent the function*, and the function is said to be *developed* or *expanded* in powers of x.

Example (a). Develop e^x in Maclaurin's series.

$$f(x) = e^x, \qquad f(0) = 1,$$
$$f'(x) = e^x, \qquad f'(0) = 1,$$

$$f^{(n)}(x) = e^x, \qquad f^{(n)}(0) = 1.$$

Therefore

$$e^x = 1 + x + \frac{x^2}{2!} + \frac{x^3}{3!} + \cdots + \frac{x^n}{n!} + \cdots .$$

This series converges for all values of x. (Ex. 7, page 575.)

Example (b). Expand $\sin x$ in powers of x.

Here

$$f(x) = \sin x, \qquad f(0) = 0,$$
$$f'(x) = \cos x, \qquad f'(0) = 1,$$
$$f''(x) = -\sin x, \qquad f''(0) = 0,$$
$$f'''(x) = -\cos x, \qquad f'''(0) = -1,$$
$$f^{(4)}(x) = \sin x, \qquad f^{(4)}(0) = 0.$$

Since we have now returned to the original function, it is clear that the sequence $0, 1, 0, -1$, occurring in the right-hand column, must repeat over and over. Hence, substituting in (2), we find

$$\sin x = x - \frac{x^3}{3!} + \frac{x^5}{5!} - \cdots + \frac{(-1)^n x^{2n+1}}{(2n+1)!} + \cdots .$$

The series converges for all values of x. (Ex. 15, page 575.)

The rather cumbersome* method, applying Maclaurin's formula directly to obtain power series for elementary functions, is to be used only on certain basic functions, those given in the next section. For other elementary functions, we obtain their power series expansions by suitable manipulations performed on the basic series. For details, see § 344–346.

---

* Try this method for getting the general term of the series for $\dfrac{x^3}{(1+x^2)^2}$, and then compare with the neat device used in Ex. 7, page 596.

336. *The Basic Expansions*

We list for reference:

(1)
$$e^x = \sum_{n=0}^{\infty} \frac{x^n}{n!}; \quad \text{for all values of } x.$$

(2)
$$\cos x = \sum_{n=0}^{\infty} \frac{(-1)^n x^{2n}}{(2n)!}; \quad \text{for all values of } x.$$

(3)
$$\sin x = \sum_{n=0}^{\infty} \frac{(-1)^n x^{2n+1}}{(2n+1)!}; \quad \text{for all values of } x.$$

(4)
$$\frac{1}{1-x} = \sum_{n=0}^{\infty} x^n; \quad -1 < x < 1.$$

(5)
$$\ln(1+x) = \sum_{n=1}^{\infty} \frac{(-1)^{n+1} x^n}{n}; \quad -1 < x \leq 1.$$

(6)
$$(1+x)^m = 1 + \sum_{n=1}^{\infty} \frac{m(m-1)(m-2)\cdots(m-n+1)x^n}{n!};$$

$$|x| < 1.$$

It is advisable that the student write out several terms of each series, as an aid in remembering these important expansions.

337. *Taylor Series*

The Maclaurin series for $f(x)$ is most useful near $x = 0$, where its convergence is rapid. In studying the function $f(x)$ near some other point $x = a$, it is natural to seek a series proceeding not in powers of x but in powers of $(x - a)$. Let

(1) $\quad f(x) = c_0 + c_1(x - a) + c_2(x - a)^2 + \cdots + c_n(x - a)^n + \cdots,$

and set $x = a$, which gives

$$c_0 = f(a).$$

Next differentiate with respect to x throughout equation (1) and then set $x = a$, proceeding just as we did in obtaining the coefficients in the Maclaurin series. The result is the Taylor series for $f(x)$:

(2) $\quad f(x) = f(a) + f'(a)(x - a) + \frac{f''(a)}{2!}(x - a)^2 + \cdots$

$$+ \frac{f^{(n)}(a)}{n!}(x - a)^n + \cdots.$$

Example.   Expand the function ln x in powers of $x - 1$.
In this case $a = 1$:

$$f(x) = \ln x, \qquad\qquad f(1) = 0,$$
$$f'(x) = \frac{1}{x}, \qquad\qquad f'(1) = 1,$$
$$f''(x) = -\frac{1}{x^2}, \qquad\qquad f''(1) = -1,$$
$$f'''(x) = \frac{2}{x^3}, \qquad\qquad f'''(1) = 2,$$
$$f^{(4)}(x) = -\frac{2 \cdot 3}{x^4}, \qquad\qquad f^{(4)}(1) = -2 \cdot 3,$$

$$f^{(n)}(x) = (-1)^{n-1}\frac{(n-1)!}{x^n}, \qquad f^{(n)}(1) = (-1)^{n-1}(n-1)!$$

Hence, by (2),

$$\ln x = (x-1) - \frac{(x-1)^2}{2} + \frac{(x-1)^3}{3} - \cdots$$

$$+ (-1)^{n-1}\frac{(x-1)^n}{n} + \cdots .$$

The series converges for $0 < x \leqq 2$.

EXERCISES

In Exs. 1–10, use the Maclaurin series directly to expand the given function in powers of x; then determine the interval of convergence.

1. $\cos x$.   See (2), § 336.

2. $\dfrac{1}{1-x}$.   See (4), § 336.

3. $\ln(1+x)$.   See (5), § 336. \qquad **4.** $\dfrac{1}{1+2x}$.

5. $\sin 3x$. \qquad\qquad **6.** $e^{-\frac{1}{2}x}$. \qquad\qquad **7.** $\ln(1-3x)$.

8. $\sqrt{1+x}$. \qquad *Ans.* $1 + \dfrac{1}{2}x + \displaystyle\sum_{n=2}^{\infty}\frac{(-1)^{n+1}\,1\cdot 3\cdot 5\,\cdots\,(2n-3)x^n}{2^n n!}$.

9. $\dfrac{1}{\sqrt{1+x}}$. \qquad *Ans.* $1 + \displaystyle\sum_{n=1}^{\infty}\frac{(-1)^n\,1\cdot 3\cdot 5\,\cdots\,(2n-1)x^n}{2^n n!}$.

10. $(1+x)^m$.   See (6), § 336.

In Exs. 11–20, obtain the power series expansion for the given function by making an appropriate substitution in one of the basic expansions of § 336.

11. $\dfrac{1}{1 - x^2}$. Put x^2 for x in (4), § 336.

12. $\ln (1 - x^2)$. Put $(-x^2)$ for x in (5), § 336.

13. $e^{-\frac{1}{2}x^2}$. 14. $\cos 4x$. 15. Ex. 4.

16. Ex. 5. 17. Ex. 6. 18. Ex. 7.

19. $\ln (1 + 4x^2)$. 20. $\dfrac{1}{1 + 3x^4}$.

21. Obtain the power series for $\dfrac{1}{\sqrt{1 - x^2}}$ from the result of Ex. 9.

22. Obtain the power series for $\dfrac{x^4}{1 - x^3}$ from (4), § 336.

23. Obtain the power series for $\dfrac{x^3}{\sqrt{1 - x^3}}$ from Ex. 9.

24. Obtain the power series for $\ln (3 - x)$ from (5), § 336, with the aid of the relation

$$\ln (3 - x) = \ln \left[3 \left(1 - \frac{x}{3} \right) \right] = \ln 3 + \ln \left(1 - \frac{x}{3} \right).$$

25. Obtain the power series for $\ln (5 - 2x)$ from (5), § 336.
26. Obtain the power series for $\sin x \cos x$ from (3), § 336.
27. Obtain the power series for $x^3 e^{-x^2}$ from (1), § 336.
28. Show that $\csc x$ cannot be expanded in a Maclaurin series.
29. Show that $x \cot^2 x$ cannot be expanded in a Maclaurin series.
30. Show that $x^2 \ln x$ cannot be expanded in a Maclaurin series.

In Exs. 31–39, use Taylor series directly to obtain the desired expansion.

31. e^x in powers of $(x - 2)$. $Ans. \displaystyle\sum_{n=0}^{\infty} \frac{e^2(x - 2)^n}{n!}.$

32. $\ln x$ in powers of $(x - 3)$.
33. $\sin x$ in powers of $(x - \frac{1}{4}\pi)$.

34. $\sqrt{x}$ in powers of $(x - 2)$. 35. $\dfrac{1}{1 + x}$ in powers of $(x + 4)$.

36. e^x in powers of $(x + 1)$. 37. $\ln x$ in powers of $(x - \frac{1}{2})$.

38. $\cos x$ in powers of $(x + \frac{1}{4}\pi)$. 39. $\dfrac{1}{1 - x}$ in powers of $(x - 3)$.

In Exs. 40–45, use appropriate devices to obtain the desired expansion from the basic formulas of § 336 without resorting to Taylor's expansion directly.

40. Ex. 31. Write $e^x = e^2 \cdot e^{x-2}$.

41. Ex. 32. Write $\ln x = \ln [3 + (x - 3)] = \ln \left[3 \left(1 + \dfrac{x - 3}{3} \right) \right]$, etc.

42. Ex. 35. Use $\dfrac{1}{1+x} = \dfrac{1}{-3+(x+4)}$, etc.

43. Ex. 36.   **44. Ex. 37.**   **45. Ex. 39.**

46. Show that, if $P(x)$ is a polynomial of the nth degree in x,

$$P(x) = P(a) + P'(a)(x-a) + \frac{P''(a)}{2!}(x-a)^2 + \cdots + \frac{P^{(n)}(a)}{n!}(x-a)^n,$$

whatever may be the values of a and x.

47. Arrange the function $y = x^3 - 3x^2 + 2x - 5$ in powers of $x - 3$. (Ex. 46.)
        Ans. $y = 1 + 11(x-3) + 6(x-3)^2 + (x-3)^3$.

48. Arrange the function $y = x^4 - 3x^2 - 6x + 8$ in powers of $x - 2$. (Ex. 46.)
        Ans. $y = 14(x-2) + 21(x-2)^2 + 8(x-2)^3 + (x-2)^4$.

49. The Maclaurin series for the function $f(x) = e^{-\frac{1}{x^2}}$ may be formally obtained, provided we define $f(0) = 0$. Prove that the series converges for all values of x but does not represent the function.

It is proved in more advanced courses that the derivatives of $f(x)$ exist and are continuous at $x = 0$.

The reader should show that the nth derivative of $f(x)$ for $x \neq 0$ is the product of $e^{-\frac{1}{x^2}}$ and a polynomial in $\dfrac{1}{x}$.

338. *Remainder Theorems*

Suppose that $f(y)$ and its derivative $f'(y)$ are continuous in a range $a \leqq y \leqq x$. We know that an integral of $f'(y)$ is $f(y)$, so that

$$(1) \qquad \int_a^x f'(y)\, dy = f(x) - f(a).$$

Let us rewrite (1) as

$$(2) \qquad f(x) = f(a) + \int_a^x f'(y)\, dy.$$

We shall use integration by parts on the integral in (2), differentiating $f'(y)$ to get $f''(y)\, dy$ and integrating dy to get $(y - x)$. The choice $(y - x)$ rather than y as an integral of dy is made to simplify the integrated portion at the upper limit of integration.

$$\begin{array}{c|c} f'(y) & dy \\ \hline f''(y)\, dy & -(x-y) \end{array}$$

If we assume the existence of $f''(y)$, the above integration by parts performed on equation (2) leads us to

$$f(x) = f(a) - \left[(x-y)f'(y)\right]_a^x + \int_a^x (x-y)f''(y)\, dy,$$

or

(3) $$f(x) = f(a) + (x - a)f'(a) + \int_a^x (x - y)f''(y)\, dy.$$

Let us now apply integration by parts again.

$$\begin{array}{c|c} f''(y) & (x - y)\, dy \\ \hline f'''(y)\, dy & -\tfrac{1}{2}(x - y)^2 \end{array}$$

The choice indicated in the table leads us from equation (3) to the form

$$f(x) = f(a) + (x - a)f'(a) - \tfrac{1}{2}\left[(x - y)^2 f''(y) \right]_a^x + \tfrac{1}{2}\int_a^x (x - y)^2 f'''(y)\, dy,$$

and thus to the equation

(4) $$f(x) = f(a) + (x - a)f'(a) + \tfrac{1}{2}(x - a)^2 f''(a) + \tfrac{1}{2}\int_a^x (x - y)^2 f'''(y)\, dy.$$

The above process may be iterated, provided the derivatives of $f(y)$ involved all exist. In n steps, we are thus led to the following result.

Theorem 68. *If in $a \leqq y \leqq x$, $f(y)$ and its first $(n + 1)$ derivatives exist,*

(5) $$f(x) = f(a) + \sum_{k=1}^{n} \frac{f^{(k)}(a)(x - a)^k}{k!} + R_n(x, a)$$

in which

(6) $$R_n(x, a) = \frac{1}{n!} \int_a^x (x - y)^n f^{(n+1)}(y)\, dy.$$

The term $R_n(x, a)$ in (5) and (6) is called the *remainder*. Equation (5) is a finite form of a Taylor series. The problem of showing that $f(x)$ is represented by its Taylor series in some interval around $x = a$ is precisely the problem of showing that in the interval

(7) $$\operatorname*{Lim}_{n \to \infty} R_n(x, a) = 0.$$

We shall now obtain another form for the remainder term R_n of equation (5). For this purpose let us extend the first law of the mean obtained in § 145.

Suppose that in the interval $a \leqq y \leqq x$, $f(y)$ and its first $(n + 1)$ derivatives exist. Define the remainder $R_n(x, a)$ by

(8) $$f(x) = f(a) + \sum_{k=1}^{n} \frac{f^{(k)}(a)(x - a)^k}{k!} + R_n(x, a).$$

Now consider the function

$$(9) \quad \varphi(y) = f(x) - f(y) - \sum_{k=1}^{n} \frac{f^{(k)}(y)(x-y)^k}{k!} - \frac{(x-y)^{n+1}r_n(x, a)}{(n+1)!}.$$

We wish to make $\varphi(y)$ satisfy the conditions of Rolle's theorem, § 144. By (9), $\varphi(x) = 0$, and

$$(10) \quad \varphi(a) = f(x) - f(a) - \sum_{k=1}^{n} \frac{f^{(k)}(a)(x-a)^k}{k!} - \frac{(x-a)^{n+1}r_n(x, a)}{(n+1)!}.$$

Because of (8) the $\varphi(a)$ of (10) will be zero if we choose $r_n(x, a)$ so that

$$R_n(x, a) = \frac{(x-a)^{n+1}r_n(x, a)}{(n+1)!}.$$

From equation (9) it follows that

$$\varphi'(y) = -f'(y) - \sum_{k=1}^{n} \frac{f^{(k+1)}(y)(x-y)^k}{k!}$$
$$+ \sum_{k=1}^{n} \frac{f^{(k)}(y)(x-y)^{k-1}}{(k-1)!} + \frac{(x-y)^n r_n(x, a)}{n!}.$$

A shift of index from k to $(k+1)$ in the last summation above permits us to write

$$\varphi'(y) = -f'(y) - \sum_{k=1}^{n} \frac{f^{(k+1)}(y)(x-y)^k}{k!}$$
$$+ \sum_{k=0}^{n-1} \frac{f^{(k+1)}(y)(x-y)^k}{k!} + \frac{(x-y)^n r_n(x, a)}{n!},$$

or

$$(11) \quad \varphi'(y) = -\frac{f^{(n+1)}(y)(x-y)^n}{n!} + \frac{(x-y)^n r_n(x, a)}{n!},$$

since all the other terms drop out. We now see that $\varphi'(y)$ exists in the interval $a \leq y \leq x$. Therefore Rolle's theorem may be applied to $\varphi(y)$. Hence there exists an x_1 in the open interval $a < x_1 < x$ such that $\varphi'(x_1) = 0$. Since $(x - x_1) \neq 0$, we may conclude from $\varphi'(x_1) = 0$ and equation (11) that

$$(12) \quad r_n(x, a) = f^{(n+1)}(x_1), \quad a < x_1 < x.$$

We have thus proved the following result.

THEOREM 69.   *If in $a \leqq y \leqq x$, $f(y)$ and its first $(n + 1)$ derivatives exist,*

(13) $$f(x) = f(a) + \sum_{k=1}^{n} \frac{f^{(k)}(a)(x - a)^k}{k!} + R_n(x, a)$$

in which

(14) $$R_n(x, a) = \frac{(x - a)^{n+1} f^{(n+1)}(x_1)}{(n + 1)!}$$

for some x_1 in the open interval $a < x_1 < x$.

Again we have a finite form of Taylor series, with the remainder term this time given by (14) corresponding to the earlier form (6), page 583. Since differentiation is frequently a more elementary process than is integration, we make more use of (14) than we do of (6).

339. *Justification of Some Basic Expansions*

We now demonstrate the validity of some of the expansions given in § 336. We may conclude from Theorem 69 of the preceding section that if all the derivatives of $f(x)$ exist, $f(x)$ is represented by its Taylor series

(1) $$f(x) = f(a) + \sum_{n=1}^{\infty} \frac{f^{(n)}(a)(x - a)^n}{n!}$$

in any interval such that

(2) $$\lim_{n \to \infty} \frac{(x - a)^{n+1} f^{(n+1)}(x_1)}{(n + 1)!} = 0, \qquad a < x_1 < x.$$

For Maclaurin series put $a = 0$ in the above statement.

First consider $f(x) = e^x$. We know that for all n,

(3) $$f^{(n)}(x) = e^x.$$

Then, using $a = 0$, we have

(4) $$e^x = 1 + \sum_{n=1}^{\infty} \frac{x^n}{n!}$$

if only

(5) $$\lim_{n \to \infty} \frac{x^{n+1} e^{x_1}}{(n + 1)!} = 0, \qquad 0 < x_1 < x.$$

But (5) is true for any fixed x, so (4) is valid for all positive x. The same argument with x replaced by $(-x)$ yields the validity for negative x. At $x = 0$, the series terminates. Therefore the expansion (4) is valid for all finite x.

The interval of validity of a Taylor (or Maclaurin) series is symmetric about the point $x = a$ (or zero). We need not discuss negative x separately in our justification of the basic Maclaurin expansions of § 336.

Next consider at once both the functions $\sin x$ and $\cos x$. We know the derivatives are each either plus or minus $\sin x$ or $\cos x$. Hence, for all finite x_1,

$$|f^{(n+1)}(x_1)| \leqq 1.$$

It follows that $R_n \to 0$ as $n \to \infty$ for $f(x) = \cos x$ or $f(x) = \sin x$. Thus the expansions (2) and (3) of § 336 are valid for all finite x.

The validity of the expansion

$$(6) \qquad\qquad \frac{1}{1 - x} = \sum_{n=0}^{\infty} x^n, \qquad -1 < x < 1,$$

is easily justified by direct appeal to the definition of the sum of an infinite series. Let the sum of the terms out to x^n in the series on the right in (6) be $S_n(x)$:

$$(7) \qquad\qquad S_n(x) = \sum_{k=0}^{n} x^k.$$

By elementary algebra

$$(8) \qquad\qquad S_n(x) = \frac{1 - x^{n+1}}{1 - x}.$$

Therefore, if $|x| < 1$,

$$\operatorname*{Lim}_{n \to \infty} S_n(x) = \frac{1}{1 - x}.$$

If $|x| \geqq 1$, the series in (6) diverges because the general term does not approach zero as $n \to \infty$. (Recall Theorem 61, page 550.)

The student may show the validity of other expansions which appear in the book, if he wishes. We have accomplished the basic aim of exhibiting the ideas upon which such proofs of validity are based.

340. *Applications of Maclaurin Series*

The most elementary application of series, and one of great importance, is in computing tables of values of various functions, e.g., logarithms, trigonometric functions, etc.

Example (a). Compute $\sin 3°$ to five decimal places.

Setting $x = 3° = \dfrac{\pi}{60}$ in the series for $\sin x$ (§ 336), we get

$$\sin 3° = \sin \frac{\pi}{60} = \frac{\pi}{60} - \frac{1}{6}\left(\frac{\pi}{60}\right)^3 + \frac{1}{120}\left(\frac{\pi}{60}\right)^5 - \cdots$$
$$= 0.052\ 360 - 0.000\ 024 + \cdots.$$

Without computing the third term, we see that it is much too small to affect the sixth decimal place, and the error committed by stopping with any term is less than the next term by Theorem 67, § 332.   Hence we need keep only two terms:

$$\sin 3° = 0.052\ 34.$$

Example (b).   Since

$$\lim_{\theta \to 0} \frac{\sin \theta}{\theta} = 1,$$

it follows that for small values of the angle, $\sin \theta$ and θ are nearly equal. Within what interval can the sine be replaced by the angle if the allowable error is 0.0005?

From the equation

$$\sin \theta = \theta - \frac{\theta^3}{3!} + \frac{\theta^5}{5!} - \cdots,$$

it follows that the error committed by stopping with the first term, i.e., by setting

$$\sin \theta = \theta,$$

is less than $\frac{1}{6}\theta^3$ for sufficiently small θ (say, $\theta < 1$), by Theorem 67 of § 332. We therefore have

$$\frac{1}{6}\theta^3 < 0.0005,$$
$$\theta^3 < 0.003,$$
$$\theta < 0.1442 \text{ (radian)}$$
$$< 8° \ 15', \text{ approximately.}$$

That is, the sine of any angle less than $8° \ 15'$ can be replaced by the angle with an error less than 0.0005.

Example (c).   Find the amount by which an arc of a great circle of the earth 1 mi. long recedes from its chord.

We have to find

$$l = R - R \cos \alpha = R(1 - \cos \alpha).$$

Since α is very small, we may safely take, in (2) of § 336,

$$\cos \alpha = 1 - \frac{1}{2} \alpha^2,$$

$$l = \frac{1}{2} R\alpha^2 = \frac{(R\alpha)^2}{2R}.$$

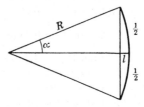

Figure 350

By hypothesis, $R\alpha = \frac{1}{2}$, so that, with $R = 4000$ mi.,

$$l = \frac{\frac{1}{4}}{8000} \text{ mi.} = \frac{5280 \cdot 12}{4 \cdot 8000} \text{ in.} = 2 \text{ in., nearly.}$$

One of the most useful elementary applications of Maclaurin series is the evaluation of certain definite integrals.   See § 347, page 599.

341. *The Value of e*

As a further application of the Maclaurin series, let us compute the value of e to five decimal places. Taking $x = 1$ in (1), § 336, we have

$$e = 1 + 1 + \frac{1}{2!} + \frac{1}{3!} + \frac{1}{4!} + \cdots + \frac{1}{n!} + \cdots .$$

This gives*

$$
\begin{array}{l}
1.000\ 000 \\
1.000\ 000 \\
0.500\ 000 \\
0.166\ 667 \\
0.041\ 667 \\
0.008\ 333 \\
0.001\ 389 \\
0.000\ 198 \\
0.000\ 025 \\
0.000\ 003 \\
\hline
2.718\ 28.
\end{array}
$$

The sum of all the remaining terms is but little greater than the first term neglected. Compare the terms neglected with the geometric series

$$\frac{1}{10!}\left(1 + \frac{1}{11} + \frac{1}{11^2} + \cdots + \frac{1}{11^n} + \cdots\right).$$

EXERCISES

In Exs. 1–8, use series to make the required computations.

  1. cos 3° to five places.
  2. sin 4° to four places.
  3. cos 6° to four places.
  4. sin 2° to five places.
  5. sin 88° to four places.
  6. cos 85° to four places.
  7. ln (1.05) to four places.
  8. ln (0.97) to six places.

  9. Compute $\dfrac{1}{e}$ by power series. *Ans.* 0.3679.

 10. Find the tenth root of e. *Ans.* 1.10517.

 11. Compute $(1.01)^7$ by the binomial theorem. *Ans.* 1.0721.

 12. Raise 0.99 to the tenth power. *Ans.* 0.9044.

 13. Extract the square root of 102 to four decimal places by using power series, first writing

$$\sqrt{102} = \sqrt{100 + 2} = 10(1 + 0.02)^{\frac{1}{2}}.$$

Ans. 10.0995.

 14. Extract the square root of 101 to four decimal places by using power series.

 15. Within what interval can sin θ be placed by θ, if the allowable error is 0.005? Check by the table.

* Note that the fourth term can be obtained by dividing the third by 3, the fifth by dividing the fourth by 4, etc.

16. Within what interval can $\cos \theta$ be taken equal to 1, with accuracy to three places (allowable error 0.0005)? Check by the table, pages 712–713.

17. Solve the equation $\cos x = 5x$ to three figures by using series.

Ans. $x = 0.196.$

18. Solve the equation $\cos x = 10x.$ *Ans.* $x = 0.0995.$

19. Solve Example (c), § 340, if the arc is 10 mi. long. *Ans.* 16 ft.

20. In Example (c), § 340, how much longer is the arc than the chord?

Ans. $\frac{1}{6000}$ in.

21. If a straight tunnel were to be bored through the earth from Detroit to Chicago (say, 300 mi.), how much distance would be saved? *Ans.* 371 ft.

22. In Ex. 21, find the greatest depth of the tunnel. *Ans.* 2.8 mi.

23. The gravitational attraction of the earth at a height h above sea level is

$$A = \frac{gR^2}{(R + h)^2},$$

where R is the radius of the earth and $g = 32.16$ ft. per sec. per sec. At what altitude is $A = 32.00$?

24. Taking the earth's circumference as 40,000,000 meters, find the difference between the circumference and the perimeter of a regular inscribed polygon of 1,000,000 sides. *Ans.* Less than $\frac{1}{15}$ mm.

25. In the computation of e, § 341, find an upper limit for the error caused by stopping with 10 terms. *Ans.* 0.000 000 3.

26. Use the forms of the remainder term in Theorems 68 and 69 of § 338 to show that: If $g(y)$ is continuous in the interval $a \leq y \leq x$, there exists an x_1 such that

$$\int_a^x (x - y)^n g(y)\, dy = \frac{(x - a)^{n+1} g(x_1)}{n + 1} \qquad a < x_1 < x.$$

342. *Applications of Taylor Series*

If a power series is to be used for computation, the coefficients must be known numbers. Hence, even though it may be theoretically possible to expand a function $f(x)$ in powers of $(x - a)$ for any value of a (this is true, for instance, for e^x, $\sin x$ and $\cos x$), actually, for purposes of computation, the only readily available values of a are those for which $f(a), f'(a), f''(a), \cdots$, are known, since these quantities appear in the coefficients. For example, if we wish to use the Taylor series for $\sin x$ for computation, the only values of a ready to hand ($0 < a < \frac{1}{2}\pi$) are $\frac{1}{6}\pi$, $\frac{1}{4}\pi$, or $\frac{1}{3}\pi$.

Maclaurin series converge rapidly, in general, for *small* values of x. Taylor series converge rapidly for values of x near a; i.e., such that $(x - a)$ is small. Hence, of the available values of a [those for which $f(a), f'(a), \cdots$, are known], we should as a rule choose the one that is *nearest the value of x for which $f(x)$ is to be computed.* For example, to compute $\sin 46°$, we would take $a = \frac{1}{4}\pi$; to compute $\sin 58°$, we would take $a = \frac{1}{3}\pi$.

Example. Find the value of $e^{1.04}$ to four decimal places.

The Maclaurin series for e^x would converge fairly rapidly for $x = 1.04$, but the successive terms would not be easy to compute. Knowing the value of e

from § 341, we may use $e^{1.04} = e \cdot e^{0.04}$,

$$e^{1.04} = e\left[1 + 0.04 + \frac{0.0016}{2!} + \frac{0.000\ 064}{3!} + \frac{0.000\ 002\ 56}{4!} + \cdots\right]$$

$$= 2.718\ 28\ (1 + 0.04 + 0.000\ 8 + 0.000\ 01) = 2.829\ 2.$$

343. *Approximate Formulas for Δy*

In (2), § 337, let us replace a by x and x by $x + \Delta x$. The formula then becomes

(1) $f(x + \Delta x) = f(x) + f'(x)\,\Delta x + \dfrac{f''(x)}{2!}\,\overline{\Delta x}^2 + \dfrac{f'''(x)}{3!}\,\overline{\Delta x}^3 + \cdots$

$$+ \frac{f^{(n)}(x)}{n!}\,\overline{\Delta x}^n + \cdots,$$

or, with

$$y = f(x), \qquad \Delta y = f(x + \Delta x) - f(x),$$

(2) $\Delta y = y'\,\Delta x + \dfrac{y''}{2!}\,\overline{\Delta x}^2 + \dfrac{y'''}{3!}\,\overline{\Delta x}^3 + \cdots + \dfrac{y^{(n)}}{n!}\,\overline{\Delta x}^n + \cdots.$

For values of x and Δx that cause the terms of the series to diminish rapidly, we have, as a first approximation to the value of Δy, the formula used in § 73:

$$\Delta y = y'\,\Delta x = dy,$$

the error in using this formula being approximately $\frac{1}{2}y''\,\overline{\Delta x}^2$; as a second approximation we have

$$\Delta y = y'\,\Delta x + \tfrac{1}{2}y''\,\overline{\Delta x}^2,$$

with an error nearly equal to $\frac{1}{6}y'''\,\overline{\Delta x}^3$; etc.

   Example.   Taking $f(x) = \cos x$ in (1), we get

$$\cos(x + \Delta x) = \cos x - \sin x\,\Delta x - \tfrac{1}{2}\cos x\,\overline{\Delta x}^2 + \cdots,$$

which gives the first approximation

(3) $\cos(x + \Delta x) = \cos x - \sin x\,\Delta x.$

If the allowable error in the cosine is 0.0005, within what range may this formula be used to compute the cosines of angles near 45°?

   The error in using (3) is approximately $-\frac{1}{2}\cos x\,\overline{\Delta x}^2$. Since $x = 45°$, we have, numerically,

$$\tfrac{1}{2} \cdot 0.7071\,\overline{\Delta x}^2 < 0.000\ 5,$$
$$\overline{\Delta x}^2 < 0.001\ 414,$$
$$\Delta x < 0.037\ 6 = 2°, \text{ roughly.}$$

Hence the approximate formula (3) may safely be used to compute the cosines of angles between 43° and 47°.

EXERCISES

1. Using $e^x = e \cdot e^{x-1}$, compute $e^{0.98}$ to four figures. *Ans.* 2.664.

2. Using Ex. 33, page 581, compute sin 44°. *Ans.* 0.695.

3. Compute cos 44°. *Ans.* 0.719.

4. Apply (1), § 343, to $y = \dfrac{1}{x}$.

Ans. $\dfrac{1}{x + \Delta x} = \displaystyle\sum_{n=0}^{\infty} \dfrac{(-1)^n \overline{\Delta x^n}}{x^{n+1}} = \dfrac{1}{x} - \dfrac{\Delta x}{x^2} + \dfrac{\overline{\Delta x^2}}{x^3} - \cdots + \dfrac{(-1)^n \overline{\Delta x^n}}{x^{n+1}} + \cdots$.

5. Compute $\frac{1}{102}$ to eight decimal places. (Ex. 4.)

6. Compute $\frac{1}{997}$ to 15 decimal places by mental arithmetic.

7. Given cos 6° = 0.994 52, find sec 6°. *Ans.* 1.005 51.

8. Show that the error in using the approximate formula of Example (*a*), § 73, is $\pi \overline{\Delta r^2}$. When $r = 10$ ft., what is the greatest allowable value of Δr if accuracy to 5% is required? *Ans.* About 1 ft.

9. Find the error in the approximate formula for the volume of a thin spherical shell (Ex. 1, page 135). What is the greatest allowable thickness for a radius of 5 ft., if accuracy to 1% is required? *Ans.* About 0.6 in.

10. Solve the example of § 343 for angles near 60°. *Ans.* 57° 30′ < *x* < 62° 30′.

11. From (1), § 343, obtain an approximate formula for $\dfrac{1}{(x + \Delta x)^2}$.

Ans. $\dfrac{1}{(x + \Delta x)^2} = \dfrac{1}{x^2} - \dfrac{2\Delta x}{x^3} + \dfrac{3\overline{\Delta x^2}}{x^4} - \dfrac{4\overline{\Delta x^3}}{x^5} + \cdots$.

12. Compute $(\frac{1}{98})^2$ to ten places by mental arithmetic.

13. Use (1), § 343, to obtain an approximate formula for $\dfrac{1}{(x + \Delta x)^3}$.

Ans. $\dfrac{1}{(x + \Delta x)^3} = \dfrac{1 \cdot 2}{2x^3} - \dfrac{2 \cdot 3\Delta x}{2x^4} + \dfrac{3 \cdot 4\overline{\Delta x^2}}{2x^5} - \dfrac{4 \cdot 5\overline{\Delta x^3}}{2x^6} + \cdots$.

14. Compute $\frac{1}{729}$ to seven places.

15. Show that $\ln (x + \Delta x) = \ln x + \dfrac{\Delta x}{x} - \dfrac{\overline{\Delta x^2}}{2x^2} + \dfrac{\overline{\Delta x^3}}{3x^3} - \cdots$.

16. If the allowable error in a logarithm is 0.000 05, within what range can the formula $\ln (x + \Delta x) = \ln x + \dfrac{\Delta x}{x}$ be used?

17. Show that $(x + \Delta x)^{\frac{1}{2}} = x^{\frac{1}{2}} + \dfrac{\Delta x}{2x^{\frac{1}{2}}} - \dfrac{1}{2} \cdot \dfrac{\overline{\Delta x^2}}{4x^{\frac{3}{2}}} + \dfrac{1 \cdot 3}{2 \cdot 4} \dfrac{\overline{\Delta x^3}}{6x^{\frac{5}{2}}} - \cdots$.

18. Extract $\sqrt{101}$ to seven decimal places. (Ex. 17.)

19. Make an accurate detail of the curve $y = x^4 - 4x^3 + 6x^2$ near the point $x = 1$. (Ex. 46, page 582.)

20. Solve Ex. 19 for the curve $y = \ln x$. (Example, § 337.)

Operations with Power Series

344. *Algebraic Operations with Power Series*

Operations that can always be performed upon series of a finite number of terms, such as rearrangement of terms, insertion or removal of parentheses, etc., cannot be assumed offhand to be allowable with infinite series, and in fact it is easily shown that they are not allowable in all cases.

In dealing with power series, it is desirable to know whether certain elementary operations are permissible. We therefore state the following theorems regarding power series; the proofs belong to a more advanced treatment of the subject, except for the proof of Theorem 70. For that theorem the student can easily construct a proof using Theorem 10, page 50.

THEOREM 70. ADDITION. *Within any common interval of convergence, the term-by-term sum of the power series for $f(x)$ and $g(x)$ is the power series for $[f(x) + g(x)]$.*

In rough language, two convergent power series may be added term by term. That is, within an interval where the series

$$f(x) = \sum_{n=0}^{\infty} a_n x^n,$$

and

$$g(x) = \sum_{n=0}^{\infty} b_n x^n,$$

are both convergent, the series obtained by adding them term by term will converge to $[f(x) + g(x)]$:

$$f(x) + g(x) = \sum_{n=0}^{\infty} (a_n + b_n) x^n.$$

Subtraction is included by a change of signs.

THEOREM 71. MULTIPLICATION. *Within any common interval of convergence of the power series,*

$$f(x) = \sum_{n=0}^{\infty} a_n x^n,$$

$$g(x) = \sum_{n=0}^{\infty} b_n x^n,$$

the power series formed by multiplying each term of one series by every term of the other series* converges to the product $f(x)g(x)$,

$$f(x)g(x) = a_0 b_0 + (a_0 b_1 + a_1 b_0)x + (a_0 b_2 + a_1 b_1 + a_2 b_0)x^2 + \cdots$$
$$+ (a_0 b_n + a_1 b_{n-1} + \cdots + a_n b_0)x^n + \cdots.$$

THEOREM 72. DIVISION. *If the power series for $f(x)$ and $g(x)$ are convergent in some common interval, the power series formed by performing ordinary long division (as with polynomials) to form $\dfrac{f(x)}{g(x)}$ will converge in some interval including $x = 0$, provided the constant term in the denominator series is not zero.*

Neither the general term nor the interval of convergence of the quotient series can be determined by elementary means. Division of power series is one instance in which we are forced to be content with the first few terms of a series.

In using these theorems, the point to be noted is that within the limits indicated, they enable us to treat infinite series *exactly like polynomials*, merely discarding all terms beyond those that we need to retain.

Example (a). Find the power series for $\dfrac{1}{x^2 - 3x + 2}$.

Since

$$\frac{1}{x^2 - 3x + 2} = \frac{1}{(1 - x)(2 - x)} = \frac{1}{1 - x} - \frac{1}{2 - x},$$

and

$$\frac{1}{1 - x} = 1 + x + x^2 + \cdots + x^n + \cdots, \qquad -1 < x < 1,$$

and

$$\frac{-1}{2 - x} = \frac{-\frac{1}{2}}{1 - \dfrac{x}{2}}$$

$$= -\frac{1}{2}\left(1 + \frac{x}{2} + \frac{x^2}{2^2} + \cdots + \frac{x^n}{2^n} + \cdots\right), \qquad -2 < x < 2,$$

---

* This is the "Cauchy product" of the two series. A similar result holds for the product of any two *absolutely convergent* series, the product series being absolutely convergent to the product of the sums of the series being multiplied.

we add the series term by term to obtain

$$\frac{1}{x^2 - 3x + 2} = \frac{1}{2} + \left(1 - \frac{1}{2^2}\right)x + \left(1 - \frac{1}{2^3}\right)x^2 + \cdots$$
$$+ \left(1 - \frac{1}{2^{n+1}}\right)x^n + \cdots, \qquad -1 < x < 1.$$

Example (*b*). Expand $\sin^2 x$ in powers of x to x^6 inclusive.
We have

$$\sin x = x - \frac{x^3}{3!} + \frac{x^5}{5!} - \cdots$$
$$= x - \tfrac{1}{6}x^3 + \tfrac{1}{120}x^5 - \cdots .$$

Squaring the trinomial and discarding all terms after x^6, we find

$$\sin^2 x = x^2 - \tfrac{1}{3}x^4 + \tfrac{2}{45}x^6 + \cdots .$$

By Theorem 71, this series converges for all values of x. See also the much more efficient method in Exs. 17–18 below.

Example (*c*). Expand $x^2 \csc^2 x$ to x^4 inclusive.
By Example (*b*),

$$x^2 \csc^2 x = \frac{x^2}{\sin^2 x} = \frac{x^2}{x^2 - \tfrac{1}{3}x^4 + \tfrac{2}{45}x^6 + \cdots}$$
$$= \frac{1}{1 - \tfrac{1}{3}x^2 + \tfrac{2}{45}x^4 + \cdots}.$$

$$1 - \tfrac{1}{3}x^2 + \tfrac{2}{45}x^4 \,\big|\, 1 \qquad\qquad \big|\, 1 + \tfrac{1}{3}x^2 + \tfrac{1}{15}x^4$$
$$1 - \tfrac{1}{3}x^2 + \tfrac{2}{45}x^4$$
$$\tfrac{1}{3}x^2 - \tfrac{2}{45}x^4$$
$$\tfrac{1}{3}x^2 - \tfrac{1}{9}x^4$$
$$\tfrac{1}{15}x^4$$

Therefore

$$x^2 \csc^2 x = 1 + \tfrac{1}{3}x^2 + \tfrac{1}{15}x^4 + \cdots .$$

The interval of convergence, obtained by more advanced methods, is $|x| < \pi$.

Example (*d*). In leveling, error is introduced, owing to the curvature of the earth. Find the correction for 1 mi.
By Ex. 11 below, we have

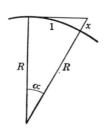

Figure 351

$$\sec \alpha = 1 + \frac{\alpha^2}{2} + \cdots,$$

and Figure 351 shows that

$$\sec \alpha = \frac{R + x}{R} = 1 + \frac{x}{R}.$$

Since α is very small, we obtain

$$1 + \frac{\alpha^2}{2} = 1 + \frac{x}{R},$$

or

$$x = \frac{R\alpha^2}{2} = \frac{(R\alpha)^2}{2R} = \frac{1}{8000} \text{ mi.}$$
$$= \frac{5280 \cdot 12}{8000} \text{ in.} = 7.9 \text{ in.}$$

345. *Differentiation of Power Series*

Within its interval of convergence (end points excluded), term-by-term differentiation of a power series yields the power series for the derivative of the original sum function, and the interval of convergence remains the same.

THEOREM 73.   DIFFERENTIATION.   *If*

$$f(x) = a_0 + a_1 x + a_2 x^2 + \cdots + a_n x^n + \cdots, \qquad |x| < h,$$

then

$$f'(x) = a_1 + 2a_2 x + \cdots + n a_n x^{n-1} + \cdots,$$

for $|x| < h$.

Example.   Derive the series for $\cos x$ from that for $\sin x$.
We know that

$$\sin x = x - \frac{x^3}{3!} + \frac{x^5}{5!} - \cdots + \frac{(-1)^n x^{2n+1}}{(2n+1)!} + \cdots,$$

for all x.   Therefore

$$\cos x = 1 - \frac{3x^2}{3!} + \frac{5x^4}{5!} - \cdots + \frac{(-1)^n (2n+1) x^{2n}}{(2n+1)!} + \cdots$$
$$= 1 - \frac{x^2}{2!} + \frac{x^4}{4!} - \cdots + \frac{(-1)^n x^{2n}}{(2n)!} + \cdots,$$

for all x, as given in § 336.

EXERCISES

In Exs. 1–23, expand the function in a Maclaurin series by appropriate application of Theorems 70–73 above.   Determine the interval of convergence (not testing end points) wherever Theorem 72 is not involved.   If Theorem 72 is used, the interval is enclosed in parentheses in the answer.

1. $\dfrac{4x}{(1+x)(1-3x)}$.   Write as $\dfrac{1}{1-3x} - \dfrac{1}{1+x}$.

$Ans.$ $\displaystyle\sum_{n=1}^{\infty} [3^n - (-1)^n] x^n, \; -\tfrac{1}{3} < x < \tfrac{1}{3}$.

2. $\cosh x$. $Ans.$ $1 + \dfrac{x^2}{2!} + \dfrac{x^4}{4!} + \cdots + \dfrac{x^{2n}}{(2n)!} + \cdots$, all values.

3. $\sinh x$. $Ans.$ $x + \dfrac{x^3}{3!} + \dfrac{x^5}{5!} + \cdots + \dfrac{x^{2n+1}}{(2n+1)!} + \cdots$, all values.

4. $\ln \dfrac{1+x}{1-x}$.   *Ans.* $2\left(x + \dfrac{x^3}{3} + \dfrac{x^5}{5} + \cdots + \dfrac{x^{2n-1}}{2n-1} + \cdots\right)$, $|x| < 1$.

5. $\ln(1 - 3x + 2x^2)$.

$$Ans. \quad -3x - \frac{5}{2}x^2 - 3x^3 - \cdots - \frac{(1+2^n)x^n}{n} + \cdots, \quad |x| < \frac{1}{2}.$$

6. From the basic series (§ 336) for $\dfrac{1}{1-x}$, find the series for $\dfrac{1}{(1-x)^2}$ by differentiation.   *Ans.* $1 + 2x + 3x^2 + \cdots + nx^{n-1} + \cdots$, $|x| < 1$.

7. Obtain the series for $\dfrac{x^3}{(1+x^2)^2}$ by replacing x by $(-x^2)$ in the answer to Ex. 6 and then multiplying throughout by x^3.

$$Ans. \quad \frac{x^3}{(1+x^2)^2} = \sum_{n=1}^{\infty} (-1)^{n-1} n x^{2n+1}, \quad |x| < 1.$$

8. $e^{-x} \cos x$, to the term in x^4.

$$Ans. \quad 1 - x + \tfrac{1}{3}x^3 - \tfrac{1}{6}x^4 + \cdots, \text{ all values of } x.$$

9. $e^{-x} \sin x$, to the term in x^5.

$$Ans. \quad x - x^2 + \tfrac{1}{3}x^3 - \tfrac{1}{30}x^5 + \cdots, \text{ all values of } x.$$

10. $\tan x$, to the term in x^5.   *Ans.* $x + \tfrac{1}{3}x^3 + \tfrac{2}{15}x^5 + \cdots$, ($|x| < \tfrac{1}{2}\pi$).

11. $\sec x$, to the term in x^6.   *Ans.* $1 + \tfrac{1}{2}x^2 + \tfrac{5}{24}x^4 + \tfrac{61}{720}x^6 + \cdots$, ($|x| < \tfrac{1}{2}\pi$).

12. $\ln^2(1+x)$, to the term in x^5.   *Ans.* $x^2 - x^3 + \tfrac{11}{12}x^4 - \tfrac{5}{6}x^5 + \cdots$, $|x| < 1$.

13. $\dfrac{\ln(1+x)}{1+x}$.   Check by Ex. 12.

14. $x \csc x$, to the term in x^4.   *Ans.* $1 + \tfrac{1}{6}x^2 + \tfrac{7}{360}x^4 + \cdots$, ($|x| < \pi$).

15. $\tan^2 x$, to the term in x^6.   *Ans.* $x^2 + \tfrac{2}{3}x^4 + \tfrac{17}{45}x^6 + \cdots$, ($|x| < \tfrac{1}{2}\pi$).

16. $\sec^2 x$, to the term in x^6, by squaring the answer to Ex. 11.   Check with Ex. 15.

17. $\cos^2 x$.   Use $\cos^2 x = \tfrac{1}{2}(1 + \cos 2x)$.

$$Ans. \quad 1 - \frac{2x^2}{2!} + \frac{2^3 x^4}{4!} - \frac{2^5 x^6}{6!} + \cdots + \frac{(-1)^n 2^{2n-1} x^{2n}}{(2n)!} + \cdots, \text{ all values of } x.$$

18. $\sin^2 x$.   Use $\sin^2 x = \tfrac{1}{2}(1 - \cos 2x)$; then check with Ex. 17.

19. From Ex. 5, find the power series for $\dfrac{4x - 3}{1 - 3x + 2x^2}$.

20. $\csc x - \cot x$, to the term in x^5.

$$Ans. \quad \tfrac{1}{2}x + \tfrac{1}{24}x^3 + \tfrac{1}{240}x^5 + \cdots, \text{ } (|x| < \pi).$$

21. $\dfrac{x}{(1 - 3x^4)^2}$.   See Exs. 6–7.

22. $\dfrac{1 + 2x}{1 - x^3}$.

23. $e^x \cos 2x$, to the term in x^4.

24. Show that for values of x so small that the fourth and higher powers of $\dfrac{x}{a}$ may be neglected, the catenary $y = a \cosh \dfrac{x}{a}$ may be replaced by the parabola $x^2 = 2a(y - a)$.

25. Check Ex. 9 with Ex. 8, with the aid of differentiation.

26. Differentiate the series for e^x.

27. From Ex. 11, find the first three terms of the power series for sec x tan x. Then check with Exs. 10–11.

28. Obtain the series for sinh x from that for cosh x.

29. Show that $\sin^3 x = \dfrac{3}{4} \displaystyle\sum_{n=1}^{\infty} \dfrac{(-1)^{n-1}(3^{2n}-1)x^{2n+1}}{(2n+1)!}$.

30. In Example (d), § 344, find the correction for 4 mi.   Solve in two ways.
Ans. 10.56 ft.

31. Two ships have masts reaching 80 ft. above the water level.   How far is each masthead visible from the other? Ans. About 22 mi.

32. What is the radius of vision (theoretically) from the top of a building 200 ft. high? Ans. 17.4 mi.

In Exs. 33–45, evaluate the limits with the aid of power series.   Note that this is one application in which the general term of the series is not of use; a few terms suffice.

33. $\displaystyle\lim_{\theta\to 0} \frac{\theta - \sin\theta}{\theta^3}$. Ans. $\frac{1}{6}$.

34. $\displaystyle\lim_{\theta\to 0} \frac{1 - \cos\theta}{\theta^2}$. Ans. $\frac{1}{2}$.

35. $\displaystyle\lim_{x\to 0} \frac{(1+x)^m - (1-x)^m}{x}$. Ans. $2m$

36. $\displaystyle\lim_{x\to 0} \frac{\sinh x - \sin x}{x^3}$. Ans. $\frac{1}{3}$.

37. $\displaystyle\lim_{x\to 0} \frac{\cosh x - \cos x}{x^2}$. Ans. 1.

38. $\displaystyle\lim_{x\to 0} \frac{\sin x - \ln(1+x)}{x^2}$. Ans. $\frac{1}{2}$.

39. $\displaystyle\lim_{x\to 0} \frac{\cos x - 1}{x \sin x}$. Ans. $-\frac{1}{2}$.

40. $\displaystyle\lim_{\theta\to 0} \frac{\sin\theta - \theta\cos\theta}{\sin^3\theta}$. Ans. $\frac{1}{3}$

41. $\displaystyle\lim_{\theta\to 0} \frac{\tan\theta - \theta}{\theta^3}$. Ans. $\frac{1}{3}$.

42. $\displaystyle\lim_{\theta\to 0} \frac{\tan^2\theta - \theta^2}{\theta^4}$. Ans. $\frac{2}{3}$.

43. $\displaystyle\lim_{x\to 0} \frac{\tan^2 x - \sin^2 x}{\sinh^3 x \ln(1+x)}$. Ans. 1.

44. $\displaystyle\lim_{\alpha\to 0} \frac{\tan 2\alpha - 2\sin\alpha}{\alpha^3}$.

45. $\displaystyle\lim_{x\to 0} \frac{\sqrt{1-x} - \sqrt{1+x}}{x}$.

In Exs. 46–52, find the sum of the given series by using the appropriate value of x in some power series of known sum.

46. $1 + \dfrac{1}{2^2 \cdot 3} + \dfrac{1}{2^4 \cdot 5} + \cdots + \dfrac{1}{2^{2n} \cdot (2n+1)} + \cdots$. Put $x = \frac{1}{2}$ in Ex. 4.

Ans. ln 3.

47. $1 + \dfrac{2}{3} + \dfrac{3}{3^2} + \dfrac{4}{3^3} + \cdots + \dfrac{n}{3^{n-1}} + \cdots$. Use Ex. 6. Ans. $\frac{9}{4}$.

48. $1 - \dfrac{1}{2 \cdot 1!} + \dfrac{1}{2^2 \cdot 2!} - \dfrac{1}{2^3 \cdot 3!} + \cdots + \dfrac{(-1)^n}{2^n \cdot n!} + \cdots$. Ans. $\dfrac{1}{\sqrt{e}}$.

49. $\displaystyle\sum_{n=0}^{\infty} \dfrac{3^{2n}}{(2n)!}$. Ans. cosh 3.

50. $\displaystyle\sum_{n=0}^{\infty} \dfrac{(-1)^n}{(2n)!}$. **51.** $\displaystyle\sum_{n=0}^{\infty} \dfrac{(-1)^n}{3^{2n}(2n+1)!}$.

52. $\displaystyle\sum_{n=1}^{\infty} \dfrac{(-1)^{n-1}n}{2^{2n+1}}$. (Ex. 7.) Ans. $\frac{2}{25}$.

346. *Integration of Power Series*

Within its interval of convergence (sometimes even including end points), term-by-term integration of a power series yields the power series for the integral of the original sum function, and the interval remains the same.

THEOREM 74. INTEGRATION. *If*

$$f(x) = a_0 + a_1x + a_2x^2 + \cdots + a_nx^n + \cdots, \qquad |x| < h,$$

then,

$$\int f(x)\,dx = C + a_0x + \frac{a_1x^2}{2} + \frac{a_2x^3}{3} + \cdots + \frac{a_nx^{n+1}}{n+1} + \cdots,$$

$$|x| < h.$$

Theorem 74 may also be worded as follows.

THEOREM 74a. *If*

$$f(x) = \sum_{n=0}^{\infty} a_nx^n, \qquad |x| < h,$$

then

$$\int_{\alpha}^{\beta} f(x)\,dx = \sum_{n=0}^{\infty} \frac{a_n}{n+1}\left[\beta^{n+1} - \alpha^{n+1}\right],$$

as long as $|\alpha|, |\beta| < h.$

Example.   Derive the series for $\ln(1 + x)$ from that for $\dfrac{1}{1 + x}$.

We know, from the basic series (4), page 579 (with x replaced by $-x$), that

$$\frac{1}{1 + x} = 1 - x + x^2 - x^3 + \cdots + (-1)^n x^n + \cdots, \qquad |x| < 1.$$

By multiplying throughout by dx and integrating, we obtain

$$\ln(1 + x) = C + x - \frac{x^2}{2} + \frac{x^3}{3} - \frac{x^4}{4} + \cdots + \frac{(-1)^n x^{n+1}}{n + 1} + \cdots,$$
$$|x| < 1.$$

Putting $x = 0$, we find that $C = 0$, so that finally

$$\ln(1 + x) = x - \frac{x^2}{2} + \frac{x^3}{3} - \frac{x^4}{4} + \cdots + \frac{(-1)^n x^{n+1}}{n + 1} + \cdots, \qquad |x| < 1.$$

347. *Application to Definite Integrals*

An important application of Theorem 74 is in the approximate evaluation of definite integrals—particularly when the integral cannot be expressed in terms of elementary functions, but sometimes also when, although evaluation in the elementary sense is possible, the result would be of inconvenient form. Although the method is available, theoretically, whenever the interval of integration lies entirely within the interval of convergence of the series, it actually works well only if the integrated series converges rapidly at both limits.

Example (a).   Find the area under the curve

$$y = \frac{\sin x}{x}$$

from $x = 0$ to $x = 1$.

The area is

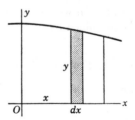

$$A = \int_0^1 y \, dx = \int_0^1 \frac{\sin x}{x} \, dx.$$

Figure 352

The integral occurring here cannot be evaluated in terms of elementary functions.   But we have

$$\sin x = x - \frac{x^3}{6} + \frac{x^5}{120} - \frac{x^7}{5040} + \cdots + \frac{(-1)^n x^{2n+1}}{(2n + 1)!} + \cdots,$$

$$\frac{\sin x}{x} = 1 - \frac{x^2}{6} + \frac{x^4}{120} - \frac{x^6}{5040} + \cdots + \frac{(-1)^n x^{2n}}{(2n + 1)!} + \cdots,$$

whence (Theorem 74)

$$A = \int_0^1 \left(1 - \frac{x^2}{6} + \frac{x^4}{120} - \frac{x^6}{5040} + \cdots \right) dx$$

$$= \left[x - \frac{x^3}{18} + \frac{x^5}{600} - \frac{x^7}{35{,}280} + \cdots \right]_0^1$$

$$= 1 - 0.055\,56 + 0.001\,67 - 0.000\,03 = 0.9461.$$

Example (b).   Evaluate $\displaystyle \int_0^1 \frac{dx}{\sqrt{100 - x^3}}$.

This is an "elliptic integral," impossible to evaluate in elementary terms. But

$$\frac{1}{\sqrt{100 - x^3}} = \frac{1}{10\sqrt{1 - \frac{1}{100}x^3}}.$$

Expanding the integrand in powers of x (Ex. 9, page 580), we find

$$\int_0^1 \frac{dx}{\sqrt{100 - x^3}} = \frac{1}{10} \int_0^1 \frac{dx}{\sqrt{1 - \frac{1}{100}x^3}} = \frac{1}{10} \int_0^1 \left(1 - \frac{1}{100}x^3 \right)^{-\frac{1}{2}} dx$$

$$= \frac{1}{10} \int_0^1 \left(1 + \frac{1}{2}\frac{x^3}{10^2} + \frac{1 \cdot 3}{2 \cdot 4}\frac{x^6}{10^4} + \cdots \right) dx$$

$$= \frac{1}{10} \left[x + \frac{1}{2 \cdot 4}\frac{x^4}{10^2} + \frac{1 \cdot 3}{2 \cdot 4 \cdot 7}\frac{x^7}{10^4} + \cdots \right]_0^1$$

$$= 0.100\,13.$$

EXERCISES

In the answers to exercises, any interval of convergence enclosed in parentheses was determined by methods more advanced than those available in this book.

1. From the basic series for $\dfrac{1}{1 - x}$, write down the series for $\dfrac{1}{1 + y^2}$, multiply by dy, and integrate from 0 to x.

Ans. Arctan x = $\displaystyle \sum_{n=0}^{\infty} \frac{(-1)^n x^{2n+1}}{2n + 1}$

$$= x - \frac{x^3}{3} + \frac{x^5}{5} - \cdots + \frac{(-1)^n x^{2n+1}}{2n + 1} + \cdots, \ |x| \leq 1.$$

2. From the series for $(1 + x)^{-\frac{1}{2}}$, Ex. 9, page 580, obtain the series for $(1 - y^2)^{-\frac{1}{2}}$, and then that for Arcsin x.

Ans. Arcsin x = x + $\displaystyle \sum_{n=1}^{\infty} \frac{1 \cdot 3 \cdot 5 \cdots (2n - 1)x^{2n+1}}{2^n n!(2n + 1)}, \ |x| < 1.$

3. Investigate the result of integrating, term by term, the series for e^x.

4. Obtain the series for cos x by integration.

5. With the aid of Ex. 10, page 596, obtain the terms, out to the x^6 term, in the power series for $\ln \cos x$.

$$Ans.\ \ln \cos x = -\frac{x^2}{2} - \frac{x^4}{12} - \frac{x^6}{45} + \cdots, \ (|x| < \tfrac{1}{2}\pi).$$

6. Using the result in Ex. 11, page 596, obtain the power series for $\ln (\sec x + \tan x)$, out to the term in x^7.

$$Ans.\ \ln (\sec x + \tan x) = x + \frac{x^3}{6} + \frac{x^5}{24} + \frac{61x^7}{5040} + \cdots, \ (|x| < \tfrac{1}{2}\pi).$$

7. In Ex. 15, page 596, we found that

$$\tan^2 x = x^2 + \tfrac{2}{3}x^4 + \tfrac{17}{45}x^6 + \cdots.$$

By integration of this series show that

$$\tan x = x + \frac{x^3}{3} + \frac{2x^5}{15} + \frac{17x^7}{315} + \cdots$$

and thus improve upon the result obtained in Ex. 10, page 596.

8. From the series for $\sinh x$, Ex. 3, page 595, obtain by integration the series for $\cosh x$.

9. In Ex. 32, page 176, we showed that

$$\text{Arctan } \tfrac{1}{3} + \text{Arctan } \tfrac{1}{2} = \tfrac{1}{4}\pi.$$

Use this result and Ex. 1 above to obtain a series for π.

$$Ans.\ \pi = 4 \sum_{n=0}^{\infty} \frac{(-1)^n[(\tfrac{1}{3})^{2n+1} + (\tfrac{1}{2})^{2n+1}]}{2n + 1}.$$

10. Use Ex. 9 to compute π to three decimal places. It is best to compute $4 \text{ Arctan } \tfrac{1}{3}$ and $4 \text{ Arctan } \tfrac{1}{2}$, each from its own series, then add them to get π.

11. Put $x = \tfrac{1}{2}$ in the answer to Ex. 2, and compute π to two decimal places.

12. Integrate the series for $\dfrac{1}{1 - x^2}$, and compare with Ex. 4, page 596.

13. Find, to three decimal places, the area under the curve $y = e^{-x^2}$, from $x = 0$ to $x = \tfrac{1}{2}$.   *Ans.* 0.461.

14. Find, to two decimal places, the centroid of the area in Ex. 13.

$$Ans.\ (0.24, 0.46).$$

15. Find, to four decimal places, the area under the curve $y = \cos (x^2)$ from $x = 0$ to $x = 1$.   *Ans.* 0.9045.

16. Find, to four decimal places, the area under the curve $y = \sin (x^2)$ from $x = 0$ to $x = 1$.

17. Evaluate $\displaystyle\int_0^{0.1} \frac{dx}{\sqrt{1 + x^5}}$ to eight decimal places.   *Ans.* 0.099 999 92.

18. Find the area under the curve $y = e^{-x^3}$, from $x = 0$ to $x = 1$.   *Ans.* 0.807.

19. Find the area under the curve $y = \dfrac{e^{-x}}{x}$ from $x = 0.001$ to $x = 0.002$.

$$Ans.\ \ln 2 - 0.001\ 00 = 0.692\ 15.$$

20. Evaluate $\displaystyle\int_0^1 \frac{x^4\, dx}{\sqrt{25 + x^4}}$ to three places.

21. Find the area under the curve $y = x^3 - 3x^2 + 2x - 5$ from $x = 2.999$ to $x = 3$.   (Ex. 47, page 582.)

22. Find the area under the curve $y = x^4 - 3x^2 - 6x + 8$ from $x = 1.99$ to $x = 2.01$.   (Ex. 48, page 582.)   *Ans.* 0.000 014 000 04.

23. Find to three places the area under the curve $y = \dfrac{\cos x}{x}$ from $x = \dfrac{1}{2}$ to $x = 1$.

Ans. 0.515.

24. Use Ex. 8, page 580 and integration of series to find, to five decimal places, the length of arc of the hyperbola $xy = 1$ from $x = 10$ to $x = 100$.   *Ans.* 90.000 17.

25. Use Ex. 8, page 580, Wallis' formula, page 368, and integration of series to show that the length of one arch of the curve $y = \cos x$ is 1.24π.

26. Evaluate $\displaystyle \lim_{x \to 0} \int_x^{2x} \frac{\cos t \, dt}{t}$.   *Ans.* ln 2.

27. Evaluate $\displaystyle \lim_{x \to 0} \int_x^{2x} \frac{e^{-t}}{t} \, dt$.   *Ans.* ln 2.

28. Evaluate $\displaystyle \int_2^{\infty} \frac{dx}{\sqrt{x^4 + 1}} \cdot \left(\frac{1}{\sqrt{x^4 + 1}} = \frac{1}{x^2} \cdot \frac{1}{\sqrt{1 + x^{-4}}} \right.$; substitute x^{-4} for x

in Ex. 9, page 580).   *Ans.* 0.497.

In Exs. 29–30, expand the integrand in powers of $\dfrac{1}{x}$.   (See Ex. 28.)

29. Find the area under the curve $y = \dfrac{1}{x^2 - 1}$, to the right of $x = 100$.

Ans. 0.010 000 333 353.

30. Find the area under the curve $y = \dfrac{1}{x^4 + x^2}$, to the right of $x = 10$.

Ans. 0.000 331.

348. *Summation of Power Series*

The general problem, given a power series, to find the sum of the series in terms of known functions, is naturally incapable of solution. Even if the sum does happen to be expressible in terms of known functions, the actual determination of that sum may be prohibitively difficult.

There are instances in which the application of our knowledge of the basic series in § 336 will yield the desired sum.

Example (a).   Sum the series $\displaystyle \sum_{n=0}^{\infty} \frac{(-1)^n (n + 2) x^n}{n!}$.

We start with a known series suggested by the series to be summed. We know that

(1) $$e^{-x} = \sum_{n=0}^{\infty} \frac{(-1)^n x^n}{n!},$$

for all finite x.

The series to be summed has a factor $(n + 2)$ in the numerator. Such a factor can be introduced by differentiation of x^{n+2}. Therefore we first introduce a factor x^2 on both sides of equation (1) to obtain

$$(2) \qquad\qquad x^2 e^{-x} = \sum_{n=0}^{\infty} \frac{(-1)^n x^{n+2}}{n!}.$$

Then differentiation of each member of equation (2) yields

$$(3) \qquad\qquad e^{-x}(2x - x^2) = \sum_{n=0}^{\infty} \frac{(-1)^n (n + 2) x^{n+1}}{n!},$$

and the desired sum is obtained by division of both members of (3) by x:

$$(4) \qquad\qquad e^{-x}(2 - x) = \sum_{n=0}^{\infty} \frac{(-1)^n (n + 2) x^n}{n!},$$

valid for all finite x.

Example (b). Sum the series $\displaystyle\sum_{n=0}^{\infty} \frac{(-1)^n x^{2n}}{(n + 1)(n + 3)}.$

A factor $(n + 1)$ can be introduced into the denominator by integrating $x^n \, dx$, a factor $(n + 3)$ by integrating $x^{n+2} \, dx$. But in this instance we can start off with a factor $(n + 1)$ in the denominator by using the basic series

$$(5) \qquad\qquad \ln(1 + x) = \sum_{n=1}^{\infty} \frac{(-1)^{n+1} x^n}{n}, \qquad |x| < 1,$$

and shifting index from n to $(n + 1)$ to obtain

$$(6) \qquad\qquad \ln(1 + x) = \sum_{n=0}^{\infty} \frac{(-1)^n x^{n+1}}{n + 1}.$$

To get the desired power x^{n+2} into the numerator, we multiply throughout by x, obtaining

$$(7) \qquad\qquad x \ln(1 + x) = \sum_{n=0}^{\infty} \frac{(-1)^n x^{n+2}}{n + 1}.$$

Then an integration yields

$$\int x \ln(1 + x) \, dx = C + \sum_{n=0}^{\infty} \frac{(-1)^n x^{n+3}}{(n + 1)(n + 3)},$$

or

$$(8) \quad \frac{1}{2}(x^2 - 1)\ln(1 + x) - \frac{1}{4}(x - 1)^2 = C + \sum_{n=0}^{\infty} \frac{(-1)^n x^{n+3}}{(n+1)(n+3)}.$$

Put $x = 0$ to obtain C. Thus we find that $C = -\frac{1}{4}$. Therefore we now have

$$(9) \quad \frac{1}{2}(x^2 - 1)\ln(1 + x) - \frac{1}{4}x^2 + \frac{1}{2}x = \sum_{n=0}^{\infty} \frac{(-1)^n x^{n+3}}{(n+1)(n+3)}.$$

To obtain the desired power x^{2n} on the right, we first divide by x^3, exclude $x = 0$, and write

$$(10) \quad \frac{x^2 - 1}{2x^3}\ln(1 + x) - \frac{1}{4x} + \frac{1}{2x^2} = \sum_{n=0}^{\infty} \frac{(-1)^n x^n}{(n+1)(n+3)}.$$

Finally we replace x by x^2, thus obtaining the desired sum

$$(11) \quad \frac{x^4 - 1}{2x^6}\ln(1 + x^2) - \frac{1}{4x^2} + \frac{1}{2x^4} = \sum_{n=0}^{\infty} \frac{(-1)^n x^{2n}}{(n+1)(n+3)}, \; 0 < |x| < 1.$$

Note the implication that the left member, near $x = 0$, is an indeterminate form, as $x \to 0$, with limit $\frac{1}{3}$ ($n = 0$ term on the right).

EXERCISES

Sum the given series with the aid of the basic series in § 336.

1. $\displaystyle\sum_{n=0}^{\infty} \frac{(n+1)(n+2)x^n}{n!}$. Start with the series for $x^2 e^x$. *Ans.* $e^x(x^2 + 4x + 2)$.

2. $\displaystyle\sum_{n=0}^{\infty} \frac{(-1)^n (n+2)(n+3)x^n}{n!}$. *Ans.* $e^{-x}(x^2 - 6x + 6)$.

3. $\displaystyle\sum_{n=0}^{\infty} \frac{x^{n+4}}{n!(n+2)}$. *Ans.* $x^2(xe^x + 1 - e^x)$.

4. $\displaystyle\sum_{n=0}^{\infty} \frac{(-1)^n x^{2n+3}}{(2n)!(2n+2)}$. Start with the series for $x \cos x$.

   Ans. $x(x \sin x + \cos x - 1)$.

5. $\displaystyle\sum_{n=0}^{\infty} \frac{(-1)^n x^{2n+5}}{(2n+1)!(2n+3)}$. *Ans.* $x^2(\sin x - x \cos x)$.

6. $\displaystyle\sum_{n=0}^{\infty} (n+2)(n+1)x^{n+2}.$ *Ans.* $\dfrac{2x^2}{(1-x)^3}.$

7. $\displaystyle\sum_{n=0}^{\infty} \dfrac{(n+3)(n-1)x^{n+1}}{n+1}.$ *Ans.* $4\ln(1-x) + \dfrac{x}{(1-x)^2}.$

8. $\displaystyle\sum_{n=0}^{\infty} (-1)^n(n+1)(n+2)x^{2n+1}.$ *Ans.* $\dfrac{2x}{(1+x^2)^3}.$

9. $\displaystyle\sum_{n=0}^{\infty} \dfrac{(-1)^n(n+4)x^{n+3}}{n!(n+3)}.$ *Ans.* $2 + e^{-x}(x^3 - x^2 - 2x - 2).$

10. $\displaystyle\sum_{n=0}^{\infty} \dfrac{1}{n!(n+3)}.$ Use the method of Ex. 3; then put $x = 1$.   *Ans.* $e - 2.$

11. $\displaystyle\sum_{n=0}^{\infty} \dfrac{(-1)^n}{n!(n+3)}.$ See Ex. 10.   *Ans.* $2 - 5e^{-1}.$

12. $\displaystyle\sum_{n=0}^{\infty} \dfrac{(-1)^n(n+1)}{4^n(2n)!}.$ *Ans.* $\cos\frac{1}{2} - \frac{1}{4}\sin\frac{1}{2}.$

349. *The Function erf x*

The purpose of this section is to convince the student that a nonelementary function is not necessarily difficult to study or to use.

It has long been conventional to use the term *elementary function* to designate any function normally studied in the first two years of collegiate mathematics. For example, polynomials, exponentials, logarithms, trigonometric and inverse trigonometric functions are elementary. All functions obtained from them by a finite number of applications of the elementary operations of addition, subtraction, multiplication, division, extraction of roots, and raising to powers are elementary. Finally we include such functions as sin (sin x) in which the argument in a function previously classed as elementary is replaced by an elementary function.* A function which is not elementary is, of course, called nonelementary.

The error function, abbreviated "erf," is defined by

$$(1) \qquad\qquad \operatorname{erf} x = \frac{2}{\sqrt{\pi}} \int_0^x e^{-\beta^2}\, d\beta.$$

---

* The term *elementary function* will probably continue to be used to mean those functions described above. Since the content of mathematics courses at various levels is currently undergoing major changes, the association of the word "elementary" with functions studied in particular courses may well drop by the wayside.

This function appears frequently in the solution of problems in heat conduction and many other physical applications. Its name comes from the use in statistics of a function closely related to (1).

We shall now show that the nonelementary function erf x is as easily handled as are the elementary functions.

From (1) it follows at once that, if

$$y = \text{erf } x,$$

(2)
$$\frac{dy}{dx} = \frac{2}{\sqrt{\pi}} e^{-x^2}.$$

We know from (1) that erf $0 = 0$. In § 311 we found that

$$\int_0^\infty e^{-\beta^2} d\beta = \frac{\sqrt{\pi}}{2}.$$

Therefore $\underset{x \to \infty}{\text{Lim}} \text{ erf } x = 1$, which also indicates why the constant $\dfrac{2}{\sqrt{\pi}}$ was inserted in the definition of erf x.

Next let us obtain the Maclaurin series for erf x. We know that for all finite z,

$$e^z = \sum_{n=0}^\infty \frac{z^n}{n!}$$

and therefore that

(3)
$$e^{-\beta^2} = \sum_{n=0}^\infty \frac{(-1)^n \beta^{2n}}{n!}.$$

By employing (3) on the right in (1), we get

(4)
$$\text{erf } x = \frac{2}{\sqrt{\pi}} \sum_{n=0}^\infty \frac{(-1)^n x^{2n+1}}{(2n + 1)n!},$$

an expansion valid for all finite x.

Next let us treat the problem of integrating the error function. Consider the integral

(5)
$$\int_0^x \text{erf } y \, dy.$$

Since we already know, by (2) above, how to differentiate erf x, let us try integration by parts. With the choice shown in the table, this integration by parts at once yields the result

erf y	dy
$\dfrac{2}{\sqrt{\pi}} e^{-y^2} dy$	y

(6)
$$\int_0^x \text{erf } y \, dy = \left[y \text{ erf } y \right]_0^x - \frac{2}{\sqrt{\pi}} \int_0^x y e^{-y^2} \, dy.$$

The integral on the right in (6) is elementary. It follows that

$$\int_0^x \text{erf } y \, dy = x \text{ erf } x - 0 + \frac{1}{\sqrt{\pi}} \left[e^{-y^2} \right]_0^x,$$

or

(7) $$\int_0^x \text{erf } y \, dy = x \text{ erf } x - \frac{1}{\sqrt{\pi}} (1 - e^{-x^2}).$$

From (7) the indefinite integral of erf x also follows. It may be written in the form

(8) $$\int \text{erf } x \, dx = x \text{ erf } x + \frac{1}{\sqrt{\pi}} e^{-x^2} + C.$$

We have now found for erf x its derivative, integral, Maclaurin series, value at $x = 0$, and its limit as $x \to \infty$. Other properties are also easily obtained. See, for instance, Exs. 1–12 below.

EXERCISES

1. Show that for all real x, $|\text{erf } x| < 1$.

2. Evaluate $\int_0^x y \text{ erf } y \, dy$.   *Ans.* $\dfrac{1}{2} \left(x^2 - \dfrac{1}{2} \right) \text{erf } x + \dfrac{xe^{-x^2}}{2\sqrt{\pi}}.$

3. Evaluate $\int_0^x y^2 \text{ erf } y \, dy$.   *Ans.* $\dfrac{1}{3} x^3 \text{ erf } x + \dfrac{1}{3\sqrt{\pi}} (x^2 e^{-x^2} - 1 + e^{-x^2}).$

4. Show that erf x is an odd function of x.

5. Sketch the curve $y = \text{erf } x$.

6. Show that for $x > 0$, erf $x > \dfrac{2}{\sqrt{\pi}} \left(x - \dfrac{1}{3} x^3 \right).$ You may use the inequality obtained in § 105.

7. Show that $\text{Lim}_{x \to 0} \dfrac{\text{erf } x}{x} = \dfrac{2}{\sqrt{\pi}}.$

8. Show that $\text{Lim}_{x \to \infty} \left[x(1 - \text{erf } x) \right] = 0.$

9. Use the result in Ex. 8 to aid you in obtaining the area in the first quadrant bounded by the curve $y = \text{erf } x$ and its asymptote $y = 1$.

Ans. $\dfrac{1}{\sqrt{\pi}}.$

10. Evaluate $\int_0^x \text{erf}^2 \beta \, d\beta$.

Ans. $x \text{ erf}^2 x + \dfrac{2}{\sqrt{\pi}} e^{-x^2} \text{ erf } x - \dfrac{2}{\sqrt{2\pi}} \text{ erf } (x \sqrt{2}).$

11. Find the area in the first quadrant bounded by the curve $y = \text{erf } x$, the x-axis, and the ordinate $x = c$.   *Ans.* Use equation (7) of this section.

12. Show that you can determine the centroid of the area in Ex. 11 with the aid of Exs. 2 and 10 above.

13. The sine-integral function $\text{Si}(x)$ is defined by

$$\text{Si}(x) = \int_0^x \frac{\sin \beta}{\beta} \, d\beta.$$

Study $\text{Si}(x)$ in a manner parallel to our study of erf x above. Show, among other things, that

$$\int_0^x \text{Si}(y) \, dy = x \, \text{Si}(x) - 1 + \cos x.$$

14. Define the function $g(x)$ by

$$g(x) = \int_1^x \frac{d\beta}{\beta}$$

and study its properties without using your previous knowledge that $g(x) = \ln x$.

15. Define $h(x)$ by

$$h(x) = \int_0^x \frac{d\beta}{\sqrt{1 - \beta^2}}$$

and study it from this definition without directly employing your knowledge that $h(x) = \text{Arcsin } x$.

16. Define $\psi(x)$ by

$$\psi(x) = \int_0^x e^{\alpha^2} \, d\alpha$$

and study the function $\psi(x)$.

Approximate Integration

350. *Approximations to Definite Integrals*

Theorem 29, page 150, exhibits the limit of a sum as a definite integral:

$$\lim_{n \to \infty} \sum_{i=1}^{n} f(x_i)\, \Delta x = \int_{a}^{b} f(x)\, dx.$$

This method of evaluating the limit may fail, however, for either of two principal reasons:

(*a*) It may not be possible to evaluate the integral in terms of known functions; or

(*b*) The function may have been determined empirically, so that no formula for it is available.

Under (*a*), we have just seen that the difficulty may frequently be overcome by expanding the integrand in a suitable power series and integrating term by term. But it is not always possible to find a power series convergent at both limits; if this is possible, the series may converge so slowly as to be useless.

Under (*b*), we may plot the points corresponding to the given (x, y)-pairs and find the equation of a curve which will pass more or less closely through the given points. (There are several well-known methods for doing this; see Chapter 22.) Then, of course, we may find the area under the approximation curve in the usual way. But in a given case, this method may be more trouble than it is worth; or, when a curve has been fitted, we may wish to have an independent means of checking the result.

In any of the above situations, we must have recourse to some form of approximate integration other than that of § 347. In addition to integrating machines, various analytic methods are known.

351. *Simpson's Rule*

When we are unable to evaluate the limit of a sum of n rectangles as $n \to \infty$, one way of approximating the result would be to evaluate the sum itself for a reasonably large value of n; e.g., $n = 10$, in Figure 103, page 149. That is, measure or compute the successive ordinates, multiply by Δx to find the areas of the rectangles, and add the areas by simple arithmetic. Since the error is a rather small fraction of the total, this gives a moderately good approximation. But we can easily do better.

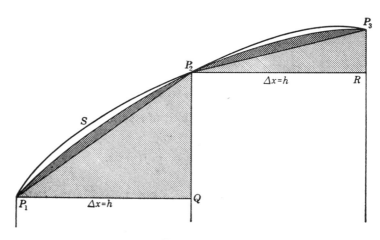

Figure 353

Figure 353 shows a magnification of the top parts of two adjacent elementary strips. Consider the left-hand one, bounded by the arc P_1SP_2. The line P_1Q is the top of our usual rectangular element. If we replace this by the *chord* P_1P_2, thus replacing the rectangle by a trapezoid, we add to the counted area the triangle P_1QP_2, greatly improving the approximation. This method, leading to the "Trapezoidal rule" stated below, is sufficiently accurate for many purposes and is therefore quite often used. But we can do much better than this.

Consider the two adjacent strips simultaneously, and pass a parabola with vertical axis through the three consecutive division-points P_1, P_2, P_3; i.e., replace the broken line $P_1P_2P_3$ by a *parabolic arc*. This adds to the count the narrow darker areas, again greatly improving the approximation.

To put this into effect, take the coordinates of P_1, P_2, P_3 as (x_0, y_0), $(x_0 + h, y_1)$, $(x_0 + 2h, y_2)$ where (temporarily), to simplify the writing, we put $\Delta x = h$. The equation

(1) $$y - y_0 = a(x - x_0)^2 + b(x - x_0)$$

represents a parabola with vertical axis (since the only terms appearing are x^2, x, y, and constant), and it passes through (x_0, y_0). Substituting $(x_0 + h, y_1)$ and $(x_0 + 2h, y_2)$, we get

$$y_1 - y_0 = ah^2 + bh,$$
$$y_2 - y_0 = 4ah^2 + 2bh.$$

Now let us compute the area under the parabola (1) from $x = x_0$ to $x = x_0 + 2h$:

$$A_1 = \int_{x_0}^{x_0+2h} y \, dx = \int_{x_0}^{x_0+2h} [a(x - x_0)^2 + b(x - x_0) + y_0] \, dx$$

$$= \left[\frac{a(x - x_0)^3}{3} + \frac{b(x - x_0)^2}{2} + y_0 x \right]_{x_0}^{x_0+2h}$$

$$= \frac{8}{3} ah^3 + 2bh^2 + 2y_0 h$$

$$= \frac{h}{3} (8ah^2 + 6bh + 6y_0)$$

$$= \frac{h}{3} [(4ah^2 + 2bh) + 4(ah^2 + bh) + 6y_0]$$

$$= \frac{h}{3} [y_2 - y_0 + 4(y_1 - y_0) + 6y_0]$$

$$= \frac{h}{3} (y_0 + 4y_1 + y_2).$$

Replacing h by Δx, we find

(2)
$$A_1 = \int_{x_0}^{x_0+2\Delta x} y \, dx = \frac{\Delta x}{3} (y_0 + 4y_1 + y_2).$$

Now divide the whole area from $x = a$ to $x = b$ into an *even number n* of strips, each of width Δx, and integrate over two strips at a time, starting with $x_0 = a$:

$$A_1 = \int_{a}^{a+2\Delta x} y \, dx = \frac{\Delta x}{3} (y_0 + 4y_1 + y_2).$$

$$A_2 = \int_{a+2\Delta x}^{a+4\Delta x} y \, dx = \frac{\Delta x}{3} (y_2 + 4y_3 + y_4),$$

$$A_3 = \int_{a+4\Delta x}^{a+6\Delta x} y \, dx = \frac{\Delta x}{3} (y_4 + 4y_5 + y_6),$$

$$\cdot \qquad \cdot \qquad \cdot$$
$$\cdot \qquad \cdot \qquad \cdot$$
$$\cdot \qquad \cdot \qquad \cdot$$

$$A_{\frac{1}{2}n} = \int_{a+(n-2)\Delta x}^{b} y \, dx = \frac{\Delta x}{3} (y_{n-2} + 4y_{n-1} + y_n).$$

Adding all these, we obtain the approximate formula called *Simpson's rule*:

$$\int_{a}^{b} y \, dx = \frac{\Delta x}{3} (y_0 + 4y_1 + 2y_2 + 4y_3 + 2y_4 + \cdots + 4y_{n-1} + y_n).$$

Simpson's rule can also be derived by using Taylor's series.*

---

* See, for example, C. E. Love and E. D. Rainville, *Differential and Integral Calculus*. 5th ed., New York: The Macmillan Company, 1954, pp. 402–403.

Although we shall not take time either to derive or to apply it, the reader may wish to have available for possible future reference the approximate formula known as the *Trapezoidal rule*:

$$\int_a^b y\, dx = \frac{\Delta x}{2}\,(y_0 + 2y_1 + 2y_2 + 2y_3 + \cdots + 2y_{n-1} + y_n).$$

The notation is the same as in Simpson's rule except that here the number of divisions need not be even.

352. *Applications*

We have developed Simpson's rule in connection with plane area. But of course, the rule applies quite independently of the physical meaning of the integral, since any function of one variable may be interpreted as the ordinate of a plane curve so that its integral becomes the area under that curve.

Example (a). Compute ln 2 from the fact that

$$A = \int_0^1 \frac{dx}{1+x} = \Big[\ln (1+x)\Big]_0^1 = \ln 2.$$

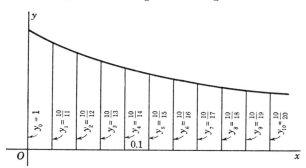

Figure 354

Let us apply Simpson's rule with $n = 10$, $\Delta x = 0.1$, so that*

$$y_0 = \frac{1}{1}, \qquad y_1 = \frac{1}{1.1} = \frac{10}{11}, \qquad y_2 = \frac{1}{1.2} = \frac{10}{12}, \text{ etc.}:$$

$$\int_0^1 \frac{dx}{1+x} = \frac{1}{30}\bigg[\frac{10}{10} + \frac{40}{11} + \frac{20}{12} + \frac{40}{13} + \frac{20}{14} + \frac{40}{15} + \frac{20}{16}$$
$$+ \frac{40}{17} + \frac{20}{18} + \frac{40}{19} + \frac{10}{20}\bigg],$$

$$(1) \qquad A = \frac{1}{3}\bigg[\frac{1}{10} + \frac{4}{11} + \frac{1}{6} + \frac{4}{13} + \frac{1}{7} + \frac{4}{15} + \frac{1}{8} + \frac{4}{17} + \frac{1}{9} + \frac{4}{19} + \frac{1}{20}\bigg],$$

* Here and in a number of the exercises following, a table of reciprocals is handy: see, for instance, the *Macmillan Logarithmic and Trigonometric Tables* (Rev. ed.; New York: The Macmillan Co.) page 94.

$$A = \tfrac{1}{3}[0.100\ 000$$
$$0.363\ 636$$
$$0.166\ 667$$
$$0.307\ 692$$
$$0.142\ 857$$
$$0.266\ 667$$
$$0.125\ 000$$
$$0.235\ 294$$
$$0.111\ 111$$
$$0.210\ 526$$
$$\underline{0.050\ 000}$$
$$\overline{2.079\ 450]} = 0.693\ 15.$$

If we were to keep the (quite untrustworthy) sixth place, the answer would be 0.693 150. The correct value is 0.693 147. Thus, with a six-place table of reciprocals, Simpson's rule produces an error of 3 points in the sixth place. The Trapezoidal rule gives an error of 6 points in the fourth place.

Example (*b*). Find the area under the curve determined by the following set of empirical data:

x	0	1	2	3	4	5	6	7	8
y	0	0.38	0.68	1.13	1.47	1.78	2.18	2.60	2.84

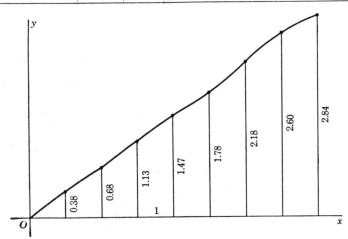

Figure 355

With $n = 8$, $\Delta x = 1$, we have

$$(2) \quad A = \int_0^8 y\ dx = \tfrac{1}{3}[0 + 1.52 + 1.36 + 4.52 + 2.94 + 7.12$$
$$+ 4.36 + 10.40 + 2.84].$$

Thus

$$A = \tfrac{1}{3}(35.06) = 11.69.$$

The points, when plotted, follow fairly closely a straight line. The equation of this line, fitted to the data by the method of averages, §§ 180–181, is

$$y = 0.363\ x.$$

Using this in (2), we get

$$A = \int_0^8 y\ dx = 0.363 \left[\frac{x^2}{2}\right]_0^8 = 11.62;$$

a difference of 0.6 of 1%.

EXERCISES

1. Evaluate $\int_1^2 \dfrac{dx}{1 + x}$ with $n = 10$.

2. Check the answers to Ex. 1 and Example (*a*) by evaluating $\int_2^3 \dfrac{dx}{1 + x}$ with $n = 10$.

3. Evaluate $\int_0^1 \dfrac{dx}{1 + x^2}$ with $n = 10$.   *Ans.* $\dfrac{\pi}{4} = 0.785\ 40.$

4. Evaluate $\int_0^1 e^{-x^2}\ dx$ with $n = 10$.   *Ans.* 0.7468.

5. Evaluate $\int_0^1 x^2 e^{-x^2}\ dx$ with $n = 10$.   *Ans.* 0.1895.

6. Check Ex. 5 by means of Ex. 4. (Integrate by parts.)

7. Show, by computation with power series, that the answer given in Ex. 4 is correct to four decimal places.

8. Show, by computation with power series, that the answer given in Ex. 5 is correct to four decimal places.

9. Check the answers to Ex. 1 and Example (*a*), § 352, by setting $x = 0.2$ in Ex. 4, page 596.

10. Evaluate $\int_0^{\frac{1}{2}} \dfrac{dx}{\sqrt{1 - x^2}}$ with $n = 4$.   *Ans.* $\dfrac{\pi}{6} = 0.5236.$

11. Evaluate $\int_0^1 \sqrt{1 + x^4}\ dx$ with $n = 10$.   *Ans.* 1.090.

In Exs. 12–17, find the area under the curve determined by the given data.*

12.

x	2	4	6	8	10
v	3.4	4.8	5.9	6.9	7.8

   Ans. 46.53.

* In some cases, the answers are given to a number of places not justified by the data. This is done in order to show the difference in results by Simpson's rule and by using the fitted equation: Exs. 12–17 versus Exs. 18–23.

13.

P	100	200	300	400	500
Q	95	185	270	350	415

Ans. 106,330.

14.

t	1	2	3	4	5
x	1.10	4.35	10.05	17.15	26.25

Ans. 44.48.

15.

x	8	10	12	14	16	18	20
y	26	115	227	358	515	684	880

Ans. 4679.

16.

x	0.6	0.8	1.0	1.2	1.4
y	0.161	0.374	0.806	1.302	2.150

Ans. 0.708.

17.

x	1	2	3	4	5	6	7
y	1.82	4.19	6.90	9.21	11.65	14.36	16.72

Ans. 55.56.

In Exs. 18–23, the given equation has been fitted to the data by the method of averages. Check the answer to the preceding exercise by using the empirical formula.

18. Ex. 12: (a) $v^2 = 5.93x$; (b) by a variation of the same method, $v^2 = 5.90x$.
Ans. (a) 46.74; (b) 46.63.

19. Ex. 13: $Q = 0.95P - 0.000\,000\,5P^3$. Ans. 106,200.
20. Ex. 14: $x = 1.071t^2$. Ans. 44.29.
21. Ex. 15: $y = 2.55x^2 - 140.02$. Ans. 4679.
22. Ex. 16: $y = 0.773x^3$. Ans. 0.717.
23. Ex. 17: (a) $y = 2.49x - 0.69$; (b) by a slight variation of the method, $y = 2.48x - 0.66$. Ans. (a) 55.62; (b) 55.56.

24. Draw a smooth curve through the points

x	0	3	5	7	9	11	12
y	0	0.59	1.56	2.83	4.36	6.05	6.90

and find the area under the curve, taking $n = 6$.

25. Solve Ex. 24 with $n = 12$.

26. Solve Ex. 24, using the fitted formula $y = 0.072x^2 - 0.002x^3$. Compare the results of Exs. 24–26.

27. Draw a smooth curve, on a large scale, through the points

x	0	50	100	150	220	300	500
y	0	22.8	49.8	85.0	128.6	192.4	328.4

and find the area under the curve, taking $n = 10$.

28. Solve Ex. 27, using the fitted formula $y = 0.233x^{1.171}$.

29. The velocity of a body, sliding from rest down a smooth inclined plane, is observed at the ends of successive seconds as shown in the table:

t	1	2	3	4	5	6	7	8
v	1.31	2.52	3.52	4.72	5.87	7.02	8.17	9.42

Find the distance traveled in 8 sec.   *Ans.* 37.8 ft.

30. In Ex. 29, the fitted formula is $v = 1.1784t$.   Check the answer.

Ans. 37.7 ft.

Differential Equations
of the First Order

353. Definitions

A *differential equation* is an equation containing derivatives or differentials. Many examples have arisen in our previous work; for instance,

$$(1) \qquad\qquad x - yy' = 0, \qquad\qquad \text{(page 90.)}$$

$$(2) \qquad\qquad y'' = -\frac{a^2}{y^3}, \qquad\qquad \text{(page 90.)}$$

$$(3) \qquad\qquad r\frac{dh}{dr} + 2h = 0, \qquad\qquad \text{(page 113.)}$$

$$(4) \qquad\qquad \frac{d^2y}{dx^2} = -k^2y, \qquad\qquad \text{(page 165.)}$$

$$(5) \qquad\qquad \frac{\partial^2u}{\partial x^2} + \frac{\partial^2u}{\partial y^2} = 0, \qquad\qquad \text{(page 431.)}$$

$$(6) \qquad\qquad \frac{\partial^2u}{\partial x^2} + \frac{\partial^2u}{\partial y^2} = \frac{\partial u}{\partial t}, \qquad\qquad \text{(page 431.)}$$

$$(7) \qquad\qquad x\frac{\partial u}{\partial x} + y\frac{\partial u}{\partial y} + z\frac{\partial u}{\partial z} = 2u. \qquad\qquad \text{(page 430.)}$$

Equations such as (1)–(4), involving only one independent variable and therefore containing only ordinary derivatives, are called *ordinary differential equations*. Equations containing partial derivatives (two or more independent variables) are *partial differential equations*—for example, (5)–(7).

The *order* of a differential equation is the order of the highest derivative that occurs in it. Thus (1), (3), (7) are of first order; (2), (4), (5), (6) are of second order. The *degree* of an ordinary differential equation is its algebraic degree in the highest-ordered derivative present in the equation.

A study of partial differential equations is beyond the limits of this book. In the elementary applications, ordinary equations of first or second order are of predominant importance.

354. *Solutions of a Differential Equation*

A *solution* of a differential equation is *any relation, free from derivatives, which involves one or more of the variables, and which is consistent with the differential equation.* For instance, the equation

(1)
$$\frac{d^2x}{dt^2} + k^2x = 0$$

has the solution

(2)
$$x = A \cos kt + B \sin kt,$$

with A and B arbitrary constants. That (2) is consistent with (1) is easily shown by twice differentiating each member of (2) with respect to t.

In a like manner, the equation

(3)
$$y(3x^2 + y^2)\, dx + (2xy^2 + 1)\, dy = 0$$

has the solution

(4)
$$x^3 + xy^2 + \ln y = c,$$

with c arbitrary. To verify that equation (4) is a solution of (3), eliminate the arbitrary constant by differentiation, obtaining

$$(3x^2 + y^2)\, dx + \left(2xy + \frac{1}{y}\right) dy = 0,$$

and then multiply throughout by y to get equation (3).

Our aim in these concluding chapters is to solve simple ordinary differential equations and to treat a few elementary applications which involve them.

By analogy with the integral calculus, a solution of a differential equation is often called an *integral* of the equation, and the arbitrary constants are called *constants of integration*.

355. *General Solutions; Particular Solutions*

Under certain rather broad conditions, a differential equation of order n can be shown to have a solution involving n distinct arbitrary constants. Such a solution is called the *general solution*. Some differential equations have solutions which are not special cases of the general solution, but such matters are beyond a brief introduction to the subject. For the differential equations to be solved in this book, every solution is a special case (some choice of the arbitrary constants) of the general solution.

A *particular solution* is any solution, not general, of the differential equation. The particular solutions used most frequently contain no arbitrary constants. For equation (1) of § 354, some particular solutions are:

$$x = \cos kt,$$
$$x = 3 \cos kt - 2 \sin kt, \quad \text{etc.}$$

In applied problems involving differential equations, we are in most cases concerned with a particular solution. Nevertheless the determination of the general solution is usually a necessary preliminary step,* after which the required particular solution is found by determining the arbitrary constant from given data, called *initial conditions*, or *boundary conditions*.

356. *Separation of Variables*

The general equation of the first order and first degree is

$$(1) \qquad\qquad M\,dx + N\,dy = 0,$$

where M and N may be functions of both x and y. Some equations of the type (1) are so simple that they can be put in the form

$$(2) \qquad\qquad A(x)\,dx + B(y)\,dy = 0;$$

i.e., the variables can be separated. Then the solution can be written down at once, for it is only a matter of finding a function F whose total differential is the left member of (2). Then $F = c$, where c is an arbitrary constant, is the desired result.

Example (a). Solve the equation

$$(3) \qquad\qquad 2(y + 3)\,dx - xy\,dy = 0.$$

Separation of the variables leads to

$$\frac{2dx}{x} - \frac{y\,dy}{y + 3} = 0,$$

$$(4) \qquad\qquad \frac{2dx}{x} - \left[1 - \frac{3}{y + 3}\right]dy = 0.$$

Hence we could write the solution as

$$(5) \qquad\qquad 2\ln x - y + 3\ln(y + 3) = c.$$

Although (5) is a correct solution, the presence of two logarithmic terms suggests that we put the arbitrary constant in logarithmic form also. Thus, directly from (4), we may write the solution in the form

$$(6) \qquad\qquad 2\ln x - y + 3\ln(y + 3) + \ln c_1 = 0,$$

where c_1 is an arbitrary constant different from the c of (5).
From (6) we get

$$y = 2\ln x + 3\ln(y + 3) + \ln c_1,$$

from which it follows that

$$(7) \qquad\qquad e^y = c_1 x^2 (y + 3)^3,$$

which is more compact than (5).

---

* As a rule this is not true when we are dealing with a partial differential equation.

Of course (5) can be transformed into (7) quite easily.   From (5)

$$y + c = 2 \ln x + 3 \ln (y + 3),$$

or

$$e^{y+c} = x^2(y + 3)^3.$$

Now we put

$$e^c = \frac{1}{c_1}$$

and arrive at (7).

The problem of changing one form of solution into another form is one which arises frequently when two or more persons solve the same differential equation and a check on the results is desired.   Unless the use to which the solution will be put is known, there is little reason for preference for one form over another, except for considerations of compactness, symmetry, and other esthetic qualities.   It is essentially a matter of individual inclination.

Example (b).   Solve the equation

$$(x^2 - 1) \, dx + xy \, dy = 0.$$

At once, we perform the separation of variables, obtaining

$$\frac{x^2 - 1}{x} \, dx + y \, dy = 0,$$

or

$$2 \left(x - \frac{1}{x} \right) dx + 2y \, dy = 0.$$

Thus the required solution is

$$x^2 - 2 \ln x + y^2 = 2 \ln c,$$

or

$$x^2 + y^2 = 2 \ln (cx).$$

EXERCISES

In Exs. 1–28 obtain the general solution.

1. $(1 - x)y' = y^2$.   *Ans.* $y \ln [c(1 - x)] = 1$.
2. $\sin x \sin y \, dx + \cos x \cos y \, dy = 0$.   *Ans.* $\sin y = c \cos x$.
3. $xy^3 \, dx + e^{x^2} \, dy = 0$.   *Ans.* $e^{-x^2} + y^{-2} = c$.
4. $2y \, dx = 3x \, dy$.   *Ans.* $x^2 = cy^3$.
5. $my \, dx = nx \, dy$.   *Ans.* $x^m = cy^n$.
6. $y' = xy^2$.   *Ans.* $y(x^2 + c) + 2 = 0$.
7. $\dfrac{dV}{dP} = \dfrac{-V}{P}$.   *Ans.* $PV = C$.
8. $ye^{2x} \, dx = (4 + e^{2x}) \, dy$.   *Ans.* $c^2y^2 = 4 + e^{2x}$.
9. $dr = b(\cos \theta \, dr + r \sin \theta \, d\theta)$.   *Ans.* $r = c(1 - b \cos \theta)$.
10. $xy \, dx - (x + 2) \, dy = 0$.   *Ans.* $e^x = cy(x + 2)^2$.
11. $x^2 \, dx + y(x - 1) \, dy = 0$.   *Ans.* $(x + 1)^2 + y^2 + 2 \ln [c(x - 1)] = 0$.

12. $(xy + x)\, dx = (x^2 y^2 + x^2 + y^2 + 1)\, dy.$

             Ans. $\ln (x^2 + 1) = y^2 - 2y + 4 \ln [c(y + 1)].$

13. $x \cos^2 y\, dx + \tan y\, dy = 0.$ *Ans.* $x^2 + \tan^2 y = c^2.$

14. $xy^3\, dx + (y + 1)e^{-x}\, dy = 0.$ *Ans.* $e^x(x - 1) = \dfrac{1}{y} + \dfrac{1}{2y^2} + c.$

15. $\dfrac{d\theta}{dz} = z(1 - z^2) \sec^2 \theta.$ *Ans.* $2\theta + \sin 2\theta = c - (1 - z^2)^2.$

16. $\dfrac{dx}{dt} = \sin^2 x \cos^3 t.$ *Ans.* $3 \cot x + 3 \sin t - \sin^3 t + c = 0.$

17. $\alpha\, d\beta + \beta\, d\alpha + \alpha\beta(d\alpha + d\beta) = 0.$ *Ans.* $\alpha\beta = ce^{-(\alpha+\beta)}.$

18. $\cos y\, dx = x\, dy.$ *Ans.* $x = c(\sec y + \tan y).$

19. $(1 + \ln x)\, dx + (1 + \ln y)\, dy = 0.$ *Ans.* $x \ln x + y \ln y = c.$

20. $x\, dx - \sqrt{a^2 - x^2}\, dy = 0.$

      Ans. $y - c = -\sqrt{a^2 - x^2}$, the lower half of the circle $x^2 + (y - c)^2 = a^2.$

21. $x\, dx + \sqrt{a^2 - x^2}\, dy = 0.$

      Ans. $y - c = \sqrt{a^2 - x^2}$, the upper half of the circle $x^2 + (y - c)^2 = a^2.$

22. $a^2\, dx = x \sqrt{x^2 - a^2}\, dy.$ *Ans.* $x = a \sec \dfrac{y + c}{a}.$

23. $y\, dx = (e^{3x} + 1)\, dy.$ *Ans.* $y^3(1 + e^{-3x}) = c^3.$

24. $y \ln x \ln y\, dx + dy = 0.$ *Ans.* $x \ln x + \ln \ln y = x + c.$

25. $(x^2 + 1)\, dy + (y^2 + 1)\, dx = 0.$ See also Ex. 29, below.

             Ans. $\operatorname{Arctan} y + \operatorname{Arctan} x = \operatorname{Arctan} c.$

26. $(y^2 + 9)\, dx = (x^2 + 9)\, dy.$ See also Ex. 30, below.

        Ans. $\operatorname{Arctan} \dfrac{x}{3} - \operatorname{Arctan} \dfrac{y}{3} = \operatorname{Arctan} \dfrac{c}{3}.$

27. $\sqrt{1 - x^2}\, dy + \sqrt{1 - y^2}\, dx = 0.$ See Ex. 31 below.

        Ans. $\operatorname{Arcsin} y + \operatorname{Arcsin} x = \operatorname{Arcsin} c.$

28. $\sqrt{4 - x^2}\, dy - \sqrt{4 - y^2}\, dx = 0.$ See Ex. 32 below.

        Ans. $\operatorname{Arcsin} \dfrac{y}{2} - \operatorname{Arcsin} \dfrac{x}{2} = \operatorname{Arcsin} \dfrac{c}{2}.$

29. Show that the answer to Ex. 25 can be put in the form $c(1 - xy) = x + y.$

30. Show that the answer to Ex. 26 can be put in the form $c(9 + xy) = 9(x - y).$

31. Show that the answer to Ex. 27 can be put in the form $x^2 + 2kxy + y^2 = 1 - k^2,$ where $k = \sqrt{1 - c^2}.$

32. Show that the answer to Ex. 28 can be put in the form $x^2 - kxy + y^2 = 4 - k^2,$ where $k = \sqrt{4 - c^2}.$

In Exs. 33–38 obtain the particular solution satisfying the boundary condition indicated.

33. $xyy' - y^2 = 1$; when $x = 2$, $y = 1.$ *Ans.* $x^2 - 2y^2 = 2.$

34. $\dfrac{dr}{dt} = -2rt$; when $t = 0$, $r = r_0.$ *Ans.* $r = r_0 e^{-t^2}.$

35. $xy^2\, dx + e^x\, dy = 0$; when $x \to \infty$, $y \to \frac{1}{2}.$ *Ans.* $y = e^x/(2e^x - x - 1).$

36. $(2a^2 - r^2)\, dr = r^3 \sin\theta\, d\theta$; when $\theta = 0$, $r = a$.   Ans. $a^2 + r^2 \ln\dfrac{r}{a} = r^2 \cos\theta$.

37. $y' = xe^{-y-x^2}$; when $x = 0$, $y = 0$.   Ans. $2e^y = 3 - e^{-x^2}$.

38. $v\dfrac{dv}{dx} = g$; when $x = x_0$, $v = v_0$.   Ans. $v^2 - v_0^2 = 2g(x - x_0)$.

39. Find the family of curves having the property $\dfrac{dy}{dx} = -\dfrac{x}{y}$, and draw several of them.   Ans. $x^2 + y^2 = c^2$.

40. Find the family of curves whose slope at any point equals the ordinate of the point.   Draw the curves $c = 1$, $c = 2$, $c = -1$, $c = 0$.   Ans. $y = ce^x$.

41. Find the family of curves whose slope equals the square of the ordinate. Draw the curves $c = 0$, $c = 1$, $c = -2$.   What happens to the curve as c changes? What form is approached as c increases indefinitely?   Ans. $xy - cy + 1 = 0$.

357. *Homogeneous Functions*

Polynomials in which all terms are of the same degree, such as

(1)
$$x^2 - 3xy + 4y^2,$$
$$x^3 + y^3,$$

are called *homogeneous* polynomials.   We wish now to extend that concept of homogeneity so that it will apply to functions other than polynomials.

If we assign a physical dimension (say, length) to each variable x and y in the polynomials in (1), then each polynomial itself also has a physical dimension, length to some power.   This suggests the desired generalization. If, when certain variables are thought of as lengths, a function has physical dimension length to the kth power, then we shall call that function homogeneous of degree k in those variables.   For example, the function

$$x^3 e^{\frac{x}{y}} - 4y^2\sqrt{x^2 + y^2}$$

is of dimension (length)^3 when x and y are lengths.   Therefore that function is said to be homogeneous of degree 3 in x and y.

We permit the degree k to be any number.   The function $\sqrt{x + 4y}$ is called homogeneous of degree $\frac{1}{2}$ in x and y.   The function

$$\frac{x}{\sqrt{x^2 + y^2}}$$

is homogeneous of degree zero in x and y.   A formal definition of homogeneity follows.

DEFINITION.   *The function $f(x, y)$ is said to be homogeneous of degree k in x and y if and only if*

(2) $f(\lambda x, \lambda y) = \lambda^k f(x, y).$

The definition is easily extended to functions of more than two variables.

For the function

$$f(x, y) = x^3 e^{\frac{x}{y}} - 4y^2 \sqrt{x^2 + y^2}$$

considered above, the formal definition of homogeneity leads us to consider

$$f(\lambda x, \lambda y) = \lambda^3 x^3 e^{\lambda x/(\lambda y)} - 4\lambda^2 y^2 \sqrt{\lambda^2 x^2 + \lambda^2 y^2}.$$

But we see at once that

$$f(\lambda x, \lambda y) = \lambda^3 f(x, y);$$

hence $f(x, y)$ is homogeneous of degree 3 in x and y, as stated previously.

The following theorems prove useful in the next section.

THEOREM 75. *If $M(x, y)$ and $N(x, y)$ are both homogeneous and of the same degree, the function $\dfrac{M(x, y)}{N(x, y)}$ is homogeneous of degree zero.*

THEOREM 76. *If $f(x, y)$ is homogeneous of degree zero in x and y, $f(x, y)$ is a function of $\dfrac{y}{x}$ alone.*

Proof of Theorem 75 is left to the student.

Proof of Theorem 76: Let us put $y = vx$. Then Theorem 76 states that if $f(x, y)$ is homogeneous of degree zero, $f(x, y)$ is a function of v alone.   Now

(3) $$f(x, y) = f(x, vx) = x^0 f(1, v) = f(1, v),$$

in which the x is now playing the role taken by λ in the definition (2) above. By (3), $f(x, y)$ depends on v alone, as stated in Theorem 76.

ORAL EXERCISES

Determine in each exercise whether the function is homogeneous or not.   If it is homogeneous, state the degree of the function.

1. $x^2 - 2xy - y^2.$

2. $x^3 - 4x^2 + y^3.$

3. $3x + \sqrt{x^2 - y^2}.$

4. $\dfrac{3x + 2y}{\sqrt{x^2 + y^2}}.$

5. $(x^3 - y^3)e^{\frac{x}{y}} + (x^2 + 4y^2)^{\frac{3}{2}}.$

6. $\sqrt{x + y}.$

7. $x \sin \dfrac{y}{x} - y \sin \dfrac{x}{y}.$

8. $3x^2 - \dfrac{x^3}{y} \text{ Arctan } \dfrac{x}{y}.$

9. $e^x.$

10. $\ln x.$

11. $e^{x/y}.$

12. $\ln (x/y).$

13. $x \tan (y/x).$

14. $x \ln x - y \ln y.$

15. $xe^x \tan (y/x).$

16. $x \ln x - x \ln y.$

17. $\dfrac{x - y}{x^2 + y^2}.$

18. $\dfrac{a^2 - 2x^2}{(a^2 - x^2)^{\frac{3}{2}}}.$

358. *Equations with Homogeneous Coefficients*

Suppose the coefficients M and N in an equation of the first order and first degree,

$$(1) \qquad M(x, y) \, dx + N(x, y) \, dy = 0,$$

are both homogeneous functions and are of the *same degree* in x and y. By Theorems 75 and 76 of § 357, the ratio M/N is a function of y/x alone. Hence equation (1) may be put in the form

$$(2) \qquad \frac{dy}{dx} + g\left(\frac{y}{x}\right) = 0.$$

This suggests the introduction of a new variable v by putting $y = vx$. Then (2) becomes

$$(3) \qquad x \frac{dv}{dx} + v + g(v) = 0,$$

in which the variables are separable. We can obtain the solution of (3) by the method of § 356, insert y/x for v, and thus arrive at the solution of (1). We have shown that the substitution $y = vx$ will transform equation (1) into an equation, in v and x, in which the variables are separable.

The above method of attack would have been equally successful had we used $x = vy$ to obtain from (1) an equation in y and v.

Example. Solve the equation

$$(4) \qquad (x^2 - xy + y^2) \, dx - xy \, dy = 0.$$

Since the coefficients in (4) are both homogeneous and of degree two in x and y, let us put $y = vx$. Then (4) becomes

$$(x^2 - x^2v + x^2v^2) \, dx - x^2v(v \, dx + x \, dv) = 0,$$

from which the factor x^2 should be removed at once. That done, we have to solve

$$(1 - v + v^2) \, dx - v(v \, dx + x \, dv) = 0,$$

or

$$(1 - v) \, dx - xv \, dv = 0.$$

Hence we separate variables to get

$$\frac{dx}{x} + \frac{v \, dv}{v - 1} = 0.$$

Then from

$$\frac{dx}{x} + \left(1 + \frac{1}{v - 1}\right) dv = 0$$

the solution is seen to be

$$\ln x + v + \ln (v - 1) = \ln c,$$

or

$$x(v - 1)e^v = c.$$

In terms of the original variables the solution is

$$x \left(\frac{y}{x} - 1 \right) e^{\frac{y}{x}} = c,$$

or

$$(y - x)e^{\frac{y}{x}} = c.$$

EXERCISES

In Exs. 1–21 obtain the general solution.

1. $(x - 2y) \, dx + (2x + y) \, dy = 0.$ *Ans.* $\ln (x^2 + y^2) + 4 \operatorname{Arctan} \frac{y}{x} = c.$

2. $xy \, dx - (x^2 + 2y^2) \, dy = 0.$ *Ans.* $x^2 = 4y^2 \ln \frac{y}{c}.$

3. $2(2x^2 + y^2) \, dx - xy \, dy = 0.$ *Ans.* $x^4 = c^2(4x^2 + y^2).$

4. $(2x^2 + xy - 2y^2) \, dx = (x^2 - 4xy) \, dy.$ *Ans.* $\operatorname{Arctan} \frac{y}{x} = 2 \ln \left(\frac{x^2 + y^2}{cx} \right).$

5. $(x^2 + 2y^2) \, dx - xy \, dy = 0.$ *Ans.* $x^4 = c^2(x^2 + y^2).$
6. $(x - y)(4x + y) \, dx + x(5x - y) \, dy = 0.$ *Ans.* $x(y + x)^2 = c(y - 2x).$
7. $(5v - u) \, du + (3v - 7u) \, dv = 0.$ *Ans.* $(3v + u)^2 = c(v - u).$
8. $(x^2 + 2xy - 4y^2) \, dx - (x^2 - 8xy - 4y^2) \, dy = 0.$ *Ans.* $x^2 + 4y^2 = c(x + y).$

9. $(x^2 + y^2) \, dx - xy \, dy = 0.$ *Ans.* $y^2 = 2x^2 \ln \frac{x}{c}.$

10. $x(x^2 + y^2)^2(y \, dx - x \, dy) + y^6 \, dy = 0.$ *Ans.* $(x^2 + y^2)^3 = 6y^6 \ln \frac{c}{y}.$

11. $(x^2 + y^2) \, dx + xy \, dy = 0.$ *Ans.* $x^2(x^2 + 2y^2) = c^4.$

12. $xy \, dx - (x + 2y)^2 \, dy = 0.$ *Ans.* $y^3(x + y) = ce^{\frac{x}{y}}.$
13. $v^2 \, dx + x(x + v) \, dv = 0.$ *Ans.* $xv^2 = c(x + 2v).$

14. $\left(x \csc \frac{y}{x} - y \right) dx + x \, dy = 0.$ *Ans.* $\ln \frac{x}{c} = \cos \frac{y}{x}.$

15. $x \, dx + \sin^2 \frac{y}{x} (y \, dx - x \, dy) = 0.$ *Ans.* $4x \ln \frac{x}{c} - 2y + x \sin \frac{2y}{x} = 0.$

16. $(x - y \ln y + y \ln x) \, dx + x(\ln y - \ln x) \, dy = 0.$
   Ans. $(x - y) \ln x + y \ln y = cx + y.$

17. $\left(x - y \operatorname{Arctan} \frac{y}{x} \right) dx + x \operatorname{Arctan} \frac{y}{x} \, dy = 0.$

   Ans. $2y \operatorname{Arctan} \frac{y}{x} = x \ln \frac{c^2(x^2 + y^2)}{x^4}.$

18. $y^2 \, dy = x(x \, dy - y \, dx)e^{\frac{x}{y}}$.

Ans. $y \ln \dfrac{y}{c} = (y - x)e^{\frac{x}{y}}$.

19. $t(s^2 + t^2) \, ds - s(s^2 - t^2) \, dt = 0$.

Ans. $s^2 = -2t^2 \ln (cst)$.

20. $y \, dx = (x + \sqrt{y^2 - x^2}) \, dy$.

Ans. Arcsin $\dfrac{x}{y} = \ln \dfrac{y}{c}$.

21. $(3x^2 - 2xy + 3y^2) \, dx = 4xy \, dy$.

Ans. $(y - x)(y + 3x)^3 = cx^3$.

22. Prove that, with the aid of the substitution $y = rx$, you can solve any equation of the form

$$y^n f(x) \, dx + H(x, y)(y \, dx - x \, dy) = 0,$$

where $H(x, y)$ is homogeneous in x and y.

In Exs. 23–35 find the particular solution indicated.

23. $(x - y) \, dx + (3x + y) \, dy = 0$; when $x = 2, y = -1$.

Ans. $2(x + 2y) + (x + y) \ln (x + y) = 0$.

24. $(y - \sqrt{x^2 + y^2}) \, dx - x \, dy = 0$; when $x = \sqrt{3}, y = 1$.   *Ans.* $x^2 = 9 - 6y$.

25. $(y + \sqrt{x^2 + y^2}) \, dx - x \, dy = 0$; when $x = \sqrt{3}, y = 1$.   *Ans.* $x^2 = 2y + 1$.

26. $\left(x \cos^2 \dfrac{y}{x} - y\right) dx + x \, dy = 0$; when $x = 1, y = \dfrac{\pi}{4}$.   *Ans.* $\tan \dfrac{y}{x} = \ln \dfrac{e}{x}$.

27. $(y^2 + 7xy + 16x^2) \, dx + x^2 \, dy = 0$; when $x = 1, y = 1$.

Ans. $x - y = 5(y + 4x) \ln x$.

28. $y^2 \, dx + (x^2 + 3xy + 4y^2) \, dy = 0$; when $x = 2, y = 1$.

Ans. $4(2y + x) \ln y = 2y - x$.

29. $xy \, dx + 2(x^2 + 2y^2) \, dy = 0$; when $x = 0, y = 1$.   *Ans.* $y^4(3x^2 + 4y^2) = 4$.

30. $y(2x^2 - xy + y^2) \, dx - x^2(2x - y) \, dy = 0$; when $x = 1, y = \frac{1}{2}$.

Ans. $y^2 \ln x = 2y^2 + xy - x^2$.

31. $y(9x - 2y) \, dx - x(6x - y) \, dy = 0$; when $x = 1, y = 1$.

Ans. $3x^3 - x^2y - 2y^2 = 0$.

32. $y(x^2 + y^2) \, dx + x(3x^2 - 5y^2) \, dy = 0$; when $x = 2, y = 1$.

Ans. $2y^5 - 2x^2y^3 + 3x = 0$.

33. $(16x + 5y) \, dx + (3x + y) \, dy = 0$; the curve to pass through the point $(1, -3)$.

Ans. $y + 3x = (y + 4x) \ln (y + 4x)$.

34. $v(3x + 2v) \, dx - x^2 \, dv = 0$; when $x = 1, v = 2$.   *Ans.* $2x^3 + 2x^2v - 3v = 0$.

35. $(3x^2 - 2y^2)y' = 2xy$; when $x = 0, y = -1$.   *Ans.* $x^2 = 2y^2(y + 1)$.

36. If $y' = F(ax + by + c)$, show that the substitution $ax + by + c = v$ produces an equation in which the variables can be separated.

37. Solve the equation $dy = (4x + y)^2 \, dx$.   (Ex. 36.)

Ans. $y = 2 \tan (2x + c) - 4x$.

38. $y' = 2(3x + y)^2 - 1$; when $x = 0, y = 1$.   *Ans.* $4 \operatorname{Arctan} (3x + y) = 8x + \pi$.

359. *Exact Equations*

In § 356 it was noticed that when an equation can be put in the form

$$A(x) \, dx + B(y) \, dy = 0,$$

the general solution may be determined by integration; i.e., by finding a function whose differential is $A(x) \, dx + B(y) \, dy$.

That idea can be extended to some equations of the form

(1) $$M(x, y)\, dx + N(x, y)\, dy = 0$$

in which separation of variables may not be possible. Suppose that a function $F(x, y)$ can be found which has for its total differential the expression $M\, dx + N\, dy$; i.e.,

(2) $$dF = M\, dx + N\, dy.$$

Then certainly

(3) $$F(x, y) = c$$

is the general solution of (1). For, from (3) it follows that

$$dF = 0,$$

or, in view of (2),

$$M\, dx + N\, dy = 0,$$

as desired.

Two things, then, are needed: first, to find out under what conditions on M and N a function F exists such that its total differential is exactly $M\, dx + N\, dy$; second, if those conditions are satisfied, actually to determine the function F. If there exists a function F such that $M\, dx + N\, dy$ is exactly the total differential of F, we call equation (1) an *exact equation*.

If the equation

(1) $$M\, dx + N\, dy = 0$$

is exact, then by definition F exists such that

$$dF = M\, dx + N\, dy.$$

But, from calculus (§ 268),

$$dF = \frac{\partial F}{\partial x}\, dx + \frac{\partial F}{\partial y}\, dy;$$

so,

$$M = \frac{\partial F}{\partial x}, \qquad N = \frac{\partial F}{\partial y}.$$

These two equations lead to

$$\frac{\partial M}{\partial y} = \frac{\partial^2 F}{\partial y\, \partial x} \quad \text{and} \quad \frac{\partial N}{\partial x} = \frac{\partial^2 F}{\partial x\, \partial y}.$$

Again from calculus

$$\frac{\partial^2 F}{\partial y\, \partial x} = \frac{\partial^2 F}{\partial x\, \partial y},$$

provided these partial derivatives are continuous. Therefore, if (1) is an exact equation, then

(4)
$$\frac{\partial M}{\partial y} = \frac{\partial N}{\partial x}.$$

Thus, for (1) to be exact, it is necessary that (4) be satisfied.

Let us now show that if condition (4) is satisfied, then (1) is an exact equation. Let $\varphi(x, y)$ be a function for which

$$\frac{\partial \varphi}{\partial x} = M.$$

The function φ is the result of integrating $M\, dx$ with respect to x while holding y constant. Now

$$\frac{\partial^2 \varphi}{\partial y\, \partial x} = \frac{\partial M}{\partial y};$$

hence, if (4) is satisfied, then also

(5)
$$\frac{\partial^2 \varphi}{\partial x\, \partial y} = \frac{\partial N}{\partial x}.$$

Let us integrate both sides of this last equation with respect to x, holding y fixed. In the integration with respect to x, the "arbitrary constant" may be any function of y. Let us call it $B'(y)$, for ease in indicating its integral. Then integration of (5) with respect to x yields

(6)
$$\frac{\partial \varphi}{\partial y} = N + B'(y).$$

Now a function F can be exhibited, namely,

$$F = \varphi(x, y) - B(y),$$

for which

$$
\begin{aligned}
dF &= \frac{\partial \varphi}{\partial x}\, dx + \frac{\partial \varphi}{\partial y}\, dy - B'(y)\, dy \\
&= M\, dx + [N + B'(y)]\, dy - B'(y)\, dy \\
&= M\, dx + N\, dy.
\end{aligned}
$$

Hence equation (1) is exact. We have completed a proof of the theorem stated below.

THEOREM 77.   *If M, N, $\dfrac{\partial M}{\partial y}$, and $\dfrac{\partial N}{\partial x}$ are continuous functions of x and y, then a necessary and sufficient condition that*

(1)
$$M\, dx + N\, dy = 0$$

be an exact equation is that

(4)
$$\frac{\partial M}{\partial y} = \frac{\partial N}{\partial x}.$$

Furthermore, the proof contains the germ of a method for obtaining the solution, a method used in Examples (*a*) and (*b*) below. It will be found, however, that with a little practice, the solutions of very many exact equations can be written down by inspection. See Examples (*c*) and (*d*). No matter what method is used the result should be checked by differentiation.

It is natural when an equation is not exact to attempt to make it exact by the introduction of an appropriate factor, which is then called an *integrating factor*. An important application of integrating factors appears in § 360.

Example (*a*).   Solve the equation

(7) $$3x(xy - 2) \, dx + (x^3 + 2y) \, dy = 0.$$

First, from the fact that

$$\frac{\partial M}{\partial y} = 3x^2 \quad \text{and} \quad \frac{\partial N}{\partial x} = 3x^2,$$

we conclude that (7) is exact. Therefore its solution is $F = c$, where

(8) $$\frac{\partial F}{\partial x} = M = 3x^2 y - 6x,$$

and

(9) $$\frac{\partial F}{\partial y} = N = x^3 + 2y.$$

Let us attempt to determine F from equation (8). Integration of both sides of (8) with respect to x, holding y constant, yields

(10) $$F = x^3 y - 3x^2 + T(y),$$

where the usual arbitrary constant in indefinite integration is now necessarily a function $T(y)$, as yet unknown. In order to determine $T(y)$, we use the fact that the function F of equation (10) must also satisfy equation (9). Hence

$$x^3 + T'(y) = x^3 + 2y,$$

so that

$$T'(y) = 2y.$$

No arbitrary constant is needed in obtaining $T(y)$, since one is being introduced on the right in the solution $F = c$. Then

$$T(y) = y^2,$$

and from (10)

$$F = x^3 y - 3x^2 + y^2.$$

Finally, the solution of equation (7) is seen to be

$$x^3 y - 3x^2 + y^2 = c,$$

a result which is easily checked by differentiation.

Example (b).   Solve the equation

(11) $$(2x^3 - xy^2 - 2y + 3) \, dx - (x^2y + 2x) \, dy = 0.$$

Here

$$\frac{\partial M}{\partial y} = -2xy - 2 = \frac{\partial N}{\partial x}$$

so that the equation (11) is exact.

The solution of (11) is $F = c$, where

(12) $$\frac{\partial F}{\partial x} = 2x^3 - xy^2 - 2y + 3$$

and

(13) $$\frac{\partial F}{\partial y} = -x^2y - 2x.$$

Because (13) is simpler than (12), and for variety's sake, let us start the determination of F from equation (13).

At once, from (13),

$$F = -\tfrac{1}{2}x^2y^2 - 2xy + Q(x),$$

where $Q(x)$ will be determined from (12).   The latter yields

$$-xy^2 - 2y + Q'(x) = 2x^3 - xy^2 - 2y + 3,$$

or

$$Q'(x) = 2x^3 + 3.$$

Therefore

$$Q(x) = \tfrac{1}{2}x^4 + 3x,$$

and the desired solution of (11) is

$$-\tfrac{1}{2}x^2y^2 - 2xy + \tfrac{1}{2}x^4 + 3x = \tfrac{1}{2}c,$$

or

$$x^4 - x^2y^2 - 4xy + 6x = c.$$

Example (c).   Solve the equation of Example (a) by inspection. Suppose that we have tested

(7) $$3x(xy - 2) \, dx + (x^3 + 2y) \, dy = 0$$

and found that it is exact.   Then we may write down the general solution by inspection; i.e., by careful observation of the left member of (7), we shall find a function of which it is the total differential.

First, the term $3x^2y \, dx$ suggests the differential of x^3y.   Hence we search (7) for the necessary companion term $x^3 \, dy$ and group the two terms.   Any term such as $-6x \, dx$, which contains only one variable, is an exact differential as it stands.   Thus we are led to rewrite equation (7) as

$$(3x^2y \, dx + x^3 \, dy) - 6x \, dx + 2y \, dy = 0,$$

from which the general solution

$$x^3y - 3x^2 + y^2 = c$$

is evident.

Example (*d*). Solve the equation

(11) $(2x^3 - xy^2 - 2y + 3) \, dx - (x^2y + 2x) \, dy = 0$

of Example (*b*) by inspection.

The grouping

$$2x^3 \, dx - (xy^2 \, dx + x^2y \, dy) - (2y \, dx + 2x \, dy) + 3dx = 0$$

leads at once to the result

$$\tfrac{1}{2}x^4 - \tfrac{1}{2}x^2y^2 - 2xy + 3x = \tfrac{1}{2}c,$$

or

$$x^4 - x^2y^2 - 4xy + 6x = c.$$

EXERCISES

Test each of the following equations for exactness and solve the equation. Those
of the equations which are not exact may, of course, be solved by methods of the
preceding sections.

1. $(x + y) \, dx + (x - y) \, dy = 0.$ *Ans.* $x^2 + 2xy - y^2 = c.$
2. $(6x + y^2) \, dx + y(2x - 3y) \, dy = 0.$ *Ans.* $3x^2 + xy^2 - y^3 = c.$
3. $(2xy - 3x^2) \, dx + (x^2 + y) \, dy = 0.$ *Ans.* $x^2y - x^3 + \tfrac{1}{2}y^2 = c.$
4. $(y^2 - 2xy + 6x) \, dx - (x^2 - 2xy + 2) \, dy = 0.$
                              Ans. $xy^2 - x^2y + 3x^2 - 2y = c.$
5. $(2xy - y) \, dx + (x^2 + x) \, dy = 0.$ *Ans.* $y(x + 1)^3 = cx.$
6. $v(2uv^2 - 3) \, du + (3u^2v^2 - 3u + 4v) \, dv = 0.$ *Ans.* $v(u^2v^2 - 3u + 2v) = c.$
7. $(\cos 2y - 3x^2y^2) \, dx + (\cos 2y - 2x \sin 2y - 2x^3y) \, dy = 0.$
                  Ans. $\tfrac{1}{2} \sin 2y + x \cos 2y - x^3y^2 = c.$
8. $(1 + y^2) \, dx + (x^2y + y) \, dy = 0.$ *Ans.* $2 \operatorname{Arctan} x + \ln (1 + y^2) = c.$
9. $(1 + y^2 + xy^2) \, dx + (x^2y + y + 2xy) \, dy = 0.$ *Ans.* $2x + y^2(1 + x)^2 = c.$
10. $(w^3 + wz^2 - z) \, dw + (z^3 + w^2z - w) \, dz = 0.$ *Ans.* $(w^2 + z^2)^2 = 4wz + c.$
11. $(2xy - \tan y) \, dx + (x^2 - x \sec^2 y) \, dy = 0.$ *Ans.* $x^2y - x \tan y = c.$
12. $(\cos x \cos y - \cot x) \, dx - \sin x \sin y \, dy = 0.$ *Ans.* $\sin x \cos y = \ln (c \sin x).$
13. $(r + \sin \theta - \cos \theta) \, dr + r(\sin \theta + \cos \theta) \, d\theta = 0.$
                  Ans. $r^2 + 2r(\sin \theta - \cos \theta) = c.$
14. $x(3xy - 4y^3 + 6) \, dx + (x^3 - 6x^2y^2 - 1) \, dy = 0.$
                  Ans. $x^3y - 2x^2y^3 + 3x^2 - y = c.$
15. $(\sin \theta - 2r \cos^2 \theta) \, dr + r \cos \theta(2r \sin \theta + 1) \, d\theta = 0.$
                  Ans. $r \sin \theta - r^2 \cos^2 \theta = c.$
16. $[2x + y \cos (xy)] \, dx + x \cos (xy) \, dy = 0.$ *Ans.* $x^2 + \sin (xy) = c.$
17. $2xy \, dx + (y^2 + x^2) \, dy = 0.$ *Ans.* $y(3x^2 + y^2) = c.$
18. $2xy \, dx + (y^2 - x^2) \, dy = 0.$ *Ans.* $x^2 + y^2 = cy.$
19. $[2xy \cos (x^2) - 2xy + 1] \, dx + [\sin (x^2) - x^2] \, dy = 0.$
                  Ans. $y[\sin (x^2) - x^2] = c - x.$

20. $(2x - 3y) \, dx + (2y - 3x) \, dy = 0.$ *Ans.* $x^2 + y^2 - 3xy = c.$

21. Do Ex. 20 by a second method.

22. $(xy^2 + y - x) \, dx + x(xy + 1) \, dy = 0.$ *Ans.* $x^2y^2 + 2xy - x^2 = c.$

23. $3y(x^2 - 1) \, dx + (x^3 + 8y - 3x) \, dy = 0;$ when $x = 0, \ y = 1.$

Ans. $xy(x^2 - 3) = 4(1 - y^2).$

24. $(1 - xy)^{-2} \, dx + [y^2 + x^2(1 - xy)^{-2}] \, dy = 0;$ when $x = 1, \ y = 1.$

Ans. $xy^4 - y^3 + 3xy - 3x - 3 = 0.$

25. $(ye^{xy} - 2y^3) \, dx + (xe^{xy} - 6xy^2 - 2y) \, dy = 0;$ when $x = 0, \ y = 2.$

Ans. $e^{xy} = 2xy^3 + y^2 - 3$

360. *The Linear Equation of Order One*

A very important concept is that of the linearity or nonlinearity of a differential equation. An equation is said to be *linear* if each term of the equation is either linear in all the dependent variables and their various derivatives or does not contain any of them. Otherwise the equation is said to be *nonlinear*. Such a term as $y \dfrac{dy}{dx}$ is of degree two in y and its derivative together and is therefore nonlinear.

An equation which is linear and of order one in the dependent variable y must be of the form

(1) $$A(x) \, dy + B(x)y \, dx = C(x) \, dx.$$

By dividing each member of equation (1) by $A(x)$, we obtain

(2) $$dy + P(x)y \, dx = Q(x) \, dx,$$

which we choose as the standard form for the linear equation of order one.

For the moment, suppose that there exists for equation (2) an integrating factor $v(x)$, a function of x alone. Then

(3) $$v \, dy + vP(x)y \, dx = vQ(x) \, dx$$

must be an exact equation. But (3) is easily put in the form

$$M \, dx + N \, dy = 0$$

with

$$M = vPy - vQ,$$

and

$$N = v,$$

in which v, P, and Q are functions of x alone.

Therefore, if equation (3) is to be exact, it follows from the requirement $\dfrac{\partial M}{\partial y} = \dfrac{\partial N}{\partial x}$ that v must satisfy the equation

(4) $$vP = \frac{dv}{dx}.$$

From (4) v may be obtained readily, for

$$P \, dx = \frac{dv}{v},$$

so that

$$\ln v = \int P \, dx,$$

or

(5) $$v = e^{\int P \, dx}.$$

That is, if the equation (2) has an integrating factor independent of y, then that factor must be as given by equation (5).

It remains to be shown that the v given by equation (5) is actually an integrating factor of

(2) $$dy + P(x)y \, dx = Q(x) \, dx.$$

Let us apply the factor throughout (2), obtaining

(6) $$e^{\int P \, dx} \, dy + P e^{\int P \, dx} y \, dx = Q e^{\int P \, dx} \, dx.$$

The left member of (6) is the differential of the product

$$y e^{\int P \, dx};$$

the right member of (6) is an exact differential, since it is independent of y. Hence equation (6) is exact, which is what we wished to show.

Of course one integrating factor is sufficient. Hence we may use in the exponent $(\int P \, dx)$ any function whose differential is $P \, dx$.

With an integrating factor at hand we can lay down the following rule for integrating any linear equation of order one:

(a) Put the equation into standard form:

$$dy + Py \, dx = Q \, dx;$$

(b) Obtain the integrating factor $e^{\int P \, dx}$;
(c) Apply the integrating factor to the equation in its standard form;
(d) Solve the resultant exact equation.

Note, in integrating the exact equation, that *the integral of the left member is always the product of the dependent variable and the integrating factor used.*
Example (a). Solve the equation

$$2(y - 4x^2) \, dx + x \, dy = 0.$$

The equation is linear in y. When put in standard form it becomes

(7) $$dy + \frac{2}{x} y \, dx = 8x \, dx.$$

Then an integrating factor is

$$e^{\int \frac{2dx}{x}} = e^{2 \ln x} = (e^{\ln x})^2 = x^2.$$

Next we apply the integrating factor to (7), thus obtaining the exact equation

(8) $$x^2 \, dy + 2xy \, dx = 8x^3 \, dx.$$

The solution of (8) is

(9) $$x^2 y = 2x^4 + c$$

and should be checked, particularly since verification of the result is so easy.

From (9) we get (8) by differentiation. Then the original differential equation follows from (8) by a simple adjustment. Hence (9) is a solution of the original equation.

Example (b). Solve the equation

$$y \, dx + (3x - xy + 2) \, dy = 0.$$

Since the product $y \, dy$ occurs here, the equation is not linear in y. It is, however, linear in x. Therefore we arrange the terms as in

$$y \, dx + (3 - y)x \, dy = -2dy$$

and pass to the standard form,

(10) $$dx + \left(\frac{3}{y} - 1\right) x \, dy = -\frac{2}{y} \, dy.$$

Now

$$\int \left(\frac{3}{y} - 1\right) dy = 3 \ln y - y + c_1,$$

so that an integrating factor for equation (10) is

$$e^{3 \ln y - y} = e^{3 \ln y} \cdot e^{-y} = (e^{\ln y})^3 \cdot e^{-y} = y^3 e^{-y}.$$

Application of this integrating factor to equation (10) leads to the exact equation

$$y^3 e^{-y} \, dx + y^2 (3 - y) e^{-y} x \, dy = -2y^2 e^{-y} \, dy,$$

from which we get

$$xy^3 e^{-y} = -2 \int y^2 e^{-y} \, dy$$

$$= 2y^2 e^{-y} + 4ye^{-y} + 4e^{-y} + c.$$

Thus we may write the solution as

$$xy^3 = 2y^2 + 4y + 4 + ce^y.$$

EXERCISES

In Exs. 1–25 find the general solution.

1. $(x^4 + 2y)\, dx - x\, dy = 0.$ *Ans.* $2y = x^4 + cx^2.$
2. $(3xy + 3y - 4)\, dx + (x + 1)^2\, dy = 0.$ *Ans.* $y = 2(x + 1)^{-1} + c(x + 1)^{-3}.$
3. $y' = \csc x - y \cot x.$ *Ans.* $y \sin x = x + c.$

4. $t\dfrac{dx}{dt} = 6te^{2t} + x(2t - 1).$ *Ans.* $xt = (3t^2 + c)e^{2t}.$

5. $dy = (x - 3y)\, dx.$ *Ans.* $9y = 3x - 1 + ce^{-3x}.$
6. $(3x - 1)y' = 6y - 10(3x - 1)^{\frac{1}{5}}.$ *Ans.* $y = 2(3x - 1)^{\frac{1}{5}} + c(3x - 1)^2.$
7. $(y - 2)\, dx + (3x - y)\, dy = 0.$ *Ans.* $12x = 3y + 2 + c(y - 2)^{-3}.$
8. $(2xy + x^2 + x^4)\, dx - (1 + x^2)\, dy = 0.$
           Ans. $y = (1 + x^2)(c + x - \operatorname{Arctan} x).$

9. $y' = x - 2xy.$ Solve by two methods.   *Ans.* $2y = 1 + ce^{-x^2}.$
10. $(y - \cos^2 x)\, dx + \cos x\, dy = 0.$ *Ans.* $y(\sec x + \tan x) = c + x - \cos x.$
11. $y' = x - 2y \cot 2x.$ *Ans.* $4y \sin 2x = c + \sin 2x - 2x \cos 2x.$
12. $(y - x + xy \cot x)\, dx + x\, dy = 0.$ *Ans.* $xy \sin x = c + \sin x - x \cos x.$

13. $\dfrac{dy}{dx} - my = c_1 e^{mx},$ where c_1 and m are constants.   *Ans.* $y = (c_1 x + c_2)e^{mx}.$

14. $\dfrac{dy}{dx} - m_2 y = c_1 e^{m_1 x},$ where $c_1,\ m_1,\ m_2$ are constants and $m_1 \neq m_2.$

         Ans. $y = c_3 e^{m_1 x} + c_2 e^{m_2 x},$ where $c_3 = \dfrac{c_1}{m_1 - m_2}.$

15. $v\, dx + (2x + 1 - vx)\, dv = 0.$ *Ans.* $xv^2 = v + 1 + ce^v.$
16. $x(x^2 + 1)y' + 2y = (x^2 + 1)^3.$ *Ans.* $x^2 y = \frac{1}{4}(x^2 + 1)^3 + c(x^2 + 1).$
17. $2x(y - x^2)\, dx + dy = 0.$ *Ans.* $y = x^2 - 1 + ce^{-x^2}.$
18. $(1 + xy)\, dx - (1 + x^2)\, dy = 0.$ *Ans.* $y = x + c(1 + x^2)^{\frac{1}{2}}.$
19. $2y\, dx = (x^2 - 1)(dx - dy).$ *Ans.* $(x - 1)y = (x + 1)[c + x - 2 \ln (x + 1)].$
20. $dx - (1 + 2x \tan y)\, dy = 0.$ *Ans.* $2x \cos^2 y = y + c + \sin y \cos y.$
21. $(1 + \cos x)y' = \sin x(\sin x + \sin x \cos x - y).$
           Ans. $y = (1 + \cos x)(c + x - \sin x).$

22. $y' = 1 + 3y \tan x.$ *Ans.* $3y \cos^3 x = c + 3 \sin x - \sin^3 x.$
23. $(x^2 + a^2)\, dy = 2x[(x^2 + a^2)^2 + 3y]\, dx;$ a is constant.
24. $(x + a)y' = bx - ny;$ $a,\ b,\ n$ are constants with $n \neq 0,\ n \neq -1.$
           Ans. $n(n + 1)y = b(nx - a) + c(x + a)^{-n}.$
25. Solve the equation of Ex. 24 for the exceptional cases $n = 0$ and $n = -1.$
         Ans. If $n = 0,\ y = bx + c - ab \ln (x + a).$
          If $n = -1,\ y = ab + c(x + a) + b(x + a) \ln (x + a).$
26. In the standard form $dy + Py\, dx = Q\, dx$ put $y = vw,$ thus obtaining

$$w(dv + Pv\, dx) + v\, dw = Q\, dx.$$

Then, by first choosing v so that

$$dv + Pv\, dx = 0$$

and later determining $w,$ show how to complete the solution of

$$dy + Py\, dx = Q\, dx.$$

In Exs. 27–33 find the particular solution indicated.

27. $(2x + 3)y' = y + (2x + 3)^{\frac{1}{2}}$; when $x = -1$, $y = 0$.

$$Ans.\ 2y = (2x + 3)^{\frac{1}{2}} \ln (2x + 3)$$

28. $y' = x^3 - 2xy$; when $x = 1$, $y = 1$.

$$Ans.\ 2y = x^2 - 1 + 2e^{1-x^2}.$$

29. $L\dfrac{di}{dt} + Ri = E$, where L, R, and E are constants; when $t = 0$, $i = 0$.

$$Ans.\ i = \frac{E}{R}\left(1 - e^{-\frac{Rt}{L}}\right).$$

30. $L\dfrac{di}{dt} + Ri = E \sin \omega t$; when $t = 0$, $i = 0$.

Ans. Let $Z^2 = R^2 + \omega^2 L^2$.   Then $i = EZ^{-2}(R \sin \omega t - \omega L \cos \omega t + \omega L e^{-\frac{Rt}{L}})$.

31. Find that solution of $y' = 2(2x - y)$ which passes through the point $(0, -1)$.

$$Ans.\ y = 2x - 1.$$

32. Find that solution of $y' = 2(2x - y)$ which passes through the point $(0, 1)$.

$$Ans.\ y = 2x - 1 + 2e^{-2x}.$$

33. $(1 + t^2)\ ds + 2t[st^2 - 3(1 + t^2)^2]\ dt = 0$; when $t = 0$, $s = 2$.

$$Ans.\ s = (1 + t^2)(3 - e^{-t^2}).$$

Elementary Applications

361. *Velocity of Escape from the Earth*

Many physical problems involve differential equations of order one and degree one.

First consider the problem of determining the velocity of a particle projected in a radial direction outward from the earth and acted upon by only one force, the gravitational attraction of the earth.

We shall assume an initial velocity in a radial direction so that the motion of the particle takes place entirely on a line through the center of the earth.

According to the Newtonian law of gravitation the acceleration of the particle will be inversely proportional to the square of the distance from the particle to the center of the earth. Let r be that variable distance, and let R be the radius of the earth. If t represents time, v the velocity of the particle, a its acceleration, and k the constant of proportionality in the Newtonian law, then

$$a = \frac{dv}{dt} = \frac{k}{r^2}.$$

The acceleration is negative because the velocity is decreasing. Hence the constant k is negative. When $r = R$, then $a = -g$, the acceleration at the surface of the earth. Thus

$$-g = \frac{k}{R^2},$$

from which

$$a = -\frac{gR^2}{r^2}.$$

We wish to express the acceleration in terms of the velocity and the distance. We have $a = \frac{dv}{dt}$ and $v = \frac{dr}{dt}.$ Hence

$$a = \frac{dv}{dt} = \frac{dr}{dt}\frac{dv}{dr} = v\frac{dv}{dr},$$

so that the differential equation for the velocity is now seen to be

637

$$(1) \qquad v\frac{dv}{dr} = -\frac{gR^2}{r^2}.$$

The method of separation of variables applies to equation (1) and leads at once to the solution

$$v^2 = \frac{2gR^2}{r} + C.$$

Suppose the particle leaves the earth's surface with the velocity v_0. Then $v = v_0$ when $r = R$, from which the constant C is easily determined to be

$$C = v_0{}^2 - 2gR.$$

Thus a particle projected in a radial direction outward from the earth's surface with an initial velocity v_0 will travel with a velocity v given by

$$(2) \qquad v^2 = \frac{2gR^2}{r} + v_0{}^2 - 2gR.$$

It is of considerable interest to determine whether the particle will escape from the earth. Now at the surface of the earth, at $r = R$, the velocity is positive, $v = v_0$. An examination of the right member of equation (2) shows that the velocity of the particle will remain positive if and only if

$$(3) \qquad v_0{}^2 - 2gR \geqq 0.$$

For, if the inequality (3) is satisfied, the velocity given by equation (2) will remain positive, since it cannot vanish, is continuous, and is positive at $r = R$. On the other hand, if the inequality (3) is not satisfied, then $v_0{}^2 - 2gR < 0$, and there will be a critical value of r for which the right member of equation (2) is zero. That is, the particle would stop, the velocity would change from positive to negative, and the particle would return to the earth.

A particle projected from the earth with a velocity v_0 such that $v_0 \geqq \sqrt{2gR}$ will escape from the earth. Hence the minimum such velocity of projection,

$$(4) \qquad v_e = \sqrt{2gR},$$

is called the *velocity of escape*.

The radius of the earth is approximately $R = 3960$ mi. The acceleration of gravity at the surface of the earth is approximately $g = 32.16$ ft per sec per sec, or $g = 6.09(10)^{-3}$ mi. per sec per sec. For the earth the velocity of escape is easily found to be $v_e = 6.95$ mi. per sec.

Of course the gravitational pull of other celestial bodies, the moon, the sun, Mars, Venus, etc., has been neglected in the idealized problem treated here. It is not difficult to see that such approximations are justified, since we are interested in only the critical initial velocity v_e. Whether the particle actually recedes from the earth forever or becomes, for instance, a satellite of some heavenly body is of no consequence in the present problem.

If in this study we happen to be thinking of the particle as an idealization of a ballistic-type rocket, then other elements must be considered. Air resistance in the first few miles may not be negligible. Methods for disposing of such difficulties are not suitable topics for discussion here.

It must be realized that the formula $v_e = \sqrt{2gR}$ applies equally well for the velocity of escape from the other members of the solar system, as long as R and g are given their appropriate values.

362. *Newton's Law of Cooling*

Experiment has shown that under certain conditions a good approximation to the temperature of an object can be obtained by using Newton's law of cooling: *The temperature of a body changes at a rate which is proportional to the difference in temperature between the outside medium and the body itself.* We assume here that the constant of proportionality is the same whether the temperature is increasing or decreasing.

Suppose, for instance, that a thermometer, which has been at the reading 70°F inside a house, is placed outside where the air temperature is 10°F. Three minutes later it is found that the thermometer reading is 25°F. We wish to predict the thermometer reading at various later times.

Let u (°F) represent the temperature of the thermometer at time t (min.), the time being measured from the instant the thermometer is placed outside. We are given that when $t = 0$, $u = 70$, and when $t = 3$, $u = 25$.

According to Newton's law the time rate of change of temperature, du/dt, is proportional to the temperature difference $(u - 10)$. Since the thermometer temperature is decreasing, it is convenient to choose $(-k)$ as the constant of proportionality. Thus the u is to be determined from the differential equation

$$(1) \qquad\qquad \frac{du}{dt} = -k(u - 10),$$

together with the conditions

$$(2) \qquad\qquad \text{When } t = 0, \quad u = 70,$$
$$(3) \qquad\qquad \text{When } t = 3, \quad u = 25.$$

We need to know the thermometer reading at two different times because there are two constants to be determined, the k in equation (1) and the "arbitrary" constant which occurs in the solution of the differential equation (1).

From equation (1) it follows at once that

$$u = 10 + Ce^{-kt}.$$

Then condition (2) yields $70 = 10 + C$ from which $C = 60$, so that we have

$$(4) \qquad\qquad u = 10 + 60e^{-kt}.$$

The value of k will be determined now by using the condition (3). Putting $t = 3$ and $u = 25$ into equation (4) we get

$$25 = 10 + 60e^{-3k},$$

from which $e^{-3k} = \frac{1}{4}$, so that $k = \frac{1}{3} \ln 4$.

Thus the temperature u is given by the equation

(5) $$u = 10 + 60e^{-\frac{t}{3} \ln 4}.$$

Since $\ln 4 = 1.39$, equation (5) may be replaced by

(6) $$u = 10 + 60e^{-0.46t},$$

which is convenient when a table of values of e^{-x} is available.

Suppose the thermometer can be read only to the nearest degree and that we wish to know when the reading will first reach 10°F. Then we need to find the smallest t such that

$$60e^{-0.46t} < 0.5.$$

The result, to the nearest minute, is $t = 10$.

363. *Simple Chemical Conversion*

It is known from the results of chemical experimentation that in certain reactions, in which a substance A is being converted into another substance, the time rate of change of the amount x of unconverted substance is proportional to x.

Let the amount of unconverted substance be known at some specified time; i.e., let $x = x_0$ at $t = 0$. Then the amount x at any time $t > 0$ is determined by the differential equation

(1) $$\frac{dx}{dt} = -kx$$

together with the condition that $x = x_0$ when $t = 0$. Since the amount x is decreasing as time increases, the constant of proportionality in equation (1) is taken to be $(-k)$.

From equation (1) it follows that

$$x = Ce^{-kt}.$$

But $x = x_0$ when $t = 0$. Hence $C = x_0$. Thus we have the result

(2) $$x = x_0 e^{-kt}.$$

Let us now add another condition which will enable us to determine k. Suppose it is known that at the end of half a minute, at $t = 30$ (sec.), two-thirds of the original amount x_0 has already been converted. Let us determine how much unconverted substance remains at $t = 60$ (sec.).

When two-thirds of the substance has been converted, one-third remains unconverted. Hence $x = \dfrac{x_0}{3}$ when $t = 30$. Equation (2) now yields the relation

$$\frac{x_0}{3} = x_0 e^{-30k}$$

from which k is easily found to be $\frac{1}{30} \ln 3$. Then with t measured in seconds, the amount of unconverted substance is given by the equation

(3) $$x = x_0 e^{-\frac{t}{30} \ln 3}.$$

At $t = 60$,

$$x = x_0 e^{-2 \ln 3} = x_0(3)^{-2} = \frac{x_0}{9}.$$

Hence one-ninth of the original amount of substance A remains unconverted at the end of one minute.

EXERCISES

1. The radius of the moon is roughly 1080 mi. The acceleration of gravity at the surface of the moon is about $0.165g$, where g is the acceleration of gravity at the surface of the earth. Determine the velocity of escape for the moon.

Ans. 1.5 mi./sec.

2. Determine to two significant figures the velocity of escape for each of the celestial bodies listed below. The data given are rough and g may be taken to be $6.1(10)^{-3}$ mi./sec.^{2}.

	Accel. of gravity at surface	Radius in miles	Ans. in mi./sec.
Venus	$0.85g$	3,800	6.3
Mars	$0.38g$	2,100	3.1
Jupiter	$2.6g$	43,000	37
Sun	$28g$	432,000	380
Ganymede	$0.12g$	1,780	1.6

3. A thermometer reading 18°F is brought into a room the temperature of which is 70°F. One minute later the thermometer reading is 31°F. Determine the temperature reading as a function of time and, in particular, find the temperature reading 5 min. after the thermometer is first brought into the room.

Ans. $u = 70 - 52e^{-0.29t}$; when $t = 5$, $u = 58$.

4. A thermometer reading 75°F is taken out where the temperature is 20°F. The reading is 30°F 4 min. later. Find (a) the thermometer reading 7 min. after the thermometer was brought outside, and (b) the time taken for the reading to drop from 75°F to within a half-degree of the air temperature.

Ans. (a) 23°F; (b) 11.5 min.

5. At 1:00 P.M. a thermometer reading 70°F is taken outside where the air temperature is −10°F, ten below zero. At 1:02 P.M. the reading is 26°F. At 1:05 P.M. the thermometer is taken back indoors where the air is at 70°F. What is the thermometer reading at 1:09 P.M.?

Ans. 56°F.

6. At 9 A.M. a thermometer reading 70°F is taken outdoors where the temperature is 15°F. At 9:05 A.M. the thermometer reading is 45°F. At 9:10 A.M. the thermometer is taken back indoors where the temperature is fixed at 70°F. Find (a) the reading at 9:20 A.M. and (b) when the reading, to the nearest degree, will show the correct (70°F) indoor temperature. *Ans.* (a) 58°F; (b) 9:46 A.M.

7. At 2:00 P.M. a thermometer reading 80°F is taken outside where the air temperature is 20°F. At 2:03 P.M. the temperature reading yielded by the thermometer is 42°F. Later the thermometer is brought inside where the air is at 80°F. At 2:10 P.M. the reading is 71°F. When was the thermometer brought indoors?

Ans. At 2:05 P.M.

8. Suppose that a chemical reaction proceeds according to the law given in § 363 above. If half the substance *A* has been converted at the end of 10 sec., find when nine-tenths of the substance will have been converted. *Ans.* 33 sec.

9. The conversion of a substance *B* follows the law used in § 363 above. If only a fourth of the substance has been converted at the end of 10 sec., find when nine-tenths of the substance will have been converted. *Ans.* 80 sec.

10. For a substance *C* the time rate of conversion is proportional to the square of the amount x of unconverted substance. Let k be the numerical value of the constant of proportionality, and let the amount of unconverted substance be x_0 at time $t = 0$. Determine x for all $t \geq 0$.

$$Ans.\ x = \frac{x_0}{1 + x_0 kt}.$$

11. Two substances, *A* and *B*, are being converted into a single compound *C*. In the laboratory it has been shown that, for these substances, the following law of conversion holds: The time rate of change of the amount x of compound *C* is proportional to the product of the amounts of unconverted substances *A* and *B*. Assume the units of measure so chosen that one unit of the compound *C* is formed from the combination of one unit of *A* together with one unit of *B*. If at time $t = 0$, there are a units of substance *A*, b units of substance *B*, and none of the compound *C* present, show that the law of conversion may be expressed by the equation

$$\frac{dx}{dt} = k(a - x)(b - x).$$

Solve this equation with the given initial condition.

$$Ans.\ \text{If}\ b \neq a,\ x = \frac{ab[e^{(b-a)kt} - 1]}{be^{(b-a)kt} - a};\ \text{if}\ b = a,\ x = \frac{a^2 kt}{akt + 1}.$$

12. In the solution of Ex. 11 above assume that $k > 0$ and investigate the behavior of x as $t \to \infty$. *Ans.* If $b \geqq a$, $x \to a$; if $b \leqq a$, $x \to b$.

13. Radium decomposes at a rate proportional to the quantity of radium present. Suppose that it is found that in 25 yr. approximately 1.1% of a certain quantity of radium has decomposed. Determine approximately how long it will take for one-half the original amount of radium to decompose. *Ans.* 1600 yr.

14. A certain radioactive substance has a half-life of 38 hr. Find how long it takes for 90% of the radioactivity to be dissipated. *Ans.* 126 hr.

15. A bacterial population *B* is known to have a rate of growth proportional to *B* itself. If between noon and 2 P.M. the population triples, at what time, no controls being exerted, should *B* become 100 times what it was at noon? *Ans.* 8:22 P.M.

16. In the motion of an object through a certain medium (air at certain pressures is an example) the medium furnishes a resisting force proportional to the square of the velocity of the moving object. Suppose a body falls, due to the action of gravity, through such a medium. Let t represent time, v represent velocity, positive downward. Let g be the usual constant acceleration of gravity and let w be the weight of the body. Use Newton's law (force equals mass times acceleration) to conclude that the differential equation of the motion is

$$\frac{w}{g}\frac{dv}{dt} = w - kv^2,$$

where kv^2 is the magnitude of the resisting force furnished by the medium.

17. Solve the differential equation of Ex. 16 with the initial condition that $v = v_0$ when $t = 0$. Introduce the constant $a^2 = \dfrac{w}{k}$ to simplify the formulas.

$$Ans. \quad \frac{a+v}{a-v} = \frac{(a+v_0)e^{\frac{2gt}{a}}}{a-v_0}.$$

18. Obtain the dimensions, in some consistent set of units, of the variables and parameters of Exs. 16–17 above.   *Ans.* t in sec. g in ft. per sec.^{2}
v in ft. per sec. k in (lb.)(sec.^{2}) per (ft.^{2})
w in lb. a in ft. per sec.

19. There are mediums which resist motion through them with a force proportional to the first power of the velocity. For such a medium state and solve problems analogous to Exs. 16–18 above, except that for convenience a constant $b = \dfrac{w}{k}$ may be introduced to replace the a^2 of Ex. 17. Show that b has the dimensions of a velocity.   *Ans.* $v = b + (v_0 - b)e^{-\frac{gt}{b}}$.

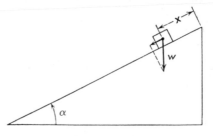

Figure 356

20. Figure 356 shows a weight, w lb., sliding down an inclined plane which makes an angle α with the horizontal. Assume that no force other than gravity is acting on the weight; i.e., there is no friction, no air resistance, etc. At time $t = 0$, let $x = x_0$ and let the initial velocity be v_0. Determine x for $t > 0$.   *Ans.* $x = \frac{1}{2}gt^2 \sin \alpha + v_0t + x_0$.

21. A long, very smooth board is inclined at an angle of 10° with the horizontal. A weight starts from rest 10 ft. from the bottom of the board and slides downward under the action of gravity alone. Find how long it will take the weight to reach the bottom of the board and determine the terminal speed.

Ans. 1.9 sec and 10.5 ft. per sec.

22. Add to the conditions of Ex. 20 above a retarding force of magnitude kv, where v is the velocity. Determine v and x under the assumption that the weight starts from rest with $x = x_0$. Use the notation $a = \dfrac{kg}{w}$.

Ans. $v = a^{-1}g \sin \alpha(1 - e^{-at})$; $x = x_0 + a^{-2}g \sin \alpha(-1 + e^{-at} + at)$.

364. *The Catenary*

Let a cable of uniformly distributed weight w (lb per ft) be suspended between two supports at points A and B as indicated in Figure 357. The cable will sag and there will be a lowest point V as indicated in the figure. We wish to determine the curve formed by the suspended cable. That curve is called the *catenary*.

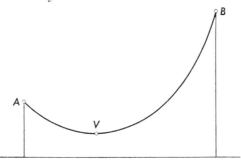

Figure 357

Choose coordinate axes as shown in Figure 358, the y-axis vertical through the point V and the x-axis horizontal and passing at a distance y_0 (to be chosen later) below V. Let s represent length (ft.) of the cable measured from V to the variable point P with coordinates (x, y). Then the portion of the cable from V to P is subject to the three forces shown in Figure 358.

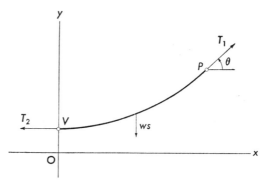

Figure 358

Those forces are: (*a*) the gravitational force ws (lb.) acting downward through the center of gravity of the portion of the cable from V to P; (*b*) the tension T_1 (lb.) acting tangentially at P; and (*c*) the tension T_2 (lb) acting horizontally (again tangentially) at V. The tension T_1 is a variable; the tension T_2 is constant.

Since equilibrium is assumed, the algebraic sum of the vertical components of these forces is zero, and the algebraic sum of the horizontal components

of these forces is also zero.   Therefore, if θ is the angle of inclination, from
the horizontal, of the tangent to the curve at the point (x, y), we have

(1) $T_1 \sin \theta - ws = 0$

and

(2) $T_1 \cos \theta - T_2 = 0.$

But $\tan \theta$ is the slope of the curve of the cable, so that

(3) $\tan \theta = \dfrac{dy}{dx}.$

   We may eliminate the variable tension T_1 from equations (1) and (2)
and obtain

(4) $\tan \theta = \dfrac{ws}{T_2}.$

The constant T_2/w has the dimension of a length.   Put $T_2/w = a$ (ft.).
Then equation (4) becomes

(5) $\tan \theta = \dfrac{s}{a}.$

   From equations (3) and (5) we see that

(6) $\dfrac{s}{a} = \dfrac{dy}{dx}.$

Now we know that, since s is the length of arc of the curve,

(7) $\dfrac{ds}{dx} = \sqrt{1 + \left(\dfrac{dy}{dx}\right)^2}.$

   We need to find a relation between x and y which satisfies (6) and (7)
together with the boundary conditions

(8)   when $x = 0$, $y = y_0$ and $\dfrac{dy}{dx} = 0.$

   Equations (6) and (7) yield

$$\dfrac{ds}{dx} = \sqrt{1 + \dfrac{s^2}{a^2}}$$

from which, by Ex. 9, page 250, we obtain

(9) $\sinh^{-1} \dfrac{s}{a} = \dfrac{x}{a} + C_1.$

When $x = 0$, $y' = 0$, so that $s = 0$.   Therefore $C_1 = 0$ and equation (9) becomes

(10)
$$\frac{s}{a} = \sinh\frac{x}{a}.$$

From (6) and (10) it follows with one more integration that

$$y = a\cosh\frac{x}{a} + C_2.$$

But at $x = 0$, $y = y_0$, so $C_2 = y_0 - a$. We may conclude that

(11)
$$y = a\cosh\frac{x}{a} + y_0 - a.$$

Then, of course, the sensible choice $y_0 = a$ is made so that the equation of the desired curve (the catenary) is

$$y = a\cosh\frac{x}{a}.$$

365. *Equation of the Tractrix*

By Ex. 19, page 251, the slope of the tractrix at any point is

$$\frac{dy}{dx} = -\frac{y}{\sqrt{a^2 - y^2}}.$$

This gives

$$dx = -\frac{\sqrt{a^2 - y^2}\,dy}{y},$$

so that

$$x = -\sqrt{a^2 - y^2} + a\ln\frac{a + \sqrt{a^2 - y^2}}{y} + C.$$

Since the point $(0, a)$ is on the curve, $C = 0$. Thus

$$x = a\ln\frac{a + \sqrt{a^2 - y^2}}{y} - \sqrt{a^2 - y^2}$$

$$= a\operatorname{sech}^{-1}\frac{y}{a} - \sqrt{a^2 - y^2},$$

by (5), § 139.

Linear Equations

with Constant

Coefficients

366. *The General Linear Equation*

The general linear differential equation of order n may be written

$$(1) \quad b_0(x)\frac{d^ny}{dx^n} + b_1(x)\frac{d^{n-1}y}{dx^{n-1}} + \cdots + b_{n-1}(x)\frac{dy}{dx} + b_n(x)y = R(x).$$

The functions $R(x)$ and $b_i(x)$; $i = 0, 1, \cdots, n$, are to be independent of the variable y. If $R(x)$ is identically zero, equation (1) is said to be *homogeneous*; if $R(x)$ is not identically zero, equation (1) is called *non-homogeneous*. Here the word homogeneous is being used with reference to the quantities $y, y', y'', \cdots, y^{(n)}$; it has nothing to do with the way in which x enters the equation.

In order to simplify the wording of statements relating to solutions of linear differential equations, we shall adopt a common convention. When a relation $y = f(x)$ is a solution of a linear differential equation, we shall also call $f(x)$ itself a solution of the differential equation.

First we prove that if y_1 and y_2 are solutions of the homogeneous equation,

$$(2) \quad b_0(x)y^{(n)} + b_1(x)y^{(n-1)} + \cdots + b_{n-1}(x)y' + b_n(x)y = 0,$$

and if c_1 and c_2 are constants, then

$$y = c_1y_1 + c_2y_2$$

is a solution of equation (2).

The statement that y_1 and y_2 are solutions of (2) means that

$$(3) \quad b_0y_1^{(n)} + b_1y_1^{(n-1)} + \cdots + b_{n-1}y_1' + b_ny_1 = 0$$

and

(4) $$b_0 y_2^{(n)} + b_1 y_2^{(n-1)} + \cdots + b_{n-1} y_2' + b_n y_2 = 0.$$

Now let us multiply each member of (3) by c_1, each member of (4) by c_2, and add the results. We get

(5) $$b_0[c_1 y_1^{(n)} + c_2 y_2^{(n)}] + b_1[c_1 y_1^{(n-1)} + c_2 y_2^{(n-1)}] + \cdots$$
$$+ b_{n-1}[c_1 y_1' + c_2 y_2'] + b_n[c_1 y_1 + c_2 y_2] = 0.$$

Since $c_1 y_1' + c_2 y_2' = (c_1 y_1 + c_2 y_2)'$, etc., equation (5) is neither more nor less than the statement that $c_1 y_1 + c_2 y_2$ is a solution of equation (2). The proof is completed. The special case $c_2 = 0$ is worth noting; that is, for a homogeneous linear equation any constant times a solution is also a solution.

In a similar manner, or by iteration of the above result, it can be seen that if

$$y_i; i = 1, 2, \cdots, k,$$

are solutions of equation (2) and if

$$c_i; i = 1, 2, \cdots, k,$$

are constants, then

$$y = c_1 y_1 + c_2 y_2 + \cdots + c_k y_k$$

is a solution of equation (2).

367. *Linear Independence*

Given the functions $f_1(x), \cdots, f_n(x)$, then if constants $c_1, c_2, \cdots, c_n$, not all zero, exist such that

(1) $$c_1 f_1(x) + c_2 f_2(x) + \cdots + c_n f_n(x) = 0$$

identically in some interval $a \le x \le b$, the functions $f_1(x), f_2(x), \cdots, f_n(x)$ are said to be *linearly dependent*. If no such relation exists, the functions are said to be *linearly independent*. That is, the functions $f_1, f_2, \cdots, f_n$ are linearly independent when equation (1) implies that

$$c_1 = c_2 = \cdots = c_n = 0.$$

If the functions of a set are linearly dependent, then at least one of them is a linear combination of the others; if they are linearly independent, then none of them is a linear combination of the others.

The functions $\cos \omega t$, $\sin \omega t$, $\sin (\omega t + \alpha)$, in which t is the variable and ω and α are constants, are linearly dependent because there exist constants c_1, c_2, c_3 such that

$$c_1 \cos \omega t + c_2 \sin \omega t + c_3 \sin (\omega t + \alpha) = 0$$

for all t. Indeed, one set of such constants is $c_1 = \sin \alpha$, $c_2 = \cos \alpha$, $c_3 = -1$.

One of the best-known sets of n linearly independent functions of x is the set $1, x, x^2, \cdots, x^{n-1}$. The linear independence of the powers of x follows at once from the fact that if $c_1, c_2, \cdots, c_n$ are not all zero, the equation

$$c_1 + c_2 x + \cdots + c_n x^{n-1} = 0$$

can have at most $(n-1)$ distinct roots and so cannot vanish identically in any interval.

368. *General Solution of a Homogeneous Equation*

Let $y_1, y_2, \cdots, y_n$ be linearly independent solutions of the homogeneous equation

(1) $$b_0(x)y^{(n)} + b_1(x)y^{(n-1)} + \cdots + b_{n-1}(x)y' + b_n(x)y = 0.$$

Then the general solution of equation (1) is

(2) $$y = c_1 y_1 + c_2 y_2 + \cdots + c_n y_n$$

where $c_1, c_2, \cdots, c_n$ are arbitrary constants.

369. *General Solution of a Nonhomogeneous Equation*

Let y_p be any particular solution (not necessarily involving any arbitrary constants) of the equation

(1) $$b_0 y^{(n)} + b_1 y^{(n-1)} + \cdots + b_{n-1} y' + b_n y = R(x)$$

and let y_c be a solution of the corresponding homogeneous equation

(2) $$b_0 y^{(n)} + b_1 y^{(n-1)} + \cdots + b_{n-1} y' + b_n y = 0.$$

Then

(3) $$y = y_c + y_p$$

is a solution of equation (1). For, using the y of equation (3) we see that

$$b_0 y^{(n)} + \cdots + b_n y = (b_0 y_c^{(n)} + \cdots + b_n y_c) + (b_0 y_p^{(n)} + \cdots + b_n y_p)$$
$$= 0 + R(x) = R(x).$$

If $y_1, y_2, \cdots, y_n$ are linearly independent solutions of equation (2), then

(4) $$y_c = c_1 y_1 + c_2 y_2 + \cdots + c_n y_n,$$

in which the c's are arbitrary constants, is the general solution of equation (2). The right member of equation (4) is called the *complementary function* for equation (1).

The general solution of the nonhomogeneous equation (1) is the sum of the complementary function and any particular solution.

370. *Differential Operators*

Let D denote differentiation with respect to x, D^2 differentiation twice with respect to x and so on; that is, for integral k,

$$D^k y = \frac{d^k y}{dx^k}.$$

The expression

(1) $$A = a_0 D^n + a_1 D^{n-1} + \cdots + a_{n-1} D + a_n$$

is called a differential operator of order n.   It may be defined as that operator which, when applied to any function* y, yields the result

(2) $$Ay = a_0 \frac{d^n y}{dx^n} + a_1 \frac{d^{n-1}y}{dx^{n-1}} + \cdots + a_{n-1}\frac{dy}{dx} + a_n y.$$

The coefficients $a_0, a_1, \cdots, a_n$ in the operator A may be functions of x, but in this book the only operators used will be those with constant coefficients.

Since for purposes of addition and multiplication the operators with constant coefficients behave just as algebraic polynomials behave, it is legitimate to use the tools of elementary algebra.   In particular, synthetic division may be used to factor operators with constant coefficients.

EXERCISES

Perform the indicated multiplications in Exs. 1–4.

1. $(2D + 1)(D - 4)$.   *Ans.* $2D^2 - 7D - 4$.
2. $(3D - 2)(3D + 2)$.   *Ans.* $9D^2 - 4$.
3. $(D - 2)(D^2 + 2D + 5)$.   *Ans.* $D^3 + D - 10$.
4. $(D + 1)(D - 2)^2$.   *Ans.* $D^3 - 3D^2 + 4$.

In Exs. 5–16 factor each of the operators.

5. $2D^2 - 5D - 3$.   *Ans.* $(D - 3)(2D + 1)$.
6. $3D^2 + 7D + 2$.
7. $D^3 - 4D^2 + D + 6$.   *Ans.* $(D + 1)(D - 2)(D - 3)$.
8. $2D^3 - 7D^2 + 2D + 3$.
9. $D^4 - 9D^2$.   *Ans.* $D^2(D - 3)(D + 3)$.
10. $D^3 - 3D + 2$.
11. $D^3 - 19D - 30$.   *Ans.* $(D + 2)(D + 3)(D - 5)$.
12. $4D^3 - 8D^2 - 11D - 3$.
13. $2D^4 - 11D^3 + 18D^2 - 4D - 8$.   *Ans.* $(D - 2)^3(2D + 1)$.
14. $2D^4 + 9D^3 + 6D^2 - 20D - 24$.
15. $D^4 + D^3 + 7D^2 + 9D - 18$.   *Ans.* $(D - 1)(D + 2)(D^2 + 9)$.
16. $D^3 + D - 10$.   *Ans.* $(D - 2)(D^2 + 2D + 5)$.

* The function y is assumed to possess as many derivatives as may be encountered in whatever operations take place.

371. *Some Properties of Differential Operators*

Since for constant m and integral k,

(1)
$$D^k e^{mx} = m^k e^{mx},$$

it is easy to find the effect an operator has upon e^{mx}. Let $f(D)$ be a polynomial in D with constant coefficients,

(2)
$$f(D) = a_0 D^n + a_1 D^{n-1} + \cdots + a_{n-1} D + a_n.$$

Then

$$f(D)e^{mx} = a_0 m^n e^{mx} + a_1 m^{n-1} e^{mx} + \cdots + a_{n-1} m e^{mx} + a_n e^{mx},$$

so that

(3)
$$f(D)e^{mx} = e^{mx} f(m).$$

If m is a root of the equation $f(m) = 0$, then in view of equation (3),

$$f(D)e^{mx} = 0.$$

Example. Let $f(D) = 2D^2 + 5D - 12$. Then the equation $f(m) = 0$ is

$$2m^2 + 5m - 12 = 0,$$

or

$$(m + 4)(2m - 3) = 0,$$

of which the roots are $m_1 = -4$ and $m_2 = \frac{3}{2}$.

With the aid of equation (3) above it can be seen that

$$(2D^2 + 5D - 12)e^{-4x} = 0$$

and that

$$(2D^2 + 5D - 12)e^{\frac{3}{2}x} = 0.$$

In other words, $y_1 = e^{-4x}$ and $y_2 = e^{\frac{3}{2}x}$ are solutions of the differential equation

$$(2D^2 + 5D - 12)y = 0.$$

Next consider the effect of the operator $(D - m)$ on the product of e^{mx} and a power of x. Since

$$(D - m)(x^k e^{mx}) = kx^{k-1}e^{mx} + mx^k e^{mx} - mx^k e^{mx},$$

we get

$$(D - m)(x^k e^{mx}) = kx^{k-1}e^{mx}.$$

Then

$$(D - m)^2(x^k e^{mx}) = k(D - m)(x^{k-1}e^{mx})$$
$$= k(k - 1)x^{k-2}e^{mx}.$$

Repeating the operation, we are led to

$$(D - m)^k(x^k e^{mx}) = k(k - 1) \cdots 2 \cdot 1 x^0 e^{mx} = k!e^{mx}.$$

But $(D - m)e^{mx} = 0$. Therefore, for all $n > k$,

(4) $$(D - m)^n(x^k e^{mx}) = 0.$$

It will be convenient to think of the exponent of x in (4) as varying rather than the exponent of the operator $(D - m)$. Hence we rewrite (4) as

(5) $$(D - m)^n(x^k e^{mx}) = 0 \text{ for } k = 0, 1, 2, \cdots, (n - 1).$$

Equation (5) forms the basis for all the solutions obtained in this chapter.

372. The Auxiliary Equation; Distinct Roots

Any linear homogeneous differential equation with constant coefficients,

(1) $$a_0 \frac{d^n y}{dx^n} + a_1 \frac{d^{n-1}y}{dx^{n-1}} + \cdots + a_{n-1} \frac{dy}{dx} + a_n y = 0,$$

may be written in the form

(2) $$f(D)y = 0,$$

where $f(D)$ is a linear differential operator. As we saw in the preceding section, if m is any root of the algebraic equation $f(m) = 0$, then

$$f(D)e^{mx} = 0,$$

which means simply that $y = e^{mx}$ is a solution of equation (2). The equation

(3) $$f(m) = 0$$

is called the *auxiliary equation* associated with (1) or (2).

The auxiliary equation for (1) is of degree n. Let its roots be $m_1, m_2, \cdots, m_n$. If those roots are all real and distinct, then the n solutions $y = e^{m_1 x}, y = e^{m_2 x}, \cdots, y = e^{m_n x}$ are linearly independent and the general solution of (1) can be written down at once. It is

$$y = c_1 e^{m_1 x} + c_2 e^{m_2 x} + \cdots + c_n e^{m_n x},$$

where $c_1, c_2, \cdots, c_n$ are arbitrary constants.

Repeated roots of the auxiliary equation will be treated in the next section.

Imaginary roots will be avoided until § 375 where the corresponding solutions will be put into a desirable form. At present the solution associated with such a root as $m_1 = 3 + 2i$ would necessarily appear in the form $y = e^{(3+2i)x}$ which is correct (with the definition given in § 374 below) but awkward in applications.

Example (a). Solve the equation

$$\frac{d^3 y}{dx^3} - 4\frac{d^2 y}{dx^2} + \frac{dy}{dx} + 6y = 0.$$

First write the auxiliary equation

$$m^3 - 4m^2 + m + 6 = 0,$$

whose roots $m = -1, 2, 3$ may be obtained by synthetic division. Then the general solution is seen to be

$$y = c_1 e^{-x} + c_2 e^{2x} + c_3 e^{3x}.$$

Example (b).   Solve the equation

$$(3D^3 + 5D^2 - 2D)y = 0.$$

The auxiliary equation is

$$3m^3 + 5m^2 - 2m = 0$$

and its roots are $m = 0, -2, \frac{1}{3}$.   Using the fact that $e^{0x} = 1$, the desired solution may be written

$$y = c_1 + c_2 e^{-2x} + c_3 e^{\frac{x}{3}}.$$

Example (c).   Solve the equation

$$\frac{d^2x}{dt^2} - 4x = 0$$

together with the conditions: when $t = 0$, $x = 0$ and $\dfrac{dx}{dt} = 3$.

The auxiliary equation is

$$m^2 - 4 = 0,$$

with roots $m = 2, -2$.   Hence the general solution of the differential equation is

$$x = c_1 e^{2t} + c_2 e^{-2t}.$$

It remains to enforce the conditions at $t = 0$.   Now

$$\frac{dx}{dt} = 2c_1 e^{2t} - 2c_2 e^{-2t}.$$

Thus the condition that $x = 0$ when $t = 0$ requires that

$$0 = c_1 + c_2,$$

while the condition that $\dfrac{dx}{dt} = 3$ when $t = 0$ requires that

$$3 = 2c_1 - 2c_2.$$

From the simultaneous equations for c_1 and c_2 we conclude that $c_1 = \frac{3}{4}$ and $c_2 = -\frac{3}{4}$.   Therefore

$$x = \tfrac{3}{4}(e^{2t} - e^{-2t}) = \tfrac{3}{2}\sinh(2t).$$

EXERCISES

In Exs. 1–22 find the general solution.   When the operator D is used it is implied that the independent variable is x.

1. $(D^2 - D - 2)y = 0$.   *Ans.* $y = c_1 e^{-x} + c_2 e^{2x}$.
2. $(D^2 + 3D)y = 0$.
3. $(D^2 - D - 6)y = 0$.   *Ans.* $y = c_1 e^{-2x} + c_2 e^{3x}$.
4. $(D^2 + 5D + 6)y = 0$.
5. $(D^3 + 2D^2 - 15D)y = 0$.   *Ans.* $y = c_1 + c_2 e^{3x} + c_3 e^{-5x}$.
6. $(D^3 + 2D^2 - 8D)y = 0$.
7. $(D^3 - D^2 - 4D + 4)y = 0$.   *Ans.* $y = c_1 e^{-2x} + c_2 e^x + c_3 e^{2x}$.
8. $(D^3 - 3D^2 - D + 3)y = 0$.

9. $(4D^3 - 13D + 6)y = 0$.   *Ans.* $y = c_1 e^{\frac{x}{2}} + c_2 e^{\frac{3x}{2}} + c_3 e^{-2x}$.
10. $(4D^3 - 49D - 60)y = 0$.

11. $\dfrac{d^3x}{dt^3} - 2\dfrac{d^2x}{dt^2} - 3\dfrac{dx}{dt} = 0$.   *Ans.* $x = c_1 + c_2 e^{-t} + c_3 e^{3t}$.

12. $\dfrac{d^3x}{dt^3} - 7\dfrac{dx}{dt} + 6x = 0$.

13. $(10D^3 + D^2 - 7D + 2)y = 0$.   *Ans.* $y = c_1 e^{-x} + c_2 e^{\frac{x}{2}} + c_3 e^{\frac{2x}{5}}$.
14. $(4D^3 - 13D - 6)y = 0$.
15. $(D^3 - 5D - 2)y = 0$.   *Ans.* $y = c_1 e^{-2x} + c_2 e^{(1+\sqrt{2})x} + c_3 e^{(1-\sqrt{2})x}$.
16. $(D^3 - 3D^2 - 3D + 1)y = 0$.

17. $(4D^4 - 15D^2 + 5D + 6)y = 0$.   *Ans.* $y = c_1 e^{-2x} + c_2 e^{-\frac{x}{2}} + c_3 e^{\frac{3x}{2}} + c_4 e^x$.
18. $(D^4 - 2D^3 - 13D^2 + 38D - 24)y = 0$.
19. $(6D^4 + 23D^3 + 28D^2 + 13D + 2)y = 0$.
20. $(4D^4 - 45D^2 - 70D - 24)y = 0$.
21. $(D^2 - 4aD + 3a^2)y = 0$, a real $\neq 0$.
22. $[D^2 - (a + b)D + ab]y = 0$, a and b real and unequal.

In Exs. 23–24 find the particular solution indicated.

23. $(D^2 - 2D - 3)y = 0$; when $x = 0$, $y = 0$ and $y' = -4$.
                                       Ans. $y = e^{-x} - e^{3x}$.
24. $(D^2 - D - 6)y = 0$; when $x = 0$, $y = 0$ and when $x = 1$, $y = e^3$.

In Exs. 25–29, find for $x = 1$ the y value for the particular solution required.

25. $(D^2 - 2D - 3)y = 0$; when $x = 0$, $y = 4$ and $y' = 0$.
                         Ans. When $x = 1$, $y = e^3 + 3e^{-1} = 21.2$.
26. $(D^3 - 4D)y = 0$; when $x = 0$, $y = 0$, $y' = 0$, and $y'' = 2$.
                         Ans. When $x = 1$, $y = \sinh^2 1$.
27. $(D^2 - D - 6)y = 0$; when $x = 0$, $y = 3$ and $y' = -1$.
                         Ans. When $x = 1$, $y = 20.4$.
28. $(D^2 + 3D - 10)y = 0$; when $x = 0$, $y = 0$ and when $x = 2$, $y = 1$.
                         Ans. When $x = 1$, $y = 0.135$.
29. $(D^3 - 2D^2 - 5D + 6)y = 0$; when $x = 0$, $y = 1$, $y' = -7$, and $y'' = -1$.
                         Ans. When $x = 1$, $y = -19.8$.

373. *The Auxiliary Equation; Repeated Roots*

Suppose that in the equation

(1)
$$f(D)y = 0$$

the operator $f(D)$ has repeated factors; i.e., the auxiliary equation $f(m) = 0$ has repeated roots. Then the method of the previous section does not yield the general solution. Let the auxiliary equation have three equal roots $m_1 = b$, $m_2 = b$, $m_3 = b$. The corresponding part of the solution yielded by the method of § 372 is

$$y = c_1 e^{bx} + c_2 e^{bx} + c_3 e^{bx},$$

or

(2)
$$y = (c_1 + c_2 + c_3)e^{bx}.$$

Now (2) can be replaced by

(3)
$$y = c_4 e^{bx}$$

with $c_4 = c_1 + c_2 + c_3$. Thus, corresponding to the three roots under consideration, this method has yielded only the solution (3). The difficulty is present, of course, because the three solutions corresponding to the roots $m_1 = m_2 = m_3 = b$ are not linearly independent.

What is needed is a method for obtaining n linearly independent solutions corresponding to n equal roots of the auxiliary equation. Suppose the auxiliary equation $f(m) = 0$ has the n equal roots

$$m_1 = m_2 = \cdots = m_n = b.$$

Then the operator $f(D)$ must have a factor $(D - b)^n$. We wish to find n linearly independent y's for which

(4)
$$(D - b)^n y = 0.$$

Turning to the result (5) near the end of § 371 and writing $m = b$, we find that

(5)
$$(D - b)^n (x^k e^{bx}) = 0 \text{ for } k = 0, 1, 2, \cdots, (n - 1).$$

The functions $y_k = x^k e^{bx}$; $k = 0, 1, 2, \cdots, (n - 1)$ are linearly independent because aside from the common factor e^{bx} they contain only the respective powers $x^0, x^1, x^2, \cdots, x^{n-1}$.

The general solution of equation (4) is

(6)
$$y = c_1 e^{bx} + c_2 x e^{bx} + \cdots + c_n x^{n-1} e^{bx}.$$

Furthermore, if $f(D)$ contains the factor $(D - b)^n$, then the equation

(1)
$$f(D)y = 0$$

can be written

(7) $$g(D)(D - b)^n y = 0$$

where $g(D)$ contains all the factors of $f(D)$ except for $(D - b)^n$. Then any solution of

(4) $$(D - b)^n y = 0$$

is also a solution of (7) and therefore of (1).

Now we are in a position to write the solution of equation (1) whenever the auxiliary equation has only real roots. Each root of the auxiliary equation is either distinct from all the other roots or it is one of a set of equal roots. Corresponding to a root m_i distinct from all others, there is the solution

(8) $$y_i = c_i e^{m_i x};$$

and corresponding to n equal roots $m_1, m_2, \cdots, m_n$ each equal to b, there is the solution

(9) $$y = c_1 e^{bx} + c_2 x e^{bx} + \cdots + c_n x^{n-1} e^{bx}.$$

The sum of such solutions (8) and (9) yields the proper number of solutions, a number equal to the order of the differential equation, because there is one solution corresponding to each root of the auxiliary equation. The solutions thus obtained can be proved to be linearly independent.

Example (a). Solve the equation

(10) $$(D^4 - 7D^3 + 18D^2 - 20D + 8)y = 0.$$

With the aid of synthetic division it is easily seen that the auxiliary equation

$$m^4 - 7m^3 + 18m^2 - 20m + 8 = 0$$

has the roots $m = 1, 2, 2, 2$. Then the general solution of equation (10) is

$$y = c_1 e^x + c_2 e^{2x} + c_3 x e^{2x} + c_4 x^2 e^{2x},$$

or

$$y = c_1 e^x + (c_2 + c_3 x + c_4 x^2)e^{2x}.$$

Example (b). Solve the equation

$$\frac{d^4 y}{dx^4} + 2\frac{d^3 y}{dx^3} + \frac{d^2 y}{dx^2} = 0.$$

The auxiliary equation is

$$m^4 + 2m^3 + m^2 = 0$$

with roots $m = 0, 0, -1, -1$. Hence the desired solution is

$$y = c_1 + c_2 x + c_3 e^{-x} + c_4 x e^{-x}.$$

EXERCISES

In Exs. 1–20 find the general solution.

1. $(4D^2 - 4D + 1)y = 0.$ Ans. $y = (c_1 + c_2x)e^{\frac{x}{2}}.$
2. $(D^2 + 6D + 9)y = 0.$
3. $(D^3 - 4D^2 + 4D)y = 0.$ Ans. $y = c_1 + (c_2 + c_3x)e^{2x}.$
4. $(9D^3 + 6D^2 + D)y = 0.$

5. $(2D^4 - 3D^3 - 2D^2)y = 0.$ Ans. $y = c_1 + c_2x + c_3e^{2x} + c_4e^{-\frac{x}{2}}.$
6. $(2D^4 - 5D^3 - 3D^2)y = 0.$
7. $(D^3 + 3D^2 - 4)y = 0.$ Ans. $y = c_1e^x + (c_2 + c_3x)e^{-2x}.$
8. $(4D^3 - 27D + 27)y = 0.$
9. $(D^3 + 3D^2 + 3D + 1)y = 0.$ Ans. $y = (c_1 + c_2x + c_3x^2)e^{-x}.$
10. $(D^3 + 6D^2 + 12D + 8)y = 0.$
11. $(D^5 - D^3)y = 0.$ Ans. $y = c_1 + c_2x + c_3x^2 + c_4e^x + c_5e^{-x};$
    or $y = c_1 + c_2x + c_3x^2 + c_6 \cosh x + c_7 \sinh x.$

12. $(D^5 - 16D^3)y = 0.$

13. $(4D^4 + 4D^3 - 3D^2 - 2D + 1)y = 0.$ Ans. $y = (c_1 + c_2x)e^{\frac{x}{2}} + (c_3 + c_4x)e^{-x}.$
14. $(4D^4 - 4D^3 - 23D^2 + 12D + 36)y = 0.$

    Ans. $y = (c_1 + c_2x)e^{-\frac{3x}{2}} + (c_3 + c_4x)e^{2x}.$
15. $(D^4 + 3D^3 - 6D^2 - 28D - 24)y = 0.$

    Ans. $y = c_1e^{3x} + (c_2 + c_3x + c_4x^2)e^{-2x}.$
16. $(27D^4 - 18D^2 + 8D - 1)y = 0.$
17. $(4D^5 - 23D^3 - 33D^2 - 17D - 3)y = 0.$

    Ans. $y = c_1e^{3x} + (c_2 + c_3x)e^{-x} + (c_4 + c_5x)e^{-\frac{x}{2}}.$
18. $(4D^5 - 15D^3 - 5D^2 + 15D + 9)y = 0.$
19. $(D^4 - 5D^2 - 6D - 2)y = 0.$
    Ans. $y = (c_1 + c_2x)e^{-x} + c_3e^{(1+\sqrt{3})x} + c_4e^{(1-\sqrt{3})x}.$
20. $(D^5 - 5D^4 + 7D^3 + D^2 - 8D + 4)y = 0.$

In Exs. 21–26, find the particular solution indicated.

21. $(D^2 + 4D + 4)y = 0$; when $x = 0$, $y = 1$ and $y' = -1$.
    Ans. $y = (1 + x)e^{-2x}.$
22. The equation of Ex. 21 with the conditions that the graph of the solution pass through the points $(0, 2)$ and $(2, 0)$.   Ans. $y = (2 - x)e^{-2x}.$
23. $(D^3 - 3D - 2)y = 0$; when $x = 0$, $y = 0$, $y' = 9$, $y'' = 0$.
    Ans. $y = 2e^{2x} + (3x - 2)e^{-x}.$
24. $(D^4 + 3D^3 + 2D^2)y = 0$; when $x = 0$, $y = 0$, $y' = 4$, $y'' = -6$, $y''' = 14$.
    Ans. $y = 2(x + e^{-x} - e^{-2x}).$
25. The equation of Ex. 24 with the conditions: when $x = 0$, $y = 0$, $y' = 3$, $y'' = -5$, $y''' = 9$.   Ans. $y = 2 - e^{-x} - e^{-2x}.$
26. $(D^3 + D^2 - D - 1)y = 0$; when $x = 0$, $y = 1$, when $x = 2$, $y = 0$, and also as $x \to \infty$, $y \to 0$.   Ans. $y = \frac{1}{2}(2 - x)e^{-x}.$

In Exs. 27–29 find for $x = 2$ the y value for the particular solution required.

27. $(4D^2 - 4D + 1)y = 0$; when $x = 0$, $y = -2$, $y' = 2$.
$$\text{Ans. When } x = 2, y = 4e.$$

28. $(D^3 + 2D^2)y = 0$; when $x = 0$, $y = -3$, $y' = 0$, $y'' = 12$.
$$\text{Ans. When } x = 2, y = 3e^{-4} + 6.$$

29. $(D^3 + 5D^2 + 3D - 9)y = 0$; when $x = 0$, $y = -1$, when $x = 1$, $y = 0$, and also as $x \to \infty$, $y \to 0$.
$$\text{Ans. When } x = 2, y = e^{-6}.$$

374. *A Definition of e^z for Imaginary z*

It is evident that such a symbol as $e^{(2+3i)}$, where $i = \sqrt{-1}$, has no meaning from the standpoint of elementary algebra; i.e., it would be meaningless to speak of "e used as a factor $(2 + 3i)$ times." Furthermore, no simple extension of the meaning of an exponent such as saves the day for the symbols $e^{\frac{1}{2}}$, e^{-2}, $e^{\frac{2}{3}}$, etc., is available for $e^{(2+3i)}$. Let us search for a reasonable definition for e^z, where z is imaginary.

Let $z = \alpha + i\beta$ with α and β real. Since it is desirable to have the ordinary laws of exponents remain valid, it is wise to require that

$$(1) \qquad e^{\alpha + i\beta} = e^{\alpha} \cdot e^{i\beta}.$$

To e^{α} with α real we attach its usual meaning.

Now consider $e^{i\beta}$, β real. In Chapter 40 it was shown that for all real x

$$(2) \qquad e^x = 1 + \frac{x}{1!} + \frac{x^2}{2!} + \frac{x^3}{3!} + \cdots + \frac{x^n}{n!} + \cdots,$$

or

$$(2) \qquad e^x = \sum_{n=0}^{\infty} \frac{x^n}{n!}.$$

If we now tentatively put $x = i\beta$ in (2) as a definition of $e^{i\beta}$, we get

$$(3) \qquad e^{i\beta} = 1 + \frac{i\beta}{1!} + \frac{i^2\beta^2}{2!} + \frac{i^3\beta^3}{3!} + \frac{i^4\beta^4}{4!} + \cdots + \frac{i^n\beta^n}{n!} + \cdots.$$

Separating the even powers of β from the odd powers of β in (3) yields

$$(4) \qquad e^{i\beta} = \sum_{k=0}^{\infty} \frac{i^{2k}\beta^{2k}}{(2k)!} + \sum_{k=0}^{\infty} \frac{i^{2k+1}\beta^{2k+1}}{(2k+1)!}.$$

Now $i^{2k} = (-1)^k$, so that we may write

$$(5) \qquad e^{i\beta} = 1 - \frac{\beta^2}{2!} + \frac{\beta^4}{4!} + \cdots + \frac{(-1)^k\beta^{2k}}{(2k)!} + \cdots$$
$$+ i\left[\frac{\beta}{1!} - \frac{\beta^3}{3!} + \cdots + \frac{(-1)^k\beta^{2k+1}}{(2k+1)!} + \cdots\right].$$

or

(5)
$$e^{i\beta} = \sum_{k=0}^{\infty} \frac{(-1)^k \beta^{2k}}{(2k)!} + i \sum_{k=0}^{\infty} \frac{(-1)^k \beta^{2k+1}}{(2k+1)!}.$$

But the series on the right in (5) are precisely those for $\cos \beta$ and $\sin \beta$ as developed in Chapter 40.   Hence we are led to the tentative result

(6)
$$e^{i\beta} = \cos \beta + i \sin \beta.$$

The student should realize that the manipulations above have no meaning in themselves at this stage (assuming that infinite series with complex terms are not a part of the content of elementary mathematics).   What has been accomplished is this: The formal manipulations above have suggested the meaningful definition (6).   Combining (6) with (1), we now put forward a reasonable *definition* of $e^{\alpha+i\beta}$, namely,

(7)
$$e^{\alpha+i\beta} = e^{\alpha}(\cos \beta + i \sin \beta), \quad \alpha \text{ and } \beta \text{ real.}$$

Replacing β by $-\beta$ in (7) yields a result which is of value to us in the next section,

$$e^{\alpha-i\beta} = e^{\alpha}(\cos \beta - i \sin \beta).$$

It is interesting and important that with the definition (7), the function e^z for complex z retains many of the properties possessed by the function e^x for real x.   Such matters are often studied in detail in books on complex variables.*   Here we need in particular to know that if

$$y = e^{(a+ib)x},$$

a, b, and x real, then

$$(D - a - ib)y = 0.$$

The result desired follows at once by differentiation, with respect to x, of the function

$$y = e^{ax}(\cos bx + i \sin bx).$$

375. *The Auxiliary Equation; Imaginary Roots*

Consider a differential equation $f(D)y = 0$ for which the auxiliary equation $f(m) = 0$ has real coefficients.   From elementary algebra we know that if the auxiliary equation has any imaginary roots, those roots must occur in conjugate pairs.   Thus if

$$m_1 = a + ib$$

is a root of the equation $f(m) = 0$, with a and b real and $b \neq 0$, then

$$m_2 = a - ib$$

---

* For example, R. V. Churchill, *Complex Variables and Applications*, 2d ed., New York: McGraw-Hill Book Co., 1960, pp. 46–49.

is also a root of $f(m) = 0$. It must be kept in mind that this result is a consequence of the reality of the coefficients in the equation $f(m) = 0$. Imaginary roots do not necessarily appear in pairs in an algebraic equation whose coefficients involve imaginaries.

We can now construct in usable form solutions of

$$(1) \qquad\qquad f(D)y = 0$$

corresponding to imaginary roots of $f(m) = 0$. For, since $f(m)$ is assumed to have real coefficients, any imaginary roots appear in conjugate pairs $m_1 = a + ib$ and $m_2 = a - ib$. Then, according to the preceding section, equation (1) is satisfied by

$$(2) \qquad\qquad y = c_1 e^{(a+ib)x} + c_2 e^{(a-ib)x}.$$

Taking x to be real along with a and b, we get from (2) the result

$$(3) \qquad y = c_1 e^{ax}(\cos bx + i \sin bx) + c_2 e^{ax}(\cos bx - i \sin bx).$$

Now (3) may be written

$$y = (c_1 + c_2)e^{ax} \cos bx + i(c_1 - c_2)e^{ax} \sin bx.$$

Finally, let $c_1 + c_2 = c_3$, and $i(c_1 - c_2) = c_4$, where c_3 and c_4 are new arbitrary constants. Then equation (1) is seen to have the solutions

$$(4) \qquad\qquad y = c_3 e^{ax} \cos bx + c_4 e^{ax} \sin bx,$$

corresponding to the two roots $m_1 = a + ib$ and $m_2 = a - ib(b \neq 0)$ of the auxiliary equation.

Taking a, b, x, and y to be real, it follows from equation (4) that c_3 and c_4 are real. But $c_1 + c_2 = c_3$, and $i(c_1 - c_2) = c_4$, so that $c_1 = \frac{1}{2}(c_3 - ic_4)$ and $c_2 = \frac{1}{2}(c_3 + ic_4)$. Hence if $c_4 \neq 0$, the c_1 and c_2 are conjugate complex numbers.

The reduction of the solution (2) above to the desirable form (4) has been done once and that is enough. Whenever a pair of conjugate imaginary roots of the auxiliary equation appears, we write at once in the form given on the right in equation (4) the particular solution corresponding to those two roots.

Example (a). Solve the equation

$$(D^3 - 3D^2 + 9D + 13)y = 0.$$

For the auxiliary equation

$$m^3 - 3m^2 + 9m + 13 = 0$$

one root, $m_1 = -1$, is easily found. When the factor $(m + 1)$ is removed by synthetic division, it is seen that the other two roots are solutions of the quadratic

$$m^2 - 4m + 13 = 0.$$

Those roots are found to be $m_2 = 2 + 3i$ and $m_3 = 2 - 3i$. The auxiliary equation has the roots $m = -1, 2 \pm 3i$. Hence the general solution of the differential equation is

$$y = c_1 e^{-x} + c_2 e^{2x} \cos 3x + c_3 e^{2x} \sin 3x.$$

Repeated imaginary roots lead to solutions analogous to those brought in by repeated real roots. For instance, if the roots $m = a \pm ib$ occur three times, then the corresponding six linearly independent solutions of the differential equation are those appearing in the expression

$$(c_1 + c_2 x + c_3 x^2)e^{ax} \cos bx + (c_4 + c_5 x + c_6 x^2)e^{ax} \sin bx.$$

Example (b). Solve the equation

$$(D^4 + 8D^2 + 16)y = 0.$$

The auxiliary equation is $m^4 + 8m^2 + 16 = 0$ and it may be written $(m^2 + 4)^2 = 0$ so that its roots are seen to be $m = \pm 2i, \pm 2i$. The roots $m_1 = 2i$ and $m_2 = -2i$ each occur twice. Thinking of $2i$ as $0 + 2i$ and recalling that $e^{0x} = 1$, we write the solution of the differential equation as

$$y = (c_1 + c_2 x) \cos 2x + (c_3 + c_4 x) \sin 2x.$$

In such exercises as those below, a fine check can be obtained by direct substitution of the result and its appropriate derivatives into the differential equation. The verification is particularly effective because the operations performed in the check are so different from those performed in obtaining the solution.

EXERCISES

Find the general solution except where the exercise stipulates otherwise.

1. Verify directly that the relation

(4) $$y = c_3 e^{ax} \cos bx + c_4 e^{ax} \sin bx$$

satisfies the equation

$$[(D - a)^2 + b^2]y = 0.$$

2. $(D^2 - 2D + 5)y = 0$. Verify your answer.

   Ans. $y = c_1 e^x \cos 2x + c_2 e^x \sin 2x.$

3. $(D^2 - 2D + 2)y = 0$.

4. $(D^2 + 9)y = 0$. Verify your answer.   *Ans.* $y = c_1 \cos 3x + c_2 \sin 3x.$

5. $(D^2 - 9)y = 0$.   *Ans.* $y = c_1 \cosh 3x + c_2 \sinh 3x.$

6. $(D^2 + 6D + 13)y = 0$. Verify your answer.

7. $(D^2 - 4D + 7)y = 0$.   *Ans.* $y = c_1 e^{2x} \cos \sqrt{3}\, x + c_2 e^{2x} \sin \sqrt{3}\, x.$

8. $(D^3 + 2D^2 + D + 2)y = 0$. Verify your answer.

9. $(D^2 - 1)y = 0$; when $x = 0$, $y = y_0$ and $y' = 0$.   *Ans.* $y = y_0 \cosh x.$

10. $(D^2 + 1)y = 0$; when $x = 0$, $y = y_0$ and $y' = 0$.   *Ans.* $y = y_0 \cos x.$

11. $(D^4 + 2D^3 + 10D^2)y = 0$.   *Ans.* $y = c_1 + c_2 x + c_3 e^{-x} \cos 3x + c_4 e^{-x} \sin 3x$.

12. $(D^3 + 7D^2 + 19D + 13)y = 0$; when $x = 0$, $y = 0$, $y' = 2$, and $y'' = -12$.

$$\text{Ans. } y = e^{-3x} \sin 2x.$$

13. $(D^5 + D^4 - 7D^3 - 11D^2 - 8D - 12)y = 0$.

$$\text{Ans. } y = c_1 \cos x + c_2 \sin x + c_3 e^{-2x} + c_4 x e^{-2x} + c_5 e^{3x}.$$

14. $(D^4 - 2D^3 + 2D^2 - 2D + 1)y = 0$.   Verify your answer.

15. $(D^4 + 18D^2 + 81)y = 0$.   *Ans.* $y = (c_1 + c_2 x) \cos 3x + (c_3 + c_4 x) \sin 3x$.

16. $(2D^4 + 11D^3 - 4D^2 - 69D + 34)y = 0$.   Verify your answer.

17. $(D^6 + 9D^4 + 24D^2 + 16)y = 0$.

$$\text{Ans. } y = c_1 \cos x + c_2 \sin x + (c_3 + c_4 x) \cos 2x + (c_5 + c_6 x) \sin 2x.$$

18. $(2D^3 - D^2 + 36D - 18)y = 0$.

$$\text{Ans. } y = c_1 e^{\frac{x}{2}} + c_2 \cos (3\sqrt{2}\, x) + c_3 \sin (3\sqrt{2}\, x).$$

19. $\dfrac{d^2 x}{dt^2} + k^2 x = 0$, k real; when $t = 0$, $x = 0$ and $\dfrac{dx}{dt} = v_0$.   Verify your result completely.

$$\text{Ans. } x = \frac{v_0}{k} \sin kt.$$

20. $(D^3 + D^2 + 4D + 4)y = 0$; when $x = 0$, $y = 0$, $y' = -1$, and $y'' = 5$.

$$\text{Ans. } y = e^{-x} - \cos 2x.$$

21. $\dfrac{d^2 x}{dt^2} + 2b \dfrac{dx}{dt} + k^2 x = 0$, $k > b > 0$; when $t = 0$, $x = 0$ and $\dfrac{dx}{dt} = v_0$.

$$\text{Ans. } x = \frac{v_0}{a} e^{-bt} \sin at, \text{ where } a = \sqrt{k^2 - b^2}.$$

MISCELLANEOUS EXERCISES

Obtain the general solution unless otherwise instructed.   Your answer can be checked by direct substitution.

1. $(D^3 - D^2 + D - 1)y = 0$.

2. $(D^3 + 4D^2 + 5D)y = 0$.

3. $(D^4 - 13D^2 + 36)y = 0$.

4. $(D^4 - 5D^3 + 5D^2 + 5D - 6)y = 0$.

5. $(4D^3 + 8D^2 - 11D + 3)y = 0$.

6. $(D^3 + D^2 - 16D - 16)y = 0$.

7. $(D^4 - D^3 - 3D^2 + D + 2)y = 0$.

8. $(D^3 - 2D^2 - 3D + 10)y = 0$.

9. $(D^5 + D^4 - 6D^3)y = 0$.

10. $(4D^3 + 28D^2 + 61D + 37)y = 0$.

11. $(4D^3 + 12D^2 + 13D + 10)y = 0$.

12. $(18D^3 - 33D^2 + 20D - 4)y = 0$.

13. $(D^2 - D - 6)y = 0$; when $x = 0$, $y = 2$ and $y' = 1$.

14. $(D^4 + 6D^3 + 9D^2)y = 0$; when $x = 0$, $y = 0$, $y' = 0$, and $y'' = 6$ and as $x \to \infty$, $y' \to 1$.   For this particular solution find the value of y when $x = 1$.

$$\text{Ans. } y = 1 - e^{-3}.$$

15. $(D^3 + 6D^2 + 12D + 8)y = 0$; when $x = 0$, $y = 1$, $y' = -2$, and $y'' = 2$.

16. $(8D^3 - 4D^2 - 2D + 1)y = 0$.

17. $(D^4 + D^3 - 4D^2 - 4D)y = 0.$
18. $(D^4 - 2D^3 + 5D^2 - 8D + 4)y = 0.$
19. $(D^4 + 2D^2 + 1)y = 0.$
20. $(D^4 + 5D^2 + 4)y = 0.$
21. $(D^4 + 3D^3 - 4D)y = 0.$
22. $(D^5 + D^4 - 9D^3 - 13D^2 + 8D + 12)y = 0.$
23. $(D^4 - 11D^3 + 36D^2 - 16D - 64)y = 0.$
24. $(D^2 + 2D + 5)y = 0.$
25. $(D^4 + 4D^3 + 2D^2 - 8D - 8)y = 0.$
26. $(4D^4 - 24D^3 + 35D^2 + 6D - 9)y = 0.$
27. $(4D^4 + 20D^3 + 35D^2 + 25D + 6)y = 0.$
28. $(D^4 - 7D^3 + 11D^2 + 5D - 14)y = 0.$
29. $(D^3 + 5D^2 + 7D + 3)y = 0.$
30. $(D^3 - 2D^2 + D - 2)y = 0.$

Nonhomogeneous Equations

376. *Construction of a Homogeneous Equation from a Specified Solution*

In preparation for the method of undetermined coefficients (§ 378), it is wise to obtain proficiency in writing down a homogeneous differential equation of which a given relation of proper form is a solution.

Recall that in solutions of homogeneous equations with constant coefficients a term such as c_1e^{ax} occurred only when the auxiliary equation $f(m) = 0$ had a root $m = a$, and then the operator $f(D)$ had a factor $(D - a)$. In like manner c_2xe^{ax} appeared only when $f(D)$ contained the factor $(D - a)^2$, $c_3x^2e^{ax}$ only when $f(D)$ contained $(D - a)^3$, etc. Such terms as $ce^{ax} \cos bx$ or $ce^{ax} \sin bx$ correspond to roots $m = a \pm ib$, or to a factor $[(D - a)^2 + b^2]$.

Example (*a*). Find a homogeneous linear equation, with constant coefficients, which has as a particular solution

$$(1) \qquad\qquad y = 7e^{3x} + 2x.$$

First note that the coefficients (7 and 2) are quite irrelevant for the present problem as long as they are not zero. We shall obtain an equation satisfied by $y = c_1e^{3x} + c_2x$, no matter what the constants c_1 and c_2 may be.

A term c_1e^{3x} occurs along with a root $m = 3$ of the auxiliary equation. The term c_2x will appear if the auxiliary equation has $m = 0, 0$; that is, a double root $m = 0$. We have recognized that the equation

$$(2) \qquad\qquad D^2(D - 3)y = 0,$$

or

$$(2) \qquad\qquad (D^3 - 3D^2)y = 0$$

has $y = c_1e^{3x} + c_2x + c_3$ as its general solution, and therefore that (2) has $y = 7e^{3x} + 2x$ as a particular solution.

Example (*b*). Find a homogeneous linear equation with real, constant coefficients which is satisfied by

$$(3) \qquad\qquad y = 6 + 3xe^x - \cos x.$$

The term 6 is associated with $m = 0$; the term $3xe^x$ with a double root $m = 1, 1$; and the term $(-\cos x)$ with the pair of imaginary roots

$$m = 0 \pm i.$$

Hence the auxiliary equation is

$$m(m - 1)^2(m^2 + 1) = 0,$$

or

$$m^5 - 2m^4 + 2m^3 - 2m^2 + m = 0.$$

Therefore the relation (3) is a solution of the differential equation

(4) $$(D^5 - 2D^4 + 2D^3 - 2D^2 + D)y = 0.$$

That is, from the general solution

$$y = c_1 + (c_2 + c_3x)e^x + c_4 \cos x + c_5 \sin x$$

of equation (4), the relation (3) follows by an appropriate choice of the constants: $c_1 = 6$, $c_2 = 0$, $c_3 = 3$, $c_4 = -1$, $c_5 = 0$.

Example (c).   Find a homogeneous linear equation with real, constant coefficients which is satisfied by

$$y = 4xe^x \sin 2x.$$

The desired equation must have its auxiliary equation with the pairs of equal roots $m = 1 \pm 2i$, $1 \pm 2i$.   The roots $m = 1 \pm 2i$ correspond to factors $(m - 1)^2 + 4$, so that the auxiliary equation must be

$$[(m - 1)^2 + 4]^2 = 0,$$

or

$$m^4 - 4m^3 + 14m^2 - 20m + 25 = 0.$$

Hence the desired equation is

$$(D^4 - 4D^3 + 14D^2 - 20D + 25)y = 0.$$

Note that in all such problems a correct (but undesirable) solution may be obtained by inserting additional roots of the auxiliary equation.

ORAL EXERCISES

In Exs. 1–14 obtain in factored form a linear differential equation, with real, constant coefficients which is satisfied by the given relation.

1. $y = 4e^{2x} + 3e^{-x}$.   *Ans.* $(D - 2)(D + 1)y = 0$.
2. $y = 7 - 2x + \frac{1}{2}e^{4x}$.   *Ans.* $D^2(D - 4)y = 0$.
3. $y = -2x + \frac{1}{2}e^{4x}$.   *Ans.* $D^2(D - 4)y = 0$.
4. $y = x^2 - 5 \sin 3x$.   *Ans.* $D^3(D^2 + 9)y = 0$.
5. $y = 2e^x \cos 3x$.
6. $y = 8xe^x + 4e^{-2x}$.
7. $y = 3e^{2x} - e^x$.

8. $y = 2 - e^{-3x}$.

9. $y = x^2 - 4$.

10. $y = \cos x$.

11. $y = \cos x - 4 \sin x$.

12. $y = \sin kx$.

13. $y = 2x \cos x$.

14. $y = 5 \cosh 2x$.

In Exs. 15–30 state the roots of the auxiliary equation for a homogeneous linear equation with real, constant coefficients and containing the given relation as a particular solution.

15. $y = 3xe^{2x}$.   *Ans. m* $= 2, 2$.

16. $y = x^2e^{-x} + 4e^x$.   *Ans. m* $= -1, -1, -1, 1$.

17. $y = e^{-x} \cos 4x$.   *Ans. m* $= -1 \pm 4i$.

18. $y = 3e^{-x} \cos 4x + 15e^{-x} \sin 4x$.   *Ans. m* $= -1 \pm 4i$.

19. $y = x(e^x - 1)$.   *Ans. m* $= 1, 1, 0, 0$.

20. $y = 7 + e^{-3x}$.

21. $y = 6x^2 - e^{-4x}$.

22. $y = 3 + 6x^2 - e^{-4x}$.

23. $y = 5 \cos 3x$.

24. $y = 5 \cos 3x - 2 \sin 3x$.

25. $y = x \cos 3x - 2 \sin 3x$.

26. $y = e^{-x}(\sin 2x + \cos 2x)$.

27. $y = e^{-x} \sin 2x$.

28. $y = x^2 - 3x + e^{-3x} + 4e^x \cos 7x$.

29. $y = \sin^3 x$.   Use the fact that $\sin^3 x = \frac{1}{4}(3 \sin x - \sin 3x)$.

30. $y = \cos^2 x$.

377. *Solution of a Nonhomogeneous Equation*

Before proceeding to the theoretical basis and the actual working technique of the useful method of undetermined coefficients, let us examine the underlying ideas as applied to a simple numerical example.

Consider the equation

(1) $$D^2(D - 1)y = 3e^x + \sin x.$$

The complementary function may be determined at once from the roots

(2) $$m = 0, 0, 1$$

of the auxiliary equation. The complementary function is

(3) $$y_c = c_1 + c_2x + c_3e^x.$$

Since the general solution of (1) is

$$y = y_c + y_p$$

where y_c is as given in (3) and y_p is any particular solution of (1), all that remains is for us to find a particular solution of (1).

The right-hand member of (1),

(4) $R(x) = 3e^x + \sin x$

is a particular solution of a homogeneous linear differential equation whose auxiliary equation has the roots

(5) $m' = 1, \pm i.$

Therefore the relation (4) is a particular solution of the equation

(6) $(D - 1)(D^2 + 1)R = 0.$

We wish to convert (1) into a homogeneous linear differential equation with constant coefficients because we know how to solve any such equation. But, by (6), the operator $(D - 1)(D^2 + 1)$ will annihilate the right member of (1). Therefore we apply that operator to both sides of equation (1) and get

(7) $(D - 1)(D^2 + 1)D^2(D - 1)y = 0.$

Any solution of (1) must be a particular solution of (7). The general solution of (7) can be written down at once from the roots of its auxiliary equation, those roots being the values $m = 0, 0, 1$ from (2) together with the values $m' = 1, \pm i$ from (5). Thus the general solution of (7) is

(8) $y = c_1 + c_2 x + c_3 e^x + c_4 x e^x + c_5 \cos x + c_6 \sin x.$

But the desired general solution of (1) is

(9) $y = y_c + y_p,$

where

$$y_c = c_1 + c_2 x + c_3 e^x,$$

the c_1, c_2, c_3 being arbitrary constants as in (8). Thus there must exist a particular solution of (1) containing at most the remaining terms in (8). Using different letters as coefficients to emphasize that they are not arbitrary, we conclude that (1) has a particular solution

(10) $y_p = Axe^x + B \cos x + C \sin x.$

It remains only to determine the numerical coefficients A, B, C by direct use of the original equation

(1) $D^2(D - 1)y = 3e^x + \sin x.$

From (10) it follows that

$$Dy_p = A(xe^x + e^x) - B \sin x + C \cos x,$$
$$D^2 y_p = A(xe^x + 2e^x) - B \cos x - C \sin x,$$
$$D^3 y_p = A(xe^x + 3e^x) + B \sin x - C \cos x.$$

Substitution of y_p into (1) then yields

(11) $Ae^x + (B + C) \sin x + (B - C) \cos x = 3e^x + \sin x.$

Since (11) is to be an identity and since e^x, $\sin x$, and $\cos x$ are linearly independent, the corresponding coefficients in the two members of (11) must be equal; i.e.,

$$A = 3$$
$$B + C = 1$$
$$B - C = 0.$$

Therefore $A = 3$, $B = \frac{1}{2}$, $C = \frac{1}{2}$.   Returning to (10), we find that a particular solution of equation (1) is

$$y_p = 3xe^x + \tfrac{1}{2} \cos x + \tfrac{1}{2} \sin x.$$

The general solution of the original equation

(1) $D^2(D - 1)y = 3e^x + \sin x$

is therefore obtained by adding to the complementary function the y_p found above:

(12) $y = c_1 + c_2 x + c_3 e^x + 3xe^x + \tfrac{1}{2} \cos x + \tfrac{1}{2} \sin x.$

A careful analysis of the ideas behind the process used above shows that in order to arrive at the solution (12), we need perform only the following steps:

(a) From (1) find the values of m and m' as exhibited in (2) and (5);
(b) From the values of m and m', write y_c and y_p as in (3) and (10);
(c) Substitute y_p into (1), equate corresponding coefficients, and obtain the numerical values of the coefficients in y_p;
(d) Write the general solution of (1).

378. *The Method of Undetermined Coefficients*

Let us examine the general problem of the type treated in the preceding section.   Let $f(D)$ be a polynomial in the operator D.   Consider the equation

(1) $f(D)y = R(x).$

Let the roots of the auxiliary equation $f(m) = 0$ be

(2) $m = m_1, m_2, \cdots, m_n.$

The general solution of (1) is

(3) $y = y_c + y_p$

where y_c can be obtained at once from the values of m in (2) and where $y = y_p$ is any particular solution (yet to be obtained) of (1).

Now suppose that the right member $R(x)$ of (1) is itself a particular solution of some homogeneous linear differential equation with constant coefficients,

$$(4) \qquad\qquad g(D)R = 0,$$

whose auxiliary equation has the roots

$$(5) \qquad\qquad m' = m_1', m_2', \cdots, m_k'.$$

Recall that the values of m' in (5) can be obtained by inspection from $R(x)$.
    The differential equation

$$(6) \qquad\qquad g(D)f(D)y = 0$$

has as the roots of its auxiliary equation the values of m from (2) and m' from (5).   Hence the general solution of (6) contains the y_c of (3) and so is of the form

$$y = y_c + y_q.$$

But also any particular solution of (1) must satisfy (6).   Now, if

$$f(D)(y_c + y_q) = R(x),$$

it follows that

$$f(D)y_q = R(x)$$

because $f(D)y_c = 0$.   Then deleting the y_c from the general solution of (6) leaves a function y_q, which for some numerical values of its coefficients must satisfy (1); i.e., the coefficients in y_q can be determined so that $y_q = y_p$. The determination of those numerical coefficients may be accomplished as in the examples below.

It must be kept in mind that the method of this section is applicable when, and only when, the right member of the equation is itself a particular solution of some homogeneous linear differential equation with constant coefficients.   Methods which apply to equations with less restricted right-hand members will be found in most books on differential equations.   For example, see Rainville, *Elementary Differential Equations* 2d ed., New York: The Macmillan Company, 1958, Chapter 11.

Example (a).   Solve the equation

$$(7) \qquad\qquad (D^2 + D - 2)y = 2x - 40 \cos 2x.$$

Here we have

$$m = 1, -2$$

and

$$m' = 0, 0, \pm 2i.$$

Therefore we may write

$$y_c = c_1 e^x + c_2 e^{-2x},$$
$$y_p = A + Bx + C \cos 2x + E \sin 2x,$$

in which c_1 and c_2 are arbitrary constants, while A, B, C, and E are to be determined numerically so that y_p will satisfy the equation (7).

Since

$$Dy_p = B - 2C \sin 2x + 2E \cos 2x$$

and

$$D^2y_p = -4C \cos 2x - 4E \sin 2x,$$

direct substitution of y_p into (7) yields

$$(8) \quad -4C \cos 2x - 4E \sin 2x + B - 2C \sin 2x$$
$$+ 2E \cos 2x - 2A - 2Bx - 2C \cos 2x$$
$$- 2E \sin 2x = 2x - 40 \cos 2x.$$

But (8) is to be an identity in x, so we must equate coefficients of each of the set of linearly independent functions $\cos 2x$, $\sin 2x$, x, 1 appearing in the identity. Thus it follows that

$$-6C + 2E = -40,$$
$$-6E - 2C = 0,$$
$$-2B = 2,$$
$$B - 2A = 0.$$

The above equations determine A, B, C, and E. Indeed, they lead to $A = -\frac{1}{2}$, $B = -1$, $C = 6$, $E = -2$.

Since the general solution of (7) is $y = y_c + y_p$, we can now write the desired result,

$$y = c_1e^x + c_2e^{-2x} - \tfrac{1}{2} - x + 6 \cos 2x - 2 \sin 2x.$$

Example (b).   Solve the equation

$$(9) \qquad\qquad (D^2 + 1)y = \sin x.$$

At once $m = \pm i$ and $m' = \pm i$. Therefore

$$y_c = c_1 \cos x + c_2 \sin x,$$
$$y_p = Ax \cos x + Bx \sin x.$$

Now

$$y_p'' = A(-x \cos x - 2 \sin x) + B(-x \sin x + 2 \cos x)$$

so that the requirement that y_p satisfy equation (9) yields

$$-2A \sin x + 2B \cos x = \sin x$$

from which $A = -\frac{1}{2}$ and $B = 0$. The general solution of (9) is

$$y = c_1 \cos x + c_2 \sin x - \tfrac{1}{2}x \cos x.$$

Example (c).   Determine y so that it will satisfy the equation

$$(10) \qquad\qquad y''' - y' = 4e^{-x} + 3e^{2x}$$

together with the conditions that when $x = 0$, $y = 0$, $y' = -1$, and $y'' = 2$.

First we note that $m = 0, 1, -1$, and $m' = -1, 2$.   Thus

$$y_c = c_1 + c_2 e^x + c_3 e^{-x}$$
$$y_p = Axe^{-x} + Be^{2x}.$$

Now

$$y_p' = A(-xe^{-x} + e^{-x}) + 2Be^{2x},$$
$$y_p'' = A(xe^{-x} - 2e^{-x}) + 4Be^{2x},$$

and

$$y_p''' = A(-xe^{-x} + 3e^{-x}) + 8Be^{2x}.$$

Then

$$y_p''' - y_p' = 2Ae^{-x} + 6Be^{2x},$$

so that from (10) we may conclude that $A = 2$ and $B = \frac{1}{2}$.

The general solution of (10) is therefore

(11) $$y = c_1 + c_2 e^x + c_3 e^{-x} + 2xe^{-x} + \frac{1}{2}e^{2x}.$$

We must determine c_1, c_2, c_3 so that (11) will satisfy the conditions: when $x = 0$, $y = 0$, $y' = -1$, and $y'' = 2$.

From (11) it follows that

(12) $$y' = c_2 e^x - c_3 e^{-x} - 2xe^{-x} + 2e^{-x} + e^{2x}$$

and

(13) $$y'' = c_2 e^x + c_3 e^{-x} + 2xe^{-x} - 4e^{-x} + 2e^{2x}.$$

We put $x = 0$ in each of (11), (12), and (13) to get the equations for the determination of c_1, c_2, and c_3.   These are

$$0 = c_1 + c_2 + c_3 + \frac{1}{2},$$
$$-1 = c_2 - c_3 + 3,$$
$$2 = c_2 + c_3 - 2,$$

from which $c_1 = -\frac{9}{2}$, $c_2 = 0$, $c_3 = 4$.   Therefore the final result is

$$y = -\frac{9}{2} + 4e^{-x} + 2xe^{-x} + \frac{1}{2}e^{2x}.$$

An important point, sometimes overlooked by students, is that it is the general solution, the y of (11), which must be made to satisfy the boundary conditions.

EXERCISES

Obtain the general solution in Exs. 1–26.

1. $(D^2 + D)y = -\cos x.$ *Ans.* $y = c_1 + c_2 e^{-x} + \frac{1}{2}\cos x - \frac{1}{2}\sin x.$
2. $(D^2 - 6D + 9)y = e^x.$ *Ans.* $y = (c_1 + c_2 x)e^{3x} + \frac{1}{4}e^x.$
3. $(D^2 - 2D - 3)y = 27x^2.$ *Ans.* $y = c_1 e^{-x} + c_2 e^{3x} - 14 + 12x - 9x^2.$
4. $(D^2 - 2D - 3)y = 4 - 8x - 6x^2.$ *Ans.* $y = c_1 e^{-x} + c_2 e^{3x} + 2x^2.$
5. $(D^2 + 4)y = 15e^x - 8x.$ *Ans.* $y = c_1 \cos 2x + c_2 \sin 2x + 3e^x - 2x.$
6. $(D^2 + 4)y = 15e^x - 8x^2.$ *Ans.* $y = c_1 \cos 2x + c_2 \sin 2x + 3e^x - 2x^2 + 1.$
7. $(D^2 + D - 2)y = 12e^{2x}.$ *Ans.* $y = c_1 e^x + c_2 e^{-2x} + 3e^{2x}.$

8. $(D^2 + D - 2)y = 12e^{-2x}$.   *Ans.* $y = c_1e^x + (c_2 - 4x)e^{-2x}$.

9. $(D^2 - 4)y = e^{2x} + 2$.   *Ans.* $y = c_1e^{-2x} + (c_2 + \frac{1}{4}x)e^{2x} - \frac{1}{2}$.

10. $(D^2 - D - 2)y = 6x + 6e^{-x}$.   *Ans.* $y = c_1e^{-x} + c_2e^{2x} - 3x + \frac{3}{2} - 2xe^{-x}$.

11. $y'' - 4y' + 3y = 20 \cos x$.   *Ans.* $y = c_1e^x + c_2e^{3x} + 2 \cos x - 4 \sin x$.

12. $y'' - 4y' + 3y = 2 \cos x + 4 \sin x$.   *Ans.* $y = c_1e^x + c_2e^{3x} + \cos x$.

13. $y'' + 2y' + y = 7 + 75 \sin 2x$.

    Ans. $y = e^{-x}(c_1 + c_2x) + 7 - 12 \cos 2x - 9 \sin 2x$.

14. $(D^2 + 4D + 5)y = 50x + 13e^{3x}$.

    Ans. $y = e^{-2x}(c_1 \cos x + c_2 \sin x) + 10x - 8 + \frac{1}{2}e^{3x}$.

15. $(D^2 + 1)y = \cos x$.   *Ans.* $y = c_1 \cos x + c_2 \sin x + \frac{1}{2}x \sin x$.

16. $(D^2 - 4D + 4)y = e^{2x}$.   *Ans.* $y = e^{2x}(c_1 + c_2x + \frac{1}{2}x^2)$.

17. $(D^2 - 1)y = e^{-x}(2 \sin x + 4 \cos x)$.   *Ans.* $y = c_1e^x + (c_2 - 2 \sin x)e^{-x}$.

18. $(D^2 - 1)y = 8xe^x$.   *Ans.* $y = c_1e^{-x} + e^x(c_2 - 2x + 2x^2)$.

19. $(D^3 - D)y = x$.   *Ans.* $y = c_1 + c_2e^x + c_3e^{-x} - \frac{1}{2}x^2$.

20. $(D^3 - D^2 + D - 1)y = 4 \sin x$.

    Ans. $y = c_1e^x + (c_2 + x) \cos x + (c_3 - x) \sin x$.

21. $(D^3 + D^2 - 4D - 4)y = 3e^{-x} - 4x - 6$.

    Ans. $y = c_1e^{2x} + c_2e^{-2x} + (c_3 - x)e^{-x} + x + \frac{1}{2}$.

22. $(D^4 - 1)y = 7x^2$.   *Ans.* $y = c_1e^x + c_2e^{-x} + c_3 \cos x + c_4 \sin x - 7x^2$.

23. $(D^4 - 1)y = e^{-x}$.   *Ans.* $y = c_1e^x + (c_2 - \frac{1}{4}x)e^{-x} + c_3 \cos x + c_4 \sin x$.

24. $(D^2 - 1)y = 10 \sin^2 x$.   Use the identity $\sin^2 x = \frac{1}{2}(1 - \cos 2x)$.

    Ans. $y = c_1e^x + c_2e^{-x} - 5 + \cos 2x$.

25. $(D^2 + 1)y = 12 \cos^2 x$.   *Ans.* $y = c_1 \cos x + c_2 \sin x + 6 - 2 \cos 2x$.

26. $(D^2 + 4)y = 4 \sin^2 x$.   *Ans.* $y = c_1 \cos 2x + c_2 \sin 2x + \frac{1}{2}(1 - x \sin 2x)$.

In Exs. 27–31 find the particular solution indicated.

27. $(D^2 + 1)y = 10e^{2x}$; when $x = 0$, $y = 0$ and $y' = 0$.

    Ans. $y = 2(e^{2x} - \cos x - 2 \sin x)$.

28. $(D^2 - 4)y = 2 - 8x$; when $x = 0$, $y = 0$ and $y' = 5$.

    Ans. $y = e^{2x} - \frac{1}{2}e^{-2x} + 2x - \frac{1}{2}$.

29. $(D^2 + 3D)y = -18x$; when $x = 0$, $y = 0$ and $y' = 5$.

    Ans. $y = 1 + 2x - 3x^2 - e^{-3x}$.

30. $(D^2 + 4D + 5)y = 10e^{-3x}$; when $x = 0$, $y = 4$ and $y' = 0$.

    Ans. $y = e^{-2x}(13 \sin x - \cos x) + 5e^{-3x}$.

31. $\dfrac{d^2x}{dt^2} + 4\dfrac{dx}{dt} + 5x = 10$; when $t = 0$, $x = 0$ and $\dfrac{dx}{dt} = 0$.

    Ans. $x = 2(1 - e^{-2t} \cos t - 2e^{-2t} \sin t)$.

In Exs. 32–35 obtain from the particular solution indicated the value of y and the value of y' at $x = 2$.

32. $y'' + 2y' + y = x$; at $x = 0$, $y = -3$ and at $x = 1$, $y = -1$.

    Ans. At $x = 2$, $y = e^{-2}$ and $y' = 1$.

33. $y'' + 2y' + y = x$; at $x = 0$, $y = -2$ and $y' = 2$.

    Ans. At $x = 2$, $y = 2e^{-2}$ and $y' = 1 - e^{-2}$.

34. $4y'' + y = 2$; at $x = \pi$, $y = 0$ and $y' = 1$.

    Ans. At $x = 2$, $y = -0.7635$ and $y' = +0.3012$.

35. $2y'' - 5y' - 3y = -9x^2 - 1$; at $x = 0$, $y = 1$ and $y' = 0$.

Ans. At $x = 2$, $y = 5.64$ and $y' = 5.68$.

36. $(D^2 + D)y = x + 1$; when $x = 0$, $y = 1$ and when $x = 1$, $y = \frac{1}{2}$. Compute the value of y at $x = 4$. *Ans.* At $x = 4$, $y = 8 - e^{-1} - e^{-2} - e^{-3}$.

37. $(D^2 + 1)y = x^3$; when $x = 0$, $y = 0$, and when $x = \pi$, $y = 0$. Show that this boundary value problem has no solution.

38. $(D^2 + 1)y = 2 \cos x$; when $x = 0$, $y = 0$ and when $x = \pi$, $y = 0$. Show that this boundary value problem has an unlimited number of solutions and obtain them. *Ans.* $y = (c + x) \sin x$.

39. For the equation $(D^3 + D^2)y = 4$, find the solution whose graph has at the origin a point of inflection with a horizontal tangent line.

Ans. $y = 4 - 4x + 2x^2 - 4e^{-x}$.

40. For the equation $(D^2 - D)y = 2 - 2x$ find a particular solution which has at some point (to be determined) on the x-axis an inflection point with a horizontal tangent line. *Ans.* The point is $(1, 0)$; the solution is $y = x^2 + 1 - 2e^{x-1}$.

41. $(D^2 + 9)y = \sin 3x$; when $x = 0$, $y = 1$ and when $x = \frac{1}{2}\pi$, $y = 1$. Compute the value of y at $x = \frac{1}{4}\pi$. *Ans.* At $x = \frac{1}{4}\pi$, $y = -1.3$.

Applications

379. *Vibration of a Spring*

Consider a steel spring attached to a rigid support and hanging downward without obstruction. The spring will obey Hooke's law; i.e., if the spring is stretched or compressed, its change in length will be proportional to the force exerted upon the spring, and when that force is removed, the spring will return to its original position with its length and other physical properties unchanged.

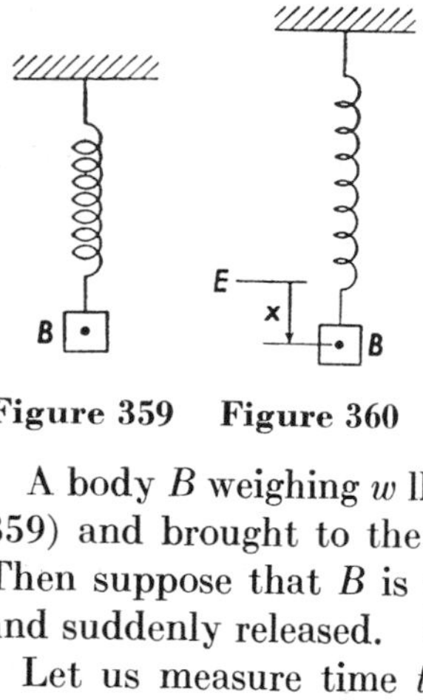

According to Hooke's law there is associated with each spring a numerical constant, the ratio of the force exerted to the displacement produced by that force. Suppose a force of magnitude f lb. stretches the spring s ft. Then the relation

$$(1) \qquad f = ks$$

defines the spring constant k in the units pounds per foot.

Figure 359   Figure 360

A body B weighing w lb. is attached to the lower end of the spring (Figure 359) and brought to the point of equilibrium where it can remain at rest. Then suppose that B is pulled down x_0 ft. below the point of equilibrium and suddenly released. Our first problem is to determine the motion of B.

Let us measure time t in seconds starting with $t = 0$ at the time B is released. Let us also indicate the position of the body B at time t by x, in feet, measured positive downward from the point of equilibrium E (Figure 360). Then the statement that B was released (i.e., without imparted velocity) from a position x_0 ft. below E can be expressed mathematically by saying that

$$(2) \qquad \text{when } t = 0, \ x = x_0 \quad \text{and} \quad \frac{dx}{dt} = 0.$$

We have used the fact that the motion of B takes place in a straight (vertical) line so that the velocity v is given by

$$v = \frac{dx}{dt}.$$

674

Let $g = 32$ ft. per sec. per sec.* be the magnitude of the acceleration due to gravity. Then B has mass w/g (lb.) (sec.^{2}) per ft., or w/g slugs.

The resultant force F acting upon B at any time is, according to Newton's law,

$$(3) \qquad\qquad F = \frac{w}{g}\frac{d^2x}{dt^2}$$

with F measured positive when it tends to move B in the positive x direction (downward). Let us neglect the force due to air resistance. Then the resultant force acting upon B is the one which by Hooke's law has magnitude $k|x|$, where k is the spring constant. This force is tending to restore equilibrium, to pull B back toward E. Therefore it is opposite in sign to x, so that

$$F = -kx,$$

or

$$(4) \qquad\qquad \frac{w}{g}\frac{d^2x}{dt^2} = -kx.$$

The problem of determining the motion of B is now seen to be one of solving a differential equation with associated boundary conditions. The displacement x from the equilibrium point E (x positive downward) must be a function of the time t such that x satisfies the differential equation

$$(5) \qquad\qquad \frac{w}{g}\frac{d^2x}{dt^2} + kx = 0$$

and the associated conditions

$$(6) \qquad\qquad \text{when } t = 0,\ x = x_0 \quad\text{and}\quad \frac{dx}{dt} = 0.$$

Let us solve the boundary value problem consisting of (5) and (6). Let $\frac{kg}{w} = \beta^2$. Then (5) may be written

$$\frac{d^2x}{dt^2} + \beta^2 x = 0$$

and we know its general solution to be

$$(7) \qquad\qquad x = c_1 \cos \beta t + c_2 \sin \beta t,$$

where c_1 and c_2 are arbitrary constants. Those constants must be determined so as to make the function x satisfy the conditions (6). From (7) it follows that

$$(8) \qquad\qquad v = \frac{dx}{dt} = -c_1\beta \sin \beta t + c_2\beta \cos \beta t.$$

Let $t = 0$ in (7) and (8). Then, using the conditions (6), we get

* The figure 32 is convenient and is in error less than $\frac{1}{2}\%$.

$$x_0 = c_1 \cdot 1 + c_2 \cdot 0$$

and

$$0 = -c_1\beta \cdot 0 + c_2\beta \cdot 1,$$

so that $c_1 = x_0$ and $c_2 = 0$.

With c_1 and c_2 known, the relation (7) becomes

(9) $$x = x_0 \cos \beta t$$

where $\beta = \sqrt{kg/w}$. Equation (9) is the solution we have been seeking. That it satisfies (5) and (6) is easily verified.

The motion described by (9) is called simple harmonic motion. It is periodic with period $2\pi/\beta$ or $2\pi(kg/w)^{-\frac{1}{2}}$. Its amplitude, the maximum deviation from the point of equilibrium, is $|x_0|$.

Variations of the above problem are obtainable by altering the boundary conditions as in the example below. Note also that the method of solution may be varied a little, replacing (7) by

(10) $$x = c_3 \sin (\beta t + c_4),$$

or by

(11) $$x = c_5 \cos (\beta t + c_6).$$

Equations (10) and (11) have the advantage that each exhibits the amplitude explicitly, as is indicated in the exercises below.

Example. A spring is such that it would be stretched 3 in. by a 6-lb. weight. Let a 12-lb. weight B be attached to the spring and pulled down 4 in. below the equilibrium point. If B is started with an upward velocity of 2 ft. per sec., describe the motion of B.

First we determine the spring constant by using the fact that when $f = 6$ (lb.), $s = \frac{3}{12} = \frac{1}{4}$ (ft.). Thus $6 = \frac{1}{4}k$, so that $k = 24$ (lb. per ft.).

With the notation of this section the problem to be solved may be expressed by

(12) $$\frac{12}{32}\frac{d^2x}{dt^2} + 24x = 0$$

together with the conditions

(13) when $t = 0$, $x = \frac{1}{3}$ and $v = -2$.

Note that the upward velocity (decreasing x) is negative and that the initial value of x must be expressed in feet to be consistent with our use of $g = 32$ (ft. per sec. per sec.).

From (12) we get

$$\frac{d^2x}{dt^2} + 64x = 0$$

so that

$$x = c_1 \cos 8t + c_2 \sin 8t.$$

Then
$$v = -8c_1 \sin 8t + 8c_2 \cos 8t.$$

Hence the conditions on x and v at $t = 0$ lead us to the values $c_1 = \frac{1}{3}$ and $c_2 = -\frac{1}{4}$. Therefore the desired solution is

(14)
$$x = \tfrac{1}{3} \cos 8t - \tfrac{1}{4} \sin 8t.$$

See also Ex. 1 below.

A detailed discussion of the motion is straightforward once (14) has been obtained. In particular it can be shown that the amplitude of the motion is $A = \frac{5}{12}$ (ft.); i.e., B oscillates between points 5 in. above and below E. The period is $\pi/4$ (sec.).

380. *Damped Vibrations*

The vibration of a spring with a suspended weight is usually retarded by damping forces, of which air resistance is an example. It has been shown by experiment that in many instances such retarding forces are fairly well approximated by a term proportional to the velocity. This retarding force will act upward when B is moving downward ($v > 0$) and downward when B is moving upward ($v < 0$). It has a sign opposite to the sign of v.

Thus, with such a resisting medium taken into consideration, the resultant force F of § 379 must be replaced by

(1)
$$F = -kx - bv,$$

where b is a positive constant determined experimentally.

Since
$$F = \frac{w}{g} \frac{d^2x}{dt^2},$$

the differential equation of motion under our present assumptions is

(2)
$$\frac{w}{g} \frac{d^2x}{dt^2} + b \frac{dx}{dt} + kx = 0.$$

In equation (2) put $\beta^2 = kg/w$ and $2\alpha = bg/w$ in order to simplify the writing. Then (2) becomes

(3)
$$\frac{d^2x}{dt^2} + 2\alpha \frac{dx}{dt} + \beta^2 x = 0,$$

which has the auxiliary equation

$$m^2 + 2\alpha m + \beta^2 = 0,$$

with roots $m = -\alpha \pm \sqrt{\alpha^2 - \beta^2}$. Often α is small compared with β. Let us assume $\alpha < \beta$ and put $\beta^2 - \alpha^2 = \gamma^2$ so that we have

$$m = -\alpha \pm i\gamma.$$

Then the general solution of (3) is

(4)
$$x = e^{-\alpha t}(c_1 \cos \gamma t + c_2 \sin \gamma t)$$

and the arbitrary constants c_1 and c_2 are available for the satisfaction of boundary conditions similar to those of § 379. The factor $e^{-\alpha t}$ is called the *damping factor*. Since $\alpha > 0$, the damping factor approaches zero as $t \to \infty$.

Example. Solve the problem of the example of § 379 with an added damping force of magnitude $0.6|v|$. Such a damping force can be realized by immersing the weight B in a thick liquid.

The problem consists in solving the differential equation

(5)
$$\frac{12}{32} \frac{d^2x}{dt^2} + 0.6 \frac{dx}{dt} + 24x = 0$$

together with the conditions

(6)
$$\text{when } t = 0, \ x = \tfrac{1}{3} \quad \text{and} \quad v = -2.$$

For (5), the auxiliary equation is

$$m^2 + 1.6m + 64 = 0,$$

so that $m = -0.80 \pm 8.0i$, in which only two significant figures are retained because of the rough nature of the data and the value of g used. Then

$$x = e^{-0.8t}(c_1 \cos 8t + c_2 \sin 8t),$$
$$v = e^{-0.8t}[(8c_2 - 0.8c_1) \cos 8t - (8c_1 + 0.8c_2) \sin 8t].$$

Because of the conditions (6) we get

$$\tfrac{1}{3} = c_1, \qquad -2 = 8c_2 - 0.8c_1.$$

Then $c_1 = 0.33$ and $c_2 = -0.22$.

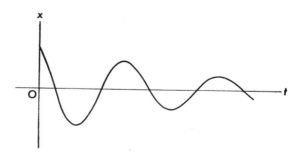

Figure 361

The desired solution is

(7)
$$x = e^{-0.8t}(0.33 \cos 8t - 0.22 \sin 8t),$$

a portion of its graph being shown in Figure 361.

EXERCISES

In these exercises the notations and approximations (including $g = 32$ ft. per sec. per sec.) of the text are used.

1. Show that the solution (14) of § 379 can be put in the form

$$x = A \cos (8t + \varphi)$$

and that $A = \frac{5}{12}$(ft.) and $\varphi = $ Arctan $\frac{3}{4}$.

In Exs. 2–14 no damping force is present.

2. A spring is such that an 8-lb. weight would stretch it 6 in. Let a 4-lb. weight be attached to the spring, pushed up 2 in. above its equilibrium point, and then released. Describe the motion.   *Ans.* $x = -\frac{1}{6} \cos 11.3t$.

3. If the 4-lb. weight of Ex. 2 starts at the same point, 2 in. above E, but with an upward velocity of 15 ft. per sec., when will the weight reach its lowest point?
          Ans. At $t = 0.4$ sec., approximately.

4. A spring is such that it is stretched 4 in. by a 10-lb. weight. Suppose the 10-lb. weight to be pulled down 5 in. below E and then given a downward velocity of 15 ft. per sec. Describe the motion.

$$\text{Ans. } x = 0.42 \cos 9.8t + 1.53 \sin 9.8t$$
$$= 1.59 \cos (9.8t - \varphi), \text{ where } \varphi = \text{Arctan } 3.64.$$

5. A spring is such that a 5-lb. weight stretches it 6 in. The 5-lb. weight is attached, the spring reaches equilibrium, then the weight is pulled down 3 in. below the equilibrium point and started off with an upward velocity of 6 ft. per sec. Find an equation giving the position of the weight at all subsequent times.
          Ans. $x = \frac{1}{4}(\cos 8t - 3 \sin 8t)$.

6. A spring is such that it is stretched 4 in. by an 8-lb. weight. Suppose the weight to be pulled down 6 in. below E and then given an upward velocity of 8 ft. per sec. Describe the motion.   *Ans.* $x = 0.50 \cos 9.8t - 0.82 \sin 9.8t$.

7. Show that the answer to Ex. 6 can be written $x = 0.96 \cos (9.8t + \varphi)$, where $\varphi = $ Arctan 1.64.

8. A spring is stretched 1.5 in. by a 2-lb. weight. Let the weight be pushed up 3 in. above E and then released. Describe the motion.   *Ans.* $x = -\frac{1}{4} \cos 16t$.

9. For the spring and weight of Ex. 8 let the weight be pulled down 4 in. below E and given a downward initial velocity of 8 ft. per sec. Describe the motion.
          Ans. $x = \frac{1}{3} \cos 16t + \frac{1}{2} \sin 16t$.

10. Show that the answer to Ex. 9 can be written $x = 0.60 \sin (16t + \varphi)$ where $\varphi = $ Arctan $\frac{2}{3}$.

11. A spring is stretched 3 in. by a 5-lb. weight. Let the weight be started from E with an upward velocity of 12 ft. per sec. Describe the motion.
          Ans. $x = -1.06 \sin 11.3t$.

12. For the spring and weight of Ex. 11, let the weight be pulled down 4 in. below E and then given an upward velocity of 8 ft. per sec. Describe the motion.
          Ans. $x = 0.33 \cos 11.3t - 0.71 \sin 11.3t$.

13. Find the amplitude of the motion in Ex. 12.   *Ans.* 0.78 ft.

14. A 20-lb. weight stretches a certain spring 10 in. Let the spring first be compressed 4 in., and then the 20-lb. weight attached and given an initial downward velocity of 8 ft. per sec. Find how far the weight would drop.   *Ans.* 35 in.

15. For the example of § 380 find the time and position of the first stop in the motion.   *Ans.* $t = 0.3$ sec., $x = -0.3$ ft.

16. For the example of § 380 find the time in which the damping factor $e^{-0.8t}$ drops to one-tenth of its initial value.   *Ans.* 2.9 sec.

17. Put (7) of § 380 into the form $x = Ae^{-0.8t} \cos (8t + \varphi)$.
    Ans. $A = 0.40$, $\varphi = $ Arctan (0.67).

18. A spring is such that a 4-lb. weight stretches it 0.64 ft. The 4-lb. weight is pushed up $\frac{1}{3}$ ft. above the point of equilibrium and then started with a downward velocity of 5 ft. per sec. The motion takes place in a medium which furnishes a damping force of magnitude $\frac{1}{4}|v|$ at all times. Find the equation describing the position of the weight at time t.   *Ans.* $x = \frac{1}{3}e^{-t}(2 \sin 7t - \cos 7t)$.

19. A spring is such that a 4-lb. weight stretches it 0.32 ft. The weight is attached to the spring and moves in a medium which furnishes a damping force of magnitude $\frac{3}{2}|v|$. The weight is drawn down $\frac{1}{2}$ ft. below the equilibrium point and given an initial upward velocity of 4 ft. per sec. Find the position of the weight thereafter.   *Ans.* $x = \frac{1}{8}e^{-6t}(4 \cos 8t - \sin 8t)$.

20. A spring is such that a 4-lb. weight stretches the spring 0.4 ft. The 4-lb. weight is attached to the spring (suspended from a fixed support), and the system is allowed to reach equilibrium. Then the weight is started from equilibrium position with an imparted upward velocity of 2 ft. per sec. Assume that the motion takes place in a medium which furnishes a retarding force of magnitude numerically equal to the speed, in feet per second, of the moving weight. Determine the position of the weight as a function of time.   *Ans.* $x = -\frac{1}{4}e^{-4t} \sin 8t$.

21. A spring is stretched 6 in. by a 3-lb. weight. The 3-lb. weight is attached to the spring and then started from equilibrium with an imparted upward velocity of 12 ft. per sec. Air resistance furnishes a retarding force equal in magnitude to $0.03|v|$. Find the equation of motion.   *Ans.* $x = -1.5e^{-0.16t} \sin 8t$.

22. A spring is stretched 10 in. by a 4-lb. weight. The weight is started 6 in. below the equilibrum point with an upward velocity of 8 ft. per sec. If a resisting medium furnishes a retarding force of magnitude $\frac{1}{4}|v|$, describe the motion.
    Ans. $x = e^{-t}[0.50 \cos 6.1t - 1.23 \sin 6.1t]$.

23. For Ex. 22 find the times of the first three stops and the position (to the nearest inch) of the weight at each stop.
    Ans. $t_1 = 0.3$ sec., $x_1 = -12$ in.; $t_2 = 0.8$ sec.,
    $x_2 = +6$ in.; $t_3 = 1.3$ sec., $x_3 = -4$ in.

24. A spring is stretched 4 in. by a 2-lb. weight. The 2-lb. weight is started from the equilibrium point with a downward velocity of 12 ft. per sec. If air resistance furnishes a retarding force of magnitude 0.02 of the velocity, describe the motion.   *Ans.* $x = 1.22e^{-0.16t} \sin 9.8t$.

25. For Ex. 24 find how long it takes the damping factor to drop to one-tenth its initial value.   *Ans.* 14.4 sec.

26. For Ex. 24 find the position of the weight: (a) at the first stop; (b) at the second stop.   *Ans.* (a) $x = 1.2$ ft.; (b) $x = -1.1$ ft.

27. Determine the constants c_1 and c_2 so that

(4) $$x = e^{-\alpha t}(c_1 \cos \gamma t + c_2 \sin \gamma t)$$

will satisfy the conditions that when $t = 0$, $x = x_0$ and $v = v_0$.
    Ans. $x = \gamma^{-1}e^{-\alpha t}[\gamma x_0 \cos \gamma t + (v_0 + \alpha x_0) \sin \gamma t]$.

381. *Critical Damping*

The problem in damped vibrations which was studied in § 380 was reduced to the problem of solving the equation

(1) $$\frac{d^2x}{dt^2} + 2\alpha \frac{dx}{dt} + \beta^2 x = 0$$

together with certain initial conditions.

The auxiliary equation for (1) is

$$m^2 + 2\alpha m + \beta^2 = 0$$

and it has the roots

(2) $$m = -\alpha \pm \sqrt{\alpha^2 - \beta^2}.$$

The general solution of equation (1) will assume various forms according to whether the two values of m:

(a) Involve imaginaries,
(b) Are equal, or
(c) Are real and distinct.

When $\alpha < \beta$, the roots of the auxiliary equation are imaginary and the solution of equation (1) takes the form

(3) $$x = e^{-\alpha t}(c_1 \cos \gamma t + c_2 \sin \gamma t),$$

or

$$x = Ae^{-\alpha t} \cos (\gamma t + \varphi),$$

in which

$$\gamma^2 = \beta^2 - \alpha^2.$$

The motion described by equation (3) is a damped oscillatory motion.

When $\alpha = \beta$, the values of m are real and equal, and the solution of equation (1) assumes the form

(4) $$x = (c_3 + c_4 t)e^{-\alpha t}.$$

The motion described by (4) is not oscillatory; it is called *critically damped* motion.

When $\alpha > \beta$, the roots of the auxiliary equation are real and distinct. Then the solution of equation (1) becomes

(5) $$x = e^{-\alpha t}(c_5 e^{\delta t} + c_6 e^{-\delta t})$$

in which $\delta^2 = \alpha^2 - \beta^2$. The motion described by equation (5) is often called *overdamped* motion; the parameter α is larger than it needs to be in order to remove the oscillations.

In Figure 362 there is a representative graph of each type of motion mentioned above, a damped oscillatory motion, a critically damped one, and an overdamped one.

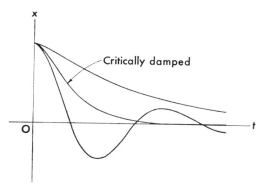

Figure 362

382. *Forced Vibrations*

Suppose next that a spring is supported as in the preceding section but that an additional vertical force is acting upon the weight attached to the spring. The additional force may, for example, be due to the presence of a magnetic field, to motion of the support, etc. The new, impressed force will depend upon time, and we may use $f(t)$ to represent the acceleration which it alone would impart to the weight B. Then the impressed force is $\dfrac{w}{g} f(t)$ and the differential equation, with damping taken into consideration, is

(1)
$$\frac{w}{g} \frac{d^2x}{dt^2} + b \frac{dx}{dt} + kx = \frac{w}{g} f(t)$$

or

(2)
$$\frac{d^2x}{dt^2} + 2\alpha \frac{dx}{dt} + \beta^2 x = f(t),$$

where again $2\alpha = bg/w$ and $\beta^2 = kg/w$.

For $f(t)$ the particular choices $f(t) = A \sin \omega t$, $f(t) = A \cos \omega t$,

$$f(t) = A_1 \cos \omega t + A_2 \sin \omega t,$$

or $f(t) = A \sin (\omega t + \sigma)$, in which A, ω, A_1, A_2, σ are constants, are of special interest in practical work. The fourth of these forms for $f(t)$ includes the others.

It will be seen in the next section that in undamped motion $(b = 0)$, the case $\omega = \beta$ is of particular interest and importance. That case will be avoided in this section.

Example. A spring is such that a 6-lb. weight stretches the spring 2 in. There is no appreciable damping present, but the spring and weight are subject to an impressed force such that the equation of motion is

(3) $$\frac{6}{32}\frac{d^2x}{dt^2} + 36x = -4.60 \sin 4t.$$

The weight B is pulled down 3 in. below the equilibrium point and then released. Describe the motion.

The problem is that of solving

(4) $$\frac{d^2x}{dt^2} + 192x = -24.5 \sin 4t$$

with the conditions

(5) $$\text{when } t = 0,\ x = 0.25 \quad \text{and} \quad v = 0.$$

The general solution of (4) is easily found to be

(6) $$x = c_1 \cos 13.9t + c_2 \sin 13.9t - 0.14 \sin 4t.$$

Then

(7) $$v = 13.9(-c_1 \sin 13.9t + c_2 \cos 13.9t) - 0.56 \cos 4t.$$

Thus the conditions (5) lead to the equations

$$0.25 = c_1$$
$$0 = 13.9c_2 - 0.56,$$

so that $c_1 = 0.25$ and $c_2 = 0.04$.

Therefore the motion under consideration is described by the relation

(8) $$x = 0.25 \cos 13.9t + 0.04 \sin 13.9t - 0.14 \sin 4t.$$

383. *Resonance*

In the undamped forced vibrations of a spring, equations of the type

(1) $$\frac{d^2x}{dt^2} + \beta^2 x = A \sin \omega t$$

can arise, as was seen in § 382. For equation (1) the roots of the auxiliary equation $m^2 + \beta^2 = 0$ are $m = \pm i\beta$. The right member of (1) is a solution of an equation whose auxiliary equation has roots $m' = \pm i\omega$. Therefore, by using the method of undetermined coefficients as in Chapter 46, we can conclude that if $\omega^2 \neq \beta^2$, then (1) has a particular solution of the form

(2) $$x_p = a_1 \sin \omega t.$$

On the other hand, if $\omega^2 = \beta^2$, then equation (1) has no particular solution of the form (2), but it does have a particular solution of the form

(3) $$x_p = b_1 t \cos \beta t.$$

Thus, if $\omega^2 \neq \beta^2$, equation (1) has the general solution

(4) $$x = c_1 \cos \beta t + c_2 \sin \beta t + Aq \sin \omega t$$

where $q = 1/(\beta^2 - \omega^2)$. An important property of the solution (4) is that the numerical value of x is bounded. Indeed, since $|\sin y| \leq 1$ and $|\cos y| \leq 1$, it follows that $|x| \leq |c_1| + |c_2| + |Aq|$. Thus there is a limit to the amplitude of the vibrations.

If $\omega = \beta$, then equation (1) has the general solution

(5) $$x = c_1 \cos \beta t + c_2 \sin \beta t - \frac{A}{2\beta} t \cos \beta t.$$

In (5) the terms $c_1 \cos \beta t$ and $c_2 \sin \beta t$ are bounded, but the term $\frac{1}{2}(A/\beta)t \cos \beta t$ is unbounded because of the factor t. When $\omega = \beta$ the resulting physical phenomenon (the building up of large amplitudes in the vibration) is called *resonance*.

In actual practice, of course, the amplitude does not exceed all bounds. The elastic limit will be reached and the spring will break unless before that happens, the weight meets with outside interference such as a floor.

EXERCISES

1. A certain straight-line motion is determined by the differential equation

$$\frac{d^2x}{dt^2} + 2\alpha \frac{dx}{dt} + 169x = 0$$

and the conditions that when $t = 0$, $x = 0$ and $v = 8$ ft. per sec.

(a) Find the value of α which leads to critical damping, determine x in terms of t, and draw the graph for $0 \leq t \leq 0.2$. $Ans.$ $\alpha = 13(1/\text{sec.})$, $x = 8te^{-13t}$.

(b) Use $\alpha = 12$. Find x in terms of t and draw the graph.
$Ans.$ $x = 1.6e^{-12t} \sin 5t$.

(c) Use $\alpha = 14$. Find x in terms of t and draw the graph.
$Ans.$ $x = 0.77(e^{-8.8t} - e^{-19.2t})$.

2. A spring is such that a 4-lb. weight stretches it 6 in. There is no appreciable damping present, but an impressed force $\frac{1}{2} \cos 8t$ is acting on the spring. If the 4-lb. weight is started from the equilibrium point with an imparted upward velocity of 4 ft. per sec., determine the position of the weight as a function of time.
$Ans.$ $x = \frac{1}{4}(t - 2) \sin 8t$.

3. A spring is such that a 2-lb. weight stretches it $\frac{1}{2}$ ft. An impressed force $\frac{1}{4} \sin 8t$ and a damping force of magnitude $|v|$ are both acting on the spring. The weight starts $\frac{1}{4}$ ft. below the equilibrium point with an imparted upward velocity of 3 ft. per sec. Find a formula for the position of the weight at time t.
$Ans.$ $x = \frac{3}{32}e^{-8t}(3 - 8t) - \frac{1}{32} \cos 8t$.

4. A spring is such that a 16-lb. weight stretches it 1.5 in. The weight is pulled down to a point 4 in. below the equilibrium point and given an initial downward velocity of 4 ft. per sec. There is no damping force present, but there is an

impressed force of 360 cos 4t lb.   Find the position and velocity of the weight at
time $t = \pi/8$ seconds.

$$Ans. \ At \ t = \frac{\pi}{8} \ (sec.), \ x = -\frac{8}{3} \ (ft.), \ v = -8 \ (ft. \ per \ sec.).$$

5. A spring is such that a 4-lb. weight stretches it 6 in.   The 4-lb. weight is
attached to the vertical spring and reaches its equilibrium point.   The weight is
then ($t = 0$) drawn downward 3 in. and released.   No damping force is present, but
there is a simple harmonic exterior force equal to sin 8t impressed upon the whole
system.   Find the time for each of the first four stops following $t = 0$.   Put the
stops in chronological order.

$$Ans. \ t = \frac{\pi}{8}, \frac{1}{2}, \frac{\pi}{4}, \frac{3\pi}{8} \ (sec.).$$

6. A spring is such that a 2-lb. weight stretches it 6 in.   There is a damping
force present, with magnitude the same as the magnitude of the velocity.   An
impressed force (2 sin 8t) is acting on the spring.   If, at $t = 0$, the weight is released
from a point 3 in. below the equilibrium point, find its position for $t > 0$.

$$Ans. \ x = (\tfrac{1}{2} + 4t)e^{-8t} - \tfrac{1}{4} \cos 8t.$$

7. In the example of § 382 change the conditions by imparting to the weight an
initial downward velocity of 4 ft. per sec.

$$Ans. \ x = 0.25 \cos 13.9t + 0.33 \sin 13.9t - 0.14 \sin 4t.$$

8. Show that the solution to Ex. 7 can be put in the form

$$x = 0.41 \cos (13.9t - \varphi) - 0.14 \sin 4t,$$

where $\varphi = $ Arctan (1.32).   In this form the first term is called the *natural* component, and the second term the *forced* component, of the motion.

9. A spring is such that it is stretched 6 in. by a 12-lb. weight (the spring of the
example in § 379).   The 12-lb. weight is pulled down 3 in. below the equilibrium
point and then released.   If no damping is present but there is an impressed force
of magnitude 9 sin 4t lb., describe the motion.   Assume that the impressed force
acts downward for very small t. $Ans. \ x = \tfrac{1}{4} \cos 8t - \tfrac{1}{4} \sin 8t + \tfrac{1}{2} \sin 4t.$

10. Show that the answer to Ex. 9 can be written

$$x = \frac{1}{4} \sqrt{2} \cos \left(8t + \frac{\pi}{4} \right) + \frac{1}{2} \sin 4t.$$

11. Alter Ex. 9 by inserting a damping force of magnitude one-half that of the
velocity and then determine x.

$$Ans. \ x = e^{-\frac{2t}{3}} (0.30 \cos 8.0t - 0.22 \sin 8.0t) - 0.05 \cos 4t + 0.49 \sin 4t.$$

12. A spring is such that a 2-lb. weight stretches it $\tfrac{1}{2}$ ft.   An impressed force
$\tfrac{1}{4}$ sin 8t is acting upon the spring.   If the 2-lb. weight is released from a point 3 in.
below the equilibrium point, determine the equation of motion.

$$Ans. \ x = \tfrac{1}{4}(1 - t) \cos 8t + \tfrac{1}{32} \sin 8t \ (ft.).$$

13. For the motion of Ex. 12 find the first four times at which stops occur and
find the position at each stop.

$Ans. \ t = \dfrac{\pi}{8}, \dfrac{\pi}{4}, 1, \dfrac{3\pi}{8}$ (sec.) and $x = -0.15, +0.05, +0.03, +0.04$ (ft.), respectively.

14. Determine the position to be expected, if nothing such as breakage interferes, at the time of the sixty-fifth stop, when $t = 8\pi$ (sec.), in Ex. 12.

15. Let the motion of Ex. 12 be retarded by a damping force of magnitude $0.6|v|$. Find the equation of motion.

Ans. $x = 0.30e^{-4.8t} \cos 6.4t + 0.22e^{-4.8t} \sin 6.4t - 0.05 \cos 8t$ (ft.).

16. Show that (to the nearest 0.01 ft.) whenever $t > 1$ (sec.), the solution of Ex. 15 may be replaced by $x = -0.05 \cos 8t$.

17. Let the motion of Ex. 12 be retarded by a damping force of magnitude $|v|$. Find the equation of motion and also determine its form (to the nearest 0.01 ft.) for $t > 1$ (sec.).

Ans. $x = \frac{9}{32}(8t + 1)e^{-8t} - \frac{1}{32} \cos 8t$ (ft.); for $t > 1$, $x = -\frac{1}{32} \cos 8t$.

18. Let the motion of Ex. 12 be retarded by a damping force of magnitude $\frac{5}{3}|v|$. Find the equation of motion.   *Ans.* $x = 0.30e^{-\frac{8}{3}t} - 0.03e^{-24t} - 0.02 \cos 8t$.

384. *The Simple Pendulum*

Figure 363

A rod of length L ft. is suspended by one end so that it can swing freely in a vertical plane. Let a weight B (the bob) of w lb. be attached to the free end of the rod, and let the weight of the rod be negligible compared with the weight of the bob.

Let θ (radians) be the angular displacement from the vertical, as shown in Figure 363, of the rod at time t (sec.). The tangential component of the force w (lb.) is $w \sin \theta$, and it tends to decrease θ. Then, neglecting the weight of the rod and using $s = L\theta$ as a measure of arc length from the vertical position, we may conclude that

$$(1) \qquad \frac{w}{g} \frac{d^2s}{dt^2} = -w \sin \theta.$$

Since $s = L\theta$ and L is constant, (1) becomes

$$(2) \qquad \frac{d^2\theta}{dt^2} + \frac{g}{L} \sin \theta = 0.$$

The solution of equation (2) is not elementary; it involves an elliptic integral. If θ is small, however, $\sin \theta$ and θ are nearly equal and (2) is closely approximated by the much simpler equation

$$(3) \qquad \frac{d^2\theta}{dt^2} + \beta^2\theta = 0; \qquad \beta^2 = \frac{g}{L}.$$

The solution of (3) with pertinent boundary conditions gives usable results whenever those conditions are such that θ remains small, say, $|\theta| < 0.3$ (radians). Recall also that in the derivation, it was assumed that the effect of the weight of the rod is negligible compared with that of the weight of the bob.

EXERCISES

1. A clock has a 6-in. pendulum. The clock ticks once for each time that the pendulum completes a swing, returning to its original position. How many times does the clock tick in 30 sec.?   *Ans.* 38 times.

2. A 6-in. pendulum is released from rest at an angle one-tenth of a radian from the vertical. Using $g = 32$ (ft. per sec. per sec.), describe the motion.

$$Ans. \ \theta = 0.1 \cos 8t \ \text{(radians)}.$$

3. For the pendulum of Ex. 2 find the maximum angular speed and its first time of occurrence.   *Ans.* 0.8 (radians per sec.) at 0.2 sec.

4. A 6-in. pendulum is started with a velocity of 1 radian per sec., toward the vertical, from a position one-tenth radian from the vertical. Describe the motion.

$$Ans. \ \theta = \tfrac{1}{10} \cos 8t - \tfrac{1}{8} \sin 8t \ \text{(radians)}.$$

5. For Ex. 4 find to the nearest degree the maximum angular displacement from the vertical.   *Ans.* 9°.

6. Interpret as a pendulum problem and solve the boundary value problem:

(A) $$\frac{d^2\theta}{dt^2} + \beta^2 \theta = 0; \qquad \beta^2 = \frac{g}{L},$$

(B) $$\text{when } t = 0, \ \theta = \theta_0 \quad \text{and} \quad \omega = \frac{d\theta}{dt} = \omega_0.$$

$$Ans. \ \theta = \theta_0 \cos \beta t + \beta^{-1}\omega_0 \sin \beta t \ \text{(radians)}.$$

7. Find the maximum angular displacement from the vertical for the pendulum of Ex. 6. $Ans. \ \theta_{\max} = (\theta_0{}^2 + \beta^{-2}\omega_0{}^2)^{\frac{1}{2}}.$

385. *Electric Circuits*

The basic laws which govern the flow of electric current in a circuit or a network will be given here without derivation. The notation used is common to most texts in electrical engineering; it is:

t (seconds) = time
q (coulombs) = quantity of electricity; e.g., charge on a capacitor
i (amperes) = current, time rate of flow of electricity
e (volts) = electromotive force or voltage
R (ohms) = resistance
L (henrys) = inductance
C (farads) = capacitance.

By the definition of q and i it follows that $i = \dfrac{dq}{dt}$.

The current at each point in a network may be determined by solving the equations which result from applying Kirchhoff's laws:

(a) *The sum of the currents into (or away from) any point is zero,*

(b) *Around any closed path the sum of the instantaneous voltage drops in a specified direction is zero.*

A circuit is treated as a network containing only one closed path.   Figure 364 exhibits an "*RLC* circuit" with some of the customary conventions for indicating various elements.

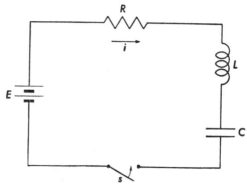

Figure 364

For a circuit, Kirchhoff's current law (*a*) indicates merely that the current is the same throughout.   That law plays a larger role in networks.

In order to apply Kirchhoff's voltage law (*b*), it is necessary to have the contributions of each of the idealized elements in Figure 364.   The *voltage drop* across the resistance is Ri, that across the inductance is $L\dfrac{di}{dt}$, while the capacitor contributes $\dfrac{1}{C}q$.   The impressed electromotive force e ($e = E$, assumed constant in Figure 364) is contributing a *voltage rise*.

Assume that at time $t = 0$ the switch s shown in Figure 364 is to be closed. If the capacitor is initially without charge, then $q = 0$ at $t = 0$, while $i = 0$ at $t = 0$, since the circuit was not closed until $t = 0$.   From Kirchhoff's law (*b*) we get the differential equation

(1)
$$ L\frac{di}{dt} + Ri + \frac{1}{C}q - E = 0, $$

in which

(2)
$$ i = \frac{dq}{dt}. $$

Equations (1) and (2) together with the initial conditions,

(3)   when $t = 0$, $q = 0$ and $i = 0$

constitute the mathematical problem to be solved in connection with Figure 364.   This problem is equivalent to one in damped vibrations.   Indeed, the analogies between electrical and mechanical systems are quite useful in practice.

Example. Consider a circuit with the schematic diagram shown in Figure 365. Here the impressed electromotive force is alternating. It is assumed that the switch s is closed at an instant ($t = 0$) when the applied voltage $E \sin \omega t$ is zero.

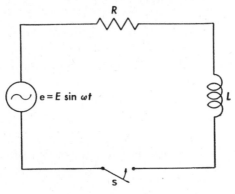

Figure 365

From Kirchhoff's voltage law it follows that, for $t > 0$,

(1) $$L \frac{di}{dt} + Ri = E \sin \omega t,$$

while

(2) $$\text{when } t = 0, \, i = 0.$$

Since L, R, E, and ω are constants, equation (1) may be integrated easily by methods developed earlier in this book. The general solution of (1) is

(3) $$i = a_1 e^{-\frac{Rt}{L}} + \frac{E}{Z^2} (R \sin \omega t - \omega L \cos \omega t),$$

where a_1 is an arbitrary constant and where

$$Z = (R^2 + \omega^2 L^2)^{\frac{1}{2}}.$$

The quantity Z is called the *steady-state impedance* of the circuit.

Since the i of equation (3) is to satisfy (2), it can be seen that $a_1 = E\omega L/Z^2$. Therefore the current in the circuit of Figure 365 is given by

(4) $$i = \frac{E}{Z^2} (R \sin \omega t - \omega L \cos \omega t + \omega L e^{-\frac{Rt}{L}}).$$

For sufficiently large t the last term on the right in (4) is negligible, while the first two terms do not change character with large t. Indeed, the current i may be split into two parts

(5) $$i = i_t + i_s,$$

where

(6) $$i_t = \frac{E\omega L}{Z^2} e^{-\frac{Rt}{L}}$$

is called the *transient current* and

(7) $$i_s = \frac{E}{Z^2} (R \sin \omega t - \omega L \cos \omega t)$$

is called the *steady-state current*. Equation (7) can also be put in the form

$$i_s = \frac{E}{Z} \sin (\omega t - \epsilon),$$

where $\epsilon = $ Arctan $(\omega L/R)$.

It is of interest to know the maximum steady-state current, which is easily found to be

(8) $$\max (i_s) = \frac{E}{Z^2} \sqrt{R^2 + \omega^2 L^2} = \frac{E}{Z}.$$

EXERCISES

1. Return to the example of this section, but assume that the switch is closed when the impressed electromotive force is at its maximum. That is, use Figure 365, page 689, with the replacement $e = E \cos \omega t$ and close the switch at $t = 0$ again, assuming that $i = 0$ when $t = 0$. Find i, i_t, i_s, and $\max (i_s)$.

Ans. $i = \dfrac{E}{Z^2} (\omega L \sin \omega t + R \cos \omega t - Re^{-\frac{Rt}{L}})$; $i_t = -\dfrac{ER}{Z^2} e^{-\frac{Rt}{L}}$;

$i_s = EZ^{-2}(\omega L \sin \omega t + R \cos \omega t)$; $\max (i_s) = \dfrac{E}{Z}.$

2. In the *RL* circuit of Figure 365, page 689, replace the alternating-current element with a direct-current element E. Assume that the switch s is closed at $t = 0$ and that $i = 0$ when $t = 0$. Determine the current i and note its steady-state and transient terms.

Ans. $i = \dfrac{E}{R} (1 - e^{-\frac{Rt}{L}})$; $i_s = \dfrac{E}{R}$; $i_t = -\dfrac{E}{R} e^{-\frac{Rt}{L}}.$

3. Figure 366 shows an *RC* circuit with an alternating-current element inserted. Assume that the switch is closed at $t = 0$, at which time $q = 0$ and $i = 0$. Use the notation $Z^2 = R^2 + (\omega C)^{-2}$, where Z is the steady-state impedance of this circuit. Find i for $t > 0$.

Ans. $i = EZ^{-2}[R \sin \omega t + (\omega C)^{-1} \cos \omega t - (\omega C)^{-1} e^{-\frac{t}{RC}}].$

4. In Figure 366 replace the alternating-current element with a direct-current element $E = 50$ volts and use $R = 10$ ohms, $C = 4(10)^{-4}$ farad. Assume that when the switch s is closed (at $t = 0$), the charge on the capacitor is 0.015 coulomb. Find the initial current in the circuit and the current for $t > 0$.

Ans. $i_0 = 1.25$ (amp.), $i = 1.25e^{-250t}.$

5. In Figure 366 replace $E \sin \omega t$ with $110 \cos 377t$ and use $R = 12$ ohms, $C = 3(10)^{-4}$ farad. Show that the impressed voltage $110 \cos 377t$ is ordinary 60-cycle alternating voltage. Assuming that $q = 0$ when $t = 0$, find the current i for $t > 0$.   *Ans.* $i = 5.94 \cos 377t - 4.38 \sin 377t + 3.23e^{-278t}$.

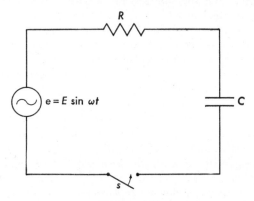

Figure 366

6. Figure 367 shows an RLC circuit with an alternating-current element. Show that the impressed electromotive force $E \sin 377t$ is ordinary 60-cycle alternating voltage. Using the values $E = 110$, $R = 100$, $L = 0.10$, $C = 5(10)^{-5}$, and assuming that when $t = 0$, $q = 0$ and $i = 0$, find the current i for $t > 0$.
        Ans. $i = 1.08 \sin 377t + 0.16 \cos 377t - 1.17e^{-276t} + 1.01e^{-724t}$.

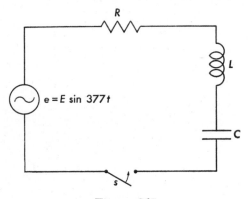

Figure 367

7. In Ex. 6 replace the 100-ohm resistance with a 10-ohm resistance, leaving everything else unchanged. Then compute the current i.
    Ans. $i = 3.28 \sin 377t + 5.03 \cos 377t - 5.03e^{-50t} \cos 444t - 3.34e^{-50t} \sin 444t$.

8. In Ex. 6 replace the 100-ohm resistance with a 40-ohm resistance, and the 0.10-henry inductance with a 0.02-henry inductance, leaving everything else unchanged. Then compute the current i.
        Ans. $i = 1.20 \sin 377t + 1.36 \cos 377t - [1.36 + 1.82(10)^3t]e^{-1000t}$.

9. In Figure 367 replace the electromotive force by $e = E \cos 377t$. Use the values $E = 110$, $R = 100$, $L = 0.10$, $C = 5(10)^{-5}$, as in Ex. 6, and compute q and i for $t > 0$, assuming that when $t = 0$, $q = 0$ and $i = 0$.

$$Ans. \ i = 1.08 \cos 377t - 0.16 \sin 377t + 0.86e^{-276t} - 1.94e^{-724t}.$$

10. In Ex. 9 replace the 100-ohm resistance with a 10-ohm resistance, leaving the rest of the problem unchanged.

$$Ans. \ i = 3.28 \cos 377t - 5.03 \sin 377t - 3.28e^{-50t} \cos 444t + 6.37e^{-50t} \sin 444t.$$

11. In Ex. 9 replace the 100-ohm resistance with a 40-ohm resistance and the 0.10-henry inductance with a 0.02-henry inductance, leaving the rest of the problem unchanged. $Ans. \ i = 1.20 \cos 377t - 1.36 \sin 377t - [1.20 - 4.82(10)^3 t]e^{-1000t}.$

12. In Ex. 9 replace the 0.10-henry inductance with 0.01-henry inductance, leaving the rest of the problem unchanged.

$$Ans. \ i = 0.88 \cos 377t - 0.44 \sin 377t + 0.26e^{-204t} - 1.14e^{-9800t}.$$

13. In Figure 364, page 688, use the values $E = 60$ volts, $R = 8$ ohms, $L = 0.06$ henry, $C = 3(10)^{-4}$ farad, and assume that when $t = 0$, $q = 0$ and $i = 0$. Set up and solve the problem without using the formulas derived in this section. Find the current for $t > 0$. $Ans. \ i = 4.42e^{-66.7t} \sin 226t.$

14. Solve Ex. 13 with the following replacements in the values of the circuit constants: $R = 30$ ohms, $C = 4(10)^{-4}$ farad, (L unchanged).

$$Ans. \ i = 6.95e^{-250t} \sinh (144t).$$

15. Solve Ex. 13 with the following replacements in the values of the circuit constants: $R = 40$ ohms, $L = 0.02$ henry, $C = 5(10)^{-5}$ farad. $Ans. \ i = 3000te^{-1000t}.$

16. In Ex. 15 find the maximum current.

$$Ans. \ i_{max} = \frac{3}{e} \ (amp).$$

TABLES

INDEFINITE INTEGRALS

[In this table, integrals immediately reducible to a standard form (p. 328) are omitted.

1. $\displaystyle\int \frac{x\,dx}{ax+b} = \frac{x}{a} - \frac{b}{a^2}\ln(ax+b) + C.$

2. $\displaystyle\int \frac{x\,dx}{(ax+b)^2} = \frac{b}{a^2(ax+b)} + \frac{1}{a^2}\ln(ax+b) + C.$

3. $\displaystyle\int x(ax+b)^n\,dx = \frac{x(ax+b)^{n+1}}{a(n+1)} - \frac{(ax+b)^{n+2}}{a^2(n+1)(n+2)} + C.$

4. $\displaystyle\int \frac{dx}{x(ax+b)} = \frac{1}{b}\ln\frac{x}{ax+b} + C.$

5. $\displaystyle\int \frac{dx}{x(ax+b)^2} = \frac{1}{b(ax+b)} + \frac{1}{b^2}\ln\frac{x}{ax+b} + C.$

6. $\displaystyle\int \frac{dx}{a^2-x^2} = \frac{1}{2a}\ln\frac{a+x}{a-x} + C.$ (See p. 360.)

7. $\displaystyle\int \frac{dx}{(ax^2+b)^2} = \frac{x}{2b(ax^2+b)} + \frac{1}{2b}\int \frac{dx}{ax^2+b}.$

8. $\displaystyle\int \frac{dx}{x(ax^2+b)} = \frac{1}{2b}\ln\frac{x^2}{ax^2+b} + C.$

9. $\displaystyle\int x\sqrt{ax+b}\,dx = \frac{2x}{3a}(ax+b)^{\frac{3}{2}} - \frac{4}{15a^2}(ax+b)^{\frac{5}{2}} + C.$

10. $\displaystyle\int \frac{x\,dx}{\sqrt{ax+b}} = \frac{2x}{a}(ax+b)^{\frac{1}{2}} - \frac{4}{3a^2}(ax+b)^{\frac{3}{2}} + C.$

11. $\displaystyle\int \sqrt{a^2-x^2}\,dx = \frac{1}{2}x\sqrt{a^2-x^2} + \frac{1}{2}a^2\,\mathrm{Arcsin}\frac{x}{a} + C.$

12. $\displaystyle\int \sqrt{x^2\pm a^2}\,dx = \tfrac{1}{2}x\sqrt{x^2\pm a^2} \pm \tfrac{1}{2}a^2\ln(x+\sqrt{x^2\pm a^2}) + C.$

13. $\displaystyle\int \frac{dx}{\sqrt{x^2\pm a^2}} = \ln(x+\sqrt{x^2\pm a^2}) + C.$

14. $\displaystyle\int \frac{dx}{x\sqrt{a^2\pm x^2}} = \frac{1}{a}\ln\frac{x}{a+\sqrt{a^2\pm x^2}} + C.$

15. $\displaystyle\int \frac{dx}{x\sqrt{x^2-a^2}} = -\frac{1}{a}\,\mathrm{Arcsin}\frac{a}{x} + C.$

16. $\displaystyle\int \frac{\sqrt{a^2\pm x^2}}{x}\,dx = \sqrt{a^2\pm x^2} + a\ln\frac{x}{a+\sqrt{a^2\pm x^2}} + C.$

17. $\displaystyle\int \frac{\sqrt{x^2 - a^2}}{x}\, dx = \sqrt{x^2 - a^2} + a \operatorname{Arcsin} \frac{a}{x} + C.$

18. $\displaystyle\int (a^2 - x^2)^{\frac{3}{2}}\, dx = \frac{1}{4} x(a^2 - x^2)^{\frac{3}{2}} + \frac{3}{8} a^2 x \sqrt{a^2 - x^2} + \frac{3}{8} a^4 \operatorname{Arcsin} \frac{x}{a} + C.$

19. $\displaystyle\int (x^2 \pm a^2)^{\frac{3}{2}}\, dx = \frac{1}{4}x(x^2 \pm a^2)^{\frac{3}{2}} \pm \frac{3}{8}a^2 x \sqrt{x^2 \pm a^2}$

$$+ \tfrac{3}{8}a^4 \ln (x + \sqrt{x^2 \pm a^2}) + C.$$

20. $\displaystyle\int \frac{dx}{(a^2 - x^2)^{\frac{3}{2}}} = \frac{x}{a^2 \sqrt{a^2 - x^2}} + C.$

21. $\displaystyle\int \frac{dx}{(x^2 \pm a^2)^{\frac{3}{2}}} = \frac{\pm x}{a^2 \sqrt{x^2 \pm a^2}} + C.$

22. $\displaystyle\int x^2 \sqrt{a^2 - x^2}\, dx$

$$= -\frac{1}{4} x(a^2 - x^2)^{\frac{3}{2}} + \frac{1}{8} a^2 x \sqrt{a^2 - x^2} + \frac{1}{8} a^4 \operatorname{Arcsin} \frac{x}{a} + C.$$

23. $\displaystyle\int x^3 \sqrt{a^2 - x^2}\, dx = \tfrac{1}{5}(a^2 - x^2)^{\frac{5}{2}} - \tfrac{1}{3}a^2(a^2 - x^2)^{\frac{3}{2}} + C.$

24. $\displaystyle\int x^2 \sqrt{x^2 \pm a^2}\, dx = \tfrac{1}{4}x(x^2 \pm a^2)^{\frac{3}{2}} \mp \tfrac{1}{8}a^2 x \sqrt{x^2 \pm a^2}$

$$- \tfrac{1}{8}a^4 \ln (x + \sqrt{x^2 \pm a^2}) + C.$$

25. $\displaystyle\int \frac{x^2\, dx}{\sqrt{a^2 - x^2}} = -\frac{1}{2} x \sqrt{a^2 - x^2} + \frac{1}{2} a^2 \operatorname{Arcsin} \frac{x}{a} + C.$

26. $\displaystyle\int \frac{x^3\, dx}{\sqrt{a^2 - x^2}} = -x^2 \sqrt{a^2 - x^2} - \frac{2}{3} (a^2 - x^2)^{\frac{3}{2}} + C.$

27. $\displaystyle\int \frac{x^2\, dx}{\sqrt{x^2 \pm a^2}} = \frac{1}{2} x \sqrt{x^2 \pm a^2} \mp \frac{1}{2} a^2 \ln (x + \sqrt{x^2 \pm a^2}) + C.$

28. $\displaystyle\int \frac{dx}{\sqrt{2ax - x^2}} = 2 \operatorname{Arcsin} \sqrt{\frac{x}{2a}} + C.$

29. $\displaystyle\int \frac{x^n\, dx}{\sqrt{2ax - x^2}} = -\frac{x^{n-1} \sqrt{2ax - x^2}}{n} + \frac{a(2n - 1)}{n} \int \frac{x^{n-1}\, dx}{\sqrt{2ax - x^2}}.$

30. $\displaystyle\int \sqrt{2ax - x^2}\, dx = \frac{1}{2} (x - a) \sqrt{2ax - x^2} + \frac{1}{2} a^2 \operatorname{Arcsin} \frac{x - a}{a} + C.$

31. $\displaystyle\int \sin^2 x\, dx = \tfrac{1}{2}x - \tfrac{1}{4} \sin 2x + C.$

32. $\displaystyle\int \cos^2 x\, dx = \tfrac{1}{2}x + \tfrac{1}{4} \sin 2x + C.$

33. $\displaystyle\int \sin^n x\, dx = -\frac{\sin^{n-1} x \cos x}{n} + \frac{n - 1}{n} \int \sin^{n-2} x\, dx.$

34. $\int \cos^n x \, dx = \frac{1}{n} \cos^{n-1} x \sin x + \frac{n-1}{n} \int \cos^{n-2} x \, dx.$

35. $\int \cos^m x \sin^n x \, dx = \frac{\cos^{m-1} x \sin^{n+1} x}{m+n} + \frac{m-1}{m+n} \int \cos^{m-2} x \sin^n x \, dx.$

36. $\int \cos^m x \sin^n x \, dx = -\frac{\sin^{n-1} x \cos^{m+1} x}{m+n} + \frac{n-1}{m+n} \int \cos^m x \sin^{n-2} x \, dx.$

37. $\int \tan x \, dx = -\ln \cos x + C.$

38. $\int \cot x \, dx = \ln \sin x + C.$

39. $\int \tan^2 x \, dx = \tan x - x + C.$

40. $\int \cot^2 x \, dx = -\cot x - x + C.$

41. $\int \tan^n x \, dx = \frac{\tan^{n-1} x}{n-1} - \int \tan^{n-2} x \, dx.$

42. $\int \cot^n x \, dx = -\frac{\cot^{n-1} x}{n-1} - \int \cot^{n-2} x \, dx.$

43. $\int \sec x \, dx = \ln (\sec x + \tan x) + C.$

44. $\int \sec^3 x \, dx = \frac{1}{2} \sec x \tan x + \frac{1}{2} \ln (\sec x + \tan x) + C.$

45. $\int \csc x \, dx = \ln (\csc x - \cot x) + C.$

46. $\int \csc^3 x \, dx = -\frac{1}{2} \csc x \cot x + \frac{1}{2} \ln (\csc x - \cot x) + C.$

47. $\int \sec^n x \, dx = \frac{\tan x \sec^{n-2} x}{n-1} + \frac{n-2}{n-1} \int \sec^{n-2} x \, dx.$

48. $\int \csc^n x \, dx = -\frac{\cot x \csc^{n-2} x}{n-1} + \frac{n-2}{n-1} \int \csc^{n-2} x \, dx.$

49. $\int x \sin x \, dx = \sin x - x \cos x + C.$

50. $\int x \cos x \, dx = \cos x + x \sin x + C.$

51. $\int x^n \sin x \, dx = -x^n \cos x + n \int x^{n-1} \cos x \, dx.$

52. $\int x^n \cos x \, dx = x^n \sin x - n \int x^{n-1} \sin x \, dx.$

53. $\int x \sin^n x \, dx = \frac{\sin^{n-1} x (\sin x - nx \cos x)}{n^2} + \frac{n-1}{n} \int x \sin^{n-2} x \, dx.$

54. $\displaystyle\int x \cos^n x\, dx = \frac{\cos^{n-1} x(\cos x + nx \sin x)}{n^2} + \frac{n-1}{n}\int x \cos^{n-2} x\, dx.$

55. $\displaystyle\int \sin mx \sin nx\, dx = \frac{\sin (m-n)x}{2(m-n)} - \frac{\sin (m+n)x}{2(m+n)} + C.$

56. $\displaystyle\int \sin mx \cos nx\, dx = -\frac{\cos (m-n)x}{2(m-n)} - \frac{\cos (m+n)x}{2(m+n)} + C.$

57. $\displaystyle\int \cos mx \cos nx\, dx = \frac{\sin (m-n)x}{2(m-n)} + \frac{\sin (m+n)x}{2(m+n)} + C.$

58. $\displaystyle\int xe^{ax}\, dx = \frac{e^{ax}}{a^2}(ax - 1) + C.$

59. $\displaystyle\int x^2 e^{ax}\, dx = \frac{e^{ax}}{a^3}(a^2 x^2 - 2ax + 2) + C.$

60. $\displaystyle\int x^n e^{ax}\, dx = \frac{x^n e^{ax}}{a} - \frac{n}{a}\int x^{n-1} e^{ax}\, dx.$

61. $\displaystyle\int e^{ax} \sin mx\, dx = \frac{e^{ax}(a \sin mx - m \cos mx)}{m^2 + a^2} + C.$

62. $\displaystyle\int e^{ax} \cos mx\, dx = \frac{e^{ax}(m \sin mx + a \cos mx)}{m^2 + a^2} + C.$

63. $\displaystyle\int \sinh x\, dx = \cosh x + C.$

64. $\displaystyle\int \cosh x\, dx = \sinh x + C.$

65. $\displaystyle\int \tanh x\, dx = \ln \cosh x + C.$

66. $\displaystyle\int \sinh^2 x\, dx = \tfrac{1}{2} \sinh x \cosh x - \tfrac{1}{2}x + C.$

67. $\displaystyle\int \cosh^2 x\, dx = \tfrac{1}{2} \sinh x \cosh x + \tfrac{1}{2}x + C.$

68. $\displaystyle\int x \sinh x\, dx = x \cosh x - \sinh x + C.$

69. $\displaystyle\int x \cosh x\, dx = x \sinh x - \cosh x + C.$

70. $\displaystyle\int \ln x\, dx = x \ln x - x + C.$

71. $\displaystyle\int x^n \ln x\, dx = x^{n+1}\left[\frac{\ln x}{n+1} - \frac{1}{(n+1)^2}\right] + C.$

72. $\displaystyle\int (\ln x)^n\, dx = x(\ln x)^n - n\int (\ln x)^{n-1}\, dx.$

N	0	1	2	3	4	5	6	7	8	9
0.0		5.395	6.088	6.493	6.781	7.004	7.187	7.341	7.474	7.592
0.1	7.697	7.793	7.880	7.960	8.034	8.103	8.167	8.228	8.285	8.339
0.2	8.391	8.439	8.486	8.530	8.573	8.614	8.653	8.691	8.727	8.762
0.3	8.796	8.829	8.861	8.891	8.921	8.950	8.978	9.006	9.032	9.058
0.4	9.084	9.108	9.132	9.156	9.179	9.201	9.223	9.245	9.266	9.287
0.5	9.307	9.327	9.346	9.365	9.384	9.402	9.420	9.438	9.455	9.472
0.6	9.489	9.506	9.522	9.538	9.554	9.569	9.584	9.600	9.614	9.629
0.7	9.643	9.658	9.671	9.685	9.699	9.712	9.726	9.739	9.752	9.764
0.8	9.777	9.789	9.802	9.814	9.826	9.837	9.849	9.861	9.872	9.883
0.9	9.895	9.906	9.917	9.927	9.938	9.949	9.959	9.970	9.980	9.990
1.0	0.00000	0995	1980	2956	3922	4879	5827	6766	7696	8618
1.1	9531	*0436	*1333	*2222	*3103	*3976	*4842	*5700	*6551	*7395
1.2	0.1 8232	9062	9885	*0701	*1511	*2314	*3111	*3902	*4686	*5464
1.3	0.2 6236	7003	7763	8518	9267	*0010	*0748	*1481	*2208	*2930
1.4	0.3 3647	4359	5066	5767	6464	7156	7844	8526	9204	9878
1.5	0.4 0547	1211	1871	2527	3178	3825	4469	5108	5742	6373
1.6	7000	7623	8243	8858	9470	*0078	*0682	*1282	*1879	*2473
1.7	0.5 3063	3649	4232	4812	5389	5962	6531	7098	7661	8222
1.8	8779	9333	9884	*0432	*0977	*1519	*2058	*2594	*3127	*3658
1.9	0.6 4185	4710	5233	5752	6269	6783	7294	7803	8310	8813
2.0	9315	9813	*0310	*0804	*1295	*1784	*2271	*2755	*3237	*3716
2.1	0.7 4194	4669	5142	5612	6081	6547	7011	7473	7932	8390
2.2	8846	9299	9751	*0200	*0648	*1093	*1536	*1978	*2418	*2855
2.3	0.8 3291	3725	4157	4587	5015	5442	5866	6289	6710	7129
2.4	7547	7963	8377	8789	9200	9609	*0016	*0422	*0826	*1228
2.5	0.9 1629	2028	2426	2822	3216	3609	4001	4391	4779	5166
2.6	5551	5935	6317	6698	7078	7456	7833	8208	8582	8954
2.7	9325	9695	*0063	*0430	*0796	*1160	*1523	*1885	*2245	*2604
2.8	1.0 2962	3318	3674	4028	4380	4732	5082	5431	5779	6126
2.9	6471	6815	7158	7500	7841	8181	8519	8856	9192	9527
3.0	9861	*0194	*0526	*0856	*1186	*1514	*1841	*2168	*2493	*2817
3.1	1.1 3140	3462	3783	4103	4422	4740	5057	5373	5688	6002
3.2	6315	6627	6938	7248	7557	7865	8173	8479	8784	9089
3.3	9392	9695	9996	*0297	*0597	*0896	*1194	*1491	*1788	*2083
3.4	1.2 2378	2671	2964	3256	3547	3837	4127	4415	4703	4990
3.5	5276	5562	5846	6130	6413	6695	6976	7257	7536	7815
3.6	8093	8371	8647	8923	9198	9473	9746	*0019	*0291	*0563
3.7	1.3 0833	1103	1372	1641	1909	2176	2442	2708	2972	3237
3.8	3500	3763	4025	4286	4547	4807	5067	5325	5584	5841
3.9	6098	6354	6609	6864	7118	7372	7624	7877	8128	8379
4.0	8629	8879	9128	9377	9624	9872	*0118	*0364	*0610	*0854
4.1	1.4 1099	1342	1585	1828	2070	2311	2552	2792	3031	3270
4.2	3508	3746	3984	4220	4456	4692	4927	5161	5395	5629
4.3	5862	6094	6326	6557	6787	7018	7247	7476	7705	7933
4.4	8160	8387	8614	8840	9065	9290	9515	9739	9962	*0185
4.5	1.5 0408	0630	0851	1072	1293	1513	1732	1951	2170	2388
4.6	2606	2823	3039	3256	3471	3687	3902	4116	4330	4543
4.7	4756	4969	5181	5393	5604	5814	6025	6235	6444	6653
4.8	6862	7070	7277	7485	7691	7898	8104	8309	8515	8719
4.9	8924	9127	9331	9534	9737	9939	*0141	*0342	*0543	*0744
5.0	1.6 0944	1144	1343	1542	1741	1939	2137	2334	2531	2728
N	0	1	2	3	4	5	6	7	8	9

(Rows 0.1–0.9, column 0: Take tabular value −10)

N	0	1	2	3	4	5	6	7	8	9
5.0	1.6 0944	1144	1343	1542	1741	1939	2137	2334	2531	2728
5.1	2924	3120	3315	3511	3705	3900	4094	4287	4481	4673
5.2	4866	5058	5250	5441	5632	5823	6013	6203	6393	6582
5.3	6771	6959	7147	7335	7523	7710	7896	8083	8269	8455
5.4	8640	8825	9010	9194	9378	9562	9745	9928	*0111	*0293
5.5	1.7 0475	0656	0838	1019	1199	1380	1560	1740	1919	2098
5.6	2277	2455	2633	2811	2988	3166	3342	3519	3695	3871
5.7	4047	4222	4397	4572	4746	4920	5094	5267	5440	5613
5.8	5786	5958	6130	6302	6473	6644	6815	6985	7156	7326
5.9	7495	7665	7834	8002	8171	8339	8507	8675	8842	9009
6.0	9176	9342	9509	9675	9840	*0006	*0171	*0336	*0500	*0665
6.1	1.8 0829	0993	1156	1319	1482	1645	1808	1970	2132	2294
6.2	2455	2616	2777	2938	3098	3258	3418	3578	3737	3896
6.3	4055	4214	4372	4530	4688	4845	5003	5160	5317	5473
6.4	5630	5786	5942	6097	6253	6408	6563	6718	6872	7026
6.5	7180	7334	7487	7641	7794	7947	8099	8251	8403	8555
6.6	8707	8858	9010	9160	9311	9462	9612	9762	9912	*0061
6.7	1.9 0211	0360	0509	0658	0806	0954	1102	1250	1398	1545
6.8	1692	1839	1986	2132	2279	2425	2571	2716	2862	3007
6.9	3152	3297	3442	3586	3730	3874	4018	4162	4305	4448
7.0	4591	4734	4876	5019	5161	5303	5445	5586	5727	5869
7.1	6009	6150	6291	6431	6571	6711	6851	6991	7130	7269
7.2	7408	7547	7685	7824	7962	8100	8238	8376	8513	8650
7.3	8787	8924	9061	9198	9334	9470	9606	9742	9877	*0013
7.4	2.0 0148	0283	0418	0553	0687	0821	0956	1089	1223	1357
7.5	1490	1624	1757	1890	2022	2155	2287	2419	2551	2683
7.6	2815	2946	3078	3209	3340	3471	3601	3732	3862	3992
7.7	4122	4252	4381	4511	4640	4769	4898	5027	5156	5284
7.8	5412	5540	5668	5796	5924	6051	6179	6306	6433	6560
7.9	6686	6813	6939	7065	7191	7317	7443	7568	7694	7819
8.0	7944	8069	8194	8318	8443	8567	8691	8815	8939	9063
8.1	9186	9310	9433	9556	9679	9802	9924	*0047	*0169	*0291
8.2	2.1 0413	0535	0657	0779	0900	1021	1142	1263	1384	1505
8.3	1626	1746	1866	1986	2106	2226	2346	2465	2585	2704
8.4	2823	2942	3061	3180	3298	3417	3535	3653	3771	3889
8.5	4007	4124	4242	4359	4476	4593	4710	4827	4943	5060
8.6	5176	5292	5409	5524	5640	5756	5871	5987	6102	6217
8.7	6332	6447	6562	6677	6791	6905	7020	7134	7248	7361
8.8	7475	7589	7702	7816	7929	8042	8155	8267	8380	8493
8.9	8605	8717	8830	8942	9054	9165	9277	9389	9500	9611
9.0	9722	9834	9944	*0055	*0166	*0276	*0387	*0497	*0607	*0717
9.1	2.2 0827	0937	1047	1157	1266	1375	1485	1594	1703	1812
9.2	1920	2029	2138	2246	2354	2462	2570	2678	2786	2894
9.3	3001	3109	3216	3324	3431	3538	3645	3751	3858	3965
9.4	4071	4177	4284	4390	4496	4601	4707	4813	4918	5024
9.5	5129	5234	5339	5444	5549	5654	5759	5863	5968	6072
9.6	6176	6280	6384	6488	6592	6696	6799	6903	7006	7109
9.7	7213	7316	7419	7521	7624	7727	7829	7932	8034	8136
9.8	8238	8340	8442	8544	8646	8747	8849	8950	9051	9152
9.9	9253	9354	9455	9556	9657	9757	9858	9958	*0058	*0158
10.0	2.3 0259	0358	0458	0558	0658	0757	0857	0956	1055	1154
N	0	1	2	3	4	5	6	7	8	9

x	e^x Value	e^x Log₁₀	e^{-x} Value	Sinh x Value	Sinh x Log₁₀	Cosh x Value	Cosh x Log₁₀	Tanh x Value
0.00	1.0000	.00000	1.0000	0.0000	$-\infty$	1.0000	.00000	.00000
0.01	1.0101	.00434	.99005	0.0100	.00001	1.0001	.00002	.01000
0.02	1.0202	.00869	.98020	0.0200	.30106	1.0002	.00009	.02000
0.03	1.0305	.01303	.97045	0.0300	.47719	1.0005	.00020	.02999
0.04	1.0408	.01737	.96079	0.0400	.60218	1.0008	.00035	.03998
0.05	1.0513	.02171	.95123	0.0500	.69915	1.0013	.00054	.04996
0.06	1.0618	.02606	.94176	0.0600	.77841	1.0018	.00078	.05993
0.07	1.0725	.03040	.93239	9.0701	.84545	1.0025	.00106	.06989
0.08	1.0833	.03474	.92312	0.0801	.90355	1.0032	.00139	.07983
0.09	1.0942	.03909	.91393	0.0901	.95483	1.0041	.00176	.08976
0.10	1.1052	.04343	.90484	0.1002	.00072	1.0050	.00217	.09967
0.11	1.1163	.04777	.89583	0.1102	.04227	1.0061	.00262	.10956
0.12	1.1275	.05212	.88692	0.1203	.08022	1.0072	.00312	.11943
0.13	1.1388	.05646	.87810	0.1304	.11517	1.0085	.00366	.12927
0.14	1.1503	.06080	.86936	0.1405	.14755	1.0098	.00424	.13909
0.15	1.1618	.06514	.86071	0.1506	.17772	1.0113	.00487	.14889
0.16	1.1735	.06949	.85214	0.1607	.20597	1.0128	.00554	.15865
0.17	1.1853	.07383	.84366	0.1708	.23254	1.0145	.00625	.16838
0.18	1.1972	.07817	.83527	0.1810	.25762	1.0162	.00700	.17808
0.19	1.2092	.08252	.82696	0.1911	.28136	1.0181	.00779	.18775
0.20	1.2214	.08686	.81873	0.2013	.30392	1.0201	.00863	.19738
0.21	1.2337	.09120	.81058	0.2115	.32541	1.0221	.00951	.20697
0.22	1.2461	.09554	.80252	0.2218	.34592	1.0243	.01043	.21652
0.23	1.2586	.09989	.79453	0.2320	.36555	1.0266	.01139	.22603
0.24	1.2712	.10423	.78663	0.2423	.38437	1.0289	.01239	.23550
0.25	1.2840	.10857	.77880	0.2526	.40245	1.0314	.01343	.24492
0.26	1.2969	.11292	.77105	0.2629	.41986	1.0340	.01452	.25430
0.27	1.3100	.11726	.76338	0.2733	.43663	1.0367	.01564	.26362
0.28	1.3231	.12160	.75578	0.2837	.45282	1.0395	.01681	.27291
0.29	1.3364	.12595	.74826	0.2941	.46847	1.0423	.01801	.28213
0.30	1.3499	.13029	.74082	0.3045	.48362	1.0453	.01926	.29131
0.31	1.3634	.13463	.73345	0.3150	.49830	1.0484	.02054	.30044
0.32	1.3771	.13897	.72615	0.3255	.51254	1.0516	.02187	.30951
0.33	1.3910	.14332	.71892	0.3360	.52637	1.0549	.02323	.31852
0.34	1.4049	.14766	.71177	0.3466	.53981	1.0584	.02463	.32748
0.35	1.4191	.15200	.70469	0.3572	.55290	1.0619	.02607	.33638
0.36	1.4333	.15635	.69768	0.3678	.56564	1.0655	.02755	.34521
0.37	1.4477	.16069	.69073	0.3785	.57807	1.0692	.02907	.35399
0.38	1.4623	.16503	.68386	0.3892	.59019	1.0731	.03063	.36271
0.39	1.4770	.16937	.67706	0.4000	.60202	1.0770	.03222	.37136
0.40	1.4918	.17372	.67032	0.4108	.61358	1.0811	.03385	.37995
0.41	1.5068	.17806	.66365	0.4216	.62488	1.0852	.03552	.38847
0.42	1.5220	.18240	.65705	0.4325	.63594	1.0895	.03723	.39693
0.43	1.5373	.18675	.65051	0.4434	.64677	1.0939	.03897	.40532
0.44	1.5527	.19109	.64404	0.4543	.65738	1.0984	.04075	.41364
0.45	1.5683	.19543	.63763	0.4653	.66777	1.1030	.04256	.42190
0.46	1.5841	.19978	.63128	0.4764	.67797	1.1077	.04441	.43008
0.47	1.6000	.20412	.62500	0.4875	.68797	1.1125	.04630	.43820
0.48	1.6161	.20846	.61878	0.4986	.69779	1.1174	.04822	.44624
0.49	1.6323	.21280	.61263	0.5098	.70744	1.1225	.05018	.45422
0.50	1.6487	.21715	.60653	0.5211	.71692	1.1276	.05217	.46212

x	e^x Value	e^x Log₁₀	e^{-x} Value	Sinh x Value	Sinh x Log₁₀	Cosh x Value	Cosh x Log₁₀	Tanh x Value
0.50	1.6487	.21715	.60653	0.5211	.71692	1.1276	.05217	.46212
0.51	1.6653	.22149	.60050	0.5324	.72624	1.1329	.05419	.46995
0.52	1.6820	.22583	.59452	0.5438	.73540	1.1383	.05625	.47770
0.53	1.6989	.23018	.58860	0.5552	.74442	1.1438	.05834	.48538
0.54	1.7160	.23452	.58275	0.5666	.75330	1.1494	.06046	.49299
0.55	1.7333	.23886	.57695	0.5782	.76204	1.1551	.06262	.50052
0.56	1.7507	.24320	.57121	0.5897	.77065	1.1609	.06481	.50798
0.57	1.7683	.24755	.56553	0.6014	.77914	1.1669	.06703	.51536
0.58	1.7860	.25189	.55990	0.6131	.78751	1.1730	.06929	.52267
0.59	1.8040	.25623	.55433	0.6248	.79576	1.1792	.07157	.52990
0.60	1.8221	.26058	.54881	0.6367	.80390	1.1855	.07389	.53705
0.61	1.8404	.26492	.54335	0.6485	.81194	1.1919	.07624	.54413
0.62	1.8589	.26926	.53794	0.6605	.81987	1.1984	.07861	.55113
0.63	1.8776	.27361	.53259	0.6725	.82770	1.2051	.08102	.55805
0.64	1.8965	.27795	.52729	0.6846	.83543	1.2119	.08346	.56490
0.65	1.9155	.28229	.52205	0.6967	.84308	1.2188	.08593	.57167
0.66	1.9348	.28663	.51685	0.7090	.85063	1.2258	.08843	.57836
0.67	1.9542	.29098	.51171	0.7213	.85809	1.2330	.09095	.58498
0.68	1.9739	.29532	.50662	0.7336	.86548	1.2402	.09351	.59152
0.69	1.9937	.29966	.50158	0.7461	.87278	1.2476	.09609	.59798
0.70	2.0138	.30401	.49659	0.7586	.88000	1.2552	.09870	.60437
0.71	2.0340	.30835	.49164	0.7712	.88715	1.2628	.10134	.61068
0.72	2.0544	.31269	.48675	0.7838	.89423	1.2706	.10401	.61691
0.73	2.0751	.31703	.48191	0.7966	.90123	1.2785	.10670	.62307
0.74	2.0959	.32138	.47711	0.8094	.90817	1.2865	.10942	.62915
0.75	2.1170	.32572	.47237	0.8223	.91504	1.2947	.11216	.63515
0.76	2.1383	.33006	.46767	0.8353	.92185	1.3030	.11493	.64108
0.77	2.1598	.33441	.46301	0.8484	.92859	1.3114	.11773	.64693
0.78	2.1815	.33875	.45841	0.8615	.93527	1.3199	.12055	.65271
0.79	2.2034	.34309	.45384	0.8748	.94190	1.3286	.12340	.65841
0.80	2.2255	.34744	.44933	0.8881	.94846	1.3374	.12627	.66404
0.81	2.2479	.35178	.44486	0.9015	.95498	1.3464	.12917	.66959
0.82	2.2705	.35612	.44043	0.9150	.96144	1.3555	.13209	.67507
0.83	2.2933	.36046	.43605	0.9286	.96784	1.3647	.13503	.68048
0.84	2.3164	.36481	.43171	0.9423	.97420	1.3740	.13800	.68581
0.85	2.3396	.36915	.42741	0.9561	.98051	1.3835	.14099	.69107
0.86	2.3632	.37349	.42316	0.9700	.98677	1.3932	.14400	.69626
0.87	2.3869	.37784	.41895	0.9840	.99299	1.4029	.14704	.70137
0.88	2.4109	.38218	.41478	0.9981	.99916	1.4128	.15009	.70642
0.89	2.4351	.38652	.41066	1.0122	.00528	1.4229	.15317	.71139
0.90	2.4596	.39087	.40657	1.0265	.01137	1.4331	.15627	.71630
0.91	2.4843	.39521	.40252	1.0409	.01741	1.4434	.15939	.72113
0.92	2.5093	.39955	.39852	1.0554	.02341	1.4539	.16254	.72590
0.93	2.5345	.40389	.39455	1.0700	.02937	1.4645	.16570	.73059
0.94	2.5600	.40824	.39063	1.0847	.03530	1.4753	.16888	.73522
0.95	2.5857	.41258	.38674	1.0995	.04119	1.4862	.17208	.73978
0.96	2.6117	.41692	.38289	1.1144	.04704	1.4973	.17531	.74428
0.97	2.6379	.42127	.37908	1.1294	.05286	1.5085	.17855	.74870
0.98	2.6645	.42561	.37531	1.1446	.05864	1.5199	.18181	.75307
0.99	2.6912	.42995	.37158	1.1598	.06439	1.5314	.18509	.75736
1.00	2.7183	.43429	.36788	1.1752	.07011	1.5431	.18839	.76159

x	e^x Value	e^x Log₁₀	e^{-x} Value	Sinh x Value	Sinh x Log₁₀	Cosh x Value	Cosh x Log₁₀	Tanh x Value
1.00	2.7183	.43429	.36788	1.1752	.07011	1.5431	.18839	.76159
1.01	2.7456	.43864	.36422	1.1907	.07580	1.5549	.19171	.76576
1.02	2.7732	.44298	.36059	1.2063	.08146	1.5669	.19504	.76987
1.03	2.8011	.44732	.35701	1.2220	.08708	1.5790	.19839	.77391
1.04	2.8292	.45167	.35345	1.2379	.09268	1.5913	.20176	.77789
1.05	2.8577	.45601	.34994	1.2539	.09825	1.6038	.20515	.78181
1.06	2.8864	.46035	.34646	1.2700	.10379	1.6164	.20855	.78566
1.07	2.9154	.46470	.34301	1.2862	.10930	1.6292	.21197	.78946
1.08	2.9447	.46904	.33960	1.3025	.11479	1.6421	.21541	.79320
1.09	2.9743	.47338	.33622	1.3190	.12025	1.6552	.21886	.79688
1.10	3.0042	.47772	.33287	1.3356	.12569	1.6685	.22233	.80050
1.11	3.0344	.48207	.32956	1.3524	.13111	1.6820	.22582	.80406
1.12	3.0649	.48641	.32628	1.3693	.13649	1.6956	.22931	.80757
1.13	3.0957	.49075	.32303	1.3863	.14186	1.7093	.23283	.81102
1.14	3.1268	.49510	.31982	1.4035	.14720	1.7233	.23636	.81441
1.15	3.1582	.49944	.31664	1.4208	.15253	1.7374	.23990	.81775
1.16	3.1899	.50378	.31349	1.4382	.15783	1.7517	.24346	.82104
1.17	3.2220	.50812	.31037	1.4558	.16311	1.7662	.24703	.82427
1.18	3.2544	.51247	.30728	1.4735	.16836	1.7808	.25062	.82745
1.19	3.2871	.51681	.30422	1.4914	.17360	1.7957	.25422	.83058
1.20	3.3201	.52115	.30119	1.5095	.17882	1.8107	.25784	.83365
1.21	3.3535	.52550	.29820	1.5276	.18402	1.8258	.26146	.83668
1.22	3.3872	.52984	.29523	1.5460	.18920	1.8412	.26510	.83965
1.23	3.4212	.53418	.29229	1.5645	.19437	1.8568	.26876	.84258
1.24	3.4556	.53853	.28938	1.5831	.19951	1.8725	.27242	.84546
1.25	3.4903	.54287	.28650	1.6019	.20464	1.8884	.27610	.84828
1.26	3.5254	.54721	.28365	1.6209	.20975	1.9045	.27979	.85106
1.27	3.5609	.55155	.28083	1.6400	.21485	1.9208	.28349	.85380
1.28	3.5966	.55590	.27804	1.6593	.21993	1.9373	.28721	.85648
1.29	3.6328	.56024	.27527	1.6788	.22499	1.9540	.29093	.85913
1.30	3.6693	.56458	.27253	1.6984	.23004	1.9709	.29467	.86172
1.31	3.7062	.56893	.26982	1.7182	.23507	1.9880	.29842	.86428
1.32	3.7434	.57327	.26714	1.7381	.24009	2.0053	.30217	.86678
1.33	3.7810	.57761	.26448	1.7583	.24509	2.0228	.30594	.86925
1.34	3.8190	.58195	.26185	1.7786	.25008	2.0404	.30972	.87167
1.35	3.8574	.58630	.25924	1.7991	.25505	2.0583	.31352	.87405
1.36	3.8962	.59064	.25666	1.8198	.26002	2.0764	.31732	.87639
1.37	3.9354	.59498	.25411	1.8406	.26496	2.0947	.32113	.87869
1.38	3.9749	.59933	.25158	1.8617	.26990	2.1132	.32495	.88095
1.39	4.0149	.60367	.24908	1.8829	.27482	2.1320	.32878	.88317
1.40	4.0552	.60801	.24660	1.9043	.27974	2.1509	.33262	.88535
1.41	4.0960	.61236	.24414	1.9259	.28464	2.1700	.33647	.88749
1.42	4.1371	.61670	.24171	1.9477	.28952	2.1894	.34033	.88960
1.43	4.1787	.62104	.23931	1.9697	.29440	2.2090	.34420	.89167
1.44	4.2207	.62538	.23693	1.9919	.29926	2.2288	.34807	.89370
1.45	4.2631	.62973	.23457	2.0143	.30412	2.2488	.35196	.89569
1.46	4.3060	.63407	.23224	2.0369	.30896	2.2691	.35585	.89765
1.47	4.3492	.63841	.22993	2.0597	.31379	2.2896	.35976	.89958
1.48	4.3929	.64276	.22764	2.0827	.31862	2.3103	.36367	.90147
1.49	4.4371	.64710	.22537	2.1059	.32343	2.3312	.36759	.90332
1.50	4.4817	.65144	.22313	2.1293	.32823	2.3524	.37151	.90515

x	e^x Value	e^x Log$_{10}$	e^{-x} Value	Sinh x Value	Sinh x Log$_{10}$	Cosh x Value	Cosh x Log$_{10}$	Tanh x Value
1.50	4.4817	.65144	.22313	2.1293	.32823	2.3524	.37151	.90515
1.51	4.5267	.65578	.22091	2.1529	.33303	2.3738	.37545	.90694
1.52	4.5722	.66013	.21871	2.1768	.33781	2.3955	.37939	.90870
1.53	4.6182	.66447	.21654	2.2008	.34258	2.4174	.38334	.91042
1.54	4.6646	.66881	.21438	2.2251	.34735	2.4395	.38730	.91212
1.55	4.7115	.67316	.21225	2.2496	.35211	2.4619	.39126	.91379
1.56	4.7588	.67750	.21014	2.2743	.35686	2.4845	.39524	.91542
1.57	4.8066	.68184	.20805	2.2993	.36160	2.5073	.39921	.91703
1.58	4.8550	.68619	.20598	2.3245	.36633	2.5305	.40320	.91860
1.59	4.9037	.69053	.20393	2.3499	.37105	2.5538	.40719	.92015
1.60	4.9530	.69487	.20190	2.3756	.37577	2.5775	.41119	.92167
1.61	5.0028	.69921	.19989	2.4015	.38048	2.6013	.41520	.92316
1.62	5.0531	.70356	.19790	2.4276	.38518	2.6255	.41921	.92462
1.63	5.1039	.70790	.19593	2.4540	.38987	2.6499	.42323	.92606
1.64	5.1552	.71224	.19398	2.4806	.39456	2.6746	.42725	.92747
1.65	5.2070	.71659	.19205	2.5075	.39923	2.6995	.43129	.92886
1.66	5.2593	.72093	.19014	2.5346	.40391	2.7247	.43532	.93022
1.67	5.3122	.72527	.18825	2.5620	.40857	2.7502	.43937	.93155
1.68	5.3656	.72961	.18637	2.5896	.41323	2.7760	.44341	.93286
1.69	5.4195	.73396	.18452	2.6175	.41788	2.8020	.44747	.93415
1.70	5.4739	.73830	.18268	2.6456	.42253	2.8283	.45153	.93541
1.71	5.5290	.74264	.18087	2.6740	.42717	2.8549	.45559	.93665
1.72	5.5845	.74699	.17907	2.7027	.43180	2.8818	.45966	.93786
1.73	5.6407	.75133	.17728	2.7317	.43643	2.9090	.46374	.93906
1.74	5.6973	.75567	.17552	2.7609	.44105	2.9364	.46782	.94023
1.75	5.7546	.76002	.17377	2.7904	.44567	2.9642	.47191	.94138
1.76	5.8124	.76436	.17204	2.8202	.45028	2.9922	.47600	.94250
1.77	5.8709	.76870	.17033	2.8503	.45488	3.0206	.48009	.94361
1.78	5.9299	.77304	.16864	2.8806	.45948	3.0492	.48419	.94470
1.79	5.9895	.77739	.16696	2.9112	.46408	3.0782	.48830	.94576
1.80	6.0496	.78173	.16530	2.9422	.46867	3.1075	.49241	.94681
1.81	6.1104	.78607	.16365	2.9734	.47325	3.1371	.49652	.94783
1.82	6.1719	.79042	.16203	3.0049	.47783	3.1669	.50064	.94884
1.83	6.2339	.79476	.16041	3.0367	.48241	3.1972	.50476	.94983
1.84	6.2965	.79910	.15882	3.0689	.48698	3.2277	.50889	.95080
1.85	6.3598	.80344	.15724	3.1013	.49154	3.2585	.51302	.95175
1.86	6.4237	.80779	.15567	3.1340	.49610	3.2897	.51716	.95268
1.87	6.4883	.81213	.15412	3.1671	.50066	3.3212	.52130	.95359
1.88	6.5535	.81647	.15259	3.2005	.50521	3.3530	.52544	.95449
1.89	6.6194	.82082	.15107	3.2341	.50976	3.3852	.52959	.95537
1.90	6.6859	.82516	.14957	3.2682	.51430	3.4177	.53374	.95624
1.91	6.7531	.82950	.14808	3.3025	.51884	3.4506	.53789	.95709
1.92	6.8210	.83385	.14661	3.3372	.52338	3.4838	.54205	.95792
1.93	6.8895	.83819	.14515	3.3722	.52791	3.5173	.54621	.95873
1.94	6.9588	.84253	.14370	3.4075	.53244	3.5512	.55038	.95953
1.95	7.0287	.84687	.14227	3.4432	.53696	3.5855	.55455	.96032
1.96	7.0993	.85122	.14086	3.4792	.54148	3.6201	.55872	.96109
1.97	7.1707	.85556	.13946	3.5156	.54600	3.6551	.56290	.96185
1.98	7.2427	.85990	.13807	3.5523	.55051	3.6904	.56707	.96259
1.99	7.3155	.86425	.13670	3.5894	.55502	3.7261	.57126	.96331
2.00	7.3891	.86859	.13534	3.6269	.55953	3.7622	.57544	.96403

x	e^x Value	e^x Log$_{10}$	e^{-x} Value	Sinh x Value	Sinh x Log$_{10}$	Cosh x Value	Cosh x Log$_{10}$	Tanh x Value
2.00	7.3891	.86859	.13534	3.6269	.55953	3.7622	.57544	.96403
2.01	7.4633	.87293	.13399	3.6647	.56403	3.7987	.57963	.96473
2.02	7.5383	.87727	.13266	3.7028	.56853	3.8355	.58382	.96541
2.03	7.6141	.88162	.13134	3.7414	.57303	3.8727	.58802	.96609
2.04	7.6906	.88596	.13003	3.7803	.57753	3.9103	.59221	.96675
2.05	7.7679	.89030	.12873	3.8196	.58202	3.9483	.59641	.96740
2.06	7.8460	.89465	.12745	3.8593	.58650	3.9867	.60061	.96803
2.07	7.9248	.89899	.12619	3.8993	.59099	4.0255	.60482	.96865
2.08	8.0045	.90333	.12493	3.9398	.59547	4.0647	.60903	.96926
2.09	8.0849	.90768	.12369	3.9806	.59995	4.1043	.61324	.96986
2.10	8.1662	.91202	.12246	4.0219	.60443	4.1443	.61745	.97045
2.11	8.2482	.91636	.12124	4.0635	.60890	4.1847	.62167	.97103
2.12	8.3311	.92070	.12003	4.1056	.61337	4.2256	.62589	.97159
2.13	8.4149	.92505	.11884	4.1480	.61784	4.2669	.63011	.97215
2.14	8.4994	.92939	.11765	4.1909	.62231	4.3085	.63433	.97269
2.15	8.5849	.93373	.11648	4.2342	.62677	4.3507	.63856	.97323
2.16	8.6711	.93808	.11533	4.2779	.63123	4.3932	.64278	.97375
2.17	8.7583	.94242	.11418	4.3221	.63569	4.4362	.64701	.97426
2.18	8.8463	.94676	.11304	4.3666	.64015	4.4797	.65125	.97477
2.19	8.9352	.95110	.11192	4.4116	.64460	4.5236	.65548	.97526
2.20	9.0250	.95545	.11080	4.4571	.64905	4.5679	.65972	.97574
2.21	9.1157	.95979	.10970	4.5030	.65350	4.6127	.66396	.97622
2.22	9.2073	.96413	.10861	4.5494	.65795	4.6580	.66820	.97668
2.23	9.2999	.96848	.10753	4.5962	.66240	4.7037	.67244	.97714
2.24	9.3933	.97282	.10646	4.6434	.66684	4.7499	.67668	.97759
2.25	9.4877	.97716	.10540	4.6912	.67128	4.7966	.68093	.97803
2.26	9.5831	.98151	.10435	4.7394	.67572	4.8437	.68518	.97846
2.27	9.6794	.98585	.10331	4.7880	.68016	4.8914	.68943	.97888
2.28	9.7767	.99019	.10228	4.8372	.68459	4.9395	.69368	.97929
2.29	9.8749	.99453	.10127	4.8868	.68903	4.9881	.69794	.97970
2.30	9.9742	.99888	.10026	4.9370	.69346	5.0372	.70219	.98010
2.31	10.074	.00322	.09926	4.9876	.69789	5.0868	.70645	.98049
2.32	10.176	.00756	.09827	5.0387	.70232	5.1370	.71071	.98087
2.33	10.278	.01191	.09730	5.0903	.70675	5.1876	.71497	.98124
2.34	10.381	.01625	.09633	5.1425	.71117	5.2388	.71923	.98161
2.35	10.486	.02059	.09537	5.1951	.71559	5.2905	.72349	.98197
2.36	10.591	.02493	.09442	5.2483	.72002	5.3427	.72776	.98233
2.37	10.697	.02928	.09348	5.3020	.72444	5.3954	.73203	.98267
2.38	10.805	.03362	.09255	5.3562	.72885	5.4487	.73630	.98301
2.39	10.913	.03796	.09163	5.4109	.73327	5.5026	.74056	.98335
2.40	11.023	.04231	.09072	5.4662	.73769	5.5569	.74484	.98367
2.41	11.134	.04665	.08982	5.5221	.74210	5.6119	.74911	.98400
2.42	11.246	.05099	.08892	5.5785	.74652	5.6674	.75338	.98431
2.43	11.359	.05534	.08804	5.6354	.75093	5.7235	.75766	.98462
2.44	11.473	.05968	.08716	5.6929	.75534	5.7801	.76194	.98492
2.45	11.588	.06402	.08629	5.7510	.75975	5.8373	.76621	.98522
2.46	11.705	.06836	.08543	5.8097	.76415	5.8951	.77049	.98551
2.47	11.822	.07271	.08458	5.8689	.76856	5.9535	.77477	.98579
2.48	11.941	.07705	.08374	5.9288	.77296	6.0125	.77906	.98607
2.49	12.061	.08139	.08291	5.9892	.77737	6.0721	.78334	.98635
2.50	12.182	.08574	.08208	6.0502	.78177	6.1323	.78762	.98661

x	e^x Value	e^x Log₁₀	e^{-x} Value	Sinh x Value	Sinh x Log₁₀	Cosh x Value	Cosh x Log₁₀	Tanh x Value
2.50	12.182	.08574	.08208	6.0502	.78177	6.1323	.78762	.98661
2.51	12.305	.09008	.08127	6.1118	.78617	6.1931	.79191	.98688
2.52	12.429	.09442	.08046	6.1741	.79057	6.2545	.79619	.98714
2.53	12.554	.09877	.07966	6.2369	.79497	6.3166	.80048	.98739
2.54	12.680	.10311	.07887	6.3004	.79937	6.3793	.80477	.98764
2.55	12.807	.10745	.07808	6.3645	.80377	6.4426	.80906	.98788
2.56	12.936	.11179	.07730	6.4293	.80816	6.5066	.81335	.98812
2.57	13.066	.11614	.07654	6.4946	.81256	6.5712	.81764	.98835
2.58	13.197	.12048	.07577	6.5607	.81695	6.6365	.82194	.98858
2.59	13.330	.12482	.07502	6.6274	.82134	6.7024	.82623	.98881
2.60	13.464	.12917	.07427	6.6947	.82573	6.7690	.83052	.98903
2.61	13.599	.13351	.07353	6.7628	.83012	6.8363	.83482	.98924
2.62	13.736	.13785	.07280	6.8315	.83451	6.9043	.83912	.98946
2.63	13.874	.14219	.07208	6.9008	.83890	6.9729	.84341	.98966
2.64	14.013	.14654	.07136	6.9709	.84329	7.0423	.84771	.98987
2.65	14.154	.15088	.07065	7.0417	.84768	7.1123	.85201	.99007
2.66	14.296	.15522	.06995	7.1132	.85206	7.1831	.85631	.99026
2.67	14.440	.15957	.06925	7.1854	.85645	7.2546	.86061	.99045
2.68	14.585	.16391	.06856	7.2583	.86083	7.3268	.86492	.99064
2.69	14.732	.16825	.06788	7.3319	.86522	7.3998	.86922	.99083
2.70	14.880	.17260	.06721	7.4063	.86960	7.4735	.87352	.99101
2.71	15.029	.17694	.06654	7.4814	.87398	7.5479	.87783	.99118
2.72	15.180	.18128	.06587	7.5572	.87836	7.6231	.88213	.99136
2.73	15.333	.18562	.06522	7.6338	.88274	7.6991	.88644	.99153
2.74	15.487	.18997	.06457	7.7112	.88712	7.7758	.89074	.99170
2.75	15.643	.19431	.06393	7.7894	.89150	7.8533	.89505	.99186
2.76	15.800	.19865	.06329	7.8683	.89588	7.9316	.89936	.99202
2.77	15.959	.20300	.06266	7.9480	.90026	8.0106	.90367	.99218
2.78	16.119	.20734	.06204	8.0285	.90463	8.0905	.90798	.99233
2.79	16.281	.21168	.06142	8.1098	.90901	8.1712	.91229	.99248
2.80	16.445	.21602	.06081	8.1919	.91339	8.2527	.91660	.99263
2.81	16.610	.22037	.06020	8.2749	.91776	8.3351	.92091	.99278
2.82	16.777	.22471	.05961	8.3586	.92213	8.4182	.92522	.99292
2.83	16.945	.22905	.05901	8.4432	.92651	8.5022	.92953	.99306
2.84	17.116	.23340	.05843	8.5287	.93088	8.5871	.93385	.99320
2.85	17.288	.23774	.05784	8.6150	.93525	8.6728	.93816	.99333
2.86	17.462	.24208	.05727	8.7021	.93963	8.7594	.94247	.99346
2.87	17.637	.24643	.05670	8.7902	.94400	8.8469	.94679	.99359
2.88	17.814	.25077	.05613	8.8791	.94837	8.9352	.95110	.99372
2.89	17.993	.25511	.05558	8.9689	.95274	9.0244	.95542	.99384
2.90	18.174	.25945	.05502	9.0596	.95711	9.1146	.95974	.99396
2.91	18.357	.26380	.05448	9.1512	.96148	9.2056	.96405	.99408
2.92	18.541	.26814	.05393	9.2437	.96584	9.2976	.96837	.99420
2.93	18.728	.27248	.05340	9.3371	.97021	9.3905	.97269	.99431
2.94	18.916	.27683	.05287	9.4315	.97458	9.4844	.97701	.99443
2.95	19.106	.28117	.05234	9.5268	.97895	9.5791	.98133	.99454
2.96	19.298	.28551	.05182	9.6231	.98331	9.6749	.98565	.99464
2.97	19.492	.28985	.05130	9.7203	.98768	9.7716	.98997	.99475
2.98	19.688	.29420	.05079	9.8185	.99205	9.8693	.99429	.99485
2.99	19.886	.29854	.05029	9.9177	.99641	9.9680	.99861	.99496
3.00	20.086	.30288	.04979	10.018	.00078	10.068	.00293	.99505

[Characteristics of Logarithms omitted—determine by the usual rule from the value]

Radians	Degrees	Sine Value	Sine Log10	Tangent Value	Tangent Log10	Cotangent Value	Cotangent Log10	Cosine Value	Cosine Log10		
.0000	0° 00′	.0000	—	.0000	—	—	—	1.0000	.0000	90° 00′	1.5708
.0029	10	.0029	.4637	.0029	.4637	343.77	.5363	1.0000	.0000	50	1.5679
.0058	20	.0058	.7648	.0058	.7648	171.89	.2352	1.0000	.0000	40	1.5650
.0087	30	.0087	.9408	.0087	.9409	114.59	.0591	1.0000	.0000	30	1.5621
.0116	40	.0116	.0658	.0116	.0658	85.940	.9342	.9999	.0000	20	1.5592
.0145	50	.0145	.1627	.0145	.1627	68.750	.8373	.9999	.0000	10	1.5563
.0175	1° 00′	.0175	.2419	.0175	.2419	57.290	.7581	.9998	.9999	89° 00′	1.5533
.0204	10	.0204	.3088	.0204	.3089	49.104	.6911	.9998	.9999	50	1.5504
.0233	20	.0233	.3668	.0233	.3669	42.964	.6331	.9997	.9999	40	1.5475
.0262	30	.0262	.4179	.0262	.4181	38.188	.5819	.9997	.9999	30	1.5446
.0291	40	.0291	.4637	.0291	.4638	34.368	.5362	.9996	.9998	20	1.5417
.0320	50	.0320	.5050	.0320	.5053	31.242	.4947	.9995	.9998	10	1.5388
.0349	2° 00′	.0349	.5428	.0349	.5431	28.636	.4569	.9994	.9997	88° 00′	1.5359
.0378	10	.0378	.5776	.0378	.5779	26.432	.4221	.9993	.9997	50	1.5330
.0407	20	.0407	.6097	.0407	.6101	24.542	.3899	.9992	.9996	40	1.5301
.0436	30	.0436	.6397	.0437	.6401	22.904	.3599	.9990	.9996	30	1.5272
.0465	40	.0465	.6677	.0466	.6682	21.470	.3318	.9989	.9995	20	1.5243
.0495	50	.0494	.6940	.0495	.6945	20.206	.3055	.9988	.9995	10	1.5213
.0524	3° 00′	.0523	.7188	.0524	.7194	19.081	.2806	.9986	.9994	87° 00′	1.5184
.0553	10	.0552	.7423	.0553	.7429	18.075	.2571	.9985	.9993	50	1.5155
.0582	20	.0581	.7645	.0582	.7652	17.169	.2348	.9983	.9993	40	1.5126
.0611	30	.0610	.7857	.0612	.7865	16.350	.2135	.9981	.9992	30	1.5097
.0640	40	.0640	.8059	.0641	.8067	15.605	.1933	.9980	.9991	20	1.5068
.0669	50	.0669	.8251	.0670	.8261	14.924	.1739	.9978	.9990	10	1.5039
.0698	4° 00′	.0698	.8436	.0699	.8446	14.301	.1554	.9976	.9989	86° 00′	1.5010
.0727	10	.0727	.8613	.0729	.8624	13.727	.1376	.9974	.9989	50	1.4981
.0756	20	.0756	.8783	.0758	.8795	13.197	.1205	.9971	.9988	40	1.4952
.0785	30	.0785	.8946	.0787	.8960	12.706	.1040	.9969	.9987	30	1.4923
.0814	40	.0814	.9104	.0816	.9118	12.251	.0882	.9967	.9986	20	1.4893
.0844	50	.0843	.9256	.0846	.9272	11.826	.0728	.9964	.9985	10	1.4864
.0873	5° 00′	.0872	.9403	.0875	.9420	11.430	.0580	.9962	.9983	85° 00′	1.4835
.0902	10	.0901	.9545	.0904	.9563	11.059	.0437	.9959	.9982	50	1.4806
.0931	20	.0929	.9682	.0934	.9701	10.712	.0299	.9957	.9981	40	1.4777
.0960	30	.0958	.9816	.0963	.9836	10.385	.0164	.9954	.9980	30	1.4748
.0989	40	.0987	.9945	.0992	.9966	10.078	.0034	.9951	.9979	20	1.4719
.1018	50	.1016	.0070	.1022	.0093	9.7882	.9907	.9948	.9977	10	1.4690
.1047	6° 00′	.1045	.0192	.1051	.0216	9.5144	.9784	.9945	.9976	84° 00′	1.4661
.1076	10	.1074	.0311	.1080	.0336	9.2553	.9664	.9942	.9975	50	1.4632
.1105	20	.1103	.0426	.1110	.0453	9.0098	.9547	.9939	.9973	40	1.4603
.1134	30	.1132	.0539	.1139	.0567	8.7769	.9433	.9936	.9972	30	1.4573
.1164	40	.1161	.0648	.1169	.0678	8.5555	.9322	.9932	.9971	20	1.4544
.1193	50	.1190	.0755	.1198	.0786	8.3450	.9214	.9929	.9969	10	1.4515
.1222	7° 00′	.1219	.0859	.1228	.0891	8.1443	.9109	.9925	.9968	83° 00′	1.4486
.1251	10	.1248	.0961	.1257	.0995	7.9530	.9005	.9922	.9966	50	1.4457
.1280	20	.1276	.1060	.1287	.1096	7.7704	.8904	.9918	.9964	40	1.4428
.1309	30	.1305	.1157	.1317	.1194	7.5958	.8806	.9914	.9963	30	1.4399
.1338	40	.1334	.1252	.1346	.1291	7.4287	.8709	.9911	.9961	20	1.4370
.1367	50	.1363	.1345	.1376	.1385	7.2687	.8615	.9907	.9959	10	1.4341
.1396	8° 00′	.1392	.1436	.1405	.1478	7.1154	.8522	.9903	.9958	82° 00′	1.4312
.1425	10	.1421	.1525	.1435	.1569	6.9682	.8431	.9899	.9956	50	1.4283
.1454	20	.1449	.1612	.1465	.1658	6.8269	.8342	.9894	.9954	40	1.4254
.1484	30	.1478	.1697	.1495	.1745	6.6912	.8255	.9890	.9952	30	1.4224
.1513	40	.1507	.1781	.1524	.1831	6.5606	.8169	.9886	.9950	20	1.4195
.1542	50	.1536	.1863	.1554	.1915	6.4348	.8085	.9881	.9948	10	1.4166
.1571	9° 00′	.1564	.1943	.1584	.1997	6.3138	.8003	.9877	.9946	81° 00′	1.4137
		Value Log10 Cosine		Value Log10 Cotangent		Value Log10 Tangent		Value Log10 Sine		Degrees	Radians

FOUR PLACE TRIGONOMETRIC FUNCTIONS

[Characteristics of Logarithms omitted—determine by the usual rule from the value]

RADIANS	DEGREES	SINE		TANGENT		COTANGENT		COSINE			
		Value	Log10	Value	Log10	Value	Log10	Value	Log10		
.1571	9° 00'	.1564	.1943	.1584	.1997	6.3138	.8003	.9877	.9946	81° 00'	1.4137
.1600	10	.1593	.2022	.1614	.2078	6.1970	.7922	.9872	.9944	50	1.4108
.1629	20	.1622	.2100	.1644	.2158	6.0844	.7842	.9868	.9942	40	1.4079
.1658	30	.1650	.2176	.1673	.2236	5.9758	.7764	.9863	.9940	3G	1.4050
.1687	40	.1679	.2251	.1703	.2313	5.8708	.7687	.9858	.9938	20	1.4021
.1716	50	.1708	.2324	.1733	.2389	5.7694	.7611	.9853	.9936	10	1.3992
.1745	10° 00'	.1736	.2397	.1763	.2463	5.6713	.7537	.9848	.9934	80° 00'	1.3963
.1774	10	.1765	.2468	.1793	.2536	5.5764	.7464	.9843	.9931	50	1.3934
.1804	20	.1794	.2538	.1823	.2609	5.4845	.7391	.9838	.9929	40	1.3904
.1833	30	.1822	.2606	.1853	.2680	5.3955	.7320	.9833	.9927	30	1.3875
.1862	40	.1851	.2674	.1883	.2750	5.3093	.7250	.9827	.9924	20	1.3846
.1891	50	.1880	.2740	.1914	.2819	5.2257	.7181	.9822	.9922	10	1.3817
.1920	11° 00'	.1908	.2806	.1944	.2887	5.1446	.7113	.9816	.9919	79° 00'	1.3788
.1949	10	.1937	.2870	.1974	.2953	5.0658	.7047	.9811	.9917	50	1.3759
.1978	20	.1965	.2934	.2004	.3020	4.9894	.6980	.9805	.9914	40	1.3730
.2007	30	.1994	.2997	.2035	.3085	4.9152	.6915	.9799	.9912	30	1.3701
.2036	40	.2022	.3058	.2065	.3149	4.8430	.6851	.9793	.9909	2G	1.3672
.2065	50	.2051	.3119	.2095	.3212	4.7729	.6788	.9787	.9907	10	1.3643
.2094	12° 00'	.2079	.3179	.2126	.3275	4.7046	.6725	.9781	.9904	78° 00'	1.3614
.2123	10	.2108	.3238	.2156	.3336	4.6382	.6664	.9775	.9901	50	1.3584
.2153	20	.2136	.3296	.2186	.3397	4.5736	.6603	.9769	.9899	40	1.3555
.2182	30	.2164	.3353	.2217	.3458	4.5107	.6542	.9763	.9896	30	1.3526
.2211	40	.2193	.3410	.2247	.3517	4.4494	.6483	.9757	.9893	20	1.3497
.2240	50	.2221	.3466	.2278	.3576	4.3897	.6424	.9750	.9890	10	1.3468
.2269	13° 00'	.2250	.3521	.2309	.3634	4.3315	.6366	.9744	.9887	77° 00'	1.3439
.2298	10	.2278	.3575	.2339	.3691	4.2747	.6309	.9737	.9884	50	1.3410
.2327	20	.2306	.3629	.2370	.3748	4.2193	.6252	.9730	.9881	40	1.3381
.2356	30	.2334	.3682	.2401	.3804	4.1653	.6196	.9724	.9878	30	1.3352
.2385	40	.2363	.3734	.2432	.3859	4.1126	.6141	.9717	.9875	20	1.3323
.2414	50	.2391	.3786	.2462	.3914	4.0611	.6086	.9710	.9872	10	1.3294
.2443	14° 00'	.2419	.3837	.2493	.3968	4.0108	.6032	.9703	.9869	76° 00'	1.3265
.2473	10	.2447	.3887	.2524	.4021	3.9617	.5979	.9696	.9866	50	1.3235
.2502	20	.2476	.3937	.2555	.4074	3.9136	.5926	.9689	.9863	40	1.3206
.2531	30	.2504	.3986	.2586	.4127	3.8667	.5873	.9681	.9859	30	1.3177
.2560	40	.2532	.4035	.2617	.4178	3.8208	.5822	.9674	.9856	20	1.3148
.2589	50	.2560	.4083	.2648	.4230	3.7760	.5770	.9667	.9853	10	1.3119
.2618	15° 00'	.2588	.4130	.2679	.4281	3.7321	.5719	.9659	.9849	75° 00'	1.3090
.2647	10	.2616	.4177	.2711	.4331	3.6891	.5669	.9652	.9846	50	1.3061
.2676	20	.2644	.4223	.2742	.4381	3.6470	.5619	.9644	.9843	40	1.3032
.2705	30	.2672	.4269	.2773	.4430	3.6059	.5570	.9636	.9839	30	1.3003
.2734	40	.2700	.4314	.2805	.4479	3.5656	.5521	.9628	.9836	20	1.2974
.2763	50	.2728	.4359	.2836	.4527	3.5261	.5473	.9621	.9832	10	1.2945
.2793	16° 00'	.2756	.4403	.2867	.4575	3.4874	.5425	.9613	.9828	74° 00'	1.2915
.2822	10	.2784	.4447	.2899	.4622	3.4495	.5378	.9605	.9825	50	1.2886
.2851	20	.2812	.4491	.2931	.4669	3.4124	.5331	.9596	.9821	40	1.2857
.2880	30	.2840	.4533	.2962	.4716	3.3759	.5284	.9588	.9817	30	1.2828
.2909	40	.2868	.4576	.2994	.4762	3.3402	.5238	.9580	.9814	20	1.2799
.2938	50	.2896	.4618	.3026	.4808	3.3052	.5192	.9572	.9810	10	1.2770
.2967	17° 00'	.2924	.4659	.3057	.4853	3.2709	.5147	.9563	.9806	73° 00'	1.2741
.2996	10	.2952	.4700	.3089	.4898	3.2371	.5102	.9555	.9802	50	1.2712
.3025	20	.2979	.4741	.3121	.4943	3.2041	.5057	.9546	.9798	40	1.2683
.3054	30	.3007	.4781	.3153	.4987	3.1716	.5013	.9537	.9794	30	1.2654
.3083	40	.3035	.4821	.3185	.5031	3.1397	.4969	.9528	.9790	20	1.2625
.3113	50	.3062	.4861	.3217	.5075	3.1084	.4925	.9520	.9786	10	1.2595
.3142	18° 00'	.3090	.4900	.3249	.5118	3.0777	.4882	.9511	.9782	72° 00'	1.2566
		Value	Log10	Value	Log10	Value	Log10	Value	Log10	DEGREES	RADIANS
		COSINE		COTANGENT		TANGENT		SINE			

[Characteristics of Logarithms omitted—determine by the usual rule from the value]

Radians	Degrees	Sine Value	Log₁₀	Tangent Value	Log₁₀	Cotangent Value	Log₁₀	Cosine Value	Log₁₀		
.3142	18° 00′	.3090	.4900	.3249	.5118	3.0777	.4882	.9511	.9782	72° 00′	1.2566
.3171	10	.3118	.4939	.3281	.5161	3.0475	.4839	.9502	.9778	50	1.2537
.3200	20	.3145	.4977	.3314	.5203	3.0178	.4797	.9492	.9774	40	1.2508
.3229	30	.3173	.5015	.3346	.5245	2.9887	.4755	.9483	.9770	30	1.2479
.3258	40	.3201	.5052	.3378	.5287	2.9600	.4713	.9474	.9765	20	1.2450
.3287	50	.3228	.5090	.3411	.5329	2.9319	.4671	.9465	.9761	10	1.2421
.3316	19° 00′	.3256	.5126	.3443	.5370	2.9042	.4630	.9455	.9757	71° 00′	1.2392
.3345	10	.3283	.5163	.3476	.5411	2.8770	.4589	.9446	.9752	50	1.2363
.3374	20	.3311	.5199	.3508	.5451	2.8502	.4549	.9436	.9748	40	1.2334
.3403	30	.3338	.5235	.3541	.5491	2.8239	.4509	.9426	.9743	30	1.2305
.3432	40	.3365	.5270	.3574	.5531	2.7980	.4469	.9417	.9739	20	1.2275
.3462	50	.3393	.5306	.3607	.5571	2.7725	.4429	.9407	.9734	10	1.2246
.3491	20° 00′	.3420	.5341	.3640	.5611	2.7475	.4389	.9397	.9730	70° 00′	1.2217
.3520	10	.3448	.5375	.3673	.5650	2.7228	.4350	.9387	.9725	50	1.2188
.3549	20	.3475	.5409	.3706	.5689	2.6985	.4311	.9377	.9721	40	1.2159
.3578	30	.3502	.5443	.3739	.5727	2.6746	.4273	.9367	.9716	30	1.2130
.3607	40	.3529	.5477	.3772	.5766	2.6511	.4234	.9356	.9711	20	1.2101
.3636	50	.3557	.5510	.3805	.5804	2.6279	.4196	.9346	.9706	10	1.2072
.3665	21° 00′	.3584	.5543	.3839	.5842	2.6051	.4158	.9336	.9702	69° 00′	1.2043
.3694	10	.3611	.5576	.3872	.5879	2.5826	.4121	.9325	.9697	50	1.2014
.3723	20	.3638	.5609	.3906	.5917	2.5605	.4083	.9315	.9692	40	1.1985
.3752	30	.3665	.5641	.3939	.5954	2.5386	.4046	.9304	.9687	30	1.1956
.3782	40	.3692	.5673	.3973	.5991	2.5172	.4009	.9293	.9682	20	1.1926
.3811	50	.3719	.5704	.4006	.6028	2.4960	.3972	.9283	.9677	10	1.1897
.3840	22° 00′	.3746	.5736	.4040	.6064	2.4751	.3936	.9272	.9672	68° 00′	1.1868
.3869	10	.3773	.5767	.4074	.6100	2.4545	.3900	.9261	.9667	50	1.1839
.3898	20	.3800	.5798	.4108	.6136	2.4342	.3864	.9250	.9661	40	1.1810
.3927	30	.3827	.5828	.4142	.6172	2.4142	.3828	.9239	.9656	30	1.1781
.3956	40	.3854	.5859	.4176	.6208	2.3945	.3792	.9228	.9651	20	1.1752
.3985	50	.3881	.5889	.4210	.6243	2.3750	.3757	.9216	.9646	10	1.1723
.4014	23° 00′	.3907	.5919	.4245	.6279	2.3559	.3721	.9205	.9640	67° 00′	1.1694
.4043	10	.3934	.5948	.4279	.6314	2.3369	.3686	.9194	.9635	50	1.1665
.4072	20	.3961	.5978	.4314	.6348	2.3183	.3652	.9182	.9629	40	1.1636
.4102	30	.3987	.6007	.4348	.6383	2.2998	.3617	.9171	.9624	30	1.1606
.4131	40	.4014	.6036	.4383	.6417	2.2817	.3583	.9159	.9618	20	1.1577
.4160	50	.4041	.6065	.4417	.6452	2.2637	.3548	.9147	.9613	10	1.1548
.4189	24° 00′	.4067	.6093	.4452	.6486	2.2460	.3514	.9135	.9607	66° 00′	1.1519
.4218	10	.4094	.6121	.4487	.6520	2.2286	.3480	.9124	.9602	50	1.1490
.4247	20	.4120	.6149	.4522	.6553	2.2113	.3447	.9112	.9596	40	1.1461
.4276	30	.4147	.6177	.4557	.6587	2.1943	.3413	.9100	.9590	30	1.1432
.4305	40	.4173	.6205	.4592	.6620	2.1775	.3380	.9088	.9584	20	1.1403
.4334	50	.4200	.6232	.4628	.6654	2.1609	.3346	.9075	.9579	10	1.1374
.4363	25° 00′	.4226	.6259	.4663	.6687	2.1445	.3313	.9063	.9573	65° 00′	1.1345
.4392	10	.4253	.6286	.4699	.6720	2.1283	.3280	.9051	.9567	50	1.1315
.4422	20	.4279	.6313	.4734	.6752	2.1123	.3248	.9038	.9561	40	1.1286
.4451	30	.4305	.6340	.4770	.6785	2.0965	.3215	.9026	.9555	30	1.1257
.4480	40	.4331	.6366	.4806	.6817	2.0809	.3183	.9013	.9549	20	1.1228
.4509	50	.4358	.6392	.4841	.6850	2.0655	.3150	.9001	.9543	10	1.1199
.4538	26° 00′	.4384	.6418	.4877	.6882	2.0503	.3118	.8988	.9537	64° 00′	1.1170
.4567	10	.4410	.6444	.4913	.6914	2.0353	.3086	.8975	.9530	50	1.1141
.4596	20	.4436	.6470	.4950	.6946	2.0204	.3054	.8962	.9524	40	1.1112
.4625	30	.4462	.6495	.4986	.6977	2.0057	.3023	.8949	.9518	30	1.1083
.4654	40	.4488	.6521	.5022	.7009	1.9912	.2991	.8936	.9512	20	1.1054
.4683	50	.4514	.6546	.5059	.7040	1.9768	.2960	.8923	.9505	10	1.1025
.4712	27° 00′	.4540	.6570	.5095	.7072	1.9626	.2928	.8910	.9499	63° 00′	1.0996
		Value Cosine	Log₁₀	Value Cotangent	Log₁₀	Value Tangent	Log₁₀	Value Sine	Log₁₀	Degrees	Radians

[Characteristics of Logarithms omitted—determine by the usual rule from the value]

Radians	Degrees	Sine Value	Sine Log₁₀	Tangent Value	Tangent Log₁₀	Cotangent Value	Cotangent Log₁₀	Cosine Value	Cosine Log₁₀		
.4712	27° 00′	.4540	.6570	.5095	.7072	1.9626	.2928	.8910	.9499	63° 00′	1.0996
.4741	10	.4566	.6595	.5132	.7103	1.9486	.2897	.8897	.9492	50	1.0966
.4771	20	.4592	.6620	.5169	.7134	1.9347	.2866	.8884	.9486	40	1.0937
.4800	30	.4617	.6644	.5206	.7165	1.9210	.2835	.8870	.9479	30	1.0908
.4829	40	.4643	.6668	.5243	.7196	1.9074	.2804	.8857	.9473	20	1.0879
.4858	50	.4669	.6692	.5280	.7226	1.8940	.2774	.8843	.9466	10	1.0850
.4887	28° 00′	.4695	.6716	.5317	.7257	1.8807	.2743	.8829	.9459	62° 00′	1.0821
.4916	10	.4720	.6740	.5354	.7287	1.8676	.2713	.8816	.9453	50	1.0792
.4945	20	.4746	.6763	.5392	.7317	1.8546	.2683	.8802	.9446	40	1.0763
.4974	30	.4772	.6787	.5430	.7348	1.8418	.2652	.8788	.9439	30	1.0734
.5003	40	.4797	.6810	.5467	.7378	1.8291	.2622	.8774	.9432	20	1.0705
.5032	50	.4823	.6833	.5505	.7408	1.8165	.2592	.8760	.9425	10	1.0676
.5061	29° 00′	.4848	.6856	.5543	.7438	1.8040	.2562	.8746	.9418	61° 00′	1.0647
.5091	10	.4874	.6878	.5581	.7467	1.7917	.2533	.8732	.9411	50	1.0617
.5120	20	.4899	.6901	.5619	.7497	1.7796	.2503	.8718	.9404	40	1.0588
.5149	30	.4924	.6923	.5658	.7526	1.7675	.2474	.8704	.9397	30	1.0559
.5178	40	.4950	.6946	.5696	.7556	1.7556	.2444	.8689	.9390	20	1.0530
.5207	50	.4975	.6968	.5735	.7585	1.7437	.2415	.8675	.9383	10	1.0501
.5236	30° 00′	.5000	.6990	.5774	.7614	1.7321	.2386	.8660	.9375	60° 00′	1.0472
.5265	10	.5025	.7012	.5812	.7644	1.7205	.2356	.8646	.9368	50	1.0443
.5294	20	.5050	.7033	.5851	.7673	1.7090	.2327	.8631	.9361	40	1.0414
.5323	30	.5075	.7055	.5890	.7701	1.6977	.2299	.8616	.9353	30	1.0385
.5352	40	.5100	.7076	.5930	.7730	1.6864	.2270	.8601	.9346	20	1.0356
.5381	50	.5125	.7097	.5969	.7759	1.6753	.2241	.8587	.9338	10	1.0327
.5411	31° 00′	.5150	.7118	.6009	.7788	1.6643	.2212	.8572	.9331	59° 00′	1.0297
.5440	10	.5175	.7139	.6048	.7816	1.6534	.2184	.8557	.9323	50	1.0268
.5469	20	.5200	.7160	.6088	.7845	1.6426	.2155	.8542	.9315	40	1.0239
.5498	30	.5225	.7181	.6128	.7873	1.6319	.2127	.8526	.9308	30	1.0210
.5527	40	.5250	.7201	.6168	.7902	1.6212	.2098	.8511	.9300	20	1.0181
.5556	50	.5275	.7222	.6208	.7930	1.6107	.2070	.8496	.9292	10	1.0152
.5585	32° 00′	.5299	.7242	.6249	.7958	1.6003	.2042	.8480	.9284	58° 00′	1.0123
.5614	10	.5324	.7262	.6289	.7986	1.5900	.2014	.8465	.9276	50	1.0094
.5643	20	.5348	.7282	.6330	.8014	1.5798	.1986	.8450	.9268	40	1.0065
.5672	30	.5373	.7302	.6371	.8042	1.5697	.1958	.8434	.9260	30	1.0036
.5701	40	.5398	.7322	.6412	.8070	1.5597	.1930	.8418	.9252	20	1.0007
.5730	50	.5422	.7342	.6453	.8097	1.5497	.1903	.8403	.9244	10	.9977
.5760	33° 00′	.5446	.7361	.6494	.8125	1.5399	.1875	.8387	.9236	57° 00′	.9948
.5789	10	.5471	.7380	.6536	.8153	1.5301	.1847	.8371	.9228	50	.9919
.5818	20	.5495	.7400	.6577	.8180	1.5204	.1820	.8355	.9219	40	.9890
.5847	30	.5519	.7419	.6619	.8208	1.5108	.1792	.8339	.9211	30	.9861
.5876	40	.5544	.7438	.6661	.8235	1.5013	.1765	.8323	.9203	20	.9832
.5905	50	.5568	.7457	.6703	.8263	1.4919	.1737	.8307	.9194	10	.9803
.5934	34° 00′	.5592	.7476	.6745	.8290	1.4826	.1710	.8290	.9186	56° 00′	.9774
.5963	10	.5616	.7494	.6787	.8317	1.4733	.1683	.8274	.9177	50	.9745
.5992	20	.5640	.7513	.6830	.8344	1.4641	.1656	.8258	.9169	40	.9716
.6021	30	.5664	.7531	.6873	.8371	1.4550	.1629	.8241	.9160	30	.9687
.6050	40	.5688	.7550	.6916	.8398	1.4460	.1602	.8225	.9151	20	.9657
.6080	50	.5712	.7568	.6959	.8425	1.4370	.1575	.8208	.9142	10	.9628
.6109	35° 00′	.5736	.7586	.7002	.8452	1.4281	.1548	.8192	.9134	55° 00′	.9599
.6138	10	.5760	.7604	.7046	.8479	1.4193	.1521	.8175	.9125	50	.9570
.6167	20	.5783	.7622	.7089	.8506	1.4106	.1494	.8158	.9116	40	.9541
.6196	30	.5807	.7640	.7133	.8533	1.4019	.1467	.8141	.9107	30	.9512
.6225	40	.5831	.7657	.7177	.8559	1.3934	.1441	.8124	.9098	20	.9483
.6254	50	.5854	.7675	.7221	.8586	1.3848	.1414	.8107	.9089	10	.9454
.6283	36° 00′	.5878	.7692	.7265	.8613	1.3764	.1387	.8090	.9080	54° 00′	.9425
		Value Log₁₀ Cosine		Value Log₁₀ Cotangent		Value Log₁₀ Tangent		Value Log₁₀ Sine		Degrees	Radians

[Characteristics of Logarithms omitted—determine by the usual rule from the value]

RADIANS	DEGREES	SINE Value	SINE Log₁₀	TANGENT Value	TANGENT Log₁₀	COTANGENT Value	COTANGENT Log₁₀	COSINE Value	COSINE Log₁₀		
.6283	36° 00′	.5878	.7692	.7265	.8613	1.3764	.1387	.8090	.9080	54° 00′	.9425
.6312	10	.5901	.7710	.7310	.8639	1.3680	.1361	.8073	.9070	50	.9396
.6341	20	.5925	.7727	.7355	.8666	1.3597	.1334	.8056	.9061	40	.9367
.6370	30	.5948	.7744	.7400	.8692	1.3514	.1308	.8039	.9052	30	.9338
.6400	40	.5972	.7761	.7445	.8718	1.3432	.1282	.8021	.9042	20	.9308
.6429	50	.5995	.7778	.7490	.8745	1.3351	.1255	.8004	.9033	10	.9279
.6458	37° 00′	.6018	.7795	.7536	.8771	1.3270	.1229	.7986	.9023	53° 00′	.9250
.6487	10	.6041	.7811	.7581	.8797	1.3190	.1203	.7969	.9014	50	.9221
.6516	20	.6065	.7828	.7627	.8824	1.3111	.1176	.7951	.9004	40	.9192
.6545	30	.6088	.7844	.7673	.8850	1.3032	.1150	.7934	.8995	30	.9163
.6574	40	.6111	.7861	.7720	.8876	1.2954	.1124	.7916	.8985	20	.9134
.6603	50	.6134	.7877	.7766	.8902	1.2876	.1098	.7898	.8975	10	.9105
.6632	38° 00′	.6157	.7893	.7813	.8928	1.2799	.1072	.7880	.8965	52° 00′	.9076
.6661	10	.6180	.7910	.7860	.8954	1.2723	.1046	.7862	.8955	50	.9047
.6690	20	.6202	.7926	.7907	.8980	1.2647	.1020	.7844	.8945	40	.9018
.6720	30	.6225	.7941	.7954	.9006	1.2572	.0994	.7826	.8935	30	.8988
.6749	40	.6248	.7957	.8002	.9032	1.2497	.0968	.7808	.8925	20	.8959
.6778	50	.6271	.7973	.8050	.9058	1.2423	.0942	.7790	.8915	10	.8930
.6807	39° 00′	.6293	.7989	.8098	.9084	1.2349	.0916	.7771	.8905	51° 00′	.8901
.6836	10	.6316	.8004	.8146	.9110	1.2276	.0890	.7753	.8895	50	.8872
.6865	20	.6338	.8020	.8195	.9135	1.2203	.0865	.7735	.8884	40	.8843
.6894	30	.6361	.8035	.8243	.9161	1.2131	.0839	.7716	.8874	30	.8814
.6923	40	.6383	.8050	.8292	.9187	1.2059	.0813	.7698	.8864	20	.8785
.6952	50	.6406	.8066	.8342	.9212	1.1988	.0788	.7679	.8853	10	.8756
.6981	40° 00′	.6428	.8081	.8391	.9238	1.1918	.0762	.7660	.8843	50° 00′	.8727
.7010	10	.6450	.8096	.8441	.9264	1.1847	.0736	.7642	.8832	50	.8698
.7039	20	.6472	.8111	.8491	.9289	1.1778	.0711	.7623	.8821	40	.8668
.7069	30	.6494	.8125	.8541	.9315	1.1708	.0685	.7604	.8810	30	.8639
.7098	40	.6517	.8140	.8591	.9341	1.1640	.0659	.7585	.8800	20	.8610
.7127	50	.6539	.8155	.8642	.9366	1.1571	.0634	.7566	.8789	10	.8581
.7156	41° 00′	.6561	.8169	.8693	.9392	1.1504	.0608	.7547	.8778	49° 00′	.8552
.7185	10	.6583	.8184	.8744	.9417	1.1436	.0583	.7528	.8767	50	.8523
.7214	20	.6604	.8198	.8796	.9443	1.1369	.0557	.7509	.8756	40	.8494
.7243	30	.6626	.8213	.8847	.9468	1.1303	.0532	.7490	.8745	30	.8465
.7272	40	.6648	.8227	.8899	.9494	1.1237	.0506	.7470	.8733	20	.8436
.7301	50	.6670	.8241	.8952	.9519	1.1171	.0481	.7451	.8722	10	.8407
.7330	42° 00′	.6691	.8255	.9004	.9544	1.1106	.0456	.7431	.8711	48° 00′	.8378
.7359	10	.6713	.8269	.9057	.9570	1.1041	.0430	.7412	.8699	50	.8348
.7389	20	.6734	.8283	.9110	.9595	1.0977	.0405	.7392	.8688	40	.8319
.7418	30	.6756	.8297	.9163	.9621	1.0913	.0379	.7373	.8676	30	.8290
.7447	40	.6777	.8311	.9217	.9646	1.0850	.0354	.7353	.8665	20	.8261
.7476	50	.6799	.8324	.9271	.9671	1.0786	.0329	.7333	.8653	10	.8232
.7505	43° 00′	.6820	.8338	.9325	.9697	1.0724	.0303	.7314	.8641	47° 00′	.8203
.7534	10	.6841	.8351	.9380	.9722	1.0661	.0278	.7294	.8629	50	.8174
.7563	20	.6862	.8365	.9435	.9747	1.0599	.0253	.7274	.8618	40	.8145
.7592	30	.6884	.8378	.9490	.9772	1.0538	.0228	.7254	.8606	30	.8116
.7621	40	.6905	.8391	.9545	.9798	1.0477	.0202	.7234	.8594	20	.8087
.7650	50	.6926	.8405	.9601	.9823	1.0416	.0177	.7214	.8582	10	.8058
.7679	44° 00′	.6947	.8418	.9657	.9848	1.0355	.0152	.7193	.8569	46° 00′	.8029
.7709	10	.6967	.8431	.9713	.9874	1.0295	.0126	.7173	.8557	50	.7999
.7738	20	.6988	.8444	.9770	.9899	1.0235	.0101	.7153	.8545	40	.7970
.7767	30	.7009	.8457	.9827	.9924	1.0176	.0076	.7133	.8532	30	.7941
.7796	40	.7030	.8469	.9884	.9949	1.0117	.0051	.7112	.8520	20	.7912
.7825	50	.7050	.8482	.9942	.9975	1.0058	.0025	.7092	.8507	10	.7883
.7854	45° 00′	.7071	.8495	1.0000	.0000	1.0000	.0000	.7071	.8495	45° 00′	.7854
		Value Log₁₀ COSINE		Value Log₁₀ COTANGENT		Value Log₁₀ TANGENT		Value Log₁₀ SINE		DEGREES	RADIANS

x Radians	Sin x	Cos x	Tan x	Equivalent of x	x Radians	Sin x	Cos x	Tan x	Equivalent of x
.00	.00000	1.0000	.00000	0° 00'.0	.50	.47943	.87758	.54630	28° 38'.9
.01	.01000	.99995	.01000	0° 34'.4	.51	.48818	.87274	.55936	29° 13'.3
.02	.02000	.99980	.02000	1° 08'.8	.52	.49688	.86782	.57256	29° 47'.6
.03	.03000	.99955	.03001	1° 43'.1	.53	.50553	.86281	.58592	30° 22'.0
.04	.03999	.99920	.04002	2° 17'.5	.54	.51414	.85771	.59943	30° 56'.4
.05	.04998	.99875	.05004	2° 51'.9	.55	.52269	.85252	.61311	31° 30'.8
.06	.05996	.99820	.06007	3° 26'.3	.56	.53119	.84726	.62695	32° 05'.1
.07	.06994	.99755	.07011	4° 00'.6	.57	.53963	.84190	.64097	32° 39'.5
.08	.07991	.99680	.08017	4° 35'.0	.58	.54802	.83646	.65517	33° 13'.9
.09	.08988	.99595	.09024	5° 09'.4	.59	.55636	.83094	.66956	33° 48'.3
.10	.09983	.99500	.10033	5° 43'.8	.60	.56464	.82534	.68414	34° 22'.6
.11	.10978	.99396	.11045	6° 18'.2	.61	.57287	.81965	.69892	34° 57'.0
.12	.11971	.99281	.12058	6° 52'.5	.62	.58104	.81388	.71391	35° 31'.4
.13	.12963	.99156	.13074	7° 26'.9	.63	.58914	.80803	.72911	36° 05'.8
.14	.13954	.99022	.14092	8° 01'.3	.64	.59720	.80210	.74454	36° 40'.2
.15	.14944	.98877	.15114	8° 35'.7	.65	.60519	.79608	.76020	37° 14'.5
.16	.15932	.98723	.16138	9° 10'.0	.66	.61312	.78999	.77610	37° 48'.9
.17	.16918	.98558	.17166	9° 44'.4	.67	.62099	.78382	.79225	38° 23'.3
.18	.17903	.98384	.18197	10° 18'.8	.68	.62879	.77757	.80866	38° 57'.7
.19	.18886	.98200	.19232	10° 53'.2	.69	.63654	.77125	.82534	39° 32'.0
.20	.19867	.98007	.20271	11° 27'.5	.70	.64422	.76484	.84229	40° 06'.4
.21	.20846	.97803	.21314	12° 01'.9	.71	.65183	.75836	.85953	40° 40'.8
.22	.21823	.97590	.22362	12° 36'.3	.72	.65938	.75181	.87707	41° 15'.2
.23	.22798	.97367	.23414	13° 10'.7	.73	.66687	.74517	.89492	41° 49'.6
.24	.23770	.97134	.24472	13° 45'.1	.74	.67429	.73847	.91309	42° 23'.9
.25	.24740	.96891	.25534	14° 19'.4	.75	.68164	.73169	.93160	42° 58'.3
.26	.25708	.96639	.26602	14° 53'.8	.76	.68892	.72484	.95045	43° 32'.7
.27	.26673	.96377	.27676	15° 28'.2	.77	.69614	.71791	.96967	44° 07'.1
.28	.27636	.96106	.28755	16° 02'.6	.78	.70328	.71091	.98926	44° 41'.4
.29	.28595	.95824	.29841	16° 36'.9	.79	.71035	.70385	1.0092	45° 15'.8
.30	.29552	.95534	.30934	17° 11'.3	.80	.71736	.69671	1.0296	45° 50'.2
.31	.30506	.95233	.32033	17° 45'.7	.81	.72429	.68950	1.0505	46° 24'.6
.32	.31457	.94924	.33139	18° 20'.1	.82	.73115	.68222	1.0717	46° 59'.0
.33	.32404	.94604	.34252	18° 54'.5	.83	.73793	.67488	1.0934	47° 33'.3
.34	.33349	.94275	.35374	19° 28'.8	.84	.74464	.66746	1.1156	48° 07'.7
.35	.34290	.93937	.36503	20° 03'.2	.85	.75128	.65998	1.1383	48° 42'.1
.36	.35227	.93590	.37640	20° 37'.6	.86	.75784	.65244	1.1616	49° 16'.5
.37	.36162	.93233	.38786	21° 12'.0	.87	.76433	.64483	1.1853	49° 50'.8
.38	.37092	.92866	.39941	21° 46'.3	.88	.77074	.63715	1.2097	50° 25'.2
.39	.38019	.92491	.41105	22° 20'.7	.89	.77707	.62941	1.2346	50° 59'.6
.40	.38942	.92106	.42279	22° 55'.1	.90	.78333	.62161	1.2602	51° 34'.0
.41	.39861	.91712	.43463	23° 29'.5	.91	.78950	.61375	1.2864	52° 08'.3
.42	.40776	.91309	.44657	24° 03'.9	.92	.79560	.60582	1.3133	52° 42'.7
.43	.41687	.90897	.45862	24° 38'.2	.93	.80162	.59783	1.3409	53° 17'.1
.44	.42594	.90475	.47078	25° 12'.6	.94	.80756	.58979	1.3692	53° 51'.5
.45	.43497	.90045	.48306	25° 47'.0	.95	.81342	.58168	1.3984	54° 25'.9
.46	.44395	.89605	.49545	26° 21'.4	.96	.81919	.57352	1.4284	55° 00'.2
.47	.45289	.89157	.50797	26° 55'.7	.97	.82489	.56530	1.4592	55° 34'.6
.48	.46178	.88699	.52061	27° 30'.1	.98	.83050	.55702	1.4910	56° 09'.0
.49	.47063	.88233	.53339	28° 04'.5	.99	.83603	.54869	1.5237	56° 43'.4
.50	.47943	.87758	.54630	28° 38'.9	1.00	.84147	.54030	1.5574	57° 17'.7

x Radians	Sin x	Cos x	Tan x	Equivalent of x	x Radians	Sin x	Cos x	Tan x	Equivalent of x
1.00	.84147	.54030	1.5574	57° 17′.7	**1.30**	.96356	.26750	3.6021	74° 29′.1
1.01	.84683	.53186	1.5922	57° 52′.1	1.31	.96618	.25785	3.7471	75° 08′.4
1.02	.85211	.52337	1.6281	58° 26′.5	1.32	.96872	.24818	3.9033	75° 37′.8
1.03	.85730	.51482	1.6652	59° 00′.9	1.33	.97115	.23848	4.0723	76° 12′.2
1.04	.86240	.50622	1.7036	59° 35′.3	1.34	.97348	.22875	4.2556	76° 46′.6
1.05	.86742	.49757	1.7433	60° 09′.6	1.35	.97572	.21901	4.4552	77° 21′.0
1.06	.87236	.48887	1.7844	60° 44′.0	1.36	.97786	.20924	4.6734	77° 55′.3
1.07	.87720	.48012	1.8270	61° 18′.4	1.37	.97991	.19945	4.9131	78° 29′.7
1.08	.88196	.47133	1.8712	61° 52′.8	1.38	.98185	.18964	5.1774	79° 04′.1
1.09	.88663	.46249	1.9171	62° 27′.1	1.39	.98370	.17981	5.4707	79° 38′.5
1.10	.89121	.45360	1.9648	63° 01′.5	**1.40**	.98545	.16997	5.7979	80° 12′.8
1.11	.89570	.44466	2.0143	63° 35′.9	1.41	.98710	.16010	6.1654	80° 47′.2
1.12	.90010	.43568	2.0660	64° 10′.3	1.42	.98865	.15023	6.5811	81° 21′.6
1.13	.90441	.42666	2.1198	64° 44′.7	1.43	.99010	.14033	7.0555	81° 56′.0
1.14	.90863	.41759	2.1759	65° 19′.0	1.44	.99146	.13042	7.6018	82° 30′.4
1.15	.91276	.40849	2.2345	65° 53′.4	1.45	.99271	.12050	8.2381	83° 04′.7
1.16	.91680	.39934	2.2958	66° 27′.8	1.46	.99387	.11057	8.9886	83° 39′.1
1.17	.92075	.39015	2.3600	67° 02′.2	1.47	.99492	.10063	9.8874	84° 13′.5
1.18	.92461	.38092	2.4273	67° 36′.5	1.48	.99588	.09067	10.983	84° 47′.9
1.19	.92837	.37166	2.4979	68° 10′.9	1.49	.99674	.08071	12.350	85° 22′.2
1.20	.93204	.36236	2.5722	68° 45′.3	**1.50**	.99749	.07074	14.101	85° 56′.6
1.21	.93562	.35302	2.6503	69° 19′.7	1.51	.99815	.06076	16.428	86° 31′.0
1.22	.93910	.34365	2.7328	69° 54′.1	1.52	.99871	.05077	19.670	87° 05′.4
1.23	.94249	.33424	2.8198	70° 28′.4	1.53	.99917	.04079	24.498	87° 39′.8
1.24	.94578	.32480	2.9119	71° 02′.8	1.54	.99953	.03079	32.461	88° 14′.1
1.25	.94898	.31532	3.0096	71° 37′.2	1.55	.99978	.02079	48.078	88° 48′.5
1.26	.95209	.30582	3.1133	72° 11′.6	1.56	.99994	.01080	92.621	89° 22′.9
1.27	.95510	.29628	3.2236	72° 45′.9	•1.57	•1.0000	•.00080	•1255.8	89° 57′.3
1.28	.95802	.28672	3.3413	73° 20′.3	1.58	.99996	−.00920	−108.65	90° 31′.6
1.29	.96084	.27712	3.4672	73° 54′.7	1.59	.99982	−.01920	−52.067	91° 06′.0
1.30	.96356	.26750	3.6021	74° 29′.1	**1.60**	.99957	−.02920	−34.233	91° 40′.4

π radians = 180°   1 radian = 57° 17′ 44″.806 = 57.°2957795
π = 3.14159265   3600″ = 60′ = 1° = 0.01745329 radian
*1 right angle = 90° = $\pi/2$ radians = 1.5707963 radians

Index